Contents in Brief

Start Smart

About the Cover

Developing fluency with fractions, decimals, and polyhedral solids are featured topics in Fifth grade. The mathematical symbols shown on the mountain goat's snowboard will help students gain momentum as they carve their way through higher levels of math. Have students locate parallel and intersecting lines on the ski lift, and use at least one of the symbols on the snowboard to describe the ski lift chairs.

Three Horizontally Aligned Programs

- Common vocabulary
- Common manipulatives
- Common technology
- Common Professional Development
- Aligned to NCTM Focal Points

Grade 5
NSF-funded, integrated performance assessment aligned with investigative instruction

Grade 5
Intensive Intervention for students two or more years below grade level (Tier 3 RTI)

The McGraw-Hill Companies

Macmillan/McGraw-Hill

Send all inquiries to:
Macmillan/McGraw-Hill
8787 Orion Place
Columbus, OH 43240-4027

ISBN: 978-0-02-106026-9 *(Teacher Edition)*
MHID: 0-02-106026-6 *(Teacher Edition)*
ISBN: 978-0-02-106024-5 *(Student Edition)*
MHID: 0-02-106024-X *(Student Edition)*

Printed in the United States of America.

5 6 7 8 9 10 11 12 13 RMN/LEH 18 17 16 15 14 13 12 11 10

Benefits of Student Edition Organization

Math Connects, grade 5 Student Edition, has a 4-part organization.

1. **Start Smart** gets students ready for grade 5 with a review of key math standards from grade 4 that are prerequisites for grade 5.
2. **Chapters 1–15** Each chapter has coherent groups of lessons focused on related grade 5 math standards and the NCTM Focal Points.
3. **Preparing for Standardized Tests** provides test success tips, step-by-step solutions for standards-based multiple-choice questions, and an extensive practice section to review before your state test.
4. **Looking Ahead** prepares students for success with lessons on several key math standards.

The organization and pacing of ***Math Connects*** helps ensure in-depth coverage of all grade 5 standards, success on your state test, and a good start for grade 6.

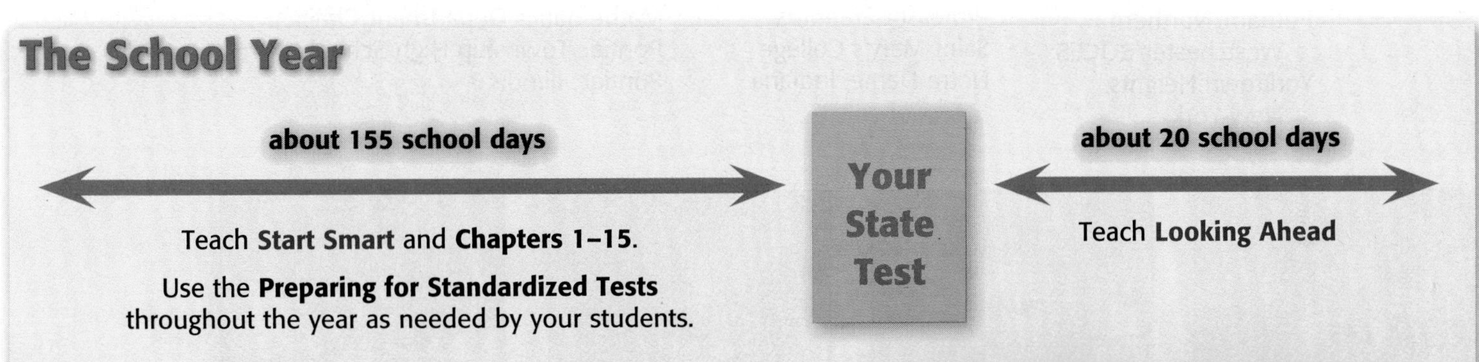

The School Year
about 155 school days
Teach Start Smart and Chapters 1–15.
Use the Preparing for Standardized Tests throughout the year as needed by your students.
Your State Test
about 20 school days
Teach Looking Ahead

Pacing Guide
Each chapter includes days for review and assessment.

Start Smart	Optional
Chapter 1	9 days
Chapter 2	10 days
Chapter 3	11 days
Chapter 4	11 days
Chapter 5	9 days
Chapter 6	11 days
Chapter 7	10 days
Chapter 8	9 days
Chapter 9	11 days
Chapter 10	14 days
Chapter 11	9 days
Chapter 12	9 days
Chapter 13	11 days
Chapter 14	14 days
Chapter 15	7 days
Total	155 days
State Test	
Looking Ahead	20 days

Authors

Mary Behr Altieri
Putnam/Northern Westchester BOCES
Yorktown Heights, New York

Don S. Balka
Professor Emeritus
Saint Mary's College
Notre Dame, Indiana

Roger Day, Ph.D.
Mathematics Department Chair
Pontiac Township High School
Pontiac, Illinois

Philip D. Gonsalves
Mathematics Coordinator
Alameda County Office of Education and California State University East Bay
Hayward, California

Ellen C. Grace
Mathematics Consultant
Albuquerque, New Mexico

Stephen Krulik
Professor Emeritus Mathematics Education
Temple University
Cherry Hill, New Jersey

Carol E. Malloy, Ph.D
Associate Professor of Mathematics Education
University of North Carolina at Chapel Hill
Chapel Hill, North Carolina

Rhonda J. Molix-Bailey
Mathematics Consultant
Mathematics by Design
Desoto, Texas

Lois Gordon Moseley
Staff Developer
NUMBERS: Mathematics Professional Development
Houston, Texas

Brian Mowry
Independent Math Educational Consultant/Part-Time Pre-K Instructional Specialist
Austin Independent School District
Austin, Texas

Christina L. Myren
Consultant Teacher
Conejo Valley Unified School District
Thousand Oaks, California

Jack Price
Professor Emeritus
California State Polytechnic University
Pomona, California

Mary Esther Reynosa
Instructional Specialist for Elementary Mathematics
Northside Independent School District
San Antonio, Texas

Rafaela M. Santa Cruz
SDSU/CGU Doctoral Program in Education
San Diego State University
San Diego, California

Robyn Silbey
Math Content Coach
Montgomery County Public Schools
Gaithersburg, Maryland

Kathleen Vielhaber
Mathematics Consultant
St. Louis, Missouri

Contributing Authors

Donna J. Long
Mathematics Consultant
Indianapolis, Indiana

FOLDABLES™ **Dinah Zike**
Educational Consultant
Dinah-Might Activities, Inc.
San Antonio, Texas

Consultants

Macmillan/McGraw-Hill wishes to thank the following professionals for their feedback. They were instrumental in providing valuable input toward the development of this program in these specific areas.

Mathematical Content

Viken Hovsepian
Professor of Mathematics
Rio Hondo College
Whittier, California

Grant A. Fraser, Ph.D.
Professor of Mathematics
California State University, Los Angeles
Los Angeles, California

Arthur K. Wayman, Ph.D.
Professor of Mathematics Emeritus
California State University, Long Beach
Long Beach, California

Assessment

Jane D. Gawronski, Ph.D.
Director of Assessment and Outreach
San Diego State University
San Diego, California

Cognitive Guided Instruction

Susan B. Empson, Ph.D.
Associate Professor of Mathematics and Science Education
University of Texas at Austin
Austin, Texas

English Learners

Cheryl Avalos
Mathematics Consultant
Los Angeles County Office of Education, Retired
Hacienda Heights, California

Kathryn Heinze
Graduate School of Education
Hamline University
St. Paul, Minnesota

Family Involvement

Paul Giganti, Jr.
Mathematics Education Consultant
Albany, California

Literature

David M. Schwartz
Children's Author, Speaker, Storyteller
Oakland, California

Vertical Alignment

Berchie Holliday
National Educational Consultant
Silver Spring, Maryland

Deborah A. Hutchens, Ed.D.
Principal
Norfolk Highlands Elementary
Chesapeake, Virginia

Reviewers

Each Reviewer reviewed at least two chapters of the Student Edition, giving feedback and suggestions for improving the effectiveness of the mathematics instruction.

Ernestine D. Austin
Facilitating Teacher/Basic Skills Teacher
LORE School
Ewing, NJ

Susie Bellah
Kindergarten Teacher
Lakeland Elementary
Humble, TX

Megan Bennett
Elementary Math Coordinator
Hartford Public Schools
Hartford, CT

Susan T. Blankenship
5th Grade Teacher – Math
Stanford Elementary School
Stanford, KY

Wendy Buchanan
3rd Grade Teacher
The Classical Center at Vial
Garland, TX

Sandra Signorelli Coelho
Associate Director for Mathematics PIMMS at Wesleyan University
Middletown, CT

Joanne DeMizio
Asst. Supt., Math and Science Curriculum
Archdiocese of New York
New York, NY

Anthony Dentino
Supervisor of Mathematics
Brick Township Schools
Brick, NJ

Lorrie L. Drennon
Math Teacher
Collins Middle School
Corsicana, TX

Ethel A. Edwards
Director of Curriculum and Instruction
Topeka Public Schools
Topeka, KS

Carolyn Elender
District Elementary Math Instructional Specialist
Pasadena ISD
Pasadena, TX

Monica Engel
Educator Second Grade
Pioneer Elementary School
Bolingbrook, IL

Anna Dahinden Flynn
Math Teacher
Coulson Tough K-6 Elementary
The Woodlands, TX

Brenda M. Foxx
Principal
University Park Elementary
University Park, MD

Katherine A. Frontier
Elementary Teacher
Laidlaw
Western Springs, IL

Susan J. Furphy
5th Grade Teacher
Nisley Elementary
Grand Jct., CO

Peter Gatz
Student Services Coordinator
Brooks Elementary
Aurora, IL

Amber Gregersen
Teacher – 2nd Grade
Nisley Elementary
Grand Junction, CO

Roberta Grindle
Math and Language Arts Academic Intervention Service Provider
Cumberland Head Elementary School
Plattsburgh, NY

Sr. Helen Lucille Habig, RSM
Assistant Superintendent/Mathematics
Archdiocese of Cincinnati
Cincinnati, OH

Holly L. Hepp
Math Facilitator
Barringer Academic Center
Charlotte, NC

Martha J. Hickman
2nd Grade Teacher
Dr. James Craik Elementary School Pomfret, MD

Margie Hill
District Coordinating Teacher for Mathematics, K-12
Blue Valley USD 229
Overland Park, KS

Carol H. Joyce
5th Grade Teacher
Nathanael Greene Elementary
Liberty, NC

Stella K. Kostante
Curriculum Coach
Roosevelt Elementary
Pittsburgh, PA

Pamela Fleming Lowe
Fourth Grade eMINTS Teacher
O'Neal Elementary
Poplar Bluff, MO

Lauren May, NBCT
4th Grade Teacher
May Watts Elementary School
Naperville, IL

Lorraine Moore
Grade 3 Math Teacher
Cowpens Elementary School
Cowpens, SC

Shannon L. Moorhead
4th Grade Teacher
Centerville Elementary
Anderson, SC

Gina M. Musselman, M.Ed
Kindergarten Teacher
Padeo Verde Elementary
Peoria, AZ

Jen Neufeld
3rd Grade Teacher
Kendall
Naperville, IL

Cathie Osiecki
K-5 Mathematics Coordinator
Middletown Public Schools
Middletown, CT

Phyllis L. Pacilli
Elementary Education Teacher
Fullerton Elementary
Addison, IL

Cindy Pearson
4th/5th Grade Teacher
John D. Spicer Elementary
Haltom City, TX

Herminio M. Planas
Mathematics Curriculum Specialist Administrative Offices-Bridgeport Public Schools
Bridgeport, CT

Jo J. Puree
Educator
Lackamas Elementary
Yelm, WA

Teresa M. Reynolds
Third Grade Teacher
Forrest View Elementary
Everett, WA

Dr. John A. Rhodes
Director of Mathematics
Indian Prairie SD #204
Aurora, IL

Amy Romm
1st Grade Teacher
Starline Elementary
Lake Havasu, AZ

Delores M. Rushing
Numeracy Coach
Dept. of Academic Services-Mathematics Department
Washington, DC

Daniel L. Scudder
Mathematics/Technology Specialist Boone Elementary
Houston, TX

Laura Seymour
Resource Teacher Leader – Elementary Math & Science, Retired
Dearborn Public Schools
Dearborn, MI

Petra Siprian
Teacher
Army Trail Elementary School
Addison, IL

Sandra Stein
K-5 Mathematics Consultant
St. Clair County Regional Educational Service Agency
Marysville, MI

Barb Stoflet
Curriculum Specialist
Roseville Area Schools
Roseville, MN

Kim Summers
Principal
Dynard Elementary
Chaptico, MD

Ann C. Teater
4th Grade Teacher
Lancaster Elementary
Lancaster, KY

Anne E. Tunney
Teacher
City of Erie School District
Erie, PA

Joylien Weathers
1st Grade Teacher
Mesa View Elementary
Grand Junction, CO

Christine F. Weiss
Third Grade Teacher
Robert C. Hill Elementary School
Romeoville, IL

Mathematics Teacher Handbook

Table of Contents

PreK–12 Mathematics: Focus on Grade 5

Welcome to Math Connects

Concepts • Skills • Problem Solving

The only true vertically aligned PreK–12 Mathematics Curriculum

Math Connects offers three dimensions of vertical alignment.

❶ Content Design

Vertical content alignment is a process that ensures you and your students experience an articulated, coherent sequence of content from grade level to grade level. This provides you with the assurance that content is introduced, reinforced, and assessed at appropriate times in the series, eliminating gaps and unnecessary duplication. You are able to target your instruction to student needs because you are not teaching content intended to be covered later or that students have previously mastered.

❷ Instructional Design

Our strong vertical alignment in instructional approach from PreKindergarten through Algebra 2 provides a smooth transition for students from elementary to middle school to high school. Our common vocabulary, technology, manipulatives, lesson planning, and Data-Driven Decision Making reduces the confusion students often encounter when transitioning between grade levels without this built-in articulation.

❸ Visual Design

The student pages of ***Math Connects*** have a consistent visual design from grade to grade. This aids students' transition from elementary school to middle school and from middle school to Algebra 1. Students are more likely to succeed when they are already familiar with how to navigate student pages.

PreK-2

3–5

5 Keys to Success

❶ Backmapping

According to College Board research, about 80% of students who successfully complete Algebra 1 and Geometry by 10th grade attend and succeed in college. (Changing the Odds: Factors Increasing Access to College, 1990) ***Math Connects*** was conceived and developed by backmapping with the final result in mind–student success in Algebra 1 and beyond.

❷ Balanced, In-Depth Content

Math Connects was developed to specifically target the skills and topics that give students the most difficulty, such as Problem Solving, in each grade span.

Grades K–2	Grades 3–5
1. Problem Solving 2. Money 3. Time 4. Measurement 5. Fractions 6. Computation	1. Problem Solving 2. Fractions 3. Measurement 4. Decimals 5. Time 6. Algebra
Grades 6–8	**Grades 9–12**
1. Fractions 2. Problem Solving 3. Measurement 4. Algebra 5. Computation	1. Problem Solving 2. Fractions 3. Algebra 4. Geometry 5. Computation 6. Probability

– *K–12 Math Market Analysis Survey,* Open Book Publishing, 2006

❸ Ongoing Assessment

Math Connects includes diagnostic, formative, and summative assessment; data-driven instruction; intervention options; and performance tracking, as well as remediation, acceleration, and enrichment tools throughout the program.

❹ Intervention and Differentiated Instruction

A three-tiered Response To Intervention (RTI) is provided.

TIER 1 **Daily Intervention** Reteach masters and Alternative Strategy suggestions address concepts from a different modality or learning style.

TIER 2 **Strategic Intervention** Teachers can use the myriad of intervention tips and ancillary materials, such as the Strategic Intervention Guide (1–5) and Study Guide and Intervention (6–8).

TIER 3 **Intensive Intervention** For students who are two or more years below grade level, ***Math Triumphs*** provides step-by-step instruction, vocabulary support, and data-driven decision making to help students succeed.

❺ Professional Development

Math Connects includes many opportunities for teacher professional development. Additional learning opportunities in various formats–video, online, and on-site instruction–are fully aligned and articulated from Kindergarten through Algebra 2.

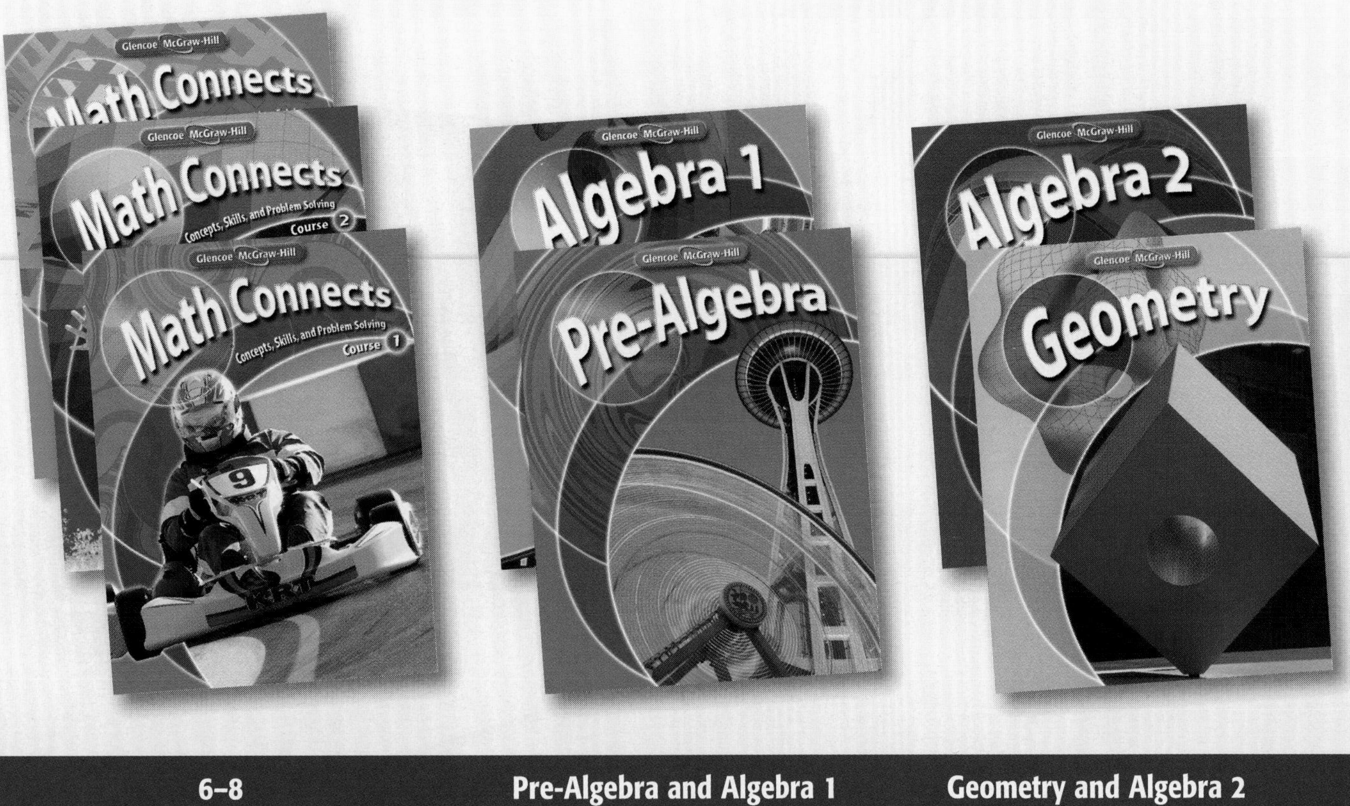

6-8 | Pre-Algebra and Algebra 1 | Geometry and Algebra 2

The Research Base

Continuous research with teachers, students, academician, and leading experts helps to build a solid foundation for ***Math Connects.***

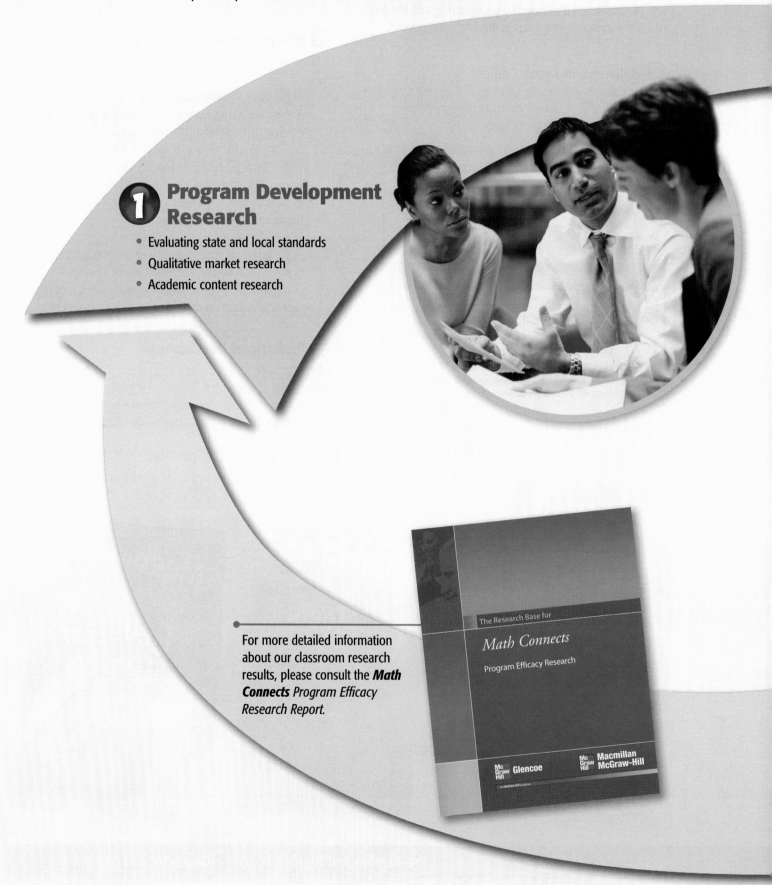

1 Program Development Research

- Evaluating state and local standards
- Qualitative market research
- Academic content research

For more detailed information about our classroom research results, please consult the ***Math Connects*** *Program Efficacy Research Report.*

for *Math Connects*

2 Formative Research

- Pedagogical research base
- Classroom field tests
- Teacher advisory boards
- Academic consultants and reviewers

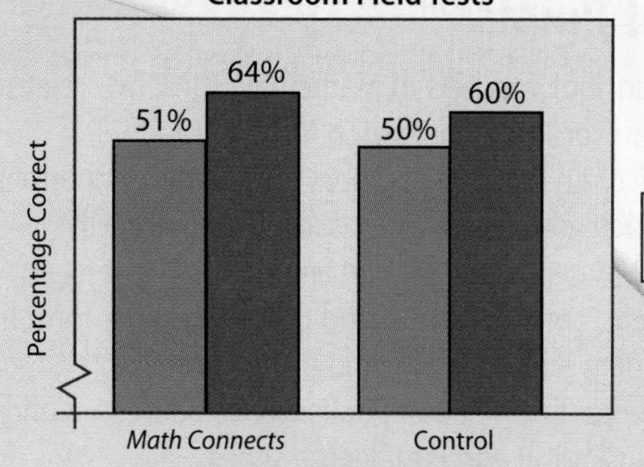

Students using a field test of the ***Math Connects*** program **(experimental group)** had ***higher*** pre-test to post-test gains than students using other textbook programs **(control group).**

3 Summative Research

- Evidence of increased test scores
- Quasi-experimental program efficacy research
- Longitudinal studies
- Qualitative program evaluations

Access all ***Math Connects*** research at macmillanmh.com.

NCTM Focal Points

The NCTM Focal Points

In 2006, the National Council of Teachers of Mathematics (NCTM) released the Curriculum Focal Points for Pre-Kindergarten through Grade 8 Mathematics. These Curriculum Focal Points focus on the most important mathematical topics for each grade level. The concepts are vertically-aligned and expect a level of depth, complexity, and rigor at each level. They comprise related ideas, concepts, skills, and procedures that form the foundation for understanding and lasting learning. The Focal Points emphasize depth versus breadth. The Focal Points will be addressed and highlighted throughout our PreK-8 and Pre-Algebra series.

What is the benefit to you in your classroom?

These Focal Points identify content for each grade level that should be mastered in order for your students to have true mathematical understanding–being able to not only calculate the answer, but to explain the answer and how to apply the calculation. The NCTM Focal Points were used as the basis in the development of ***Math Connects.*** The authors have incorporated the Focal Points into the content to assist you in building depth of understanding.

NCTM Focal Points for Grade 5	Supporting Chapters in *Math Connects*
Number and Operations and Algebra	Chapters 3, 4
Number and Operations	Chapters 2, 8, 9, 10
Geometry and Measurement and Algebra	Chapters 13, 14
Connections to the Focal Points	
Algebra	Chapters 5, 6, 7, 8, 9, 10
Measurement	Chapters 11, 12, 14
Data Analysis	Chapters 7, 15
Number and Operations	Chapters 1, 3, 4

KEY	
G5-FP1 Grade 5 Focal Point 1	**G5-FP5C** Grade 5 Focal Point 5 Connection
G5-FP2 Grade 5 Focal Point 2	**G5-FP6C** Grade 5 Focal Point 6 Connection
G5-FP3 Grade 5 Focal Point 3	**G5-FP7C** Grade 5 Focal Point 7 Connection
G5-FP4 Grade 5 Focal Point 4 Connection	

The Curriculum Focal Points identify key mathematical ideas for this grade. They are not discrete topics or a checklist to be mastered; rather, they provide a framework for the majority of instruction at a particular grade level and the foundation for future mathematics study. The complete document may be viewed at www.nctm.org/focalpoints.

G5-FP1 *Number and Operations* **and** *Algebra:* **Developing an understanding of and fluency with division of whole numbers**

Students apply their understanding of models for division, place value, properties, and the relationship of division to multiplication as they develop, discuss, and use efficient, accurate, and generalizable procedures to find quotients involving multidigit dividends. They select appropriate methods and apply them accurately to estimate quotients or calculate them mentally, depending on the context and numbers involved. They develop fluency with efficient procedures, including the standard algorithm, for dividing whole numbers, understand why the procedures work (on the basis of place value and properties of operations), and use them to solve problems. They consider the context in which a problem is situated to select the most useful form of the quotient for the solution, and they interpret it appropriately.

G5-FP2 *Number and Operations:* **Developing an understanding of and fluency with addition and subtraction of fractions and decimals**

Students apply their understanding of fractions and fraction models to represent the addition and subtraction of fractions with unlike denominators as equivalent calculations with like denominators. They apply their understandings of decimal models, place value, and properties to add and subtract decimals. They develop fluency with standard procedures for adding and subtracting fractions and decimals. They make reasonable estimates of fraction and decimal sums and differences. Students add and subtract fractions and decimals to solve problems, including problems involving measurement.

G5-FP3 *Geometry* **and** *Measurement* **and** *Algebra:* **Describing three-dimensional shapes and analyzing their properties, including volume and surface area**

Students relate two-dimensional shapes to three-dimensional shapes and analyze properties of polyhedral solids, describing them by the number of edges, faces, or vertices as well as the types of faces. Students recognize volume as an attribute of three-dimensional space. They understand that they can quantify volume by finding the total number of same-sized units of volume that they need to fill the space without gaps or overlaps. They understand that a cube that is 1 unit on an edge is the standard unit for measuring volume. They select appropriate units, strategies, and tools for solving problems that involve estimating or measuring volume. They decompose three-dimensional shapes and find surface areas and volumes of prisms. As they work with surface area, they find and justify relationships among the formulas for the areas of different polygons. They measure necessary attributes of shapes to use area formulas to solve problems.

Connections to the Focal Points

G5-FP4C *Algebra:* Students use patterns, models, and relationships as contexts for writing and solving simple equations and inequalities. They create graphs of simple equations. They explore prime and composite numbers and discover concepts related to the addition and subtraction of fractions as they use factors and multiples, including applications of common factors and common multiples. They develop an understanding of the order of operations and use it for all operations.

G5-FP5C *Measurement:* Students' experiences connect their work with solids and volume to their earlier work with capacity and weight or mass. They solve problems that require attention to both approximation and precision of measurement.

G5-FP6C *Data Analysis:* Students apply their understanding of whole numbers, fractions, and decimals as they construct and analyze double-bar and line graphs and use ordered pairs on coordinate grids.

G5-FP7C *Number and Operations:* Building on their work in grade 4, students extend their understanding of place value to numbers through millions and millionths in various contexts. They apply what they know about multiplication of whole numbers to larger numbers. Students also explore contexts that they can describe with negative numbers (e.g., situations of owing money or measuring elevations above and below sea level).

Program Philosophy

Balanced Instruction, Vertically-Aligned from Grades PreK through Algebra 1

The vertical alignment of ***Math Connects*** PreK-8 and ***Algebra 1*** incorporates a balance of instruction throughout. These programs provide students a balanced approach to mathematics by:

- investigating concepts and building conceptual understanding.
- developing, reinforcing, and mastering computational and procedural skills.
- applying mathematics to problem-solving situations.

This sequence of Student Edition pages illustrates the vertically-aligned development of the conceptual understanding and corresponding computational and procedural skills for an important algebra topic.

Primary Students use two-color counters to model addition sentences. This activity forms a basis for future understanding of and success in solving algebraic equations.

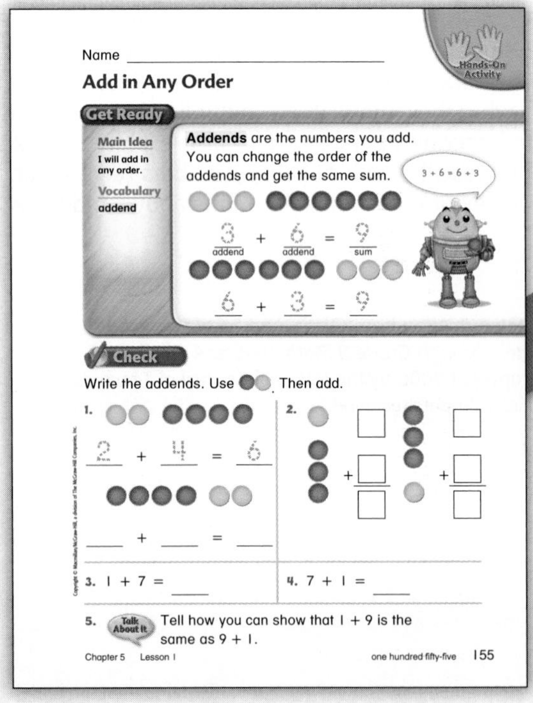

Name ____________________

Add in Any Order

Hands-On Activity

Get Ready

Main Idea
I will add in any order.

Vocabulary
addend

Addends are the numbers you add. You can change the order of the addends and get the same sum.

$3 + 6 = 6 + 3$

$3 + 6 = 9$ (addend, addend, sum)

$6 + 3 = 9$

Check

Write the addends. Use counters. Then add.

1. $2 + 4 = 6$
   ___ + ___ = ___

2. $\square + \square = \square$ $\square + \square = \square$

3. $1 + 7 =$ ___

4. $7 + 1 =$ ___

5. Talk About It Tell how you can show that $1 + 9$ is the same as $9 + 1$.

Chapter 5 Lesson 1 one hundred fifty-five 155

Math Connects, Grade 1, Student Edition, page 155

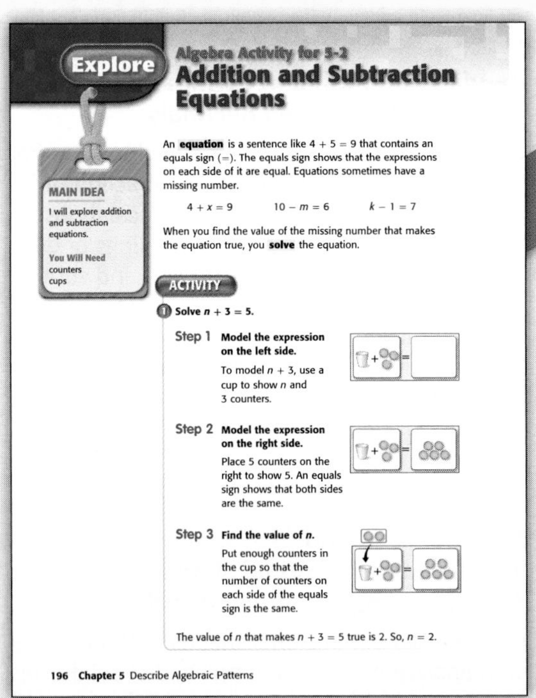

Explore Algebra Activity for 5-2

Addition and Subtraction Equations

MAIN IDEA
I will explore addition and subtraction equations.

You Will Need
counters
cups

An **equation** is a sentence like $4 + 5 = 9$ that contains an equals sign (=). The equals sign shows that the expressions on each side of it are equal. Equations sometimes have a missing number.

$4 + x = 9$ $10 - m = 6$ $k - 1 = 7$

When you find the value of the missing number that makes the equation true, you **solve** the equation.

ACTIVITY

1 **Solve $n + 3 = 5$.**

Step 1 **Model the expression on the left side.**
To model $n + 3$, use a cup to show n and 3 counters.

Step 2 **Model the expression on the right side.**
Place 5 counters on the right to show 5. An equals sign shows that both sides are the same.

Step 3 **Find the value of n.**
Put enough counters in the cup so that the number of counters on each side of the equals sign is the same.

The value of n that makes $n + 3 = 5$ true is 2. So, $n = 2$.

196 **Chapter 5** Describe Algebraic Patterns

Math Connects, Grade 4, Student Edition, page 196

Intermediate Students build on their experience with counters to using cups and counters to model and solve addition and subtraction equations. The exercises are designed to help students bridge the gap from using cups and counters to solving equations symbolically.

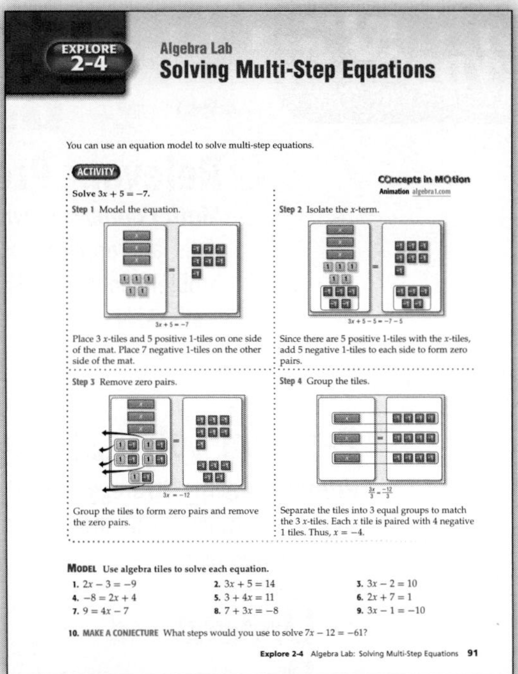

EXPLORE 2-4

Algebra Lab

Solving Multi-Step Equations

You can use an equation model to solve multi-step equations.

ACTIVITY

Concepts in MOtion
Animation algebra1.com

Solve $3x + 5 = -7$.

Step 1 Model the equation.

$3x + 5 = -7$

Place 3 x-tiles and 5 positive 1-tiles on one side of the mat. Place 7 negative 1-tiles on the other side of the mat.

Step 2 Isolate the x-term.

$3x + 5 - 5 = -7 - 5$

Since there are 5 positive 1-tiles with the x-tiles, add 5 negative 1-tiles to each side to form zero pairs.

Step 3 Remove zero pairs.

$3x = -12$

Group the tiles to form zero pairs and remove the zero pairs.

Step 4 Group the tiles.

$\frac{3x}{3} = \frac{-12}{3}$

Separate the tiles into 3 equal groups to match the 3 x-tiles. Each x tile is paired with 4 negative 1 tiles. Thus, $x = -4$.

MODEL Use algebra tiles to solve each equation.

1. $2x - 3 = -9$
2. $3x + 5 = 14$
3. $3x - 2 = 10$
4. $-8 = 2x + 4$
5. $3 + 4x = 11$
6. $2x + 7 = 1$
7. $9 = 4x - 7$
8. $7 + 3x = -8$
9. $3x - 1 = -10$

10. MAKE A CONJECTURE What steps would you use to solve $7x - 12 = -61$?

Explore 2-4 Algebra Lab: Solving Multi-Step Equations 91

Glencoe Algebra 1, Student Edition, page 91

Algebra 1 Students continue the use of algebra tiles to investigate solving multi-step equations. In the next lesson, students apply the procedure developed in the Algebra Lab to a symbolic approach.

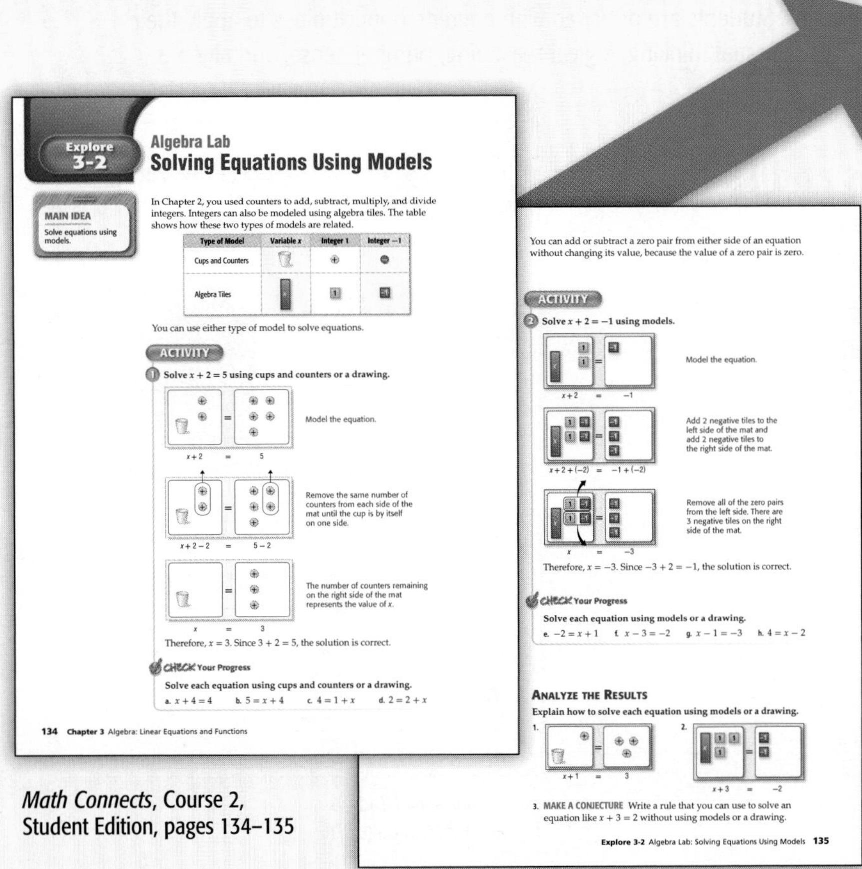

Explore 3-2

Algebra Lab

Solving Equations Using Models

MAIN IDEA

Solve equations using models.

In Chapter 2, you used counters to add, subtract, multiply, and divide integers. Integers can also be modeled using algebra tiles. The table shows how these two types of models are related.

Type of Model	Variable x	Integer 1	Integer −1
Cups and Counters			
Algebra Tiles			

You can use either type of model to solve equations.

ACTIVITY

1 Solve $x + 2 = 5$ using cups and counters or a drawing.

Model the equation.

$x + 2 = 5$

Remove the same number of counters from each side of the mat until the cup is by itself on one side.

$x + 2 - 2 = 5 - 2$

The number of counters remaining on the right side of the mat represents the value of x.

$x = 3$

Therefore, $x = 3$. Since $3 + 2 = 5$, the solution is correct.

CHECK Your Progress

Solve each equation using cups and counters or a drawing.

a. $x + 4 = 4$ b. $5 = x + 4$ c. $4 = 1 + x$ d. $2 = 2 + x$

134 Chapter 3 Algebra: Linear Equations and Functions

You can add or subtract a zero pair from either side of an equation without changing its value, because the value of a zero pair is zero.

ACTIVITY

2 Solve $x + 2 = -1$ using models.

Model the equation.

$x + 2 = -1$

Add 2 negative tiles to the left side of the mat and add 2 negative tiles to the right side of the mat.

$x + 2 + (-2) = -1 + (-2)$

Remove all of the zero pairs from the left side. There are 3 negative tiles on the right side of the mat.

$x = -3$

Therefore, $x = -3$. Since $-3 + 2 = -1$, the solution is correct.

CHECK Your Progress

Solve each equation using models or a drawing.

e. $-2 = x + 1$ f. $x - 3 = -2$ g. $x - 1 = -3$ h. $4 = x - 2$

ANALYZE THE RESULTS

Explain how to solve each equation using models or a drawing.

1. $x + 1 = 3$
2. $x + 3 = -2$

3. MAKE A CONJECTURE Write a rule that you can use to solve an equation like $x + 3 = 2$ without using models or a drawing.

Explore 3-2 Algebra Lab: Solving Equations Using Models 135

Math Connects, Course 2, Student Edition, pages 134–135

Middle School Students represent the variable *x* as a cup, as a counter, or as a written *x*. In this Algebra Lab, students make the transition from cups and counters to the more abstract algebra tiles. In the next lesson, students solve simple equations symbolically.

Continuity of Instruction The instructional sequence described demonstrates the power of backward mapping from the desired result, success in Algebra 1. This process of development avoids gaps and overlaps between grade levels and ensures that at each grade level the concepts and skills are built on the strong foundation developed in previous grades. The same approach was used across all strands throughout the entire PreK-12 series.

Program Philosophy Balance of Instruction

Relevant Problem Solving

Math Connects provides students with the appropriate development of problem-solving strategies, skills, and applications from PreK through grade 5. In grades 6–8, students continue to learn and apply problem-solving skills and strategies. Students are provided with ongoing opportunities to apply their math skills and solve problems using visual thinking, logical reasoning, number sense, and algebra.

Problem-Solving Strategies and Skills

Problem-Solving Strategy or **Skill** lessons introduce students to multiples methods for solving problems all using the *four-step* plan.

- **Understand**
- **Plan**
- **Solve**
- **Check**

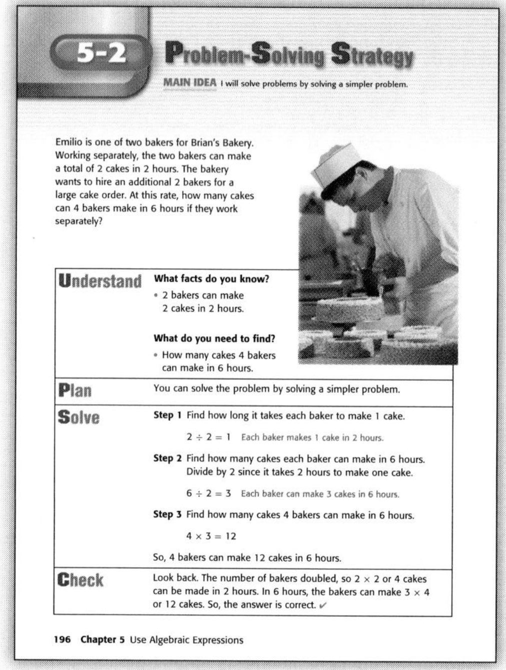

5-2 Problem-Solving Strategy

MAIN IDEA I will solve problems by solving a simpler problem.

Emilio is one of two bakers for Brian's Bakery. Working separately, the two bakers can make a total of 2 cakes in 2 hours. The bakery wants to hire an additional 2 bakers for a large cake order. At this rate, how many cakes can 4 bakers make in 6 hours if they work separately?

Understand	**What facts do you know?** • 2 bakers can make 2 cakes in 2 hours. **What do you need to find?** • How many cakes 4 bakers can make in 6 hours.
Plan	You can solve the problem by solving a simpler problem.
Solve	**Step 1** Find how long it takes each baker to make 1 cake. $2 \div 2 = 1$ Each baker makes 1 cake in 2 hours. **Step 2** Find how many cakes each baker can make in 6 hours. Divide by 2 since it takes 2 hours to make one cake. $6 \div 2 = 3$ Each baker can make 3 cakes in 6 hours. **Step 3** Find how many cakes 4 bakers can make in 6 hours. $4 \times 3 = 12$ So, 4 bakers can make 12 cakes in 6 hours.
Check	Look back. The number of bakers doubled, so 2×2 or 4 cakes can be made in 2 hours. In 6 hours, the bakers can make 3×4 or 12 cakes. So, the answer is correct. ✓

196 **Chapter 5** Use Algebraic Expressions

Math Connects, Grade 5
Student Edition, page 196

Problem-Solving Investigations

Problem-Solving Investigation lessons help students learn to choose appropriate strategies and apply them in problem-solving situations.

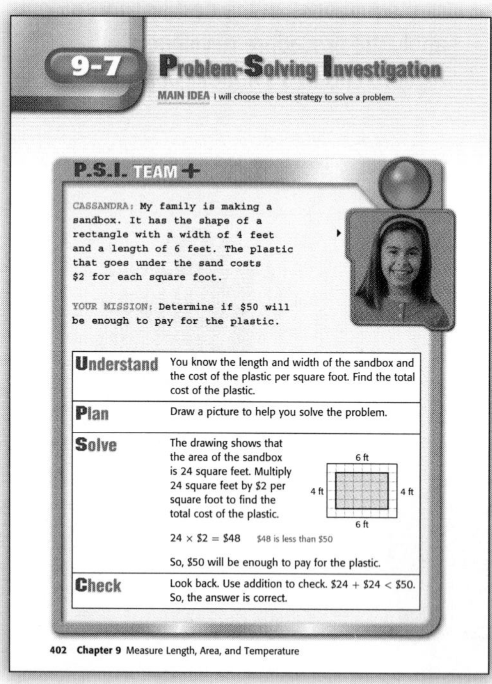

9-7 Problem-Solving Investigation

MAIN IDEA I will choose the best strategy to solve a problem.

P.S.I. TEAM +

CASSANDRA: My family is making a sandbox. It has the shape of a rectangle with a width of 4 feet and a length of 6 feet. The plastic that goes under the sand costs $2 for each square foot.

YOUR MISSION: Determine if $50 will be enough to pay for the plastic.

Understand	You know the length and width of the sandbox and the cost of the plastic per square foot. Find the total cost of the plastic.
Plan	Draw a picture to help you solve the problem.
Solve	The drawing shows that the area of the sandbox is 24 square feet. Multiply 24 square feet by $2 per square foot to find the total cost of the plastic. (6 ft, 4 ft, 4 ft, 6 ft) 24 × $2 = $48 $48 is less than $50 So, $50 will be enough to pay for the plastic.
Check	Look back. Use addition to check. $24 + $24 < $50. So, the answer is correct.

402 **Chapter 9** Measure Length, Area, and Temperature

Math Connects, Grade 3
Student Edition, page 402

Real-World Problem Solving

Each chapter has a Problem Solving lesson that makes a tie to another discipline. These lessons encourage students to see problem solving in real-world applications.

Problem Solving in Science

EMPERORS OF THE ICE

There are 17 different types of penguins. Emperor penguins are the tallest and heaviest penguins. An Emperor penguin is over 3 feet tall and can weigh from 42 to 101 pounds. The average Emperor penguin weighs 66 pounds and can swim 15 miles per hour.

About 200,000 pairs of Emperor penguins live in 40 different groups in Antarctica. Penguins huddle together to share their body heat during the cold winter temperatures and bitter winds.

Did You Know? Emperor penguins usually dive 60 to 70 feet. An average dive lasts 3 to 6 minutes.

Real-World Math

Use the information on pages 256 and 257 to solve each problem.

1. Suppose that eight average-sized Emperor penguins are standing together. What is their total weight?
2. Six penguins of varying weights are standing together. What is the least they can weigh? the most?
3. Suppose a penguin's dive lasts 4 minutes. How many times did its heart beat during the dive?
4. How many miles can a penguin swim in 3 hours?
5. Suppose it takes a penguin 3 minutes to walk from its resting place to the place where it dives. What is a reasonable number of times its heart beats in these three minutes before it dives?
6. Based on the following table, estimate how many times a penguin's heart beats after completing all of the activities listed for two minutes each.

PENGUIN HEARTBEAT

Activity	Heartbeat (beats per minute)
Resting	65
Before a dive	180–200
Hitting the water	100
Diving	20
Returning to surface	200

256 **Chapter 6** Multiply by One-Digit Numbers

Problem Solving in Science 257

Math Connects, Grade 4
Student Edition, pages 256–257

Real-World Problem Solving Readers

Fiction and nonfiction leveled readers extend problem-solving skills and strategies and make real-world applications. The books are provided for On Level, Sheltered English, and Spanish readers.

Multi-Step Word Problems

Multi-step word problems are not simple computation problems using the numbers given. Students must analyze exactly what the problem is asking and how to use the information given. These problems are starred in the Teacher Edition.

H.O.T. Problems

H.O.T. Problems require students to use **Higher Order Thinking** skills to solve problems.

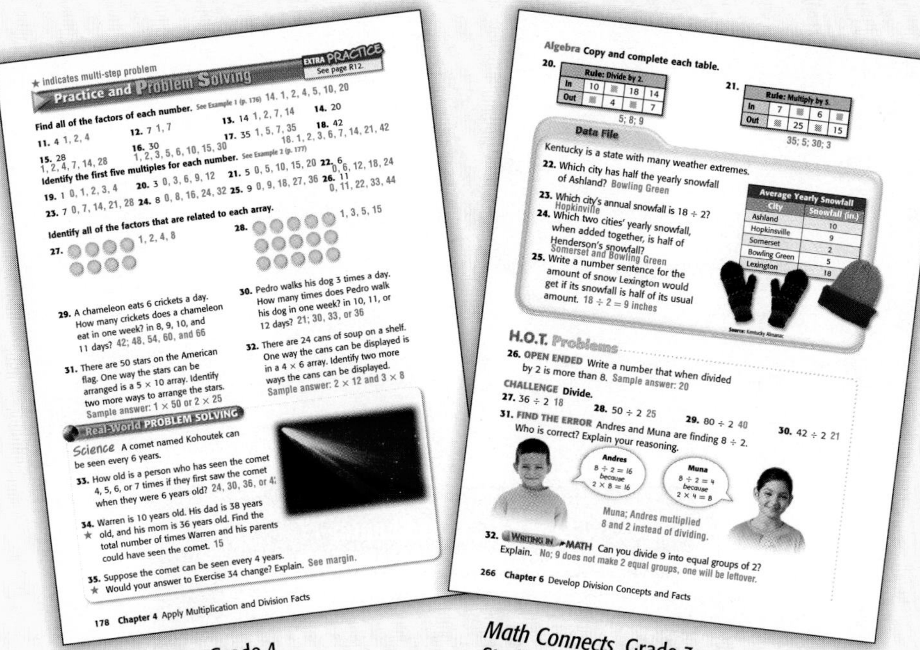

★ indicates multi-step problem

Practice and Problem Solving — EXTRA PRACTICE See page R12.

Find all of the factors of each number. See Example 1 (p. 176)

11. 4 1, 2, 4
12. 7 1, 7
13. 14 1, 2, 7, 14
14. 20 1, 2, 4, 5, 10, 20
15. 28 1, 2, 4, 7, 14, 28
16. 30 1, 2, 3, 5, 6, 10, 15, 30
17. 35 1, 5, 7, 35
18. 42 1, 2, 3, 6, 7, 14, 21, 42

Identify the first five multiples for each number. See Example 2 (p. 177)

19. 1 0, 1, 2, 3, 4
20. 3 0, 3, 6, 9, 12
21. 5 0, 5, 10, 15, 20
22. 6 0, 6, 12, 18, 24
23. 7 0, 7, 14, 21, 28
24. 8 0, 8, 16, 24, 32
25. 9 0, 9, 18, 27, 36
26. 11 0, 11, 22, 33, 44

Identify all of the factors that are related to each array.

27. 1, 2, 4, 8
28. 1, 3, 5, 15

29. A chameleon eats 6 crickets a day. How many crickets does a chameleon eat in one week? in 8, 9, 10, and 11 days? 42; 48, 54, 60, and 66
30. Pedro walks his dog 3 times a day. How many times does Pedro walk his dog in one week? in 10, 11, or 12 days? 21; 30, 33, or 36
31. There are 50 stars on the American flag. One way the stars can be arranged is a 5 × 10 array. Identify two more ways to arrange the stars. Sample answer: 1 × 50 or 2 × 25
32. There are 24 cans of soup on a shelf. One way the cans can be displayed is in a 4 × 6 array. Identify two more ways the cans can be displayed. Sample answer: 2 × 12 and 3 × 8

Real-World PROBLEM SOLVING

Science A comet named Kohoutek can be seen every 6 years.

33. How old is a person who has seen the comet 4, 5, 6, or 7 times if they first saw the comet when they were 6 years old? 24, 30, 36, or 4
34. ★ Warren is 10 years old. His dad is 38 years old, and his mom is 36 years old. Find the total number of times Warren and his parents could have seen the comet. 15
35. ★ Suppose the comet can be seen every 4 years. Would your answer to Exercise 34 change? Explain. See margin.

178 Chapter 4 Apply Multiplication and Division Facts

Math Connects, Grade 4
Student Edition, page 162

Algebra Copy and complete each table.

20.

Rule: Divide by 2.				
In	10	▒	18	14
Out	▒	4	▒	7

5; 8; 9

21.

Rule: Multiply by 5.				
In	7	▒	6	▒
Out	▒	25	▒	15

35; 5; 30; 3

Data File

Kentucky is a state with many weather extremes.

22. Which city has half the yearly snowfall of Ashland? Bowling Green
23. Which city's annual snowfall is 18 ÷ 2? Hopkinville
24. Which two cities' yearly snowfall, when added together, is half of Henderson's snowfall? Somerset and Bowling Green
25. Write a number sentence for the amount of snow Lexington would get if its snowfall is half of its usual amount. 18 ÷ 2 = 9 inches

Average Yearly Snowfall	
City	Snowfall (in.)
Ashland	10
Hopkinsville	9
Somerset	2
Bowling Green	5
Lexington	18

Source: Kentucky Almanac

H.O.T. Problems

26. OPEN ENDED Write a number that when divided by 2 is more than 8. Sample answer: 20

CHALLENGE Divide.

27. 36 ÷ 2 18
28. 50 ÷ 2 25
29. 80 ÷ 2 40
30. 42 ÷ 2 21

31. FIND THE ERROR Andres and Muna are finding 8 ÷ 2. Who is correct? Explain your reasoning.

Andres: 8 ÷ 2 = 16 because 2 × 8 = 16
Muna: 8 ÷ 2 = 4 because 2 × 4 = 8

Muna; Andres multiplied 8 and 2 instead of dividing.

32. WRITING IN MATH Can you divide 9 into equal groups of 2? Explain. No; 9 does not make 2 equal groups, one will be leftover.

266 Chapter 6 Develop Division Concepts and Facts

Math Connects, Grade 3
Student Edition, page 266

Looking Ahead

Looking Ahead lessons introduce important concepts and skills that students can use.

Math Connects, Grade 5
Student Edition, page LA0–LA1

Comprehensive Assessment System

Data-Driven Decision Making

Math Connects offers frequent and meaningful assessment of student progress within the curriculum structure and printed teacher support materials. See pages T22 and T23 for digital assessment solutions.

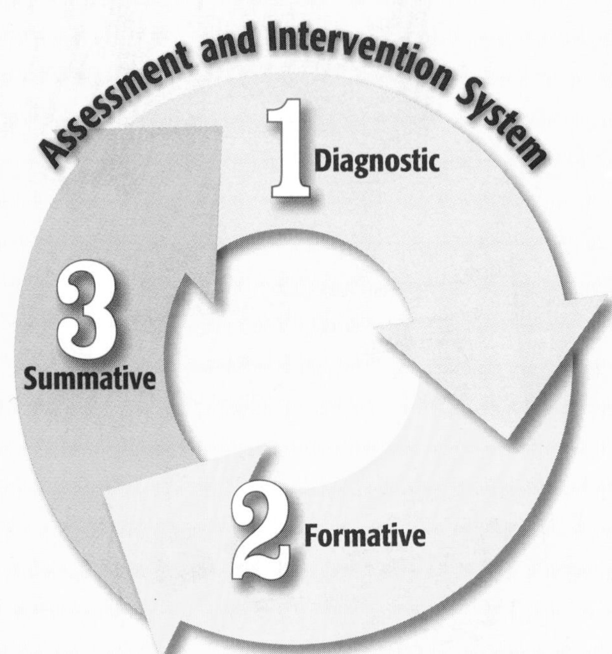

1 Diagnostic

Initial Assessment Assess students' knowledge **at the beginning of the year** with the *Diagnostic and Placement Tests*. This booklet will help you determine whether your students need additional materials and resources to meet grade-level standards.

Entry–Level Assessment Assess students' prior knowledge **at the beginning of a chapter or lesson** with one of the following options.

Student Edition

- Are You Ready?

Teacher Edition

- Intervention Options
- 5-Minute Check

Additional Resources

- Chapter Resource Masters, Chapter Diagnostic Test

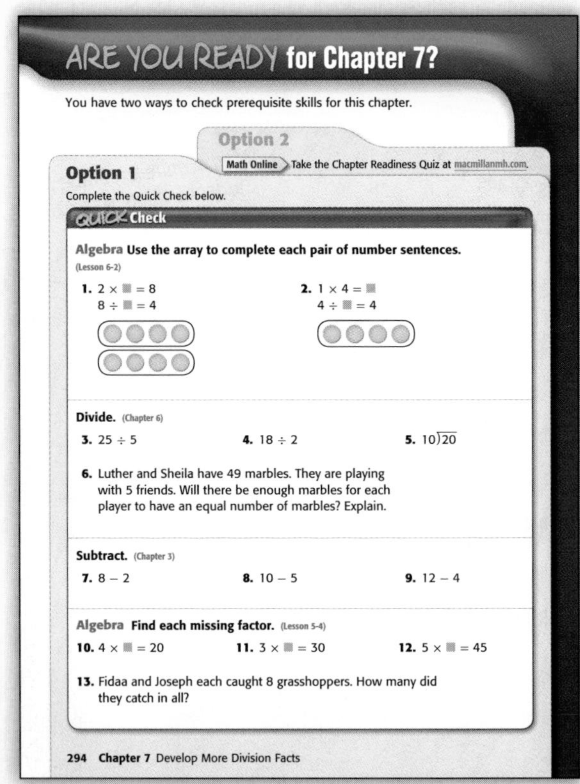

ARE YOU READY for Chapter 7?

You have two ways to check prerequisite skills for this chapter.

Option 2

Math Online Take the Chapter Readiness Quiz at macmillanmh.com.

Option 1

Complete the Quick Check below.

QUICK Check

Algebra Use the array to complete each pair of number sentences. (Lesson 6-2)

1. 2 × ■ = 8
   8 ÷ ■ = 4
2. 1 × 4 = ■
   4 ÷ ■ = 4

Divide. (Chapter 6)

3. 25 ÷ 5
4. 18 ÷ 2
5. 10)20
6. Luther and Sheila have 49 marbles. They are playing with 5 friends. Will there be enough marbles for each player to have an equal number of marbles? Explain.

Subtract. (Chapter 3)

7. 8 − 2
8. 10 − 5
9. 12 − 4

Algebra Find each missing factor. (Lesson 5-4)

10. 4 × ■ = 20
11. 3 × ■ = 30
12. 5 × ■ = 45
13. Fidaa and Joseph each caught 8 grasshoppers. How many did they catch in all?

294 Chapter 7 Develop More Division Facts

Math Connects, Grade 3
Student Edition, page 294

Formative

Progress Monitoring Determine if students are progressing adequately as you teach each lesson. Use the assessments to differentiate lesson instruction and practice.

Student Edition

- Mid-Chapter Check
- Find the Error
- Check What You Know
- Talk About It
- Writing in Math
- Study Guide and Review
- Foldables™

Teacher Edition

- Alternate Teaching Strategy
- Step 4 (Assess) of the Teaching Plan
- Quick Check
- Data-Driven Decision Making

Additional Resources

Chapter Resource Masters

- Mid-Chapter Test
- 3 Quizzes

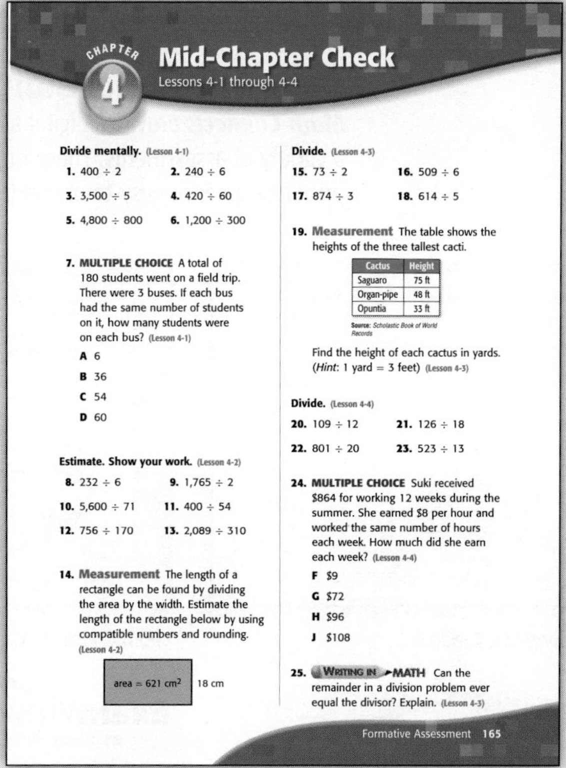

CHAPTER 4 **Mid-Chapter Check**
Lessons 4-1 through 4-4

Divide mentally. (Lesson 4-1)

1. 400 ÷ 2
2. 240 ÷ 6
3. 3,500 ÷ 5
4. 420 ÷ 60
5. 4,800 ÷ 800
6. 1,200 ÷ 300
7. **MULTIPLE CHOICE** A total of 180 students went on a field trip. There were 3 buses. If each bus had the same number of students on it, how many students were on each bus? (Lesson 4-1)
   A 6
   B 36
   C 54
   D 60

Estimate. Show your work. (Lesson 4-2)

8. 232 ÷ 6
9. 1,765 ÷ 2
10. 5,600 ÷ 71
11. 400 ÷ 54
12. 756 ÷ 170
13. 2,089 ÷ 310
14. **Measurement** The length of a rectangle can be found by dividing the area by the width. Estimate the length of the rectangle below by using compatible numbers and rounding. (Lesson 4-2)

area = 621 cm² | 18 cm

Divide. (Lesson 4-3)

15. 73 ÷ 2
16. 509 ÷ 6
17. 874 ÷ 3
18. 614 ÷ 5
19. **Measurement** The table shows the heights of the three tallest cacti.

Cactus	Height
Saguaro	75 ft
Organ-pipe	48 ft
Opuntia	33 ft

Source: Scholastic Book of World Records

Find the height of each cactus in yards. (*Hint:* 1 yard = 3 feet) (Lesson 4-3)

Divide. (Lesson 4-4)

20. 109 ÷ 12
21. 126 ÷ 18
22. 801 ÷ 20
23. 523 ÷ 13
24. **MULTIPLE CHOICE** Suki received $864 for working 12 weeks during the summer. She earned $8 per hour and worked the same number of hours each week. How much did she earn each week? (Lesson 4-4)
   F $9
   G $72
   H $96
   J $108
25. WRITING IN MATH Can the remainder in a division problem ever equal the divisor? Explain. (Lesson 4-3)

Formative Assessment 165

Math Connects, Grade 5
Student Edition, page 165

Summative

Summative Evaluation Assess student success in learning the concepts in each chapter.

Student Edition

- Chapter Test
- Test Practice
- Foldables™

Teacher Edition

- Data-Driven Decision Making

Additional Resources

Chapter Resource Masters

- Oral Assessment
- Listening Assessment
- 4 Leveled Chapter Tests
- Cumulative Test

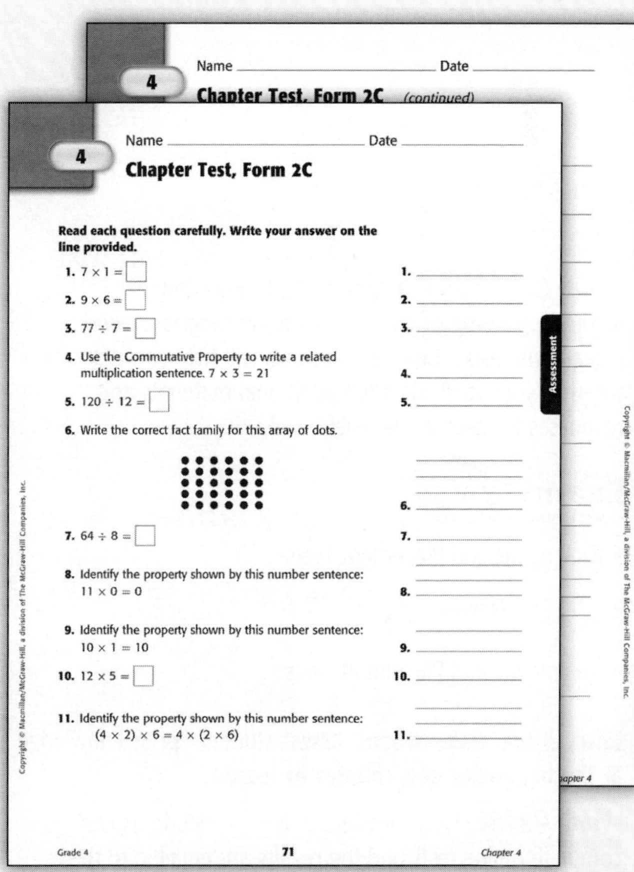

4 Name ______ Date ______
Chapter Test, Form 2C *(continued)*

4 Name ______ Date ______
Chapter Test, Form 2C

Read each question carefully. Write your answer on the line provided.

1. 7 × 1 = □ 1. ______
2. 9 × 6 = □ 2. ______
3. 77 ÷ 7 = □ 3. ______
4. Use the Commutative Property to write a related multiplication sentence. 7 × 3 = 21 4. ______
5. 120 ÷ 12 = □ 5. ______
6. Write the correct fact family for this array of dots. 6. ______
7. 64 ÷ 8 = □ 7. ______
8. Identify the property shown by this number sentence: 11 × 0 = 0 8. ______
9. Identify the property shown by this number sentence: 10 × 1 = 10 9. ______
10. 12 × 5 = □ 10. ______
11. Identify the property shown by this number sentence: (4 × 2) × 6 = 4 × (2 × 6) 11. ______

Assessment

Grade 4 71 Chapter 4

Math Connects, Grade 4
Chapter 8 Resource Masters, pages 71–72

Comprehensive Assessment System

Data-Driven Decision Making

Math Connects provides digital assessment options to create, customize, administer, and instantly score a variety of assessments. These digital solutions offer the same quality assessments and reporting as the print resources in easy-to-use technology tools.

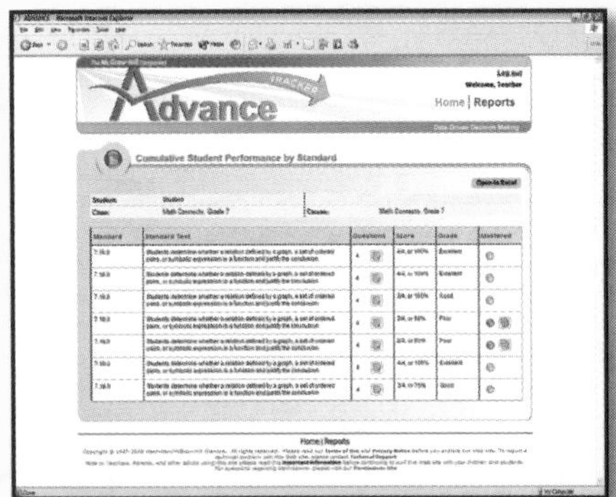

Math Connects, Grade 4

Advance Tracker helps teachers administer online tests, diagnose student achievement, and create prescriptive reports for a student or class.

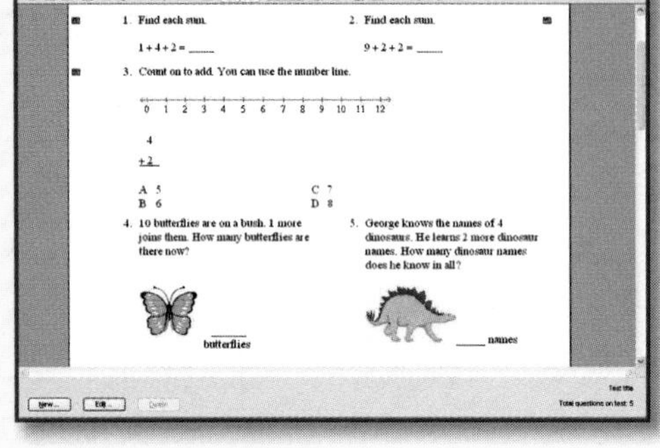

Math Connects, Grade 4

ExamView Assessment Suite allows teachers to create and customize their own assessment and assignments. Print in one or two columns to match state test.

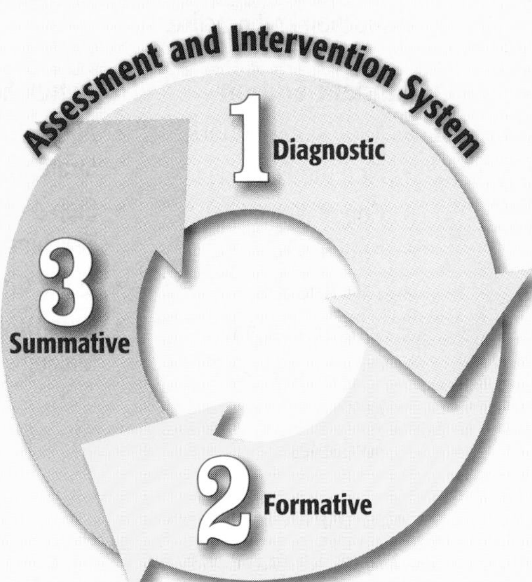

1 Diagnostic

Initial Assessment Assess students' knowledge **at the beginning of the year** with the *Diagnostic and Placement Tests.* These assessments will help you determine whether your students need additional materials and resources to meet grade-level standards.

- Diagnostic and Placement Tests

- Diagnostic and Placement Tests

Entry-Level Assessment Assess students' prior knowledge **at the beginning of a chapter or lesson.**

Math Online macmillanmh.com Students can complete online tests and the results are emailed to the teacher.

- Chapter Readiness

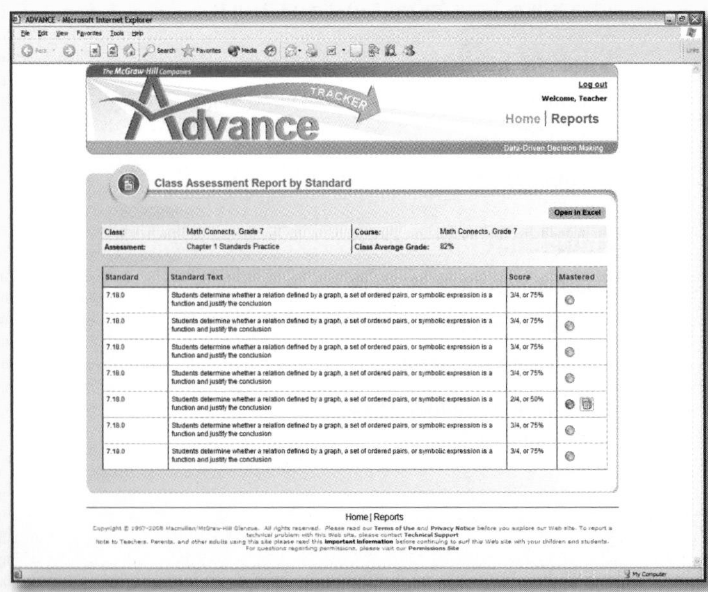

Standard	Standard Text	Score	Mastered
7.18.0	Students determine whether a relation defined by a graph, a set of ordered pairs, or symbolic expression is a function and justify the conclusion	3/4, or 75%	
7.18.0	Students determine whether a relation defined by a graph, a set of ordered pairs, or symbolic expression is a function and justify the conclusion	3/4, or 75%	
7.18.0	Students determine whether a relation defined by a graph, a set of ordered pairs, or symbolic expression is a function and justify the conclusion	3/4, or 75%	
7.18.0	Students determine whether a relation defined by a graph, a set of ordered pairs, or symbolic expression is a function and justify the conclusion	3/4, or 75%	
7.18.0	Students determine whether a relation defined by a graph, a set of ordered pairs, or symbolic expression is a function and justify the conclusion	2/4, or 50%	
7.18.0	Students determine whether a relation defined by a graph, a set of ordered pairs, or symbolic expression is a function and justify the conclusion	3/4, or 75%	
7.18.0	Students determine whether a relation defined by a graph, a set of ordered pairs, or symbolic expression is a function and justify the conclusion	3/4, or 75%	

Math Connects, Grade 5 Advance Tracker

Real-World Problem Solving Readers

Fiction and nonfiction leveled readers extend problem-solving skills and strategies and make real-world applications. The books are provided for On Level, Sheltered English, and Spanish readers.

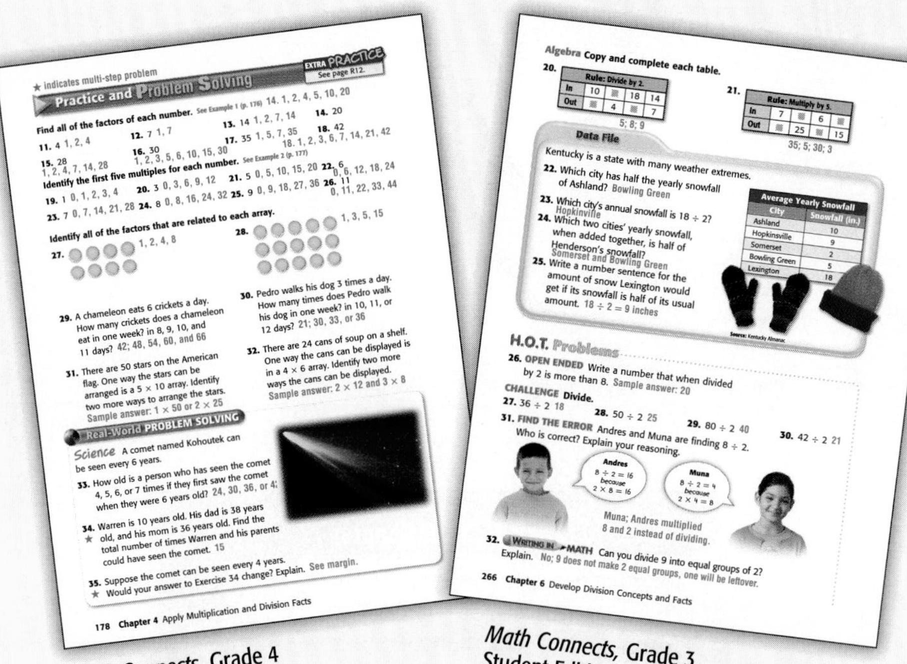

★ indicates multi-step problem

Practice and Problem Solving EXTRA PRACTICE See page R12.

Find all of the factors of each number. See Example 1 (p. 176)

11. 4 1, 2, 4
12. 7 1, 7
13. 14 1, 2, 7, 14
14. 20 1, 2, 4, 5, 10, 20
15. 28 1, 2, 4, 7, 14, 28
16. 30 1, 2, 3, 5, 6, 10, 15, 30
17. 35 1, 5, 7, 35
18. 42 1, 2, 3, 6, 7, 14, 21, 42

Identify the first five multiples for each number. See Example 2 (p. 177)

19. 1 0, 1, 2, 3, 4
20. 3 0, 3, 6, 9, 12
21. 5 0, 5, 10, 15, 20
22. 6 0, 6, 12, 18, 24
23. 7 0, 7, 14, 21, 28
24. 8 0, 8, 16, 24, 32
25. 9 0, 9, 18, 27, 36
26. 11 0, 11, 22, 33, 44

Identify all of the factors that are related to each array.

27. 1, 2, 4, 8
28. 1, 3, 5, 15

29. A chameleon eats 6 crickets a day. How many crickets does a chameleon eat in one week? in 8, 9, 10, and 11 days? 42; 48, 54, 60, and 66

30. Pedro walks his dog 3 times a day. How many times does Pedro walk his dog in one week? in 10, 11, or 12 days? 21; 30, 33, or 36

31. There are 50 stars on the American flag. One way the stars can be arranged is a 5 × 10 array. Identify two more ways to arrange the stars. Sample answer: 1 × 50 or 2 × 25

32. There are 24 cans of soup on a shelf. One way the cans can be displayed is in a 4 × 6 array. Identify two more ways the cans can be displayed. Sample answer: 2 × 12 and 3 × 8

Real-World PROBLEM SOLVING

Science A comet named Kohoutek can be seen every 6 years.

33. How old is a person who has seen the comet 4, 5, 6, or 7 times if they first saw the comet when they were 6 years old? 24, 30, 36, or 42

34. ★ Warren is 10 years old. His dad is 38 years old, and his mom is 36 years old. Find the total number of times Warren and his parents could have seen the comet. 15

35. ★ Suppose the comet can be seen every 4 years. Would your answer to Exercise 34 change? Explain. See margin.

178 **Chapter 4** Apply Multiplication and Division Facts

Math Connects, Grade 4
Student Edition, page 162

Algebra Copy and complete each table.

20.

Rule: Divide by 2.				
In	10	■	18	14
Out	■	4	■	7

5; 8; 9

21.

Rule: Multiply by 5.				
In	7	■	6	■
Out	■	25	■	15

35; 5; 30; 3

Data File

Kentucky is a state with many weather extremes.

22. Which city has half the yearly snowfall of Ashland? Bowling Green

23. Which city's annual snowfall is 18 ÷ 2? Hopkinville

24. Which two cities' yearly snowfall, when added together, is half of Henderson's snowfall? Somerset and Bowling Green

25. Write a number sentence for the amount of snow Lexington would get if its snowfall is half of its usual amount. 18 ÷ 2 = 9 inches

Average Yearly Snowfall	
City	Snowfall (in.)
Ashland	10
Hopkinsville	9
Somerset	2
Bowling Green	5
Lexington	18

Source: Kentucky Almanac

H.O.T. Problems

26. **OPEN ENDED** Write a number that when divided by 2 is more than 8. Sample answer: 20

CHALLENGE Divide.

27. 36 ÷ 2 18
28. 50 ÷ 2 25
29. 80 ÷ 2 40
30. 42 ÷ 2 21

31. **FIND THE ERROR** Andres and Muna are finding 8 ÷ 2. Who is correct? Explain your reasoning.

Muna; Andres multiplied 8 and 2 instead of dividing.

32. **WRITING IN MATH** Can you divide 9 into equal groups of 2? Explain. No; 9 does not make 2 equal groups, one will be leftover.

266 **Chapter 6** Develop Division Concepts and Facts

Math Connects, Grade 3
Student Edition, page 266

Multi-Step Word Problems

Multi-step word problems are not simple computation problems using the numbers given. Students must analyze exactly what the problem is asking and how to use the information given. These problems are starred in the Teacher Edition.

H.O.T. Problems

H.O.T. Problems require students to use **Higher Order Thinking** skills to solve problems.

Looking Ahead

Looking Ahead lessons introduce important concepts and skills that students can use.

Looking Ahead

Let's Look Ahead!

Math Connects, Grade 5
Student Edition, page LA0–LA1

Comprehensive Assessment System

Data-Driven Decision Making

Math Connects offers frequent and meaningful assessment of student progress within the curriculum structure and printed teacher support materials. See pages T22 and T23 for digital assessment solutions.

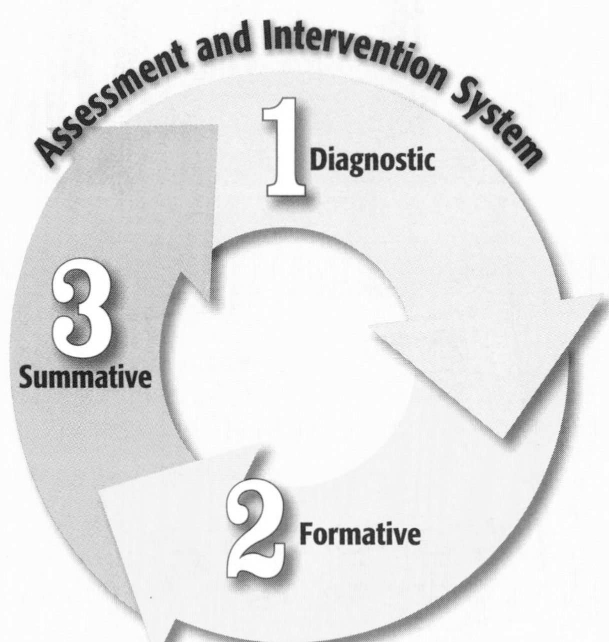

1 Diagnostic

Initial Assessment Assess students' knowledge **at the beginning of the year** with the *Diagnostic and Placement Tests*. This booklet will help you determine whether your students need additional materials and resources to meet grade-level standards.

Entry–Level Assessment Assess students' prior knowledge **at the beginning of a chapter or lesson** with one of the following options.

Student Edition

- Are You Ready?

Teacher Edition

- Intervention Options
- 5-Minute Check

Additional Resources

- Chapter Resource Masters, Chapter Diagnostic Test

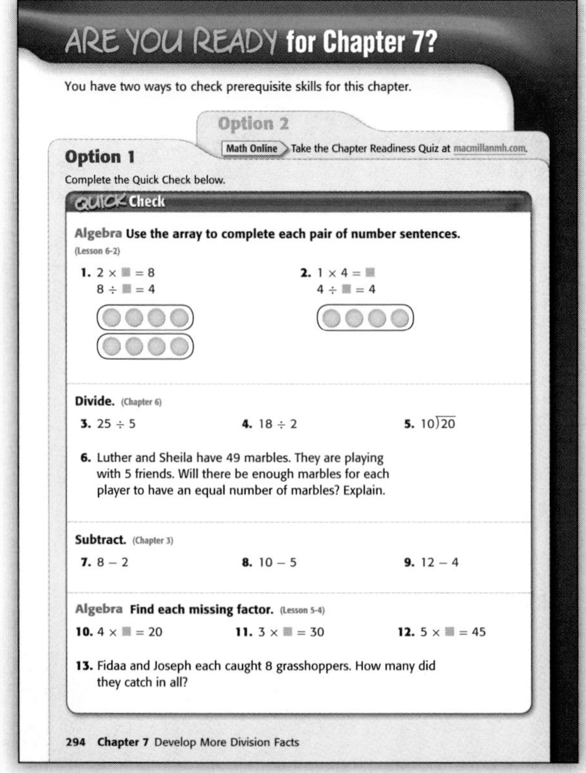

ARE YOU READY for Chapter 7?

You have two ways to check prerequisite skills for this chapter.

Option 2

Math Online Take the Chapter Readiness Quiz at macmillanmh.com.

Option 1

Complete the Quick Check below.

QUICK Check

Algebra Use the array to complete each pair of number sentences. (Lesson 6-2)

1. 2 × ■ = 8
   8 ÷ ■ = 4
2. 1 × 4 = ■
   4 ÷ ■ = 4

Divide. (Chapter 6)

3. 25 ÷ 5
4. 18 ÷ 2
5. 10)20
6. Luther and Sheila have 49 marbles. They are playing with 5 friends. Will there be enough marbles for each player to have an equal number of marbles? Explain.

Subtract. (Chapter 3)

7. 8 − 2
8. 10 − 5
9. 12 − 4

Algebra Find each missing factor. (Lesson 5-4)

10. 4 × ■ = 20
11. 3 × ■ = 30
12. 5 × ■ = 45
13. Fidaa and Joseph each caught 8 grasshoppers. How many did they catch in all?

294 Chapter 7 Develop More Division Facts

Math Connects, Grade 3
Student Edition, page 294

2 Formative

Progress Monitoring Determine if students are progressing adequately as you teach each lesson. Use the assessments to differentiate lesson instruction and practice.

Student Edition

- Mid-Chapter Check
- Find the Error
- Check What You Know
- Talk About It
- Writing in Math
- Study Guide and Review
- Foldables™

Teacher Edition

- Alternate Teaching Strategy
- Step 4 (Assess) of the Teaching Plan
- Quick Check
- Data-Driven Decision Making

Additional Resources

Chapter Resource Masters

- Mid-Chapter Test
- 3 Quizzes

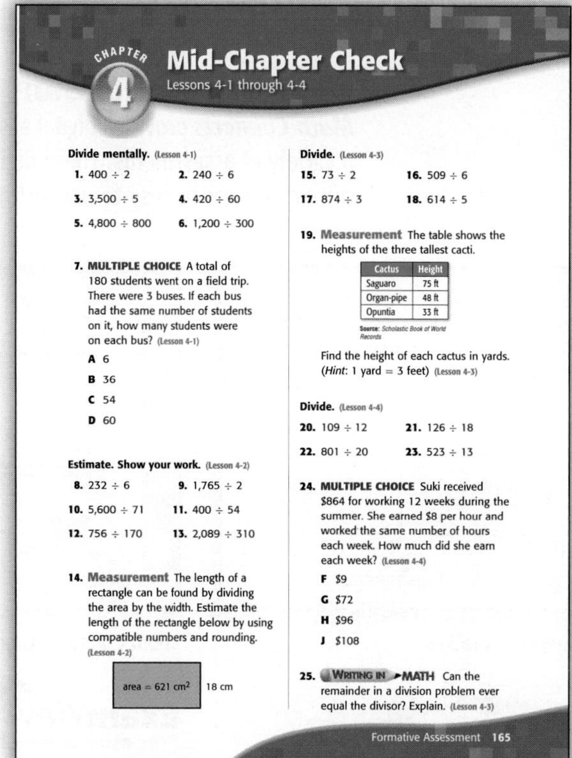

CHAPTER 4 **Mid-Chapter Check**
Lessons 4-1 through 4-4

Divide mentally. (Lesson 4-1)

1. 400 ÷ 2
2. 240 ÷ 6
3. 3,500 ÷ 5
4. 420 ÷ 60
5. 4,800 ÷ 800
6. 1,200 ÷ 300

7. **MULTIPLE CHOICE** A total of 180 students went on a field trip. There were 3 buses. If each bus had the same number of students on it, how many students were on each bus? (Lesson 4-1)
A 6
B 36
C 54
D 60

Estimate. Show your work. (Lesson 4-2)

8. 232 ÷ 6
9. 1,765 ÷ 2
10. 5,600 ÷ 71
11. 400 ÷ 54
12. 756 ÷ 170
13. 2,089 ÷ 310

14. **Measurement** The length of a rectangle can be found by dividing the area by the width. Estimate the length of the rectangle below by using compatible numbers and rounding. (Lesson 4-2)

area = 621 cm² 18 cm

Divide. (Lesson 4-3)

15. 73 ÷ 2
16. 509 ÷ 6
17. 874 ÷ 3
18. 614 ÷ 5

19. **Measurement** The table shows the heights of the three tallest cacti.

Cactus	Height
Saguaro	75 ft
Organ-pipe	48 ft
Opuntia	33 ft

Source: Scholastic Book of World Records

Find the height of each cactus in yards. (*Hint*: 1 yard = 3 feet) (Lesson 4-3)

Divide. (Lesson 4-4)

20. 109 ÷ 12
21. 126 ÷ 18
22. 801 ÷ 20
23. 523 ÷ 13

24. **MULTIPLE CHOICE** Suki received $864 for working 12 weeks during the summer. She earned $8 per hour and worked the same number of hours each week. How much did she earn each week? (Lesson 4-4)
F $9
G $72
H $96
J $108

25. WRITING IN MATH Can the remainder in a division problem ever equal the divisor? Explain. (Lesson 4-3)

Formative Assessment 165

Math Connects, Grade 5
Student Edition, page 165

3 Summative

Summative Evaluation Assess student success in learning the concepts in each chapter.

Student Edition

- Chapter Test
- Test Practice
- Foldables™

Teacher Edition

- Data-Driven Decision Making

Additional Resources

Chapter Resource Masters

- Oral Assessment
- Listening Assessment
- 4 Leveled Chapter Tests
- Cumulative Test

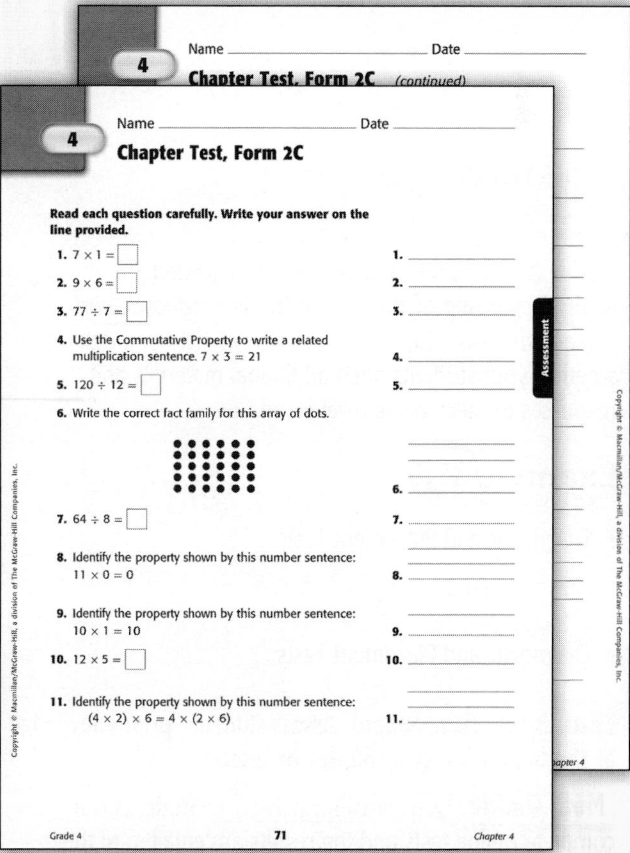

4 Name ______ Date ______
Chapter Test, Form 2C *(continued)*

4 Name ______ Date ______
Chapter Test, Form 2C

Read each question carefully. Write your answer on the line provided.

1. 7 × 1 = ☐
2. 9 × 6 = ☐
3. 77 ÷ 7 = ☐
4. Use the Commutative Property to write a related multiplication sentence. 7 × 3 = 21
5. 120 ÷ 12 = ☐
6. Write the correct fact family for this array of dots.
7. 64 ÷ 8 = ☐
8. Identify the property shown by this number sentence: 11 × 0 = 0
9. Identify the property shown by this number sentence: 10 × 1 = 10
10. 12 × 5 = ☐
11. Identify the property shown by this number sentence: (4 × 2) × 6 = 4 × (2 × 6)

Assessment

Copyright © Macmillan/McGraw-Hill, a division of The McGraw-Hill Companies, Inc.

Grade 4 71 Chapter 4

Math Connects, Grade 4
Chapter 8 Resource Masters, pages 71–72

Comprehensive Assessment System

Data-Driven Decision Making

Math Connects provides digital assessment options to create, customize, administer, and instantly score a variety of assessments. These digital solutions offer the same quality assessments and reporting as the print resources in easy-to-use technology tools.

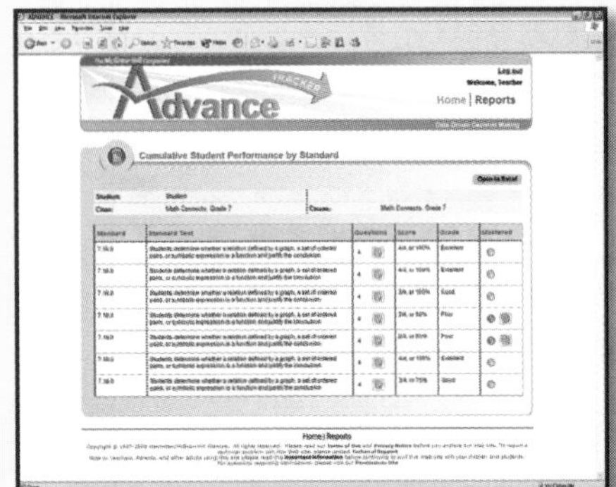

Math Connects, Grade 4

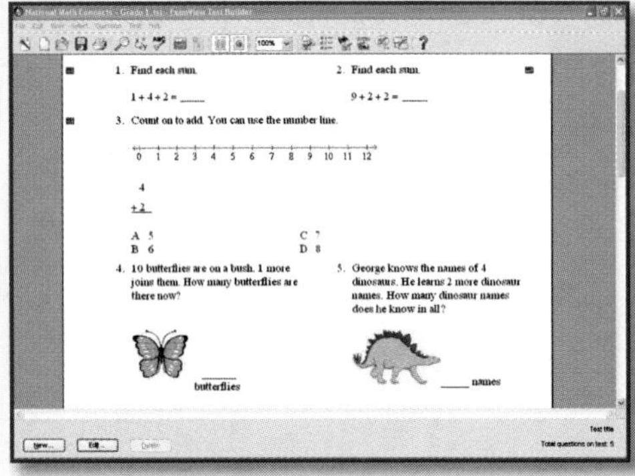

Math Connects, Grade 4

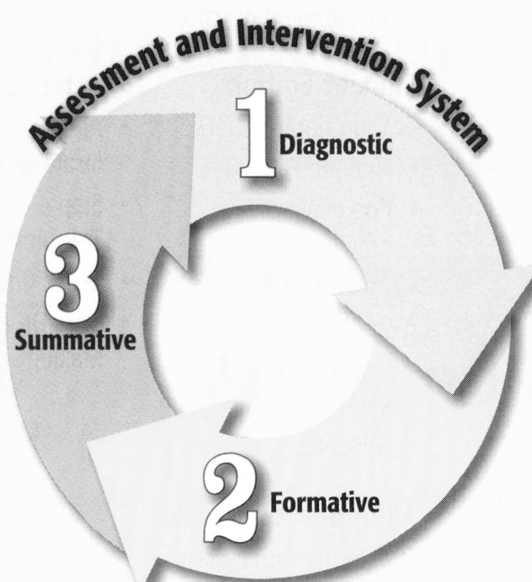

Advance Tracker helps teachers administer online tests, diagnose student achievement, and create prescriptive reports for a student or class.

ExamView Assessment Suite allows teachers to create and customize their own assessment and assignments. Print in one or two columns to match state test.

1 Diagnostic

Initial Assessment Assess students' knowledge **at the beginning of the year** with the *Diagnostic and Placement Tests.* These assessments will help you determine whether your students need additional materials and resources to meet grade-level standards.

- Diagnostic and Placement Tests

- Diagnostic and Placement Tests

Entry-Level Assessment Assess students' prior knowledge **at the beginning of a chapter or lesson.**

ath Online macmillanmh.com Students can ...plete online tests and the results are emailed to the ...r.

...er Readiness

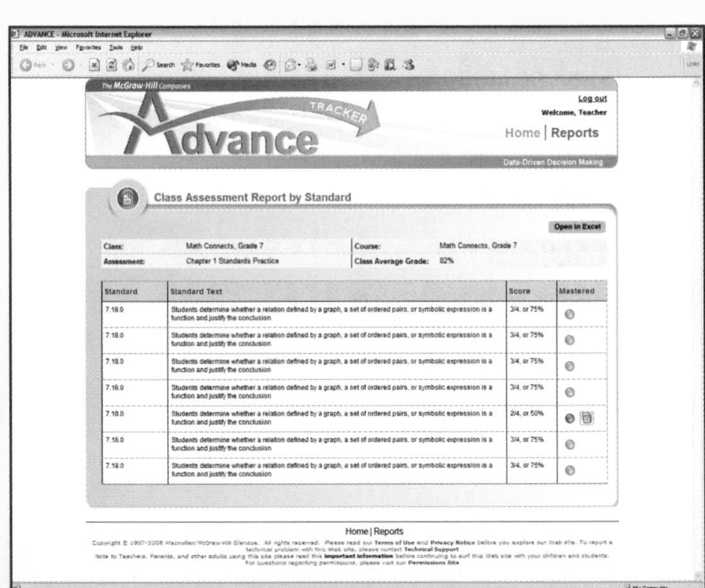

ADVANCE - Microsoft Internet Explorer

Advance TRACKER — Log out | Welcome, Teacher | Home | Reports | Data-Driven Decision Making

Class Assessment Report by Standard

Open in Excel

Class:	Math Connects, Grade 7	Course:	Math Connects, Grade 7
Assessment:	Chapter 1 Standards Practice	Class Average Grade:	82%

Standard	Standard Text	Score	Mastered
7.18.0	Students determine whether a relation defined by a graph, a set of ordered pairs, or symbolic expression is a function and justify the conclusion	3/4, or 75%	
7.18.0	Students determine whether a relation defined by a graph, a set of ordered pairs, or symbolic expression is a function and justify the conclusion	3/4, or 75%	
7.18.0	Students determine whether a relation defined by a graph, a set of ordered pairs, or symbolic expression is a function and justify the conclusion	3/4, or 75%	
7.18.0	Students determine whether a relation defined by a graph, a set of ordered pairs, or symbolic expression is a function and justify the conclusion	3/4, or 75%	
7.18.0	Students determine whether a relation defined by a graph, a set of ordered pairs, or symbolic expression is a function and justify the conclusion	2/4, or 50%	
7.18.0	Students determine whether a relation defined by a graph, a set of ordered pairs, or symbolic expression is a function and justify the conclusion	3/4, or 75%	
7.18.0	Students determine whether a relation defined by a graph, a set of ordered pairs, or symbolic expression is a function and justify the conclusion	3/4, or 75%	

Home | Reports

Copyright © 1997-2008 Macmillan/McGraw-Hill Glencoe. All rights reserved.

Math Connects, Grade 5 Advance Tracker

Formative

Progress Monitoring Determine if students are progressing adequately as you teach each lesson. Use the assessments to differentiate lesson instruction and practice.

- Mid-Chapter Test
- Study Guide and Review

Math Online macmillanmh.com

- Self-Check Quizzes

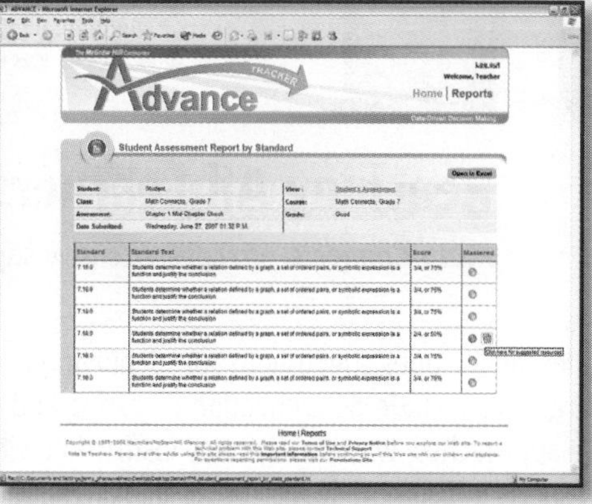

Math Connects, Grade 3, Advance Tracker

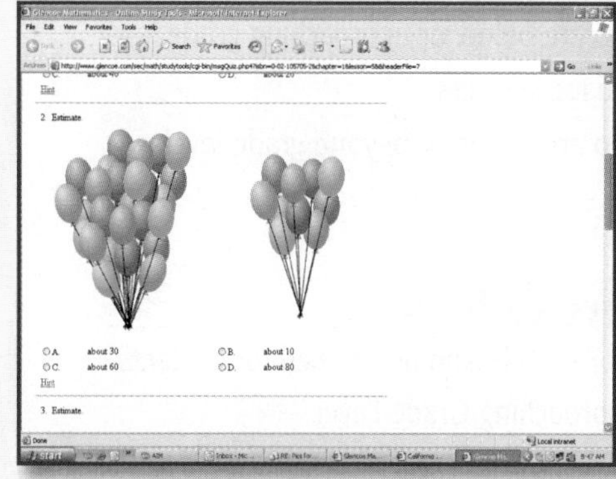

Math Connects, Grade 4, Self-Check Quiz

Summative

Summative Evaluation Assess students' success in learning the concepts in each chapter.

- Chapter Tests
- Cumulative Standardized Test Practice

- Chapter Tests
- Cumulative Standardized Test Practice

Math Online macmillanmh.com

- Chapter Tests

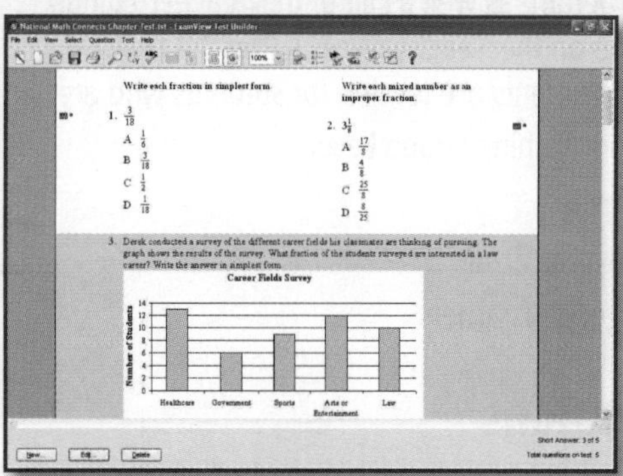

Math Connects, Grade 5, ExamView Assessment Suite

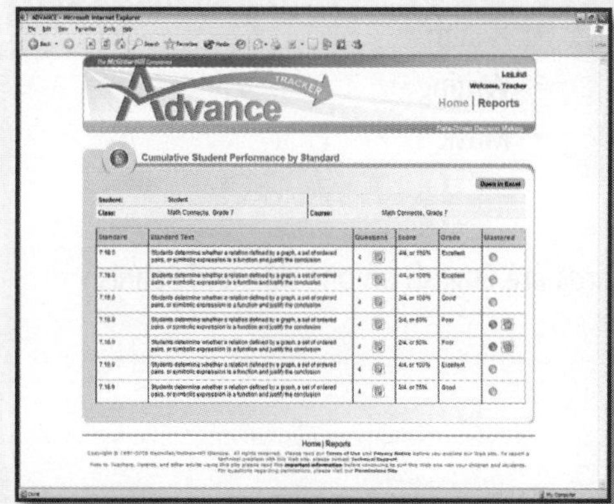

Math Connects, Grade 4, Advance Tracker

Differentiated Instruction

Reaching All Learners

Math Connects, provides extensive support for reaching all learners.

Every chapter and lesson includes suggestions for identifying and meeting your students' needs. Strategies include differentiation in pacing and student grouping, alternate approaches, ways to enhance instruction with manipulatives, questions to promote higher-order thinking, and language hints.

Personalize instruction for:

- BL Students who are below or approaching grade level
- ELL English language learners
- AL Students who are above or beyond grade level

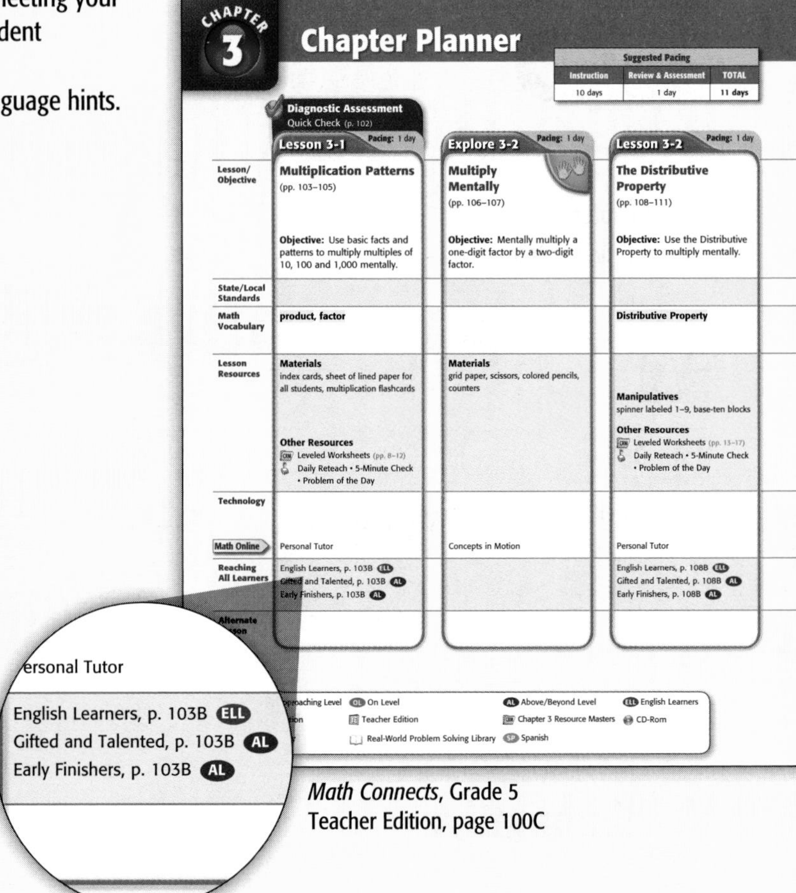

Chapter 3 **Chapter Planner**

Suggested Pacing		
Instruction	Review & Assessment	TOTAL
10 days	1 day	11 days

Diagnostic Assessment
Quick Check (p. 102)

	Lesson 3-1 (Pacing: 1 day)	Explore 3-2 (Pacing: 1 day)	Lesson 3-2 (Pacing: 1 day)
Lesson/ Objective	**Multiplication Patterns** (pp. 103–105) **Objective:** Use basic facts and patterns to multiply multiples of 10, 100 and 1,000 mentally.	**Multiply Mentally** (pp. 106–107) **Objective:** Mentally multiply a one-digit factor by a two-digit factor.	**The Distributive Property** (pp. 108–111) **Objective:** Use the Distributive Property to multiply mentally.
State/Local Standards			
Math Vocabulary	**product, factor**		**Distributive Property**
Lesson Resources	**Materials** index cards, sheet of lined paper for all students, multiplication flashcards **Other Resources** Leveled Worksheets (pp. 8–12) Daily Reteach • 5-Minute Check • Problem of the Day	**Materials** grid paper, scissors, colored pencils, counters	**Manipulatives** spinner labeled 1–9, base-ten blocks **Other Resources** Leveled Worksheets (pp. 13–17) Daily Reteach • 5-Minute Check • Problem of the Day
Technology Math Online	Personal Tutor	Concepts in Motion	Personal Tutor
Reaching All Learners	English Learners, p. 103B ELL Gifted and Talented, p. 103B AL Early Finishers, p. 103B AL		English Learners, p. 108B ELL Gifted and Talented, p. 108B AL Early Finishers, p. 108B AL
Alternate Lesson			

Key: Approaching Level · OL On Level · AL Above/Beyond Level · ELL English Learners · Teacher Edition · Chapter 3 Resource Masters · CD-Rom · Real-World Problem Solving Library · SP Spanish

Personal Tutor
English Learners, p. 103B ELL
Gifted and Talented, p. 103B AL
Early Finishers, p. 103B AL

Math Connects, Grade 5
Teacher Edition, page 100C

Leveled Exercise Sets

The assignments for each lesson are leveled for students.

- BL Below or Approaching Grade Level
- OL on Grade Level
- AL Above or Beyond Grade Level

Leveled Resources

All of the blackline masters and transparencies that accompany the program, as well as all of the Teacher Edition pages, are available on the **TeacherWorks Plus™ CD-ROM.** Resources and assignments are leveled for students who are:

- BL Below or Approaching Grade Level
- OL On Grade Level
- AL Above or Beyond Grade Level
- ELL English Language Learners

Learning Stations

Cross-curricular learning centers offer students guided opportunities to explore chapter concepts as individuals or in small groups. Content areas include:

- Science
- Social Studies
- Reading
- Art
- Health
- Writing
- Music

Learning Station cards are English on one side and Spanish on the other.

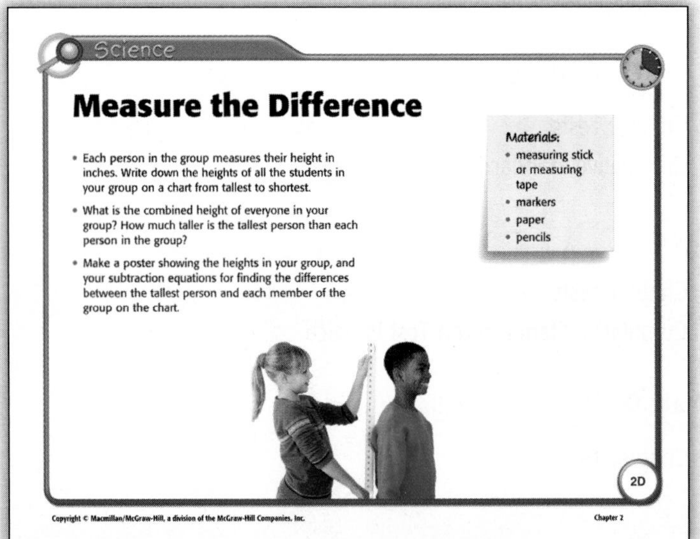

Science

Measure the Difference

- Each person in the group measures their height in inches. Write down the heights of all the students in your group on a chart from tallest to shortest.
- What is the combined height of everyone in your group? How much taller is the tallest person than each person in the group?
- Make a poster showing the heights in your group, and your subtraction equations for finding the differences between the tallest person and each member of the group on the chart.

Materials:
- measuring stick or measuring tape
- markers
- paper
- pencils

2D

Copyright © Macmillan/McGraw-Hill, a division of the McGraw-Hill Companies, Inc.

Chapter 2

Math Connects, Grade 4
Learning Station Card 2D

Advanced Learners

Acceleration and Enrichment Resources and assignments for students who are above level may be used with advanced learners. In particular, the **Enrich Masters** provide students with valuable opportunities for extending your lessons.

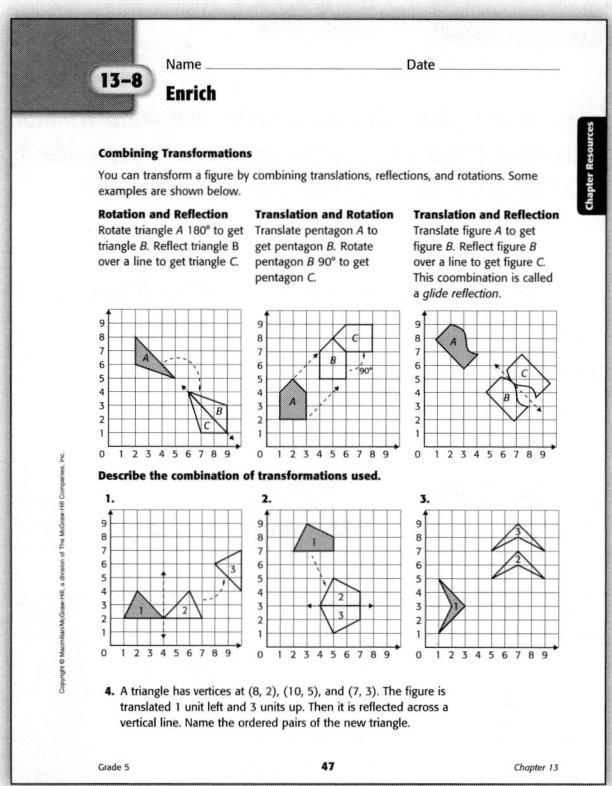

13-8 Name ______ Date ______

Enrich

Combining Transformations

You can transform a figure by combining translations, reflections, and rotations. Some examples are shown below.

Rotation and Reflection Rotate triangle *A* 180° to get triangle *B*. Reflect triangle B over a line to get triangle *C*.

Translation and Rotation Translate pentagon *A* to get pentagon *B*. Rotate pentagon *B* 90° to get pentagon *C*.

Translation and Reflection Translate figure *A* to get figure *B*. Reflect figure *B* over a line to get figure *C*. This coombination is called a *glide reflection*.

Describe the combination of transformations used.

1.

2.

3.

4. A triangle has vertices at (8, 2), (10, 5), and (7, 3). The figure is translated 1 unit left and 3 units up. Then it is reflected across a vertical line. Name the ordered pairs of the new triangle.

Grade 5 47 Chapter 13

Math Connects, Grade 5,
Chapter 13 Resource Masters, page 47

ELL English Language Learners

Our authors have identified seven keys for effective instruction with English language learner students and used them throughout the program.

1. Simplify language, not concepts.
2. Activate background knowledge.
3. Teach in multiple modalities.
4. Use core vocabulary and common use verbs.
5. Express mathematical understanding in different ways.
6. Incorporate higher-level problem-solving skills.
7. Provide a mathematics-rich classroom environment.

The English Language Learners Guide provides additional support for English language learner students that can be used alone or with core instruction in the Student Edition and Teacher Edition.

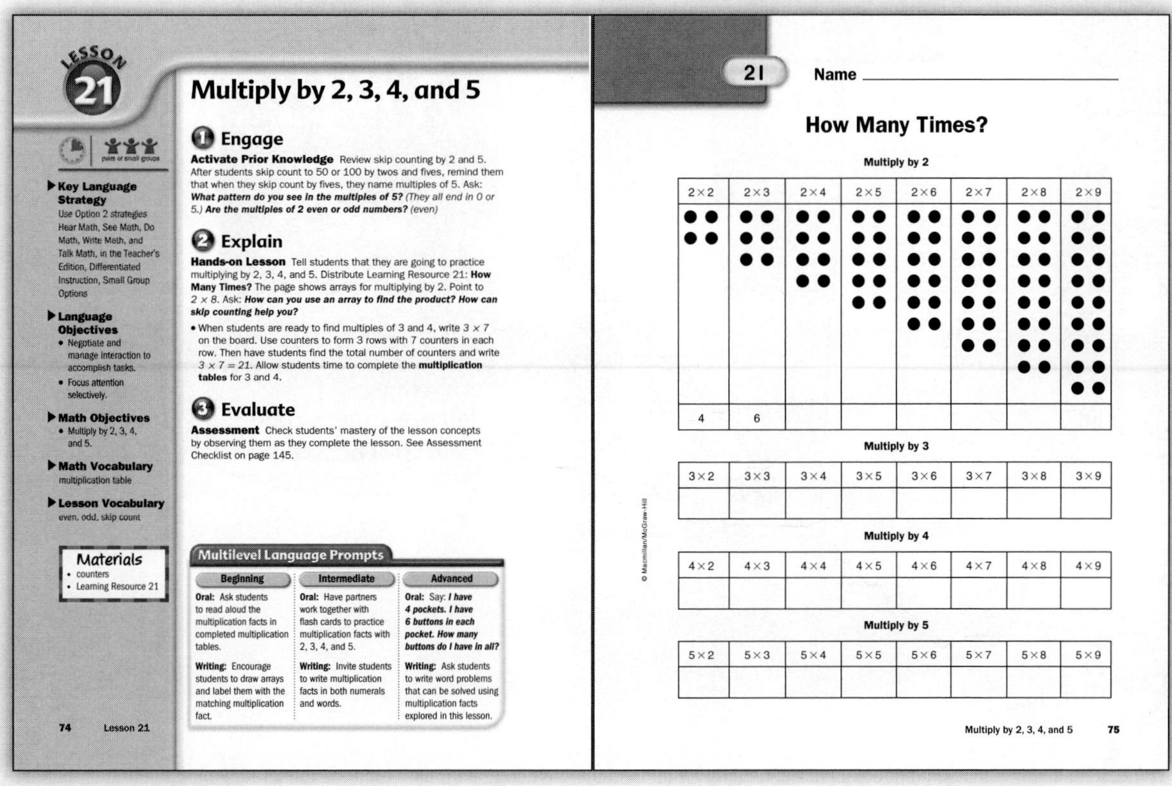

LESSON 21

Multiply by 2, 3, 4, and 5

pairs or small groups

Key Language Strategy
Use Option 2 strategies Hear Math, See Math, Do Math, Write Math, and Talk Math, in the Teacher's Edition, Differentiated Instruction, Small Group Options

Language Objectives
- Negotiate and manage interaction to accomplish tasks.
- Focus attention selectively.

Math Objectives
- Multiply by 2, 3, 4, and 5.

Math Vocabulary
multiplication table

Lesson Vocabulary
even, odd, skip count

Materials
- counters
- Learning Resource 21

1 Engage

Activate Prior Knowledge Review skip counting by 2 and 5. After students skip count to 50 or 100 by twos and fives, remind them that when they skip count by fives, they name multiples of 5. Ask: ***What pattern do you see in the multiples of 5?*** *(They all end in 0 or 5.)* ***Are the multiples of 2 even or odd numbers?*** *(even)*

2 Explain

Hands-on Lesson Tell students that they are going to practice multiplying by 2, 3, 4, and 5. Distribute Learning Resource 21: **How Many Times?** The page shows arrays for multiplying by 2. Point to 2×8. Ask: ***How can you use an array to find the product? How can skip counting help you?***

- When students are ready to find multiples of 3 and 4, write 3×7 on the board. Use counters to form 3 rows with 7 counters in each row. Then have students find the total number of counters and write $3 \times 7 = 21$. Allow students time to complete the **multiplication tables** for 3 and 4.

3 Evaluate

Assessment Check students' mastery of the lesson concepts by observing them as they complete the lesson. See Assessment Checklist on page 145.

Multilevel Language Prompts

Beginning	Intermediate	Advanced
Oral: Ask students to read aloud the multiplication facts in completed multiplication tables.	**Oral:** Have partners work together with flash cards to practice multiplication facts with 2, 3, 4, and 5.	**Oral:** Say: ***I have 4 pockets. I have 6 buttons in each pocket. How many buttons do I have in all?***
Writing: Encourage students to draw arrays and label them with the matching multiplication fact.	**Writing:** Invite students to write multiplication facts in both numerals and words.	**Writing:** Ask students to write word problems that can be solved using multiplication facts explored in this lesson.

74 Lesson 21

21 Name ______

How Many Times?

Multiply by 2

2×2	2×3	2×4	2×5	2×6	2×7	2×8	2×9
4	6						

Multiply by 3

3×2	3×3	3×4	3×5	3×6	3×7	3×8	3×9

Multiply by 4

4×2	4×3	4×4	4×5	4×6	4×7	4×8	4×9

Multiply by 5

5×2	5×3	5×4	5×5	5×6	5×7	5×8	5×9

Multiply by 2, 3, 4, and 5 75

Math Connects, Grade 3
ELL Guide, pages 74–75

Blending Your Instruction

Basal – NSF-Funded – Tier 3 Intervention

Math Connects, IMPACT Mathematics, and ***Math Triumphs*** provide a three-pronged approach to mathematics instruction. This unique combination provides built-in strategies to easily tip the balance of instruction to a more conceptual approach or to a more skills-based approach, depending on the needs of your students.

These programs are horizontally aligned in the following ways.

- Common vocabulary
- Common manipulatives
- Common teacher planning guides
- Common technology
- Common authors
- Common professional development

Basal Program–Focused on Comprehensive Instruction

NSF Program–Focused on Investigations

Intensive Intervention (Tier 3 RTI)–Focused on Skills

RTI (Response to Intervention)

In the ***Math Connects*** Teacher Editions, the Data-Driven Decision Making chart provides a comprehensive RTI (Response to Intervention) beginning with diagnostic review and continuing with prescriptions at all three RTI tiers.

- **Tier 1** – Leveled exercise sets and leveled resources
- **Tier 2** – Strategic Intervention Guide (1–5), Study Guide and Intervention (6–8)
- **Tier 3** – Intensive Intervention, ***Math Triumphs***

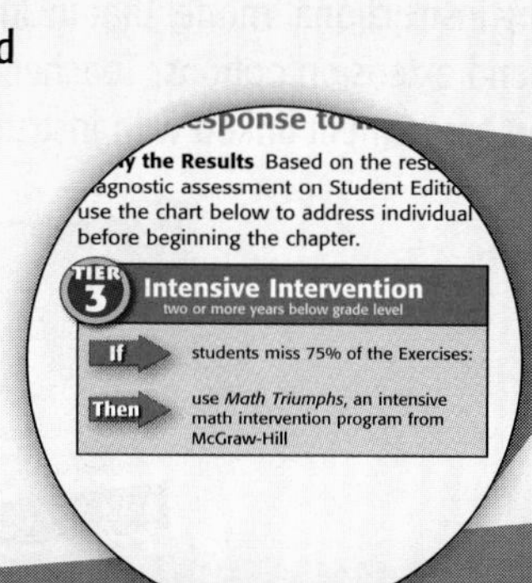

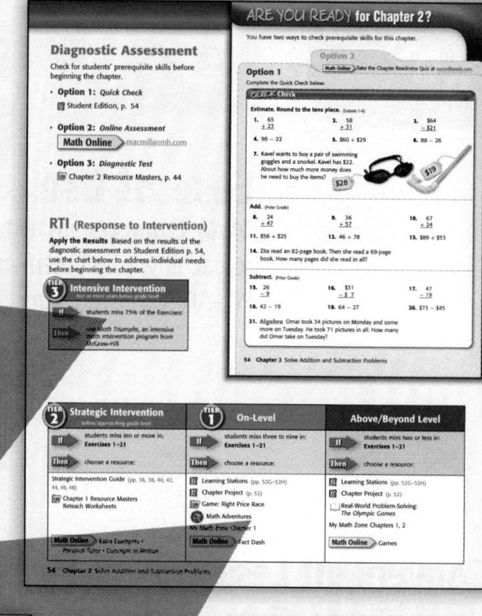

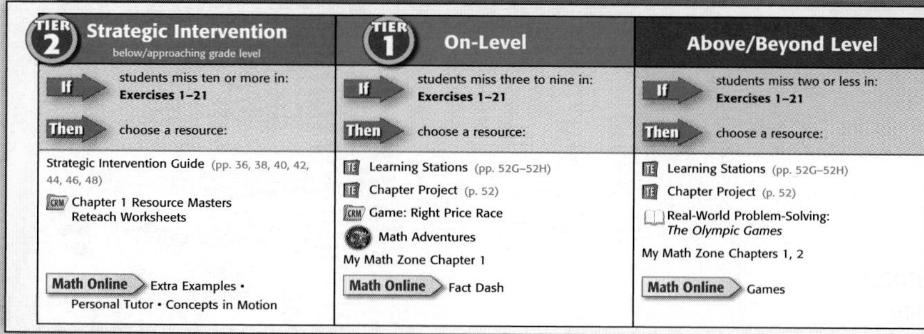

TIER 2 Strategic Intervention (below/approaching grade level)	TIER 1 On-Level	Above/Beyond Level
If students miss ten or more in: **Exercises 1–21**	**If** students miss three to nine in: **Exercises 1–21**	**If** students miss two or less in: **Exercises 1–21**
Then choose a resource:	**Then** choose a resource:	**Then** choose a resource:
Strategic Intervention Guide (pp. 36, 38, 40, 42, 44, 46, 48) CRM Chapter 1 Resource Masters Reteach Worksheets Math Online Extra Examples • Personal Tutor • Concepts in Motion	TE Learning Stations (pp. 52G–52H) TE Chapter Project (p. 52) CRM Game: Right Price Race Math Adventures My Math Zone Chapter 1 Math Online Fact Dash	TE Learning Stations (pp. 52G–52H) TE Chapter Project (p. 52) Real-World Problem-Solving: *The Olympic Games* My Math Zone Chapters 1, 2 Math Online Games

Math Connects, Grade 4
Teacher Edition, page 54

The Chapter Planner, also in the Teacher Edition of ***Math Connects,*** references alternative lessons found in ***IMPACT Mathematics.*** These lessons provide opportunities for investigative instruction with hands-on explorations.

Personal Tutor
English Learners, p. 333B ELL
Below Level, p. 333B BL
Early Finishers, p. 333B AL
IMPACT Mathematics: Unit C
KEY
Below/Approaching Level · OL On Level · Teacher Edition · Real-World Problem Solving

Chapter 8 Chapter Planner

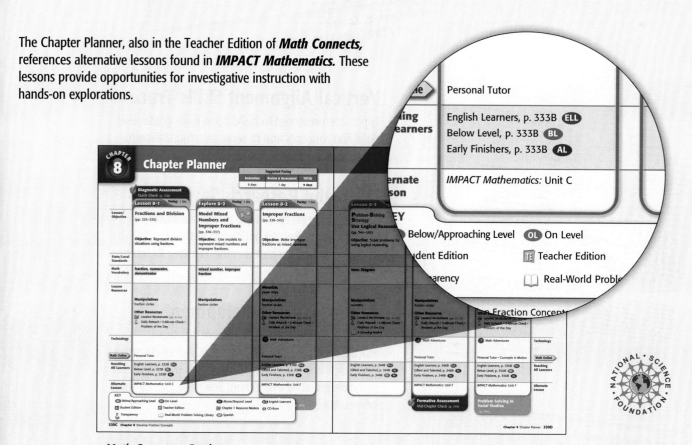

Math Connects, Grade 5
Teacher Edition, pages 330C–330D

Planning for Success

Ease of Use

Math Connects has a strong instructional model that includes differentiated instructional options, reteaching, reinforcement, and extension options, Teacher Tips to help address various learners, Pre-AP/Advanced items, and assessment linked with instruction.

Convenient Lesson Planning at Your Fingertips

The **Chapter Overview** helps you plan your instruction by showing the objectives to be covered, suggested pacing, and coverage of Focal Points.

TeacherWorks™ Plus

This electronic lesson planner contains multi-purpose management software including the Teacher Edition pages, program blackline masters, and daily calendars that make planning a snap.

CHAPTER 4 **Chapter Overview**

Chapter-at-a-Glance

In Chapter 4, the emphasis is on the meaning of multiplication and multiplication facts with 2, 4, 5, and 10.

Lesson	Math Objective	State/Local Standards
EXPLORE 4-1 **Meaning of Multiplication** (pp. 157–158)	Use models to explore multiplication.	
4-1 **Arrays and Multiplication** (pp. 159–161)	Use arrays to multiply.	
4-2 **Multiply by 2** (pp. 162–164)	Multiply by 2.	
EXTEND 4-2 **Model Multiplication** (pp. 165–166)	Use technology to multiply.	
4-3 **Multiply by 4** (pp. 168–170)	Multiply by 4.	
4-4 **Problem-Solving Skill: Extra or Missing Information** (pp. 172–173)	Solve a problem by identifying extra or missing information.	
4-5 **Multiply by 5** (pp. 174–176)	Multiply by 5.	
4-6 **Multiply by 10** (pp. 178–181)	Multiply by 10.	
4-7 **Problem-Solving Investigation: Choose a Strategy** (pp. 184–185)	Choose the best strategy to solve a problem.	
4-8 **Multiply by 0 and 1** (pp. 186–188)	Multiply by 0 and 1.	

Develop Multiplication Concepts and Facts

BIG Idea There are 144 multiplication combinations from 1×1 to 12×12, most of which are learned without difficulty. Students can use several different strategies to make sense of multiplication facts.

- Multiplication is repeated addition. For example, 4×3 is the same as adding the number 4 three times. ($4 \times 3 = 4 + 4 + 4 = 12$)
- Multiplication can be represented visually using arrays. The fact 4×3 can be demonstrated by an array of pictures or objects with 4 columns and 3 rows.
- Skip counting by a number is the same as multiplying by 1, 2, 3, and so on. To count by 4s, say 4, 8, 12, 16. . .

Use these and other strategies to emphasize the meaning of multiplication. Continued practice in a variety of contexts will lead students to commit facts to memory.

Algebra Students learn about the properties of multiplication. This concept will help prepare them for algebra concepts, such as solving equations and inequalities. (Lessons 4-1 and 4-8)

G3-FP1 *Number and Operations and Algebra:* **Developing understandings of multiplication an[illegible] and strategies for basic multiplication facts [illegible] division facts**

Students understand the meanings of m[illegible] of whole numbers through the use of [illegible] equal-sized groups, arrays, area mod[illegible] number lines for multiplication, an[illegible] partitioning, and sharing for divisi[illegible] addition and multiplication (e.g., [illegible] the distributive property) to mult[illegible] increasingly sophisticated strate[illegible] solve multiplication and division [illegible] By comparing a variety of solutio[illegible] multiplication and division as inv[illegible]

G3-FP4C *Algebra:* Understand[illegible] and the relationship between mult[illegible] of algebra readiness that develops a[illegible] analysis of patterns and relationships [illegible] division should occur at this grade level. [illegible] foundation for later understanding of func[illegible] describing relationships in context with such [illegible] number of legs is 4 times the number of chairs."

154A Chapter 4 Develop Multiplication Concepts and Facts

Math Connects, Grade 3
Teacher Edition, page 154A

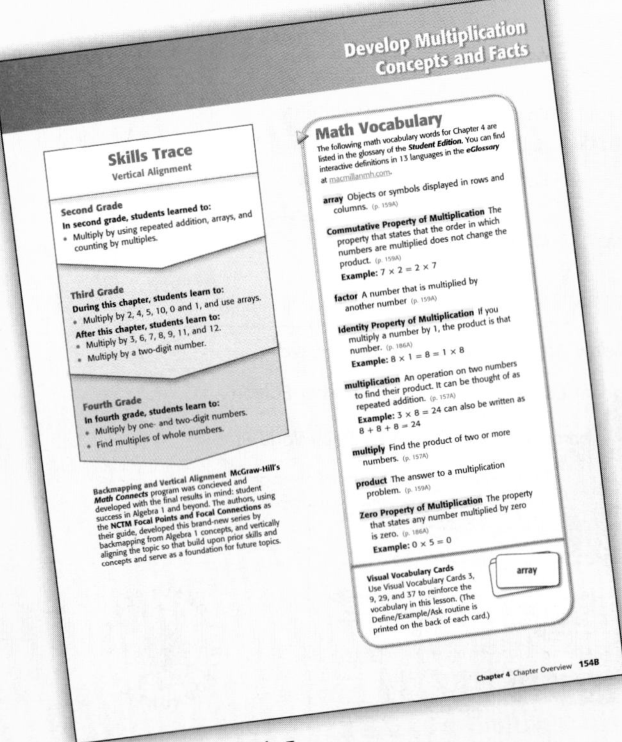

Develop Multiplication Concepts and Facts

Skills Trace
Vertical Alignment

Second Grade
In second grade, students learned to:
- Multiply by using repeated addition, arrays, and counting by multiples.

Third Grade
During this chapter, students learn to:
- Multiply by 2, 4, 5, 10, 0 and 1, and use arrays.

After this chapter, students learn to:
- Multiply by 3, 6, 7, 8, 9, 11, and 12.
- Multiply by a two-digit number.

Fourth Grade
In fourth grade, students learn to:
- Multiply by one- and two-digit numbers.
- Find multiples of whole numbers.

Backmapping and Vertical Alignment McGraw-Hill's ***Math Connects*** program was concieved and developed with the final results in mind: student success in Algebra 1 and beyond. The authors, using the **NCTM Focal Points and Focal Connections** as their guide, developed this brand-new series by backmapping from Algebra 1 concepts, and vertically aligning the topic so that build upon prior skills and concepts and serve as a foundation for future topics.

Math Vocabulary

The following math vocabulary words for Chapter 4 are listed in the glossary of the ***Student Edition.*** You can find interactive definitions in 13 languages in the ***eGlossary*** at macmillanmh.com.

array Objects or symbols displayed in rows and columns. (p. 159A)

Commutative Property of Multiplication The property that states that the order in which numbers are multiplied does not change the product. (p. 159A)
Example: $7 \times 2 = 2 \times 7$

factor A number that is multiplied by another number (p. 159A)

Identity Property of Multiplication If you multiply a number by 1, the product is that number. (p. 186A)
Example: $8 \times 1 = 8 = 1 \times 8$

multiplication An operation on two numbers to find their product. It can be thought of as repeated addition. (p. 157A)
Example: $3 \times 8 = 24$ can also be written as $8 + 8 + 8 = 24$

multiply Find the product of two or more numbers. (p. 157A)

product The answer to a multiplication problem. (p. 159A)

Zero Property of Multiplication The property that states any number multiplied by zero is zero. (p. 186A)
Example: $0 \times 5 = 0$

Visual Vocabulary Cards
Use Visual Vocabulary Cards 3, 9, 29, and 37 to reinforce the vocabulary in this lesson. (The Define/Example/Ask routine is printed on the back of each card.)

array

Chapter 4 Chapter Overview 154B

Math Connects, Grade 3
Teacher Edition, page 154B

Vertical Alignment Skills Trace

Topics are presented to build upon prior grade level skills and concepts and to serve as a foundation for future topics.

What the Research Says

Citations from research help to validate ***Math Connects*** program. An additional Research Bibliography can be found in the **Teacher Reference Handbook.**

Professional Development

Targeted professional development has been articulated throughout the program. Actual classroom video clips are especially helpful when planning lessons and differentiating instruction. See page T32 for more information.

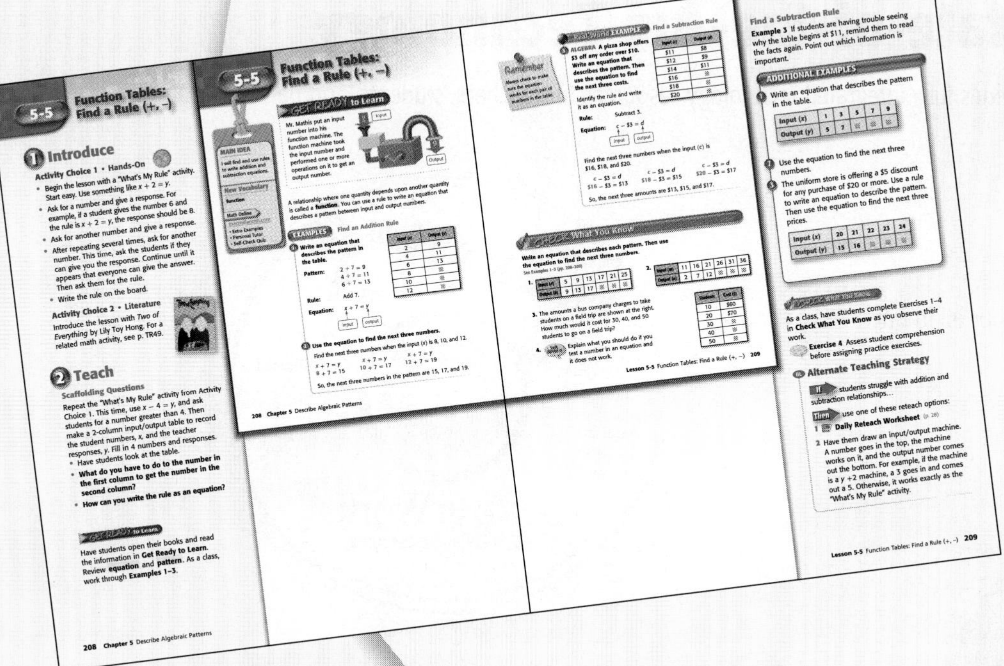

Math Connects, Grade 4
Teacher Edition, pages 208–209

Four-Step Teaching Plan

Organizes your instruction as you **Focus** and **Teach** and help your students **Practice** and **Assess** what they've learned.

Scaffolding Questions

Each lesson contains **Scaffolding Questions** for you to use to help students investigate and understand the main ideas of the lesson.

Additional Examples

Each **Additional Example** mirrors the example in the Student Edition. The Additional Examples are also available as a PowerPoint® presentation on the **Interactive Classroom** CD-ROM.

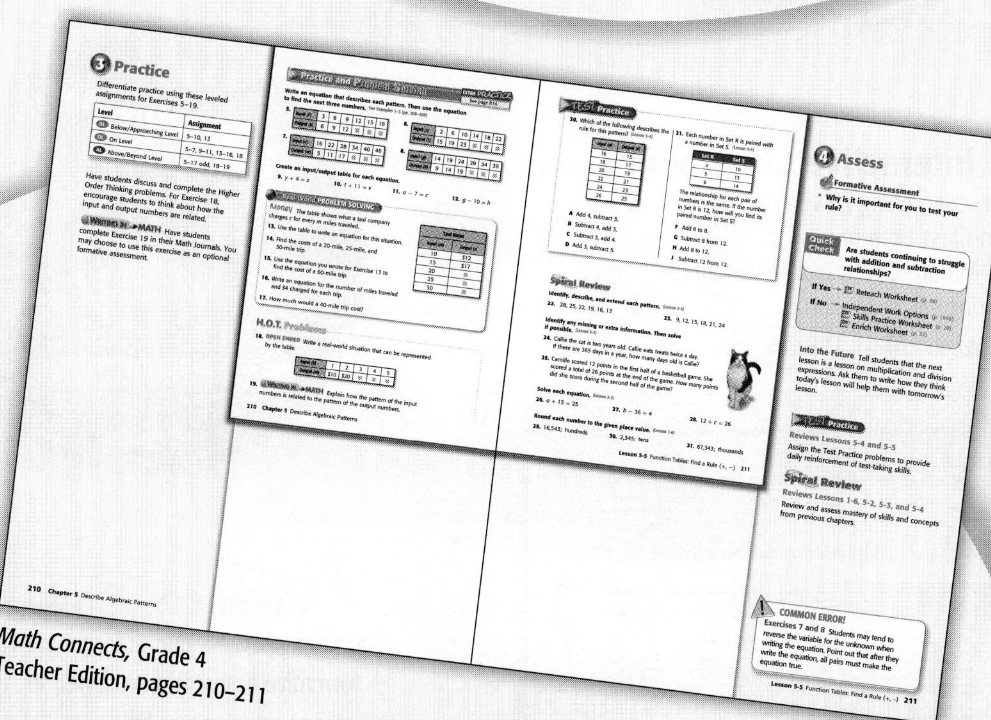

Math Connects, Grade 4
Teacher Edition, pages 210–211

Differentiated Practice

Because most classrooms include students at a wide range of ability levels, **Differentiated Practice** allows you to customize your assignments.

Vertical Alignment

Vertical Alignment at the beginning of each chapter shows the objectives that lead into and follow the current lesson's content for a coherent PreK–12 scope and sequence.

Planning for Success
State-of-the-Art Technology

Math Connects provides fully integrated technology resources for teachers, students, and parents.

For Teachers

TeacherWorks™ Plus is your all-in-one planner and resource center.
- entire Teacher Edition
- all print ancillaries
- electronic lesson planner

ExamView® Assessment Suite allows teachers to create and customize their own assessment and assignments.

New features:
- correlated to state standards
- online content update
- one- or two-column formatting

Use **Interactive Classroom** to guide instruction using PowerPoint ™
- In-Class Examples
- 5-Minute Check Transparencies
- Concepts in Motion
- links to **Math Online**

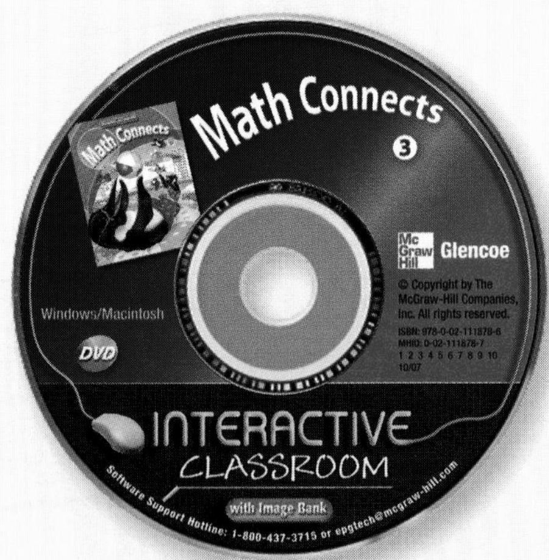

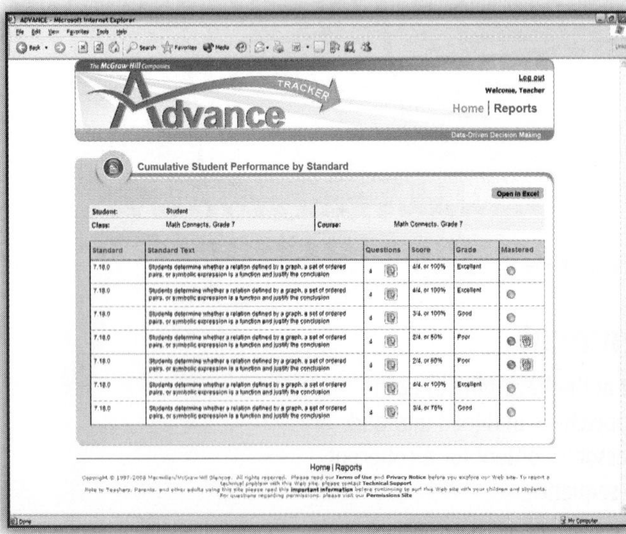

The McGraw-Hill Companies

Advance TRACKER

Log out
Welcome, Teacher
Home | Reports

Data-Driven Decision Making

Cumulative Student Performance by Standard

Open in Excel

Student: Student
Class: Math Connects, Grade 7 | Course: Math Connects, Grade 7

Standard	Standard Text	Questions	Score	Grade	Mastered
7.18.0	Students determine whether a relation defined by a graph, a set of ordered pairs, or symbolic expression is a function and justify the conclusion	4	4/4, or 100%	Excellent	
7.18.0	Students determine whether a relation defined by a graph, a set of ordered pairs, or symbolic expression is a function and justify the conclusion	4	4/4, or 100%	Excellent	
7.18.0	Students determine whether a relation defined by a graph, a set of ordered pairs, or symbolic expression is a function and justify the conclusion	4	3/4, or 100%	Good	
7.18.0	Students determine whether a relation defined by a graph, a set of ordered pairs, or symbolic expression is a function and justify the conclusion	4	2/4, or 50%	Poor	
7.18.0	Students determine whether a relation defined by a graph, a set of ordered pairs, or symbolic expression is a function and justify the conclusion	4	2/4, or 50%	Poor	
7.18.0	Students determine whether a relation defined by a graph, a set of ordered pairs, or symbolic expression is a function and justify the conclusion	4	4/4, or 100%	Excellent	
7.18.0	Students determine whether a relation defined by a graph, a set of ordered pairs, or symbolic expression is a function and justify the conclusion	4	3/4, or 75%	Good	

Home | Reports

Copyright © 1997-2008 Macmillan/McGraw-Hill Glencoe. All rights reserved. Please read our **Terms of Use** and **Privacy Notice** before you explore our Web site. To report a technical problem with this Web site, please contact **Technical Support**
Note to Teachers, Parents, and other adults using this site please read this **important information** before continuing to surf this Web site with your children and students. For questions regarding permissions, please visit our **Permissions Site**

Advance TRACKER Learner Management System helps you track progress and differentiate your instruction.
- formative assessments aligned to standards
- links to intervention help

Other Technology: My Math Zone (CD-ROM)
Math Songs (English and Spanish, CD-ROM)

For Students

StudentWorks™ Plus is your students' backpack solution.

- entire Student Edition
- all student worksheets
- links to **Math Online**

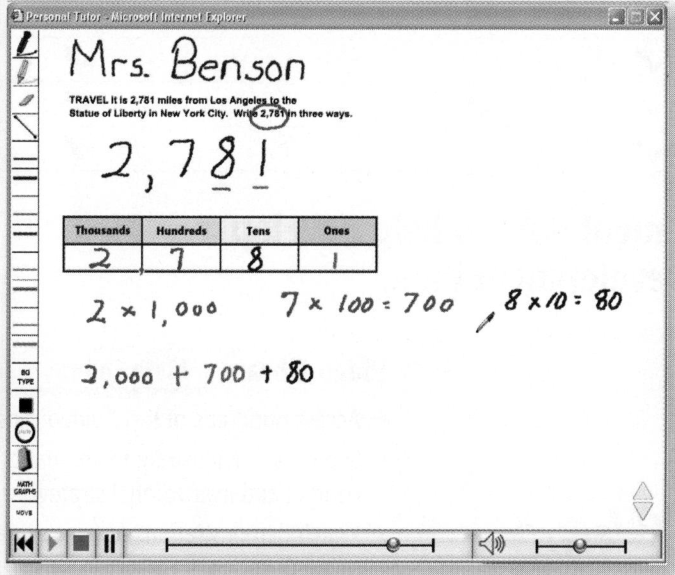

Math Online provides a wealth of resources – convenient for students and parents!

- Self-Check Quizzes
- Personal Tutor
- Concepts in Motion
- eGlossary (14 languages)
- And much, much more!

Math Online *Math Connect's* **eBook** is easy to use, easy to read, and packed with features.

- links to online study tools and resources right from the page
- includes audio

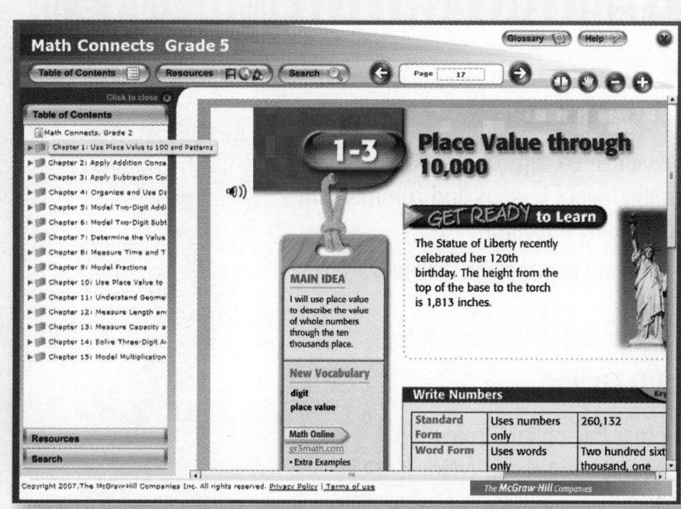

Other Technology: Math Adventures with Dot and Ray (online and CD-ROM)
Math Tool Chest (online and CD-ROM)

PreK-12 Data-Driven Professional Development

McGraw-Hill Professional Development (MHPD) provides a comprehensive plan for mathematics that is fully aligned and articulated with ***Math Connects K–8*** and the ***Glencoe Mathematics*** high school series.

Professional Development Needs	Online Courses	DVD Workshops	Video Library	Teach-Use-Succeed	Ready-Access Math
Has immediate classroom application	✓	✓	✓	✓	✓
Builds content knowledge	✓	✓			✓
Promotes best teaching practices		✓	✓		
Supports new and experienced teachers	✓	✓	✓	✓	✓
Allows customization of courses	✓	✓			✓
Can be self-paced	✓	✓		✓	✓
Adaptable for various timeframes	✓	✓	✓	✓	✓
Is grade-level specific			✓	✓	✓
Promotes a learning community	✓	✓			✓
Provides vertically-aligned content	✓	✓	✓		✓
Helps with RTI (Response to Intervention), Tiers 1–3	✓	✓	✓		✓

Use students' mathematics achievement data to help develop a targeted Professional Development Plan.

Accredited Online Courses

(available for purchase)

- Watch video clips of math classrooms Complete interactive exercises Develop electronic portfolios.
- Complete each 3- to 5-hour online module one segment at a time.
- University credit (additional tuition charge)

DVD Workshops

- Watch video clips of classroom mathematics lessons and commentaries by leading educators.
- Complete lessons and activities.

MHPD Online

- Access this online Professional Development resource for K–12 educators.
- Link to relevant Web sites.
- Download grade-level student resources.

Video Library **Math Online**

- Access hundreds of K–12 video clips.
- See clips that illustrate mathematics content and instructional strategies.
- Watch demonstrations or commentaries by math specialists

Teach-Use-Succeed Textbook Implementation Modules

- Watch an experienced teacher demonstrate the *Math Connects* K–8 Student Editions, Teacher Editions, and program ancillaries
- Online or DVD

Ready-Access Math, Personalized Professional Development

- Access training materials for nearly 300 mathematics professional development lessons.
- Create a customized sequence of professional development sessions.
- Deliver 45–60 minute after-school professional development sessions.

Program Components

	Grade K	Grade 1	Grade 2	Grade 3	Grade 4	Grade 5	Grade 6	Grade 7
Chapter Resource Masters	●	●	●	●	●	●	●	●
Daily Reteach Transparencies	●	●	●	●	●	●		
5-Minute Check Transparencies		●	●	●	●	●	●	●
Noteables Interactive Notebook							●	●
Hands-On Activity Tools and Resources	●	●	●	●	●	●		
Teaching Math with Manipulatives							●	●
ELL Guide	●	●	●	●	●	●	●	
Strategic Intervention Guide		●	●	●	●	●		
Problem of the Day/Week	●	●	●	●	●	●	●	●
Learning Station Cards	●	●	●	●	●	●		
Math Routines on the Go	●	●	●					
Quick Review Math Handbook							●	●
Visual Vocabulary Cards	●	●	●	●	●	●		
Transition Blackline Masters				●				
Math Skills Maintenance							●	●
Real-World Problem Solving Readers	●	●	●	●	●	●		
Graphic Novels							●	●
Dinah Zike's Teaching with Foldables	●	●	●	●	●	●	●	●
Diagnostic and Placement Tests	●	●	●	●	●	●	●	●
StudentWorks Plus CD-ROM	●	●	●	●	●	●	●	●
TeacherWorks Plus DVD	●	●	●	●	●	●	●	●
ExamView CD-ROM	●	●	●	●	●	●	●	●
Interactive Classroom PowerPoint™				●	●	●	●	●
Math Adventures with Dot and Ray CD-ROM	●	●	●	●	●	●	●	
Classroom Games CD-ROM	●	●	●	●	●	●		
AssignmentWorks CD-ROM							●	●
Math Songs CD-ROM	●	●	●	●	●	●		
Individual Manipulative Kit	●	●	●	●	●	●	●	●
Classroom Manipulative Kit	●	●	●	●	●	●	●	●
Overhead Manipulative Kit	●	●	●	●	●	●	●	●
Teacher Tool Kit	●	●	●	●	●	●		
Magnetic Manipulative Kit	●	●	●	●	●	●		
Student Edition Flip Book	●							
Activity Flip Chart	●							
Robot Puppet	●	●	●					
WorkMats	●	●	●	●	●	●		
Professional Development	●	●	●	●	●	●	●	●

Macmillan/McGraw-Hill's EL Support

A Comprehensive Plan

Macmillan/McGraw-Hill's EL support combines language acquisition and math instruction through exploration, discovery, and solving meaningful problems based on conceptual knowledge. These flexible pieces provide the tools needed to integrate EL students into the math curriculum.

English Language Learner Guide
A comprehensive ancillary that compliments the basal curriculum, provides targeted EL vocabulary, and multiple ideas for how to integrate new math vocabulary into context. Activities, games, and assessments are grouped by mathematical strand and learning modality that supplement and reinforce the concepts and skills in the Student Edition.

EL Strategies in the Teacher Edition

Every lesson in the Teacher Edition is supported by an EL strategy that presents the vocabulary that the EL student will need to **approach, understand, practice,** or **extend** the targeted math skill. These strategies in the Teachers Edition form the basis for ESL content instruction. The strategies require little or no teacher preparation, can be used as an entrance, exit, or extension of the regular lesson, and keep the EL student on grade level regardless of language.

Assessment and Standards Alignment The **TeacherWorks®** program provides Math planning and assessment tools. English learner skills are dually aligned to math skills, so with a simple click, both standards are covered. Online, the standards alignment is sortable and includes the objectives, vocabulary, language focus and teaching modalities that encapsulate all the skills required for EL success and achievement. National and state specific alignments are found at macmillanmh.com/math. As additional support, there are skill and language checklists in the English Language Learners Guide.

Real-World Problem Solving Readers are leveled for sheltered English readers. These problem solving books provide reading materials that are grade level appropriate and can be included in regular classroom instruction or content. On-level readers are available in English and Spanish.

Foldables® create new ways for EL students to translate and record their learning process; to not only master the math skills and the English language, but to become self-motivated learners.

Language Support

Macmillan/McGraw-Hill's comprehensive support of language learners provides the basic language skills needed to approach the math concepts taught in the Student Edition.

Option 2 Teacher Edition
Differentiated Strategy Instruction

Small Group Options

Each lesson in the **Teacher Edition** features a teaching strategy written specifically for English Language Learners. These strategies provide language support for ELs that can be used before, during, or after whole group instruction.

There are five different types of strategies featured in the Teacher Edition.

- **Do Math**
- **Say Math**
- **Write Math**
- **Hear Math**
- **See Math**

Each English Language Learners strategy in the **Teacher Edition** provides language support appropriate for the math skill. Strategies:

- activate background knowledge
- align with the math lesson
- use modalities to integrate English into usable language
- use context to make the math skill meaningful
- supply common vocabulary that is needed to understand the math
- keep students on grade level, regardless of their language proficiency

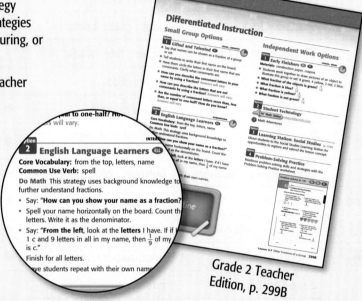

Grade 2 Teacher Edition, p. 299B

Each English Language Learners strategy can be used in a variety of ways: in cooperative groups, small groups, whole class, pairs, or individually. This flexibility allows the teacher to change when or how the strategy is introduced, based on the needs of the students.

Here are two sample approaches.

EL Instruction

Before the Lesson

- Use the Teacher Edition EL strategy to show the concept in separate groups.
- Teach the lesson to the whole class using the Student Edition pages.
- Pair language learners with native speakers for peer tutoring.
- Reinforce with Foldables® and use the EL worksheet.

After the Lesson

- Teach the lesson to the whole class using the Student Edition pages.
- Have native speakers work independently at Learning Stations while you work with language learners.
- Extend with a literary connection.

Program Manipulatives

Manipulative	Suggested Alternative	PreK	Grade K	Grade 1	Grade 2	Grade 3	Grade 4	Grade 5	Grade 6	Grade 7	Grade 8
Attribute Buttons	real buttons, pasta	●	●								
Color Tiles	blocks, buttons	●	●								
Graphing Mats	posterboard	●	●								
Attribute Blocks	pasta, buttons	●	●	●	●						
Student Clock	paper plate, brads		●	●	●	●	●	●			
Demonstration Clock	paper plate, brads		●	●	●	●	●	●			
Connecting Cubes	paper clips	●	●	●	●	●	●	●			
Number Cubes	spinner, cards	●	●	●	●	●	●	●	●	●	●
Spinners	construction paper, paperclip, pencil	●	●	●	●	●	●	●	●	●	●
Two-Colored Counters	buttons, coins, beans	●	●	●	●	●	●	●	●	●	●
Pattern Blocks	construction paper	●	●	●	●	●	●	●	●	●	
Geometric Solids/Models	cans, boxes, balls	●	●	●	●	●	●	●			
Bucket Balance	ruler, paper cups, string	●	●	●	●	●	●	●			
Base-Ten Blocks	grid paper			●	●	●	●	●	●	●	
Money	real money, construction paper			●	●	●	●	●			
Ruler	straightedge, book			●	●	●	●	●	●	●	●
Fraction Circles	construction paper			●	●	●	●	●			
Fraction Models						●	●	●			
Geoboards	dot paper			●	●	●	●	●	●	●	●
Compass	paperclip					●	●	●	●	●	●
Protractor						●	●	●	●	●	●
Plastic Cups	paper cups					●	●	●	●	●	●
Algebra Tiles	block, buttons, coins								●	●	●
Centimeter Cubes	block								●	●	●
Equation Mats	construction paper								●	●	●
Stopwatch	clock, watch								●	●	
Measuring Cups	paper cups								●	●	
Geomirrors	mirror								●	●	
Tangrams	construction paper								●	●	

Teacher Edition

Macmillan McGraw-Hill

Math Connects

5

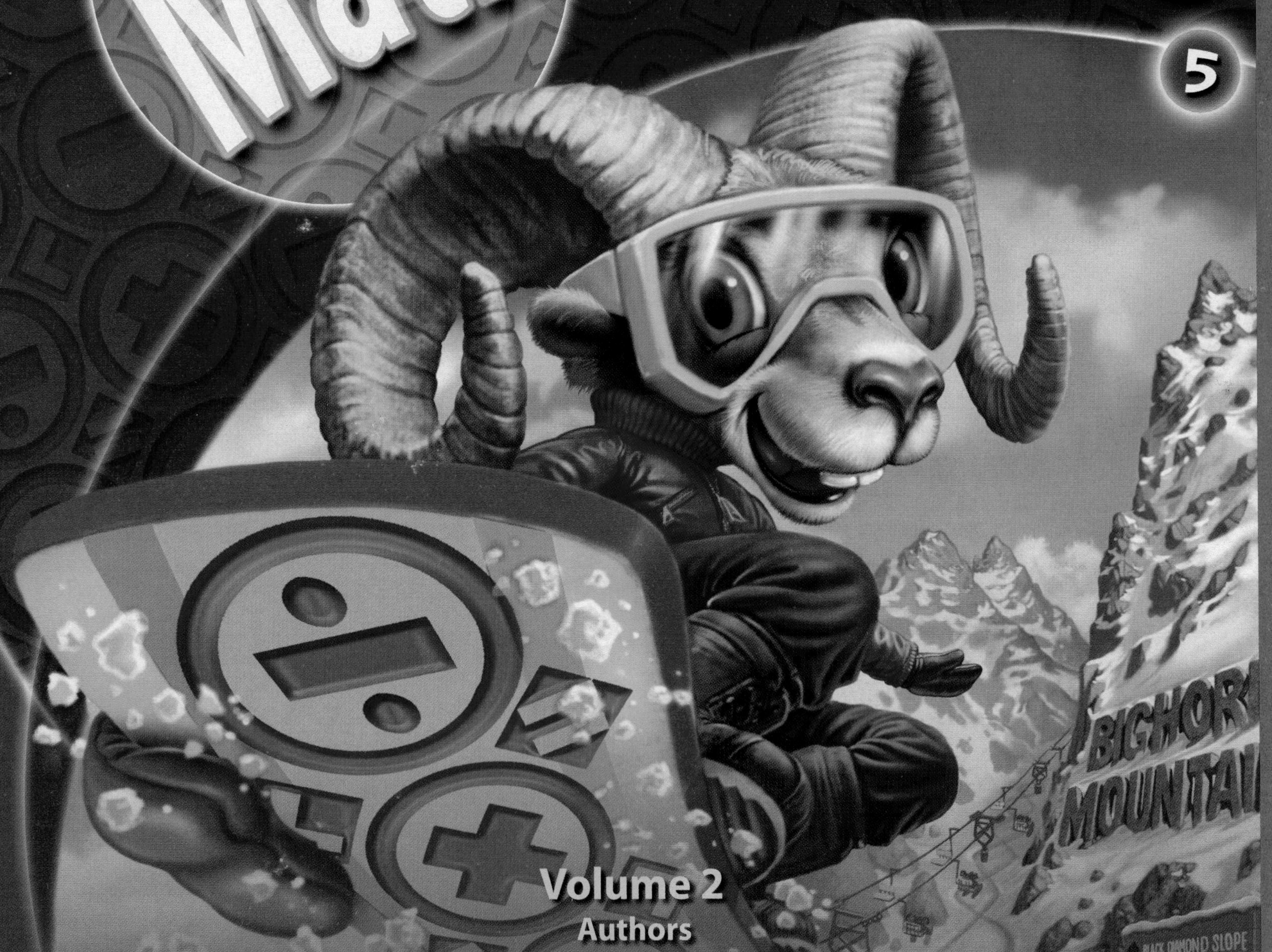

Volume 2

Authors

Altieri • Balka • Day • Gonsalves • Grace • Krulik
Malloy • Molix-Bailey • Moseley • Mowry • Myren
Price • Reynosa • Santa Cruz • Silbey • Vielhaber

Mc Graw Hill Macmillan/McGraw-Hill

Contents

Start Smart

H.O.T. Problems

Use Place Value

Focal Points and Connections

G5-FP7C *Number and Operations*

Add and Subtract Whole Numbers and Decimals

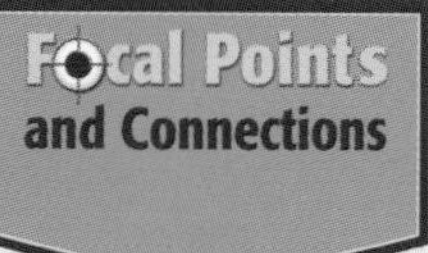

G5-FP2 *Number and Operations*

Test Practice 67, 73, 87, 91, 97, 98, 99

H.O.T. Problems
Higher Order Thinking 63, 66, 72, 82, 87, 90

WRITING IN MATH 63, 66, 69, 72, 73, 75, 79, 82, 87, 90, 97

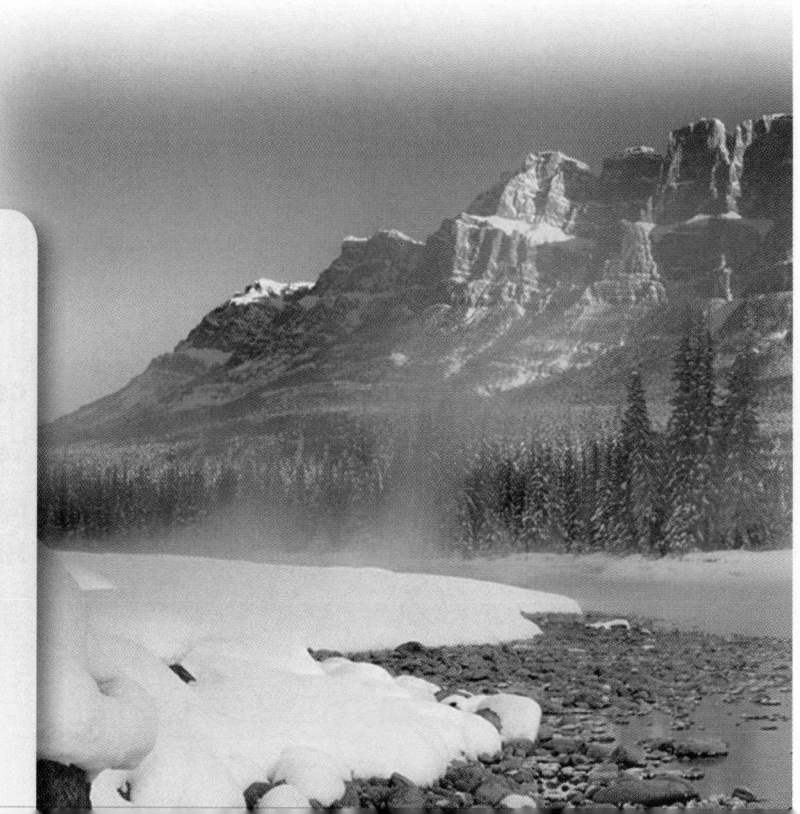

CHAPTER 3 Multiply Whole Numbers

Focal Points and Connections

G5-FP1 *Number and Operations and Algebra*
G5-FP7C *Number and Operations*

Chapter 4 Divide Whole Numbers

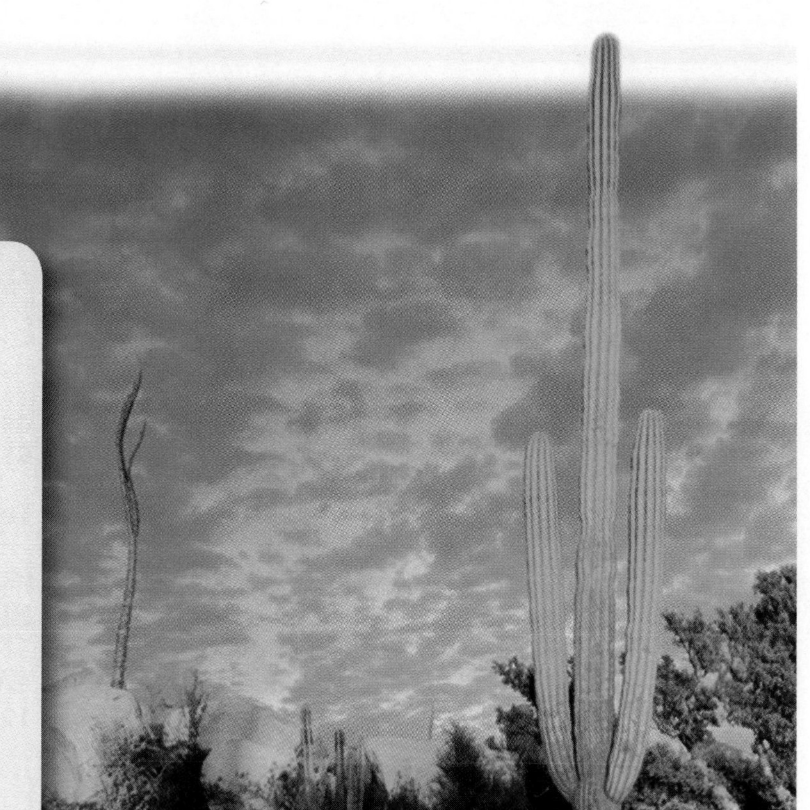

Focal Points and Connections

G5-FP1 *Number and Operations and Algebra*
G5-FP7C *Number and Operations*

CHAPTER 5 Use Algebraic Expressions

Focal Points and Connections

G5-FP4C *Algebra*

Use Equations and Function Tables

G5-FP4C *Algebra*

Test Practice 245, 253, 257, 273, 274, 275

H.O.T. Problems
Higher Order Thinking 239, 245, 252, 257, 262

WRITING IN MATH 236, 239, 241, 245, 247, 252, 253, 257, 262, 267, 273

CHAPTER 7 Display and Interpret Data

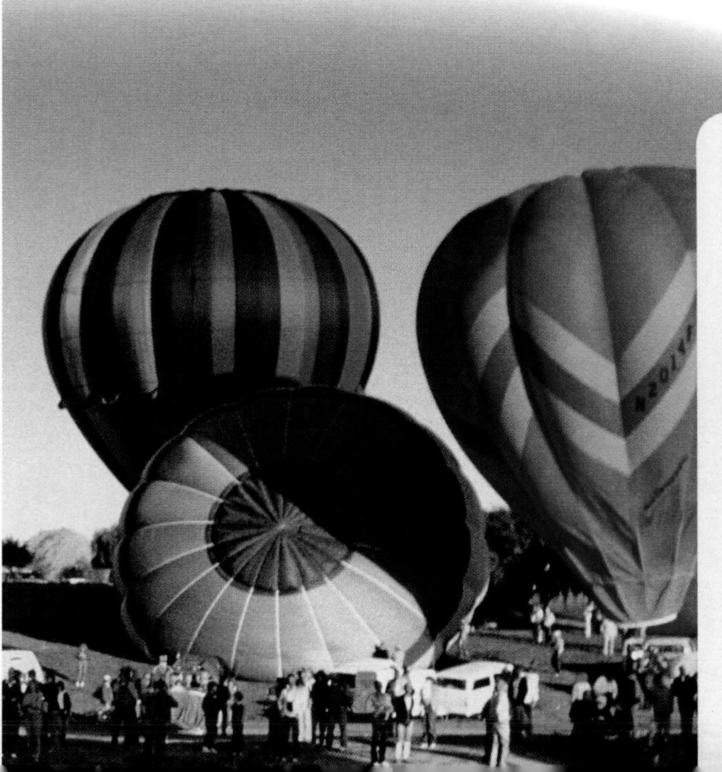

Focal Points and Connections

G5-FP6C *Data Analysis*
G5-FP4C *Algebra*

Develop Fraction Concepts

Focal Points and Connections

G5-FP2 *Number and Operations*
G5-FP4C *Algebra*

CHAPTER 9 Use Factors and Multiples

Focal Points and Connections

G5-FP2 *Number and Operations*
G5-FP4C *Algebra*

Test Practice 381, 389, 390, 399, 405, 415, 416, 417

H.O.T. Problems
Higher Order Thinking 375, 381, 384, 393, 399, 405

WRITING IN MATH 375, 381, 384, 389, 390, 393, 399, 405, 415, 416, 417

CHAPTER 10 Add and Subtract Fractions

Focal Points and Connections

G5-FP2 *Number and Operations*
G5-FP4C *Algebra*

Use Measures in the Customary System

Focal Points and Connections

G5-FP5C ***Measurement***

Test Practice 480, 487, 491, 495, 503, 509, 510, 511

H.O.T. Problems
Higher Order Thinking 480, 486, 490, 495, 502

WRITING IN MATH 476, 480, 483, 486, 490, 491, 495, 497, 502, 509

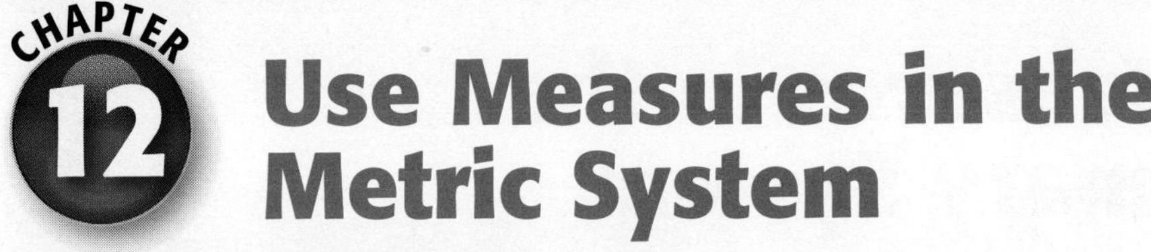

Chapter 12 Use Measures in the Metric System

Focal Points and Connections

G5-FP5C *Measurement*

Test Practice 530, 532, 541, 551, 552, 553

H.O.T. Problems
Higher Order Thinking 521, 526, 529, 535, 541

WRITING IN MATH 516, 521, 523, 526, 529, 532, 535, 541, 545, 551

CHAPTER 13 Identify, Compare, and Classify Geometric Figures

Focal Points and Connections

G5-FP3 *Geometry and Measurement and Algebra*

Measure Perimeter, Area, and Volume

G5-FP3 *Geometry and Measurement and Algebra*
G5-FP5C *Measurement*

Test Practice 615, 623, 626, 635, 655, 656, 657

H.O.T. Problems
Higher Order Thinking 611, 615, 619, 627, 635, 643, 647

WRITING IN MATH 611, 615, 619, 621, 623, 627, 629, 630, 635, 639, 643, 647, 655

CHAPTER 15 Use Probability to Make Predictions

Focal Points and Connections

G5-FP6C *Data Analysis*

Looking Ahead

Problem-Solving Projects

Student Handbook

Built-In Workbook

Reference

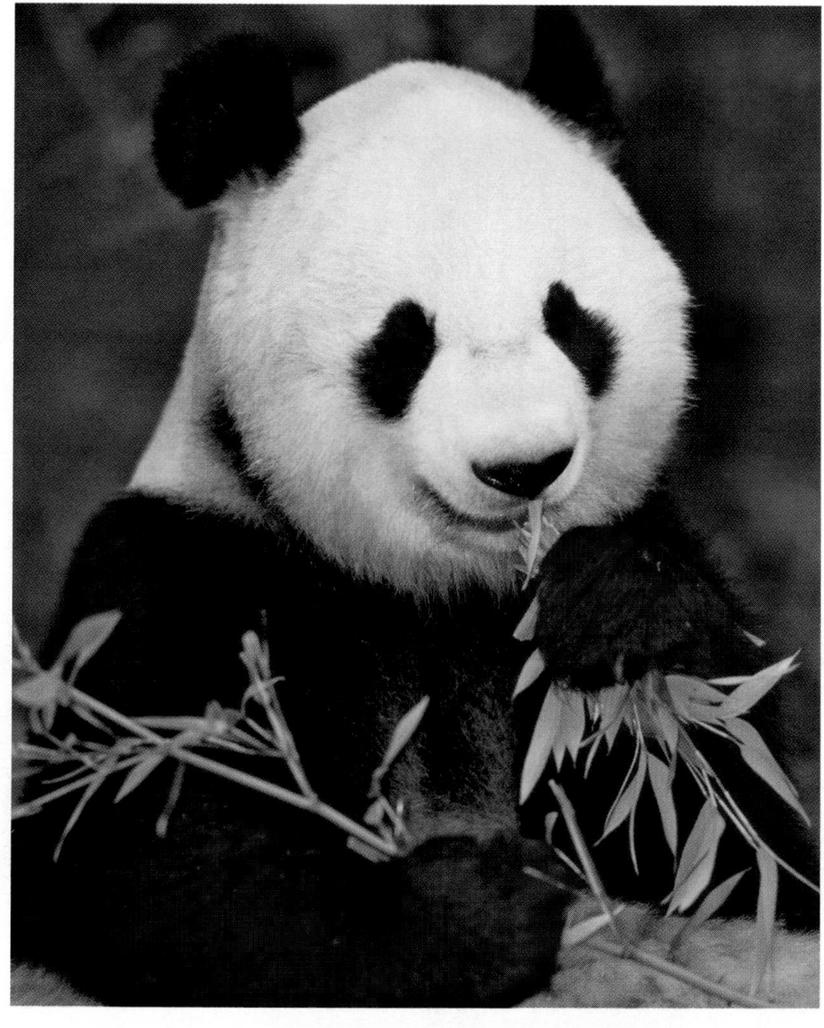

To the Student

As you gear up to study mathematics, you are probably wondering, "What will I learn this year?"

- **Number and Operations:** Estimate and find quotients of whole numbers, including quotients of multidigit numbers.
- **Number and Operations:** Add and subtract fractions with unlike denominators.
- **Geometry and Measurement:** Find volume and surface area of three dimensional figures.

Along the way, you'll learn more about problem solving, how to use the tools and language of mathematics, and how to THINK mathematically.

How to Use Your Math Book

Have you ever been in class and not understood all of what was being presented? Or, you understood everything in class, but got stuck on how to solve some of the homework problems? Don't worry. You can find answers in your math book!

- **Read** the MAIN IDEA at the beginning of the lesson.
- **Find** the New Vocabulary words, **highlighted in yellow**, and read their definitions.
- **Review** the EXAMPLE problems, solved step-by-step, to remind you of the day's material.
- **Refer** to the EXTRA PRACTICE boxes that show you where you can find extra exercises to practice a concept.
- **Go** to Math Online where you can find extra examples to coach you through difficult problems.
- **Review** the notes you've taken on your FOLDABLES®.
- **Refer** to the Remember boxes for information that may help you with your examples and homework practice.

Chapter Overview

Chapter-at-a-Glance

In Chapter 9, the emphasis is on using factors and multiples, finding equivalent fractions, and comparing fractions.

Lesson	Math Objective	State/Local Standards
9-1 Common Factors (pp. 373–375)	Identify common factors of a set of whole numbers.	
EXPLORE **9-2 Prime and Composite Numbers** (pp. 376–377)	Use objects or pictures to identify prime and composite numbers.	
9-2 Prime and Composite Numbers (pp. 378–381)	Identify prime and composite numbers.	
9-3 Equivalent Fractions (pp. 382–384)	Write a fraction that is equivalent to a given fraction.	
9-4 Simplest Form (pp. 386–389)	Write a fraction in simplest form.	
9-5 Decimals and Fractions (pp. 391–393)	Relate decimals to fractions.	
9-6 Problem-Solving Strategy: Look for a Pattern (pp. 394–395)	Solve problems by looking for a pattern.	
9-7 Multiples (pp. 396–399)	Identify common multiples of a set of whole numbers.	
9-8 Problem-Solving Investigation: Choose a Strategy (pp. 400–401)	Choose the best strategy to solve a problem.	
EXPLORE **9-9 Compare Fractions** (pp. 402–403)	Use technology to compare fractions.	
9-9 Compare Fractions (pp. 404–407)	Compare fractions using common denominators.	

Use Factors and Multiples

BIG Idea The chapter begins with lessons on number theory concepts including finding common factors and identifying prime and composite numbers. Without the understanding of these foundational concepts, students will have difficulties with equivalent fractions and simplifying fractions, two concepts introduced in later lessons in the chapter.

Algebra Students solve problems by finding a pattern. This concept will help prepare them for algebra concepts, such as writing equations to describe patterns. (Lesson 9-6)

G5-FP4C Algebra: Students use patterns, models, and relationships as contexts for writing and solving simple equations and inequalities. They create graphs of simple equations. They explore prime and composite numbers and discover concepts related to the addition and subtraction of fractions as they use factors and multiples, including applications of common factors and common multiples. They develop an understanding of the order of operations and use it for all operations.

G5-FP2 Number and Operations: Developing an understanding of a fluency with addition and subtraction of fractions and decimals Students apply their understandings of fractions and fraction models to represent the addition and subtraction of fractions with unlike denominators as equivalent calculations with like denominators. They apply their understandings of decimal models, place value, and properties to add and subtract decimals. They develop fluency with standard procedures for adding and subtracting fractions and decimals. They make reasonable estimates of fraction and decimal sums and differences. Students add and subtract fractions and decimals to solve problems, including problems involving measurement.

Skills Trace

Vertical Alignment

Fourth Grade

In fourth grade, students learned to:

- Find factors and multiples of whole numbers and multiply three factors.
- Understand how multiplication and division are related and multiply multiples of 10 and 100 using basic facts and patterns.

Fifth Grade

During this chapter, students learn to:

- Write a fraction that is equivalent to a given fraction and compare fractions using common denominators.
- Write decimals as fractions.
- Identify common factors of a set of whole numbers.
- Identify prime and composite numbers.

After this chapter, students learn to:

- Add and subtract like fractions.

Sixth Grade

In sixth grade, students learn to:

- Find the prime factorization of a composite number.
- Find the greatest common factor and least common multiple of two or more numbers.

Backmapping and Vertical Alignment **McGraw-Hill's *Math Connects*** program was conceived and developed with the final results in mind: student success in Algebra 1 and beyond. The authors, using the **NCTM Focal Points and Focal Connections** as their guide, developed this brand-new series by backmapping from Algebra 1 concepts, and vertically aligning the topics so that they build upon prior skills and concepts and serve as a foundation for future topics.

Math Vocabulary

The following math vocabulary words for Chapter 9 are listed in the glossary of the ***Student Edition***. You can find interactive definitions in 13 languages in the ***eGlossary*** at macmillanmh.com.

common factor A whole number that is a factor of two or more numbers. (p. 373A)
Example: 3 is a common factor of both 6 and 12.

composite number A whole number that has more than two factors. (p. 376)
Example: 12 has the factors 1, 2, 3, 4, 6, and 12.

equivalent fractions Fractions that represent the same number. (p. 382A)
Example: $\frac{3}{4} = \frac{6}{8} = \frac{9}{12} = \frac{12}{16}$

greatest common factor (GCF) The largest number that divides evenly into two or more numbers. (p. 373A)
Example: The greatest common factor of 12, 18, and 30 is 6.

multiple A multiple of a number is the product of that number and any whole number. (p. 396A)
Example: 15 is a multiple of 5 because $3 \times 5 = 15$.

prime factorization A way of expressing a composite number as a product of its prime factors. (p. 378A)

prime number Any whole number with exactly two factors, 1 and itself. (p. 376)
Examples: 7, 13, and 19

simplest form A fraction in which the numerator and the denominator have no common factor greater than 1. (p. 386A)
Example: $\frac{5}{12}$ is in simplest form because 5 and 12 have no common factor greater than 1.

Visual Vocabulary Cards
Use Visual Vocabulary Card 35 to reinforce the vocabulary in this lesson. (The Define/Example/Ask routine is printed on the back of each card.)

prime factorization

Chapter Planner

Suggested Pacing		
Instruction	**Review & Assessment**	**TOTAL**
10 days	1 day	**11 days**

Diagnostic Assessment
Quick Check (p. 372)

	Lesson 9-1 Pacing: 1 day	**Explore 9-2** Pacing: 1 day	**Lesson 9-2** Pacing: 1 day
Lesson/ Objective	**Common Factors** (pp. 373–375) **Objective:** Identify common factors of a set of whole numbers.	**Prime and Composite Numbers** (pp. 376–377) **Objective:** Use objects or pictures to identify prime and composite numbers.	**Prime and Composite Numbers** (pp. 378–381) **Objective:** Identify prime and composite numbers.
State/Local Standards			
Math Vocabulary	**common factor, greatest common factor (GCF)**	**composite number, prime number**	**prime factorization**
Lesson Resources	**Materials** grid paper **Manipulatives** color tiles, counters **Other Resources** CRM Leveled Worksheets (pp. 8–12) Daily Reteach • 5-Minute Check • Problem of the Day	**Materials** square tiles, grid paper, markers, index cards, hundreds chart **Manipulatives** two color counters	**Materials** grid paper, markers **Manipulatives** square tiles **Other Resources** CRM Leveled Worksheets (pp. 13–17) Daily Reteach • 5-Minute Check • Problem of the Day
Technology			Math Adventures
Math Online	Personal Tutor		Personal Tutor
Reaching All Learners	English Learners, p. 373B ELL Gifted and Talented, p. 373B AL Early Finishers, p. 373B AL		English Learners, p. 378B ELL Below Level, p. 378B BL Early Finishers, p. 378B AL
Alternate Lesson			

KEY

BL Below/Approaching Level — OL On Level — AL Above/Beyond Level — ELL English Learners
SE Student Edition — TE Teacher Edition — CRM Chapter 1 Resource Masters — CD-Rom
Transparency — Real-World Problem Solving Library

	Lesson 9-3 (Pacing: 1 day)	Lesson 9-4 (Pacing: 1 day)	Lesson 9-5 (Pacing: 1 day)
Lesson/ Objective	**Equivalent Fractions** (pp. 382–384) **Objective:** Write a fraction that is equivalent to a given fraction.	**Simplest Form** (pp. 386–389) **Objective:** Write a fraction in simplest form.	**Decimals and Fractions** (pp. 391–393) **Objective:** Relate decimals to fractions.
State/Local Standards			
Math Vocabulary	**equivalent fractions**	**simplest form**	
Lesson Resources	**Manipulatives** fraction tiles, fraction circles **Other Resources** CRM Leveled Worksheets (pp. 18–22) Daily Reteach • 5-Minute Check • Problem of the Day	**Materials** index cards **Manipulatives** counters **Other Resources** CRM Leveled Worksheets (pp. 23–27) Daily Reteach • 5-Minute Check • Problem of the Day	**Materials** overhead decimal squares for tenths, hundredths, and thousandths, decimal square workmat, crayons or markers, fraction bars or fraction bar poster **Other Resources** CRM Leveled Worksheets (pp. 28–32) Daily Reteach • 5-Minute Check • Problem of the Day
Technology **Math Online**	Math Adventures Personal Tutor	Math Adventures Personal Tutor	Math Adventures Personal Tutor
Reaching All Learners	English Learners, p. 382B ELL Gifted and Talented, p. 382B AL Early Finishers, p. 382B AL	English Learners, p. 386B ELL Below Level, p. 386B BL Early Finishers, p. 386B AL	English Learners, p. 391B ELL Below Level, p. 391B BL Early Finishers, p. 391B AL
Alternate Lesson	*IMPACT Mathematics:* Unit E	*IMPACT Mathematics:* Unit E	*IMPACT Mathematics:* Unit E

Game Time
Match Up (p. 385)

Formative Assessment
Mid-Chapter Check (p. 390)

Chapter Planner

	Lesson 9-6 (Pacing: 1 day)	Lesson 9-7 (Pacing: 1 day)	Lesson 9-8 (Pacing: 1 day)
Lesson/ Objective	**Problem-Solving Strategy** **Look for a Pattern** (pp. 394–395) **Objective:** Solve problems by looking for a pattern.	**Multiples** (pp. 396–399) **Objective:** Identify common multiples of a set of whole numbers.	**Problem-Solving Investigation** **Choose a Strategy** (pp. 400–401) **Objective:** Choose the best strategy to solve a problem.
State/Local Standards			
Math Vocabulary		**multiple, common multiple, least common multiple (LCM)**	
Lesson Resources	**Materials** calculator, blocks **Other Resources** CRM Leveled Worksheets (pp. 33–37) Daily Reteach • 5-Minute Check • Problem of the Day *Nature's Delicate Balance*	**Materials** hundred chart, crayons or markers, number lines **Manipulatives** connecting cubes **Other Resources** CRM Leveled Worksheets (pp. 38–42) Daily Reteach • 5-Minute Check • Problem of the Day	**Other Resources** CRM Leveled Worksheets (pp. 43–47) Daily Reteach • 5-Minute Check • Problem of the Day *Nature's Delicate Balance*
Technology / **Math Online**		Math Adventures Personal Tutor	
Reaching All Learners	English Learners, p. 394B ELL Below Level, p. 394B BL Early Finishers, p. 394B OL AL	English Learners, p. 396B ELL Below Level, p. 396B BL Early Finishers, p. 396B AL	English Learners, p. 400B ELL Below Level, p. 400B BL Early Finishers, p. 400B OL AL
Alternate Lesson			

Explore 9-9

Pacing: $\frac{1}{2}$ day

Tech Link

Compare Fractions
(pp. 402–403)

Objective: Use technology to compare fractions.

Math Tool Chest

Lesson 9-9

Pacing: $\frac{1}{2}$ day

Compare Fractions
(pp. 404–407)

Objective: Compare fractions using common denominators.

common denominators, least common denominator (LCD)

Materials
masking tape

Manipulatives
fraction tiles, number lines

Other Resources
CRM Leveled Worksheets (pp. 48–52)
Daily Reteach • 5-Minute Check • Problem of the Day

Math Adventures

Personal Tutor • Concepts in Motion

English Learners, p. 404B ELL
Gifted and Talented, p. 404B AL
Early Finishers, p. 404B AL

IMPACT Mathematics: Unit E

Problem Solving: Social Studies (p. 408)

Summative Assessment
- Study Guide and Review (p. 410)
- Chapter Test (p. 415)
- Test Practice (p. 416)

Assessment Options

Diagnostic Assessment

SE *Option 1:* Quick Check (p. 372)
Option 2: Online Quiz macmillanmh.com
CRM *Option 3:* Diagnostic Test (p. 54)
CRM *Option 4:* Chapter Pretest (p. 55)

Formative Assessment

TE Alternate Teaching Strategies (every lesson)
SE Talk About It (every lesson)
SE Writing in Math (every lesson)
SE Check What You Know (every lesson)
TE Ticket Out the Door (pp. 375, 393)
TE Yesterday's News (pp. 389, 407)
SE Mid-Chapter Check (p. 390)
CRM Lesson Quizzes (pp. 56–58)
CRM Mid-Chapter Test (p. 59)

Summative Assessment

SE Chapter Test (p. 415)
SE Test Practice (p. 416)
CRM Vocabulary Test (p. 60)
CRM Leveled Chapter Tests (pp. 65–76)
CRM Cumulative Test Practice (pp. 79–81)
CRM Oral Assessment (pp. 61–62)
ExamView® Assessment Suite
Advance Tracker

Mc Graw Hill Professional Development

Targeted professional development has been articulated throughout **McGraw-Hill's *Math Connects*** program. The **McGraw-Hill Professional Development Video Library** provides short videos that support the **NCTM Focal Points and Focal Connections.** For more information visit macmillanmh.com.

Model Lessons

Instructional Strategies

Learning Stations
Cross-Curricular Links

pair | LOGICAL 

Where Is It?

Archeologists plot their finds to record them for later use.

- Make your own dig site by measuring a 4-meter by 4-meter coordinate plane on the floor. Use masking tape to mark your axes, and write the meter and decimeter markers on the masking tape. Write the decimeters as fractions.
- One person places seashells on the coordinate plane and writes the coordinates down on a separate piece of paper as decimals.
- The other person tries to find the shells using the coordinates. They pick up a shell when they locate it using the coordinates.

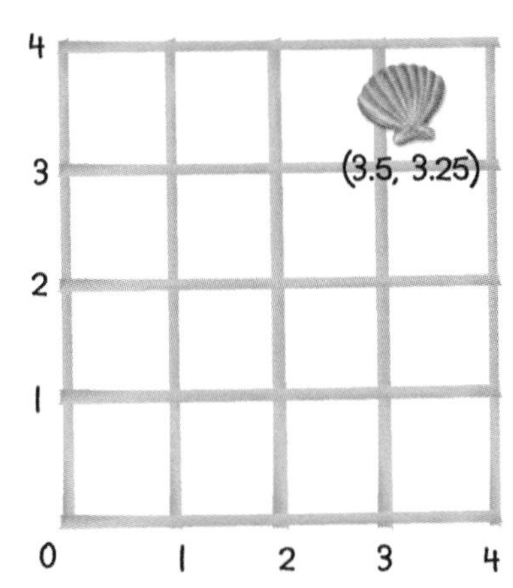

Materials:
- measuring tape
- masking tape
- seashells
- pencils
- paper

Art

 individual | VISUAL 

It is In The Mix

Using an eyedropper and two colors of paint, make a painted gradation color strip using decimal mixtures.

- Into the first cup, drop 1.0 quantity, or 10 drops, of the first color, and 0 of the second color. Into the second cup, the mix is 0.9 of one color to 0.1 of the second color (9 drops of the first color and 1 drop of the second color). Keep reducing the first color by 0.1 or and increasing the second color by 0.1 until you have all 10 cups full. Notice how the mix changes the color.
- Now paint a picture using the colors you just created.

Materials:
- tempera paints (two colors)
- 10 plastic cups
- eyedroppers
- paintbrushes
- access to water
- paper

Writing

 individual | LOGICAL 

Denominator Dilemma

- Write a story about a party two friends are attending. The two friends each go shopping for food to bring and divide among the party guests. But each friend thinks there will be a different number of people at the party. Describe what happens when they get to the party and discover that they're both wrong, and there are more people than they both counted on. How can they use common multiples to solve their dilemma?

Louisa and Angel both went out to buy snacks for the party, but Louisa thought there would be 20 people to buy for. Angel had been told there were only 15 people invited.

Materials:
- paper
- pencil

Health

pair | LOGICAL

What's For Dinner?

- Suppose the daily requirements for dairy are three servings per day, and you need two servings of meat/fish/eggs/legumes, five servings of fruit/vegetables, and eight servings of grains.
- Each person expresses what he or she had for dinner using equivalent fractions. For example, if you had one serving of vegetables, that would be $\frac{1}{5}$ of your daily fruit/vegetable requirement, and you could write down $\frac{3}{15}$ fruit/vegetable.
- Challenge each other to figure out exactly how many servings of each food group you had for dinner.

For dinner, I had 3/15 of my daily fruit and vegetable requirement...

Materials:
- paper
- pencils

Music

pair | LOGICAL

Musical Code

- In music, in 4/4 time, a quarter note is $\frac{1}{4}$ of a measure. A half note is $\frac{1}{2}$ of a measure. A whole note lasts one whole measure.
- Make up four measures using decimal code for the notes. Then give it to your partner and see if he or she can write the proper notes in the measure. For example, if one person's measures had a quarter note in it, you would write it as a 0.25 note.
- Challenge each other to crack these musical codes.

♩ $= \frac{1}{4}$

𝅗𝅥 $= \frac{1}{2}$

𝅝 $= 1$

Materials:
- paper
- pencils

Social Studies

individual | VISUAL

Eratosthenes' Sieve

- Make a 10 × 10 number chart with cardstock: 1–10 on the first line, 11–20 on the second line, and so on until you reach 100. Cut out small circles of colored paper to cover one number at a time.
- 1 has only one factor, so it is not prime. Since 2 has only two factors, it is prime, but anything divisible by 2 has more than two factors. Cover up numbers greater than 2 that are divisible by 2.
- Now, cover up numbers greater than 3 and divisible by 3. If you keep going like this, you will see that only the primes are left uncovered. Then, use your chart as a portable prime number finder.

●	2	3	4	5	6	7	8	9	10
11	12	13	14	15	16	17	18	19	20
21	22	23	24	25	26	27	28	29	30
31	32	33	34	35	36	37	38	39	40
41	42	43	44	45	46	47	48	49	50
51	52	53	54	55	56	57	58	59	60
61	62	63	64	65	66	67	68	69	70
71	72	73	74	75	76	77	78	79	80
81	82	83	84	85	86	87	88	89	90
91	92	93	94	95	96	97	98	99	

Materials:
- cardstock
- colored construction paper
- scissors
- markers

CHAPTER 9

Introduce the Chapter

 Real World: Got Pizza!

Materials: fraction circles, index cards

Share with students that they are going to learn about factors and multiples in this chapter. Remind them that a factor is a number that is multiplied by another number. Explain that a factor is also a number that divides a whole number evenly.

- Have students work in pairs to play a factor game.
- Distribute 10 index cards to each group or have students use pieces of paper. Students should write 0–9, one digit per card. Cards are shuffled and placed facedown.
- Player 1 turns over two cards. Player 2 names the greatest two-digit number possible with the digits.
- Player 1 names as many factors of the number as they can.
- Students repeat, switching roles.

Direct students to Student Edition p. 370. Have students read the paragraph at the top of the page.

- **Can you name some other multiples of 6?** Sample answers: 6, 12, 18, 24, etc.

WRITING IN MATH

Starting the Chapter
Pose the following question to students: What do you know about factors and multiples? Ask students to write their answers in their Math Journals. Then have volunteers share their answers with the class.

Key Vocabulary Introduce the key vocabulary in the chapter using the routine below.

Define: A prime number is any whole number with exactly two factors, 1 and itself.

Example: 19, 23, 31

Ask: How can we determine if a number is prime?

Read-Aloud Anthology For an optional reading activity to introduce this chapter's math concepts, see the Read-Aloud Anthology on p. TR28.

CHAPTER 9

Use Factors and Multiples

BIG Idea What are multiples?

A **multiple** of a number is the product of that number and any whole number.

Example It costs $6 for a fifth grade student to enter the Frederik Meijer Gardens and Sculpture Park in Grand Rapids, Michigan. If two fifth grade students enter the park, the cost would be 6×2, or 12. So, 12 is a multiple of 6.

What will I learn in this chapter?

- Identify common factors and common multiples of a set of whole numbers.
- Identify prime and composite numbers.
- Find equivalent fractions and simplify fractions.
- Relate decimals to fractions.
- Compare fractions using a variety of methods, including common denominators.
- Solve problems by using the *look for a pattern* strategy.

Key Vocabulary

common factor
composite number
equivalent fractions
prime number
simplest form

Math Online Student Study Tools at macmillanmh.com

 Chapter 9 Project

A Portable Sieve

Students make a "Sieve of Eratosthenes."

- Students use cardstock to make a 10×10 number table. Then they use paper circles to cover up the numbers that are not prime. They begin by covering 1 and then covering all multiples of 2 except 2. They then cover all multiples of 3 except 3. 4 is covered already because it is a multiple of 2. They cover all multiples of 5 except 5, and so on, until all primes are uncovered and all composite numbers are covered.
- This sieve strains out all the composite numbers and leaves the primes. Students can roll up their grid and store the colored circles with the grid for a portable prime number finder.
- Challenge students to find the next prime number after 100.

CRM *Refer to Chapter 9 Resource Masters, p. 63, for a rubric to assess students' progress on this project.*

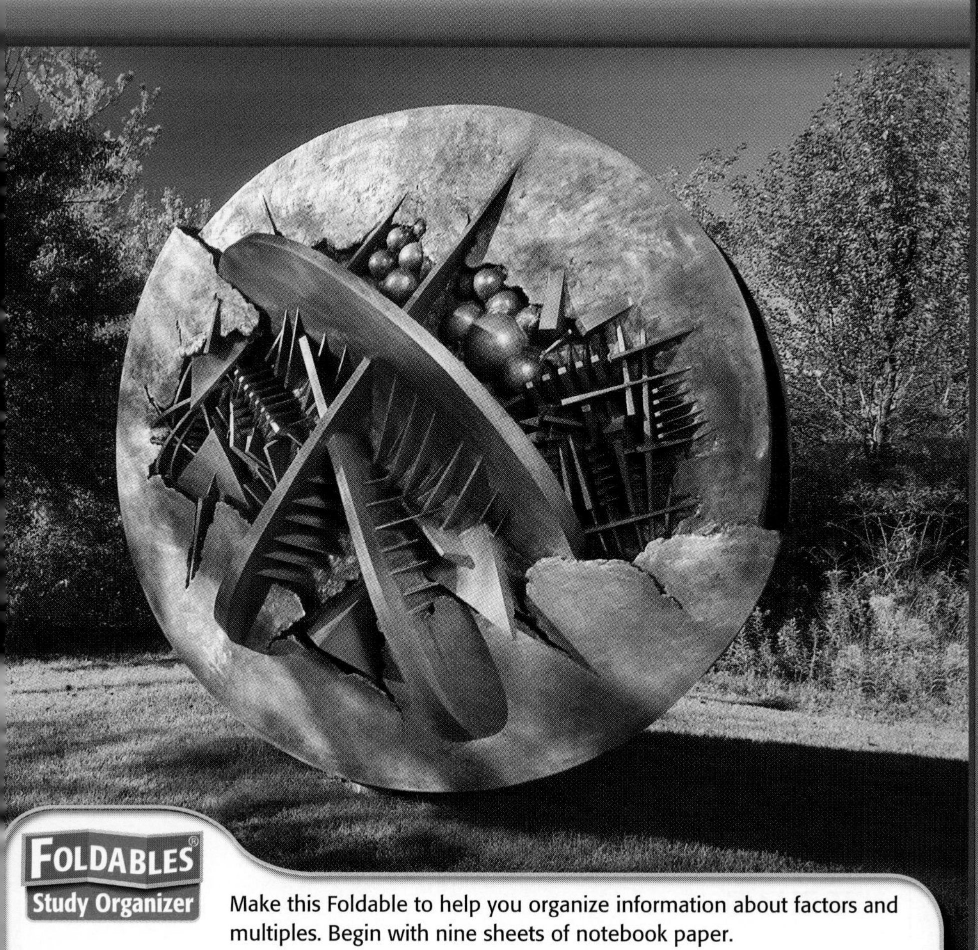

FOLDABLES Study Organizer Make this Foldable to help you organize information about factors and multiples. Begin with nine sheets of notebook paper.

1. **Fold** 9 sheets of paper in half along the width.

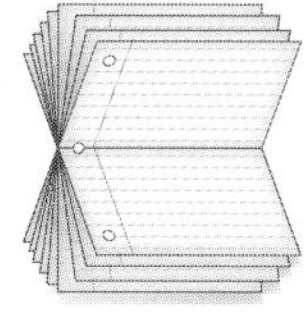

2. **Cut** a 1″ tab along the left edge through one thickness.

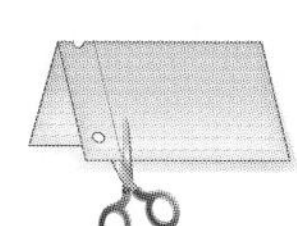

3. **Glue** the 1″ tab down. Write the lesson number and title on the front tab.

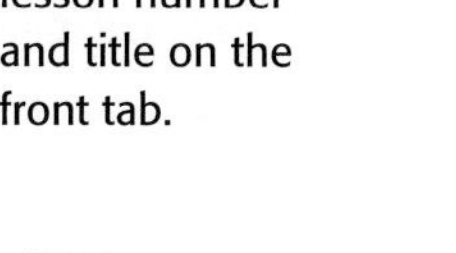

4. **Repeat** Steps 2 and 3 for the remaining sheets. Staple them together on the glued tabs to form a booklet.

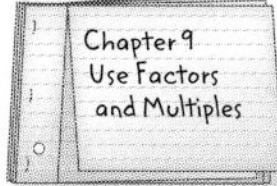

Chapter 9 Use Factors and Multiples **371**

ELL National ESL Standards Alignment for Chapter 9			
Lesson, Page	ESL Standards	Modality	Level
9-1, p. 373B	Goal 2, Standard 2, f	Visual, Linguistic	Intermediate
9-2, p. 378B	Goal 2, Standard 2, d	Social, Visual	Intermediate
9-3, p. 382B	Goal 2, Standard 2, i	Spatial, Kinesthetic	Beginning
9-4, p. 386B	Goal 2, Standard 1, d	Logical, Auditory	Advanced
9-5, p. 391B	Goal 1, Standard 3, c	Linguistic, Auditory	Intermediate
9-6, p. 394B	Goal 1, Standard 3, d	Linguistic, Auditory	Intermediate
9-7, p. 396B	Goal 2, Standard 1, h	Visual, Kinesthetic	Intermediate
9-8, p. 400B	Goal 2, Standard 1, f	Linguistic, Logical	Advanced
9-9, p. 404B	Goal 2, Standard 3, k	Visual, Spatial	Intermediate

The National ESL Standards can be found in the Teacher Reference Handbook.

FOLDABLES Dinah Zike's Foldables

Guide students through the directions on p. 371 to create their own Foldable graphic organizers for information about factors and multiples. Students may also use their Foldables to study and review for chapter assessments.

When to Use It Lessons 9-1, 9-2, 9-3, 9-4, and 9-5. (Additional instructions for using the Foldables with these lessons are found on pp. 390 and 410.)

Chapter 9 Literature List

Lesson	Book Title
9-1	**Sea Squares** Joy N. Hulme
9-2	**Among the Odds and Evens: A Tale of Adventure** Priscilla Turner
9-3	**Fraction Fun** David A. Adler
9-4	**Give Me Half!** Stuart J. Murphy
9-5	**Henry Hikes to Fitchburg** D.B. Johnson
9-6	**Polar Bear Math: Learning About Fractions from Klondike and Snow** Ann Whitehead Nagda and Cindy Bickel
9-7	**Marvelous Multiplication: Games and Activities that Make Math Easy and Fun** Lynette Long
9-9	**Fraction Fun** David A. Adler

- Read the Math at Home letter found on Chapter 9 Resource Masters, p. 4, with the class and have each student sign it. (A Spanish version is found on p. 5.)
- Send home copies of the Math at Home letter with each student.

Diagnostic Assessment

Check for students' prerequisite skills before beginning the chapter.

- **Option 1:** ***Quick Check***
  SE Student Edition, p. 372
- **Option 2:** ***Online Assessment***
  Math Online macmillanmh.com
- **Option 3:** ***Diagnostic Test***
  CRM Chapter 9 Resource Masters, p. 63

RTI (Response to Intervention)

Apply the Results Based on the results of the diagnostic assessment on Student Edition p. 372, address individual needs before beginning the chapter.

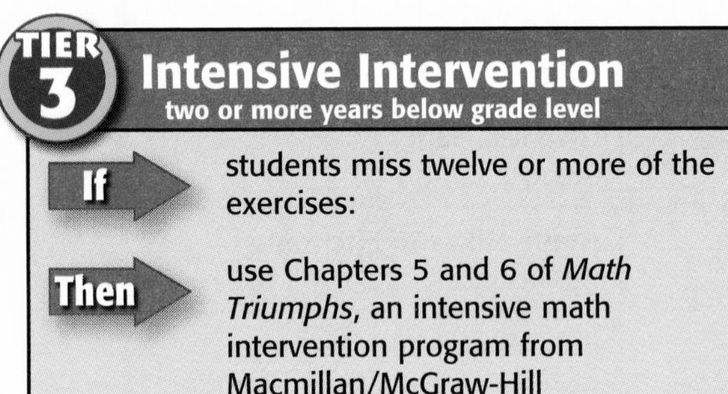

TIER 3 Intensive Intervention
two or more years below grade level

If students miss twelve or more of the exercises:

Then use Chapters 5 and 6 of *Math Triumphs*, an intensive math intervention program from Macmillan/McGraw-Hill

ARE YOU READY for Chapter 9?

You have two ways to check prerequisite skills for this chapter.

Option 2

Math Online Take the Chapter Readiness Quiz at macmillanmh.com.

Option 1

Complete the Quick Check below.

QUICK Check

Write all of the factors of each number. (Prior Grade) (Used in Lesson 9-1)

1. 8 1, 2, 4, 8 **2.** 11 1, 11 **3.** 6 1, 2, 3, 6

4. 15 1, 3, 5, 15 **5.** 32 1, 2, 4, 8, 16, 32 **6.** 24 1, 2, 3, 4, 6, 8, 12, 24

Identify the number of rows and columns in each figure. (Prior Grade) (Used in Lesson 9-2)

7. 1 row, 6 columns **8.** 2 rows, 3 columns

9. 5 rows, 4 columns **10.** 4 rows, 5 columns

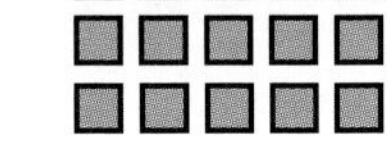

Write each decimal in words. (Lesson 1-4) (Used in Lesson 9-5)

11. 0.3 three tenths **12.** 0.8 eight tenths **13.** 0.1 one tenth

14. 0.45 forty-five hundredths **15.** 0.06 six hundredths **16.** 0.04 four hundredths

17. Measurement A rock has a mass of 0.925 kilogram. Write this measure in words. nine hundred twenty-five thousandths kilogram

18. Measurement A bottle of water contains 0.85 pint. Write this amount in words. eighty-five hundredths

TIER 2 Strategic Intervention below/approaching grade level	**TIER 1 On-Level**	**Above/Beyond Level**
If students miss six to eleven in: **Exercises 1–18**	**If** students miss three to five in: **Exercises 1–18**	**If** students miss two or less: **Exercises 1–18**
Then Choose a resource:	**Then** Choose a resource:	**Then** Choose a resource:
Strategic Intervention Guide (pp. 90, 92, 94, 100, 104, 112) CRM Chapter 8 Resource Master (Reteach Worksheets) **Math Online** Extra Examples • Personal Tutor • Concepts in Motion • Online Games	TE Learning Stations (pp. 370G–370H) TE Chapter Project (p. 370) Math Adventures My Math Zone Chapter 8 **Math Online** Fact Dash	TE Learning Stations (pp. 370G–370H) TE Chapter Project (p. 370) Real-World Problems Solving Reader: *Nature's Delicate Balance* My Math Zone Chapter 8, 9 **Math Online** Games

LESSON **9-1**

Common Factors

Lesson Planner

Objective

Identify common factors of a set of whole numbers.

Vocabulary

common factor, greatest common factor (GCF)

Resources

Materials: grid paper
Manipulatives: color tiles, counters
Literature Connection: *Sea Squares* by Joy N. Hulme
Teacher Technology
TeacherWorks • Interactive Classroom

Focus on Math Background

In a product of two numbers $a \cdot b$, the first factor a can be called the *multiplier* and b the *multiplicand*. Since multiplication is commutative, the distinction is usually unnecessary. However, the meaning of the product may depend on which number is the multiplier: $4 \cdot 3$ and $3 \cdot 4$ are both equal to 12, but "four groups of three" and "three groups of four" have different interpretations. In this lesson, students use factorization to help them identify the greatest common factor (GCF), also called the greatest common divisor. The GCF can be found by listing all the factors of each number and identifying the greatest common factor. All natural numbers have 1 as a common factor. The GCF can also be found using prime factors.
For example:
24: $1 \times 2 \times 2 \times 2 \times 3$ 18: $1 \times 2 \times 3 \times 3$
GCF of 24 and 18: $1 \times 2 \times 3 = 6$

Daily Routine

Use these suggestions before beginning the lesson on p. 373.

5-Minute Check

(Reviews Lesson 8-7)

Use any strategy to solve. Tell what strategy you used.

Jake went to see a play at his high school. It started at 6:35 P.M. and lasted 1 hour and 55 minutes. At what time did the play end? 8:30 P.M.; *solve a simpler problem*

Problem of the Day

How much did Juan earn babysitting? Create a new graph that shows how much Juan will earn if he works the same number of jobs but earns only half as much. $44; Check students' graphs.

Dollars Earned by Babysitting

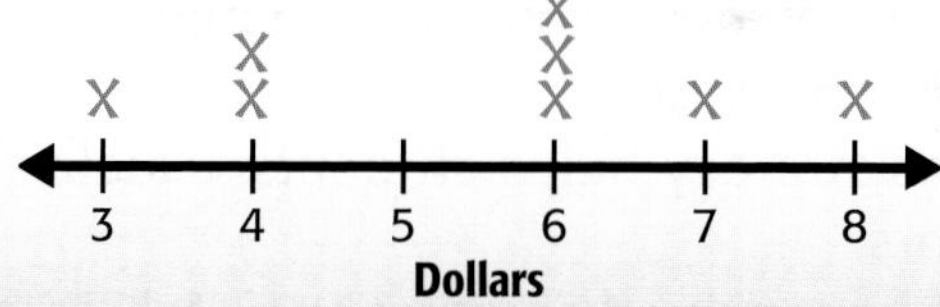

Building Math Vocabulary

Write the lesson vocabulary words and their definitions on the board.

Call on several volunteers to use the term *common* in a sentence. The ask students to write the terms *common factor* and *greatest common factor* in separate sentences.

Differentiated Instruction

Small Group Options

LOGICAL

Option 1 Gifted and Talented AL

- Ask students to find the GCF of 225 and 270. 45

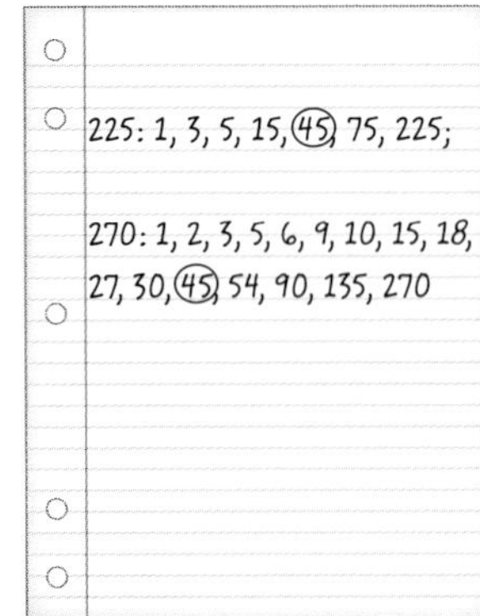

225: 1, 3, 5, 15, 45, 75, 225;
270: 1, 2, 3, 5, 6, 9, 10, 15, 18, 27, 30, 45, 54, 90, 135, 270

VISUAL, LINGUISTIC

Option 2 English Language Learners ELL

Materials: transparency cut in half, permanent and transparency markers

Core Vocabulary: greatest, common, on both

Common Use Verb: circle

See Math This strategy helps students visualize common factors.

- With the permanent marker write: "18." Ask: "What are the factors for 18?" Prompt students as you write pairs underneath. Repeat for 24 on the other sheet.
- Ask: "What numbers are *on both*?" With the transparency marker, circle the *common* factors as students call them out.
- Prompt students to describe what *common* factor means based on the demonstration.
- Repeat until students show understanding.
- Continue finding the *greatest* common factors as time permits.

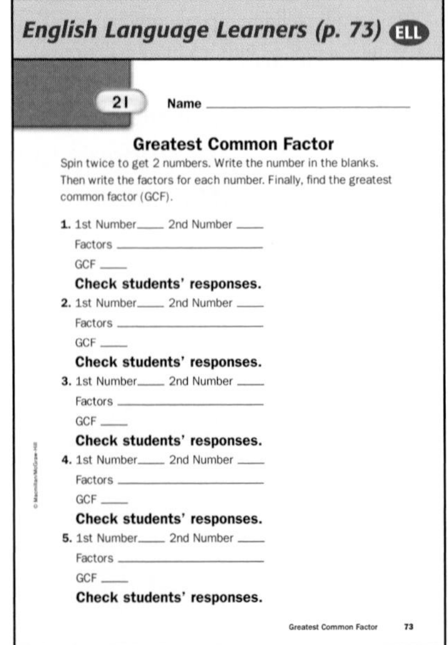

English Language Learners (p. 73) ELL

21 Name

Greatest Common Factor

Spin twice to get 2 numbers. Write the number in the blanks. Then write the factors for each number. Finally, find the greatest common factor (GCF).

1. 1st Number____ 2nd Number____
   Factors ____
   GCF ____
   Check students' responses.
2. 1st Number____ 2nd Number____
   Factors ____
   GCF ____
   Check students' responses.
3. 1st Number____ 2nd Number____
   Factors ____
   GCF ____
   Check students' responses.
4. 1st Number____ 2nd Number____
   Factors ____
   GCF ____
   Check students' responses.
5. 1st Number____ 2nd Number____
   Factors ____
   GCF ____
   Check students' responses.

Greatest Common Factor 73

Use this worksheet to provide additional support for English Language Learners.

Independent Work Options

VISUAL/SPATIAL

Option 1 Early Finishers AL

Materials: two number cubes

- Have students work with a partner. The first student rolls both number cubes to form a two-digit number. For example, if a 5 and a 2 are rolled, the two-digit number can be 25 or 52. Let students decide which number to use. The second student repeats the same process to generate a two-digit number.
- Have each student find all the factors of their two-digit number.
- Together have the students find the common factors of their numbers. Then have them find the GCF.
- Repeat as time allows.

Option 2 Student Technology

Math Online macmillanmh.com

Personal Tutor • Extra Examples

Option 3 Learning Station: Writing (p. 370G)

Direct students to the Writing Learning Station for opportunities to explore and extend the lesson concept.

Option 4 Problem-Solving Practice

Reinforce problem-solving skills and strategies with the Problem-Solving Practice worksheet.

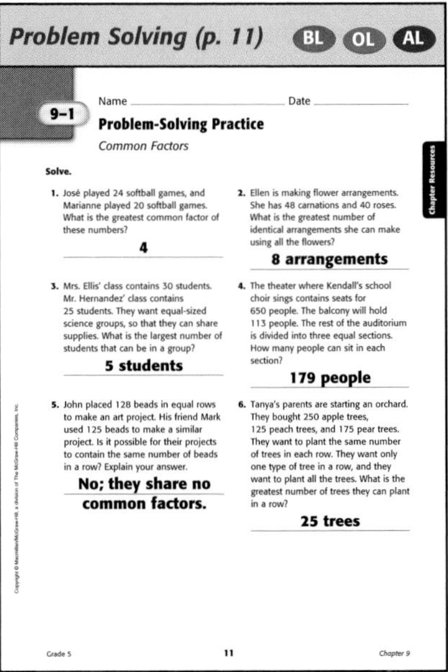

Problem Solving (p. 11) BL OL AL

9–1 Name ____ Date ____

Problem-Solving Practice

Common Factors

Chapter Resources

Solve.

1. José played 24 softball games, and Marianne played 20 softball games. What is the greatest common factor of these numbers?
   4
2. Ellen is making flower arrangements. She has 48 carnations and 40 roses. What is the greatest number of identical arrangements she can make using all the flowers?
   8 arrangements
3. Mrs. Ellis' class contains 30 students. Mr. Hernandez' class contains 25 students. They want equal-sized science groups, so that they can share supplies. What is the largest number of students that can be in a group?
   5 students
4. The theater where Kendall's school choir sings contains seats for 650 people. The balcony will hold 113 people. The rest of the auditorium is divided into three equal sections. How many people can sit in each section?
   179 people
5. John placed 128 beads in equal rows to make an art project. His friend Mark used 125 beads to make a similar project. Is it possible for their projects to contain the same number of beads in a row? Explain your answer.
   No; they share no common factors.
6. Tanya's parents are starting an orchard. They bought 250 apple trees, 125 peach trees, and 175 pear trees. They want to plant the same number of trees in each row. They want only one type of tree in a row, and they want to plant all the trees. What is the greatest number of trees they can plant in a row?
   25 trees

Grade 5 11 Chapter 9

9-1 Common Factors

MAIN IDEA

I will identify common factors of a set of whole numbers.

New Vocabulary

common factor

greatest common factor (GCF)

Math Online macmillanmh.com

- Extra Examples
- Personal Tutor
- Self-Check Quiz

GET READY to Learn

A pet store has 6 dog bones and 18 dog biscuits to give away as samples. They put an equal number of bones and an equal number of biscuits in each sample bag. What is the greatest number of sample bags they can give away? 6

The factors of 6 and 18 are listed below.

Product	Factors
6	1×6
6	2×3

Product	Factors
18	1×18
18	2×9
18	3×6

factors of 6: **1**, **2**, **3**, **6**

factors of 18: **1**, **2**, **3**, **6**, 9, 18

A **common factor** is a number that is a factor of two or more numbers. So, 1, 2, 3, and 6 are common factors of 6 and 18. Since 6 is the greatest of these common factors, the greatest number of sample bags that can be made is 6.

EXAMPLE Find Common Factors

1 Find the common factors of 16 and 20.

Step 1 List all the factors of each number.

$16 = 1 \times 16 \quad 16 = 2 \times 8 \quad 16 = 4 \times 4$

factors of 16: 1, 2, 4, 8, 16

$20 = 1 \times 20 \quad 20 = 2 \times 10 \quad 20 = 4 \times 5$

factors of 20: 1, 2, 4, 5, 10, 20

Step 2 Find the common factors.

factors of 16: **1**, **2**, **4**, 8, 16

factors of 20: **1**, **2**, **4**, 5, 10, 20

The common factors of 16 and 20 are 1, 2, and 4.

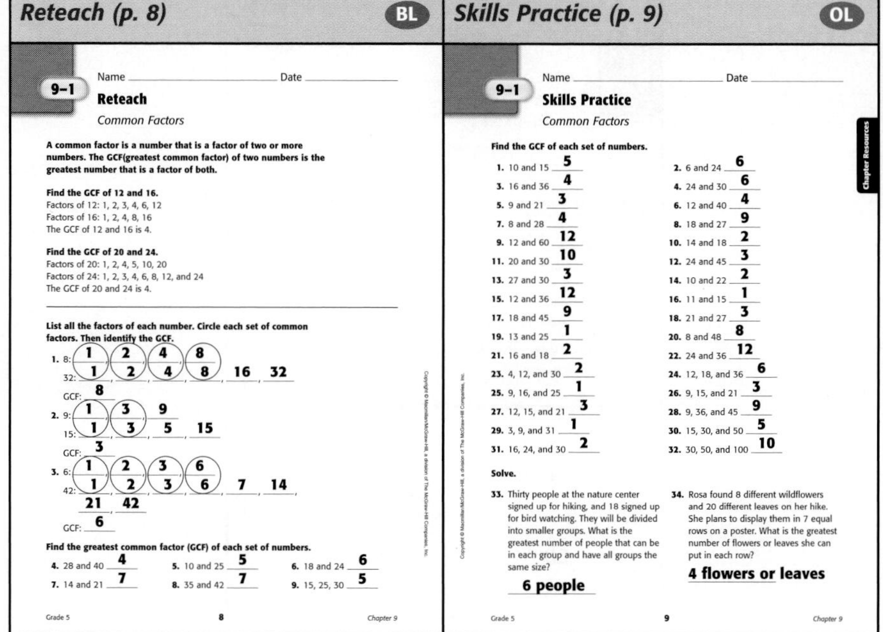

Reteach (p. 8) BL

9-1 Name ____ Date ____

Reteach

Common Factors

A common factor is a number that is a factor of two or more numbers. The GCF(greatest common factor) of two numbers is the greatest number that is a factor of both.

Find the GCF of 12 and 16.
Factors of 12: 1, 2, 3, 4, 6, 12
Factors of 16: 1, 2, 4, 8, 16
The GCF of 12 and 16 is 4.

Find the GCF of 20 and 24.
Factors of 20: 1, 2, 4, 5, 10, 20
Factors of 24: 1, 2, 3, 4, 6, 8, 12, and 24
The GCF of 20 and 24 is 4.

List all the factors of each number. Circle each set of common factors. Then identify the GCF.

1. 8: **1**, **2**, **4**, **8**
32: **1**, **2**, **4**, **8**, **16**, **32**
GCF: **8**

2. 9: **1**, **3**, **9**
15: **1**, **3**, **5**, **15**
GCF: **3**

3. 6: **1**, **2**, **3**, **6**
42: **1**, **2**, **3**, **6**, **7**, **14**, **21**, **42**
GCF: **6**

Find the greatest common factor (GCF) of each set of numbers.

4. 28 and 40 **4** 5. 10 and 25 **5** 6. 18 and 24 **6**
7. 14 and 21 **7** 8. 35 and 42 **7** 9. 15, 25, 30 **5**

Grade 5 8 Chapter 9

Skills Practice (p. 9) OL

9-1 Name ____ Date ____

Skills Practice

Common Factors

Find the GCF of each set of numbers.

1. 10 and 15 **5**
2. 6 and 24 **6**
3. 16 and 36 **4**
4. 24 and 30 **6**
5. 9 and 21 **3**
6. 12 and 40 **4**
7. 8 and 28 **4**
8. 18 and 27 **9**
9. 12 and 60 **12**
10. 14 and 18 **2**
11. 20 and 30 **10**
12. 24 and 45 **3**
13. 27 and 30 **3**
14. 10 and 22 **2**
15. 12 and 36 **12**
16. 11 and 15 **1**
17. 18 and 45 **9**
18. 21 and 27 **3**
19. 13 and 25 **1**
20. 8 and 48 **8**
21. 16 and 18 **2**
22. 24 and 36 **12**
23. 4, 12, and 30 **2**
24. 12, 18, and 36 **6**
25. 9, 16, and 25 **1**
26. 9, 15, and 21 **3**
27. 12, 15, and 21 **3**
28. 9, 36, and 45 **9**
29. 3, 9, and 31 **1**
30. 15, 30, and 50 **5**
31. 16, 24, and 30 **2**
32. 30, 50, and 100 **10**

Solve.

33. Thirty people at the nature center signed up for hiking, and 18 signed up for bird watching. They will be divided into smaller groups. What is the greatest number of people that can be in each group and have all groups the same size?
6 people

34. Rosa found 8 different wildflowers and 20 different leaves on her hike. She plans to display them in 7 equal rows on a poster. What is the greatest number of flowers or leaves she can put in each row?
4 flowers or leaves

Grade 5 9 Chapter 9

Chapter Resources

9-1 Common Factors

1 Introduce

Activity Choice 1 • Hands-On

- Ask two volunteers to stand in front of the class. As a class, list some attributes of each student, for example, eye color, color of clothes, wearing or not wearing glasses, etc.
- Draw a Venn diagram on the board and record the attributes of each student. Ask the students to identify any attributes that both students have in common. List those in the center of the Venn diagram.
- Tell the students that they will be learning about common attributes of two or more numbers.

Activity Choice 2 • Literature

Introduce the lesson with *Sea Squares* by Joy N. Hulme. For a related math activity, see p. TR49.

2 Teach

Scaffolding Questions

- Ask students to use square tiles or grid paper to model the factors of 24. Ask a volunteer to list the factors from least to greatest on a T-table on the board. 1, 2, 3, 4, 6, 12
- Repeat the process for 15. 1, 3, 5, 15
- **What are the common factors?** 1, 3 Circle the common factors.
- Draw a Venn diagram. List the factors of 15 that are not circled in the left side of the Venn diagram and the factors not circled for 24 in the right. List the common factors in the center of the diagram.
- **What is the GCF?** 3

GET READY to Learn

Have students open their books and read the information in **Get Ready to Learn.** Introduce **common factor** and **greatest common factor (GCF)**. As a class, work through **Examples 1–4**.

Numbers with One Common Factor

Example 2 Some students find it difficult to understand that some numbers have only one factor in common, the factor 1. Provide ample opportunity for students to explore numbers, such as 6, 7, 9, and 9, 20, 21. Guide the students through the process of finding the common factors of each number set. Allow them to use either grid paper or color tiles to model each problem.

ADDITIONAL EXAMPLES

1. Find the common factors of 12 and 18. 1, 2, 3, and 6
2. Find the common factors of 8, 14, and 21. 1
3. Find the greatest common factor of 12, 16, and 18. 2
4. Olimpia is making a vegetable platter using 32 tomato slices and 48 cucumber slices. She wants to put the same number of tomato slices as the number of cucumber slices on each plate. What is the greatest number of plates she can make? 16

CHECK What You Know

As a class, have students complete Exercises 1–10 in **Check What You Know** as you observe their work.

Exercise 10 Assess student comprehension before assigning practice exercises.

BL Alternate Teaching Strategy

If students have trouble remembering how to find the GCF,

Then use one of these reteach options:

1 CRM **Daily Reteach Worksheet** (p. 8)

2 have students use the letters of GCF backward:

F - find factors

C - find common factors

G - find greatest common factor

This will help them to remember the order in which to work the problems.

Remember

The number 1 is always a common factor of two or more numbers.

EXAMPLE Numbers with One Common Factor

2 Find the common factors of 4, 8, and 15.

factors of 4: 1, 2, 4
factors of 8: 1, 2, 4, 8
factors of 15: 1, 3, 5, 15

The only factor common to all three numbers is 1.

The greatest of the common factors of two or more numbers is called the **greatest common factor (GCF)**.

EXAMPLE Find the Greatest Common Factor

3 Find the greatest common factor of 10, 15, and 20.

List all the factors of 10, 15, and 20 to find the common factors.

factors of 10: 1, 2, 5, 10
factors of 15: 1, 3, 5, 15
factors of 20: 1, 2, 4, 5, 10, 20

The common factors are 1 and 5. The greatest of these is 5. So, the greatest common factor, or GCF, of 10, 15, and 20 is 5.

Real-World EXAMPLE Use the Greatest Common Factor

4 FOOD A chef made 24 baked cheese sticks and 36 egg rolls to arrange on plates. Each plate will have an equal number of cheese sticks and an equal number of egg rolls. What is the greatest number of plates he can arrange?

First, find the common factors of each number.

factors of 24: 1, 2, 3, 4, 6, 8, 12, 24
factors of 36: 1, 2, 3, 4, 6, 9, 12, 18, 36

common factors of 24 and 36: 1, 2, 3, 4, 6, 12

The chef can arrange 1, 2, 3, 4, 6, or 12 plates with each plate having an equal number of cheese sticks and an equal number of egg rolls. Since 12 is the GCF, the greatest number of plates the chef can arrange is 12.

Check There will be 24 ÷ 12, or 2 cheese sticks and 36 ÷ 12, or 3 egg rolls on each plate. ✓

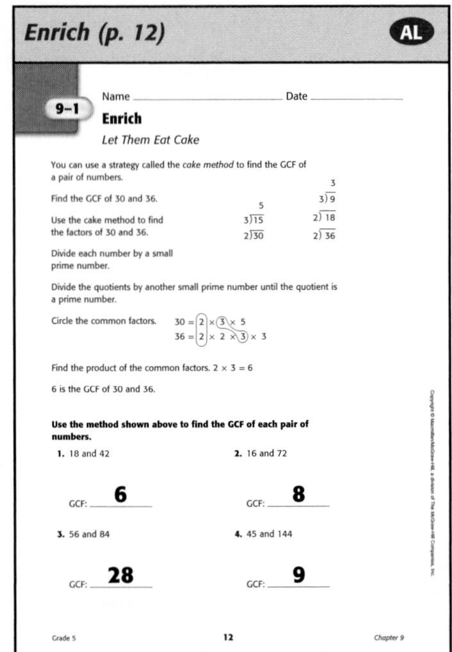

Enrich (p. 12) AL

Name ______________ Date ______________

9–1 Enrich

Let Them Eat Cake

You can use a strategy called the *cake method* to find the GCF of a pair of numbers.

Find the GCF of 30 and 36.

Use the cake method to find the factors of 30 and 36.

$$\begin{array}{r} 5 \\ 3\overline{)15} \\ 2\overline{)30} \end{array} \qquad \begin{array}{r} 3 \\ 3\overline{)9} \\ 2\overline{)18} \\ 2\overline{)36} \end{array}$$

Divide each number by a small prime number.

Divide the quotients by another small prime number until the quotient is a prime number.

Circle the common factors. $30 = 2 \times 3 \times 5$
$36 = 2 \times 2 \times 3 \times 3$

Find the product of the common factors. $2 \times 3 = 6$

6 is the GCF of 30 and 36.

Use the method shown above to find the GCF of each pair of numbers.

1. 18 and 42

GCF: **6**

2. 16 and 72

GCF: **8**

3. 56 and 84

GCF: **28**

4. 45 and 144

GCF: **9**

CHECK What You Know

Find the common factors of each set of numbers. See Examples 1, 2 (pp. 373–374)

1. 9, 12 1, 3
2. 13, 15 1
3. 24, 28, 32 1, 2, 4
4. 10, 30, 50 1, 2, 5, 10

Find the GCF of each set of numbers. See Examples 3, 4 (p. 374)

5. 8, 14 2
6. 15, 20 5
7. 21, 24, 27 3
8. 30, 48, 60 6

9. Fourteen boys and 21 girls will be divided into equal groups. Find the greatest number of children that can be in each group if no one is left out. 7 children

10. Talk About It Explain the steps for finding the GCF of two numbers. Give an example. See margin.

Practice and Problem Solving

Find the common factors of each set of numbers. See Examples 1, 2 (pp. 373–374)

11. 5, 20 1, 5
12. 6, 15 1, 3
13. 8, 9 1
14. 14, 25 1
15. 12, 18, 30 1, 2, 3, 6
16. 27, 36, 45 1, 3, 9
17. 21, 28, 35 1, 7
18. 18, 36, 54 1, 2, 3, 6, 9, 18

Find the GCF of each set of numbers. See Examples 3, 4 (p. 374)

19. 4, 10 2
20. 15, 18 3
21. 18, 42 6
22. 20, 35 5
23. 21, 35, 49 7
24. 24, 30, 42 6
25. 12, 18, 26 2
26. 24, 40, 56 8

27. A grocery store clerk has 16 oranges, 20 apples, and 24 pears. The clerk needs to put an equal number of apples, oranges, and pears into each basket. What is the greatest number of apples that can be in each basket? 4 apples

28. A gardener has 27 pansies and 36 daisies. If the gardener plants an equal number of each type of flower in each row, what is the greatest number of pansies in each row? 9 pansies

H.O.T. Problems

29–31. See Ch. 9 Answer Appendix.

29. OPEN ENDED Write two numbers that have common factors of 1, 3, and 5. Explain how you found the numbers.

30. NUMBER SENSE Three numbers have a GCF of 4. The largest number is 12. Explain how to find the other numbers.

31. WRITING IN ►MATH Can the GCF of two numbers ever be 1? Explain your answer. Give an example to support it.

Additional Answer

10. Sample answer: List the factors of each number and find the factors that are common to both numbers. The greatest of these is the GCF. The GCF of 6 and 8 is 2.

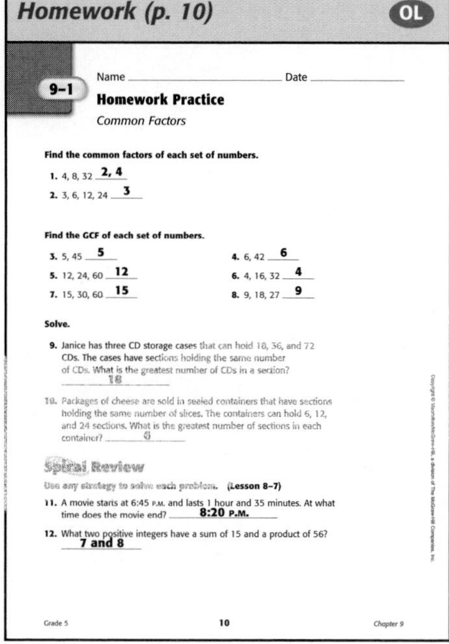

Homework (p. 10) OL

9-1 Name ________ Date ________

Homework Practice

Common Factors

Find the common factors of each set of numbers.

1. 4, 8, 32 2, 4
2. 3, 6, 12, 24 3

Find the GCF of each set of numbers.

3. 5, 45 5
4. 6, 42 6
5. 12, 24, 60 12
6. 4, 16, 32 4
7. 15, 30, 60 15
8. 9, 18, 27 9

Solve.

9. Janice has three CD storage cases that can hold 18, 36, and 72 CDs. The cases have sections holding the same number of CDs. What is the greatest number of CDs in a section? 18

10. Packages of cheese are sold in sealed containers that have sections holding the same number of slices. The containers can hold 6, 12, and 24 sections. What is the greatest number of sections in each container? 6

Spiral Review

Use any strategy to solve each problem. (Lesson 8–7)

11. A movie starts at 6:45 P.M. and lasts 1 hour and 35 minutes. At what time does the movie end? 8:20 P.M.

12. What two positive integers have a sum of 15 and a product of 56? 7 and 8

Grade 5 10 Chapter 9

3 Practice

Differentiate practice using these leveled assignments for Exercises 11–31.

Level	Assignment
BL Below/ Approaching Level	11–15, 19–22, 27
OL On Level	15–28, 31
AL Above/Beyond Level	11–27 odd, 29–31

Have students discuss and complete the Higher Order Thinking problems. Encourage students to use *the guess and check* strategy to solve each problem.

WRITING IN ►MATH Have students complete Exercise 31 in their Math Journals. You may choose to use this exercise as an optional formative assessment.

4 Assess

Formative Assessment

Explain how to find the greatest common factor of 20 and 50. List all the factors of each number. Then select the greatest factor on both lists: 10.

- **Could the greatest common factor be 25? Why or why not?** No, because a factor of 20 cannot be greater than 20.

Quick Check **Are students continuing to struggle with common factors?**

If Yes → Strategic Intervention Guide (p. 92)

If No → Independent Work Options (p. 373B)
CRM Skills Practice Worksheet (p. 9)
CRM Enrich Worksheet (p. 12)

Ticket Out the Door Have students write the GCF of 18 and 24 on a piece of paper and hand it to you as they leave the room. 6

COMMON ERROR!

Exercise 18 Students may forget to list a factor. Have them separate pairs of factors, starting with 1 and the number, then list pairs from the least and greatest working inward.

Math Activity for 9-2

Lesson Planner

Objective

Use objects or pictures to identify prime and composite numbers.

Vocabulary

prime number, **composite number**

Resources

Materials: square tiles, grid paper, markers, index cards, hundreds chart
Manipulatives: two color counters

1 Introduce

- Divide the class into groups of two. Make one set of index cards labeled with the numbers 7, 9, 13, 15, 17, 18, 19, 27, 29, and 30, one number per card.
- Randomly give each group of students an index card. Have students use grid paper to draw all the rectangular arrays possible for the given number.
- Have students place numbers that only have two factors, itself and 1, on the left side of the board and numbers with more than two factors on the right.

2 Teach

Activity 1 Have students work in groups of two to model the factor pairs of 6 using color tiles. Have them display the four different factor pairs on a poster board or display mat. Have them check to see if their display matches the model in the text.

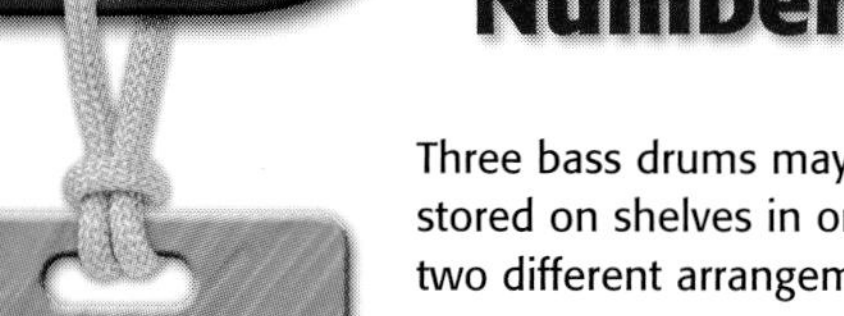

Math Activity for 9-2

Prime and Composite Numbers

MAIN IDEA

I will use models to identify prime and composite numbers.

New Vocabulary

prime
composite

Three bass drums may be stored on shelves in only two different arrangements.

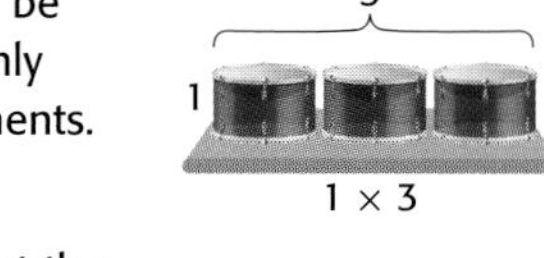

These rectangular arrangements show that the only factors of 3 are 1 and 3.

When a number, like 3, has exactly two factors, the number is **prime**.

You can store 4 drums in any of the three ways shown at the right. What are the factors of 4? 1, 2, 4

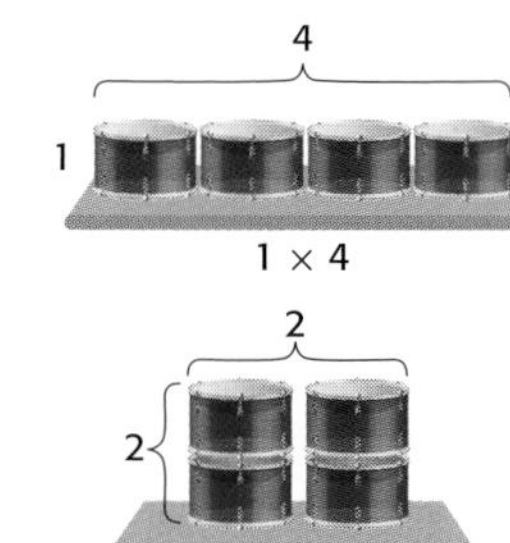

When a number, like 4, has more than two factors, the number is **composite**.

ACTIVITY

1. **Use models to determine whether 6 is *prime* or *composite*.**

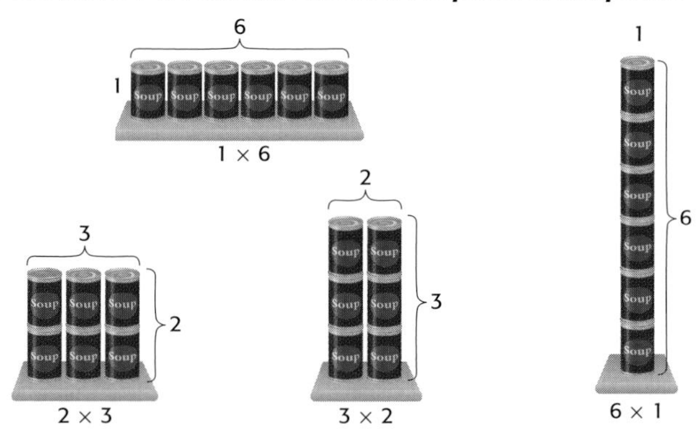

You can arrange the 6 soup cans in four different ways. So, 6 is a composite number.

ACTIVITY

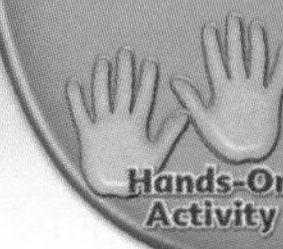

2 **Use models to determine whether 7 is *prime* or *composite*.**

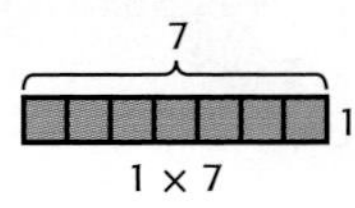

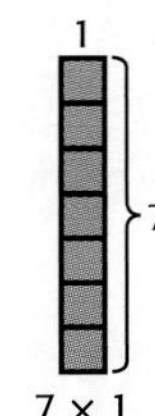

You can arrange the 7 tiles in only 2 ways: 7 × 1 and 1 × 7. So, 7 is a prime number.

Think About It 1–2. See Ch. 9 Answer Appendix.

1. Are all even numbers composite? Use a drawing in your explanation.
2. Are all odd numbers prime? Support your explanation with a drawing.

CHECK What You Know

Use objects or pictures to determine whether each number is *prime* or *composite*. Describe the models that you used. 4, 6, 8. See margin.

3. 13 prime; 1 × 13, 13 × 1
4. 10
5. 11 prime; 1 × 11, 11 × 1
6. 8
7. 17 prime; 1 × 17, 17 × 1
8. 9
9. Caleb made 12 dinner rolls. He placed the rolls in 3 rows of 4 on a table. In what other ways could he have arranged the rolls in equal rows? 4 rows of 3, 1 row of 12, 12 rows of 1, 2 rows of 6, 6 rows of 2
10. Write a number between 20 and 30. Then use objects or pictures to show whether the number is prime or composite. See Ch. 9 Answer Appendix.
11. **WRITING IN ▶MATH** Is there a connection between the number of rectangular arrangements that are possible when modeling a number and the number of factors the number has? Explain your reasoning. Sample answer: Yes, the number of arrangements equals the number of factors.

Additional Answers

4. composite; 1 × 10, 10 × 1, 2 × 5, 5 × 2
6. composite; 1 × 8, 8 × 1, 2 × 4, 4 × 2
8. composite; 1 × 9, 9 × 1, 3 × 3

Activity 2 Have students use color tiles to model the different factor pairs of 7.

- **How many factor pairs are there for the number 7? What are they?** two; 7 × 1, 1 × 7
- **What kind of number is 7?** a prime number

Tips for New Teachers

You may wish to provide students with a hundreds chart to use as a reference as they work through Activities 1 and 2 and the exercises.

Think About It

Assign Exercises 1–2 to assess student comprehension of the concept presented in the activity.

3 Assess

Formative Assessment

Use **Check What You Know** exercises to assess whether students understand prime and composite numbers.

From Concrete to Abstract Use Exercise 11 to help students to make the connection between the number of different rectangular arrangements that are possible for a number and the number of factors.

Extending the Concept Prime numbers have exactly two factors, the number itself and 1. Have students list the prime numbers less than 20. 2, 3, 5, 7, 11, 13, 17, and 19 Point out that 2 is the only even prime number. If needed, have students use objects or draw pictures.

LESSON 9-2

Prime and Composite Numbers

Lesson Planner

Objective

Identify prime and composite numbers.

Vocabulary

prime factorization

Resources

Materials: grid paper, markers
Manipulatives: square tiles
Literature Connection: *Among the Odds and Evens: A Tale of Adventure* by Priscilla Turner
Alternate Lesson: Use *IMPACT Mathematics:* Unit E to provide practice with prime and composite numbers.
Teacher Technology
TeacherWorks • Interactive Classroom • Concepts in Motion

Focus on Math Background

A prime number is any *whole number* that has exactly two unique factors, 1 and the number itself. A composite number is a *whole number* that has more than two factors. The whole number 1 is a special number. It is not prime because it does not have exactly two unique factors. It is not composite because it does not have more than two factors. Factoring a whole number into its prime factors is called prime factorization. Each whole number has exactly one prime factorization (except for the order of the factors). To help find the prime factors of a composite number, you can use divisibility rules. A whole number is divisible by:

- 2 if the ones digit is divisible by 2.
- 3 if the sum of the digits is divisible by 3.
- 5 if the ones digit is 0 or 5.
- 10 if the ones digit is 0.

Daily Routine

Use these suggestions before beginning the lesson on p. 378.

5-Minute Check

(Reviews Lesson 9-1)

Find the common factors of each set of numbers.

1. 12 and 18 1, 2, 3, 6
2. 20, 24 and 28 1, 2, 4

Find the GCF of each set of numbers.

3. 15 and 20 5
4. 21, 28 and 35 7

Problem of the Day

A number has four digits. It is greater than 11 but less than 12. The sum of the four digits is 13. The digit in the hundredths place is 6. What is the number? Explain how you found the number.
11.56; Answers will vary.

Building Math Vocabulary

Write the lesson vocabulary word and its definition on the board.

Have students write the definition in their Math Journals. Ask them to give you an example of a prime number and a composite number. Show students the prime factorization of one of their numbers.

Visual Vocabulary Cards

Use Visual Vocabulary Card 35 to reinforce the vocabulary introduced in this lesson. (The Define/Example/Ask routine is written on the back of each card.)

Differentiated Instruction

Small Group Options

SPATIAL, KINESTHETIC

Option 1 Below Level BL

Materials: connecting cubes

- Have students work with connecting cubes to see why some numbers are prime and some are composite.
- For example, to examine 15, take 15 connecting cubes and try to form a rectangle that contains more than one row and column. Since you can form a 3×5 rectangle, 15 is composite.

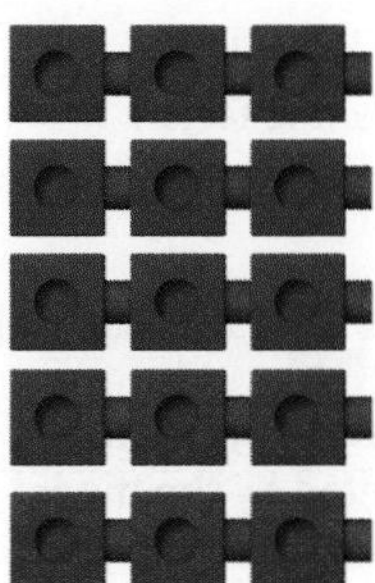

SOCIAL, VISUAL

Option 2 English Language Learners ELL

Core Vocabulary: family, related, relatives
Common Use Verb: group

Do Math This strategy activates background knowledge by associating families with number families.

- Say: "Families are groups of related people." Model drawing a picture of your family inside the frame. Say: "Numbers also have families." Flip the picture.
- Draw a second frame on the back. Write "12" on it and the factors 1,12; 2,6; 3,4 inside it. Say: "This is the Twelve Family." Repeat for 7, 18, and 23.
- Allow students to group number families. Label each as "prime" or "composite."
- Have students draw and count the relatives and factor the total. Prompt students label their family as prime or composite.

Independent Work Options

LOGICAL

Option 1 Early Finishers AL

Materials: index cards

- Ask students to choose a number to factor on index cards. Students should create a factor tree showing the prime factorization of their number without revealing the number being factored.
- When students finish factoring, have them write the number they factored on the back of the card, and exchange cards with a partner.
- Students will use the factor tree on the card to figure out what the original number was. After partners are done solving, have them discuss their solving strategies.

Option 2 Student Technology

Math Online macmillanmh.com

Personal Tutor • Extra Examples

Math Adventures

Option 3 Learning Station: Social Studies (p. 370H)

Direct students to the Social Studies Learning Station for opportunities to explore and extend the lesson concept.

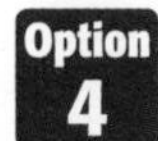

Option 4 Problem-Solving Practice

Reinforce problem-solving skills and strategies with the Problem-Solving Practice worksheet.

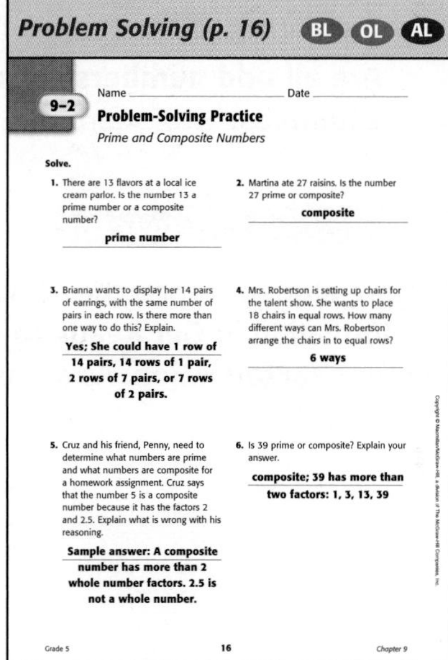

Problem Solving (p. 16) BL OL AL

9–2 Name ________ Date ________

Problem-Solving Practice

Prime and Composite Numbers

Solve.

1. There are 13 flavors at a local ice cream parlor. Is the number 13 a prime number or a composite number?
   prime number
2. Martina ate 27 raisins. Is the number 27 prime or composite?
   composite
3. Brianna wants to display her 14 pairs of earrings, with the same number of pairs in each row. Is there more than one way to do this? Explain.
   Yes; She could have 1 row of 14 pairs, 14 rows of 1 pair, 2 rows of 7 pairs, or 7 rows of 2 pairs.
4. Mrs. Robertson is setting up chairs for the talent show. She wants to place 18 chairs in equal rows. How many different ways can Mrs. Robertson arrange the chairs in to equal rows?
   6 ways
5. Cruz and his friend, Penny, need to determine what numbers are prime and what numbers are composite for a homework assignment. Cruz says that the number 5 is a composite number because it has the factors 2 and 2.5. Explain what is wrong with his reasoning.
   Sample answer: A composite number has more than 2 whole number factors. 2.5 is not a whole number.
6. Is 39 prime or composite? Explain your answer.
   composite; 39 has more than two factors: 1, 3, 13, 39

Grade 5 16 Chapter 9

9-2 Prime and Composite Numbers

1 Introduce

Activity Choice 1 • Hands-On

- Divide the class into 3 teams. Provide each team with 20 color tiles and grid paper. Challenge the teams to find the prime numbers from 2–10. 2, 3, 5, and 7
- If a team declares that a number is a prime number, another team can challenge their conclusion. The original team or the challenger must use color tiles or grid paper to justify their answer.

Activity Choice 2 • Literature

Introduce the lesson with *Among the Odds and Evens: A Tale of Adventure* by Priscilla Turner. For a related math activity, see p. TR50.

2 Teach

Scaffolding Questions

Have students decide whether the following numbers are prime or composite. Have them use grid paper or color tiles to support their answers.

- **Is 13 prime or composite?** prime
- **Why is 13 a prime number? What are the factors of 13?** 13 is a prime number because 13 only has two factors, 13 and 1.
- **Is 15 prime or composite? How do you know?** 15 is a composite number because 15 has more than two factors: 1, 3, 5, and 15.
- **Are all prime numbers, except 2, odd numbers?** yes
- **Are all odd numbers prime numbers? Give examples.** No; examples will vary.

GET READY to Learn

Have students open their books and read the information in **Get Ready to Learn.** Introduce **prime factorization**. As a class, work through **Examples 1–3**.

9-2 Prime and Composite Numbers

MAIN IDEA

I will identify prime and composite numbers.

New Vocabulary

prime factorization

Math Online

macmillanmh.com

- Extra Examples
- Personal Tutor
- Self-Check Quiz

GET READY to Learn

Stella makes and sells jewelry at craft shows. She has 12 rings that she wants to display in equal rows.

1 row of 12 rings

2 rows of 6 rings

3 rows of 4 rings

In the Math Activity, you learned that a *composite* number has more than two factors. So, 12 is a composite number because its factors are 1, 2, 3, 4, 6, and 12.

The number 5 has only two factors: 1 and 5. So, 5 is a *prime* number.

The numbers 1 and 0 are neither prime nor composite.

- 1 has only one factor: 1
- 0 has a never ending number of factors: $0 \times 1, 0 \times 2, 0 \times 3, \ldots$

EXAMPLE Use Models

1 **Tell whether the number 10 represented by the model at the right is *prime* or *composite*.**

The model shows 2 rows of 5 squares. The squares could also be arranged in 5 rows of 2 squares, 10 rows of 1 square, or 1 row of 10 squares.

So, the number 10 is a composite number because it has more than 2 factors.

Reteach (p. 13) BL

9–2 Name ______ Date ______

Reteach

Prime and Composite Numbers

- A number is **prime** if it is a whole number that has exactly two factors, 1 and the number itself.
  Example: $7 = 1 \times 7$
- A number is **composite** if it is greater than 1 and has more than two factors.
  Example: $4 = 2 \times 2, 1 \times 4$

You can use models and factor pairs to identify prime and composite numbers.

Tell whether the number 12 represented by the model below is *prime* or *composite*.	**A classroom has 20 desks that are to be placed in equal rows. Is 20 prime or composite? What does it mean in this problem?**
The model shows 2 rows of 6 squares. The squares could also be arranged in 6 rows of 2 squares, 12 rows of 1 square, or 1 row of 12 squares, 4 rows of 3 squares, 3 rows of 4 squares, as shown below. So, the number 12 is a composite number because it has more than 2 factors.	Factors of 20: 1, 2, 4, 5, 10, 20. Since 20 has more than two factors, it is a composite number. This means there are more than two ways to arrange the desks. Some ways are listed below. • 2 rows of 10 desks • 10 rows of 2 desks • 4 rows of 5 desks • 5 rows of 4 desks

Tell whether the number represented by each model is *prime* or *composite*.

1. 8 **composite**

2. 5 **prime**

3. 10 **composite**

Grade 5 13 Chapter 9

Chapter Resources

Skills Practice (p. 14) OL

9–2 Name ______ Date ______

Skills Practice

Prime and Composite Numbers

Tell whether the number represented by each model is *prime* or *composite*.

1. 6 **composite**

2. 12 **composite**

3. 7 **prime**

Tell whether each number is *prime* or *composite*.

4. 64 **composite**

5. 45 **composite**

6. 18 **composite**

7. 23 **prime**

8. 39 **composite**

9. 55 **composite**

10. 28 **composite**

11. 79 **prime**

12. 62 **composite**

Problem Solving.

Solve.

13. There are 24 students in Mrs. Blackwell's class. The number of boys and the number of girls are both prime numbers. There are 2 more boys than girls. How many boys and how many girls are in the class? **13 boys and 11 girls**

14. There are 27 students in Mr. Rodriguez's class. The number of boys and the number of girls are both composite numbers. There are 3 more girls than boys. How many girls and how many boys are in the class? **15 girls and 12 boys**

Grade 5 14 Chapter 9

Prime and composite numbers can help you solve real-world situations.

Real-World EXAMPLE Use Factor Pairs

2 **GEOMETRY A banquet hall has 24 square tables that are to be placed together to form a rectangle. Is 24 prime or composite? What does this mean in the problem? What would happen if the banquet hall had only 23 tables?**

factors of 24: 1, 2, 3, 4, 6, 8, 12, 24

Since 24 has more than two factors, it is a composite number. This means that there are more than two ways to arrange the 24 tables. Some of the ways are listed below.

- 1 row of 24 tables
- 3 rows of 8 tables
- 2 rows of 12 tables
- 4 rows of 6 tables

If the banquet hall had only 23 tables, there could be only two possible arrangements, since 23 has only two factors. This is because 23 is a prime number.

- 1 row of 23 tables
- 23 rows of 1 table

Remember

You can use models to identify 24 as prime or composite. Twenty-four counters can be arranged in equal rows in more than two ways. So, 24 is composite.

You can write every composite number as a product of prime numbers. This is called the **prime factorization** of a number. A *factor tree* can be used to find the prime factorization of a number.

EXAMPLE Find the Prime Factorization of a Number

3 **Find the prime factorization of 36.**

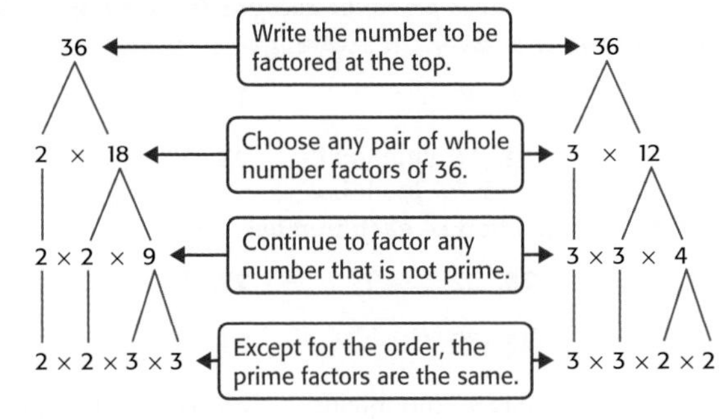

In order, the prime factorization of 36 is $2 \times 2 \times 3 \times 3$.

Enrich (p. 17) AL

Name ______________ Date ______________

9-2 **Enrich**

Number Patterns

Mathematicians have found interesting patterns among prime and composite numbers. Complete each table. See what pattern you find.

1.

Prime number	11	23	37	41	59	67	73	83	89	97
Remainder when divided by 6	**5**	**5**	**1**	**5**	**5**	**1**	**1**	**5**	**5**	**1**

2. What do you notice about remainders when prime numbers are divided by 6? **the remainders are either 1 or 5.**

3. Try three prime numbers of your choice. Divide by 6. Does the pattern continue? Explain. **Yes, the remainder is always 1 or 5.**

4.

Prime number	11	23	37	41	59	67	73	83	89	97
Remainder when divided by 4	**3**	**3**	**1**	**1**	**3**	**3**	**1**	**3**	**1**	**1**

5. What do you notice about remainders when prime numbers are divided by 4? **The remainders are either 1 or 3.**

6. Try three prime numbers of your choice. Divide by 4. Does the pattern continue? Explain. **Yes, the remainder is always 1 or 3.**

7. Find out if a similar pattern exists when dividing prime numbers by other 1-digit numbers. Make tables like those above to find out what happens when you divide by 3, by 5, by 7, by 8, and by 9. Describe your findings.
When you divide a prime number by 1-digit numbers, the remainders will always be 1 and another number.

A **perfect number** is a composite number whose factors, not including the number itself, add up to the number. The first perfect number is 6. The factors of 6 are 1, 2, and 3. $6 = 1 + 2 + 3$

8. Find the next perfect number. Show the number as a sum of its factors.
28; $1 + 2 + 4 + 7 + 14 = 28$

Chapter Resources

Grade 5 17 Chapter 9

Use Factor Pairs

Example 2 If students have difficulty finding all of the factor pairs of 24, have the students act out this problem using paper squares or color tiles.

ADDITIONAL EXAMPLES

1 Tell whether the number 14 represented by the model is *prime* or *composite*. composite

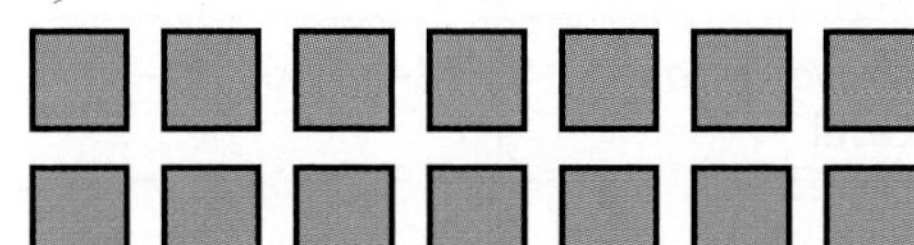

2 19 square tables are to be placed together to form a rectangle. Is 19 a prime or composite number? What does it mean in this problem? Prime; since the number 19 is a prime number, there is only one way to place the tables.

3 Find the prime factorization of 54.
$2 \times 3 \times 3 \times 3$

CHECK What You Know

As a class, have students complete Exercises 1–12 in **Check What You Know** as you observe their work.

Exercise 12 Assess student comprehension before assigning practice exercises.

BL Alternate Teaching Strategy

If students have trouble identifying prime and composite numbers...

Then use one of these reteach options:

1. CRM **Daily Reteach Worksheet** (p. 13)
2. Review basic multiplication facts with students. Students may need to keep a list of these facts on their desks as a reference.

3 Practice

Differentiate practice using these leveled assignments for Exercises 13–37.

Level	Assignment
BL Below/ Approaching Level	13–16, 17–22, 29–31
OL On Level	13–30, 37
AL Above/Beyond Level	13–33 odd, 35–37

Have students discuss and complete the Higher Order Thinking problems. Encourage them to draw a picture to model the prime or composite numbers they choose.

WRITING IN ▶MATH Have students complete Exercise 37 in their Math Journals. You may choose to use this as an optional formative assessment.

COMMON ERROR!

Exercise 19 Students may think that odd numbers are prime numbers. Have students skip count by 5s to see that every other number is an odd number, and it is also a composite number. For example, 3×5 equals 15.

CHECK What You Know

Tell whether the number represented by each model is *prime* or *composite*. See Example 1 (p. 378)

1. prime
2. composite

Tell whether each number is *prime* or *composite*. Use objects or models to justify your answer. See Examples 1, 2 (pp. 378–379)

3. 9 composite
4. 24 composite
5. 17 prime
6. 31 prime

3–6. See students' work for models.

Find the prime factorization of each number. See Example 3 (p. 379)

7. 18 $2 \times 3 \times 3$
8. 20 $2 \times 2 \times 5$
9. 24 $2 \times 2 \times 2 \times 3$
10. 45 $3 \times 3 \times 5$

11. Is there more than one way for Mark to display 21 model cars if each row has the same number of cars? Explain. See Ch. 9 Answer Appendix.
12. Talk About It Is 33 prime or composite? Explain how you know. Composite; 33 has 4 factors: 1, 3, 11, and 33.

Practice and Problem Solving

See page R24.

Tell whether the number represented by each model is *prime* or *composite*. See Example 1 (p. 378)

13. 2 prime
14. 8 composite
15. 7 prime
16. 4 composite

Tell whether each number is *prime* or *composite*. Use objects or models to justify your answer. See Examples 1, 2 (pp. 378–379)

17. 18 composite
18. 29 prime
19. 15 composite
20. 26 composite
21. 13 prime
22. 16 composite
23. 37 prime
24. 53 prime

17–24. See students' work for models.

Find the prime factorization of each number. See Example 3 (p. 379)

25. 16 $2 \times 2 \times 2 \times 2$
26. 22 2×11
27. 30 $2 \times 3 \times 5$
28. 42 $2 \times 3 \times 7$
29. 63 $3 \times 3 \times 7$
30. 70 $2 \times 5 \times 7$
31. 50 $2 \times 5 \times 5$
32. 88 $2 \times 2 \times 2 \times 11$

33. A mountain range has 90 mountains that are one mile or more tall. Is 90 a prime or composite number? composite
34. Alex's birthday is February 29. Is 29 a prime or composite number? prime

H.O.T. Problems

35. NUMBER SENSE Find the least prime number that is greater than 100. Explain. 101; The only factors of 101 are 1 and 101

36. CHALLENGE Two prime numbers that have a difference of 2 are called *twin primes*. For example, 5 and 7 are twin primes. Find all pairs of twin primes less than 50. 3 and 5, 5 and 7, 11 and 13, 17 and 19, 29 and 31, 41 and 43

37. WRITING IN ▸MATH Explain how you can use objects or models to tell if a number is prime or composite. See Ch. 9 Answer Appendix.

38. The table shows how many Calories you can burn in 10 minutes for certain activities.

Activity	Number of Calories
Basketball	64
Dancing	35
Hiking	47
Roller skating	57

For which activity is the number of Calories a prime number? (Lesson 9-2) C

A basketball **C** hiking

B dancing **D** roller skating

39. Which group names all the common factors of 27 and 54? (Lesson 9-1) H

F 1, 3, 9

G 1, 3, 9, 18

H 1, 3, 9, 27

J 1, 3, 9, 27, 54

40. What is the missing number in the prime factorization of 156? C

$2 \times 2 \times 3 \times \blacksquare$ 13

A 3 **C** 13

B 5 **D** 17

Spiral Review

Find the GCF of each set of numbers. (Lesson 9-1)

41. 6, 15 3 **42.** 18, 24 6 **43.** 14, 28 14 **44.** 10, 25 5

45. Jackie bought 5 papayas for $1.99 each and 3 yogurts for $0.75 each. The cashier gave her $8 change. What is the least number of coins she could have given the cashier? What would they have been? (Lesson 8-7) 2; 2 dimes

46. The Jackson family went swimming $2\frac{5}{6}$ hours on Saturday and $1\frac{3}{6}$ hours on Sunday. On which day did they spend more time swimming? (Lesson 8-5) Saturday

Homework Practice (p. 15) OL

9-2 Name ____ Date ____

Homework Practice

Prime and Composite Numbers

Tell whether each number is *prime* or *composite*.

1. 75 **composite** 2. 61 **prime** 3. 96 **composite**
4. 48 **composite** 5. 29 **prime** 6. 95 **composite**
7. 68 **composite** 8. 54 **composite** 9. 171 **composite**
10. 143 **composite** 11. 117 **composite** 12. 209 **composite**

Problem Solving.
Solve.

13. A board is 24 inches long. Find all the whole-number lengths into which it can be evenly divided. **in inches: 1, 2, 3, 4, 6, 8, 12, 24**

14. A ribbon is 36 inches long. Find all the whole-number lengths into which it can be evenly divided. **in inches: 1, 2, 3, 4, 6, 9, 12, 18, 36**

Spiral Review

Find the GCF of each set of numbers. (Lesson 9-1)

15. 6, 18 **6** 16. 16, 30 **2** 17. 14, 28 **14**
18. 27, 54 **27** 19. 8, 12 **4** 20. 49, 63 **7**

Grade 5 15 Chapter 9

4 Assess

Formative Assessment

Have students discuss and answer the following questions.

- **Except for the number 2, is an even number prime or composite? How do you know?** Composite; all even numbers have 2 as a factor as well as 1 and the number itself.
- **Is an odd number prime or composite?** An odd number can be either prime or composite.
- **When is an odd number a composite number? Give an example.** An odd number is a composite number when it has more than two factors. Examples will vary.

Quick Check **Are students continuing to struggle with prime and composite numbers?**

If Yes → Small Group Options (p. 380B)
Strategic Intervention Guide (p. 90)

If No → Independent Work Options (p. 380B)
CRM Skills Practice Worksheet (p. 14)
CRM Enrich Worksheet (p. 17)

Name the Math Determine whether 95 is prime or composite. Show all your work and explain the steps you used to decide.

Reviews Lessons 9-1 and 9-2

Assign the Test Practice problems to provide daily reinforcement of test-taking skills.

Reviews Lessons 8-5, 8-7, and 9-1

Review and assess mastery of skills and concepts from previous chapters.

LESSON 9-3

Equivalent Fractions

Lesson Planner

Objective

Write a fraction that is equivalent to a given fraction.

Vocabulary

equivalent fractions

Resources

Materials: colored pencils, construction paper strips, grid paper, scissors
Manipulatives: fraction tiles, fraction circles
Literature Connection: *Fraction Fun* by David A. Adler
Alternate Lesson: Use *IMPACT Mathematics:* Unit E to provide practice with equivalent fractions.
Teacher Technology
TeacherWorks • Interactive Classroom

Focus on Math Background

Fractions that contain different numerals can name the same number. When you find an equivalent fraction, you are "renaming" a number while letting its value remain the same. All operations with fractions (in Chapter 10 and higher grades) rely on the ability to find equivalent fractions. Students must be able to find equivalent fractions with larger numerators and denominators as well as ones with smaller numerators and denominators. For example,

$\frac{2}{5} = \frac{2 \times 3}{5 \times 3} = \frac{6}{15}$ using multiplication

$\frac{20}{35} = \frac{20 \div 5}{35 \div 5} = \frac{4}{7}$ using division

Open-ended practice with a variety of concrete models like fraction strips or fraction circles can be very helpful. Measuring lengths with rulers marked in inches is particularly effective.

Daily Routine

Use these suggestions before beginning the lesson on p. 382.

5-Minute Check

(Reviews Lesson 9-2)

Tell whether each number is *prime* or *composite*.

1. 6 composite
2. 13 prime
3. 29 prime
4. 49 composite

Problem of the Day

What number between 420 and 480 is divisible by 2, 3, 5, 6, 9, and 10? Explain how you solved this problem. 450; explanations may vary.

Building Math Vocabulary

Write the lesson vocabulary word and its definition on the board.

Ask students to explain what they know about the word *equal*. Discuss, as a class, what they think the term *equivalent fractions* might mean.

Differentiated Instruction

Small Group Options

Option 1 Gifted and Talented AL

LOGICAL

Materials: paper and pencil

- Pass out six index cards to partners, with a different fraction on each.
- Pass out six more blank cards for partners to write an equivalent fraction to match the fractions on the first six cards.
- Students can play a memory matching game with their 12 cards.

Option 2 English Language Learners ELL

SPATIAL, KINESTHETIC

Materials: transparency fractions, transparency
Core Vocabulary: one half, two halves, quarters
Common Use Verb: layer
Do Math: This strategy helps students see equivalent fractions.

- Draw a circle on the transparency. Lay a half circle on the transparencyand write $\frac{1}{2}$ on the uncovered part of the circle. Say: "This is one half of a circle. $\frac{1}{2}$ and $\frac{1}{2} = \frac{2}{2} =$ a circle."
- Repeat modeling with $\frac{1}{4}$, layering the quarters over the $\frac{1}{2}$ circle. Write: "$\frac{2}{4} = \frac{1}{2}$." Repeat for $\frac{4}{4} =$ a circle.
- Continue this process, showing equivalent fractions using square transparency tiles.
- Restate and write equivalents in identical language to fully illustrate the core math skill.
- Model folding paper to show equivalent fractions, allowing students to repeat as time permits.

Independent Work Options

Option 1 Early Finishers AL

SOCIAL

Materials: number cubes

- Have students work with a partner.
- One student rolls two number cubes. He or she uses the two numbers to form a fraction; the lesser number should always be in the numerator.
- Both students race to write three fractions equivalent to the fraction created using the number cube.
- Repeat as time allows.

Option 2 Student Technology

Math Online macmillanmh.com

Personal Tutor • Extra Examples

 Math Adventures

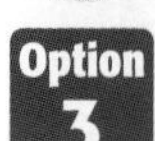

Option 3 Learning Station: Health (p. 370D)

Direct students to the Health Learning Station for opportunities to explore and extend the lesson concept.

Option 4 Problem-Solving Practice

Reinforce problem-solving skills and strategies with the Problem-Solving Practice worksheet.

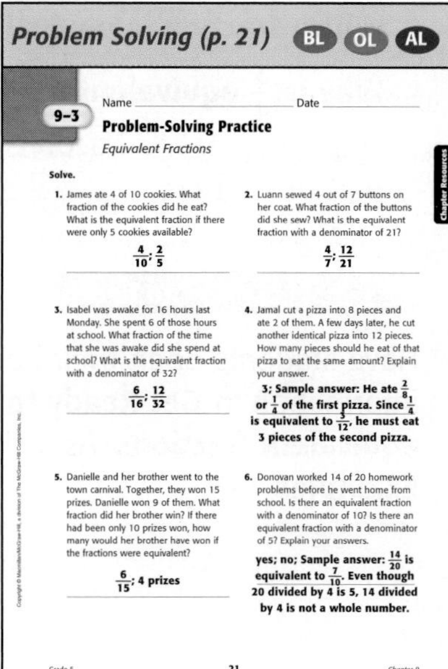

Problem Solving (p. 21) BL OL AL

9–3 Name ______ Date ______

Problem-Solving Practice

Equivalent Fractions

Solve.

1. James ate 4 of 10 cookies. What fraction of the cookies did he eat? What is the equivalent fraction if there were only 5 cookies available?
   $\frac{4}{10}$; $\frac{2}{5}$
2. Luann sewed 4 out of 7 buttons on her coat. What fraction of the buttons did she sew? What is the equivalent fraction with a denominator of 21?
   $\frac{4}{7}$; $\frac{12}{21}$
3. Isabel was awake for 16 hours last Monday. She spent 6 of those hours at school. What fraction of the time that she was awake did she spend at school? What is the equivalent fraction with a denominator of 32?
   $\frac{6}{16}$; $\frac{12}{32}$
4. Jamal cut a pizza into 8 pieces and ate 2 of them. A few days later, he cut another identical pizza into 12 pieces. How many pieces should he eat of that pizza to eat the same amount? Explain your answer.
   3; Sample answer: He ate $\frac{2}{8}$ or $\frac{1}{4}$ of the first pizza. Since $\frac{1}{4}$ is equivalent to $\frac{3}{12}$, he must eat 3 pieces of the second pizza.
5. Danielle and her brother went to the town carnival. Together, they won 15 prizes. Danielle won 9 of them. What fraction did her brother win? If there had been only 10 prizes won, how many would her brother have won if the fractions were equivalent?
   $\frac{6}{15}$; 4 prizes
6. Donovan worked 14 of 20 homework problems before he went home from school. Is there an equivalent fraction with a denominator of 10? Is there an equivalent fraction with a denominator of 5? Explain your answers.
   yes; no; Sample answer: $\frac{14}{20}$ is equivalent to $\frac{7}{10}$. Even though 20 divided by 4 is 5, 14 divided by 4 is not a whole number.

Chapter Resources

Grade 5 21 Chapter 9

9-3 Equivalent Fractions

1 Introduce

Activity Choice 1 • Hands-On 

- Divide the class into pairs. Provide fraction circles, colored pencils, and unlined paper for each group.
- Write the fraction $\frac{1}{2}$ on the board. Have students use the fraction circles to find other fractions that name the same part of a whole as this fraction.
- Have students use different colors to draw these fractions for a bulletin board display.
- Tell students that fractions that name the same part of a whole are called *equivalent* fractions.

Activity Choice 2 • Literature

Introduce the lesson with *Fraction Fun* by David A. Adler. For a related math activity, see p. TR50.

2 Teach

Scaffolding Questions

Provide students with four construction paper strips 12-cm long. Have them divide one into halves, one into thirds, one into fourths, and one into twelfths.

- **Which fractions are equivalent to $\frac{1}{2}$?** $\frac{2}{4}$ and $\frac{6}{12}$
- **Which fraction is equivalent to $\frac{2}{3}$?** $\frac{8}{12}$
- **Why is $\frac{3}{4}$ equivalent to $\frac{9}{12}$?** The fraction strips match. The fractions name the same part of a whole.

GET READY to Learn

Have students open their books and read the information in **Get Ready to Learn.** Introduce **equivalent fractions**. As a class, work through **Examples 1–3**.

9-3 Equivalent Fractions

MAIN IDEA

I will write a fraction that is equivalent to a given fraction.

New Vocabulary

equivalent fractions

Math Online

macmillanmh.com

- Extra Examples
- Personal Tutor
- Self-Check Quiz

GET READY to Learn

Mrs. Bahn is dividing her garden into thirds. One third of her garden will be used for tomatoes. If her garden is 9 feet wide, she figures that she needs to save a width of 3 feet of the garden for tomatoes. Did she figure correctly?

Equivalent fractions are fractions that have the same value. The fractions $\frac{1}{3}$ and $\frac{3}{9}$ name the same part of the whole. So, they are equivalent fractions. Mrs. Bahn figured correctly.

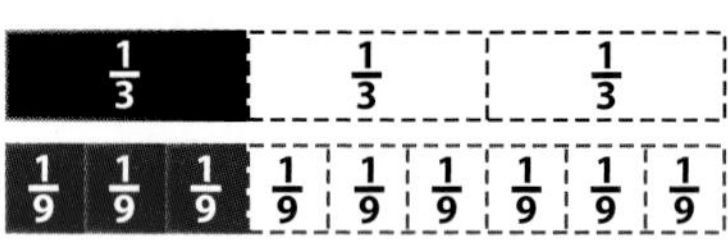

Multiplying the numerator and denominator each by 3 gives $\frac{3}{9}$.

$$\frac{1}{3} \times \frac{3}{3} = \frac{1 \times 3}{3 \times 3} = \frac{3}{9}$$

Recall that $\frac{3}{3}$ is an equivalent form of 1. To find equivalent fractions, you can multiply a fraction by an equivalent form of 1, such as $\frac{2}{2}$, $\frac{3}{3}$, or $\frac{4}{4}$.

EXAMPLE Find Equivalent Fractions by Multiplying

1 **Find two fractions that are equivalent to $\frac{1}{4}$.**

Multiply $\frac{1}{4}$ by equivalent forms of one, such as $\frac{2}{2}$ and $\frac{3}{3}$.

Multiply $\frac{1}{4}$ by $\frac{2}{2}$.

$$\frac{1}{4} \times \frac{2}{2} = \frac{1 \times 2}{4 \times 2} = \frac{2}{8}$$

Multiply $\frac{1}{4}$ by $\frac{3}{3}$.

$$\frac{1}{4} \times \frac{3}{3} = \frac{1 \times 3}{4 \times 3} = \frac{3}{12}$$

So, $\frac{2}{8}$ and $\frac{3}{12}$ are both equivalent to $\frac{1}{4}$.

382 Chapter 9 Use Factors and Multiples

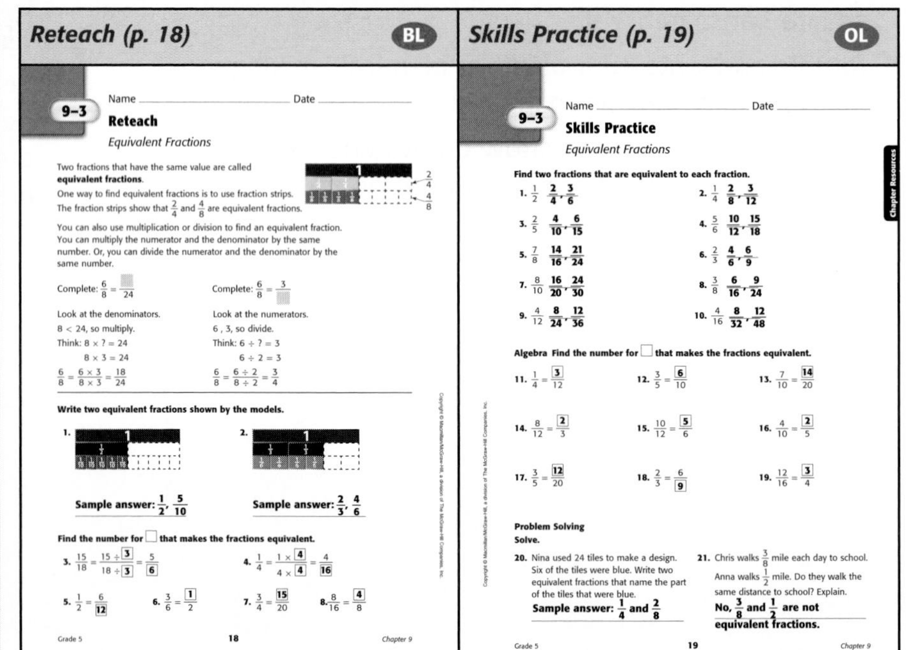

Reteach (p. 18) BL

9-3 Name ______ Date ______

Reteach

Equivalent Fractions

Two fractions that have the same value are called **equivalent fractions**.

One way to find equivalent fractions is to use fraction strips. The fraction strips show that $\frac{2}{4}$ and $\frac{4}{8}$ are equivalent fractions.

You can also use multiplication or division to find an equivalent fraction. You can multiply the numerator and the denominator by the same number. Or, you can divide the numerator and the denominator by the same number.

Complete: $\frac{6}{8} = \frac{\square}{24}$

Look at the denominators.

8 < 24, so multiply.

Think: $8 \times ? = 24$

$8 \times 3 = 24$

$\frac{6}{8} = \frac{6 \times 3}{8 \times 3} = \frac{18}{24}$

Complete: $\frac{6}{8} = \frac{3}{\square}$

Look at the numerators.

6 , 3, so divide.

Think: $6 \div ? = 3$

$6 \div 2 = 3$

$\frac{6}{8} = \frac{6 \div 2}{8 \div 2} = \frac{3}{4}$

Write two equivalent fractions shown by the models.

1. **Sample answer: $\frac{1}{2}$, $\frac{5}{10}$**
2. **Sample answer: $\frac{2}{3}$, $\frac{4}{6}$**

Find the number for $\square$ that makes the fractions equivalent.

3. $\frac{15}{18} = \frac{15 \div \boxed{3}}{18 \div \boxed{3}} = \frac{5}{\boxed{6}}$
4. $\frac{1}{4} = \frac{1 \times \boxed{4}}{4 \times \boxed{4}} = \frac{4}{\boxed{16}}$
5. $\frac{1}{2} = \frac{6}{\boxed{12}}$
6. $\frac{3}{6} = \frac{\boxed{1}}{2}$
7. $\frac{3}{4} = \frac{\boxed{15}}{20}$
8. $\frac{8}{16} = \frac{\boxed{4}}{8}$

Grade 5 18 Chapter 9

Copyright © Macmillan/McGraw-Hill, a division of The McGraw-Hill Companies, Inc.

Skills Practice (p. 19) OL

9-3 Name ______ Date ______

Skills Practice

Equivalent Fractions

Find two fractions that are equivalent to each fraction.

1. $\frac{1}{2}$ **$\frac{2}{4}$, $\frac{3}{6}$**
2. $\frac{1}{4}$ **$\frac{2}{8}$, $\frac{3}{12}$**
3. $\frac{2}{5}$ **$\frac{4}{10}$, $\frac{6}{15}$**
4. $\frac{5}{6}$ **$\frac{10}{12}$, $\frac{15}{18}$**
5. $\frac{7}{8}$ **$\frac{14}{16}$, $\frac{21}{24}$**
6. $\frac{2}{3}$ **$\frac{4}{6}$, $\frac{6}{9}$**
7. $\frac{8}{10}$ **$\frac{16}{20}$, $\frac{24}{30}$**
8. $\frac{3}{8}$ **$\frac{6}{16}$, $\frac{9}{24}$**
9. $\frac{4}{12}$ **$\frac{8}{24}$, $\frac{12}{36}$**
10. $\frac{4}{16}$ **$\frac{8}{32}$, $\frac{12}{48}$**

Algebra Find the number for $\square$ that makes the fractions equivalent.

11. $\frac{1}{4} = \frac{\boxed{3}}{12}$
12. $\frac{3}{5} = \frac{\boxed{6}}{10}$
13. $\frac{7}{10} = \frac{\boxed{14}}{20}$
14. $\frac{8}{12} = \frac{\boxed{2}}{3}$
15. $\frac{10}{12} = \frac{\boxed{5}}{6}$
16. $\frac{4}{10} = \frac{\boxed{2}}{5}$
17. $\frac{3}{5} = \frac{\boxed{12}}{20}$
18. $\frac{2}{3} = \frac{6}{\boxed{9}}$
19. $\frac{12}{16} = \frac{\boxed{3}}{4}$

Problem Solving

Solve.

20. Nina used 24 tiles to make a design. Six of the tiles were blue. Write two equivalent fractions that name the part of the tiles that were blue.
Sample answer: $\frac{1}{4}$ and $\frac{2}{8}$
21. Chris walks $\frac{3}{8}$ mile each day to school. Anna walks $\frac{1}{2}$ mile. Do they walk the same distance to school? Explain.
No, $\frac{3}{8}$ and $\frac{1}{2}$ are not equivalent fractions.

Grade 5 19 Chapter 9

Chapter Resources

Copyright © Macmillan/McGraw-Hill, a division of The McGraw-Hill Companies, Inc.

Real-World EXAMPLE

Remember

There are many different fractions that are equivalent to a given fraction.

2 SCIENCE Ethan measured the length of an insect to be $\frac{7}{8}$ inch. Find two equivalent measurements for the length of the insect, in inches.

Multiply $\frac{7}{8}$ by equivalent forms of one, such as $\frac{2}{2}$ and $\frac{3}{3}$.

Multiply $\frac{7}{8}$ by $\frac{2}{2}$. Multiply $\frac{7}{8}$ by $\frac{3}{3}$.

$\frac{7}{8} \times \frac{2}{2} = \frac{7 \times 2}{8 \times 2} = \frac{14}{16}$ $\frac{7}{8} \times \frac{3}{3} = \frac{7 \times 3}{8 \times 3} = \frac{21}{24}$

So, the insect's length is equivalent to $\frac{14}{16}$ inch and $\frac{21}{24}$ inch.

EXAMPLE Find a Missing Number

3 ALGEBRA Find the number for ■ that makes the fractions in $\frac{2}{7} = \frac{■}{21}$ equivalent.

$\frac{2}{7} = \frac{2 \times ?}{7 \times ?} = \frac{■}{21}$ THINK What number times 7 equals 21?

$\frac{2}{7} = \frac{2 \times 3}{7 \times 3} = \frac{6}{21}$ 7 × 3 = 21, so multiply the numerator by 3.

The missing number is 6. So, $\frac{2}{7} = \frac{6}{21}$.

CHECK What You Know

Find two fractions that are equivalent to each fraction. Check your answer using fraction tiles or number lines. See Examples 1, 2 (pp. 382–383) 1–6. Sample answers are given.

1. $\frac{2}{5}$ $\frac{4}{10}, \frac{6}{15}$
2. $\frac{3}{4}$ $\frac{9}{12}, \frac{12}{16}$
3. $\frac{6}{10}$ $\frac{12}{20}, \frac{18}{30}$
4. $\frac{2}{8}$ $\frac{4}{16}, \frac{6}{24}$
5. $\frac{1}{3}$ $\frac{2}{6}, \frac{3}{9}$
6. $\frac{5}{6}$ $\frac{10}{12}, \frac{15}{18}$

Algebra Find the number for ■ that makes the fractions equivalent. See Example 3 (p. 383)

7. $\frac{1}{2} = \frac{■}{4}$ 2
8. $\frac{2}{5} = \frac{10}{■}$ 25
9. $\frac{4}{18} = \frac{12}{■}$ 54

11. Sample answer: Multiply the numerator and the denominator by 2 to get $\frac{8}{18}$.

10. **Measurement** How many sixteenths of an inch are equal to $\frac{5}{8}$ inch? $\frac{10}{16}$ in.

11. 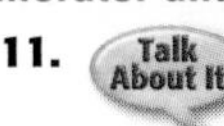

Explain how to find an equivalent fraction for $\frac{4}{9}$.

Enrich (p. 22) AL

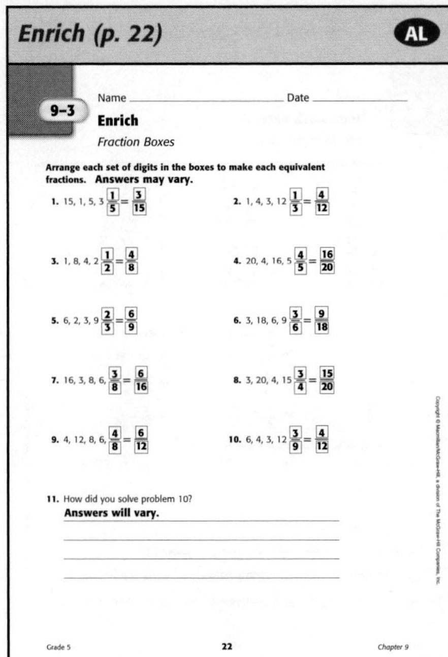

9-3 Name ______ Date ______

Enrich

Fraction Boxes

Arrange each set of digits in the boxes to make each equivalent fraction. Answers may vary.

1. 15, 1, 5, 3 $\frac{1}{5} = \frac{3}{15}$
2. 1, 4, 3, 12 $\frac{1}{3} = \frac{4}{12}$
3. 1, 8, 4, 2 $\frac{1}{2} = \frac{4}{8}$
4. 20, 4, 16, 5 $\frac{4}{5} = \frac{16}{20}$
5. 6, 2, 3, 9 $\frac{2}{3} = \frac{6}{9}$
6. 3, 18, 6, 9 $\frac{3}{6} = \frac{9}{18}$
7. 16, 3, 8, 6, $\frac{3}{8} = \frac{6}{16}$
8. 3, 20, 4, 15 $\frac{3}{4} = \frac{15}{20}$
9. 4, 12, 8, 6, $\frac{4}{8} = \frac{6}{12}$
10. 6, 4, 3, 12 $\frac{3}{9} = \frac{4}{12}$
11. How did you solve problem 10?
Answers will vary.

Grade 5 22 Chapter 9

Find Equivalent Fractions by Multiplying

Example 1 Remind students that what they do to the numerator they must also do to the denominator.

ADDITIONAL EXAMPLES

1. Find two fractions that are equivalent to $\frac{3}{4}$. Sample answers: $\frac{6}{8}$; $\frac{9}{12}$
2. Reynaldo measured the width of a dime and found it to be $\frac{5}{8}$ inch. Find two equivalent measurements for the width in inches. Sample answers: $\frac{10}{16}$ inch; $\frac{20}{32}$ inch
3. Find the number for ■ that makes the fractions in $\frac{3}{5} = \frac{■}{20}$ equivalent. The missing number is 12, so, $\frac{3}{5} = \frac{12}{20}$.

CHECK What You Know

As a class, have students complete Exercises 1–11 in **Check What You Know** as you observe their work.

Exercise 11 Assess student comprehension before assigning practice exercises.

BL Alternate Teaching Strategy

If students have trouble remembering to multiply the numerator and denominator by the same number…

Then use one of these reteach options:

1. CRM **Daily Reteach Worksheet** (p. 18)
2. Have students cut one piece of paper in half, and write the fraction each piece represents. $\frac{1}{2}$ Then have them cut each piece in half again. **How many fourths equals one half?** 2
   Repeat by cutting each fourth to create 8ths. Show that four of these equal one half. Help students make the connection between the multiple pieces of paper, to multiplying to find equivalent fractions.

COMMON ERROR!

Exercises 28–30 Have struggling students use fraction strips to help them solve these problems.

3 Practice

Differentiate practice using these leveled assignments for Exercises 12–34.

Level	Assignment
BL Below/ Approaching Level	12–17, 24–26, 28–29, 34
OL On Level	12–20, 24–30, 34
AL Above/Beyond Level	13–31 odd, 32–34

Have students discuss and complete the Higher Order Thinking problems. Have students use fraction models to check their answers.

WRITING IN MATH Have students complete Exercise 34 in their Math Journals. You may choose to use this exercise as an optional formative assessment.

4 Assess

Formative Assessment

Write $\frac{2}{3}$, $\frac{6}{9}$, and $\frac{6}{12}$ on the board.

- **Are $\frac{2}{3}$ and $\frac{6}{9}$ equivalent fractions? How do you know?** Yes; you multiply $\frac{2}{3} \times \frac{3}{3}$ and get $\frac{6}{9}$.
- **Are $\frac{2}{3}$ and $\frac{6}{12}$ equivalent fractions? Why or why not?** No; 2×3 is 6 but 3×3 is not 12.

Quick Check **Are students continuing to struggle with equivalent fractions?**

If Yes → Strategic Intervention Guide (p. 104)

If No → Independent Work Options (p. 382B)
CRM Skills Practice Worksheet (p. 19)
CRM Enrich Worksheet (p. 22)

Into the Future Tell students that the next lesson is about simplifying fractions. Ask students to write how they think today's lesson will help them with tomorrow's lesson.

29. $\frac{10}{12}$, $\frac{15}{18}$

31. 1 minute/10 people = 5 minutes/50 people; 1 minute/10 people = 30 minutes/300 people; in 5 minutes, 50 people can go down the slides. In 30 minutes, 300 people can go down the slides.

★ indicates multi-step problem

Practice and Problem Solving

EXTRA PRACTICE See page R24.

Find two fractions that are equivalent to each fraction. Check your answer using fraction tiles or number lines. See Examples 1, 2 (pp. 382–383) 12–23. Sample answers are given.

12. $\frac{2}{3}$ $\frac{4}{6}$, $\frac{6}{9}$
13. $\frac{1}{2}$ $\frac{2}{4}$, $\frac{3}{6}$
14. $\frac{2}{6}$ $\frac{4}{12}$, $\frac{6}{18}$
15. $\frac{1}{5}$ $\frac{2}{10}$, $\frac{3}{15}$
16. $\frac{2}{12}$ $\frac{4}{24}$, $\frac{6}{36}$
17. $\frac{3}{6}$ $\frac{6}{12}$, $\frac{9}{18}$
18. $\frac{3}{5}$ $\frac{6}{10}$, $\frac{9}{15}$
19. $\frac{6}{8}$ $\frac{12}{16}$, $\frac{18}{24}$
20. $\frac{4}{16}$ $\frac{8}{32}$, $\frac{12}{48}$
21. $\frac{2}{7}$ $\frac{4}{14}$, $\frac{6}{21}$
22. $\frac{5}{10}$ $\frac{10}{20}$, $\frac{15}{30}$
23. $\frac{6}{14}$ $\frac{12}{28}$, $\frac{18}{42}$

Algebra **Find the number for ■ that makes the fractions equivalent.**
See Example 3 (p. 383)

24. $\frac{1}{3} = \frac{■}{9}$ 3
25. $\frac{8}{16} = \frac{16}{■}$ 32
26. $\frac{6}{9} = \frac{18}{■}$ 27
27. $\frac{3}{5} = \frac{9}{■}$ 15

28. Fatima read $\frac{2}{5}$ of a book. Gary read $\frac{4}{10}$ of the same book. Did Gary read more than, less than, or the same amount as Fatima? same

★29. **Measurement** Mr. Bixler ran $\frac{5}{6}$ mile. How many twelfths and how many eighteenths of a mile are equal to $\frac{5}{6}$ mile? See margin.

30. Rodolfo ate $\frac{1}{4}$ of a cantaloupe. Aida ate the same amount from another cantaloupe, cut into eighths. How many pieces did Aida eat? 2 pieces

★31. In 1 minute, 10 people can slide down a water slide. Complete the following. Explain what the equivalent fractions mean. See margin.
$\frac{1}{10} = \frac{5}{■}$ $\frac{1}{10} = \frac{■}{300}$

H.O.T. Problems

32. **OPEN ENDED** Using fraction tiles or a number line, show 3 fractions that are equivalent to each other. Sample answer: $\frac{1}{5} = \frac{2}{10} = \frac{4}{20}$

33. **FIND THE ERROR** Jeremy and Antwon are finding an equivalent fraction for $\frac{3}{7}$. Who is correct? Explain. See Ch. 9 Answer Appendix.

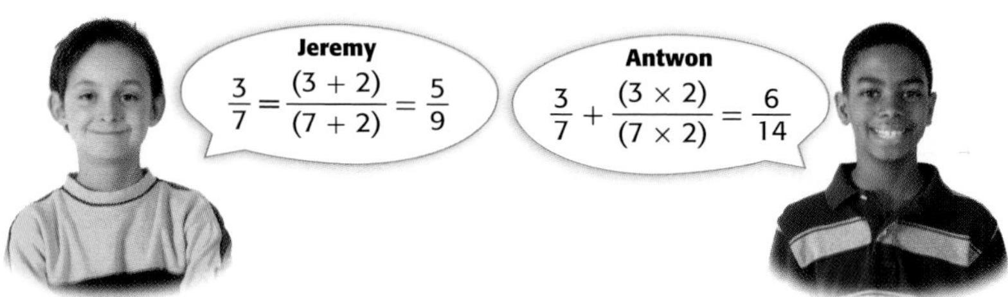

Jeremy
$\frac{3}{7} = \frac{(3 + 2)}{(7 + 2)} = \frac{5}{9}$
Antwon
$\frac{3}{7} + \frac{(3 \times 2)}{(7 \times 2)} = \frac{6}{14}$

34. WRITING IN MATH Write about a real-world situation that can be represented by $\frac{3}{4}$. Then write an equivalent fraction and describe the meaning of the equivalent fraction. See Ch. 9 Answer Appendix.

384 Chapter 9 Use Factors and Multiples

Homework Practice (p. 20) OL

9-3 Name ______ Date ______

Homework Practice
Equivalent Fractions

Write two fractions that are equivalent to each fraction. **Sample answers are given.**

1. $\frac{2}{5}$ $\frac{4}{10}$, $\frac{6}{15}$
2. $\frac{6}{18}$ $\frac{12}{36}$, $\frac{18}{54}$
3. $\frac{5}{10}$ $\frac{10}{20}$, $\frac{15}{30}$
4. $\frac{3}{12}$ $\frac{6}{24}$, $\frac{9}{36}$
5. $\frac{21}{35}$ $\frac{42}{70}$, $\frac{63}{105}$
6. $\frac{6}{8}$ $\frac{12}{16}$, $\frac{18}{24}$
7. $\frac{8}{20}$ $\frac{16}{40}$, $\frac{24}{60}$
8. $\frac{3}{9}$ $\frac{6}{18}$, $\frac{9}{27}$
9. $\frac{12}{15}$ $\frac{24}{30}$, $\frac{36}{45}$
10. $\frac{6}{24}$ $\frac{12}{48}$, $\frac{18}{72}$
11. $\frac{12}{20}$ $\frac{24}{40}$, $\frac{36}{60}$
12. $\frac{8}{10}$ $\frac{16}{20}$, $\frac{24}{30}$

Algebra Find the number for □ that makes the fractions equivalent.

13. $\frac{4}{5} = \frac{12}{15}$
14. $\frac{14}{16} = \frac{7}{8}$
15. $\frac{3}{7} = \frac{12}{28}$
16. $\frac{2}{6} = \frac{1}{3}$
17. $\frac{12}{16} = \frac{3}{4}$
18. $\frac{3}{4} = \frac{6}{8}$
19. $\frac{14}{42} = \frac{1}{3}$
20. $\frac{5}{9} = \frac{15}{27}$
21. $\frac{9}{30} = \frac{3}{10}$

Are the fractions equivalent? Write yes or no.

22. $\frac{3}{4} = \frac{6}{8}$ yes
23. $\frac{3}{8} = \frac{7}{16}$ no
24. $\frac{5}{9} = \frac{15}{27}$ yes
25. $\frac{2}{3} = \frac{4}{5}$ no
26. $\frac{5}{7} = \frac{15}{21}$ yes
27. $\frac{10}{13} = \frac{7}{14}$ no

Spiral Review

Tell whether each number is prime or composite. (Lesson 9–2)

28. 14 composite
29. 33 composite
30. 29 prime
31. 47 prime
32. 18 composite
33. 28 composite

Grade 5 20 Chapter 9

Match Up

Equivalent Fractions

Get Ready!

Players: 2 players

You will need: 32 index cards

Get Set!

Label each index card with one fraction as shown.

$\frac{1}{2}$	$\frac{1}{3}$	$\frac{2}{3}$	$\frac{1}{4}$	$\frac{2}{4}$	$\frac{3}{4}$	$\frac{2}{5}$	$\frac{3}{5}$
$\frac{4}{5}$	$\frac{1}{6}$	$\frac{5}{6}$	$\frac{2}{7}$	$\frac{1}{8}$	$\frac{2}{8}$	$\frac{3}{8}$	$\frac{2}{9}$
$\frac{6}{9}$	$\frac{4}{10}$	$\frac{5}{10}$	$\frac{8}{10}$	$\frac{2}{12}$	$\frac{4}{12}$	$\frac{2}{16}$	$\frac{4}{16}$
$\frac{4}{18}$	$\frac{6}{18}$	$\frac{15}{18}$	$\frac{12}{20}$	$\frac{15}{20}$	$\frac{6}{21}$	$\frac{3}{24}$	$\frac{9}{24}$

Go!

- Shuffle the cards. Then one player deals 5 cards to each player. The remaining cards are placed in a pile facedown on the table.
- Players place any pairs of cards that are equivalent fractions on the table. If 3 cards are equivalent, the player must choose a pair.
- Player 1 chooses a card from the pile and tries to form an equivalent fraction pair. He or she then discards any other card facedown on a discard pile of cards.
- Player 2 takes a turn choosing a card, forming pairs of equivalent fractions, and placing a card facedown on the discard pile.
- Continue playing until there are no more cards in the pile or until neither player can make an equivalent fraction pair. The player with the most pairs of equivalent fractions wins.

Differentiated Practice

Use these leveled suggestions to differentiate the game for all learners.

Level	Assignment
BL Below/ Approaching Level	Students use fraction strips to help them find matching pairs.
OL On Level	Have students play the game with the rules as written.
AL Above/Beyond Level	Students come up with their own equivalent fractions for the card set.

Match Up

Math Concept: Equivalent Fractions

Materials: 32 index cards, paper, pencils

Introduce the game on p. 385 to your students to play as a class, in small groups, or at a learning workstation to review concepts introduced in this chapter.

Instructions

- Students play in pairs. They create a set of 32 fraction cards, as shown on p. 385.
- Students shuffle the cards and deal 5 cards to each player. The remaining cards are placed in a pile face down on the table. Players check their hands for pairs of cards that are equivalent fractions, and place them on the table. If 3 cards are equivalent, the player must choose two of the cards to make a pair.
- Player 1 chooses a card from the pile and tries to form an equivalent fraction pair. He or she then discards any other card from the hand face-down on a discard pile of cards. Player 2 takes a turn choosing a card and tries to form an equivalent fraction pair. Player 2 discards one card from the hand to the discard pile.
- Play continues until there are no more cards in the pile or until neither player can make an equivalent fraction pair. The player with the most pairs of equivalent fractions wins.

Extend the Game

Have students make the game using more cards and have the winners of five games in a row then play each other in a class matching game tournament.

LESSON 9-4

Simplest Form

Lesson Planner

Objective

Write a fraction in simplest form.

Vocabulary

simplest form

Resources

Materials: index cards
Manipulatives: counters
Literature Connection: *Give Me Half!* by Stuart J. Murphy
Alternate Lesson: Use *IMPACT Mathematics:* Unit E to provide practice with simplest form.
Teacher Technology
TeacherWorks • Interactive Classroom

Focus on Math Background

A strong foundation in identifying common factors and greatest common factor (GCF), introduced in Lesson 9-1, is key to simplifying fractions in this lesson. Students will simplify fractions in two ways:

- divide the numerator and denominator by common factors until the only common factor is 1; or
- divide the numerator and denominator by their GCF.

In a set of many equivalent fractions, students should be able to see that only one can be in simplest form. But they may mistakenly believe that "simplest" always means "best." Point out that, in some cases, it is preferable to leave a fraction in something other than simplest form.

Daily Routine

Use these suggestions before beginning the lesson on p. 386.

5-Minute Check

(Reviews Lesson 9-3)

Write two fractions that are equivalent to each fraction. 1-2. Sample answers are given.

1. $\frac{2}{5}$ $\frac{4}{10}, \frac{6}{15}$ **2.** $\frac{6}{12}$ $\frac{12}{24}, \frac{18}{36}$

Find the number for ■ that makes the fractions equivalent.

3. $\frac{1}{5} = \frac{■}{15}$ $\frac{1}{5} = \frac{3}{15}$ **4.** $\frac{2}{3} = \frac{■}{15}$ $\frac{2}{3} = \frac{10}{15}$

Problem of the Day

A pizza is divided into 8 slices. Anne eats $\frac{6}{24}$ of the pizza. How many slices of the pizza did she eat? 2 slices; $\frac{6}{24} = \frac{1}{4} = \frac{2}{8}$

Building Math Vocabulary

Write the lesson vocabulary word and its definition on the board.

Ask students to model $\frac{8}{10}$ using fraction pieces.

- **Find an equivalent fraction using fewer fraction pieces.** $\frac{4}{5}$
- **Can you find another fraction equivalent to $\frac{4}{5}$ that has fewer fraction pieces?** no

Explain that $\frac{4}{5}$ is in *simplest form*.

Differentiated Instruction

Small Group Options

LOGICAL

Option 1 Below Level BL

Materials: paper and pencil

- Have students list the numbers 1–20 on a sheet of paper. Then have them list the factors of all the numbers.
- As they come across a number greater than 20 in the exercises, have them add that number and its factors to their list.
- Allow them to use this list as they simplify fractions. For example, to simplify $\frac{4}{6}$, students use their list to first find the GCF of 4 and 6: 2. Then divide by the GCF to simplify $\frac{4}{6}$: $\frac{4}{6} = \frac{4 \div 2}{6 \div 2} = \frac{2}{3}$.

LOGICAL, AUDITORY

Option 2 English Language Learners ELL

Core Vocabulary: why/why not?, is it true?, what goes in the blank?
Common Use Verb: balance
Hear Math: This strategy helps students hear vocabulary used to find the simplest form.

- Write: "23 ×___= 23" on the board. Ask: "What goes in the blank?" Prompt "1."
- Solicit different ways to write 1 one, 1.0, $\frac{2}{2}$ etc. Ask if writing a form of '1' on the blank will make the problem true. yes
- Have pairs decide a way 1 can be written as a fraction $\frac{2}{2}$, $\frac{45}{45}$, etc.
- Insert one of their fractions into the scaffold for example, $23 \times \frac{4}{4} = 23$. Ask: "Is it true?
- Accept responses and discuss why or why not their answers are correct.
- Repeat for all pairs as time permits.

Independent Work Options

LOGICAL

Option 1 Early Finishers AL

Materials: paper and pencil

- Have students solve the following problem and explain their work.

Joanne has half as many markers as Victor. Victor has one third as many markers as Tim. Tim has one fourth as many as Patrick. If Patrick has 120 markers, how many markers does each person have?

Joanne: 5 markers,
Victor: 10 markers,
Tim: 30 markers

Option 2 Student Technology

Math Online macmillanmh.com

Personal Tutor • Extra Examples

Math Adventures

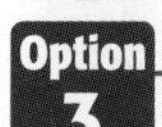

Option 3 Learning Station: Science (p. 370G)

Direct students to the Science Learning Station for opportunities to explore and extend the lesson concept.

Option 4 Problem-Solving Practice

Reinforce problem-solving skills and strategies with the Problem-Solving Practice worksheet.

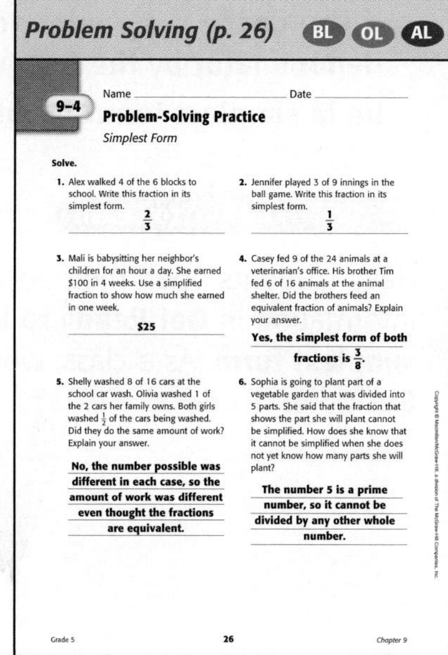

Problem Solving (p. 26) BL OL AL

9-4 Name ________ Date ________

Problem-Solving Practice

Simplest Form

Solve.

1. Alex walked 4 of the 6 blocks to school. Write this fraction in its simplest form. **$\frac{2}{3}$**
2. Jennifer played 3 of 9 innings in the ball game. Write this fraction in its simplest form. **$\frac{1}{3}$**
3. Mali is babysitting her neighbor's children for an hour a day. She earned $100 in 4 weeks. Use a simplified fraction to show how much she earned in one week. **$25**
4. Casey fed 9 of the 24 animals at a veterinarian's office. His brother Tim fed 6 of 16 animals at the animal shelter. Did the brothers feed an equivalent fraction of animals? Explain your answer. **Yes, the simplest form of both fractions is $\frac{3}{8}$.**
5. Shelly washed 8 of 16 cars at the school car wash. Olivia washed 1 of the 2 cars her family owns. Both girls washed $\frac{1}{2}$ of the cars being washed. Did they do the same amount of work? Explain your answer. **No, the number possible was different in each case, so the amount of work was different even thought the fractions are equivalent.**
6. Sophia is going to plant part of a vegetable garden that was divided into 5 parts. She said that the fraction that shows the part she will plant cannot be simplified. How does she know that it cannot be simplified when she does not yet know how many parts she will plant? **The number 5 is a prime number, so it cannot be divided by any other whole number.**

Grade 5 26 Chapter 9

9-4 Simplest Form

1 Introduce

Activity Choice 1 • Hands-On

- Give pairs of students a set of index cards with one digit, 0–9, on each card. Write the numbers 12 and 18 on the board.
- Ask students to find the GCF of the two numbers. Give them time to find the answer. At the signal, "answers up," all team leaders hold up the digit card that represents the GCF. 6
- Repeat the process using the numbers 12 and 22. 2
- Tell students that in today's lesson they will be finding the GCF of numbers to help them simplify fractions.

Activity Choice 2 • Literature

Introduce the lesson with *Give Me Half!* by Stuart J. Murphy. For a related math activity, see p. TR50.

2 Teach

Scaffolding Questions

Write the fraction $\frac{12}{16}$ on the board.

- **Is 2 a common factor of 12 and 16?** yes
- **What fraction will you get if you divide both the numerator and denominator by 2? Is the fraction in simplest form?** $\frac{6}{8}$; no
- **What is the GCF of 12 and 16?** 4
- **If you divide the numerator and denominator by the GCF, will the fraction be in simplest form? What is it?** yes; $\frac{3}{4}$

GET READY to Learn

Have students open their books and read the information in **Get Ready to Learn.** Introduce **simplest form**. As a class, work through **Examples 1 and 2**.

9-4 Simplest Form

MAIN IDEA
I will write a fraction in simplest form.
New Vocabulary
simplest form
Math Online
macmillanmh.com
• Extra Examples
• Personal Tutor
• Self-Check Quiz

GET READY to Learn

A praying mantis is 12 centimeters long, and a walking stick is 22 centimeters long. So, a praying mantis is $\frac{12}{22}$ the length of a stick insect. Is this the simplest way to write this fraction?

A fraction is written in **simplest form** when the GCF of the numerator and the denominator is 1. The simplest form of a fraction is one of its many equivalent fractions.

Real-World EXAMPLE Simplest Form

1 MEASUREMENT Refer to the information above. What fraction of a walking stick's length is the length of a praying mantis? Write the fraction in simplest form.

Step 1 Find the GCF of the numerator and the denominator.

factors of 12: 1, **2**, 3, 4, 6, 12
factors of 22: 1, **2**, 11, 22 The GCF of 12 and 22 is 2.

Step 2 Divide both the numerator and the denominator by the GCF. Dividing both the numerator and the denominator by the same number is equivalent to dividing by one. The appearance of the fraction changes, not its value.

$\frac{12}{22} = \frac{12 \div 2}{22 \div 2} = \frac{6}{11}$ The GCF of 6 and 11 is 1.

So, a praying mantis' length is $\frac{6}{11}$ the length of a walking stick.

You can see from the models at the right that $\frac{12}{22} = \frac{6}{11}$.

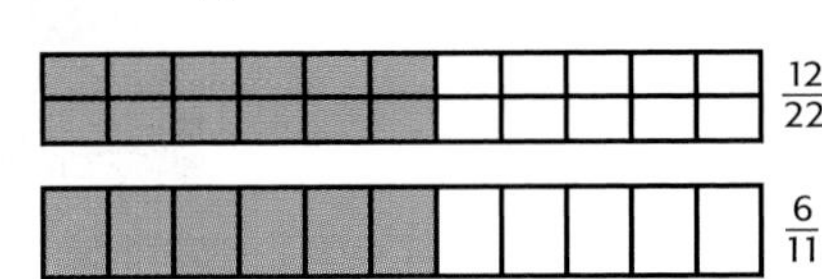

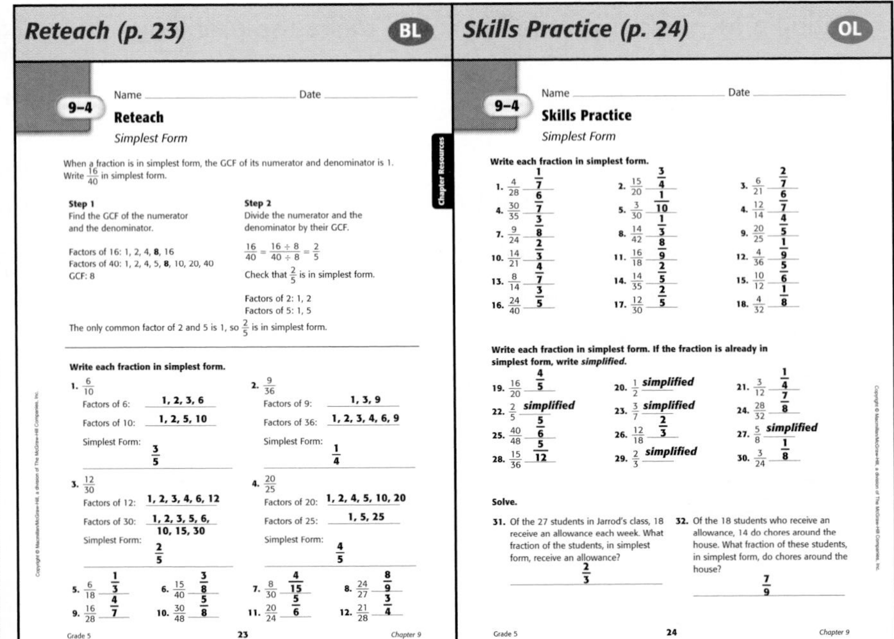

Reteach (p. 23) BL

9-4 Name ______ Date ______

Reteach

Simplest Form

When a fraction is in simplest form, the GCF of its numerator and denominator is 1. Write $\frac{16}{40}$ in simplest form.

Step 1
Find the GCF of the numerator and the denominator.

Factors of 16: 1, 2, 4, **8**, 16
Factors of 40: 1, 2, 4, 5, **8**, 10, 20, 40
GCF: 8

Step 2
Divide the numerator and the denominator by their GCF.

$\frac{16}{40} = \frac{16 \div 8}{40 \div 8} = \frac{2}{5}$

Check that $\frac{2}{5}$ is in simplest form.

Factors of 2: 1, 2
Factors of 5: 1, 5

The only common factor of 2 and 5 is 1, so $\frac{2}{5}$ is in simplest form.

Write each fraction in simplest form.

1. $\frac{6}{10}$
Factors of 6: **1, 2, 3, 6**
Factors of 10: **1, 2, 5, 10**
Simplest Form: $\frac{3}{5}$

2. $\frac{9}{36}$
Factors of 9: **1, 3, 9**
Factors of 36: **1, 2, 3, 4, 6, 9**
Simplest Form: $\frac{1}{4}$

3. $\frac{12}{30}$
Factors of 12: **1, 2, 3, 4, 6, 12**
Factors of 30: **1, 2, 3, 5, 6, 10, 15, 30**
Simplest Form: $\frac{2}{5}$

4. $\frac{20}{25}$
Factors of 20: **1, 2, 4, 5, 10, 20**
Factors of 25: **1, 5, 25**
Simplest Form: $\frac{4}{5}$

5. $\frac{6}{18}$ $\frac{1}{3}$ 6. $\frac{15}{40}$ $\frac{3}{8}$ 7. $\frac{8}{30}$ $\frac{4}{15}$ 8. $\frac{24}{27}$ $\frac{8}{9}$

9. $\frac{16}{28}$ $\frac{4}{7}$ 10. $\frac{30}{48}$ $\frac{5}{8}$ 11. $\frac{20}{24}$ $\frac{5}{6}$ 12. $\frac{21}{28}$ $\frac{3}{4}$

Grade 5 23 Chapter 9

Skills Practice (p. 24) OL

9-4 Name ______ Date ______

Skills Practice

Simplest Form

Write each fraction in simplest form.

1. $\frac{4}{28}$ $\frac{1}{7}$ 2. $\frac{15}{20}$ $\frac{3}{4}$ 3. $\frac{6}{21}$ $\frac{2}{7}$

4. $\frac{30}{35}$ $\frac{6}{7}$ 5. $\frac{3}{30}$ $\frac{1}{10}$ 4. $\frac{12}{14}$ $\frac{6}{7}$

7. $\frac{9}{24}$ $\frac{3}{8}$ 8. $\frac{14}{42}$ $\frac{1}{3}$ 9. $\frac{20}{25}$ $\frac{4}{5}$

10. $\frac{14}{21}$ $\frac{2}{3}$ 11. $\frac{16}{18}$ $\frac{8}{9}$ 12. $\frac{4}{36}$ $\frac{1}{9}$

13. $\frac{8}{14}$ $\frac{4}{7}$ 14. $\frac{14}{35}$ $\frac{2}{5}$ 15. $\frac{10}{12}$ $\frac{5}{6}$

16. $\frac{24}{40}$ $\frac{3}{5}$ 17. $\frac{12}{30}$ $\frac{2}{5}$ 18. $\frac{4}{32}$ $\frac{1}{8}$

Write each fraction in simplest form. If the fraction is already in simplest form, write *simplified*.

19. $\frac{16}{20}$ $\frac{4}{5}$ 20. $\frac{1}{2}$ ***simplified*** 21. $\frac{3}{12}$ $\frac{1}{4}$

22. $\frac{2}{5}$ ***simplified*** 23. $\frac{3}{7}$ ***simplified*** 24. $\frac{28}{32}$ $\frac{7}{8}$

25. $\frac{40}{48}$ $\frac{5}{6}$ 26. $\frac{12}{18}$ $\frac{2}{3}$ 27. $\frac{5}{8}$ ***simplified***

28. $\frac{15}{36}$ $\frac{5}{12}$ 29. $\frac{2}{3}$ ***simplified*** 30. $\frac{3}{24}$ $\frac{1}{8}$

Solve.

31. Of the 27 students in Jarrod's class, 18 receive an allowance each week. What fraction of the students, in simplest form, receive an allowance? $\frac{2}{3}$

32. Of the 18 students who receive an allowance, 14 do chores around the house. What fraction of these students, in simplest form, do chores around the house? $\frac{7}{9}$

Grade 5 24 Chapter 9

Remember

The divisibility rules are useful for finding common factors.

EXAMPLE Simplest Form

2 Write $\frac{18}{30}$ in simplest form.

One Way: **Divide by Common Factors**

$\frac{18}{30} = \frac{18 \div 2}{30 \div 2} = \frac{9}{15}$ Divide 18 and 30 by the common factor 2.

$\frac{9}{15} = \frac{9 \div 3}{15 \div 3} = \frac{3}{5}$ Divide 9 and 15 by the common factor 3.

Since 3 and 5 have no common factors other than 1, stop dividing.

Another Way: **Divide by the GCF**

factors of 18: 1, 2, 3, 6, 9, 18

factors of 30: 1, 2, 3, 5, 6, 10, 15, 30

The GCF of 18 and 30 is 6.

$\frac{18}{30} = \frac{18 \div 6}{30 \div 6} = \frac{3}{5}$ Divide by the GCF 6.

Using either method, $\frac{18}{30}$ written in simplest form is $\frac{3}{5}$.

Check

You can see from the models at the right that $\frac{18}{30} = \frac{3}{5}$. ✓

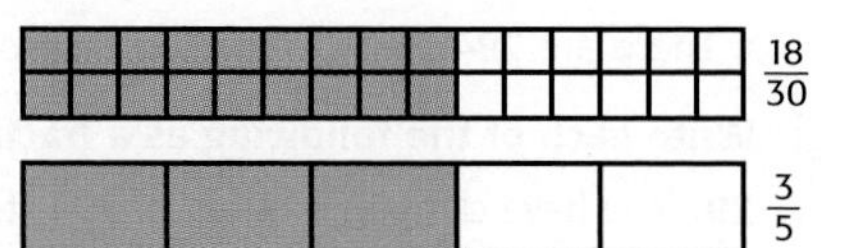

10. Sample answer: Find the GCF of the numerator and the denominator. Then divide the numerator and the denominator by the GCF.

CHECK What You Know

Write each fraction in simplest form. If the fraction is already in simplest form, write *simplified*. See Examples 1, 2 (pp. 386–387)

1. $\frac{4}{6}$ $\frac{2}{3}$
2. $\frac{2}{12}$ $\frac{1}{6}$
3. $\frac{8}{24}$ $\frac{1}{3}$
4. $\frac{8}{9}$ simplified
5. $\frac{9}{18}$ $\frac{1}{2}$
6. $\frac{4}{14}$ $\frac{2}{7}$
7. $\frac{15}{20}$ $\frac{3}{4}$
8. $\frac{21}{35}$ $\frac{3}{5}$
9. Kara buys 24 bagels. Ten are whole wheat. What fraction of the bagels are whole wheat, in simplest form? $\frac{5}{12}$
10. **Talk About It** Use at least 2 sentences to explain how to find the simplest form of any fraction.

Enrich (p. 27) AL

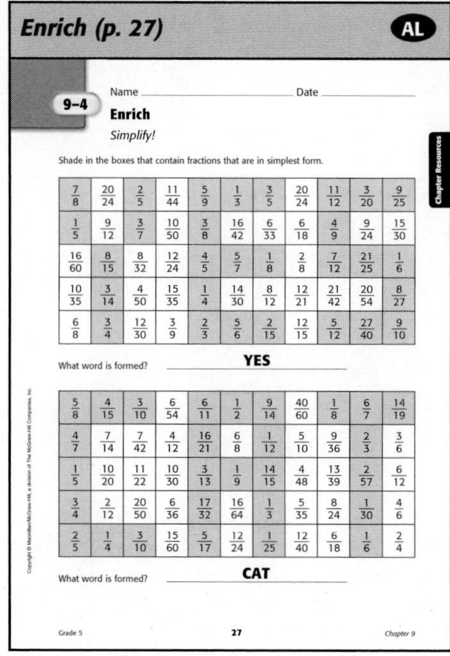

9–4 Name ______ Date ______

Enrich

Simplify!

Shade in the boxes that contain fractions that are in simplest form.

7/8	20/24	2/5	11/44	5/9	1/3	3/5	20/24	11/12	3/20	9/25
1/5	9/12	3/7	10/50	3/8	16/42	6/33	6/18	4/9	9/24	15/30
16/60	8/15	8/32	12/24	4/5	5/7	1/8	2/8	7/12	21/25	1/6
10/35	3/14	4/50	15/35	1/4	14/30	8/12	12/21	21/42	20/54	8/27
6/8	3/4	12/30	3/9	2/3	5/6	2/15	12/15	5/12	27/40	9/10

What word is formed? **YES**

5/8	4/15	3/10	6/54	6/11	1/2	9/14	40/60	1/8	6/7	14/19
4/7	7/14	7/42	4/12	16/21	6/8	1/12	5/10	9/36	2/3	3/6
1/5	10/20	11/22	10/30	3/13	1/9	14/15	4/48	13/39	2/57	6/12
3/4	2/12	20/50	6/36	17/32	16/64	1/3	5/35	8/24	1/30	4/6
2/5	1/4	3/10	15/60	5/17	12/24	1/25	12/40	6/18	1/6	2/4

What word is formed? **CAT**

Chapter Resources

Grade 5 27 Chapter 9

Simplest Form

Example 2 Be sure that students understand that a fraction is not in simplest form if the numerator and denominator have a common factor.

ADDITIONAL EXAMPLES

1. Xiang has a ribbon 24 inches long. Urmi has a ribbon 36 inches long. Xiang's ribbon is $\frac{24}{36}$ the length of Urmi's ribbon. Write $\frac{24}{36}$ in simplest form. $\frac{2}{3}$
2. Write $\frac{20}{28}$ in simplest form. $\frac{5}{7}$

CHECK What You Know

As a class, have students complete Exercises 1–10 in **Check What You Know** as you observe their work.

Exercise 10 Assess student comprehension before assigning practice exercises.

BL Alternate Teaching Strategy

If students have trouble writing a fraction in simplest form…

Then use one of these reteach options:

1. CRM **Daily Reteach Worksheet** (p. 23)
2. Present students with the following problem: *Marina has 10 yellow balls, 12 purple balls, and 8 green balls. What fraction of the balls are yellow, in simplest form?*
   - Remind students that a fraction compares a part of the whole to the total number of parts.
   - Have students use 10 yellow counters to represent the 10 yellow balls and 30 red counters to represent the total number of balls.
   - Have students divide the counters into as many groups as they can that have the same number of yellow counters in each group and the same number of red counters in each group.
   - Guide students to see that they can divide the groups into 10 groups of 1 yellow counter and 3 red counters. There is 1 yellow ball for every 3 balls, thus $\frac{1}{3}$ of the balls are yellow.

3 Practice

Differentiate practice using these leveled assignments for Exercises 11–33.

Level	Assignment
BL Below/Approaching Level	11–18, 27, 29, 33
OL On Level	11–22, 27–30, 33
AL Above/Beyond Level	12–30 even, 31–33

Have students discuss and complete the Higher Order Thinking problems. Allow students to use fraction circles to check their answer.

WRITING IN ▶MATH Have students complete Exercise 33 in their Math Journals. You may choose to use this as an optional formative assessment.

COMMON ERROR!

Exercise 16 Students may incorrectly simplify this fraction by writing $\frac{6}{12}$ as the simplest form of $\frac{12}{24}$. Have students use prime factorization to find common factors. $\frac{12}{24} = \frac{2 \times 2 \times 3}{2 \times 2 \times 2 \times 3} = \frac{1}{2}$.

Practice and Problem Solving

See page R24.

Write each fraction in simplest form. If the fraction is already in simplest form, write *simplified*. See Examples 1, 2 (pp. 386–387)

11. $\frac{6}{8}$ $\frac{3}{4}$ **12.** $\frac{6}{10}$ $\frac{3}{5}$ **13.** $\frac{3}{18}$ $\frac{1}{6}$ **14.** $\frac{2}{15}$ simplified

15. $\frac{4}{16}$ $\frac{1}{4}$ **16.** $\frac{12}{24}$ $\frac{1}{2}$ **17.** $\frac{6}{25}$ simplified **18.** $\frac{21}{30}$ $\frac{7}{10}$

19. $\frac{12}{40}$ $\frac{3}{10}$ **20.** $\frac{4}{11}$ simplified **21.** $\frac{8}{28}$ $\frac{2}{7}$ **22.** $\frac{9}{24}$ $\frac{3}{8}$

23. $\frac{3}{36}$ $\frac{1}{12}$ **24.** $\frac{25}{30}$ $\frac{5}{6}$ **25.** $\frac{18}{45}$ $\frac{2}{5}$ **26.** $\frac{36}{48}$ $\frac{3}{4}$

27. A basket of fruit has 10 oranges, 12 apples, and 18 peaches. Express in simplest form the fraction of fruit that are oranges. $\frac{1}{4}$

28. Measurement Andeana is 4 feet tall. Her brother Berto is 38 inches tall. What fractional part of Andeana's height is Berto's height? $\frac{19}{24}$

Data File

The Bunker Hill Monument in Charlestown, Massachusetts, is at the location of the first major battle of the American Revolution.

- The current monument is 221 feet tall. The original monument at the site was a little more than 17 feet tall.
- There are 294 steps to the top look-out window.

Write each of the following as a fraction in simplest form.

29. You have climbed 147 out of 294 steps. $\frac{1}{2}$

30. The original monument is $\frac{17}{221}$ as tall as the current Bunker Hill Monument. $\frac{1}{13}$

H.O.T. Problems

31–33. See Ch. 9 Answer Appendix.

31. OPEN ENDED Write a real-world problem that uses $\frac{14}{18}$ in the problem. Write the fraction in simplest form.

32. WHICH ONE DOESN'T BELONG? Identify the fraction that does not belong with the other three. Explain your reasoning.

$\frac{3}{12}$ $\frac{4}{16}$ $\frac{5}{25}$ $\frac{6}{24}$

33. WRITING IN ▶MATH Explain how you would write $\frac{24}{36}$ in simplest form.

TEST Practice

34. Gil's aunt cut his birthday cake into 32 equal pieces, as shown below. Eighteen pieces were eaten at his birthday party. What fraction of the cake was left? **(Lesson 9-4)** A

A $\frac{7}{16}$ **C** $\frac{7}{12}$

B $\frac{9}{16}$ **D** $\frac{9}{14}$

35. The fractions $\frac{2}{8}$, $\frac{3}{12}$, $\frac{4}{16}$, and $\frac{5}{20}$ are each equivalent to $\frac{1}{4}$. What is the relationship between the numerator and denominator in each fraction that is equivalent to $\frac{1}{4}$? **(Lesson 9-3)** G

F The numerator is 4 times the denominator.

G The denominator is 4 times the numerator.

H The numerator is 4 more than the denominator.

J The denominator is 4 more than the numerator.

Spiral Review

Write two fractions that are equivalent to each fraction. (Lesson 9-3)

36. $\frac{4}{7}$ $\frac{8}{14}$, $\frac{12}{21}$ **37.** $\frac{2}{9}$ $\frac{4}{18}$, $\frac{6}{27}$ **38.** $\frac{4}{8}$ $\frac{1}{2}$, $\frac{8}{16}$ **39.** $\frac{1}{6}$ $\frac{2}{12}$, $\frac{3}{18}$

40. A tangerine has about 37 Calories. Is 37 *prime* or *composite*? **(Lesson 9-2)** prime

41. Thirty-six fourth graders, 48 fifth graders, and 24 sixth graders will attend a play. An equal number of students must sit in each row, and only students from the same grade can sit in a row. What is the greatest number of fifth graders that can sit in each row? **(Lesson 9-1)** 12 fifth graders

Write each mixed number as an improper fraction. Check using models. (Lesson 8-4)

42. $1\frac{2}{5}$ $\frac{7}{5}$ **43.** $3\frac{1}{8}$ $\frac{25}{8}$ **44.** $5\frac{2}{3}$ $\frac{17}{3}$

45. The table shows the distances that Terrell threw a flying disk. Find the median and mode of the data. **(Lesson 7-1)** 28 ft; 26 ft

Throw	Distance (ft)
1	30
2	26
3	26
4	37

46. Swimming lessons cost $62 per swimmer. A total of $806 was collected for swimming lessons. How many people took swimming lessons? **(Lesson 4-4)** 13

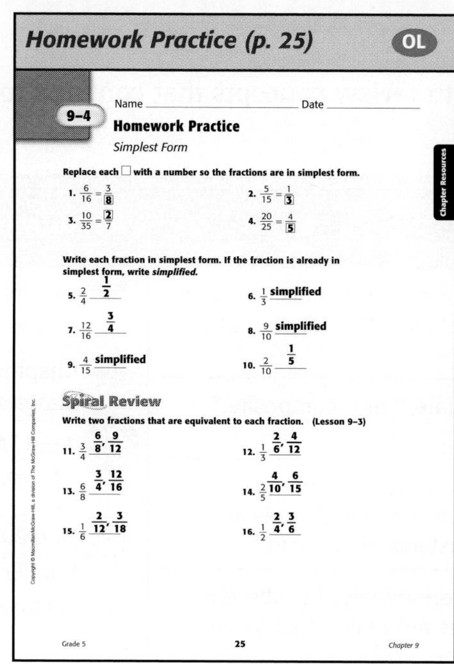
Homework Practice (p. 25) OL

9–4 Name ________ Date ________

Homework Practice

Simplest Form

Replace each □ with a number so the fractions are in simplest form.

1. $\frac{6}{16} = \frac{3}{\boxed{8}}$
2. $\frac{5}{15} = \frac{1}{\boxed{3}}$
3. $\frac{10}{35} = \frac{\boxed{2}}{7}$
4. $\frac{20}{25} = \frac{4}{\boxed{5}}$

Write each fraction in simplest form. If the fraction is already in simplest form, write *simplified.*

5. $\frac{2}{4}$ $\frac{1}{2}$
6. $\frac{1}{3}$ simplified
7. $\frac{12}{16}$ $\frac{3}{4}$
8. $\frac{9}{10}$ simplified
9. $\frac{4}{15}$ simplified
10. $\frac{2}{10}$ $\frac{1}{5}$

Spiral Review

Write two fractions that are equivalent to each fraction. (Lesson 9–3)

11. $\frac{3}{4}$ $\frac{6}{8}$, $\frac{9}{12}$
12. $\frac{1}{3}$ $\frac{2}{6}$, $\frac{4}{12}$
13. $\frac{6}{8}$ $\frac{3}{4}$, $\frac{12}{16}$
14. $\frac{2}{5}$ $\frac{4}{10}$, $\frac{6}{15}$
15. $\frac{1}{6}$ $\frac{2}{12}$, $\frac{3}{18}$
16. $\frac{1}{2}$ $\frac{2}{4}$, $\frac{3}{6}$

Chapter Resources

Grade 5 25 Chapter 9

4 Assess

Formative Assessment

Write $\frac{18}{30}$ on the board.

- **What fraction do you get if you divide the numerator and denominator by 3? Is it in simplest form?** $\frac{6}{10}$; no
- **Why does dividing by the GCF take fewer steps to simplify the fraction?** Sample answer: You only divide by one number to find the simplest form.

Quick Check **Are students continuing to struggle with writing fractions in simplest form?**

If Yes → Small Group Options (p. 386B)
Strategic Intervention Guide (p. 100)

If No → Independent Work Options (p. 386B)
CRM Skills Practice Worksheet (p. 24)
CRM Enrich Worksheet (p. 27)

Yesterday's News Have students explain how yesterday's lesson on equivalent fractions helped them with today's lesson on finding the simplest form of a fraction.

TEST Practice

Reviews Lessons 9-3 and 9-4

Assign the Test Practice problems to provide daily reinforcement of test-taking skills.

Spiral Review

Reviews Lessons 4-4, 7-1, 8-4, 9-1, 9-2, and 9-3

Review and assess mastery of skills and concepts from previous chapters.

Mid-Chapter Check

Lessons 9-1 through 9-4

Formative Assessment

Use the Mid-Chapter Check to assess students' progress in the first half of the chapter.

Customize and create multiple versions of your Mid-Chapter Check and the test answer keys.

FOLDABLES Dinah Zike's Foldables

Use these lesson suggestions to incorporate the Foldables during the chapter.

Lesson 9-1 Students record information, define terms, and identify common factors of a set of whole numbers beneath the first tab of the Foldable.

Lesson 9-2 Students demonstrate their ability to identify prime and composite numbers beneath the second tab of the Foldable.

Lessons 9-3, 9-4 Ask students to provide examples showing equivalent fractions, and to convert fractions into their simplest forms beneath the third tab of the Foldable.

Chapter 9 Mid-Chapter Check

Lessons 9-1 through 9-4

Find the common factors of each set of numbers. (Lesson 9-1)

1. 5, 15 1, 5
2. 12, 30 1, 2, 3, 6
3. 24, 32, 40 1, 2, 4, 8
4. 10, 22, 30 1, 2
5. **MULTIPLE CHOICE** Which group shows all the numbers that are common factors of 24 and 40? (Lesson 9-1) C
   - **A** 1, 2, 4
   - **B** 1, 2, 4, 6
   - **C** 1, 2, 4, 8
   - **D** 1, 2, 4, 6, 8, 12

Find the GCF of each set of numbers. (Lesson 9-1)

6. 9, 21 3
7. 12, 26 2
8. 20, 30, 40 10
9. 8, 24, 32 8

Tell whether each number is *prime* or *composite*. (Lesson 9-2)

10. 20 composite
11. 36 composite
12. 19 prime
13. 28 composite
14. **MULTIPLE CHOICE** Which model does NOT represent a composite number? (Lesson 9-2) G
   - **F**
   - **G**
   - **H**
   - **J**

15–18. See Ch. 9 Answer Appendix.

Find two fractions that are equivalent to each fraction. (Lesson 9-3)

15. $\frac{2}{7}$
16. $\frac{1}{5}$
17. $\frac{4}{10}$
18. $\frac{3}{8}$
19. **Algebra** What number makes $\frac{4}{9} = \frac{16}{■}$ a true statement? (Lesson 9-3) 36
20. **MULTIPLE CHOICE** Devin recorded the shirt color of the 30 students who rode his bus on Monday. The results are shown below.

Shirt Color	Number of Students
Blue	12
White	9
Red	5
Green	3
Other	1

Which fraction of shirts were red? (Lesson 9-4) D

A $\frac{1}{3}$ **B** $\frac{1}{4}$ **C** $\frac{1}{5}$ **D** $\frac{1}{6}$

Write each fraction in simplest form. If the fraction is already in simplest form, write *simplified*. (Lesson 9-4)

21. $\frac{8}{24}$ $\frac{1}{3}$
22. $\frac{6}{14}$ $\frac{3}{7}$
23. $\frac{9}{20}$ simplified
24. $\frac{25}{30}$ $\frac{5}{6}$
25.  WRITING IN MATH Explain how you would find two fractions that are equivalent to $\frac{6}{10}$. (Lesson 9-3) See Ch. 9 Answer Appendix.

390 **Chapter 9** Use Factors and Multiples

Data-Driven Decision Making

Based on the results of the Mid-Chapter Check, use the following resources to review concepts that continue to give students problems.

Exercises	State/Local Standards	What's the Math?	Error Analysis	Resources for Review
1–9 Lesson 9-1		Identify common factors of a set of whole numbers.	Does not put 1 as a factor of all numbers. Does not understand "common factors," "GCF." Does not list all factors.	Strategic Intervention Guide (pp. 92, 100, 102, 104) CRM Chapter 9 Resource Masters (Reteach) Math Adventures My Math Zone Chapter 9 **Math Online** Extra Examples • Concepts in Motion
10–14 Lesson 9-2		Identify prime or composite numbers.	Does not understand "prime," and "composite."	
15–19, 25 Lesson 9-3		Write equivalent fractions.	Does not multiply/divide numerator and denominator by same number to find equivalent fractions. Does not understand "equivalent."	
20–24 Lesson 9-4		Write a fraction in simplest form.	Divides numerator and denominator by different numbers to simplify. Does not realize that same number on top and bottom equals 1.	

LESSON

9-5 Decimals and Fractions

Lesson Planner

Objective

Relate decimals to fractions.

Review Vocabulary

decimal, fraction

Resources

Materials: overhead decimal squares for tenths, hundredths, and thousandths, decimal square workmat, crayons or markers, fraction bars or fraction bar poster
Literature Connection: *Henry Hikes to Fitchburg* by D.B. Johnson
Alternate Lesson: Use *IMPACT Mathematics:* Unit E to provide practice with decimals and fractions.
Teacher Technology
TeacherWorks • Interactive Classroom

Focus on Math Background

In this lesson, students use their knowledge of decimal place value from Chapter 1 to help them represent decimals as fractions. Students may write decimals in place-value charts before converting them to fractions, or write or say the word form of the decimal to help them write an equivalent fraction. The name of the rightmost place value will be the denominator of the fraction. For example, 0.425 = *four hundred twenty-five thousandths* = $\frac{425}{1,000}$. Fractions should usually be written in simplest form. To simplify a fraction, divide the numerator and the denominator by the greatest common factor. For example, $\frac{425 \div 25}{1,000 \div 25} = \frac{17}{40}$

Daily Routine

Use these suggestions before beginning the lesson on p. 391.

5-Minute Check 

(Reviews Lesson 9-4)

Write each fraction in simplest form. If the fraction is already in simplest form, write *simplified*.

1. $\frac{15}{45}$ $\frac{1}{3}$
2. $\frac{12}{30}$ $\frac{2}{5}$
3. $\frac{7}{26}$ simplified
4. $\frac{28}{42}$ $\frac{2}{3}$

Problem of the Day 

Fifteen students take the bus to and from school each day. The bus fare is $1.50 one way. They decide to walk to save money. How long will it take them to save $1,100? 25 days

Review Math Vocabulary

Write the lesson vocabulary words and their definition on the board.

Have students compare and contrast decimals and fractions. Have them tell how they are alike and how they are different. Ask for examples of each.

Visual Vocabulary Cards

Use Visual Vocabulary Card 6 to reinforce the vocabulary reviewed in this lesson. (The Define/Example/Ask routine is printed on the back of each card.)

Differentiated Instruction

Small Group Options

LOGICAL

Option 1 Below Level BL

Materials: number line

- Have students write these common fractions as decimals: $\frac{1}{2}$; $\frac{1}{4}$; $\frac{3}{4}$; $\frac{1}{5}$; $\frac{3}{5}$; $\frac{1}{8}$; $\frac{3}{8}$; $\frac{5}{8}$; $\frac{7}{8}$
  0.5; 0.25; 0.75; 0.2; 0.6; 0.125; 0.375; 0.625; 0.875
- Then have students place the fractions on top and decimal equivalents underneath a number line, from least to greatest.

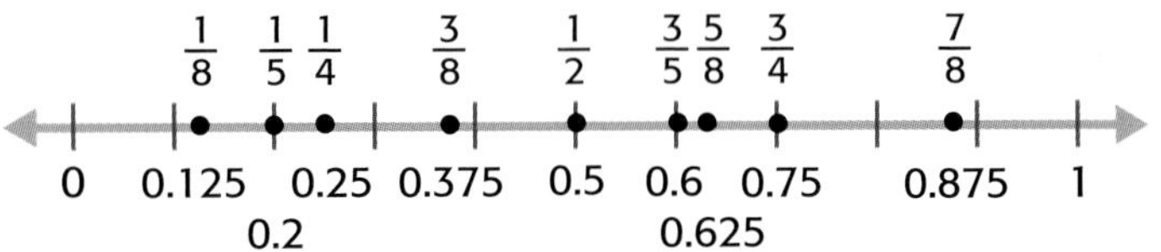

LINGUISTIC, AUDITORY

Option 2 English Language Learners ELL

Materials: index cards, pocket chart
Core Vocabulary: and, before, after
Common Use Verb: splits

Talk Math This strategy clarifies the written use of the decimal point and the verbal use of "and" in numbers and decimals to help students read numbers correctly.

- Pass out cards and have students write "and" while you display these numbers on large index cards: $3\frac{1}{2}$, 1.35, $45\frac{3}{4}$, $12\frac{1}{6}$, $26\frac{3}{8}$, 34.136, 2.13.
- Say the number. Cut or tear apart on the decimal point or at the fraction. Re-read while separating the torn card and inserting an "and" card.
- Practice reading "and" between whole numbers, fractions, and decimals.

Independent Work Options

LOGICAL

Option 1 Early Finishers AL

Materials: index cards, pencils

- Have students label an index card with the title, Fourths. Have them write $\frac{1}{4}$, $\frac{2}{4}$, and $\frac{3}{4}$ down the left edge of the card. Then have them write the decimal equivalents for each fraction.
- Have the students repeat the procedure with all of the fifths and twentieths.

Fourths	
$\frac{1}{4}$	0.25
$\frac{2}{4}$	0.5
$\frac{3}{4}$	0.75

Option 2 Student Technology

Tech Link

Math Online macmillanmh.com

Personal Tutor • Extra Examples

Math Adventures

Option 3 Learning Station: Art (p. 370G)

Direct students to the Art Learning Station for opportunities to explore and extend the lesson concept.

Option 4 Problem-Solving Practice

Reinforce problem-solving skills and strategies with the Problem-Solving Practice worksheet.

Problem Solving (p. 31) BL OL AL

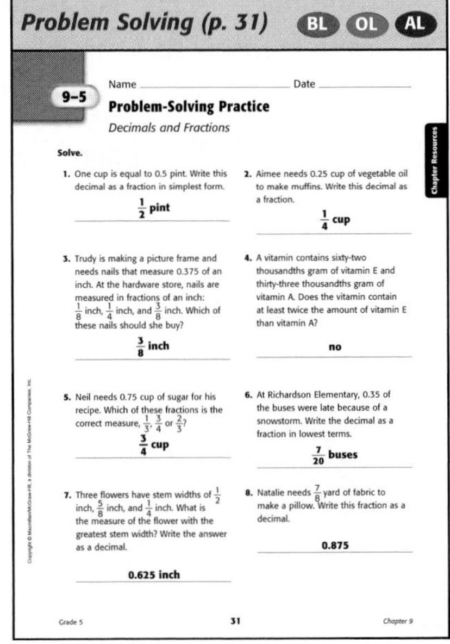

Name ______ Date ______

9–5 **Problem-Solving Practice**

Decimals and Fractions

Chapter Resources

Solve.

1. One cup is equal to 0.5 pint. Write this decimal as a fraction in simplest form.
   $\frac{1}{2}$ pint
2. Aimee needs 0.25 cup of vegetable oil to make muffins. Write this decimal as a fraction.
   $\frac{1}{4}$ cup
3. Trudy is making a picture frame and needs nails that measure 0.375 of an inch. At the hardware store, nails are measured in fractions of an inch: $\frac{1}{8}$ inch, $\frac{1}{4}$ inch, and $\frac{3}{8}$ inch. Which of these nails should she buy?
   $\frac{3}{8}$ inch
4. A vitamin contains sixty-two thousandths gram of vitamin E and thirty-three thousandths gram of vitamin A. Does the vitamin contain at least twice the amount of vitamin E than vitamin A?
   no
5. Neil needs 0.75 cup of sugar for his recipe. Which of these fractions is the correct measure, $\frac{1}{3}$, $\frac{3}{4}$ or $\frac{2}{3}$?
   $\frac{3}{4}$ cup
6. At Richardson Elementary, 0.35 of the buses were late because of a snowstorm. Write the decimal as a fraction in lowest terms.
   $\frac{7}{20}$ buses
7. Three flowers have stem widths of $\frac{1}{2}$ inch, $\frac{5}{8}$ inch, and $\frac{1}{4}$ inch. What is the measure of the flower with the greatest stem width? Write the answer as a decimal.
   0.625 inch
8. Natalie needs $\frac{7}{8}$ yard of fabric to make a pillow. Write this fraction as a decimal.
   0.875

Grade 5 31 Chapter 9

9-5 Decimals and Fractions

GET READY to Learn

A cashier weighs two peaches. The scale reads 0.75 pound. What fraction of a pound do the peaches weigh?

MAIN IDEA

I will relate decimals to fractions.

Math Online

macmillanmh.com

- Extra Examples
- Personal Tutor
- Self-Check Quiz

You can use models to write any decimal that names tenths, hundredths, or thousandths as a fraction. Use the place value of the right most digit in the decimal to name the denominator of the fraction.

Real-World EXAMPLE — Write a Decimal as a Fraction

1 FOOD Refer to the information above. Write the weight of the peaches as a fraction in simplest form.

Step 1 Shade a model of 0.75.

THINK 0.75 is 75 hundredths.

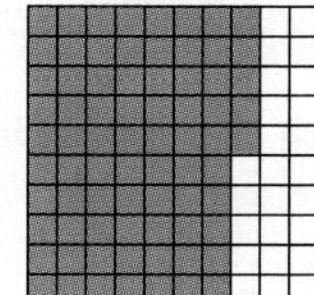

Step 2 Write a fraction with 100 as the denominator.

$0.75 = \frac{75}{100}$

Step 3 If necessary, simplify the fraction.

$\frac{75}{100} = \frac{75 \div 25}{100 \div 25}$ Divide by the GCF, 25.

$= \frac{3}{4}$ Simplify.

So, the peaches weigh $\frac{3}{4}$ pound.

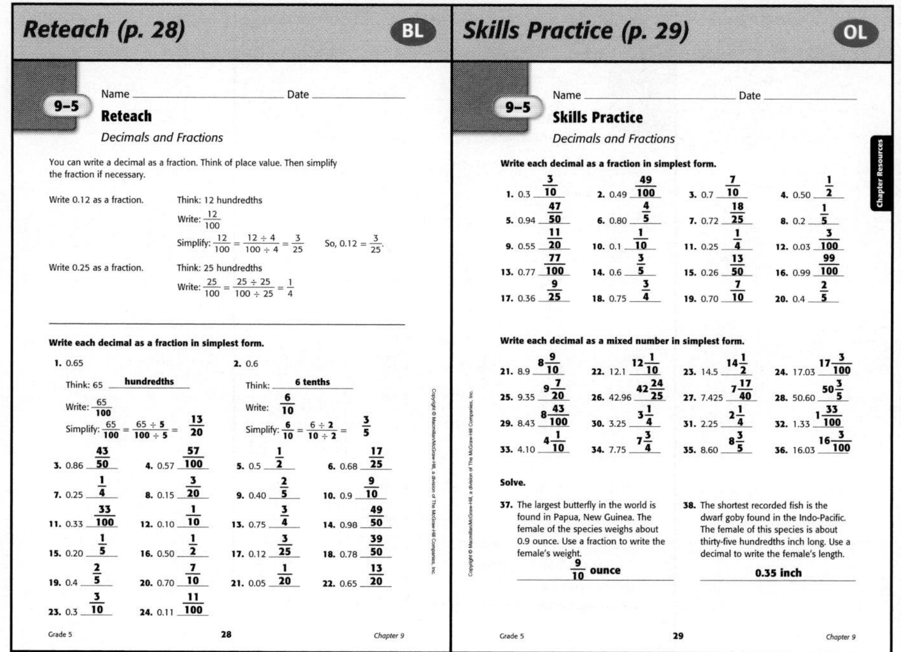

Reteach (p. 28) BL

9–5 Name ________ Date ________

Reteach

Decimals and Fractions

You can write a decimal as a fraction. Think of place value. Then simplify the fraction if necessary.

Write 0.12 as a fraction. Think: 12 hundredths

Write: $\frac{12}{100}$

Simplify: $\frac{12}{100} = \frac{12 \div 4}{100 \div 4} = \frac{3}{25}$ So, $0.12 = \frac{3}{25}$.

Write 0.25 as a fraction. Think: 25 hundredths

Write: $\frac{25}{100} = \frac{25 \div 25}{100 \div 25} = \frac{1}{4}$

Write each decimal as a fraction in simplest form.

1. 0.65
Think: 65 **hundredths**
Write: $\frac{65}{100}$
Simplify: $\frac{65}{100} = \frac{65 \div 5}{100 \div 5} = \frac{13}{20}$

2. 0.6
Think: **6 tenths**
Write: $\frac{6}{10}$
Simplify: $\frac{6}{10} = \frac{6 \div 2}{10 \div 2} = \frac{3}{5}$

3. 0.86 $\frac{43}{50}$ 4. 0.57 $\frac{57}{100}$ 5. 0.5 $\frac{1}{2}$ 6. 0.68 $\frac{17}{25}$

7. 0.25 $\frac{1}{4}$ 8. 0.15 $\frac{3}{20}$ 9. 0.40 $\frac{2}{5}$ 10. 0.9 $\frac{9}{10}$

11. 0.33 $\frac{33}{100}$ 12. 0.10 $\frac{1}{10}$ 13. 0.75 $\frac{3}{4}$ 14. 0.98 $\frac{49}{50}$

15. 0.20 $\frac{1}{5}$ 16. 0.50 $\frac{1}{2}$ 17. 0.12 $\frac{3}{25}$ 18. 0.78 $\frac{39}{50}$

19. 0.4 $\frac{2}{5}$ 20. 0.70 $\frac{7}{10}$ 21. 0.05 $\frac{1}{20}$ 22. 0.65 $\frac{13}{20}$

23. 0.3 $\frac{3}{10}$ 24. 0.11 $\frac{11}{100}$

Grade 5 28 Chapter 9

Skills Practice (p. 29) OL

9–5 Name ________ Date ________

Skills Practice

Decimals and Fractions

Chapter Resources

Write each decimal as a fraction in simplest form.

1. 0.3 $\frac{3}{10}$ 2. 0.49 $\frac{49}{100}$ 3. 0.7 $\frac{7}{10}$ 4. 0.50 $\frac{1}{2}$

5. 0.94 $\frac{47}{50}$ 6. 0.80 $\frac{4}{5}$ 7. 0.72 $\frac{18}{25}$ 8. 0.2 $\frac{1}{5}$

9. 0.55 $\frac{11}{20}$ 10. 0.1 $\frac{1}{10}$ 11. 0.25 $\frac{1}{4}$ 12. 0.03 $\frac{3}{100}$

13. 0.77 $\frac{77}{100}$ 14. 0.6 $\frac{3}{5}$ 15. 0.26 $\frac{13}{50}$ 16. 0.99 $\frac{99}{100}$

17. 0.36 $\frac{9}{25}$ 18. 0.75 $\frac{3}{4}$ 19. 0.70 $\frac{7}{10}$ 20. 0.4 $\frac{2}{5}$

Write each decimal as a mixed number in simplest form.

21. 8.9 $8\frac{9}{10}$ 22. 12.1 $12\frac{1}{10}$ 23. 14.5 $14\frac{1}{2}$ 24. 17.03 $17\frac{3}{100}$

25. 9.35 $9\frac{7}{20}$ 26. 42.96 $42\frac{24}{25}$ 27. 7.425 $7\frac{17}{40}$ 28. 50.60 $50\frac{3}{5}$

29. 8.43 $8\frac{43}{100}$ 30. 3.25 $3\frac{1}{4}$ 31. 2.25 $2\frac{1}{4}$ 32. 1.33 $1\frac{33}{100}$

33. 4.10 $4\frac{1}{10}$ 34. 7.75 $7\frac{3}{4}$ 35. 8.60 $8\frac{3}{5}$ 36. 16.03 $16\frac{3}{100}$

Solve.

37. The largest butterfly in the world is found in Papua, New Guinea. The female of the species weighs about 0.9 ounce. Use a fraction to write the female's weight.
$\frac{9}{10}$ ounce

38. The shortest recorded fish is the dwarf goby found in the Indo-Pacific. The female of this species is about thirty-five hundredths inch long. Use a decimal to write the female's length.
0.35 inch

Grade 5 29 Chapter 9

9-5 Decimals and Fractions

1 Introduce

Activity Choice 1 • Hands-On

- Have pairs of students draw a fraction model on a sheet of paper. Have all the pairs order themselves from least to greatest around the room.
- Write 0.75 on a sheet of paper. **Where can we place 0.75 to order it with your fractions?** Allow time for discussion.
- Lead students to see that 0.75 is 75 hundredths or $\frac{75}{100}$. **What is $\frac{75}{100}$ in simplest form?** $\frac{3}{4}$
- Have students draw a model of 0.75.
- Now have students find a place for 0.75 among them.

Activity Choice 2 • Literature

Introduce the lesson with *Henry Hikes to Fitchburg* by D.B. Johnson. For a related math activity, see p. TR50.

2 Teach

Scaffolding Questions

Write 0.25 on the board.

- **What is the name of 0.25?** twenty-five hundredths
- **How do you write this as a fraction?** $\frac{25}{100}$
- **What is the GCF of 25 and 100?** 25
- **What is $\frac{25}{100}$ in simplest form?** $\frac{1}{4}$

GET READY to Learn

Have students open their books and read the information in **Get Ready to Learn.** Review **decimal** and **fraction**. As a class, work through **Examples 1–3**.

Write a Decimal as a Fraction

Example 2 Be sure that students understand that 0.8 means 8 tenths and 0.75 means 75 hundredths. Encourage students to use decimal models.

ADDITIONAL EXAMPLES

1. A cashier weighs two apples. The scale reads 0.35 pound. Write the weight of the apples as a fraction in simplest form. $\frac{7}{20}$ pound
2. Write 0.2 as a fraction in simplest form. $\frac{1}{5}$
3. Write 0.003 as a fraction in simplest form. $\frac{3}{1,000}$

CHECK What You Know

As a class, have students complete Exercises 1–8 in **Check What You Know** as you observe their work.

Exercise 8 Assess student comprehension before assigning practice exercises.

BL Alternate Teaching Strategy

If students have trouble writing decimals as fractions in simplest form...

Then use one of these reteach options:

1. CRM **Daily Reteach Worksheet** (p. 28)
2. Have students create study strips. Have them write frequently used decimals from 0.1 to 0.9 and the fraction equivalents on a strip of paper. They can laminate the strip and use it as a bookmark.

$0.1 = \frac{1}{10}$	$0.6 = \frac{3}{5}$
$0.2 = \frac{1}{5}$	$0.7 = \frac{7}{10}$
$0.25 = \frac{1}{4}$	$0.75 = \frac{3}{4}$
$0.3 = \frac{3}{10}$	$0.8 = \frac{4}{5}$
$0.4 = \frac{2}{5}$	$0.9 = \frac{9}{10}$
$0.5 = \frac{1}{2}$	

COMMON ERROR!

Exercise 25 Remind students that a dollar is equivalent to 100 pennies.

Remember

Use the place value of the right most digit in the decimal as the denominator.

EXAMPLE Write a Decimal as a Fraction

2 **Write 0.8 as a fraction in simplest form.**

Step 1 Shade a model of 0.8.

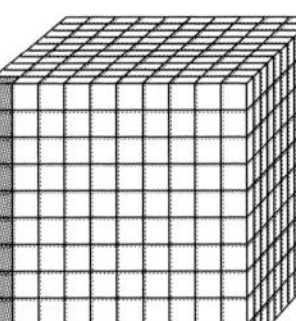

Step 2 Write a fraction with 10 as the denominator.

$0.8 = \frac{8}{10}$

Step 3 If necessary, simplify the fraction.

$\frac{8}{10} = \frac{8 \div 2}{10 \div 2}$ Divide by the GCF, 2.

$= \frac{4}{5}$ Simplify.

EXAMPLE Write a Decimal as a Fraction

3 **Write 0.009 as a fraction in simplest form.**

Shade a model of 0.009.

Write a fraction with 1,000 as the denominator.

$0.009 = \frac{9}{1,000}$ $\frac{9}{1,000}$ is in simplest form.

CHECK What You Know

Write each decimal or decimal model as a fraction in simplest form. See Examples 1–3 (pp. 391–392)

1. 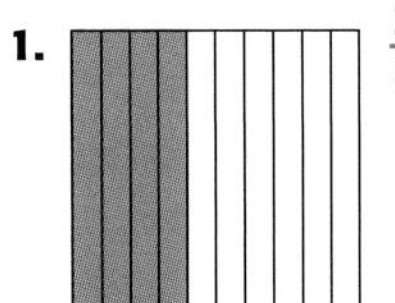 $\frac{2}{5}$

2. 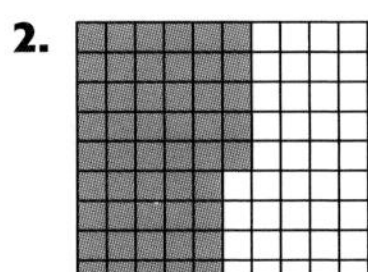 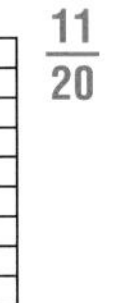 $\frac{11}{20}$

3. 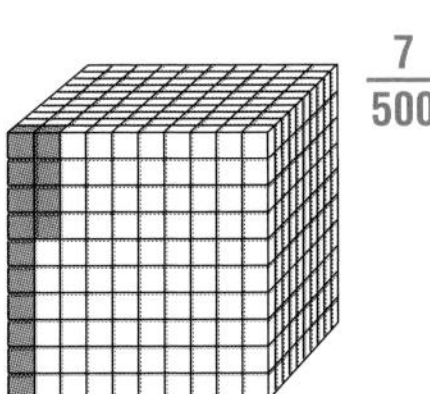 $\frac{7}{500}$

4. 0.6 $\frac{3}{5}$

5. 0.17 $\frac{17}{100}$

6. 0.125 $\frac{1}{8}$

7. It rained 0.68 inch last night. What fraction of an inch did it rain? Write in simplest form. $\frac{17}{25}$ in.

8. Talk About It How would you write a decimal as a fraction? Provide an example. See Ch. 9 Answer Appendix.

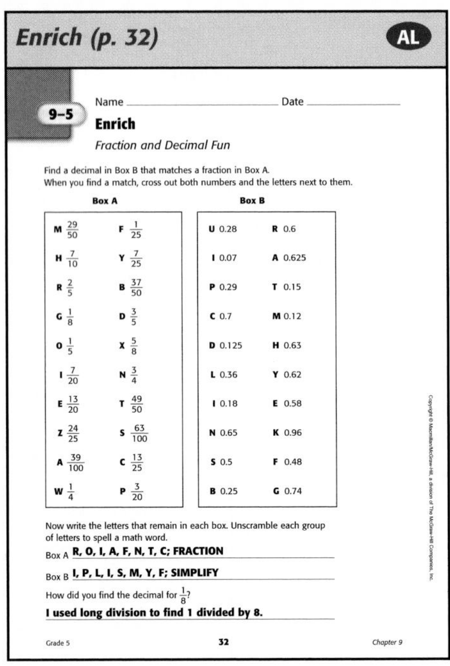

Enrich (p. 32) AL

9–5 Name ______ Date ______

Enrich

Fraction and Decimal Fun

Find a decimal in Box B that matches a fraction in Box A. When you find a match, cross out both numbers and the letters next to them.

Box A		Box B	
M $\frac{29}{50}$	F $\frac{1}{25}$	U 0.28	R 0.6
H $\frac{7}{10}$	Y $\frac{7}{25}$	I 0.07	A 0.625
R $\frac{2}{5}$	B $\frac{37}{50}$	P 0.29	T 0.15
G $\frac{1}{8}$	D $\frac{3}{5}$	C 0.7	M 0.12
O $\frac{1}{5}$	X $\frac{5}{8}$	D 0.125	H 0.63
I $\frac{7}{20}$	N $\frac{3}{4}$	L 0.36	Y 0.62
E $\frac{13}{20}$	T $\frac{49}{50}$	I 0.18	E 0.58
Z $\frac{24}{25}$	S $\frac{63}{100}$	N 0.65	K 0.96
A $\frac{39}{100}$	C $\frac{13}{25}$	S 0.5	F 0.48
W $\frac{1}{4}$	P $\frac{3}{20}$	B 0.25	G 0.74

Now write the letters that remain in each box. Unscramble each group of letters to spell a math word.

Box A **R, O, I, A, F, N, T, C; FRACTION**

Box B **I, P, L, I, S, M, Y, F; SIMPLIFY**

How did you find the decimal for $\frac{1}{8}$?

I used long division to find 1 divided by 8.

Grade 5 32 Chapter 9

Practice and Problem Solving

See page R25.

Write each decimal or decimal model as a fraction in simplest form.
See Examples 1–3 (pp. 391–392)

9. 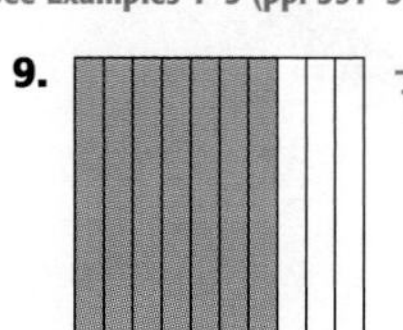 $\frac{7}{10}$

10. 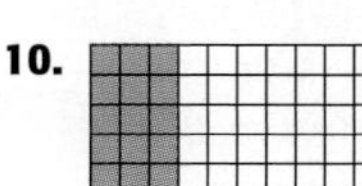  $\frac{1}{4}$

11. 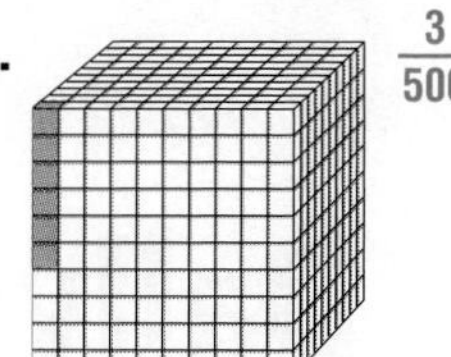 $\frac{3}{500}$

12. 0.9 $\frac{9}{10}$ **13.** 0.2 $\frac{1}{5}$ **14.** 0.5 $\frac{1}{2}$ **15.** 0.1 $\frac{1}{10}$

16. 0.65 $\frac{13}{20}$ **17.** 0.87 $\frac{87}{100}$ **18.** 0.45 $\frac{9}{20}$ **19.** 0.06 $\frac{3}{50}$

20. 0.875 $\frac{7}{8}$ **21.** 0.255 $\frac{51}{200}$ **22.** 0.045 $\frac{9}{200}$ **23.** 0.008 $\frac{1}{125}$

24. A three-toed sloth can travel at a rate of 0.07 mile per hour. Write 0.07 as a fraction in simplest form. $\frac{7}{100}$

25. What fraction of a dollar is a penny, a nickel, a dime, a quarter, and a half dollar? Write each in simplest form. See margin.

Real-World PROBLEM SOLVING

Science The *radius* of a planet is the distance from the planet's center to its surface. The table compares the radius of three planets in the solar system to the radius of Earth.

Comparing a Planet's Radius with Earth's

Planet	Radius (in Earth radii)
Mercury	0.38 × Earth
Venus	0.95 × Earth
Earth	1 × Earth
Mars	0.53 × Earth

What fraction times Earth's radius is the radius of each planet? Write in simplest form.

26. Mercury $\frac{19}{50}$

27. Venus $\frac{19}{20}$

28. Mars $\frac{53}{100}$

H.O.T. Problems

29–30. See Ch. 9 Answer Appendix.

29. OPEN ENDED Write a real-world problem that relates a decimal to a fraction between $\frac{30}{100}$ and $\frac{40}{100}$.

30. **WRITING IN ▶MATH** Explain why 0.08 is not equal to $\frac{8}{10}$.

Additional Answer

25. penny: $\frac{1}{100}$;

nickel: $\frac{1}{20}$; dime: $\frac{1}{10}$;

quarter: $\frac{1}{4}$;

half-dollar: $\frac{1}{2}$

Homework Practice (p. 30) OL

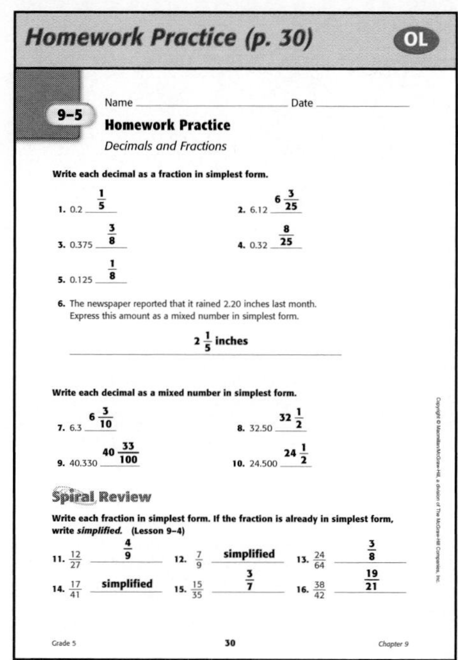

9-5 Name ____ Date ____

Homework Practice

Decimals and Fractions

Write each decimal as a fraction in simplest form.

1. 0.2 $\frac{1}{5}$ 2. 6.12 $6\frac{3}{25}$

3. 0.375 $\frac{3}{8}$ 4. 0.32 $\frac{8}{25}$

5. 0.125 $\frac{1}{8}$

6. The newspaper reported that it rained 2.20 inches last month. Express this amount as a mixed number in simplest form.

$2\frac{1}{5}$ inches

Write each decimal as a mixed number in simplest form.

7. 6.3 $6\frac{3}{10}$ 8. 32.50 $32\frac{1}{2}$

9. 40.330 $40\frac{33}{100}$ 10. 24.500 $24\frac{1}{2}$

Spiral Review

Write each fraction in simplest form. If the fraction is already in simplest form, write *simplified*. (Lesson 9-4)

11. $\frac{12}{27}$ $\frac{4}{9}$ 12. $\frac{7}{9}$ simplified 13. $\frac{24}{64}$ $\frac{3}{8}$

14. $\frac{17}{41}$ simplified 15. $\frac{15}{35}$ $\frac{3}{7}$ 16. $\frac{38}{42}$ $\frac{19}{21}$

Grade 5 30 Chapter 9

3 Practice

Differentiate practice using these leveled assignments for Exercises 9–30.

Level	Assignment
BL Below/ Approaching Level	9-15, 18, 27
OL On Level	9–22, 27–30
AL Above/Beyond Level	12–28 even, 29–30

Have students discuss and complete the Higher Order Thinking problems. For Exercise 29, tell students that they may want to simplify the fractions before they write their word problem.

WRITING IN ▶MATH Have students complete Exercise 30 in their Math Journals. You may choose to use this exercise as an optional formative assessment.

4 Assess

Formative Assessment

Write 0.8 and 0.08 on the board.

- **What is 0.8 written as a fraction in simplest form?** $\frac{4}{5}$ **How did you find the simplest form of $\frac{8}{10}$?** Sample answer: Divide the numerator and denominator by the GCF.
- **What is 0.08 written as a fraction in simplest form?** $\frac{2}{25}$ **How did you find the simplest form of $\frac{8}{100}$?** Sample answer: Divide the numerator and denominator by the GCF.

Quick Check **Are students continuing to struggle with writing decimals as fractions?**

If Yes → Small Group Options (p. 391B)
Strategic Intervention Guide (p. 112)

If No → Independent Work Options (p. 391B)
CRM Skills Practice Worksheet (p. 29)
CRM Enrich Worksheet (p. 32)

Ticket Out the Door On a piece of paper, have students write 0.5, 0.05, and 0.005 as fractions in simplest form and hand it to you as they leave the room. $\frac{1}{2}$, $\frac{1}{20}$, $\frac{1}{200}$

9-6 Problem-Solving Strategy
Look for a Pattern

Lesson Planner

Objective

Solve problems by looking for a pattern.

Resources

Materials: calculator, blocks

Literature Connection: *Polar Bear Math: Learning About Fractions from Klondike and Snow* by Ann Whitehead Nagda and Cindy Bickel

Teacher Technology

TeacherWorks • Interactive Classroom

Real-World Problem Solving Library
Math and Science: Nature's Delicate Balance

Use these leveled books to reinforce and extend problem-solving skills and strategies.

Leveled for:

- OL On Level
- ELL Sheltered English
- SP Spanish

For additional support, see the Real-World Problem Solving Teacher Guide.

Daily Routine

Use these suggestions before beginning the lesson on p. 394.

5-Minute Check

(Reviews Lesson 9-5)

Write each decimal as a fraction in simplest form.

1. 0.6 $\frac{3}{5}$ **2.** 0.75 $\frac{3}{4}$

3. 0.15 $\frac{3}{20}$ **4.** 0.48 $\frac{12}{25}$

Problem of the Day

Miss Hernandez had a hole in her purse. She lost 1 dime and 1 quarter every day. At the end of 2 weeks, she has 1 dime left. How much money did she begin with? $5

Differentiated Instruction

Small Group Options

LOGICAL, SOCIAL

Option 1 Below Level BL

Materials: chart paper, markers

- Assign partners.
- Copy this problem on the chart paper:

  Copy and complete this pattern: 2, 8, 6, 12, 10, 16, 14, 20, 18, ■, ■, ■. 24, 22, 28
- Upon completion, the students should discuss with their partner how they got their answer. +6, − 2

LINGUISTIC, AUDITORY

Option 2 English Language Learners ELL

Materials: index cards with the word "and" written on them
Core Vocabulary: and, before, after
Common Use Verb: tear
Talk Math: This strategy helps students find a pattern when reading whole numbers, decimals and fractions.

- Pass out cards. Write "and" while you display these numbers on large index cards: $3\frac{1}{2}$, 1.35, $45\frac{5}{8}$, $12\frac{1}{3}$, $26\frac{2}{3}$, 34.136, 2.13
- Say the number. Tear it apart on the decimal point or between the whole number and the fraction
- Read with the torn card on either side of the "and".
- Model the difference between a whole number before "and" and a fraction or decimal after it.
- Repeat for remaining numbers, having students raise up their card when they hear and say "and."
- Discuss the pattern of using "and" to separate decimals and fractions.

Independent Work Options

LINGUISTIC

Option 1 Early Finishers OL AL

Materials: index cards

- Give each student five index cards. Have each student write a pattern on the front of each card and the rule for the pattern on the back.
- Have the students exchange cards and find the next three numbers for each pattern they receive. Have them check their answers with the rule on the back.

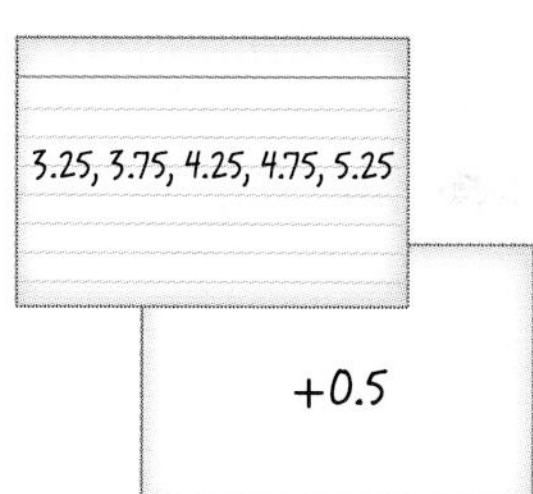

Option 2 Student Technology

macmillanmh.com

Personal Tutor • Extra Examples

Option 3 Learning Station: Music (p. 370H)

Direct students to the Music Learning Station for opportunities to explore and extend the lesson concept.

9-6 Problem-Solving Strategy

1 Introduce

Activity Choice 1 • Review

- Write the following problem on the board.

  During the first hour, 5 people entered a store. In the second hour, twice as many people came and no one left. In the third hour, 3 times as many people came as were in the store during the second hour and 20 people left. How many customers were in the store at the end of the third hour? 25 people

- **Which strategy would you use to solve this problem?** *make a list or table*

Activity Choice 2 • Literature

Introduce the lesson with *Polar Bear Math: Learning About Fractions from Klondike and Snow* by Ann Whitehead Nagda and Cindy Bickel. For a related math activity, see p. TR51.

2 Teach

Have students read the problem. Guide them through the problem-solving steps.

Understand Using the questions, review what students know and need to find.

Plan Have them discuss their strategy.

Solve Guide students to use the *look for a pattern* strategy to solve the problem.

- **How many miles did Shawna run the first day? How many miles did Shawna run the second day?** 1.25; 1.85
- **How many more miles did she run the second day than the first?** 0.6 **How many more miles did Shawna run each day than the day before?** 0.6
- **How many miles did she run on the sixth day?** 4.25

Check Have students look back at the problem to make sure that the answer fits the facts given.

- **How does subtracting help you to check?** subtraction undoes addition

9-6 Problem-Solving Strategy

MAIN IDEA I will solve problems by looking for a pattern.

Shawna is training to run in a half-marathon. A half-marathon is about 13 miles. On her first day of training, she ran 1.25 miles. Then she increased her distance each day according to a pattern. Here are the number of miles Shawna ran the first five days of training.

1.25, 1.85, 2.45, 3.05, 3.65

Based on her pattern, how many miles will Shawna run on the sixth day?

Understand

What facts do you know?

- We know how many miles Shawna ran each day for five days.
- She increased the distance she ran each day according to a pattern.

What do you need to find?

- The number of miles Shawna will run on the sixth day.

Plan

One way to solve the problem is by looking for a pattern among the number of miles she ran each day for five days. Then extend the pattern to find the number of miles she will run on the sixth day.

Solve

Use your plan to solve the problem.

Find the amounts by which Shawna increased her distances.

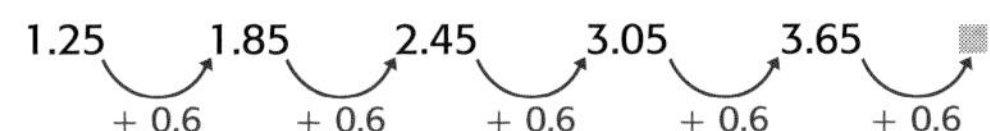

Shawna increases her distance by 0.6 mile each day. Add 0.6 to 3.65 to find the number of miles Shawna will run on the sixth day.

$$3.65 + 0.6 = 4.25$$

So, on the sixth day, she will run 4.25 miles.

Check

Look back. $4.25 - 0.6 = 3.65$. So, the answer is correct. ✓

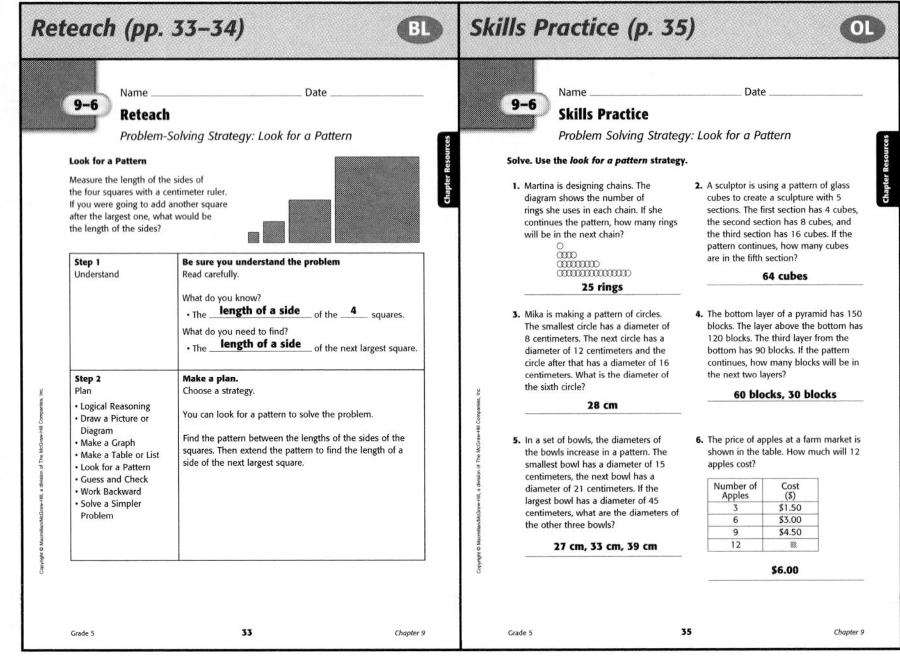

Reteach (pp. 33–34) BL

9–6 Name ______ Date ______

Reteach

Problem-Solving Strategy: Look for a Pattern

Look for a Pattern

Measure the length of the sides of the four squares with a centimeter ruler. If you were going to add another square after the largest one, what would be the length of the sides?

Step 1 Understand	**Be sure you understand the problem** Read carefully. What do you know? • The **length of a side** of the **4** squares. What do you need to find? • The **length of a side** of the next largest square.
Step 2 Plan • Logical Reasoning • Draw a Picture or Diagram • Make a Graph • Make a Table or List • Look for a Pattern • Guess and Check • Work Backward • Solve a Simpler Problem	**Make a plan.** Choose a strategy. You can look for a pattern to solve the problem. Find the pattern between the lengths of the sides of the squares. Then extend the pattern to find the length of a side of the next largest square.

Chapter Resources

Grade 5 33 Chapter 9

Skills Practice (p. 35) OL

9–6 Name ______ Date ______

Skills Practice

Problem Solving Strategy: Look for a Pattern

Solve. Use the *look for a pattern* strategy.

1. Martina is designing chains. The diagram shows the number of rings she uses in each chain. If she continues the pattern, how many rings will be in the next chain? **25 rings**
2. A sculptor is using a pattern of glass cubes to create a sculpture with 5 sections. The first section has 4 cubes, the second section has 8 cubes, and the third section has 16 cubes. If the pattern continues, how many cubes are in the fifth section? **64 cubes**
3. Mika is making a pattern of circles. The smallest circle has a diameter of 8 centimeters. The next circle has a diameter of 12 centimeters and the circle after that has a diameter of 16 centimeters. What is the diameter of the sixth circle? **28 cm**
4. The bottom layer of a pyramid has 150 blocks. The layer above the bottom has 120 blocks. The third layer from the bottom has 90 blocks. If the pattern continues, how many blocks will be in the next two layers? **60 blocks, 30 blocks**
5. In a set of bowls, the diameters of the bowls increase in a pattern. The smallest bowl has a diameter of 15 centimeters, the next bowl has a diameter of 21 centimeters. If the largest bowl has a diameter of 45 centimeters, what are the diameters of the other three bowls? **27 cm, 33 cm, 39 cm**
6. The price of apples at a farm market is shown in the table. How much will 12 apples cost?

Number of Apples	Cost ($)
3	$1.50
6	$3.00
9	$4.50
12	■

$6.00

Chapter Resources

Grade 5 35 Chapter 9

4. Sample answer: No, there isn't always a pattern when solving a problem.

ANALYZE the Strategy

Refer to the problem on the previous page.

1. How many miles will Shawna run on day seven if she wants to double her normal increase? 5.45 miles
2. Explain why Shawna cannot continue her pattern forever. See Ch. 9 Answer Appendix.

3. Sample answer: Use this strategy when the change between events is the same.

3. Explain when to use the *look for a pattern* strategy to solve a problem.
4. Can you always use the *look for a pattern* strategy when solving a problem?

PRACTICE the Strategy

Solve. Use the *look for a pattern* strategy.

5. Draw the next two figures in the pattern. See Ch. 9 Answer Appendix.

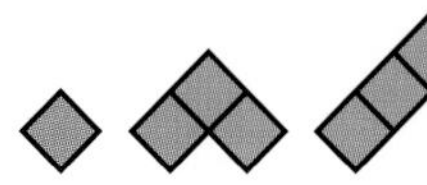

6. Stefano is buying a few pencils. The table shows the price of different numbers of pencils.

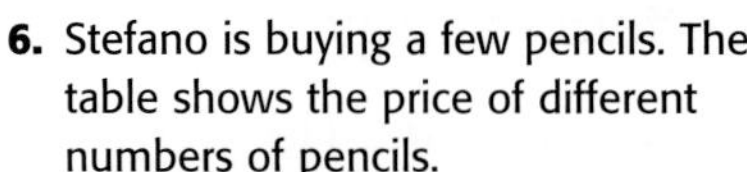

Number of Pencils	Price
10	$2.00
15	$3.00
20	$4.00
25	$5.00
30	$6.00

What is the relationship between the number of pencils and price? See Ch. 9 Answer Appendix.

7. **Measurement** Cheryl is filling a pool. She measures the depth in feet every 5 minutes. Her measurements are 2.5, 3.6, 4.7, and 5.8. If this pattern continues, how deep will the water be the next time she measures? 6.9 feet

For Exercises 8–10, use the following information.

Gavin rode his bike for a longer distance each day while training. Here is his record of the number of miles he rode.

Mon	Tues	Wed	Thurs	Fri
3.5 mi	4.2 mi	5.0 mi	■	6.9 mi

8. Based on Gavin's pattern, how long did he ride on Thursday? 5.9 mi
9. **Algebra** If the pattern continues, how far will Gavin ride on Saturday? 8.0 mi

10–12. See Ch. 9 Answer Appendix

10. Explain how to find the number of miles Gavin will ride on Sunday, if the pattern continues.
11. The Fibonacci sequence is a famous pattern of numbers. The first seven numbers in the Fibonacci sequence are 1, 1, 2, 3, 5, 8, and 13. Find the next three numbers. Explain the pattern.
12. WRITING IN MATH Write a real-world problem that uses the *look for a pattern* strategy. Use the pattern below.

    2.45, 2.8, 3.15, 3.5, . . .

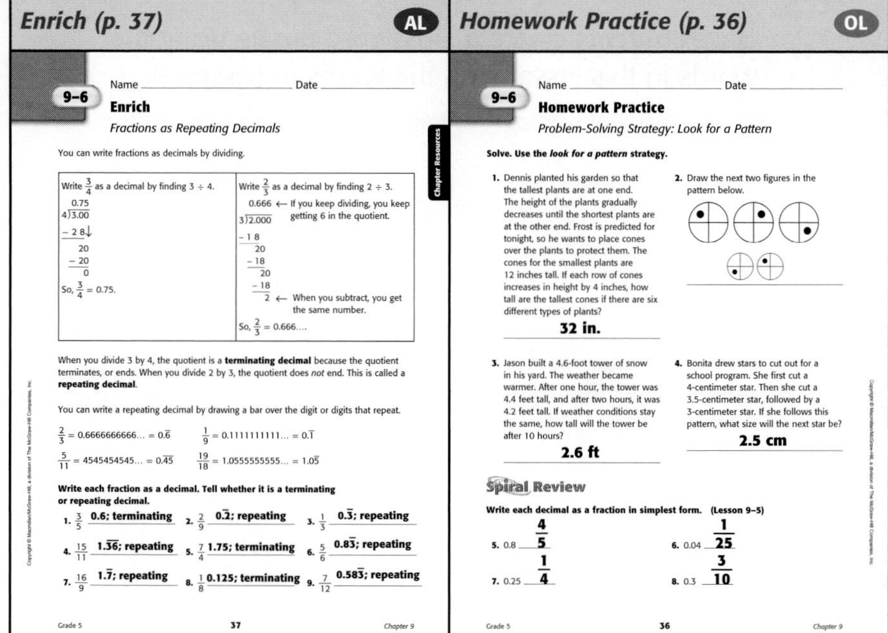

Enrich (p. 37) AL

9–6 Name ________ Date ________

Enrich

Fractions as Repeating Decimals

You can write fractions as decimals by dividing.

Write $\frac{3}{4}$ as a decimal by finding 3 ÷ 4.	Write $\frac{2}{3}$ as a decimal by finding 2 ÷ 3.
$4\overline{)3.00}$ = 0.75; − 28, 20, − 20, 0. So, $\frac{3}{4}$ = 0.75.	$3\overline{)2.000}$ = 0.666 ← If you keep dividing, you keep getting 6 in the quotient. − 18, 20, − 18, 20, − 18, 2 ← When you subtract, you get the same number. So, $\frac{2}{3}$ = 0.666....

When you divide 3 by 4, the quotient is a **terminating decimal** because the quotient terminates, or ends. When you divide 2 by 3, the quotient does *not* end. This is called a **repeating decimal**.

You can write a repeating decimal by drawing a bar over the digit or digits that repeat.

$\frac{2}{3} = 0.6666666666... = 0.\overline{6}$ $\frac{1}{9} = 0.1111111111... = 0.\overline{1}$

$\frac{5}{11} = 4545454545... = 0.\overline{45}$ $\frac{19}{18} = 1.0555555555... = 1.0\overline{5}$

Write each fraction as a decimal. Tell whether it is a terminating or repeating decimal.

1. $\frac{3}{5}$ **0.6; terminating**
2. $\frac{2}{9}$ **$0.\overline{2}$; repeating**
3. $\frac{1}{3}$ **$0.\overline{3}$; repeating**
4. $\frac{15}{11}$ **$1.\overline{36}$; repeating**
5. $\frac{7}{4}$ **1.75; terminating**
6. $\frac{5}{6}$ **$0.8\overline{3}$; repeating**
7. $\frac{16}{9}$ **$1.\overline{7}$; repeating**
8. $\frac{1}{8}$ **0.125; terminating**
9. $\frac{7}{12}$ **$0.58\overline{3}$; repeating**

Grade 5 37 Chapter 9

Homework Practice (p. 36) OL

9–6 Name ________ Date ________

Homework Practice

Problem-Solving Strategy: Look for a Pattern

Solve. Use the *look for a pattern* strategy.

1. Dennis planted his garden so that the tallest plants are at one end. The height of the plants gradually decreases until the shortest plants are at the other end. Frost is predicted for tonight, so he wants to place cones over the plants to protect them. The cones for the smallest plants are 12 inches tall. If each row of cones increases in height by 4 inches, how tall are the tallest cones if there are six different types of plants? **32 in.**
2. Draw the next two figures in the pattern below.
3. Jason built a 4.6-foot tower of snow in his yard. The weather became warmer. After one hour, the tower was 4.4 feet tall, and after two hours, it was 4.2 feet tall. If weather conditions stay the same, how tall will the tower be after 10 hours? **2.6 ft**
4. Bonita drew stars to cut out for a school program. She first cut a 4-centimeter star. Then she cut a 3.5-centimeter star, followed by a 3-centimeter star. If she follows this pattern, what size will the next star be? **2.5 cm**

Spiral Review

Write each decimal as a fraction in simplest form. (Lesson 9–5)

5. 0.8 **$\frac{4}{5}$**
6. 0.04 **$\frac{1}{25}$**
7. 0.25 **$\frac{1}{4}$**
8. 0.3 **$\frac{3}{10}$**

Grade 5 36 Chapter 9

Analyze the Strategy Use Exercises 1–4 to analyze and discuss the problem-solving strategy.

BL Alternate Teaching Strategy

If students have trouble finding the pattern…

Then use one of these reteach options:

1 CRM **Daily Reteach Worksheet** (p. 33)

2 Have them begin with the last number in the sequence and subtract.

- **What is 3.65 minus 3.05?** 0.6
- **What is 3.05 minus 2.45?** 0.6

3 Practice

Using the Exercises

Exercises 6 Have students use a calculator to help them solve this problem.

Exercise 5 Suggest students use blocks to model this pattern.

4 Assess

Formative Assessment

- **How can you tell if the pattern is addition?** The numbers increase.
- **How can you tell if the pattern is subtraction?** The numbers decrease.

Quick Check **Are students continuing to struggle with looking for a pattern?**

If Yes → Small Group Options (p. 394B)
Strategic Intervention Guide (p. 94)

If No → Independent Work Options (p. 394B)
CRM Skills Practice Worksheet (p. 35)
CRM Enrich Worksheet (p. 37)

COMMON ERROR!

Exercises 8 and 9 Students may have difficulty finding the pattern because of the decimals. Review how to subtract decimals.

LESSON 9-7

Multiples

Lesson Planner

Objective

Identify common multiples of a set of whole numbers.

Vocabulary

multiple, common multiple, least common multiple (LCM)

Resources

Materials: hundred chart, crayons or markers, number lines
Manipulatives: connecting cubes
Literature Connection: *Marvelous Multiplication: Games and Activities that Make Math Easy and Fun* by Lynette Long
Teacher Technology
TeacherWorks • Interactive Classroom

Focus on Math Background

To find multiples of a number, students find the product of the number and other factors. If two or more numbers share the same nonzero multiple, that multiple is called a common multiple of the numbers. Students can identify the least common multiple (LCM), or the least number that is a multiple of two or more numbers, in two ways:

- List several multiples of each number n, starting with $1 \times n$, $2 \times n$, etc., and find the least multiple that they share.
- Write the prime factorization of each number, multiply each factor the greatest number of times it occurs in any of the factorizations. For example, to find the LCM of 9 and 15, write the prime factorizations of both numbers: $9 = 3 \times 3$; $15 = 3 \times 5$. 9 has two 3s and 15 only has one. 15 has one 5 and 9 has none. So the LCM is two 3s times one 5, i.e., $3 \times 3 \times 5 = 45$.

Daily Routine

Use these suggestions before beginning the lesson on p. 396.

5-Minute Check

(Reviews Lesson 9-6)

Solve. Use the *look for a pattern* strategy.

Azibo starts with $22 in a savings account. He makes the same deposit every week. After the first week, his account has $24.50. After the second, $27.00. After the third, $29.50, and after the fourth week, he has $32.00 in his account. How much does he have after 5 weeks? $34.50

Problem of the Day

Suppose this pattern continues:

FRIDAYFRIDAYFRIDAYFRIDAYFRIDAY

What will be the letter in the 35th position? A

Building Math Vocabulary

Write the lesson vocabulary words and their definitions on the board.

Have students create a crossword puzzle using the words in this lesson and the words in Lesson 9.

Differentiated Instruction

Small Group Options

Option 1 Below Level BL

LOGICAL

Materials: paper and pencil

- Ask students to revisit Exercise 9 from this lesson.
- *Inez needs to pull the weeds from her garden. Would it be better for her to do this every 6th or 7th day? She does not want to increase the number of days she spends in the garden. Make a chart if needed to help you solve this problem.* Weeding will work best every 6 days.

Watering	0, 2, 4, 6, 8, 10, 12, 14, 16, 18, 20, 22, 24, 26, 28, 30
Trims	0 15, 30
(6th day) Weeding	0 6, 12, 18, 24, 30
(7th day)	0 7, 14, 21, 28

Option 2 English Language Learners ELL

VISUAL, KINESTHETIC

Materials: multiplication tables, one per group; strips of colored transparency paper

Core Vocabulary: multiple, both

Common Use Verb: find

Do Math This strategy helps make the concept of putting fractions in the simplest form more concrete for students.

- Model how to use the multiplication table. Say: "Look at the row for 6. The numbers are 6, 12, 18, 24, and so on. These numbers are **multiples** of 6."
- Ask: "What are the first six **multiples** of 3?"
- Say: "Cover the **multiples** of 3 with a strip of transparency. Cover the **multiples** of 6 with another."

English Language Learners (p. 75) ELL

22 Name ______

Least Common Denominators

Roll a number cube four times to make two fractions.
Find the least common multiple (LCM) of the denominators.
Find the least common denominator (LCD).

NUMBERS	FIRST FRACTION	NUMBERS	SECOND FRACTION	LCM	LCD
__ __	—	__ __	—		
__ __	—	__ __	—		
__ __	—	__ __	—		
__ __	—	__ __	—		
__ __	—	__ __	—		
__ __	—	__ __	—		
__ __	—	__ __	—		
__ __	—	__ __	—		
__ __	—	__ __	—		

Check students' responses.

© Macmillan/McGraw-Hill

Common Multiples 75

Use this worksheet to provide additional support for English Language Learners.

Independent Work Options

Option 1 Early Finishers AL

LOGICAL

Materials: pencil and paper

- Ask students to solve this problem. *Large plastic cups are sold in packages of 20 and large foam dinner plates are sold in packages of 50. What is the least number of packages of plastic cups and packages of plates needed so the number of cups matches the number of plates?* 5 packages of cups and 2 packages of plates
- **How many people could eat and have a drink?** 100 **How is this related to the LCM?** 100 is the LCM of 20 and 50.

Option 2 Student Technology

Math Online macmillanmh.com

Personal Tutor • Extra Examples

 Math Adventures

Option 3 Learning Station: Writing (p. 370G)

Direct students to the Writing Learning Station for opportunities to explore and extend the lesson concept.

Option 4 Problem-Solving Practice

Reinforce problem-solving skills and strategies with the Problem-Solving Practice worksheet.

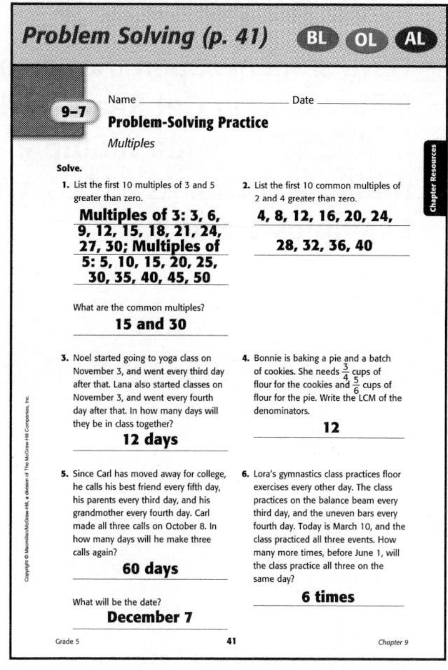

Problem Solving (p. 41) BL OL AL

Name ______ Date ______

9–7 **Problem-Solving Practice**

Multiples

Chapter Resources

Solve.

1. List the first 10 multiples of 3 and 5 greater than zero.
   Multiples of 3: 3, 6, 9, 12, 15, 18, 21, 24, 27, 30; Multiples of 5: 5, 10, 15, 20, 25, 30, 35, 40, 45, 50
   What are the common multiples?
   15 and 30
2. List the first 10 common multiples of 2 and 4 greater than zero.
   4, 8, 12, 16, 20, 24, 28, 32, 36, 40
3. Noel started going to yoga class on November 3, and went every third day after that. Lana also started classes on November 3, and went every fourth day after that. In how many days will they be in class together?
   12 days
4. Bonnie is baking a pie and a batch of cookies. She needs $\frac{3}{4}$ cups of flour for the cookies and $\frac{5}{6}$ cups of flour for the pie. Write the LCM of the denominators.
   12
5. Since Carl has moved away for college, he calls his best friend every fifth day, his parents every third day, and his grandmother every fourth day. Carl made all three calls on October 8. In how many days will he make three calls again?
   60 days
   What will be the date?
   December 7
6. Lora's gymnastics class practices floor exercises every other day. The class practices on the balance beam every third day, and the uneven bars every fourth day. Today is March 10, and the class practiced all three events. How many more times, before June 1, will the class practice all three on the same day?
   6 times

Copyright © Macmillan/McGraw-Hill, a division of The McGraw-Hill Companies, Inc.

Grade 5 41 Chapter 9

9-7 Multiples

1 Introduce

Activity Choice 1 • Hands-On

- Divide the class into teams of 6–8 to play *Zap*. Pick a number, such as 3.
- One team begins. A member recites the numbers 1, 2, *zap*. The next team member continues 4, 5, *zap*. Each time a student comes to a multiple of 3, he or she says *zap*.
- When a team member does not say *zap* for a multiple of 3, the play goes to the next team and you choose another number.

Activity Choice 2 • Literature

Introduce the lesson with *Marvelous Multiplication: Games and Activities that Make Math Easy and Fun* by Lynette Long. For a related math activity, see p. TR51.

2 Teach

Scaffolding Questions

Have one student skip count by 2s. Another student skip counts by 3s.

- **What multiples do 2 and 3 have in common?** 6, 12, 18, and so on
- **What multiples do 3 and 4 have in common?** 12, 24, 36, and so on
- **What is the least common multiple of 3 and 4? Explain.** 12; all other common multiples are greater than 12.

GET READY to Learn

Have students open their books and read the information in **Get Ready to Learn.** Introduce **multiple, common multiple** and **least common multiple (LCM)**. As a class, work through **Examples 1 and 2**.

9-7 Multiples

MAIN IDEA

I will identify common multiples of a set of whole numbers.

New Vocabulary

multiple

common multiple

least common multiple (LCM)

Math Online

macmillanmh.com

- Extra Examples
- Personal Tutor
- Self-Check Quiz

GET READY to Learn

Hands-On Mini Activity

A **multiple** of a number is the product of the number and any whole number. The first few multiples of 4 are 4, 8, 12, and 16.

1, 2. See students' work.

1. Use a hundreds chart to place a colored cube on the multiples of 4. Part of a hundreds chart is shown.

×	1	2	3	4	5	6	7	8	9	10
1	1	2	3	4	5	6	7	8	9	10
2	2	4	6	8	10	12	14	16	18	20
3	3	6	9	12	15	18	21	24	27	30
4	4	8	12	16	20	24	28	32	36	40

2. On the same chart, place a different colored cube on the multiples of 6.
3. List all the numbers that have two cubes. 12, 24, 36, 48, 60, 72, 84, 96
4. What is the least number that has two cubes? 12

In the Mini Activity, you found common multiples of 4 and 6. A whole number that is a multiple of two or more whole numbers is a **common multiple**.

EXAMPLE Find Common Multiples

1 List multiples to find the first two common multiples of 8 and 12.

multiples of 8: 8, 16, **24**, 32, 40, **48**, ... $8 \times 1, 8 \times 2, 8 \times 3, 8 \times 4, 8 \times 5, 8 \times 6...$

multiples of 12: 12, **24**, 36, **48**, 60, ... $12 \times 1, 12 \times 2, 12 \times 3, 12 \times 4, 12 \times 5, 12 \times 6, ...$

The first two common multiples of 8 and 12 are 24 and 48.

396 **Chapter 9** Use Factors and Multiples

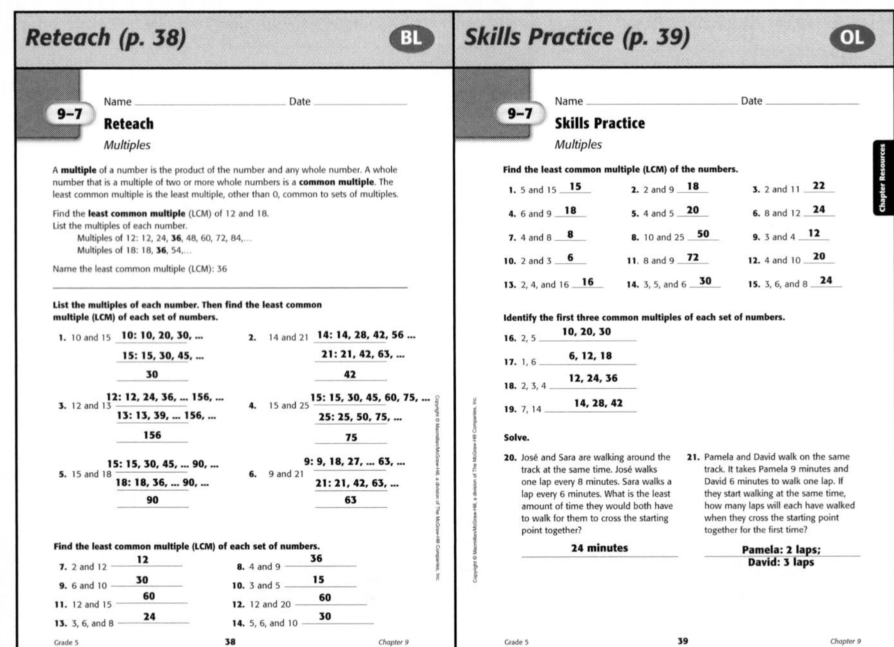

Reteach (p. 38) BL

9-7 Name ______ Date ______

Reteach

Multiples

A **multiple** of a number is the product of the number and any whole number. A whole number that is a multiple of two or more whole numbers is a **common multiple**. The least common multiple is the least multiple, other than 0, common to sets of multiples.

Find the **least common multiple** (LCM) of 12 and 18.
List the multiples of each number.
Multiples of 12: 12, 24, **36**, 48, 60, 72, 84,...
Multiples of 18: 18, **36**, 54,...

Name the least common multiple (LCM): 36

List the multiples of each number. Then find the least common multiple (LCM) of each set of numbers.

1. 10 and 15 **10: 10, 20, 30, ...** **15: 15, 30, 45, ...** **30**
2. 14 and 21 **14: 14, 28, 42, 56 ...** **21: 21, 42, 63, ...** **42**
3. 12 and 13 **12: 12, 24, 36, ... 156, ...** **13: 13, 39, ... 156, ...** **156**
4. 15 and 25 **15: 15, 30, 45, 60, 75, ...** **25: 25, 50, 75, ...** **75**
5. 15 and 18 **15: 15, 30, 45, ... 90, ...** **18: 18, 36, ... 90, ...** **90**
6. 9 and 21 **9: 9, 18, 27, ... 63, ...** **21: 21, 42, 63, ...** **63**

Find the least common multiple (LCM) of each set of numbers.

7. 2 and 12 **12**
8. 4 and 9 **36**
9. 6 and 10 **30**
10. 3 and 5 **15**
11. 12 and 15 **60**
12. 12 and 20 **60**
13. 3, 6, and 8 **24**
14. 5, 6, and 10 **30**

Grade 5 38 *Chapter 9*

Skills Practice (p. 39) OL

9-7 Name ______ Date ______

Skills Practice

Multiples

Find the least common multiple (LCM) of the numbers.

1. 5 and 15 **15**
2. 2 and 9 **18**
3. 2 and 11 **22**
4. 6 and 9 **18**
5. 4 and 5 **20**
6. 8 and 12 **24**
7. 4 and 8 **8**
8. 10 and 25 **50**
9. 3 and 4 **12**
10. 2 and 3 **6**
11. 8 and 9 **72**
12. 4 and 10 **20**
13. 2, 4, and 16 **16**
14. 3, 5, and 6 **30**
15. 3, 6, and 8 **24**

Identify the first three common multiples of each set of numbers.

16. 2, 5 **10, 20, 30**
17. 1, 6 **6, 12, 18**
18. 2, 3, 4 **12, 24, 36**
19. 7, 14 **14, 28, 42**

Solve.

20. José and Sara are walking around the track at the same time. José walks one lap every 8 minutes. Sara walks a lap every 6 minutes. What is the least amount of time they would both have to walk for them to cross the starting point together? **24 minutes**
21. Pamela and David walk on the same track. It takes Pamela 9 minutes and David 6 minutes to walk one lap. If they start walking at the same time, how many laps will each have walked when they cross the starting point together for the first time? **Pamela: 2 laps; David: 3 laps**

Grade 5 39 *Chapter 9*

Chapter Resources

The **least common multiple (LCM)** is the least multiple, other than 0, common to sets of multiples. In the Mini Activity, the LCM of 4 and 6 is 12.

Real-World EXAMPLE Find and Use the LCM

> **Remember**
> You can always find a common multiple by finding the product of the numbers. This does not always give the LCM. In Example 2, $2 \times 3 \times 4 = 24$ which is a multiple of all three numbers. But the LCM of 2, 3, and 4 is 12.

2 FOOD Ben's Burgers gives away a free order of fries every 2 days, a free milkshake every 3 days, and a free hamburger every 4 days. If they gave away all three items today, in how many days will they give away all three items again?

To solve, find the LCM of 2, 3 and 4.

multiples of 2: 2, 4, 6, 8, 10, **12** ... $2 \times 1, 2 \times 2, 2 \times 3, 2 \times 4, \ldots$

multiples of 3: 3, 6, 9, **12**, 15, 18... $3 \times 1, 3 \times 2, 3 \times 3, 3 \times 4, \ldots$

multiples of 4: 4, 8, **12**, 16, 20... $4 \times 1, 4 \times 2, 4 \times 3, 4 \times 4, \ldots$

Notice that 12 is the least common multiple of 2, 3, and 4. So, Ben's Burgers will give away all three items again in 12 days.

Draw a number line to check. Use F for fries, M for milkshake, and H for hamburger. You can see that the first day that all three items appear again, after today, is day 12. So, the answer is correct.

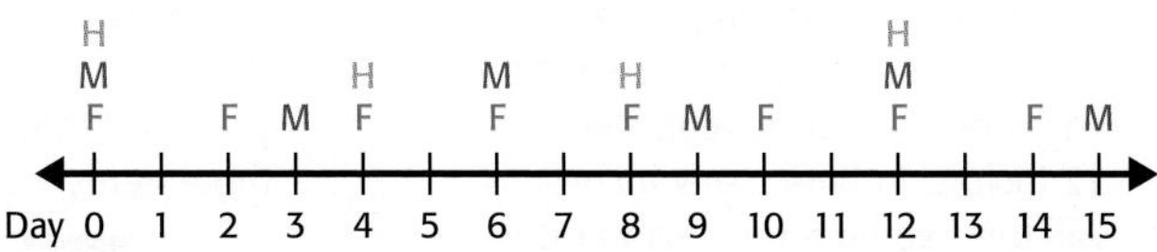

CHECK What You Know

List multiples to find the first two common multiples of each set of numbers. See Example 1 (p. 396)

1. 2 and 6 6, 12 **2.** 4 and 10 20, 40 **3.** 5, 6, and 10 30, 60 **4.** 3, 4, and 6 12, 24

Find the LCM of each set of numbers. Make a table or a number line.
See Example 2 (p. 397) 5–8. See students' work for tables and number lines.

5. 3 and 4 12 **6.** 2 and 7 14 **7.** 4, 5, and 10 20 **8.** 3, 6, and 7 42

9. Inez waters her plants every two days. She trims them every 15 days. She did both today. When will she do both again? 30 days

10. Talk About It When is the LCM of two numbers one of the numbers? Give an example. See margin.

Find and Use the LCM

Example 2 Students use number lines to find common multiples.

ADDITIONAL EXAMPLES

1 List multiples to find the first two common multiples of 6 and 10. 30, 60

2 Aaron has film studies every 4 days and math class every 5 days. If he had both classes today, in how many days will Aaron have both classes again? 20 days

CHECK What You Know

As a class, have students complete Exercises 1–10 in **Check What You Know** as you observe their work.

Exercise 10 Assess student comprehension before assigning practice exercises.

BL Alternate Teaching Strategy

If students have trouble finding common multiples...

Then use one of these reteach options:

1 CRM **Daily Reteach Worksheet** (p. 38)

2 On a number line, students circle the multiples of one number in one color and the multiples of the other in a different color. Point out to students that the colors overlap at the common multiples.

Additional Answer

10. Sample answer: When one number is a factor of the other number, the LCM is the greater number. For example, the LCM of 2 and 6 is 6.

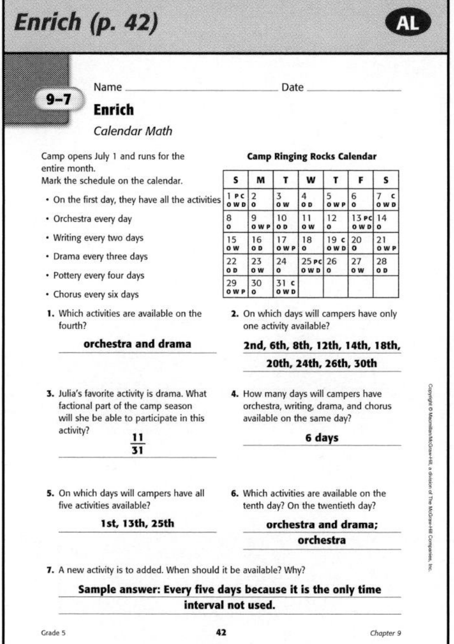
Enrich (p. 42) AL

9–7 Name ______ Date ______

Enrich

Calendar Math

Camp opens July 1 and runs for the entire month.
Mark the schedule on the calendar.

- On the first day, they have all the activities
- Orchestra every day
- Writing every two days
- Drama every three days
- Pottery every four days
- Chorus every six days

Camp Ringing Rocks Calendar

S	M	T	W	T	F	S
1 P C O W D	2 O	3 O W	4 O D	5 O W P	6 O	7 C O W D
8 O	9 O W P	10 O D	11 O W	12 O	13 P C O W D	14 O
15 O W	16 O D	17 O W P	18 O	19 C O W D	20 O	21 O W P
22 O D	23 O W	24 O	25 P C O W D	26 O	27 O W	28 O D
29 O W P	30 O	31 C O W D				

1. Which activities are available on the fourth?
orchestra and drama

2. On which days will campers have only one activity available?
2nd, 6th, 8th, 12th, 14th, 18th, 20th, 24th, 26th, 30th

3. Julia's favorite activity is drama. What factional part of the camp season will she be able to participate in this activity?
$\mathbf{\frac{11}{31}}$

4. How many days will campers have orchestra, writing, drama, and chorus available on the same day?
6 days

5. On which days will campers have all five activities available?
1st, 13th, 25th

6. Which activities are available on the tenth day? On the twentieth day?
orchestra and drama; orchestra

7. A new activity is to added. When should it be available? Why?
Sample answer: Every five days because it is the only time interval not used.

Grade 5 42 Chapter 9

Tips for New Teachers

If students continue to struggle, you may wish to complete this short activity.

- Provide each student with a hundreds chart and connecting cubes.
- Have students choose one color and put this color of cube on the first few multiples of 4 on the hundred chart (4, 8, 12, 16, 20, 24...).
- Next, put cubes of a second color on the multiples of 10 (10, 20, 30...). Tell students that the first time two cubes land on the same number, that number is the least common multiple of the two numbers.
- Using the hundreds chart as a recording sheet, color half of each square the color of the cube for the first number. Repeat with the second color. When both colors appear in a square, that number is a common multiple.

3 Practice

Differentiate practice using these leveled assignments for Exercises 11–34.

Level	Assignment
BL Below/ Approaching Level	11–14, 19–22, 27, 34
OL On Level	15–30, 33, 34
AL Above/Beyond Level	11–29 odd, 31–34

Have students discuss and complete the Higher Order Thinking problems. In Exercise 33, write organized lists of multiples to help determine the answer.

WRITING IN ►MATH Have students complete Exercise 34 in their Math Journals. You may choose to use this as an optional formative assessment.

COMMON ERROR!

Exercises 22 and 26 Students may get confused and find the GCF instead of the LCM. Have students circle the letter M in LCM and write out the word for which it stands, *multiple*. Remind them that multiple is the product of that number and any whole number.

Practice and Problem Solving

See page R25.

List multiples to find the first two common multiples of each set of numbers. See Example 1 (p. 396)

11. 2 and 4 4, 8

12. 8 and 12 24, 48

13. 3 and 12 12, 24

14. 4 and 8 8, 16

15. 2, 5, and 10 10, 20

16. 3, 4, and 8 24, 48

17. 2, 3, and 9 18, 36

18. 6, 10, and 15 30, 60

Find the LCM of each set of numbers. Make a table or a number line.
See Example 2 (p. 397) 19–26. See students' work for tables and number lines.

19. 5 and 6 30

20. 3 and 5 15

21. 6 and 9 18

22. 12 and 18 36

23. 6, 12, and 15 60

24. 5, 10, and 15 30

25. 3, 9, and 15 45

26. 9, 12, and 18 36

27. Macy is painting a design that contains two repeating patterns. One pattern repeats every 8 inches. The other pattern repeats every 12 inches. In how many inches will the two patterns begin at the same place? 24 in.

28. The science department buys the following equipment. They bought all three items this year. In how many years will they again have to buy all three items? 20 yr

Item	Time Bought
Microscopes	every 5 years
Safety goggles	every 4 years
Test tubes	every 2 years

Real-World PROBLEM SOLVING

Music A trumpet player plays a note on the fourth beat and every 4 beats after that. A saxophone player plays a note on the eighth beat and every 8 beats after that.

29. On which beat will the musicians play a note together? eighth beat

30. Suppose a clarinet player joins them. He plays a note on the sixth beat and every 6 beats after that. On which beat will all three musicians play a note together? twenty-fourth beat

H.O.T. Problems 31–32. See Ch. 9 Answer Appendix.

31. OPEN ENDED Write a real-world problem that involves two numbers between 9 and 21. Find the LCM of the numbers and describe what it means in the problem.

32. FIND THE ERROR Carrie and Bryant are finding the least common multiple of 18 and 24. Who is correct? Explain.

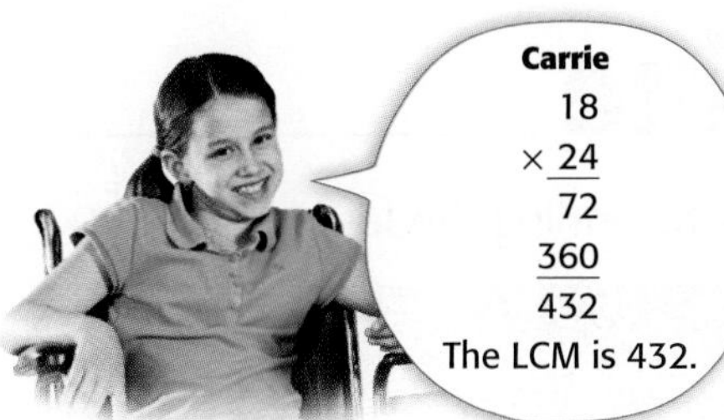

Bryant
multiples of 18:
18, 36, 54 0, ...
multiples of 24:
24, 48, 72, 96, ...
The LCM is 72.

33. CHALLENGE Consider the numbers from 2 to 10. For which two numbers is the LCM the greatest? Explain. 9 and 10; The LCM is 90, the product of the two numbers.

34. WRITING IN MATH How is the GCF of 36 and 45 different from their LCM? See Ch. 9 Answer Appendix.

TEST Practice

35. A tree grew 0.85 inch in the first year. What fraction of an inch did it grow in the first year? (Lesson 9-5) B

A $\frac{4}{5}$ **C** $\frac{21}{25}$

B $\frac{17}{20}$ **D** $\frac{17}{50}$

36. Look for the pattern in the sequence of numbers below. Each sequence is an example of which kind of numbers? (Lesson 9-7) H

3, 6, 12, 24, 48
5, 10, 20, 40, 80
8, 16, 32, 64, 128

F even numbers **H** multiples

G odd numbers **J** prime numbers

Spiral Review

37. The table shows the heights of different sizes of bleachers. If the pattern continues, what would be the height of bleachers that have 7 rows? (Lesson 9-6) 14

Number of Rows	Height of Bleachers (ft)
1	2
2	4
3	6

Write each decimal as a fraction in simplest form. (Lesson 9-5)

38. 0.2 $\frac{1}{5}$ **39.** 0.12 $\frac{3}{25}$ **40.** 0.08 $\frac{2}{25}$

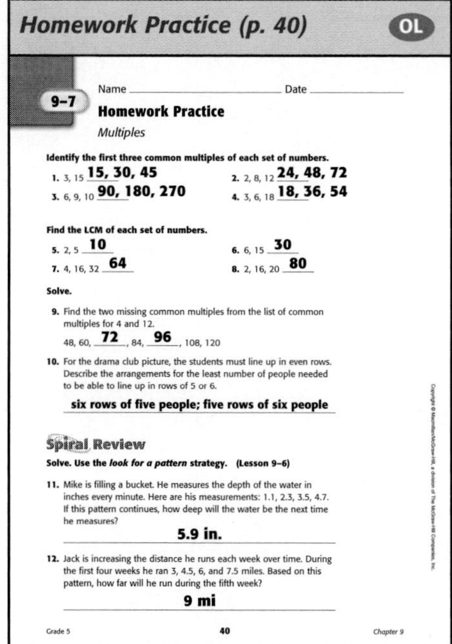

Homework Practice (p. 40) OL

9-7 Name ____ Date ____

Homework Practice

Multiples

Identify the first three common multiples of each set of numbers.

1. 3, 15 **15, 30, 45**
2. 2, 8, 12 **24, 48, 72**
3. 6, 9, 10 **90, 180, 270**
4. 3, 6, 18 **18, 36, 54**

Find the LCM of each set of numbers.

5. 2, 5 **10**
6. 6, 15 **30**
7. 4, 16, 32 **64**
8. 2, 16, 20 **80**

Solve.

9. Find the two missing common multiples from the list of common multiples for 4 and 12.
48, 60, **72**, 84, **96**, 108, 120

10. For the drama club picture, the students must line up in even rows. Describe the arrangements for the least number of people needed to be able to line up in rows of 5 or 6.
six rows of five people; five rows of six people

Spiral Review

Solve. Use the *look for a pattern* strategy. (Lesson 9–6)

11. Mike is filling a bucket. He measures the depth of the water in inches every minute. Here are his measurements: 1.1, 2.3, 3.5, 4.7. If this pattern continues, how deep will the water be the next time he measures?
5.9 in.

12. Jack is increasing the distance he runs each week over time. During the first four weeks he ran 3, 4.5, 6, and 7.5 miles. Based on this pattern, how far will he run during the fifth week?
9 mi

Grade 5 40 Chapter 9

4 Assess

Formative Assessment

Write the numbers 5 and 7 on the board.

- **What is the least common multiple of 5 and 7?** 35
- **Will multiplying two numbers always give you the least common multiple? Explain.** No; it will be a common multiple but not necessarily the least common multiple.
- **Give an example.** Sample answer: 6 and 8; 6 × 8 = 48; the LCM of 6 and 8 is 24.

Quick Check **Are students continuing to struggle with identifying common multiples?**

If Yes → Small Group Options (p. 396B)

If No → Independent Work Options (p. 396B)
CRM Skills Practice Worksheet (p. 39)
CRM Enrich Worksheet (p. 42)

Name the Math Write the steps needed to find the LCM of two numbers. Give an example.

Reviews Lessons 9-5 and 9-7

Assign the Test Practice problems to provide daily reinforcement of test-taking skills.

Reviews Lessons 9-5 and 9-6

Review and assess mastery of skills and concepts from previous chapters.

9-8 Problem-Solving Investigation
Choose the Best Strategy

Lesson Planner

Objective

Choose the best strategy to solve a problem.

Resources

Teacher Technology

TeacherWorks • Interactive Classroom

Real-World Problem Solving Library
Math and Science: Nature's Delicate Balance

Use these leveled books to reinforce and extend problem-solving skills and strategies.

Leveled for:

- OL On Level
- ELL Sheltered English
- SP Spanish

For additional support, see the Real-World Problem Solving Teacher Guide.

Daily Routine

Use these suggestions before beginning the lesson on p. 400.

5-Minute Check

(Reviews Lesson 9-7)

List multiples to find the first two common multiples of each set of numbers.

1. 6 and 8 24, 48
2. 5 and 7 35, 70

Find the LCM of each set of numbers.

3. 8 and 12 24
4. 9 and 15 45

Problem of the Day

Guess the fraction. It is equivalent to $\frac{1}{4}$. The numerator is a multiple of 3. The denominator is between 25 and 40. $\frac{9}{36}$

Differentiated Instruction

Small Group Options

LOGICAL

Option 1 Below Level BL

Materials: paper and pencil

- Share this problem with students:

  Mr. Johnson began a new job at a furniture store selling couch and chair sets. He sells: 3 sets on Tuesday, 5 sets on Wednesday, 4 sets on Thursday, 2 sets on Friday, and 4 sets on Saturday. His boss hoped he would sell on average 3 sets per day. After 5 days did he meet his boss' goal? Yes, he did better than his boss expected.

LINGUISTIC, LOGICAL

Option 2 English Language Learners ELL

Materials: paper, pencil
Core Vocabulary: higher, lower, tries
Common Use Verb: guess

Talk Math This strategy uses cooperative groups to help students internalize language and logical reasoning for choosing strategies.

- Say: "I am thinking of a number between 1 and 100. ***Guess*** what it is."
- Students take turns guessing. Write a tally for each guess. Respond only "higher" or "lower" to each guess. When number is guessed, count the tallies.
- Challenge students to try to guess the next number in less tries.
- Repeat if time permits.
- Allow students to brainstorm ways to minimize tries.
- Use this strategy as an ongoing challenge for students. Prompt them to challenge by saying: "I can name your number in __ tries or less."

Independent Work Options

LINGUISTIC

Option 1 Early Finishers   

Materials: index cards

- Have each student choose the strategy he or she likes best.
- Then on an index card, the student writes a word problem that can be solved using his or her strategy.
- On the other side of the index card, the student writes the solution to the problem, using the strategy he or she chose.
- Save the index cards in a box for other early finishers to solve.

Option 2 Student Technology

 macmillanmh.com

Personal Tutor • Extra Examples

Tech Link

Option 3 Learning Station: Science (p. 370H)

Direct students to the Science Learning Station for opportunities to explore and extend the lesson concept.

9-8 Problem-Solving Investigation

1 Introduce

Activity Choice • Review

- Write the following on the board:

  Domingo starts at his home. He walks 5 blocks east, 2 blocks south, and 8 blocks west to the library. To go home, he walks north and east. How many blocks will he walk home?
- Ask students to think about the problem-solving strategies they have used so far.
- **Which strategy would you use to solve this problem?** *draw a diagram*
- **Solve the problem.** 5 blocks

2 Teach

Have students read the problem on goldfish. Guide them through the problem-solving steps.

Understand Using the questions, review what students know and need to find.

Plan Have them discuss their strategy.

Solve Guide students to use the *guess and check* strategy to solve the problem.

- **What happens when we use 5 as a guess? Explain.** There are too many.
- **What happens when we use 3?** There are too few.
- **What happens when we use 4?** It is correct.

Check Have students look back at the problem to make sure that the answer fits the facts given.

- **How can you tell 4 is the correct answer?** Gisela has 4, Liseta 8, and Clara 16. Add, and there are 28 goldfish in all.

! COMMON ERROR!

Exercise 8 Students may increase the numbers they guess rather than adjust downward. Have them organize and track their work.

9-8 Problem-Solving Investigation

MAIN IDEA I will choose the best strategy to solve a problem.

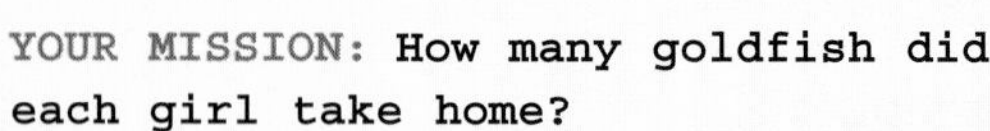

MYKAELA: My science teacher is giving goldfish to some of my classmates to take care of during the summer. He gave some of them to Gisela. Then he gave twice as many to Liseta. He gave twice as many to Clara as he gave to Liseta. He gave out all 28 goldfish.

YOUR MISSION: How many goldfish did each girl take home?

Understand There are 28 goldfish. He gave some to Gisela. He gave twice as many to Liseta as to Gisela. He gave twice as many to Clara as to Liseta. You need to determine how many goldfish each girl took home.

Plan You can use the *guess and check* strategy to find how many goldfish each girl took home.

Solve Make a guess as to how many goldfish the teacher gave Gisela. See if it is correct. Then adjust the guess, if necessary.

Number of Goldfish				
Gisela	Liseta	Clara	Total	
5	$2 \times 5 = 10$	$2 \times 10 = 20$	35	$35 > 28$; too many
3	$2 \times 3 = 6$	$2 \times 6 = 12$	21	$21 < 28$; too few
4	$2 \times 4 = 8$	$2 \times 8 = 16$	28	$28 = 28$; correct

So, the teacher gave 4 goldfish to Gisela, 8 goldfish to Liseta, and 16 goldfish to Clara.

Check Look back. $4 + 8 + 16 = 28$. So, the answer is correct. ✓

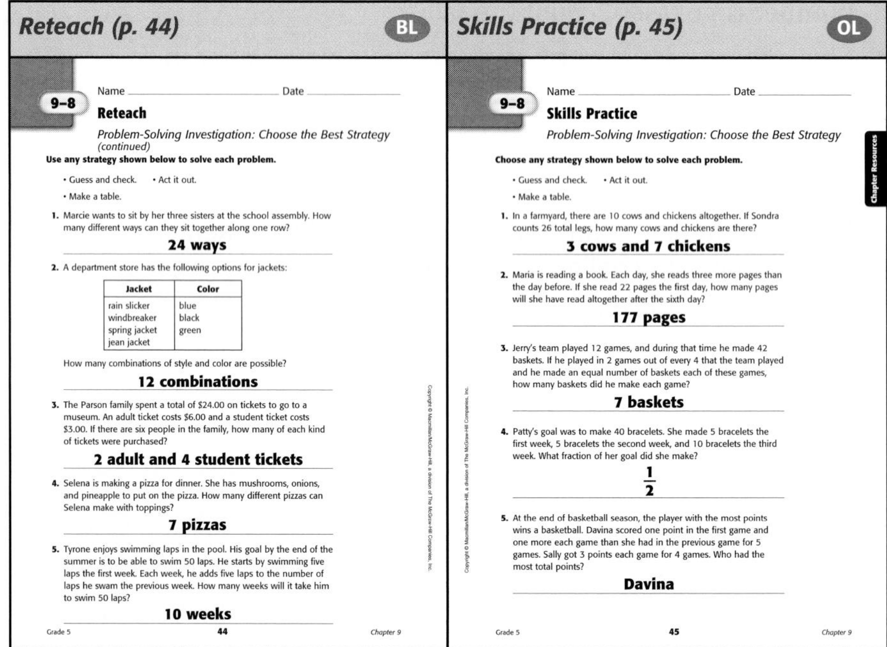

Reteach (p. 44) BL

Name ______ Date ______

9-8 **Reteach**

Problem-Solving Investigation: Choose the Best Strategy (continued)

Use any strategy shown below to solve each problem.

- Guess and check. • Act it out.
- Make a table.

1. Marcie wants to sit by her three sisters at the school assembly. How many different ways can they sit together along one row?

   24 ways
2. A department store has the following options for jackets:

Jacket	Color
rain slicker windbreaker spring jacket jean jacket	blue black green

   How many combinations of style and color are possible?

   12 combinations
3. The Parson family spent a total of $24.00 on tickets to go to a museum. An adult ticket costs $6.00 and a student ticket costs $3.00. If there are six people in the family, how many of each kind of tickets were purchased?

   2 adult and 4 student tickets
4. Selena is making a pizza for dinner. She has mushrooms, onions, and pineapple to put on the pizza. How many different pizzas can Selena make with toppings?

   7 pizzas
5. Tyrone enjoys swimming laps in the pool. His goal by the end of the summer is to be able to swim 50 laps. He starts by swimming five laps the first week. Each week, he adds five laps to the number of laps he swam the previous week. How many weeks will it take him to swim 50 laps?

   10 weeks

Grade 5 44 Chapter 9

Skills Practice (p. 45) OL

Name ______ Date ______

9-8 **Skills Practice**

Problem-Solving Investigation: Choose the Best Strategy

Chapter Resources

Choose any strategy shown below to solve each problem.

- Guess and check. • Act it out.
- Make a table.

1. In a farmyard, there are 10 cows and chickens altogether. If Sondra counts 26 total legs, how many cows and chickens are there?

   3 cows and 7 chickens
2. Maria is reading a book. Each day, she reads three more pages than the day before. If she read 22 pages the first day, how many pages will she have read altogether after the sixth day?

   177 pages
3. Jerry's team played 12 games, and during that time he made 42 baskets. If he played in 2 games out of every 4 that the team played and he made an equal number of baskets each of these games, how many baskets did he make each game?

   7 baskets
4. Patty's goal was to make 40 bracelets. She made 5 bracelets the first week, 5 bracelets the second week, and 10 bracelets the third week. What fraction of her goal did she make?

   $\frac{1}{2}$
5. At the end of basketball season, the player with the most points wins a basketball. Davina scored one point in the first game and one more each game than she had in the previous game for 5 games. Sally got 3 points each game for 4 games. Who had the most total points?

   Davina

Grade 5 45 Chapter 9

5–7. See Ch. 9 Answer Appendix

Mixed Problem Solving

See page R26.

Use any strategy shown below to solve each problem.

PROBLEM-SOLVING STRATEGIES
- Guess and check.
- Look for a pattern.
- Solve a simpler problem.

1. Lorraine and Yori have 12 plants between them. Yori has 4 more than Lorraine. How many does each girl have? **Lorraine has 4 plants; Yori has 8 plants.**
2. **Algebra** When Cesar's Pizza Parlor makes a pizza, they use the following amount of cheese on each pizza:

Number of Pizzas	Amount of Cheese (ounces)
1	4
2	8
3	12
5	20
7	■ **28**
8	■ **32**

Complete the table and find how much cheese Cesar's uses to make 8 pizzas.

3. Annette put $5 in her bank account each week for 14 weeks. Isabel put $7 in her bank account each week for 11 weeks. Who saved more money? How much more? **See Ch. 9 Answer Appendix.**
4. During the World Series, one pitcher used a pattern when he pitched. The pattern was two fastballs followed by two sliders followed by a change-up. If the pattern continues, what kind of pitch will the eleventh pitch be? **See Ch. 9 Answer Appendix.**
5. Mr. Whitmore bought tickets for a movie. Adult tickets cost $5 each and children's tickets cost $3 each. He spent a total of $22 for the tickets. How many adult tickets and how many children's tickets did he buy?
6. Liu has $53 in his bank account. Each week for 5 weeks, he adds $2.50 to the account. How much does he now have in his bank account?
7. Maggie and her younger brother, Ty, went to lunch. Ty had a sandwich and soft drink. Maggie had a hamburger and milkshake. How much more did Maggie's lunch cost than Ty's?

Menu			
Item	Cost	Item	Cost
Sandwich	$2.25	Milkshake	$3.00
Hamburger	$4.50	Soft drink	$0.75

8. A total of 48 students joined the math team. There were 12 more girls than boys who joined. How many boys and how many girls joined the math team? **18 boys; 30 girls**
9. Oscar makes leather belts. If he continues his pattern below, what will be the design of the seventeenth link in the belt? **See Ch. 9 Answer Appendix.**

10. 

Explain how you use the *guess and check* strategy. **See Ch. 9 Answer Appendix.**

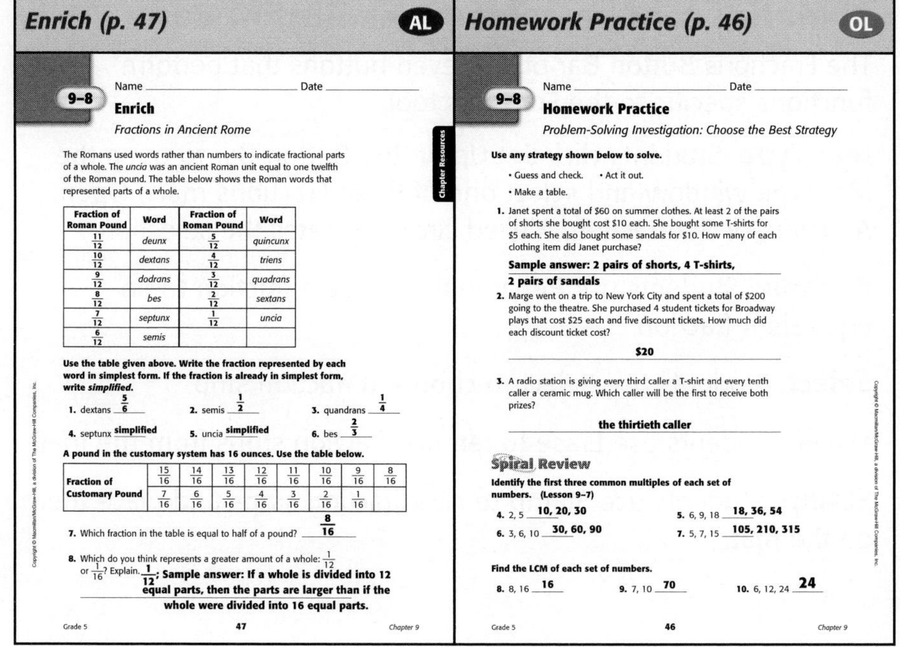

Enrich (p. 47) AL

9–8 Name ______ Date ______

Enrich

Fractions in Ancient Rome

The Romans used words rather than numbers to indicate fractional parts of a whole. The *uncia* was an ancient Roman unit equal to one twelfth of the Roman pound. The table below shows the Roman words that represented parts of a whole.

Fraction of Roman Pound	Word	Fraction of Roman Pound	Word
$\frac{11}{12}$	*deunx*	$\frac{5}{12}$	*quincunx*
$\frac{10}{12}$	*dextans*	$\frac{4}{12}$	*triens*
$\frac{9}{12}$	*dodrans*	$\frac{3}{12}$	*quadrans*
$\frac{8}{12}$	*bes*	$\frac{2}{12}$	*sextans*
$\frac{7}{12}$	*septunx*	$\frac{1}{12}$	*uncia*
$\frac{6}{12}$	*semis*		

Use the table given above. Write the fraction represented by each word in simplest form. If the fraction is already in simplest form, write *simplified*.

1. dextans $\frac{5}{6}$
2. semis $\frac{1}{2}$
3. quandrans $\frac{1}{4}$
4. septunx **simplified**
5. uncia **simplified**
6. bes $\frac{2}{3}$

A pound in the customary system has 16 ounces. Use the table below.

Fraction of Customary Pound	$\frac{15}{16}$	$\frac{14}{16}$	$\frac{13}{16}$	$\frac{12}{16}$	$\frac{11}{16}$	$\frac{10}{16}$	$\frac{9}{16}$	$\frac{8}{16}$
	$\frac{7}{16}$	$\frac{6}{16}$	$\frac{5}{16}$	$\frac{4}{16}$	$\frac{3}{16}$	$\frac{2}{16}$	$\frac{1}{16}$	

7. Which fraction in the table is equal to half of a pound? $\frac{8}{16}$
8. Which do you think represents a greater amount of a whole: $\frac{1}{12}$ or $\frac{1}{16}$? Explain. **$\frac{1}{12}$; Sample answer: If a whole is divided into 12 equal parts, then the parts are larger than if the whole were divided into 16 equal parts.**

Grade 5 47 Chapter 9

Chapter Resources

Homework Practice (p. 46) OL

9–8 Name ______ Date ______

Homework Practice

Problem-Solving Investigation: Choose the Best Strategy

Use any strategy shown below to solve.

- Guess and check.
- Act it out.
- Make a table.

1. Janet spent a total of $60 on summer clothes. At least 2 of the pairs of shorts she bought cost $10 each. She bought some T-shirts for $5 each. She also bought some sandals for $10. How many of each clothing item did Janet purchase?
Sample answer: 2 pairs of shorts, 4 T-shirts, 2 pairs of sandals
2. Marge went on a trip to New York City and spent a total of $200 going to the theatre. She purchased 4 student tickets for Broadway plays that cost $25 each and five discount tickets. How much did each discount ticket cost?
$20
3. A radio station is giving every third caller a T-shirt and every tenth caller a ceramic mug. Which caller will be the first to receive both prizes?
the thirtieth caller

Spiral Review

Identify the first three common multiples of each set of numbers. (Lesson 9–7)

4. 2, 5 **10, 20, 30**
5. 6, 9, 18 **18, 36, 54**
6. 3, 6, 10 **30, 60, 90**
7. 5, 7, 15 **105, 210, 315**

Find the LCM of each set of numbers.

8. 8, 16 **16**
9. 7, 10 **70**
10. 6, 12, 24 **24**

Grade 5 46 Chapter 9

BL Alternate Teaching Strategy

If students have trouble choosing the best strategy to solve a problem…

Then use one of these reteach options:

1. CRM **Daily Reteach Worksheet** (p. 44)
2. Discuss each problem before students start working to determine what strategies could be used to solve each problem.

3 Practice

Using the Exercises

Exercises 2, 4, 6, and 9 require students to *look for a pattern*.

Exercise 3 is a multi-step that can be solved using multiplication and subtraction.

Exercises 1, 5, and 8 can be solved using *guess and check*

4 Assess

Formative Assessment

Suppose you are using the *guess and check* strategy to solve a word problem.

- **What should you do if the number you choose is too high?** Pick a smaller number.
- **What should you do if the number you choose is too low?** Pick a larger number.

Quick Check **Are students continuing to struggle with choosing a strategy to solve a problem?**

If Yes → Small Group Options (p. 400B)

If No → Independent Work Options (p. 400B)
CRM Skills Practice Worksheet (p. 45)
CRM Enrich Worksheet (p. 47)

Technology Activity for 9-9

Lesson Planner

Objective

Use technology to compare fractions.

Resources

Math Online macmillanmh.com

 **Math Tool Chest**

Getting Started

- The activities and exercises on pp. 402–403 use the Fractions Tool in Math Tool Chest. They may be completed as a class, in pairs, or individually.
- Have students read each example on pp. 402–403.
- As a class, work through each activity in each example following the instructions on the page.

Technology Activity for 9-9

Compare Fractions

MAIN IDEA

I will use technology to compare fractions.

ACTIVITY

1 **Jeffrey studied for $\frac{3}{4}$ hour and Estella studied for $\frac{5}{6}$ hour. Who studied longer?**

You can use the Fractions option from the Math Tool Chest™.

- Choose Fractions. Click on Level 2.
- Click on Math Type. Select the 2 Sections option.
- At the bottom of the first section, stamp out three of the $\frac{1}{4}$ stamps in a horizontal line to represent $\frac{3}{4}$.
- Directly under the $\frac{1}{4}$ stamps and lined up with the left edge, place five of the $\frac{1}{6}$ stamps. This represents $\frac{5}{6}$.

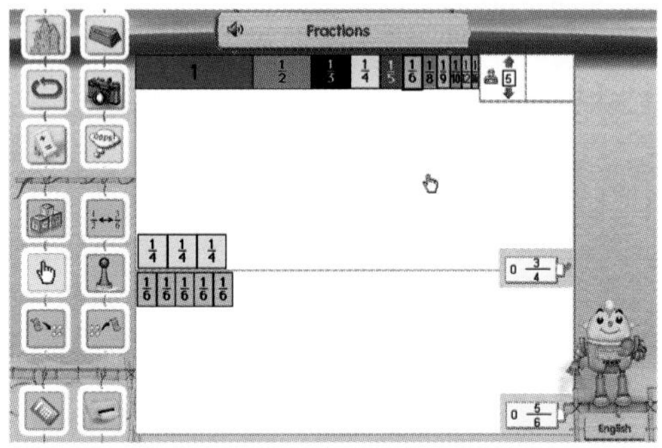

The model shows that $\frac{5}{6} > \frac{3}{4}$. So, Estella studied longer.

CHECK What You Know

Use the Fraction Option from Math Tools Chest™ to compare fractions. Then name the fraction that is greater.

1. $\frac{2}{3}$ and $\frac{3}{4}$ $\frac{3}{4}$ **2.** $\frac{2}{5}$ and $\frac{1}{4}$ $\frac{2}{5}$ **3.** $\frac{5}{8}$ and $\frac{7}{9}$ $\frac{7}{9}$ **4.** $\frac{11}{12}$ and $\frac{9}{10}$ $\frac{11}{12}$

5. $\frac{7}{8}$ and $\frac{5}{6}$ $\frac{7}{8}$ **6.** $\frac{2}{9}$ and $\frac{3}{10}$ $\frac{3}{10}$ **7.** $\frac{7}{12}$ and $\frac{1}{2}$ $\frac{7}{12}$ **8.** $\frac{3}{12}$ and $\frac{3}{8}$ $\frac{3}{8}$

Math Tool Chest: Fractions Button Bar

The Fractions Button Bar offers seven buttons that perform functions specific to the Fractions tool.

Mat Type Students click Set Up on the Button Bar to open the Mat Type window and select one of three Fractions mats: Open, Addition, or Subtraction. A filled circle indicates the selection.

Rename Students use Rename to change a fraction to an equivalent fraction.

Select Students use Select to choose a fraction strip.

Erase Students use Erase to remove fraction strips from the mat.

Stamp Students use Stamp to click fraction strips and place them on the mat.

ACTIVITY

Tech Link

2 **Terrence, Yasmin, and Delsin were kicking soccer balls into a net. Terrence made $\frac{6}{10}$ of his shots, Yasmin made $\frac{3}{8}$ of her shots, and Delsin made $\frac{7}{9}$ of his shots. Compare the fractions and arrange them in order from least to greatest.**

Follow the same steps as in Activity 1, with the following exceptions.

- Select the 3 Sections option from Mat Type.
- Align the stamps with the left most edge of the screen to ensure accuracy when comparing fractions.

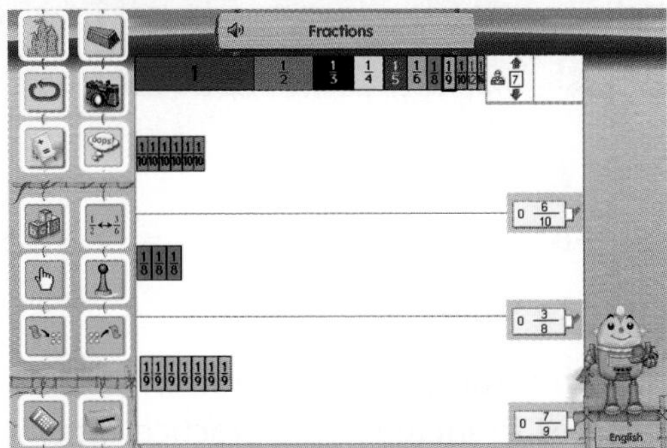

The model shows that $\frac{3}{8} < \frac{6}{10} < \frac{7}{9}$.

CHECK What You Know

Use Math Tool Chest™ to order the fractions from least to greatest.

9. $\frac{2}{5}$, $\frac{3}{16}$, and $\frac{3}{4}$ $\frac{3}{16}, \frac{2}{5}, \frac{3}{4}$ **10.** $\frac{8}{9}$, $\frac{3}{4}$, and $\frac{1}{2}$ $\frac{1}{2}, \frac{3}{4}, \frac{8}{9}$ **11.** $\frac{4}{12}$, $\frac{2}{5}$, and $\frac{4}{5}$ $\frac{4}{12}, \frac{2}{5}, \frac{4}{5}$

Solve. Use Math Tool Chest™.

12. Francisca lives $\frac{7}{10}$ mile from the park and Sereeta lives $\frac{3}{4}$ mile from the park. Who lives closer to the park? Francisca

13. Keith and Ines are sharing a pizza. Keith ate $\frac{5}{12}$ of the pizza and Ines ate $\frac{1}{3}$ of the pizza. Who ate more pizza? Keith

Tech Link

Using Math Tool Chest

Fractions

- Through Math Tool Chest, students can compare fractions with like and unlike denominators.
- In Activity 1, students are asked to stamp out $\frac{3}{4}$. Students can either stamp out three of the $\frac{1}{4}$ fractions or increase the amount of $\frac{1}{4}$ fractions to three by using the arrows. No matter which method they choose, make sure they are careful when lining them up to compare with the fraction in the other mat.

CHECK What You Know

Alone or in pairs, have students complete Exercises 1–13 in **Check What You Know** as you observe their work.

Extending the Link

- Students can find equivalent fractions using Math Tool Chest.
- Stamp out the fraction $\frac{1}{4}$ on your mat. Click on the select arrow and then on the $\frac{1}{4}$ fraction again. Make sure it is highlighted.
- Now click on the rename button and a list of equivalent fractions for $\frac{1}{4}$ will appear.

LESSON 9-9

Compare Fractions

Lesson Planner

Objective

Compare fractions using common denominators.

Vocabulary

common denominators, least common denominator (LCD)

Resources

Materials: masking tape
Manipulatives: fraction tiles, number lines
Literature Connection: *Fraction Fun* by David A. Adler
Alternate Lesson: Use *IMPACT Mathematics:* Unit E to provide practice with comparing fractions.
Teacher Tech Tools
TeacherWorks • Interactive Classroom • Concepts in Motion

Focus on Math Background

Students can compare two or more fractions using models, number lines, or equivalent fractions. When one uses equivalent fractions, the fractions being compared must have the same denominator. Once this is achieved, the fraction with the greater numerator is the greater fraction. One technique is to find the least common denominator and use it to write equivalent fractions. For example, for denominators of 3 and 4, write several multiples for each number and look for the least common multiple.

Multiples of 3: 3, 6, 9, **12**, 15

Multiple of 4: 4, 8, **12**, 16, 20

In this case, 12 is the least common multiple and therefore the least common denominator.

Daily Routine

Use these suggestions before beginning the lesson on p. 404.

5-Minute Check

(Reviews Lesson 9-8)

Use any strategy to solve.

Haloke practiced the trumpet for 1 hour on Monday. He decides to increase his practice time by 15 minutes each day. How long will he practice on the sixth day? 2 hours 15 minutes; strategies will vary.

Problem of the Day

Find the first seven multiples of 6. What is the median of these numbers? 24

Review Math Vocabulary

Write the lesson vocabulary words and their definitions on the board.

Have students look up the word common in the dictionary. Discuss the meaning of *common factor* and *common multiple*.

- **What do you think common denominator means?** Ask for examples of fractions that have a common denominator.

Visual Vocabulary Cards

Use Visual Vocabulary Card 20 to reinforce the vocabulary in this lesson. (The Define/Example/Ask routine is printed on the back of each card.)

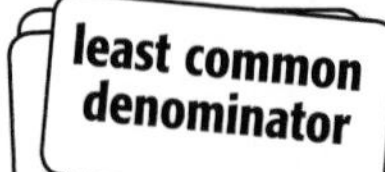

Differentiated Instruction

Small Group Options

Option 1 Gifted and Talented AL

LOGICAL

Materials: paper and pencil

- Hand students this problem:
- *Carol and Abebi wear either T-shirts, sweaters, or blouses with their blue jeans. Carol says that $\frac{3}{4}$ of her tops are T-shirts. Abebi says that $\frac{2}{3}$ of her tops are T-shirts. Each girl has 12 T-shirts. How can this be? Find a way to illustrate the answer.*

$\frac{3}{4} = \frac{12}{?}$ $\frac{3 \times 4 = 12}{4 \times 4 = 16}$ Carol has 16 tops in all.

$\frac{2}{3} = \frac{12}{?}$ $\frac{2 \times 6 = 12}{3 \times 6 = 18}$ Abebi has 18 tops in all.

Option 2 English Language Learners ELL

VISUAL, SPATIAL

Materials: large sheet of art paper or poster with pepperoni and other toppings drawn on it
Core Vocabulary: more friends, will share, greater/less than
Common Use Verb: get
Hear Math: This strategy activates background knowledge to help students compare fractions.

- Say: "I am going to eat all of this pizza."
- Pantomine with a student a "friend" ringing the doorbell.
- Say: "I will ***share*** my pizza." Fold paper in half. Say: "You ***get*** one half and I ***get*** one half." Write $\frac{1}{2}$ on the board.
- Repeat for 4 more friends.
- Say: "We **will share**." Fold the paper in sixths. Show students $\frac{1}{6}$. Ask: "How much do we each ***get?*** Is that **greater than** or **less than** $\frac{1}{2}$?"
- Write: "$\frac{1}{2} > \frac{1}{6}$" and "$\frac{1}{6} < \frac{1}{2}$."

Use this worksheet to provide additional support for English Language Learners.

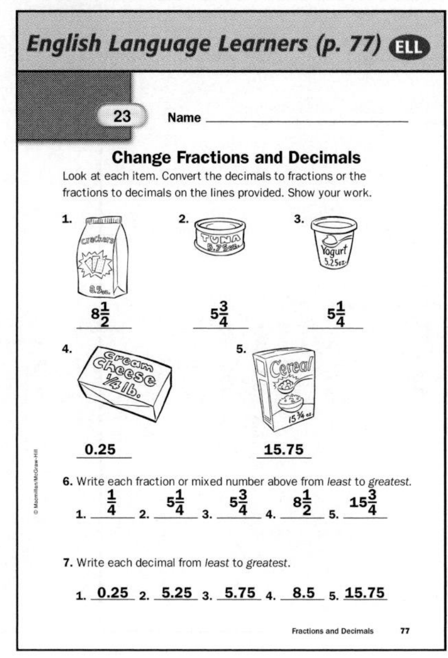

English Language Learners (p. 77) ELL

23 Name ____________

Change Fractions and Decimals

Look at each item. Convert the decimals to fractions or the fractions to decimals on the lines provided. Show your work.

1. $8\frac{1}{2}$
2. $5\frac{3}{4}$
3. $5\frac{1}{4}$
4. 0.25
5. 15.75

6. Write each fraction or mixed number above from *least* to *greatest*.

1. $\frac{1}{4}$ 2. $5\frac{1}{4}$ 3. $5\frac{3}{4}$ 4. $8\frac{1}{2}$ 5. $15\frac{3}{4}$

7. Write each decimal from *least* to *greatest*.

1. 0.25 2. 5.25 3. 5.75 4. 8.5 5. 15.75

Fractions and Decimals 77

Independent Work Options

Option 1 Early Finishers AL

VISUAL, TACTILE

Materials: two number cubes

- Have students roll two number cubes and create a fraction with the numbers rolled. The smaller number should be the numerator. The larger number should be the denominator.
- Have the student roll again to create another fraction.
- Then, have the students compare the two fractions. Have them record the results.

Option 2 Student Technology

Math Online macmillanmh.com

Personal Tutor • Extra Examples

Math Adventures

Option 3 Learning Station: Science (p. 370H)

Direct students to the Science Learning Station for opportunities to explore and extend the lesson concept.

Option 4 Problem-Solving Practice

Reinforce problem-solving skills and strategies with the Problem-Solving Practice worksheet.

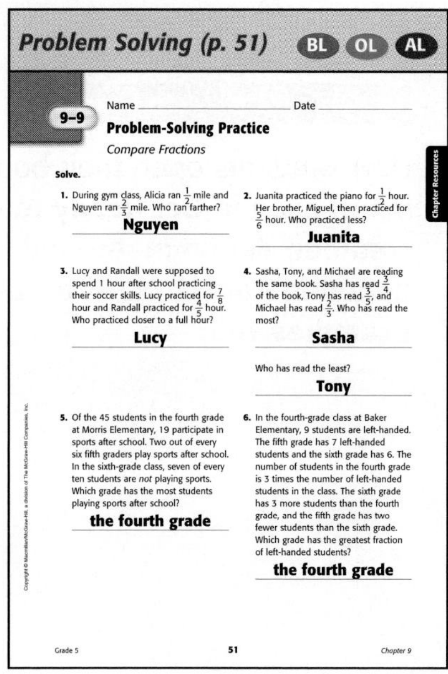

Problem Solving (p. 51) BL OL AL

9–9 Name ____________ Date ____________

Problem-Solving Practice

Compare Fractions

Chapter Resources

Solve.

1. During gym class, Alicia ran $\frac{1}{2}$ mile and Nguyen ran $\frac{2}{3}$ mile. Who ran farther?
Nguyen

2. Juanita practiced the piano for $\frac{1}{2}$ hour. Her brother, Miguel, then practiced for $\frac{5}{6}$ hour. Who practiced less?
Juanita

3. Lucy and Randall were supposed to spend 1 hour after school practicing their soccer skills. Lucy practiced for $\frac{7}{8}$ hour and Randall practiced for $\frac{4}{5}$ hour. Who practiced closer to a full hour?
Lucy

4. Sasha, Tony, and Michael are reading the same book. Sasha has read $\frac{3}{4}$ of the book, Tony has read $\frac{3}{5}$, and Michael has read $\frac{2}{3}$. Who has read the most?
Sasha
Who has read the least?
Tony

5. Of the 45 students in the fourth grade at Morris Elementary, 19 participate in sports after school. Two out of every six fifth graders play sports after school. In the sixth-grade class, seven of every ten students are *not* playing sports. Which grade has the most students playing sports after school?
the fourth grade

6. In the fourth-grade class at Baker Elementary, 9 students are left-handed. The fifth grade has 7 left-handed students and the sixth grade has 6. The number of students in the fourth grade is 3 times the number of left-handed students in the class. The sixth grade has 3 more students than the fourth grade, and the fifth grade has two fewer students than the sixth grade. Which grade has the greatest fraction of left-handed students?
the fourth grade

Grade 5 51 Chapter 9

9-9 Compare Fractions

1 Introduce

Activity Choice 1 • Hands-On

- Write the following fractions each on an index card: $\frac{1}{2}, \frac{1}{3}, \frac{2}{3}, \frac{1}{4}, \frac{3}{4}, \frac{1}{6}, \frac{5}{6}, \frac{1}{8}, \frac{3}{8}, \frac{5}{8}, \frac{7}{8}, \frac{3}{24}, \frac{8}{24}, \frac{12}{24}, \frac{13}{24}, \frac{17}{24}, \frac{21}{24}$, and $\frac{2}{24}$.
- Tape a piece of masking tape on the floor in the front of the classroom. Label the left end 0 and the right end 1.
- Working as a class, students place the fractions on the line.
- Have them justify the placement.

Activity Choice 2 • Literature

Introduce the lesson *Fraction Fun* by David A. Adler. For a related math activity, see p. TR51.

2 Teach

Scaffolding Questions

Discuss Activity Choice 1.

- **Which fractions were easier to place on the line?** fractions that have the same denominator
- **Which fractions are equivalent fractions?** $\frac{3}{24}$ and $\frac{1}{8}$; $\frac{8}{24}$ and $\frac{1}{3}$; $\frac{12}{24}$ and $\frac{1}{2}$; $\frac{21}{24}$ and $\frac{7}{8}$
- **How does knowing $\frac{12}{24} = \frac{1}{2}$ help you to place $\frac{13}{24}$?** $\frac{13}{24}$ will be to the right of $\frac{1}{2}$.

GET READY to Learn

Have students open their books and read the information in **Get Ready to Learn.** Introduce **common denominator** and **least common denominator (LCD).** As a class, work through **Examples 1–3.**

9-9 Compare Fractions

MAIN IDEA

I will compare fractions using common denominators.

New Vocabulary

common denominator
least common denominator (LCD)

Math Online

macmillanmh.com
- Extra Examples
- Personal Tutor
- Self-Check Quiz
- Concepts in Motion

GET READY to Learn

A class survey showed that $\frac{5}{8}$ of the class favored apple pie, $\frac{1}{4}$ favored peach pie, and $\frac{1}{8}$ of class liked pumpkin pie. Which type of pie was favored most? apple

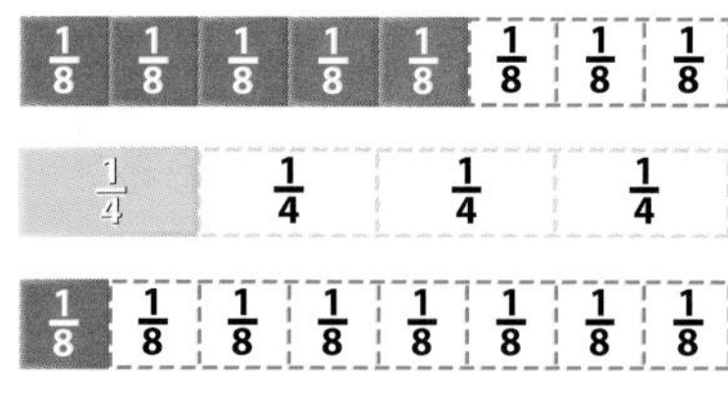

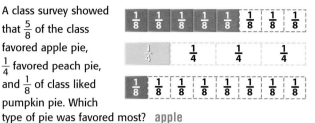

You can use models to compare fractions. If fractions have the same denominators, compare the numerators. If the fractions have different denominators, first write equivalent fractions with a common denominator. A **common denominator** of two or more fractions is a number that is a multiple of the denominators of the fractions.

Use the **least common denominator (LCD)**, or the least common multiple of the denominators, to compare fractions.

EXAMPLE Compare Fractions

1 **Compare $\frac{3}{5}$ and $\frac{1}{2}$ using models and the least common denominator.**

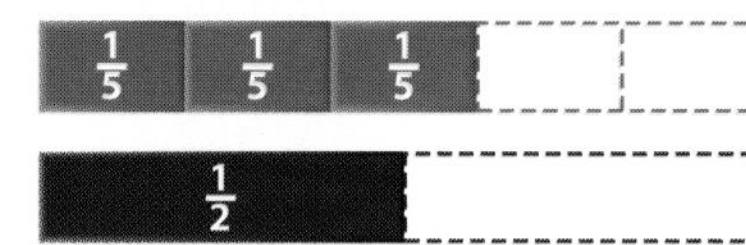

The models show that $\frac{3}{5} > \frac{1}{2}$.

Step 1 Find the LCM of the denominators. The LCM of 5 and 2 is 10.

Step 2 Find equivalent fractions with a denominator of 10.

$\frac{3}{5} = \frac{6}{10}$ THINK $5 \times 2 = 10$, $3 \times 2 = 6$

$\frac{1}{2} = \frac{5}{10}$ THINK $2 \times 5 = 10$, $1 \times 5 = 5$

Step 3 Compare the numerators. Since $6 > 5$, then $\frac{6}{10} > \frac{5}{10}$.
So, $\frac{3}{5} > \frac{1}{2}$.

404 Chapter 9 Use Factors and Multiples

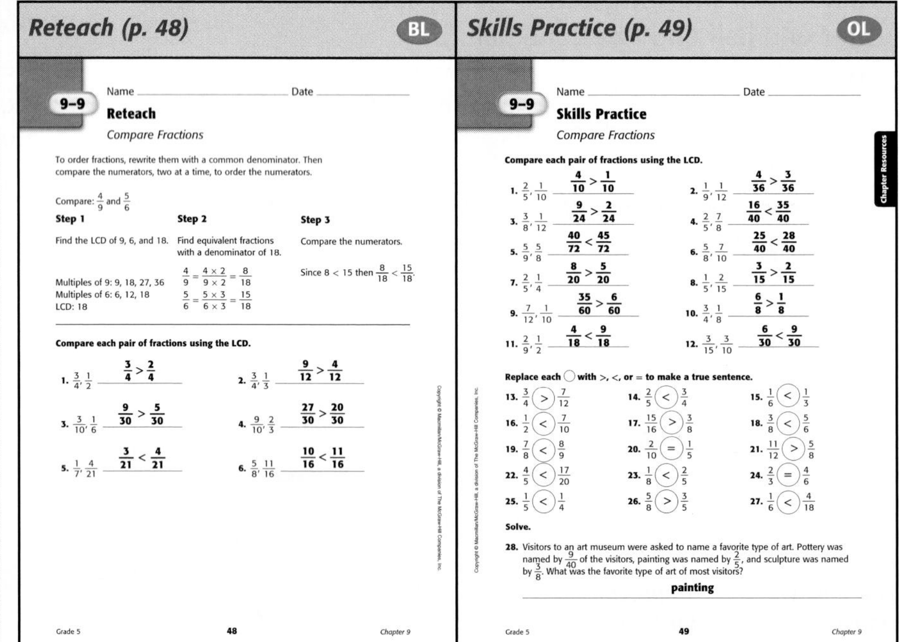

Reteach (p. 48) BL

9-9 Name ____________ Date ____________

Reteach

Compare Fractions

To order fractions, rewrite them with a common denominator. Then compare the numerators, two at a time, to order the numerators.

Compare: $\frac{4}{9}$ and $\frac{5}{6}$

Step 1	Step 2	Step 3
Find the LCD of 9, 6, and 18.	Find equivalent fractions with a denominator of 18.	Compare the numerators.
Multiples of 9: 9, 18, 27, 36 Multiples of 6: 6, 12, 18 LCD: 18	$\frac{4}{9} = \frac{4 \times 2}{9 \times 2} = \frac{8}{18}$ $\frac{5}{6} = \frac{5 \times 3}{6 \times 3} = \frac{15}{18}$	Since $8 < 15$ then $\frac{8}{18} < \frac{15}{18}$.

Compare each pair of fractions using the LCD.

1. $\frac{3}{4}, \frac{1}{2}$ $\frac{3}{4} > \frac{2}{4}$
2. $\frac{3}{4}, \frac{1}{3}$ $\frac{9}{12} > \frac{4}{12}$
3. $\frac{3}{10}, \frac{1}{6}$ $\frac{9}{30} > \frac{5}{30}$
4. $\frac{9}{10}, \frac{2}{3}$ $\frac{27}{30} > \frac{20}{30}$
5. $\frac{1}{7}, \frac{4}{21}$ $\frac{3}{21} < \frac{4}{21}$
6. $\frac{5}{8}, \frac{11}{16}$ $\frac{10}{16} < \frac{11}{16}$

Grade 5 48 Chapter 9

Skills Practice (p. 49) OL

9-9 Name ____________ Date ____________

Skills Practice

Compare Fractions

Chapter Resources

Compare each pair of fractions using the LCD.

1. $\frac{2}{5}, \frac{1}{10}$ $\frac{4}{10} > \frac{1}{10}$
2. $\frac{1}{9}, \frac{1}{12}$ $\frac{4}{36} > \frac{3}{36}$
3. $\frac{3}{8}, \frac{1}{12}$ $\frac{9}{24} > \frac{2}{24}$
4. $\frac{2}{5}, \frac{7}{8}$ $\frac{16}{40} < \frac{35}{40}$
5. $\frac{5}{9}, \frac{5}{8}$ $\frac{40}{72} < \frac{45}{72}$
6. $\frac{5}{8}, \frac{7}{10}$ $\frac{25}{40} < \frac{28}{40}$
7. $\frac{2}{5}, \frac{1}{4}$ $\frac{8}{20} > \frac{5}{20}$
8. $\frac{1}{5}, \frac{2}{15}$ $\frac{3}{15} > \frac{2}{15}$
9. $\frac{7}{12}, \frac{1}{10}$ $\frac{35}{60} > \frac{6}{60}$
10. $\frac{3}{4}, \frac{1}{8}$ $\frac{6}{8} > \frac{1}{8}$
11. $\frac{2}{9}, \frac{1}{2}$ $\frac{4}{18} < \frac{9}{18}$
12. $\frac{3}{15}, \frac{3}{10}$ $\frac{6}{30} < \frac{9}{30}$

Replace each ○ with >, <, or = to make a true sentence.

13. $\frac{3}{4}$ (>) $\frac{7}{12}$
14. $\frac{2}{5}$ (<) $\frac{3}{4}$
15. $\frac{1}{6}$ (<) $\frac{1}{3}$
16. $\frac{1}{2}$ (<) $\frac{7}{10}$
17. $\frac{15}{16}$ (>) $\frac{3}{8}$
18. $\frac{3}{8}$ (<) $\frac{5}{6}$
19. $\frac{7}{8}$ (<) $\frac{8}{9}$
20. $\frac{2}{10}$ (=) $\frac{1}{5}$
21. $\frac{11}{12}$ (>) $\frac{5}{8}$
22. $\frac{4}{5}$ (<) $\frac{17}{20}$
23. $\frac{1}{8}$ (<) $\frac{2}{5}$
24. $\frac{2}{3}$ (=) $\frac{4}{6}$
25. $\frac{1}{5}$ (<) $\frac{1}{4}$
26. $\frac{5}{8}$ (>) $\frac{3}{5}$
27. $\frac{1}{6}$ (<) $\frac{4}{18}$

Solve.

28. Visitors to an art museum were asked to name a favorite type of art. Pottery was named by $\frac{9}{40}$ of the visitors, painting was named by $\frac{2}{5}$, and sculpture was named by $\frac{3}{8}$. What was the favorite type of art of most visitors?

painting

Grade 5 49 Chapter 9

Remember

You can also find a set of equivalent fractions for $\frac{5}{6}$ and $\frac{7}{9}$ to find the LCD.

$\frac{5}{6}, \frac{10}{12}, \frac{15}{18}, \frac{20}{24}, \ldots$

$\frac{7}{9}, \frac{14}{18}, \frac{21}{27}, \ldots$

In Example 1, the LCD of $\frac{3}{5}$ and $\frac{1}{2}$ is 10, which can also be found by multiplying 5 and 2. You can always multiply the denominators of two fractions to find a common denominator. This method does not always give the LCD.

EXAMPLE Compare Fractions Using the LCD

2 **Compare $\frac{5}{6}$ and $\frac{7}{9}$ using the least common denominator.**

Step 1 Find the LCM of the denominators. The LCM of 6 and 9 is 18. Note that multiplying 6 by 9 gives a common denominator of 54, which is not the LCD, 18.

Step 2 Find an equivalent fraction with a denominator of 18 for each fraction.

$\frac{5}{6} = \frac{15}{18}$ THINK $6 \times 3 = 18, 5 \times 3 = 15$

$\frac{7}{9} = \frac{14}{18}$ THINK $9 \times 2 = 18, 7 \times 2 = 14$

Step 3 Compare the numerators. Since $15 > 14$, then $\frac{15}{18} > \frac{14}{18}$. So, $\frac{5}{6} > \frac{7}{9}$.

Real-World EXAMPLE

3 **SPORTS Trevor made 2 out of 3 field goals and Tyler made 5 out of 6. Who made a greater fraction of field goals?**

The models show $\frac{5}{6} > \frac{2}{3}$.

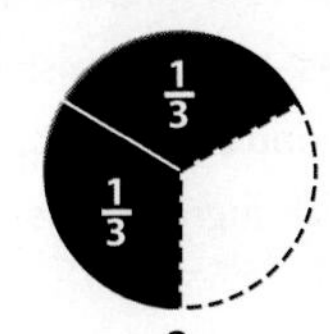

$\frac{2}{3}$

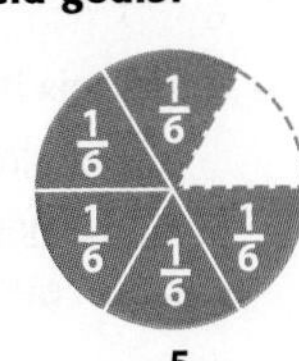

$\frac{5}{6}$

Step 1 Find the LCM of the denominators. The LCM of 3 and 6 is 6.

Step 2 Find an equivalent fraction with a denominator of 6 for each fraction.

$\frac{2}{3} = \frac{4}{6}$ THINK $3 \times 2 = 6, 2 \times 2 = 4$

$\frac{5}{6} = \frac{5}{6}$ THINK $6 \times 1 = 6, 5 \times 1 = 5$

Step 3 Compare the numerators. Since $5 > 4$, then $\frac{5}{6} > \frac{4}{6}$. So, $\frac{5}{6} > \frac{2}{3}$. Tyler made a greater fraction of field goals.

Enrich (p. 52) AL

9–9 Name ________ Date ________

Enrich

More Fraction Boxes

Arrange each set of digits in the boxes to make each statement true. Sample answers are given.

1. 3, 1, 7, 5 $\frac{1}{3} < \frac{5}{7}$
2. 1, 8, 4, 2 $\frac{4}{8} = \frac{1}{2}$
3. 6, 9, 5, 4 $\frac{4}{5} > \frac{6}{9}$
4. 2, 3, 7, 6 $\frac{3}{7} > \frac{2}{6}$
5. 8, 3, 1, 5 $\frac{1}{3} < \frac{5}{8}$
6. 4, 6, 5, 3 $\frac{3}{4} < \frac{5}{6}$
7. 1, 3, 4, 5, 7, 9 $\frac{1}{4} < \frac{3}{9} < \frac{5}{7}$
8. 4, 2, 8, 6, 5, 1 $\frac{1}{8} < \frac{2}{5} < \frac{4}{6}$
9. 7, 1, 8, 3, 2, 9 $\frac{2}{9} < \frac{1}{3} < \frac{7}{8}$
10. 3, 5, 2, 6, 4, 7 $\frac{4}{7} < \frac{3}{4} < \frac{5}{6}$
11. How did you solve problem 10? **Answers will vary.**

Grade 5 52 Chapter 9

Compare Fractions Using the LCD

Example 2 Have students use fraction tiles to check their work.

ADDITIONAL EXAMPLES

1 Compare $\frac{2}{3}$ and $\frac{2}{4}$ using models and the least common denominator.

$\frac{1}{12}$	$\frac{1}{12}$	$\frac{1}{12}$	$\frac{1}{12}$	$\frac{1}{12}$	$\frac{1}{12}$	$\frac{1}{12}$	$\frac{1}{12}$				
$\frac{1}{12}$	$\frac{1}{12}$	$\frac{1}{12}$	$\frac{1}{12}$	$\frac{1}{12}$	$\frac{1}{12}$						

$\frac{2}{3} > \frac{2}{4}$

2 Compare $\frac{3}{4}$ and $\frac{7}{8}$ using the least common denominator. $\frac{3}{4} < \frac{7}{8}$

3 Idalia made 1 out of 2 baskets and Susan made 3 out of 5 baskets. Who made a greater fraction of baskets? Susan

CHECK What You Know

As a class, have students complete Exercises 1–10 in **Check What You Know** as you observe their work.

Exercise 10 Assess student comprehension before assigning practice exercises.

BL Alternate Teaching Strategy

If students have trouble finding the least common denominator…

Then use one of these reteach options:

1. CRM **Daily Reteach Worksheet** (p. 48)
2. Have them list the multiples of each denominator and circle the least common multiple.

3 Practice

Differentiate practice using these leveled assignments for Exercises 11–33.

Level	Assignment
BL Below/ Approaching Level	11–14, 19–22, 27, 33
OL On Level	11–14, 27–29, 33
AL Above/Below Level	12–30 even, 31–33

Have students discuss and complete the Higher Order Thinking problems. For Exercise 32, have the students verify their answer with several examples.

WRITING IN ▸MATH Have students complete Exercise 33 in their Math Journals. You may choose to use this as an optional formative assessment.

Additional Answers

10. The LCM is the least common multiple of two or more numbers. It is used to find the LCD, which is the least common denominator of two or more fractions.

33. Sample answer: $\frac{5}{6}$ of the students have a bike and $\frac{3}{8}$ have both a bike and a scooter. Do a greater fraction of students have both a bike and a scooter? Answer: no, because $\frac{5}{6} > \frac{3}{8}$.

COMMON ERROR!

Exercise 17 Students may try to change $\frac{3}{10}$ to $\frac{5}{12}$ by adding 2 to the numerator and denominator. Stress that you multiply the fraction by a fraction whose value is 1 so that you do not change its value. Fractions such as $\frac{2}{2}$, $\frac{3}{3}$, and so on are other names for 1.

★ indicates multi-step problem

CHECK What You Know

Compare each pair of fractions using models or the LCD.
See Examples 1–3 (pp. 404–405) See students' work for models.

1. $\frac{1}{5}$ and $\frac{1}{3}$ $\frac{3}{15} < \frac{5}{15}$ **2.** $\frac{1}{2}$ and $\frac{1}{6}$ $\frac{3}{6} > \frac{1}{6}$ **3.** $\frac{3}{4}$ and $\frac{7}{8}$ $\frac{6}{8} < \frac{7}{8}$ **4.** $\frac{2}{3}$ and $\frac{7}{10}$ $\frac{20}{30} < \frac{21}{30}$

Algebra Replace each ● with <, >, or = to make a true statement. See Examples 1–3 (pp. 404–405)

5. $\frac{1}{3}$ ● $\frac{5}{9}$ < **6.** $\frac{2}{3}$ ● $\frac{7}{12}$ > **7.** $\frac{1}{4}$ ● $\frac{1}{6}$ > **8.** $\frac{2}{5}$ ● $\frac{6}{15}$ =

9. A recipe calls for $\frac{5}{8}$ cup of brown sugar and $\frac{2}{3}$ cup of flour. Which ingredient is greater? flour

10. 

Explain how the LCM and the LCD are alike. How are they different? See margin.

Practice and Problem Solving

See page R26.

Compare each pair of fractions using models or the LCD.
See Examples 1–3 (pp. 404–405) See students' work for models.

11. $\frac{2}{3}$ and $\frac{3}{4}$ $\frac{8}{12} < \frac{9}{12}$ **12.** $\frac{1}{5}$ and $\frac{3}{15}$ $\frac{3}{15} = \frac{3}{15}$ **13.** $\frac{1}{6}$ and $\frac{1}{3}$ $\frac{1}{6} < \frac{2}{6}$ **14.** $\frac{2}{5}$ and $\frac{3}{4}$ $\frac{8}{20} < \frac{15}{20}$

15. $\frac{4}{5}$ and $\frac{5}{6}$ $\frac{24}{30} < \frac{25}{30}$ **16.** $\frac{7}{8}$ and $\frac{2}{3}$ $\frac{21}{24} > \frac{16}{24}$ **17.** $\frac{3}{10}$ and $\frac{1}{12}$ $\frac{18}{60} > \frac{5}{60}$ **18.** $\frac{5}{6}$ and $\frac{4}{9}$ $\frac{15}{18} > \frac{8}{18}$

Algebra Replace each ● with <, >, or = to make a true statement. See Examples 1–3 (pp. 404–405)

19. $\frac{2}{5}$ ● $\frac{3}{10}$ > **20.** $\frac{3}{4}$ ● $\frac{3}{7}$ > **21.** $\frac{1}{5}$ ● $\frac{1}{4}$ < **22.** $\frac{1}{2}$ ● $\frac{6}{12}$ =

23. $\frac{2}{6}$ ● $\frac{3}{7}$ < **24.** $\frac{11}{12}$ ● $\frac{5}{8}$ > **25.** $\frac{3}{8}$ ● $\frac{5}{6}$ < **26.** $\frac{15}{16}$ ● $\frac{3}{8}$ >

27. A trail mix has $\frac{1}{2}$ cup of raisins, $\frac{1}{4}$ cup of almonds, and $\frac{2}{3}$ cup of peanuts. Which ingredient is greater? peanuts

28. A class survey showed that $\frac{7}{15}$ of the class liked soccer, $\frac{3}{10}$ liked tennis, and $\frac{2}{5}$ liked basketball. Which sport was liked the least? tennis

★29. The amounts of water four runners drank are shown at the right. Who drank the most? Keisha

★30. The fifth graders were given sandwiches for lunch during their field trip. Nathan ate $\frac{5}{6}$ of his sandwich, Leroy ate $\frac{7}{8}$ of his sandwich, and Sofia ate $\frac{5}{8}$ of her sandwich. Who had the least amount of sandwich left to eat? Leroy

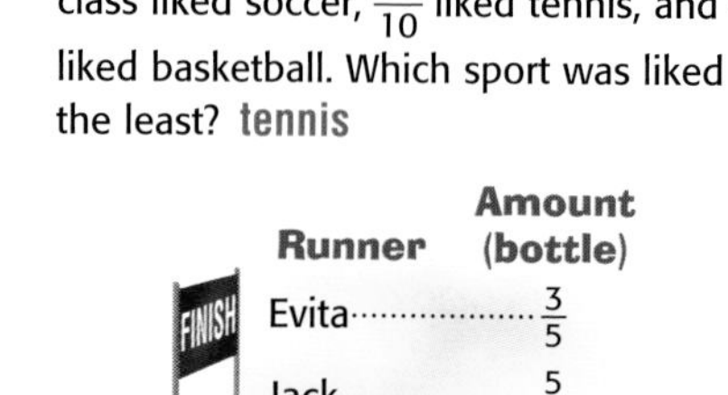

Runner	Amount (bottle)
Evita	$\frac{3}{5}$
Jack	$\frac{5}{8}$
Keisha	$\frac{3}{4}$
Sirjo	$\frac{5}{10}$

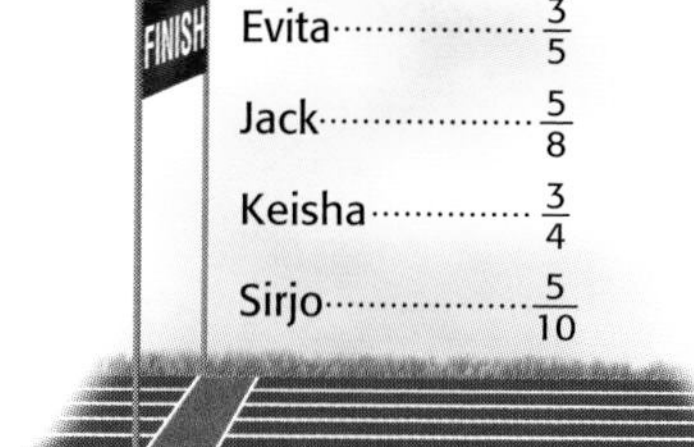

H.O.T. Problems

31. OPEN ENDED Replace ■ with a number to make $\frac{■}{24} > \frac{1}{4}$ a true statement. Sample answer: 7

32. NUMBER SENSE Suppose two fractions have the same numerator and different denominators. How can you decide which fraction is greater without finding the LCD? Sample answer: The fraction with the smaller denominator is greater.

33. WRITING IN MATH Write a real-world problem that can be solved by comparing two fractions with different denominators. Then solve. Support your answer with a model. See margin.

TEST Practice

34. The table shows the cost of renting a bicycle. If the pattern continues, how much will it cost to rent a bicycle for 6 hours? (Lesson 9-7) C

Number of Hours	Cost ($)
2	12
3	18
4	24
5	30

A $6 **C** $36

B $32 **D** $42

35. Eighteen out of 24 of Emil's CDs are country music. Five out of 8 of Imani's CDs are country music. Which is a true statement? (Lesson 9-9) J

F Both of their CD collections are half country music.

G Both of their CD collections are less than half country music.

H Emil's collection is closer to half country than Imani's collection.

J Imani's collection is closer to half country than Emil's collection.

Spiral Review

36. Find the missing number in the pattern 1, 2, 4, 7, ■, 16, … . (Lesson 9-8) 11

Find the first two common multiples of each pair of numbers. (Lesson 9-7)

37. 4 and 6 12, 24 **38.** 3, 9 9, 18 **39.** 2, 5 10, 20 **40.** 8, 20 40, 80

41. The table shows the number of games won and lost by the girls' basketball team. What fraction of the games did the team win? Write the fraction in simplest form. (Lesson 9-4) $\frac{3}{4}$

Number of Wins	Number of Losses
12	4

Homework Practice (p. 50) OL

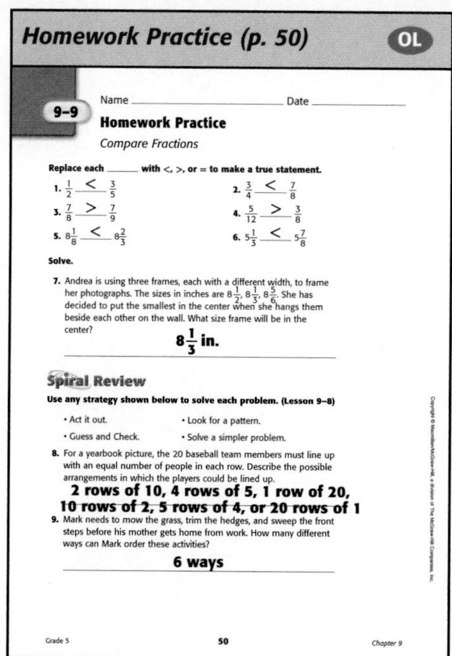

9-9 Name ______ Date ______

Homework Practice

Compare Fractions

Replace each ____ with <, >, or = to make a true statement.

1. $\frac{1}{2}$ < $\frac{3}{5}$
2. $\frac{3}{4}$ < $\frac{7}{8}$
3. $\frac{7}{8}$ > $\frac{7}{9}$
4. $\frac{5}{12}$ > $\frac{3}{8}$
5. $8\frac{1}{8}$ < $8\frac{2}{3}$
6. $5\frac{1}{3}$ < $5\frac{7}{8}$

Solve.

7. Andrea is using three frames, each with a different width, to frame her photographs. The sizes in inches are $8\frac{1}{2}$, $8\frac{1}{3}$, $8\frac{5}{6}$. She has decided to put the smallest in the center when she hangs them beside each other on the wall. What size frame will be in the center? $8\frac{1}{3}$ in.

Spiral Review

Use any strategy shown below to solve each problem. (Lesson 9-8)

- Act it out.
- Look for a pattern.
- Guess and Check.
- Solve a simpler problem.

8. For a yearbook picture, the 20 baseball team members must line up with an equal number of people in each row. Describe the possible arrangements in which the players could be lined up. **2 rows of 10, 4 rows of 5, 1 row of 20, 10 rows of 2, 5 rows of 4, or 20 rows of 1**

9. Mark needs to mow the grass, trim the hedges, and sweep the front steps before his mother gets home from work. How many different ways can Mark order these activities? **6 ways**

Grade 5 50 Chapter 9

4 Assess

Formative Assessment

Write $\frac{3}{4}$, $\frac{2}{3}$, and $\frac{7}{8}$ on the board.

- **How do you find the least common multiple of the denominators?** List the multiples of each denominator and circle the least one they all have in common.
- **What is the least common denominator of the fractions?** 24
- **What fraction do you multiply $\frac{3}{4}$ by to make it have the denominator 24?** $\frac{6}{6}$
- Have students change each fraction to twenty-fourths and arrange the fractions in order from least to greatest. $\frac{16}{24}$, $\frac{18}{24}$, $\frac{21}{14}$
- Then, have them place the original fraction in order from least to greatest. $\frac{2}{3}$, $\frac{3}{4}$, $\frac{7}{8}$

Quick Check **Are students continuing to struggle with comparing fractions using common denominators?**

If Yes → CRM Reteach Worksheet (p. 48)

If No → Independent Work Options (p. 402B)
CRM Skills Practice Worksheet (p. 49)
CRM Enrich Worksheet (p. 52)

Yesterday's News Ask students to explain how finding the common multiple of two numbers helped them to find the least common denominator of two fractions.

TEST Practice

Reviews Lessons 9-7 and 9-9

Assign the Test Practice problems to provide daily reinforcement of test-taking skills.

Spiral Review

Reviews Lessons 9-4, 9-7, and 9-8

Review and assess mastery of skills and concepts from previous chapters.

Lesson Planner

Objective

Interpret information and data from social studies to solve problems.

National Standard 

Students will understand the folklore and other cultural contributions from various regions of the United States and how they helped to form a national heritage.

Activate Prior Knowledge

Before you turn students' attention to the pages, ask them to discuss dreamcatchers.

- **What is a dreamcatcher?** a decoration you hang over your bed
- **Who invented dreamcatchers?** A Native American tribe; the Chippewa people.

Use the Student Page

Ask students to read the information on p. 404 and answer these questions:

- **What is the prime factorization of the number of groups of Chippewas in North America?** $2 \times 2 \times 3 \times 5 \times 5 = 300$
- **Is the number of beads in a simple dreamcatcher a prime or a composite number?** composite
- **The fraction, in simplest form, that represents the number of yards of string to the the number of beads in a simple dreamcatcher is $\frac{1}{4}$. Find an equivalent fraction for $\frac{1}{4}$.** Sample answer: $\frac{7}{28}$

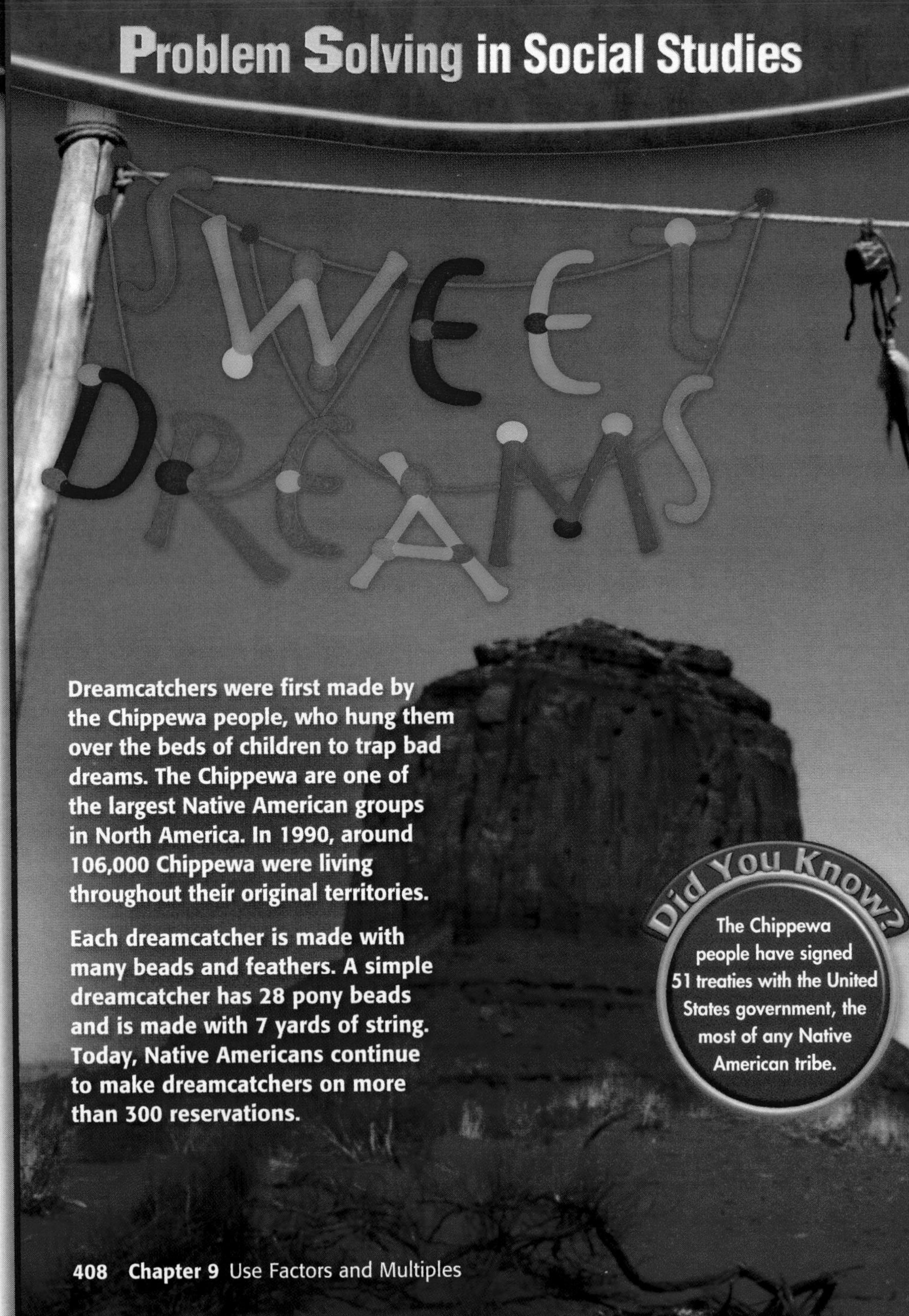

Problem Solving in Social Studies
SWEET DREAMS
Dreamcatchers were first made by the Chippewa people, who hung them over the beds of children to trap bad dreams. The Chippewa are one of the largest Native American groups in North America. In 1990, around 106,000 Chippewa were living throughout their original territories.
Each dreamcatcher is made with many beads and feathers. A simple dreamcatcher has 28 pony beads and is made with 7 yards of string. Today, Native Americans continue to make dreamcatchers on more than 300 reservations.
Did You Know?
The Chippewa people have signed 51 treaties with the United States government, the most of any Native American tribe.
408 Chapter 9 Use Factors and Multiples

Real-World Math

Use the information on page 408 to solve each problem.

1. In a simple dreamcatcher, how many beads do you use for each yard of string? **4**
2. For each dreamcatcher you made, you used 12 beads. If you had 144 beads, how many dreamcatchers did you make? **12**
3. Each time you add a feather to a dreamcatcher, you add 3 turquoise beads. Use a function table to find out how many beads you will need if you have 2, 5, 8, or 13 feathers in your dreamcatcher. **See margin.**
4. Find the rule for the function table you created in Exercise 3. **3x**
5. You are making dreamcatchers that require 6 beads for every 1 feather. Let *f* represent the number of feathers. Then write a function rule that relates the total number of beads to the number of feathers. **6*f***
6. Use the function rule from Exercise 5 to find the number of beads you would use if you made a dreamcatcher with 17 feathers. **102**
7. Suppose you use 12 feathers and a certain amount of beads to make a dreamcatcher. If you had 48 feathers and beads, how many beads did you use? **36**

Real-World Math

Assign the exercises on p. 409. Encourage students to choose a problem-solving strategy before beginning each exercise. If necessary, review the strategies suggested in Lesson 9-8, p. 401.

Exercise 2 Remind students that they may want to use a factor tree to find the prime factorization of 28.

Exercise 4 Tell students that they will need to create their function table for Exercise 3 first before completing this exercise.

WRITING IN MATH Have students create a word problem that uses the information found in the text and in the chart on p. 409.

Extend the Activity

Have students figure out how many feathers Orlando would use in his dreamcatcher if he doubled the number of beads.

Additional Answer

3.

Number of feathers, *f*	Number of beads, *b*
2	6
5	15
8	24
13	39

Chapter 9 Study Guide and Review

FOLDABLES Dinah Zike's Foldables

Use these lesson suggestions to incorporate the Foldable during the chapter. Students can then use their Foldables to review for the test.

Lesson 9-5 Students write decimals as fractions and fractions as decimals beneath the fourth tab of the Foldable.

Key Vocabulary

The page references after each word denote where that term was first introduced. If students have difficulty answer Exercises 1–6, remind them they can use the page references to review the vocabulary terms.

Vocabulary Review

Review chapter vocabulary using one of the following options.

- **Visual Vocabulary Cards** (6, 20, 35)
- **eGlossary** at macmillanmh.com

Additional Answers

1. prime number
2. equivalent fractions

Chapter 9 Study Guide and Review

Math Online macmillanmh.com
- STUDY TO GO
- Vocabulary Review

FOLDABLES Study Organizer GET READY to Study

Be sure the following Big Ideas are written in your Foldable.

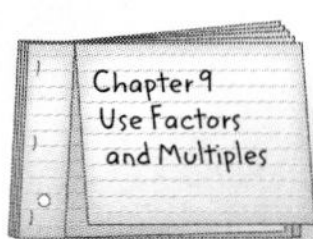

Key Concepts

Prime and Composite Numbers

- A prime number has exactly two factors, 1 and itself. A composite number has more than two factors. (p. 376)

prime numbers: 2, 3, 11, 29
composite numbers: 4, 8, 12, 20

Equivalent Fractions and Fractions in Simplest Form

- Fractions that have the same value are **equivalent fractions**. (p. 382)

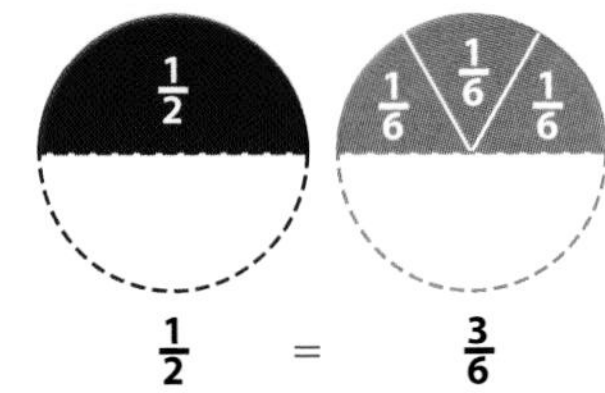

$\frac{1}{2}$  $\frac{3}{6}$

- A fraction is in **simplest form** when the GCF of the numerator and denominator is 1. (p. 386)

Compare Fractions

- To compare fractions with different denominators, rename the fractions using common denominators.

Key Vocabulary

common factor (p. 373)
composite number (p. 376)
equivalent fractions (p. 382)
prime number (p. 376)
simplest form (p. 386)

Vocabulary Check

Complete. Use a word from the Key Vocabulary list.

1–2. See margin.

1. A whole number greater than 1 that has exactly two factors, 1 and itself, is called a(n) __?__.
2. $\frac{3}{5}$ and $\frac{6}{10}$ are called __?__.
3. A whole number that has more than two factors is called a(n) __?__. composite number
4. A fraction is written in __?__ when the numerator and denominator have no common factor greater than 1. simplest form
5. A whole number that is a factor of two or more numbers is called a(n) __?__. common factor
6. The fraction $\frac{5}{12}$ is written in __?__. simplest form

Chapter 9 Project

A Portable Sieve

Alone, in pairs, or in small groups, have students discuss the results of their completed chapter project with the class. Assess their work using the Chapter Project rubric found in Chapter 9 Resource Masters, p. 63.

Lesson-by-Lesson Review

9-1 Common Factors (pp. 373–375)

Example 1
Find the greatest common factor of 6 and 21.

First, list the factors of 6 and 21.

factors of 6: 1, 2, 3, 6

factors of 21: 1, 3, 7, 21

The common factors are 1 and 3. The greatest of these is 3. So, the greatest common factor of 6 and 21 is 3.

Find the common factors of each set of numbers.

7. 6, 8 1, 2

8. 9, 21, and 24 1, 3

Find the GCF of each set of numbers.

9. 12, 30 6

10. 18, 45 9

11. Twelve pens and 16 pencils will be placed in bags with an equal number of each item. What is the most number of bags that can be made? 4 bags

9-2 Prime and Composite Numbers (pp. 378–381)

Example 2
Tell whether 51 is *prime* or *composite*.

$51 = 1 \times 51$ $51 = 3 \times 17$

factors of 51: 1, 3, 17, 51

Since 51 has more than two factors, it is a composite number.

Tell whether each number is *prime* or *composite*. 12–14. See margin.

12. 23 **13.** 48 **14.** 34

15. A goliath birdeater is a spider that can grow up to 28 centimeters. Find the prime factorization of 28. $2 \times 2 \times 7$

9-3 Equivalent Fractions (pp. 382–384) 16–18. Sample answers are given.

Example 3
Find two fractions that are equivalent to $\frac{2}{9}$.

Multiply $\frac{2}{9}$ by $\frac{2}{2}$. $\frac{2}{9} = \frac{2 \times 2}{9 \times 2} = \frac{4}{18}$

Multiply $\frac{2}{9}$ by $\frac{3}{3}$. $\frac{2}{9} = \frac{2 \times 3}{9 \times 3} = \frac{6}{27}$

So, $\frac{2}{9} = \frac{4}{18}$ and $\frac{2}{9} = \frac{6}{27}$.

Find two fractions that are equivalent to each fraction.

16. $\frac{1}{6}$ $\frac{2}{12}, \frac{3}{18}$ **17.** $\frac{4}{5}$ $\frac{8}{10}, \frac{12}{15}$ **18.** $\frac{2}{7}$ $\frac{4}{14}, \frac{6}{21}$

19. Lucinda cut her birthday cake into 16 slices. If Lucinda and her friends ate $\frac{1}{4}$ of the cake, how many pieces of cake did they eat? Support your answer with a model. See margin.

Lesson-by-Lesson Review

Have students complete the Lesson-by-Lesson Review on pp. 411–414. Then you can use ExamView® Assessment Suite to customize another review worksheet that practices all the objectives of this chapter or only the objectives on which your students need more help.

Intervention If the given examples are not sufficient to review the topics covered by the questions, use the page references next to the exercises to review that topic in the Student Edition.

Additional Answers

12. prime

13. composite

14. composite

19. 4; $\frac{4}{16} = \frac{1}{4}$

Study Guide and Review

Study Guide and Review

9-4 Simplest Form (pp. 386–389)

Example 4
Write $\frac{4}{20}$ in simplest form.

factors of 4: 1, 2, 4

factors of 20: 1, 2, 4, 5, 10, 20

The GCF of 4 and 20 is 4.

$\frac{4}{20} = \frac{4 \div 4}{20 \div 4} = \frac{1}{5}$ Divide the numerator and denominator by 4.

So, $\frac{4}{20}$ in simplest form is $\frac{1}{5}$.

Write each fraction in simplest form. If the fraction is already in simplest form, write *simplified*.

20. $\frac{2}{10}$ $\frac{1}{5}$
21. $\frac{4}{18}$ $\frac{2}{9}$
22. $\frac{6}{21}$ $\frac{2}{7}$
23. $\frac{8}{24}$ $\frac{1}{3}$
24. $\frac{12}{25}$ simplified
25. $\frac{20}{32}$ $\frac{5}{8}$
26. What fraction is represented by the model shown below? Write the fraction in simplest form. $\frac{6}{15}$; $\frac{2}{5}$

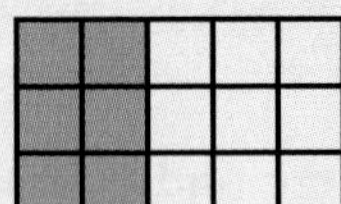

9-5 Decimals and Fractions (pp. 391–393)

Example 5
Write 0.45 as a fraction in simplest form.

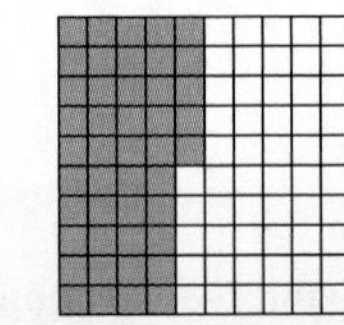

0.45 is 45 hundredths.

Step 1
Write a fraction with 100 as the denominator.

$0.45 = \frac{45}{100}$

Step 2
Simplify the fraction.

$\frac{45}{100} = \frac{45 \div 5}{100 \div 5}$ Divide by the GCF, 5.

$= \frac{9}{20}$ Simplify.

So, $0.45 = \frac{9}{20}$.

Write each decimal as a fraction in simplest form.

27. 0.9 $\frac{9}{10}$
28. 0.4 $\frac{2}{5}$
29. 0.13 $\frac{13}{100}$
30. 0.88 $\frac{22}{25}$
31. 0.28 $\frac{7}{25}$
32. 0.06 $\frac{3}{50}$
33. A model train is 0.025 the length of an actual train. What fraction of the actual train length is the model? Write the fraction in simplest form. $\frac{1}{40}$
34. A small black-legged tick is 0.125 inch long. What fraction of an inch is the black-legged tick? Write the fraction in simplest form. $\frac{1}{8}$

9-6 Problem-Solving Strategy: Look for a Pattern (pp. 394–395)

Example 6
This stairway is made of cubes. How many cubes would be needed to make it 7 steps high?

Understand You know how many cubes are 1, 2, and 3 steps.

Plan Look for a pattern.

Solve 2 steps: 2 + 1, or 3
3 steps: 3 + (2 + 1), or 6
4 steps: 4 + (3 + 2 + 1), or 10
7 steps: 7 + (6 + 5 + 4 + 3 + 2 + 1), or 28

Check Draw a picture and count the cubes. There are 28 cubes, so the answer is correct. ✓

35. Find the next three numbers.
3, 7, 12, 18, 25,... **33, 42, 52**

36. Bena makes bracelets. She uses red, white, and gray beads. If she continues her pattern, what color is the 15th bead? **gray**

37. Draw the next two figures in the pattern. **See margin.**

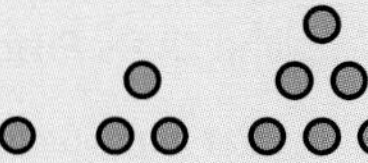

38. Jackson wrote the following fractions on the board.

$\frac{1}{2}, \frac{2}{5}, \frac{3}{8}, \frac{4}{11}, \frac{5}{14}$

If he continues writing fractions according to the pattern, what will be the next three fractions? **See margin.**

9-7 Multiples (pp. 396–399) **39, 40. See students' work for tables/graphs.**

Example 7
Find the LCM of 12 and 16.

List multiples of each number to find the least common multiple.

multiples of 12: 12, 24, 36, **48**, 60 ...

multiples of 16: 16, 32, **48**, 64, 80...

The LCM of 12 and 16 is 48.

Find the LCM of each set of numbers. Make a table or a graph.

39. 5 and 9 **45** **40.** 4, 7, and 14 **28**

41. Every 7 days, a video store gives free popcorn with movie rentals. Every 5 days, they offer a free movie. If they gave away popcorn and a movie today, when will they give away both again? **35 days**

Additional Answers

37.

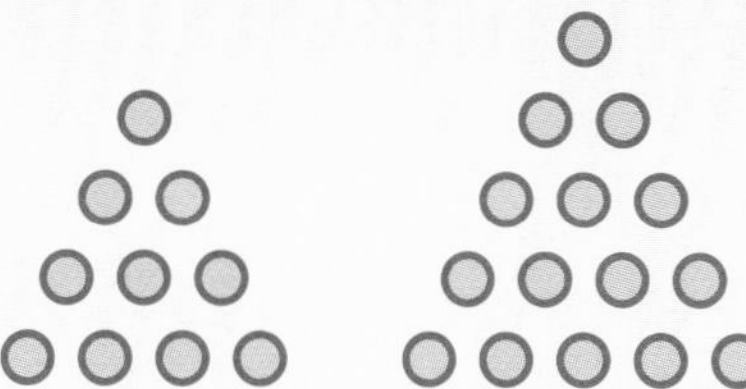

38. $\frac{6}{17}, \frac{7}{20}, \frac{8}{23}$

CHAPTER 9 Study Guide and Review

9-8 Problem-Solving Investigation: Choose a Strategy (pp. 400–401)

Example 8

Pilar has $69 to spend on presents. CDs cost $13, and DVDs cost $15. How many CDs and DVDs can she buy?

Understand You know how much money Pilar has. You know how much CDs and DVDs cost.

Plan Use can guess and check to find how many CDs and DVDs Pilar can buy.

Solve Pilar can buy 3 CDs and 2 DVDs with $69.

Check Look back. $13 + $13 + $13 + $15 + $15 = $69. So, Pilar is correct. ✓

43. 4 packages of hot dogs and 5 packages of buns

Solve. Use any strategy.

42. Charlotte has two hamster cages. When she cleans them, she uses $\frac{3}{8}$ bag of hamster bedding for one cage and $\frac{1}{4}$ bag for the other cage. Does she need 1 bag or 2 bags when she cleans the cages? 1 bag

43. Hot dogs are sold in packages of 10. Hot dog buns are sold in packages of 8. What are the fewest packages of hot dogs and packages of buns needed so the number of hot dogs matches the number of buns?

44. The table shows the number of tickets sold for the school play. If adult tickets were $3.50 and student tickets were $2, what were the total sales? $851

Ticket	Number Sold
Adult	126
Student	205

9-9 Compare Fractions (pp. 402–405)

Example 9

Replace ● with <, >, or = to make $\frac{2}{5}$ ● $\frac{3}{4}$ a true statement.

The LCM of 5 and 4 is 20. So, 20 is the LCD of $\frac{2}{5}$ and $\frac{3}{4}$.

$\frac{2}{5} = \frac{8}{20}$ THINK $5 \times 4 = 20, 2 \times 4 = 8$

$\frac{3}{4} = \frac{15}{20}$ THINK $4 \times 5 = 20, 3 \times 5 = 15$

Since $8 < 15$, $\frac{8}{20} < \frac{15}{20}$. So, $\frac{2}{5} < \frac{3}{4}$.

Replace each ● with <, >, or = to make a true statement.

45. $\frac{1}{4}$ ● $\frac{6}{8}$ <

46. $\frac{2}{3}$ ● $\frac{3}{5}$ >

47. $\frac{2}{3}$ ● $\frac{7}{12}$ >

48. $\frac{5}{8}$ ● $\frac{7}{12}$ >

49. Christine worked on social studies homework $\frac{3}{4}$ of an hour. She worked on math for $\frac{5}{6}$ of an hour. On which subject did she spend more time? math

Chapter Test

Find the common factors of each set of numbers.

1. 15, 45 1, 3, 5, 15
2. 24, 32, and 40 1, 2, 4, 8

Find the GCF of each set of numbers.

3. 8, 28 4
4. 21, 24, and 27 3

5. **MULTIPLE CHOICE** Which is a prime factor of the composite number 24? A
   - A 3
   - B 4
   - C 5
   - D 12

6. The table shows the countries with the most wins for the Tour De France cycling race. Tell whether each number in the table is *prime* or *composite*.

Country	Number of Wins
Belgium	18
France	36
Netherlands	2
Spain	8
United States	7

See Ch. 9 Answer Appendix.

7. Which fractions below are equivalent? $\frac{4}{5}$ and $\frac{24}{30}$

$\frac{4}{5}$ $\frac{6}{10}$ $\frac{24}{30}$ $\frac{2}{5}$ $\frac{16}{25}$

Write each fraction in simplest form. If the fraction is already in simplest form, write *simplified*.

8. $\frac{9}{18}$ $\frac{1}{2}$
9. $\frac{15}{16}$ simplified
10. $\frac{28}{32}$ $\frac{7}{8}$
11. $\frac{6}{27}$ $\frac{2}{9}$

12. The table shows when customers at Maltey's Burgers receive items free with the purchase of a burger deal.

Free Item	When
Milkshake	every 4 days
Tater tots	every 10 days

If they gave away both items today, in how many days will a customer be able to get both a milkshake and tater tots free again? 20 days

Write each decimal as a fraction in simplest form.

13. 0.7 $\frac{7}{10}$
14. 0.24 $\frac{6}{25}$
15. 0.875 $\frac{7}{8}$
16. 0.02 $\frac{1}{50}$

17. What is the least common multiple of 12 and 20? 60

18. **Measurement** Grasshoppers can jump 40 times the length of their body. If one foot equals 12 inches, how many feet could a 3-inch grasshopper jump? 10 ft

19. **MULTIPLE CHOICE** Amber went to the library after school 3 of the 5 school days this week. Which fraction is less than $\frac{3}{5}$? F
   - F $\frac{1}{2}$
   - G $\frac{3}{4}$
   - H $\frac{4}{5}$
   - J $\frac{5}{6}$

20. **WRITING IN MATH** Explain the steps you would take to make the following a true statement. See Ch. 9 Answer Appendix.

$\frac{3}{10} \bullet \frac{9}{20}$

Summative Assessment 415

Chapter 9 Chapter Test

Summative Assessment

Use these alternate leveled chapter tests to differentiate assessment for the specific needs of your students.

Leveled Chapter 9 Tests			
Form	**Type**	**Level**	**CRM Pages**
1	Multiple Choice	BL	65–66
2A	Multiple Choice	OL	67–68
2B	Multiple Choice	OL	69–70
2C	Free Response	AL	71–72
2D	Free Response	AL	73–74
3	Free Response	AL	75–76

BL = below/approaching grade level
OL = on grade level
AL = above/beyond grade level

Vocabulary Test

CRM **Chapter 9 Resource Masters** (p. 63)

ExamView Assessment Suite Customize and create multiple versions of your Chapter Test and the test answer keys.

Data-Driven Decision Making

Based on the results of the Chapter Test, use the following to review concepts that continue to present students with problems.

Exercises	State/Local Standards	What's the Math?	Error Analysis	Resources for Review
1–4, 12 17		Identify common factors of a set of whole numbers. Identify multiples.	Does not put 1 as a factor of all numbers. Does not list all factors. Does not understand term "GCF," or "least common multiple."	Strategic Intervention Guide (pp. 20, 92, 94, 100, 102, 104, 112, 116) CRM Chapter 9 Resource Masters (Reteach) Math Adventures My Math Zone Chapter 9 Math Online Extra Examples • Concepts in Motion
5–6		Identify prime and composite numbers.	Does not understand "prime factor," "composite."	
7–11 19-20		Write fractions in simplest form. Compare fractions.	Divides numerator and denominator by different numbers when reducing. Does not know how to compare fractions.	
13–16		Write fractions as decimals and decimals as fractions.	Does not know how to convert a decimal to a fraction. Does not compute accurately. Does not know how to put in simplest form.	

Test Practice

Formative Assessment

- Use student pp. 416–417 as practice and cumulative review. The questions are written in the same style as many state tests.
- You can also use these two pages to benchmark student progress, or as an alternate homework assignment.

Additional practice pages can be found in the Chapter 9 Resource Masters.

CRM **Chapter 9 Resource Masters**
Cumulative Test Practice

- Multiple Choice format (pp. 65–70)
- Free Response format (pp. 71–76)

ExamView® Assessment Suite Create practice worksheets or tests that align to your state standards.

Math Online Have students visit macmillanmh.com for additional practice to reinforce your state standards.

Math Online macmillanmh.com
• Test Practice

9 Test Practice
Cumulative, Chapters 1–9

PART 1 Multiple Choice

Read each question. Then fill in the correct answer on the answer sheet provided by your teacher or on a sheet of paper.

1. Sancho picked up a handful of coins from a jar without looking. He got 7 pennies, 5 nickels, 3 dimes, and 2 quarters. What fraction of the coins that he picked were nickels? C

A $\frac{2}{17}$ **C** $\frac{5}{17}$
B $\frac{3}{17}$ **D** $\frac{7}{17}$

2. Paige cut a cake into 20 pieces. If 14 pieces have been eaten, what fraction of the cake remains? H

F $\frac{1}{10}$ **H** $\frac{3}{10}$
G $\frac{1}{5}$ **J** $\frac{2}{5}$

3. Natalie has washed the dishes 8 out of the last 12 nights. Which fraction shows the portion of time spent washing dishes? C

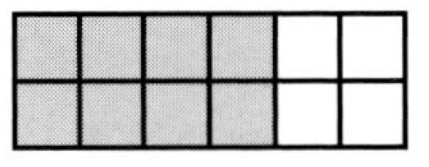

A $\frac{1}{3}$ **C** $\frac{2}{3}$
B $\frac{1}{2}$ **D** $\frac{5}{6}$

4. Emilia used 4 of her 8 stamps to mail letters. Which fraction is less than $\frac{4}{8}$? J

F $\frac{5}{8}$ **H** $\frac{1}{2}$
G $\frac{3}{4}$ **J** $\frac{3}{7}$

5. Which is a prime factor of the composite number 32? A

A 2 **C** 4
B 3 **D** 5

6. The table shows the number of bills of each value that Bree received for her birthday. In all, what fraction of the number of bills that Bree received for her birthday were $10 or $20 bills? H

Birthday Money	
Value of Bill	Number of bills
$5	5
$10	3
$20	2
$50	1

F $\frac{5}{22}$ **H** $\frac{5}{11}$
G $\frac{3}{11}$ **J** $\frac{8}{11}$

7. Clarence bought a 3-pound can of mixed nuts for a party. One-fourth of the can is made up of walnuts, and two-fifths of the can is made up of peanuts. Which of the following shows the correct relationship between $\frac{1}{4}$ and $\frac{2}{5}$? C

A $\frac{1}{4} = \frac{2}{5}$ **C** $\frac{1}{4} < \frac{2}{5}$
B $\frac{1}{4} > \frac{2}{5}$ **D** $\frac{1}{5} < \frac{3}{10}$

Test-Taking Tip

Tell students to read the question carefully. They can break it into smaller parts to make it easier to solve.

Preparing for Standardized Tests
For test-taking strategies and practice, see pages R42–R55.

8. An assembly hall was set up with 20 rows of chairs. Each row had 16 chairs. In addition, there were 15 chairs on stage. Which expression can be used to find how many chairs there were in all? F

F $(20 \times 16) + 15$
G $(20 + 16) + 15$
H $(20 \times 15) + 16$
J $(20 + 15) \times 16$

9. Which group shows the prime factorization of the number 252? C

A $2 \times 3 \times 3 \times 7$
B $2 \times 2 \times 2 \times 3 \times 5$
C $2 \times 2 \times 3 \times 3 \times 7$
D $2 \times 2 \times 2 \times 3 \times 3 \times 7$

10. A florist sells vases of roses for $35 each. If the florist sold 62 vases last weekend, how much money did she collect? H

F $1,855
G $1,930
H $2,170
J $2,310

PART 2 Short Response

Record your answers on the answer sheet provided by your teacher or on a sheet of paper.

11. List all of the factors of 68. 1, 2, 34, 68, 4,17

12. A pizza was divided into eighths. You ate $\frac{3}{4}$ of the pizza. How many slices did you eat? 6

PART 3 Extended Response

Record your answers on the answer sheet provided by your teacher or on a sheet of paper. Show your work.

13. Explain the difference between a prime number and a composite number. Be sure to include examples of each. See margin.

14. Determine if $\frac{1}{3}$ and $\frac{3}{9}$ are equivalent fractions by using a drawing. See margin.

NEED EXTRA HELP?														
If You Missed Question...	1	2	3	4	5	6	7	8	9	10	11	12	13	14
Go to Lesson...	9-4	9-4	9-4	9-9	9-2	9-9	9-9	6-6	9-2	9-4	9-1	9-3	9-2	9-3

Answer Sheet Practice

Have students simulate taking a state test by recording their answers on a practice recording sheet.

CRM **Chapter 9 Resource Masters**
Student Recording Sheet (p. 81)

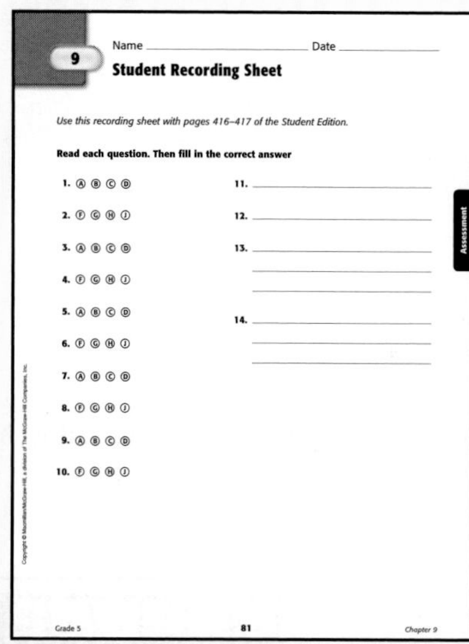
9 Name ______ Date ______
Student Recording Sheet

Use this recording sheet with pages 416–417 of the Student Edition.

Read each question. Then fill in the correct answer

1. Ⓐ Ⓑ Ⓒ Ⓓ 11. ______
2. Ⓕ Ⓖ Ⓗ Ⓙ 12. ______
3. Ⓐ Ⓑ Ⓒ Ⓓ 13. ______
4. Ⓕ Ⓖ Ⓗ Ⓙ
5. Ⓐ Ⓑ Ⓒ Ⓓ 14. ______
6. Ⓕ Ⓖ Ⓗ Ⓙ
7. Ⓐ Ⓑ Ⓒ Ⓓ
8. Ⓕ Ⓖ Ⓗ Ⓙ
9. Ⓐ Ⓑ Ⓒ Ⓓ
10. Ⓕ Ⓖ Ⓗ Ⓙ

Assessment

Grade 5 81 Chapter 9

Additional Answers

13. A prime number has exactly two factors. A composite number has more than two factors.

14. Yes, they are equivalent.

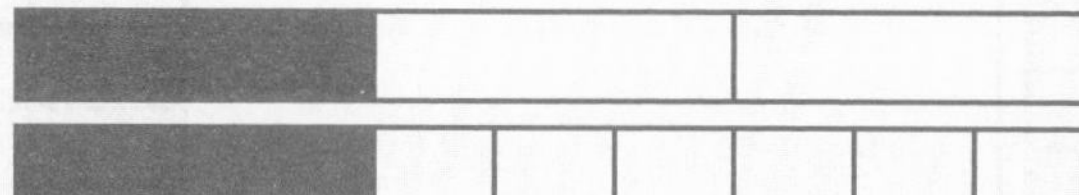

Page 375, Lesson 9-1

29. Sample answers: 15 and 30; Find $1 \times 3 \times 5$ to get the first number, 15. Then multiply by another number, such as 2, to get the second number. In this case, the second number is 30. Both 15 and 30 have factors of 1, 3, and 5.

30. 4 and 8; sample answer: since 4 is a factor of the number find multiples of 4. 12 is the largest number, so the 2 multiples of 4 less than 12 are 4 and 8.

31. Sample answer: Yes; when 1 is the only common factor of two numbers, then the GCF is 1. For example, the GCF of 5 and 7 is 1 because 1 is the only common factor of the numbers.

Page 377, Explore 9-2

1. No; 2 is a prime number because it only has two factors: 1 and 2. It can be shown in exactly two different arrangements.

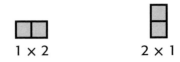

2. Sample answer: No, not all odd numbers are prime. For example, 9 is an odd number. You can show the number 9 in 3 ways.

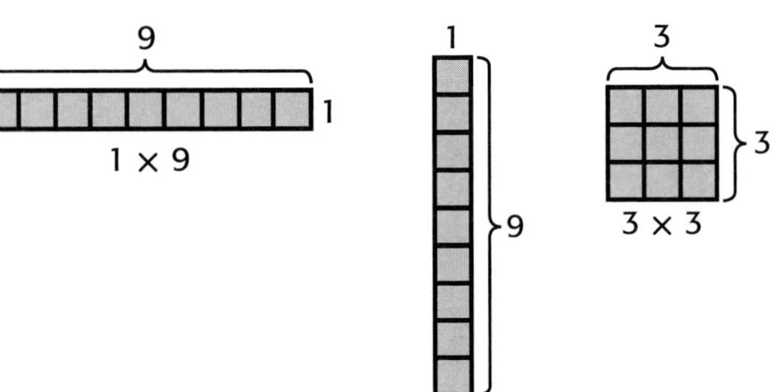

10. Sample answer: 21 is composite because it can be shown in four different rectangular arrangements: 1×21, 21×1, 3×7, and 7×3.

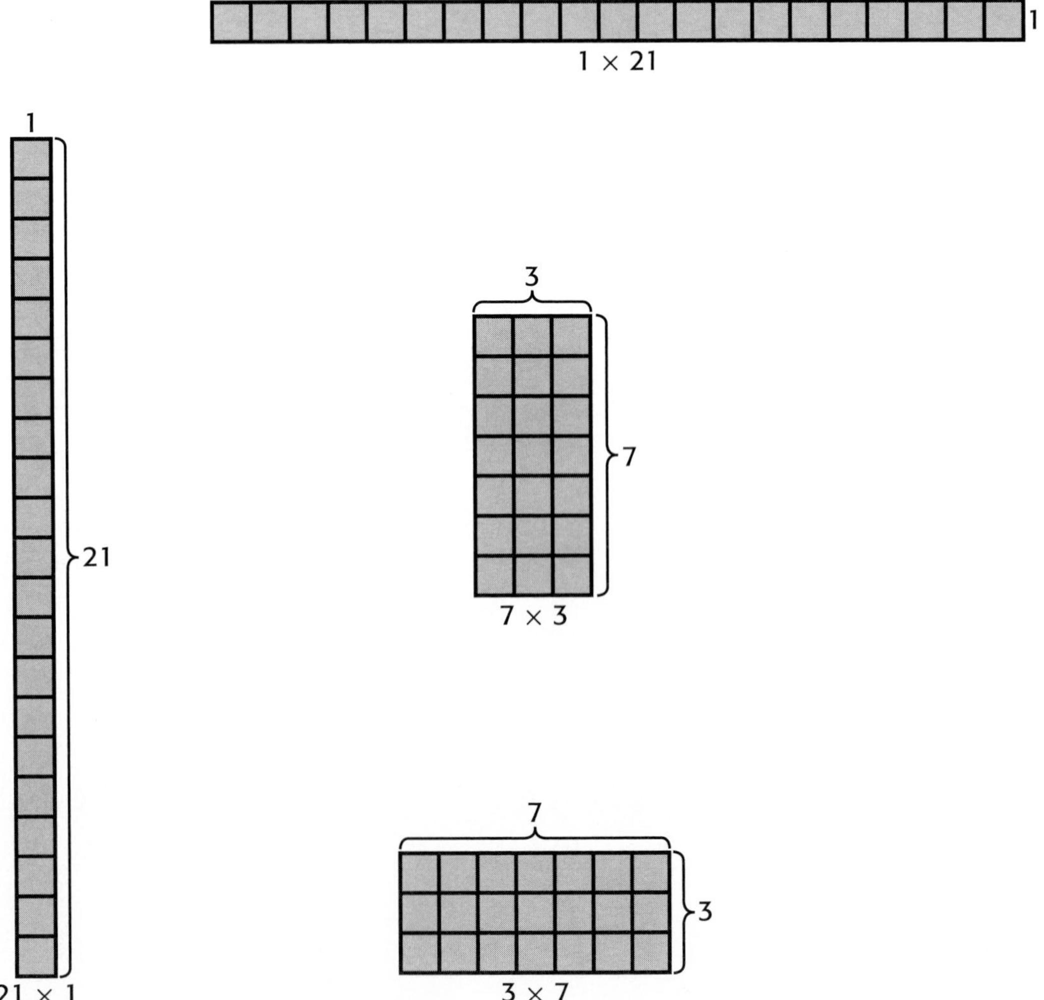

Page 380, Lesson 9-2

11. Yes; he could have 1 row of 21 cars, 21 rows of 1 car, 3 rows of 7 cars, or 7 rows of 3 cars.

37. Sample answer: If a number of objects can be arranged as a rectangle in exactly two ways, then the number is prime. If a number of objects can be arranged as a rectangle in more than two ways, then the number is composite.

Page 384, Lesson 9-3

33. Sample answer: Antwon; Jeremy incorrectly added 2 to the numerator and denominator. He should have multiplied each by 2, like Antwon did.

34. Sample answer: A pizza is cut into 4 slices and 3 slices are taken. $\frac{3}{4} = \frac{6}{8}$; the same pizza is cut into 8 slices and 6 slices are taken.

Page 388, Lesson 9-4

31. Sample answer: A fifth grade student has answered 14 out 18 questions on the math test. What fraction of the math test has the student completed?; $\frac{7}{9}$

32. $\frac{5}{25}$; It is the only fraction that equals $\frac{1}{5}$ when written in simplest form. The other fractions equal $\frac{1}{4}$.

33. Sample answer: Find the GCF of 24 and 36, which is 12. Then divide 24 and 36 by 12 to get the fraction $\frac{2}{3}$.

Page 390, Mid-Chapter Check

15. Sample answers: $\frac{4}{14}, \frac{6}{21}$

16. Sample answers: $\frac{2}{10}, \frac{3}{15}$

17. Sample answers: $\frac{2}{5}, \frac{8}{20}$

18. Sample answers: $\frac{6}{16}, \frac{9}{24}$

25. Sample answer: Multiply the numerator and denominator of $\frac{6}{10}$ by 2 to get $\frac{12}{20}$. Divide the numerator and denominator of $\frac{6}{10}$ by 2 to get $\frac{3}{5}$.

Pages 392–393, Lesson 9-5

8. Sample answer: Write the decimal number as the numerator of a fraction with a denominator of 10, 100, or 1,000, and so on. Then simplify the fraction.; For example, 0.9 would be written as $\frac{9}{10}$.

29. Sample answer: Marcella used a piece of fabric that measures 0.35 yard long. What would this length be as a fraction?

30. Sample answer: Since the last place value of the decimal is the hundredths place, the decimal is 8 hundredths which is written as $\frac{8}{100}$.

Page 395, Lesson 9-6

2. Shawna's pattern is to increase her distance ran each day. Eventually, she will exceed her physical capacity or her time limits.

5.

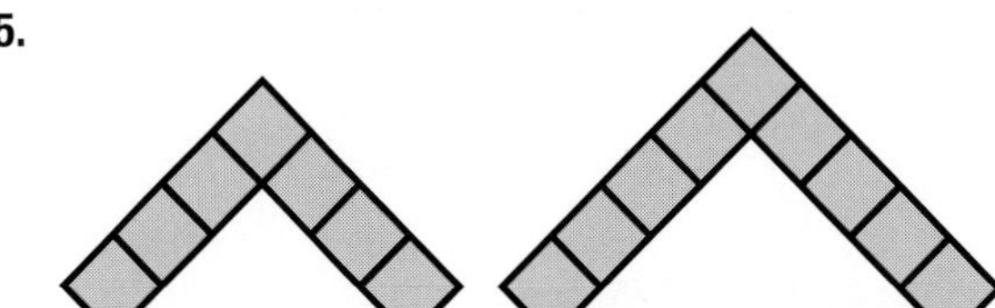

6. The price is \$0.20 more than the number of pencils.

10. Sample answer: Add 1.2 to the number of miles he will ride on Saturday; $8.0 + 1.2 = 9.2$ mi

11. 21, 34, 55; sample answer: Each number is the sum of the previous two numbers.

12. Sample answer: Marcella put \$2.45 in her piggy bank on Monday. Each day, she increased the amount she added to her bank by \$0.35. How much money did she add to her bank on Friday? \$3.85

Page 398, Lesson 9-7

31. Sample answer: Mrs. Cook washes her windows every 12th day. Mrs. Henderson washes her windows every 15th day. On what day will they both was their windows?; LCM: 60

32. Bryant; the LCM of 18 and 24 is 72. 432 is a common multiple of the numbers, but not the least common multiple.

34. The GCF is 9; it is the greatest number that is a factor of both 36 and 45. The LCM of 36 and 45 is 180; it is the least number that is a multiple of both 36 and 45.

Page 401, Lesson 9-8

3. Annette saved $14 \times \$5.00 = \$70.00$. Isabel saved $\$7.00 \times 11 = \$77.00$. Isabel saved \$7.00 more than Annette.; solve a simpler problem

4. The 11th pitch will be a fastball. The pattern repeats:
F F S S C F F S S C
F

5. He bought 2 adult tickets and 4 children's tickets.

6. He adds $5 \times \$2.50$ or \$12.50. He has \$65.50 altogether.

7. Maggie's lunch cost \$7.50; Ty's lunch cost \$3.00. Maggie's lunch cost \$4.50 more than Ty's.

9. The pattern repeats every four links. The 17th design will be the same as the first one.

10. First, you guess, or estimate, a reasonable answer. Then, check it by working the problem. If needed, guess again, re-work the problem, and see if you have a reasonable answer. Keep guessing until your answer works.

Page 415, Chapter Test

6. composite; composite; prime; composite; prime

20. Sample answer: Find the LCM of the denominators, 20. Then write an equivalent fraction with a denominator of 20 for each fraction, $\frac{6}{20}$ and $\frac{9}{20}$. Compare the numerators.; $\frac{6}{20} < \frac{9}{20}$ or $\frac{3}{10} < \frac{9}{20}$

Chapter Overview

Chapter-at-a-Glance

In Chapter 10, the emphasis is on adding and subtracting fractions and mixed numbers and estimating sums and differences.

Lesson	Math Objective	State/Local Standards
EXPLORE 10-1 **Add Like Fractions** (pp. 421–422)	Use models to add fractions with like denominators.	
10-1 **Add Like Fractions** (pp. 423–425)	Add fractions with like denominators.	
EXPLORE 10-2 **Subtract Like Fractions** (pp. 426–427)	Use models to subtract fractions with like denominators.	
10-2 **Subtract Like Fractions** (pp. 428–431)	Subtract fractions with like denominators.	
EXPLORE 10-3 **Add Unlike Fractions** (pp. 432–433)	Use models to add unlike fractions.	
10-3 **Add Unlike Fractions** (pp. 434–436)	Add unlike fractions.	
EXPLORE 10-4 **Subtract Unlike Fractions** (pp. 437–438)	Use models to subtract unlike fractions.	
10-4 **Subtract Unlike Fractions** (pp. 439–441)	Subtract unlike fractions.	
10-5 **Problem-Solving Skill: Determine Reasonable Answers** (pp. 442–443)	Solve problems by determining reasonable answers.	
10-6 **Estimate Sums and Differences** (pp. 444–446)	Estimate sums and differences of mixed numbers.	
10-7 **Add Mixed Numbers** (pp. 448–451)	Add mixed numbers.	
10-8 **Subtract Mixed Numbers** (pp. 452–454)	Subtract mixed numbers.	
10-9 **Problem-Solving Investigation: Choose a Strategy** (pp. 456–457)	Choose a strategy to solve a problem.	
10-10 **Subtraction With Renaming** (pp. 458–561)	Subtract mixed numbers with renaming.	

Add and Subtract Fractions

BIG Idea The focus of this chapter is addition and subtraction of fractions. The goal is to develop a strong foundation and fraction sense. Although the majority of the chapter focuses on adding and subtracting fractions, two of the lessons involve estimating sums and differences of fractions and mixed numbers with unlike denominators. This allows students to use proportional reasoning skills. The remainder of the lessons use, visual models and hands-on activities in engaging contexts that help students make sense of the fraction algorithms.

Algebra In lessons 1 through 4, students add and subtract fractions. This concept will help prepare them for algebra concepts, such as solving equations that include fractions. (Lessons 10-1 and 10-2)

G5-FP2 Number and Operations: Developing an understanding of and fluency with addition and subtraction of fractions and decimals Students apply their understandings of fractions and fraction models to represent the addition and subtraction of fractions with unlike denominators as equivalent calculations with like denominators. They apply their understandings of decimal models, place value, and properties to add and subtract decimals. They develop fluency with standard procedures for adding and subtracting fractions and decimals. They make reasonable estimates of fraction and decimal sums and differences. Students add and subtract fractions and decimals to solve problems, including problems involving measurement.

G5-FP4C Algebra: Students use patterns, models, and relationships as contexts for writing and solving simple equations and inequalities. They create graphs of simple equations. They explore prime and composite numbers and discover concepts related to the addition and subtraction of fractions as they use factors and multiples, including applications of common factors and common multiples. They develop an understanding of the order of operations and use it for all operations.

Skills Trace

Vertical Alignment

Fourth Grade

In fourth grade, students learned to:

- Identify, read, write, and model fractions for part of a set and part of a whole.
- Find equivalent fractions.
- Write mixed numbers and improper fractions.
- Compare and order simple fractions.

Fifth Grade

During this chapter, students learn to:

- Add and subtract like and unlike fractions, and add and subtract mixed numbers.
- Estimate sums and differences.

After this chapter, students learn to:

- Add and subtract measures.
- Use fractions to describe probability.

Sixth Grade

In sixth grade, students learn to:

- Add and subtract mixed numbers.
- Round and estimate sums and differences of fractions and mixed numbers.

Backmapping and Vertical Alignment McGraw-Hill's ***Math Connects*** program was conceived and developed with the final results in mind: student success in Algebra 1 and beyond. The authors, using the **NCTM Focal Points and Focal Connections** as their guide, developed this brand new series by backmapping from Algebra 1 concepts, and vertically aligning the topics so that they build upon prior skills and concepts and serve as a foundation for future topics.

Math Vocabulary

The following math vocabulary words for Chapter 10 are listed in the glossary of the ***Student Edition***. You can find interactive definitions in 13 languages in the ***eGlossary*** at macmillanmh.com.

fraction A number that represents part of a whole or part of a set. (p. 448A)
Example: $\frac{1}{2}, \frac{1}{3}, \frac{1}{4}, \frac{3}{4}$

greatest common factor (GCF) The largest number that divides evenly into two or more numbers. (p. 428A)
Example: The greatest common factor of 12, 18, and 30 is 6

improper fraction A fraction with a numerator that is greater than or equal to the denominator. (p. 458A)
Example: $\frac{17}{3}$, or $\frac{5}{5}$

mixed number A number that has a whole number part and a fraction part. (p. 444A)
Example: $6\frac{1}{2}$

simplest form A fraction in which the numerator and the denominator have no common factor greater than 1. (p. 423A)
Example: $\frac{5}{12}$ is in simplest form because 5 and 12 have no common factor greater than 1.

unlike fraction Fractions with different denominators. (p. 434A)
Example: $\frac{1}{2}$ and $\frac{2}{3}$.

whole number The numbers 0, 1, 2, 3, 4.... (p. 448A)

Visual Vocabulary Cards
Use Visual Vocabulary Cards 17 and 24 to reinforce the vocabulary in this lesson. (The Define/Example/Ask routine is printed on the back of each card.)

improper fraction

Chapter Planner

Suggested Pacing		
Instruction	Review & Assessment	TOTAL
13 days	1 day	**14 days**

Diagnostic Assessment
Quick Check (p. 420)

	Explore 10-1 (Pacing: $\frac{1}{2}$ day)	Lesson 10-1 (Pacing: $\frac{1}{2}$ day)	Explore 10-2 (Pacing: 1 day)
Lesson/ Objective	**Add Like Fractions** (pp. 421–422) **Objective:** Use models to add fractions with like denominators.	**Add Like Fractions** (pp. 423–425) **Objective:** Add fractions with like denominators.	**Subtract Like Fractions** (pp. 426–427) **Objective:** Use models to subtract fractions with like denominators.
State/Local Standards			
Math Vocabulary	**like fractions**	**simplest form**	
Lesson Resources	**Manipulatives** fraction circles, fraction tiles	**Manipulatives** fraction tiles, fraction circles **Other Resources** CRM Leveled Worksheets (pp. 8–12) Daily Reteach • 5-Minute Check • Problem of the Day	**Manipulatives** fraction tiles
Technology		Math Adventures Math Song Track 15	
Math Online	Concepts in Motion	Personal Tutor	
Reaching All Learners		English Learners, p. 423B ELL Below Level, p. 423B BL Early Finishers, p. 423B OL AL	
Alternate Lesson			

KEY

- BL Below/Approaching Level
- OL On Level
- AL Above/Beyond Level
- ELL English Learners
- SE Student Edition
- TE Teacher Edition
- CRM Chapter 1 Resource Masters
- CD-Rom
- Transparency
- Real-World Problem Solving Library

	Lesson 10-2 (Pacing: 1 day)	Explore 10-3 (Pacing: 1 day)	Lesson 10-3 (Pacing: 1 day)
Lesson/ Objective	**Subtract Like Fractions** (pp. 428–431) **Objective:** Subtract fractions with like denominators.	**Add Unlike Fractions** (pp. 432–433) **Objective:** Use models to add unlike fractions.	**Add Unlike Fractions** (pp. 434–436) **Objective:** Add unlike fractions.
State/Local Standards			
Math Vocabulary	**greatest common factor (GCF)**		**unlike fraction**
Lesson Resources	**Materials** dry-erase boards, dry-erase markers **Manipulatives** fraction tiles, fraction circles **Other Resources** CRM Leveled Worksheets (pp. 13–17) Daily Reteach • 5-Minute Check • Problem of the Day	**Manipulatives** fraction tiles	**Other Resources** CRM Leveled Worksheets (pp. 18–22) Daily Reteach • 5-Minute Check • Problem of the Day
Technology **Math Online**	Math Adventures Personal Tutor		Math Tool Chest
Reaching All Learners	English Learners, p. 428B ELL Below Level, p. 423B BL Early Finishers, p. 428B OL		English Learners, p. 434B ELL Below Level, p. 423B BL Early Finishers, p. 434B OL
Alternate Lesson			

Chapter Planner

	Explore 10-4 (Pacing: 1 day)	Lesson 10-4 (Pacing: 1 day)	Lesson 10-5 (Pacing: 1 day)
Lesson/ Objective	**Subtract Unlike Fractions** (pp. 437–438) **Objective:** Use models to subtract unlike fractions.	**Subtract Unlike Fractions** (pp. 439–441) **Objective:** Subtract unlike fractions.	**Problem-Solving Skill Determine Reasonable Answers** (pp. 442–443) **Objective:** Solve problems by determining reasonable answers.
State/Local Standards			
Math Vocabulary			
Lesson Resources	**Manipulatives** fraction tiles	**Other Resources** CRM Leveled Worksheets (pp. 23–27) Daily Reteach • 5-Minute Check • Problem of the Day	**Other Resources** CRM Leveled Worksheets (pp. 28–32) Daily Reteach • 5-Minute Check • Problem of the Day *Life in Colonial America*
Technology		Math Adventures	Math Adventures
Math Online		Personal Tutor	
Reaching All Learners		English Learners, p. 439B ELL Gifted and Talented, p. 439B AL Early Finishers, p. 439B OL AL	English Learners, p. 442B ELL Gifted and Talented, p. 442B AL Early Finishers, p. 442B OL AL
Alternate Lesson			

	Lesson 10-6 (Pacing: 1 day)	Lesson 10-7 (Pacing: 1 day)	Lesson 10-8 (Pacing: 1 day)
Lesson/ Objective	**Estimate Sums and Differences** (pp. 444–446) **Objective:** Estimate sums and differences of mixed numbers.	**Add Mixed Numbers** (pp. 444–451) **Objective:** Add mixed numbers.	**Subtract Mixed Numbers** (pp. 452–454) **Objective:** Subtract mixed numbers.
State/Local Standards			
Math Vocabulary	**mixed number, estimate**	**whole number, fraction**	
Lesson Resources	**Materials** masking tape, index cards **Manipulatives** fraction tiles **Other Resources** CRM Leveled Worksheets (pp. 33–37) Daily Reteach • 5-Minute Check • Problem of the Day	**Manipulatives** clocks, fraction models **Other Resources** CRM Leveled Worksheets (pp. 38–42) Daily Reteach • 5-Minute Check • Problem of the Day	**Manipulatives** play money, fraction models **Other Resources** CRM Leveled Worksheets (pp. 43–47) Daily Reteach • 5-Minute Check • Problem of the Day
Technology / **Math Online**	Math Adventures Personal Tutor	Math Adventures Personal Tutor	Math Adventures Personal Tutor
Reaching All Learners	English Learners, p. 444B ELL Below Level, p. 423B BL Early Finishers, p. 444B OL	English Learners, p. 444B ELL Gifted and Talented, p. 444B AL Early Finishers, p. 444B OL	English Learners, p. 452B ELL Gifted and Talented, p. 452B AL Early Finishers, p. 452B OL AL
Alternate Lesson		*IMPACT Mathematics*: Unit F	*IMPACT Mathematics*: Unit F

Formative Assessment
Mid-Chapter Check (p. 447)

Game Time
Fraction Subtraction (p. 455)

Chapter Planner

	Lesson 10-9 (Pacing: 1 day)	Lesson 10-10 (Pacing: 1 day)
Lesson/ Objective	**Problem-Solving Investigation** **Choose a Strategy** (pp. 456–457) **Objective:** Choose a strategy to solve a problem.	**Subtraction with Renaming** (pp. 458–461) **Objective:** Subtract mixed numbers.
State/Local Standards		
Math Vocabulary		**improper fraction**
Lesson Resources	**Materials** yard stick, masking tape, ruler **Manipulatives** play money **Other Resources** CRM Leveled Worksheets (pp. 48–52) Daily Reteach • 5-Minute Check • Problem of the Day *Life in Colonial America*	**Manipulatives** play money, fraction models **Other Resources** CRM Leveled Worksheets (pp. 53–57) Daily Reteach • 5-Minute Check • Problem of the Day
Technology		
Math Online		Personal Tutor
Reaching All Learners	English Learners, p. 456B ELL Gifted and Talented, p. 456B AL Early Finishers, p. 456B OL AL	English Learners, p. 458B ELL Below Level, p. 458B BL Early Finishers, p. 458B OL
Alternate Lesson		*IMPACT Mathematics*: Unit F

Problem Solving: Science
(p. 462–463)

Summative Assessment
- Study Guide and Review (p. 464)
- Chapter Test (p. 469)
- Test Practice (p. 470)

Assessment Options

Diagnostic Assessment

- SE *Option 1:* Quick Check (p. 420)
- *Option 2:* Online Quiz macmillanmh.com
- CRM *Option 3:* Diagnostic Test (p. 59)
- CRM *Option 4:* Chapter Test (p. 60)

Formative Assessment

- TE Alternate Teaching Strategies (every lesson)
- SE Talk About It (every lesson)
- SE Writing in Math (every lesson)
- SE Check What You Know (every lesson)
- TE Yesterday's News (pp. 431, 454)
- TE Name the Math (p. 446)
- SE Mid-Chapter Check (p. 447)
- CRM Lesson Quizzes (pp. 61–63)
- CRM Mid-Chapter Test (p. 64)

Summative Assessment

- SE Chapter Test (p. 469)
- SE Test Practice (p. 470)
- CRM Vocabulary Test (p. 65)
- CRM Leveled Chapter Tests (pp. 70–80)
- CRM Cumulative Test Practice (p. 84)
- CRM Oral Assessment (p. 66)
- ExamView® Assessment Suite
- Advance Tracker

Mc Graw Hill Professional Development

Targeted professional development has been articulated throughout **McGraw-Hill's *Math Connects*** program. The **McGraw-Hill Professional Development Video Library** provides short videos that support the **NCTM Focal Points and Focal Connections.** For more information, visit macmillanmh.com.

Model Lessons

Instructional Strategies

Teacher Notes

Learning Stations

Cross-Curricular Links

Science

individual | LOGICAL

I Will Take Two, Please

- Choose a recipe that has fractions in its ingredient measurements. Read the recipe to see how many people it will serve.
- Now, look back at the list of ingredients. If you want to serve twice as many people as the recipe serves now, you have to add like fractions in order to double the recipe. For example, if a recipe calls for $\frac{1}{4}$ of a cup of flour, you have to add $\frac{1}{4}$ to $\frac{1}{4}$ to get the doubled amount. Double all of the ingredients and rewrite the recipe to show your new measurements.
- How many people can you serve now?

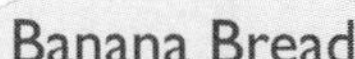

Banana Bread
2 eggs
$1\frac{3}{4}$ c. sifted flour
2 tsp. baking powder
$\frac{1}{4}$ tsp. baking soda
$\frac{1}{2}$ tsp. salt
$\frac{1}{3}$ c. vegetable shortening
$\frac{2}{3}$ c. sugar
1 c. mashed bananas (about 3 bananas)
Serves 16 32

Materials:
- recipes from cookbooks or cooking magazines
- paper
- pencil

Art

individual | SPATIAL

How Much Space?

Make a mosaic collage using paper squares.

- Roll a number cube once to get a numerator, and once to get a denominator. Round this fraction to the nearest half-inch. This will be the length and width of the picture squares you will cut out from magazines to make your mosaic collage.
- Estimate how many of your picture squares you can fit on your paper. You may try this with or without rounding. Place your squares on the paper to see if your estimation was accurate. Then glue them down to make your collage.

Materials:
- number cube
- art magazines for clipping
- glue
- scissors
- ruler
- paper

Writing

individual | LOGICAL

Add It Up

- Write a poem in two-line stanzas, and count the number of words in each line. (A stanza is a group of lines in a poem).
- What fraction of the whole poem do each of the lines represent?
- What fraction of the whole poem do each of the stanzas represent? Add the fractions for each of the lines in a stanza to find out.
- You can check your line and stanza fractions by adding them up to see if the total gives you a fraction equivalent to one.

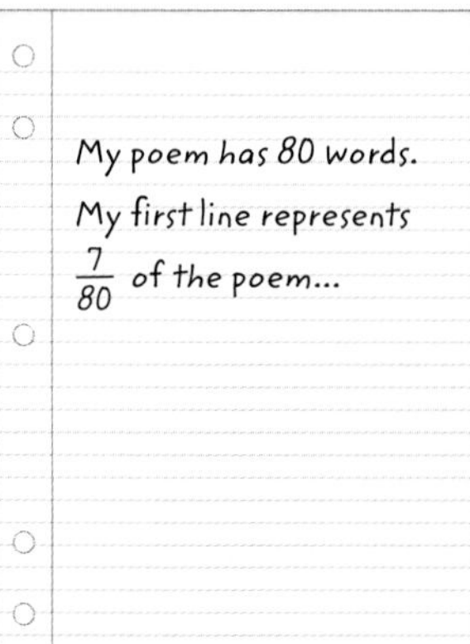

My poem has 80 words.
My first line represents
$\frac{7}{80}$ of the poem...

Materials:
- paper
- pencils

Reading

An Educated Guess

- Read *Betcha!* by Stuart J. Murphy by yourself or with a partner.
- Write the name of each classmate and his or her height in inches on one index card per person. Place the index cards into a basket and shake the basket to shuffle the cards.
- One person pulls two cards from the basket, estimates the difference between the two heights, then records the amount on paper. Do this until all the cards are gone. The other person keeps time of how long it takes to estimate all the cards in the basket. Then switch roles.

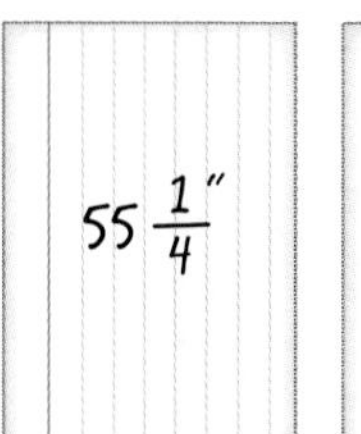

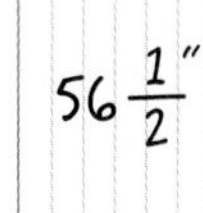

Estimated Height Difference = 2″

Materials:
- *Betcha!* by Stuart J. Murphy
- list of heights of each student in classroom
- index cards
- basket
- stopwatch

Health

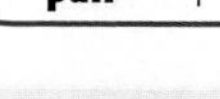

Beanbag Toss

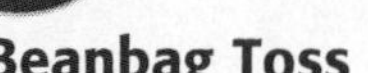

Beanbag tossing contests can be won by measuring accuracy.

- Make a starting line with masking tape on the floor. Each person takes a turn standing at the line to toss the beanbag twice. Use an underhand toss.
- The other person measures how far the beanbag was tossed, records the distance in inches for each toss, then adds them up.
- The person who can get both of their tosses closest to $120\frac{1}{2}$ inches combined is the winner.

Materials:
- beanbags
- masking tape
- measuring tape
- paper
- pencils

Social Studies

Voting Age

- In the United States, citizens must be 18 years old in order to vote. How much longer until you can vote?
- 18 years can be written as the mixed number $17\frac{12}{12}$. Subtract your age rounded to the nearest twelfth from $17\frac{12}{12}$ to find out how many years and months until you are able to vote.
- Find the age difference of everyone in your classroom and display it on a poster.

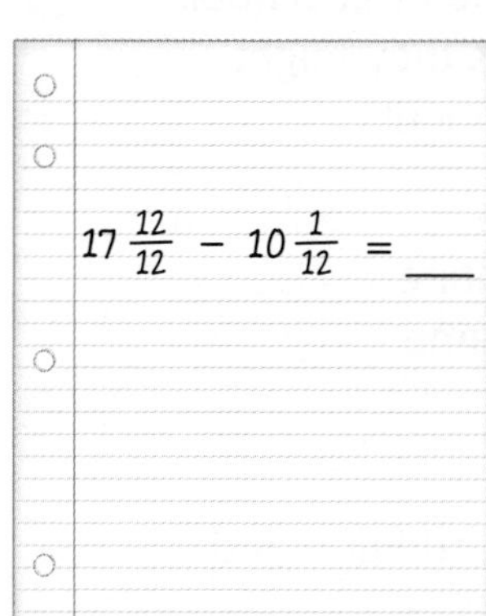

Materials:
- list of names and birthdays of students in the classroom
- paper
- pencils
- poster board

CHAPTER 10

Introduce the Chapter

 Real World: Parts of Pie

Manipulatives: fraction models

Review with students what they have learned about fractions so far this year. Tell them that they will learn how to add and subtract fractions and mixed numbers in this chapter.

Tell students to suppose they have an apple pie that is cut into eight equal-sized pieces. Provide students with a fraction circle of eighths to represent the pie.

- **What fraction represents one piece of the pie?** $\frac{1}{8}$ **two pieces?** $\frac{2}{8}$

Pose the following problem:

Suppose Tim ate $\frac{2}{8}$ of the pie and Kenji ate $\frac{1}{8}$ of the pie. What fraction of the pie did they eat in all?

Write $\frac{2}{8} + \frac{1}{8}$ on the board. Guide students to use the fraction circles to model the addition and solve the problem. $\frac{3}{8}$

Direct students to Student Edition p. 414. Have students read the paragraph at the top of the page.

- **Name two like fractions. How do you know they are like fractions?** Sample answer: $\frac{1}{4}$ and $\frac{3}{4}$; because they have the same denominator, 4
- **What is $\frac{1}{2} - \frac{1}{2}$? How do you know?** 0; Sample answer: Any number subtracted from itself is 0.

WRITING IN ▶MATH

Starting the Chapter

Ask students to write a paragraph describing situations where they might add or subtract fractions or mixed numbers at home or at school. Suggest that they think about times they might combine or compare two measurements.

Key Vocabulary Introduce the key vocabulary in the chapter using the following routine.

Define: Like fractions have the same denominator.

Example: $\frac{4}{7}$ and $\frac{2}{7}$

Ask: How do like fractions make addition and subtraction easier?

Read-Aloud Anthology For an optional reading activity to introduce this chapter's math concepts, see the Read-Aloud Anthology on p. TR28.

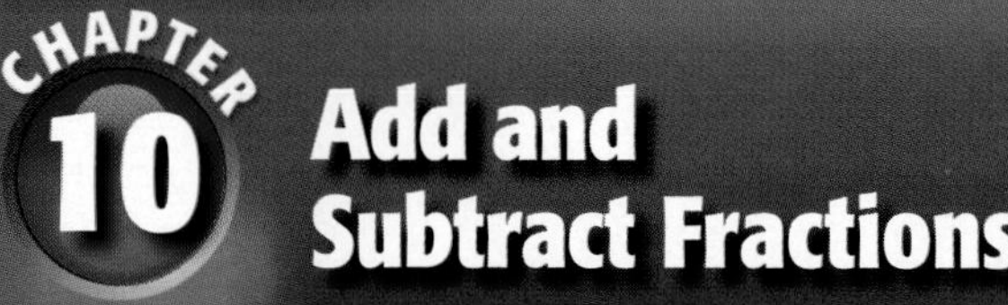

Chapter 10 Add and Subtract Fractions

BIG Idea What are like fractions?

Fractions that have the same denominator are **like fractions**.

$\frac{1}{8}$ $\frac{3}{8}$ $2\frac{5}{8}$ $5\frac{7}{8}$

You can add and subtract like fractions.

Example The average height of an African penguin is $26\frac{1}{2}$ inches. The average height of an Emperor penguin is $36\frac{1}{2}$ inches. You can subtract $26\frac{1}{2}$ from $36\frac{1}{2}$ to find the difference in height between the two penguins.

What will I learn in this chapter?

- Add and subtract like and unlike fractions.
- Estimate sums and differences of mixed numbers.
- Add and subtract mixed numbers.
- Solve problems by determining reasonable answers.

Key Vocabulary

like fractions

unlike fractions

Math Online Student Study Tools at macmillanmh.com

 Chapter 10 Project

Number Line Rounding Race

Teams challenge each other to a race using rounded fractions.

- Students create a number line on the floor, marked in $\frac{1}{2}$-foot increments to at least 10 feet. They split into two teams and write 20 fractions on slips of paper to put into two baskets.
- Each team chooses a caller. The callers stand at the far end of the number line. Each caller pulls a fraction and reads it out to the team at the zero end. The first runner from each team rounds the fraction to the nearest $\frac{1}{2}$ and moves to that spot on the number line. The fraction is placed back in the basket.
- Repeat until the runner reaches the end of the line; then the next runner starts. This continues until all runners have reached the end. The first team to get all its runners across the line wins.

CRM *Refer to Chapter 10 Resource Masters, p. 68, for a rubric to assess students' progress on this project.*

FOLDABLES Study Organizer Make this Foldable to organize information about like and unlike fractions. Begin with a sheet of $8\frac{1}{2}'' \times 11''$ paper, four index cards, and glue.

1. **Fold** the paper in half widthwise.
2. **Open** and fold along the length about $2\frac{1}{2}''$ from the bottom.
3. **Glue** the edges on either side to form two pockets.
4. **Label** the pockets *Like Fractions* and *Unlike Fractions*. Place two index cards in each pocket.

Chapter 10 Add and Subtract Fractions **419**

ELL National ESL Standards Alignment for Chapter 10			
Lesson, Page	ESL Standards	Modality	Level
10-1, p. 423B	Goal 2, Standard 3, h	Visual, Social	Intermediate
10-2, p. 428B	Goal 1, Standard 3, c	Auditory, Logical	Beginning
10-3, p. 434B	Goal 2, Standard 1, c	Logical, Visual	Intermediate
10-4, p. 439B	Goal, Standard,	Visual, Logical	
10-5, p. 442B	Goal 2, Standard 2, f	Linguistic	Advanced
10-6, p. 444B	Goal 2, Standard 2, j	Interpersonal, Kinesthetic	Intermediate
10-7, p. 448B	Goal 2, Standard 3, i	Visual, Linguistic	Intermediate
10-8, p. 452B	Goal 2, Standard 2, i	Logical, Auditory	Intermediate
10-9, p. 456B	Goal 3, Standard 1, c	Social	Advanced
10-10, p. 458B	Goal 2, Standard 1, g	Kinesthetic	Intermediate

The National ESL Standards can be found in the Teacher Reference Handbook.

FOLDABLES Dinah Zike's Foldables

Guide students through the directions on Student Edition p. 419 to create their own Foldables graphic organizers for like and unlike fractions. Students may also use their Foldables to study and review for chapter assessments.

When to Use It Lessons 10-1, 10-2, 10-3, 10-4, 10-6, 10-7, and 10-9. (Additional instructions for using the Foldables with these lessons are found on pp. 447 and 464.)

Chapter 10 Literature List

Lesson	Book Title
10-1	**Pizza Counting** Christina Dobson
10-2	**Gator Pie** Louise Mathews
10-3	**How Pizza Came to Queens** Dayal Kaur Khalsa
10-4	**How Pizza Came to Queens** Dayal Kaur Khalsa
10-5	**Minnie's Diner: A Multiplying Menu** Dayle Ann Dodds
10-6	**Fractions and Decimals** Lucille Caron and Philip M. St. Jacques
10-7	**Fraction Action** Loreen Leedy
10-8	**The Missing Piece** Shel Silverstein
10-10	**Fractions and Decimals** Lucille Caron and Philip M. St. Jacques

- Read the Math at Home letter found in Chapter 10 Resource Masters, p. 4, with the class and have each student sign it. (A Spanish version is found on p. 5.)
- Send home copies of the Math at Home letter with each student.

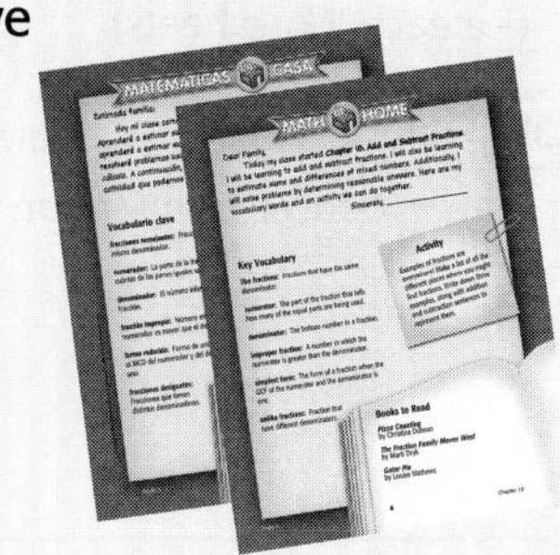

Diagnostic Assessment

Check for students' prerequisite skills before beginning the chapter.

- **Option 1:** ***Quick Check***

  SE Student Edition, p. 420

- **Option 2:** ***Online Assessment***

  Math Online macmillanmh.com

- **Option 3:** ***Diagnostic Test***

  CRM Chapter 10 Resource Masters, p. 59

RTI (Response to Intervention)

Apply the Results Based on the results of the diagnostic assessment on student p. 420, use the chart below to address individual needs before and during the chapter.

TIER 3 Intensive Intervention

If students miss eleven or more of the exercises:

Then use Chapter 6 of *Math Triumphs*, an intensive math intervention program from McGraw-Hill

ARE YOU READY for Chapter 10?

You have two ways to check prerequisite skills for this chapter.

Option 2

Math Online Take the Chapter Readiness Quiz at macmillanmh.com.

Option 1

Complete the Quick Check below.

QUICK Check

Write each fraction in simplest form.
(Lesson 9-4) (Used in Lessons 10-1, 10-2, 10-5, 10-6, and 10-8)

1. $\frac{4}{8}$ $\frac{1}{2}$ **2.** $\frac{4}{12}$ $\frac{1}{3}$ **3.** $\frac{15}{20}$ $\frac{3}{4}$ **4.** $\frac{4}{24}$ $\frac{1}{6}$

5. Monica made 4 out of 16 free throws. Write the fraction of free throws she made in simplest form. $\frac{1}{4}$

Write each improper fraction as a mixed number.
(Lesson 8-2) (Used in Lessons 10-1, 10-2, 10-5, and 10-6)

6. $\frac{10}{7}$ $1\frac{3}{7}$ **7.** $\frac{3}{2}$ $1\frac{1}{2}$ **8.** $\frac{14}{6}$ $2\frac{1}{3}$ **9.** $\frac{22}{4}$ $5\frac{1}{2}$

10. A recipe for potato casserole calls for $\frac{7}{4}$ cups of cheese. Write the fraction as a mixed number. $1\frac{3}{4}$

Estimate each sum or difference by rounding. Show your work. (Lesson 2-1) (Used in Lesson 10-4)

11. $10.5 - 7.1$ $11 - 7 = 4$ **12.** $6.2 + 4.7$ $6 + 5 = 11$ **13.** $5.2 + 2.1$ $5 + 2 = 7$ **14.** $12.7 - 6.6$ $13 - 7 = 6$

15. Sierra bought the two items shown at the right. About how much did she spend? Round to the nearest dollar. $13

16. Two classes are recycling. One class earns $17.69, and the other earns $31.15. About how much more did the second class earn? Round to the nearest dollar. Sample answer: $31 − $18 = $13

420 **Chapter 10** Add and Subtract Fractions

TIER 2 Strategic Intervention (below/approaching grade level)	TIER 1 On-Level	Above/Beyond-Level
If students miss five to ten in: **Exercises 1–16**	**If** students miss three or four in: **Exercises 1–16**	**If** students miss two or less: **Exercises 1–16**
Then choose a resource:	**Then** choose a resource:	**Then** choose a resource:
CRM Chapter 8 Resource Masters (Reteach Worksheets) **Math Online** Extra Examples • Personal Tutor • Concepts in Motion	TE Learning Stations (pp. 418I–418J) TE Chapter Project (p. 418) CRM Game: Add It All Up Math Adventures My Math Zone Chapter 9 **Math Online** Fact Dash	TE Learning Stations (pp. 418I–418J) TE Chapter Project (pp. 418) Real-World Problems Solving Reader: *Life in Colonial America* Math Adventures My Math Zone Chapter 9, 10 **Math Online** Games

Math Activity for 10-1

Add Like Fractions

You can use fraction tiles to add fractions with the same denominator. Fractions with the same denominator are called **like fractions**. For example, $\frac{3}{5}$ and $\frac{1}{5}$ are like fractions because they both have a denominator of 5.

MAIN IDEA

I will use models to add fractions with like denominators.

New Vocabulary

like fractions

Math Online

macmillanmh.com

- Concepts in Motion

ACTIVITY

1. **Lauren sliced an apple to eat as a snack. She ate $\frac{3}{5}$ of the apple and gave $\frac{1}{5}$ of the apple to her sister. How much of the apple did they eat?**

Step 1 **Model $\frac{3}{5}$.**

Use three $\frac{1}{5}$-fraction tiles to show $\frac{3}{5}$.

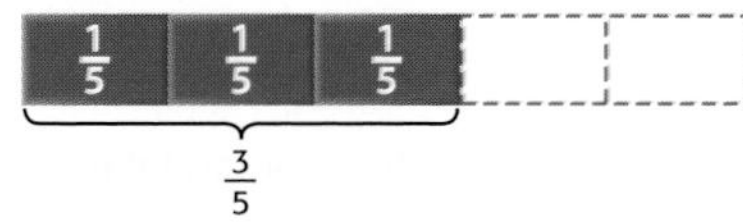

Step 2 **Model $\frac{1}{5}$.**

Add one $\frac{1}{5}$-fraction tile to show $\frac{1}{5}$.

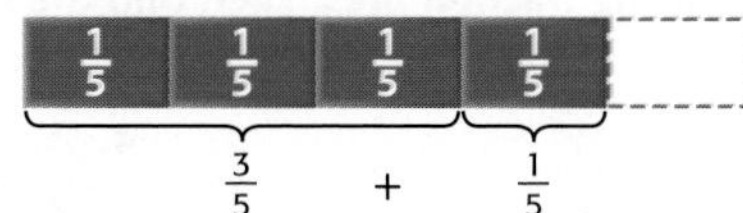

Step 3 **Add.**

Count the total number of $\frac{1}{5}$-fraction tiles.

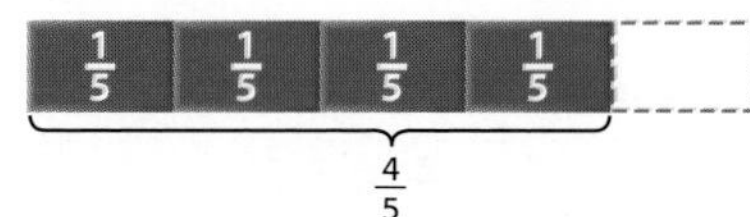

Since $\frac{3}{5} + \frac{1}{5} = \frac{4}{5}$, you can say that Lauren and her sister ate $\frac{4}{5}$ or *four fifths* of the apple.

Math Activity for 10-1

Lesson Planner

Objective

Use models to add fractions with like denominators.

Resources

Manipulatives: fraction circles, fraction tiles
Teacher Technology

Math Online Concepts in Motion

1 Introduce

- Distribute fraction circles (halves through twelfths) to small groups of students.
- Have students discuss different items their fraction circles could represent at a carnival, rodeo, or parade, for example, a pizza or a pie.
- Ask students to identify the number of equal parts in each fraction circle. Then have them name the fraction for one part of each circle (one half through one twelfth).

2 Teach

Activity 1 Provide students with fraction tiles. Have students first place five $\frac{1}{5}$-fraction tiles directly under one whole fraction tile to illustrate that five fifths is equivalent to one whole.

Guide students to model $\frac{3}{5}$ with the fraction tiles, then model $\frac{1}{5}$ directly to the right to show the addition. Have them count the total number of $\frac{1}{5}$-fraction tiles to find the sum, $\frac{4}{5}$.

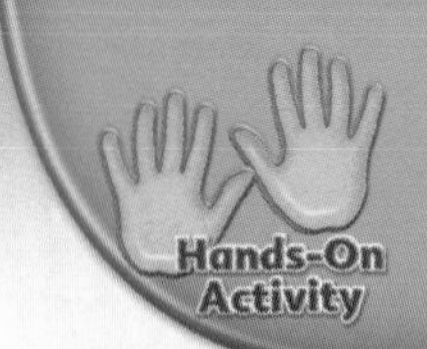

Activity 2 Have students repeat the process for $\frac{3}{10} + \frac{4}{10}$: first model $\frac{3}{10}$ with three $\frac{1}{10}$-fraction tiles, then model $\frac{4}{10}$ directly to the right and count the total number of $\frac{1}{10}$-fraction tiles to find the sum.

Think About It

Assign Exercises 1 and 2 to assess student comprehension of the concept presented in the activity.

3 Assess

Formative Assessment

Use **Check What You Know** Exercises 3–10 to assess whether students understand how to use models to add fractions with like denominators.

From Concrete to Abstract Use Exercise 10 to bridge the gap between modeling addition with fraction tiles and adding fractions with like denominators without the use of models or drawings.

Extending the Concept Have students use fraction tiles to find the sum of $\frac{3}{8} + \frac{1}{8} + \frac{5}{8}$. Challenge them to write the sum in simplest form.

Additional Answers

1. Use one $\frac{1}{8}$-fraction piece to show $\frac{1}{8}$. Then use six $\frac{1}{8}$-fraction pieces to show $\frac{6}{8}$.
2. Count the total number of $\frac{1}{8}$-fraction pieces; $\frac{7}{8}$

7. $\frac{2}{3}$;

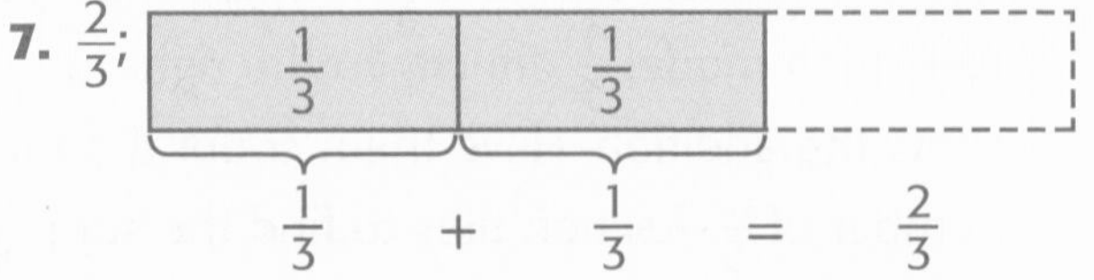

ACTIVITY

2 **Theo asked his class what type of pet they like the best. Of the class, $\frac{3}{10}$ said they like dogs, and $\frac{4}{10}$ said they like cats. What fraction of the class likes dogs or cats?**

Step 1 **Model $\frac{3}{10}$.**

Use three $\frac{1}{10}$-fraction tiles to show $\frac{3}{10}$.

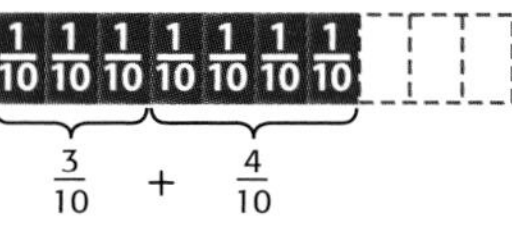

Step 2 **Model $\frac{4}{10}$.**

Use four $\frac{1}{10}$-fraction tiles to show $\frac{4}{10}$.

Step 3 **Add.**

Count the total number of $\frac{1}{10}$-fraction tiles.

$\frac{3}{10} + \frac{4}{10} = \frac{7}{10}$. So, $\frac{7}{10}$ or *seven tenths* of the class likes dogs or cats.

Think About It 1–2. See margin.

1. Describe how you would model $\frac{1}{8} + \frac{6}{8}$.
2. Explain how to find $\frac{1}{8} + \frac{6}{8}$. Then find and write the sum in words.

CHECK What You Know

Model each sum using fraction tiles. Then find the sum and write it in words. 3–6. See students' work for models.

3.

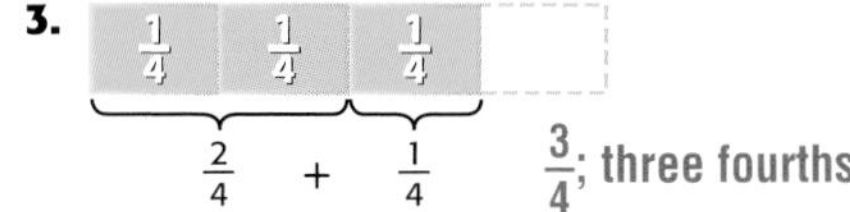

$\frac{3}{4}$; three fourths

4.

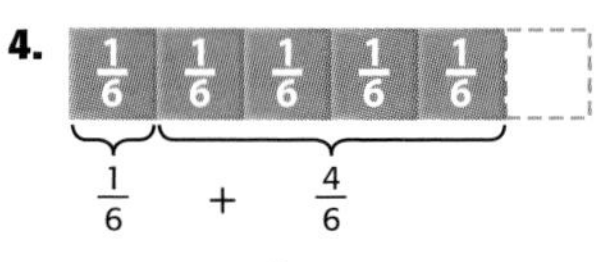

$\frac{5}{6}$; five sixths

5. $\frac{3}{8} + \frac{4}{8}$ $\frac{7}{8}$; seven eighths

6. $\frac{5}{10} + \frac{4}{10}$ $\frac{9}{10}$; nine tenths

Find each sum. Use fraction tiles if needed. 7–10. See margin.

7. $\frac{1}{3} + \frac{1}{3}$
8. $\frac{2}{8} + \frac{5}{8}$
9. $\frac{5}{12} + \frac{6}{12}$
10. **WRITING IN MATH** Look at the numerators and denominators in each exercise. Do you notice a pattern? Explain how you could find the sum of $\frac{1}{5} + \frac{1}{5}$ without using fraction tiles.

Additional Answers

8. $\frac{7}{8}$;

$\frac{1}{8}$	$\frac{1}{8}$	$\frac{1}{8}$	$\frac{1}{8}$	$\frac{1}{8}$	$\frac{1}{8}$	$\frac{1}{8}$

$\frac{2}{8} + \frac{5}{8} = \frac{7}{8}$

9. $\frac{11}{12}$;

$\frac{1}{12}$	$\frac{1}{12}$	$\frac{1}{12}$	$\frac{1}{12}$	$\frac{1}{12}$	$\frac{1}{12}$	$\frac{1}{12}$	$\frac{1}{12}$	$\frac{1}{12}$	$\frac{1}{12}$	$\frac{1}{12}$

$\frac{5}{12} + \frac{6}{12} = \frac{11}{12}$

10. Sample answer: The numerator is the sum of the numerators of the addends and the denominator is the same as the addends; Add 1 and 2 to get the numerator and the denominator is 5.

LESSON 10-1

Add Like Fractions

Lesson Planner

Objective

Add fractions with like denominators.

Review Vocabulary

simplest form

Resources

Manipulatives: fraction tiles, fraction circles
Literature Connection: *Pizza Counting* by Christina Dobson
Teacher Technology
Interactive Classroom • TeacherWorks

Focus on Math Background

It is important that students understand why fractions with like denominators can be added by adding the numerators. Since like fractions have denominators that name the same fractional part, the numerators count identical units. When adding fractions, the denominators are left alone, as they identify the parts that are being combined and just the numerators are added. So 1 *fifth* plus 3 *fifths*, must be equal to 4 *fifths*. In addition to modeling fraction addition with concrete objects such as fraction tiles, it can be modeled on a number line; consider $\frac{3}{5} + \frac{4}{5}$:

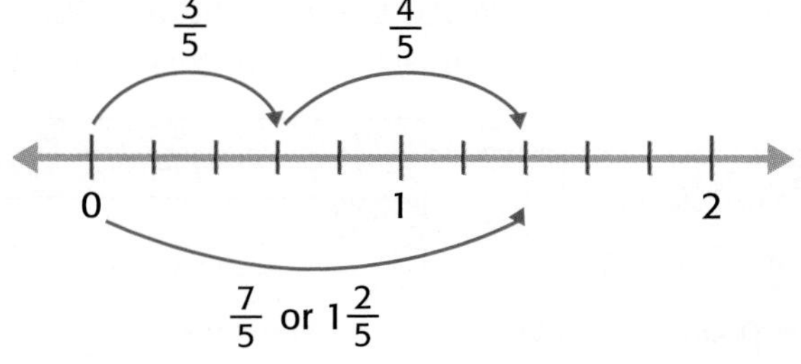

Daily Routine

Use these suggestions before beginning the lesson on p. 423.

5-Minute Check 

(Reviews Lesson 9-9)

Compare each pair of fractions using models or the LCD.

1. $\frac{1}{4}$ and $\frac{2}{3}$ $\frac{3}{12} < \frac{8}{12}$
2. $\frac{3}{10}$ and $\frac{2}{5}$ $\frac{3}{10} < \frac{4}{10}$
3. $\frac{5}{6}$ and $\frac{1}{9}$ $\frac{15}{18} > \frac{2}{18}$
4. $\frac{4}{15}$ and $\frac{9}{10}$ $\frac{8}{30} < \frac{27}{30}$

Replace each ● with <, >, or = to make a true statement.

5. $\frac{3}{5}$ ● $\frac{4}{10}$ $>$
6. $\frac{4}{8}$ ● $\frac{1}{2}$ $=$
7. $\frac{1}{6}$ ● $\frac{1}{5}$ $<$
8. $\frac{4}{7}$ ● $\frac{2}{3}$ $<$

Problem of the Day 

Yusuf walked 20 miles last week. He walked 3.6 miles each day on Tuesday, Thursday, and Friday. He walked 2.25 miles each day on Monday, Saturday, and Sunday. How far did Yusuf walk on Wednesday? 2.45 miles

Review Math Vocabulary

Write the lesson vocabulary word and its definition on the board.

Write the following fractions on the board: $\frac{5}{10}$, $\frac{2}{6}$, $\frac{4}{4}$, $\frac{15}{25}$, $\frac{4}{12}$, $\frac{7}{21}$, $\frac{8}{10}$, $\frac{8}{12}$, and $\frac{8}{16}$. Have students write each fraction in simplest form.

Differentiated Instruction

Small Group Options

SPATIAL

Option 1 Below Level BL

Materials: measuring cups

- Have students figure out different ways to use measuring cups to form 1 cup of water, for example, one way is to add $\frac{1}{2}$ cup, $\frac{1}{4}$ cup, and $\frac{1}{4}$ cup.
- Translate each method to a number sentence on the board.

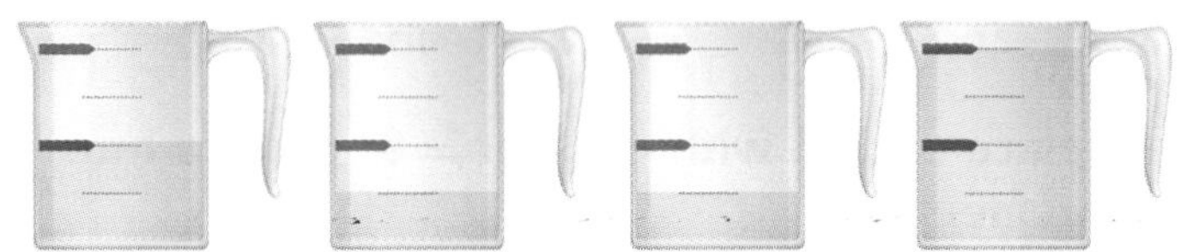

VISUAL, SOCIAL

Option 2 English Language Learners ELL

Materials: paper, pencil
Core Vocabulary: what if, whole number, fractional pieces
Common Use Verb: stay the same

See Math This strategy uses background knowledge and conditional language to peer teach adding and subtracting fractions.

- Ask students to tell you how to add 2 + 5.
- Say: "**What if** each number was not a **whole number**? **What if** it was a **fractional piece**?"
- Write $\frac{2}{8} + \frac{5}{8}$. Say: "How would we add them?
- Draw 2 + 5 and $\frac{2}{8} + \frac{5}{8}$. Say: "When the bottom ***stays the same***, we can just add the top." Count out and write the answer, $\frac{7}{8}$.
- Repeat with the concept of subtraction.
- Extend understanding by having students reteach each other how to add and subtract fractions.

Use this worksheet to provide additional support for English Language Learners.

English Language Learners (p. 29) ELL

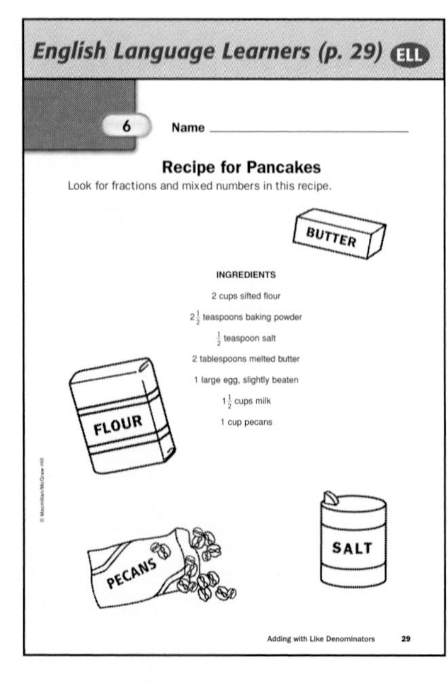

6 Name ____________

Recipe for Pancakes

Look for fractions and mixed numbers in this recipe.

INGREDIENTS

2 cups sifted flour

$2\frac{1}{2}$ teaspoons baking powder

$\frac{1}{2}$ teaspoon salt

2 tablespoons melted butter

1 large egg, slightly beaten

$1\frac{1}{2}$ cups milk

1 cup pecans

Adding with Like Denominators 29

Independent Work Options

LINGUISTIC/LOGICAL

Option 1 Early Finishers OL AL

Materials: pencil, paper

- Have students look over their answers to Practice Exercises 9–16 on p. 425 of their books.
- Challenge students to write a new addition sentence for each sum.

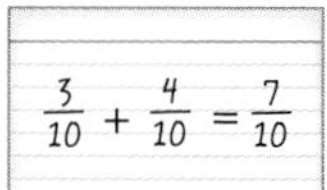

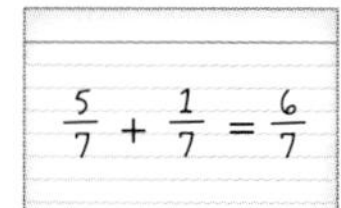

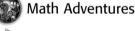

For example, for Exercise 9's sum of $\frac{6}{7}$, they may write $\frac{5}{7} + \frac{1}{7} = \frac{6}{7}$.

- For each new addition sentence they write, have students draw a picture to check their work.
- Allow students to share their addition sentences with their classmates.

Option 2 Student Technology

Tech Link

Personal Tutor • Extra Examples

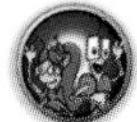 Math Adventures

 Math Songs, "Equivalent Fractions" Track #15

Option 3 Learning Station: Science (p. 418I)

Direct students to the Science Learning Station for opportunities to explore and extend the lesson concept.

Option 4 Problem-Solving Practice

Reinforce problem-solving skills and strategies with the Problem-Solving Practice worksheet.

Problem Solving (p. 11) BL OL AL

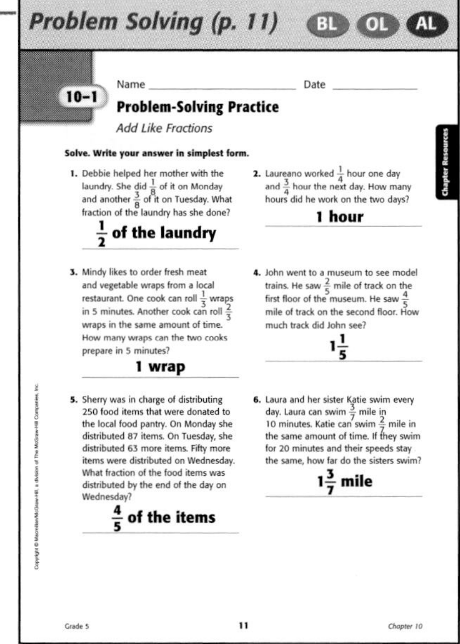

Name ____________ Date ____________

10–1 **Problem-Solving Practice**

Add Like Fractions

Chapter Resources

Solve. Write your answer in simplest form.

1. Debbie helped her mother with the laundry. She did $\frac{1}{8}$ of it on Monday and another $\frac{3}{8}$ of it on Tuesday. What fraction of the laundry has she done? **$\frac{1}{2}$ of the laundry**
2. Laureano worked $\frac{1}{4}$ hour one day and $\frac{3}{4}$ hour the next day. How many hours did he work on the two days? **1 hour**
3. Mindy likes to order fresh meat and vegetable wraps from a local restaurant. One cook can roll $\frac{1}{3}$ wraps in 5 minutes. Another cook can roll $\frac{2}{3}$ wraps in the same amount of time. How many wraps can the two cooks prepare in 5 minutes? **1 wrap**
4. John went to a museum to see model trains. He saw $\frac{2}{5}$ mile of track on the first floor of the museum. He saw $\frac{4}{5}$ mile of track on the second floor. How much track did John see? **$1\frac{1}{5}$**
5. Sherry was in charge of distributing 250 food items that were donated to the local food pantry. On Monday she distributed 87 items. On Tuesday, she distributed 63 more items. Fifty more items were distributed on Wednesday. What fraction of the food items was distributed by the end of the day on Wednesday? **$\frac{4}{5}$ of the items**
6. Laura and her sister Katie swim every day. Laura can swim $\frac{3}{7}$ mile in 10 minutes. Katie can swim $\frac{2}{7}$ mile in the same amount of time. If they swim for 20 minutes and their speeds stay the same, how far do the sisters swim? **$1\frac{3}{7}$ mile**

Grade 5 11 Chapter 10

10-1 Add Like Fractions

MAIN IDEA

I will add fractions with like denominators.

Math Online

macmillanmh.com
- Extra Examples
- Personal Tutor
- Self-Check Quiz

GET READY to Learn

At the county fair, Lorena and her father decided to share a foot-long sub sandwich. Lorena ate $\frac{2}{6}$ of the sandwich, and her father ate $\frac{3}{6}$ of the sandwich. How much of the sandwich did they eat?

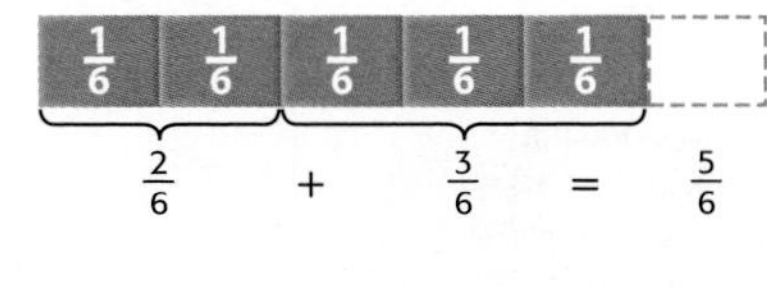

To find how much of the sub sandwich Lorena and her father ate, you can add the like fractions. When you add like fractions, the denominator names the units.

EXAMPLE Add Like Fractions

1 **Find $\frac{2}{6} + \frac{3}{6}$. Use models to check.**

$\frac{2}{6} + \frac{3}{6} = \frac{2+3}{6}$

$= \frac{5}{6}$ Add.

So, $\frac{2}{6} + \frac{3}{6} = \frac{5}{6}$.

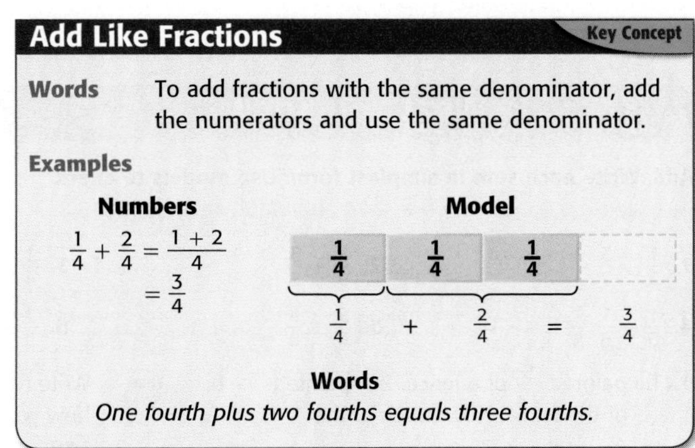

Add Like Fractions Key Concept

Words To add fractions with the same denominator, add the numerators and use the same denominator.

Examples

Numbers

$\frac{1}{4} + \frac{2}{4} = \frac{1+2}{4}$

$= \frac{3}{4}$

Model

$\frac{1}{4}$ $\frac{1}{4}$ $\frac{1}{4}$

$\frac{1}{4} + \frac{2}{4} = \frac{3}{4}$

Words

One fourth plus two fourths equals three fourths.

10-1 Add Like Fractions

1 Introduce

Activity Choice 1 • Hands-On

- Review fractional parts of a whole by having 24 (or 12) students stand up.
- Organize students into groups according to a common characteristic, such as shirt color. Ask students to name the fractional part of 24 for each group.
- For example: Six out of 24 students are wearing red shirts. **What fraction of the students are wearing red shirts?** $\frac{6}{24}$
- **What is this fraction in simplest form?** $\frac{1}{4}$
- Next, challenge students to organize themselves into groups to model fractions. For example, ask them to make a group that shows $\frac{1}{8}$ of 24 students.
- **How many students are in this group?** 3 Encourage students to rewrite the fraction with a denominator of 24 to solve.
- Tell students that they will use their understanding of equivalent fractions and simplest form as they add fractions.

Activity Choice 2 • Literature

Introduce the lesson with *Pizza Counting* by Christina Dobson. For a related math activity, see p. TR51.

2 Teach

Scaffolding Questions

Have students use fraction tiles to model $\frac{4}{8} + \frac{1}{8}$.

- **How do you model $\frac{4}{8}$?** Place four $\frac{1}{8}$-tiles next to each other.
- **What do you do next?** Model adding $\frac{1}{8}$ by placing one $\frac{1}{8}$-tile next to the four-$\frac{1}{8}$ tiles.
- **How can you count to find the sum?** Count the number of $\frac{1}{8}$-tiles in all to find the sum. **How can you add?** 4 tiles + 1 tile = 5 tiles. So $\frac{4}{8} + \frac{1}{8} = \frac{5}{8}$.

GET READY to Learn

Have students open their books and read the information in **Get Ready to Learn.** Review **like fractions**. As a class, work through **Examples 1–3.**

Add Like Fractions

Example 2 Help students read the table. Locate the fractions for Monday and Wednesday and explain that they must add the two fractions to solve the problem. You may also have students use fraction tiles to check that $\frac{2}{5}$ is equivalent to $\frac{1}{10} + \frac{3}{10}$ by lining up two $\frac{1}{5}$-tiles directly above one $\frac{1}{10}$-tile and three $\frac{1}{10}$-tiles.

ADDITIONAL EXAMPLES

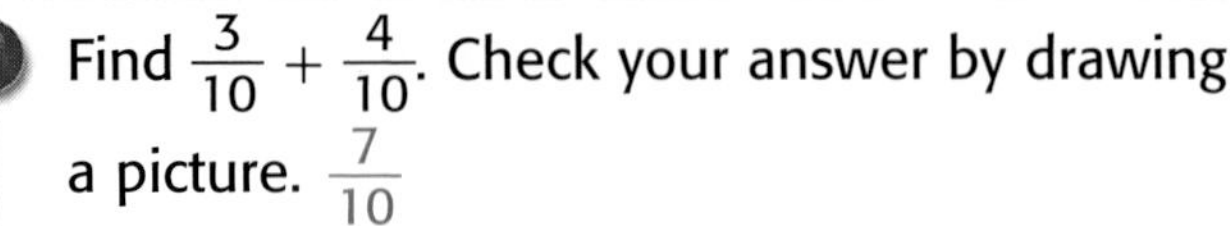

1. Find $\frac{3}{10} + \frac{4}{10}$. Check your answer by drawing a picture. $\frac{7}{10}$

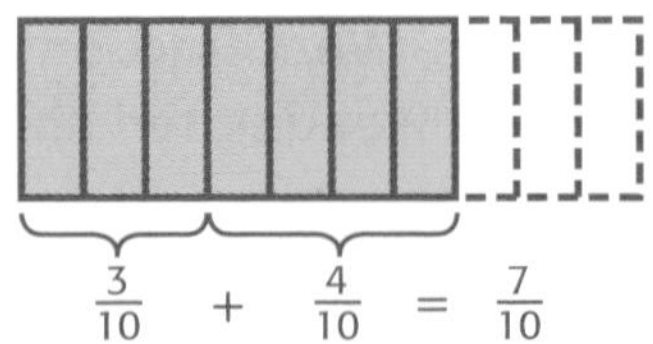

2. Marco ate $\frac{3}{8}$ of a pizza and Jen ate $\frac{1}{8}$ of it. What fraction of the pizza did the two friends eat in all? $\frac{1}{2}$
3. Find $\frac{5}{6} + \frac{2}{6}$. $1\frac{1}{6}$

CHECK What You Know

As a class, have students complete Exercises 1–8 in **Check What You Know** as you observe their work.

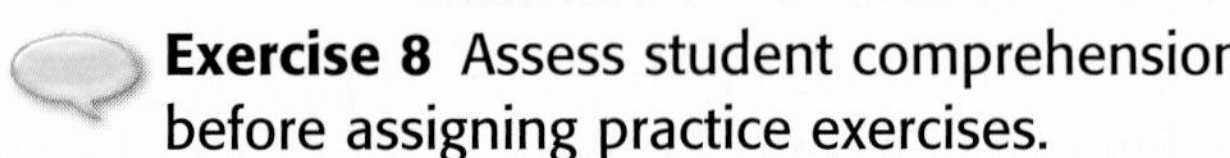

Exercise 8 Assess student comprehension before assigning practice exercises.

BL Alternate Teaching Strategy

If students have trouble adding fractions with like denominators...

Then use one of these reteach options:

1. CRM **Daily Reteach Worksheet** (p. 8)
2. Have students use fraction circles to model addition problems or to check their work. Have them look at the denominators of the like fractions and choose the fraction circle with that number of equal parts. Then have them model each addend with the circle pieces, combine, and count to find the sum.

COMMON ERROR!

Students may add denominators when adding fractions. Have students use fraction models to check their work. The models will illustrate that the denominator of the sum must be the same as the denominators of the addends.

Real-World EXAMPLE Add Like Fractions

2. **READING The table shows how much of a book Cleveland read each day. What fraction of the book did Cleveland read on Monday and Wednesday?**

Day	Fraction
Monday	$\frac{1}{10}$
Tuesday	$\frac{4}{10}$
Wednesday	$\frac{3}{10}$
Thursday	$\frac{2}{10}$

Add $\frac{1}{10}$ and $\frac{3}{10}$.

$\frac{1}{10} + \frac{3}{10} = \frac{1+3}{10}$ Add the numerators.

$= \frac{4}{10}$ Simplify.

$= \frac{4 \div 2}{10 \div 2}$ Divide the numerator and denominator by the GCF, 2.

$= \frac{2}{5}$ Simplify. Check by drawing a picture.

So, Cleveland read $\frac{2}{5}$ of the book on Monday and Wednesday.

Remember

To review writing an improper fraction as a mixed number, see Lesson 8-2 on pages 338–342.

EXAMPLE Add Like Fractions

3. **Find $\frac{2}{5} + \frac{4}{5}$. Use models to check.**

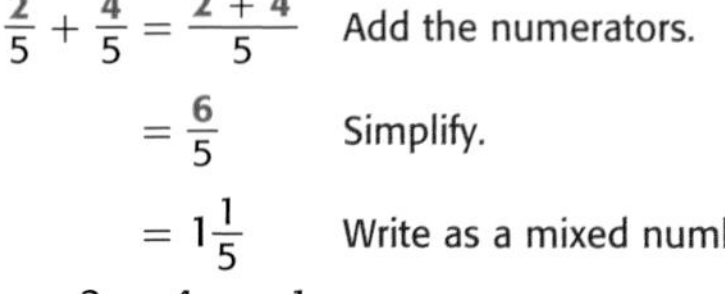

$\frac{2}{5} + \frac{4}{5} = \frac{2+4}{5}$ Add the numerators.

$= \frac{6}{5}$ Simplify.

$= 1\frac{1}{5}$ Write as a mixed number.

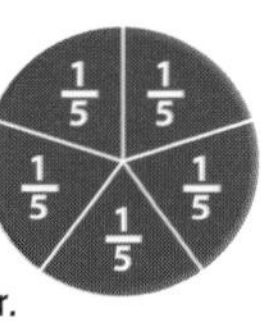

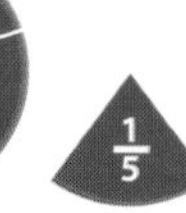

So, $\frac{2}{5} + \frac{4}{5} = 1\frac{1}{5}$.

CHECK What You Know

Add. Write each sum in simplest form. Use models to check.

See Examples 1–3 (pp. 423–424) 1–6. See students' work for models.

1. $\frac{1}{7} + \frac{3}{7}$ $\frac{4}{7}$
2. $\frac{2}{9} + \frac{3}{9}$ $\frac{5}{9}$
3. $\frac{1}{4} + \frac{1}{4}$ $\frac{1}{2}$
4. $\frac{1}{6} + \frac{1}{6}$ $\frac{1}{3}$
5. $\frac{5}{8} + \frac{3}{8}$ $\frac{8}{8}$ or 1
6. $\frac{2}{9} + \frac{8}{9}$ $1\frac{1}{9}$
7. Tia painted $\frac{5}{12}$ of a fence. Rey painted $\frac{4}{12}$ of the fence. How much of the fence did they paint? $\frac{3}{4}$
8.  Talk About It Write two sentences to explain how you solved Exercise 7. See Ch. 10 Answer Appendix.

424 **Chapter 10** Add and Subtract Fractions

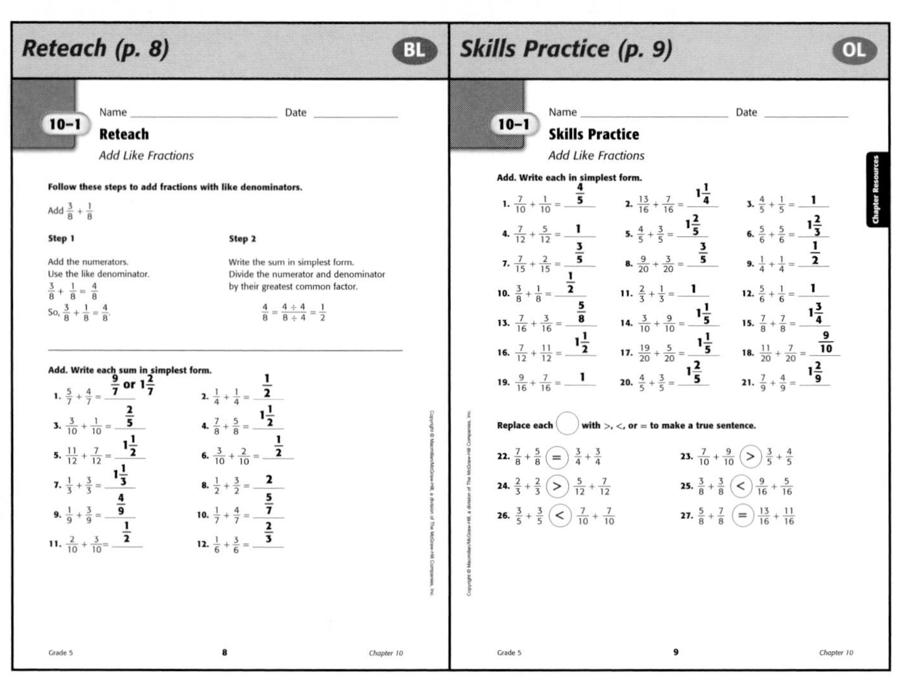

Reteach (p. 8) BL

10-1 Name ______ Date ______

Reteach

Add Like Fractions

Follow these steps to add fractions with like denominators.

Add $\frac{3}{8} + \frac{1}{8}$

Step 1

Add the numerators.
Use the like denominator.
$\frac{3}{8} + \frac{1}{8} = \frac{4}{8}$
So, $\frac{3}{8} + \frac{1}{8} = \frac{4}{8}$.

Step 2

Write the sum in simplest form.
Divide the numerator and denominator by their greatest common factor.
$\frac{4}{8} = \frac{4 \div 4}{8 \div 4} = \frac{1}{2}$

Add. Write each sum in simplest form.

1. $\frac{5}{7} + \frac{4}{7} =$ $\frac{9}{7}$ or $1\frac{2}{7}$
2. $\frac{1}{4} + \frac{1}{4} =$ $\frac{1}{2}$
3. $\frac{3}{10} + \frac{1}{10} =$ $\frac{2}{5}$
4. $\frac{7}{8} + \frac{5}{8} =$ $1\frac{1}{2}$
5. $\frac{11}{12} + \frac{7}{12} =$ $1\frac{1}{2}$
6. $\frac{3}{10} + \frac{2}{10} =$ $\frac{1}{2}$
7. $\frac{1}{3} + \frac{3}{3} =$ $1\frac{1}{3}$
8. $\frac{1}{2} + \frac{3}{2} =$ 2
9. $\frac{1}{9} + \frac{3}{9} =$ $\frac{4}{9}$
10. $\frac{1}{7} + \frac{4}{7} =$ $\frac{5}{7}$
11. $\frac{2}{10} + \frac{3}{10} =$ $\frac{1}{2}$
12. $\frac{1}{6} + \frac{3}{6} =$ $\frac{2}{3}$

Grade 5 8 Chapter 10

Skills Practice (p. 9) OL

10-1 Name ______ Date ______

Skills Practice

Add Like Fractions

Chapter Resources

Add. Write each in simplest form.

1. $\frac{7}{10} + \frac{1}{10} =$ $\frac{4}{5}$
2. $\frac{13}{16} + \frac{7}{16} =$ $1\frac{1}{4}$
3. $\frac{4}{5} + \frac{1}{5} =$ 1
4. $\frac{7}{12} + \frac{5}{12} =$ 1
5. $\frac{4}{5} + \frac{3}{5} =$ $1\frac{2}{5}$
6. $\frac{5}{6} + \frac{5}{6} =$ $1\frac{2}{3}$
7. $\frac{7}{15} + \frac{2}{15} =$ $\frac{3}{5}$
8. $\frac{9}{20} + \frac{3}{20} =$ $\frac{3}{5}$
9. $\frac{1}{4} + \frac{1}{4} =$ $\frac{1}{2}$
10. $\frac{3}{8} + \frac{1}{8} =$ $\frac{1}{2}$
11. $\frac{2}{3} + \frac{1}{3} =$ 1
12. $\frac{5}{6} + \frac{1}{6} =$ 1
13. $\frac{7}{16} + \frac{3}{16} =$ $\frac{5}{8}$
14. $\frac{3}{10} + \frac{9}{10} =$ $1\frac{1}{5}$
15. $\frac{7}{8} + \frac{7}{8} =$ $1\frac{3}{4}$
16. $\frac{7}{12} + \frac{11}{12} =$ $1\frac{1}{2}$
17. $\frac{19}{20} + \frac{5}{20} =$ $1\frac{1}{5}$
18. $\frac{11}{20} + \frac{7}{20} =$ $\frac{9}{10}$
19. $\frac{9}{16} + \frac{7}{16} =$ 1
20. $\frac{4}{5} + \frac{3}{5} =$ $1\frac{2}{5}$
21. $\frac{7}{9} + \frac{4}{9} =$ $1\frac{2}{9}$

Replace each ◯ with >, <, or = to make a true sentence.

22. $\frac{7}{8} + \frac{5}{8}$ (=) $\frac{3}{4} + \frac{3}{4}$
23. $\frac{7}{10} + \frac{9}{10}$ (>) $\frac{3}{5} + \frac{4}{5}$
24. $\frac{2}{3} + \frac{2}{3}$ (>) $\frac{5}{12} + \frac{7}{12}$
25. $\frac{3}{8} + \frac{3}{8}$ (<) $\frac{9}{16} + \frac{5}{16}$
26. $\frac{3}{5} + \frac{3}{5}$ (<) $\frac{7}{10} + \frac{7}{10}$
27. $\frac{5}{8} + \frac{7}{8}$ (=) $\frac{13}{16} + \frac{11}{16}$

Grade 5 9 Chapter 10

★ indicates multi-step problem

Practice and Problem Solving

EXTRA PRACTICE
See page R26.

Add. Write each sum in simplest form. Use models to check. See Examples 1–3 (pp. 423–424) 9–16. See students' work for models.

9. $\frac{4}{7} + \frac{2}{7}$ $\frac{6}{7}$ **10.** $\frac{2}{10} + \frac{5}{10}$ $\frac{7}{10}$ **11.** $\frac{2}{6} + \frac{2}{6}$ $\frac{2}{3}$ **12.** $\frac{3}{8} + \frac{1}{8}$ $\frac{1}{2}$

13. $\frac{3}{4} + \frac{1}{4}$ $\frac{4}{4}$ or 1 **14.** $\frac{4}{9} + \frac{5}{9}$ $\frac{9}{9}$ or 1 **15.** $\frac{3}{5} + \frac{4}{5}$ $1\frac{2}{5}$ **16.** $\frac{2}{3} + \frac{2}{3}$ $1\frac{1}{3}$

17. What is the sum of *two fifths and one fifth*? Write your answer in words. three fifths

18. What is the sum of *six ninths and three ninths*? Write your answer in words. nine ninths or one

19. Mia walked $\frac{9}{10}$ of a mile to the park. She walked the same distance home. How much did she walk altogether? See Ch. 10 Answer Appendix.

★**20.** It rained $\frac{2}{8}$ of an inch in one hour. It rained twice as much in the next hour. Find the total amount of rain. $\frac{3}{4}$ inch

For Exercises 21 and 22, refer to the table.

Type of Parade Float	Number
Sports Team	6
Radio Station	5
High School	3
Dance Group	4

21. What fraction of the floats were from either a dance group or a radio station? $\frac{1}{2}$

22. What fraction of the floats were *not* from a sports team? $\frac{2}{3}$

Algebra **Find the value of *x* that makes a true sentence.**

23. $\frac{3}{8} + \frac{x}{8} = \frac{7}{8}$ 4 **24.** $\frac{x}{9} + \frac{5}{9} = \frac{7}{9}$ 2 **25.** $\frac{5}{12} + \frac{x}{12} = 1$ 7

Data File

The recipe for North Carolina pulled pork sauce is shown.

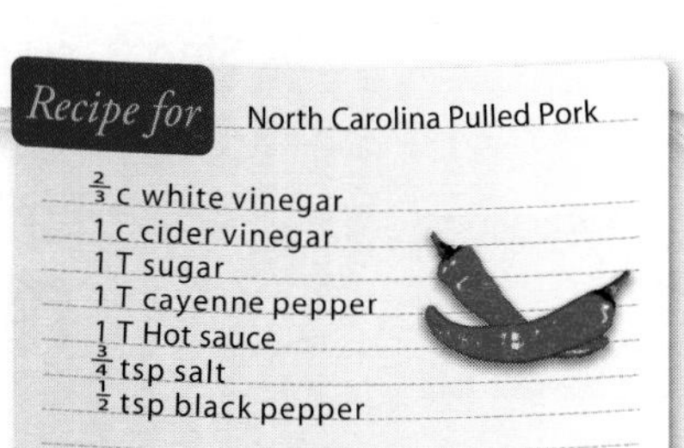

Recipe for North Carolina Pulled Pork
$\frac{2}{3}$ c white vinegar
1 c cider vinegar
1 T sugar
1 T cayenne pepper
1 T Hot sauce
$\frac{3}{4}$ tsp salt
$\frac{1}{2}$ tsp black pepper

26. If you double the recipe, how much white vinegar will you need? $1\frac{1}{3}$ cup

27. Mr. Gellar triples the recipe. For what ingredient will he need $1\frac{1}{2}$ tsp? black pepper

H.O.T. Problems

28. **OPEN ENDED** Select two fractions whose sum is $\frac{3}{4}$ and whose denominators are the same, but not 4. Justify your selection.

29. WRITING IN ▸MATH Write a real-world problem that can be solved by adding like fractions. Then solve.
28–29. See Ch. 10 Answer Appendix.

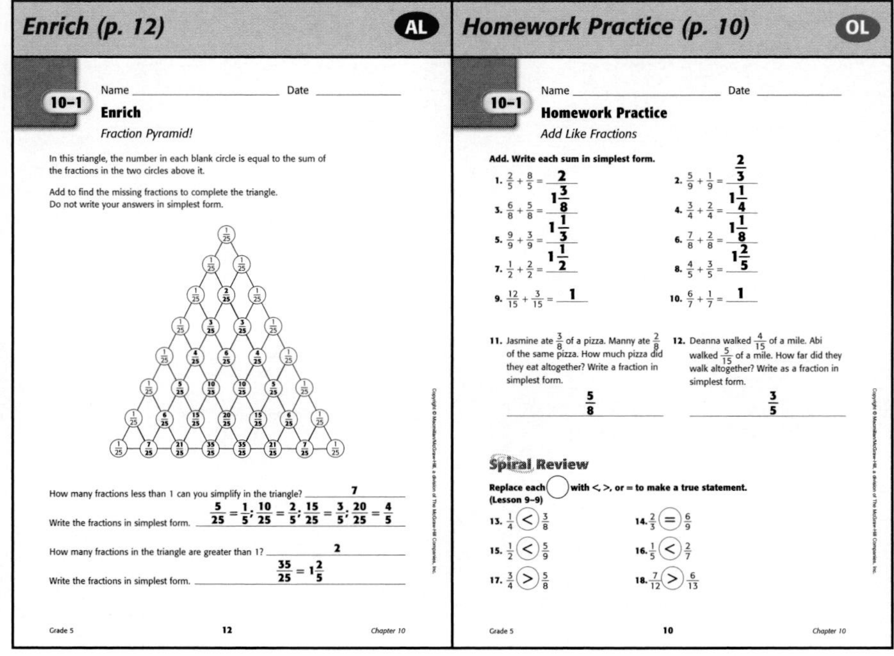

Enrich (p. 12) AL

10–1 Name ______ Date ______

Enrich

Fraction Pyramid!

In this triangle, the number in each blank circle is equal to the sum of the fractions in the two circles above it.

Add to find the missing fractions to complete the triangle. Do not write your answers in simplest form.

How many fractions less than 1 can you simplify in the triangle? **7**

Write the fractions in simplest form. $\frac{5}{25} = \frac{1}{5}; \frac{10}{25} = \frac{2}{5}; \frac{15}{25} = \frac{3}{5}; \frac{20}{25} = \frac{4}{5}$

How many fractions in the triangle are greater than 1? **2**

Write the fractions in simplest form. $\frac{35}{25} = 1\frac{2}{5}$

Grade 5 12 Chapter 10

Homework Practice (p. 10) OL

10–1 Name ______ Date ______

Homework Practice

Add Like Fractions

Add. Write each sum in simplest form.

1. $\frac{2}{5} + \frac{8}{5} =$ **2**
2. $\frac{5}{9} + \frac{1}{9} =$ $\frac{2}{3}$
3. $\frac{6}{8} + \frac{5}{8} =$ $1\frac{3}{8}$
4. $\frac{3}{4} + \frac{2}{4} =$ $1\frac{1}{4}$
5. $\frac{9}{9} + \frac{3}{9} =$ $1\frac{1}{3}$
6. $\frac{7}{8} + \frac{2}{8} =$ $1\frac{1}{8}$
7. $\frac{1}{2} + \frac{2}{2} =$ $1\frac{1}{2}$
8. $\frac{4}{5} + \frac{3}{5} =$ $1\frac{2}{5}$
9. $\frac{12}{15} + \frac{3}{15} =$ **1**
10. $\frac{6}{7} + \frac{1}{7} =$ **1**

11. Jasmine ate $\frac{3}{8}$ of a pizza. Manny ate $\frac{2}{8}$ of the same pizza. How much pizza did they eat altogether? Write a fraction in simplest form. $\frac{5}{8}$

12. Deanna walked $\frac{4}{15}$ of a mile. Abi walked $\frac{5}{15}$ of a mile. How far did they walk altogether? Write as a fraction in simplest form. $\frac{3}{5}$

Spiral Review

Replace each ◯ with <, >, or = to make a true statement. (Lesson 9–9)

13. $\frac{1}{4}$ (<) $\frac{3}{8}$
14. $\frac{2}{3}$ (=) $\frac{6}{9}$
15. $\frac{1}{2}$ (<) $\frac{5}{9}$
16. $\frac{1}{5}$ (<) $\frac{2}{7}$
17. $\frac{3}{4}$ (>) $\frac{5}{8}$
18. $\frac{7}{12}$ (>) $\frac{6}{13}$

Grade 5 10 Chapter 10

3 Practice

Differentiate practice using these leveled assignments for Exercises 9–29.

Level	Assignment
BL Below/Approaching Level	9–10, 17–18, 21–22, 23–24, 26–27
OL On Level	11–14, 17–20, 21–20, 23–25, 26–27, 28
AL Above/Beyond Level	9–27 odd, 28–29

Have students discuss and complete the Higher Order Thinking problems. Students may use the *guess and check* strategy to solve Exercise 28.

WRITING IN ▸MATH Have students complete Exercise 29 in their Math Journals. You may choose to use this exercise as an optional formative assessment.

4 Assess

Formative Assessment

- **Is $\frac{3}{5} + \frac{4}{5}$ more or less than 1? Tell how you know.** more than 1; $\frac{3}{5} + \frac{4}{5} = \frac{7}{5}$; $\frac{5}{5} = 1$; $\frac{7}{5}$ is greater than $\frac{5}{5}$, so $\frac{7}{5}$ is greater than 1.

Quick Check **Are students continuing to struggle with adding fractions with like denominators?**

If Yes → Small Group Options (p. 423B)

If No → Independent Work Options (p. 423B)
CRM Skills Practice Worksheet (p. 9)
CRM Enrich Worksheet (p. 12)

Into the Future Ask students to think about what they learned to do with fractions today and predict what they may learn to do next. Ask them to write a problem they think they may be asked to solve.

Math Activity for 10-2

Lesson Planner

Objective

Use models to subtract fractions with like denominators.

Resources

Manipulatives: fraction tiles

1 Introduce

- Provide students with $\frac{1}{6}$-fraction tiles. Write $\frac{3}{6} + \frac{2}{6}$ on the board. Have students model the addition.
- **What did you do first?** I put down three $\frac{1}{6}$ tiles to show $\frac{3}{6}$.
- **How do you show the addition of $\frac{2}{6}$?** Place two $\frac{1}{6}$-fraction tiles next to the three $\frac{1}{6}$-fraction tiles.
- **How do you find the sum?** Count the total number of $\frac{1}{6}$-tiles. There are 5 tiles, so the sum is $\frac{5}{6}$.
- Have students discuss how they think they might use fraction tiles to model subtraction of like fractions.

2 Teach

Activity 1 Give students $\frac{1}{8}$-fraction tiles. Have them model $\frac{5}{8}$ by placing five $\frac{1}{8}$-tiles side-by-side. Point out that students should physically remove, or take away, two of the five tiles to show the subtraction of $\frac{2}{8}$ from $\frac{5}{8}$. The number of $\frac{1}{8}$-tiles that are left show the difference.

Math Activity for 10-2

Subtract Like Fractions

MAIN IDEA

I will use models to subtract fractions with like denominators.

You can use fraction tiles to subtract fractions with like denominators.

ACTIVITY

1 Miguel has a bag of marbles. Of the marbles, $\frac{5}{8}$ are blue, and $\frac{2}{8}$ are red. How many more blue marbles than red marbles are in the bag?

Step 1 **Model $\frac{5}{8}$.**

Use five $\frac{1}{8}$-fraction tiles to show $\frac{5}{8}$.

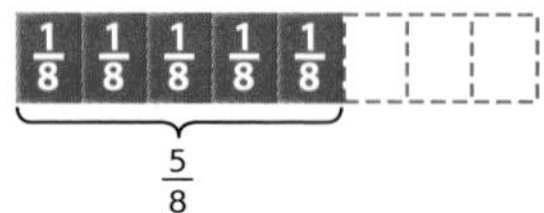

Step 2 **Subtract $\frac{2}{8}$.**

Remove two $\frac{1}{8}$-fraction tiles to show the subtraction of $\frac{2}{8}$.

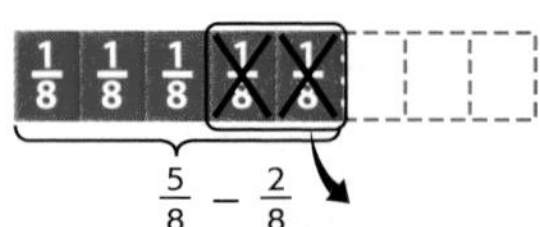

Step 3 Count the total number of $\frac{1}{8}$-fraction tiles that are left.

$\frac{5}{8} - \frac{2}{8} = \frac{3}{8}$. So, there are $\frac{3}{8}$ or *three eighths* more blue marbles.

ACTIVITY

2 **Abbi bought $\frac{9}{10}$ pound of Swiss cheese and $\frac{6}{10}$ pound of cheddar cheese. How much more Swiss cheese did she buy?**

Step 1 **Model $\frac{9}{10}$.**

Use nine $\frac{1}{10}$-fraction tiles to show $\frac{9}{10}$.

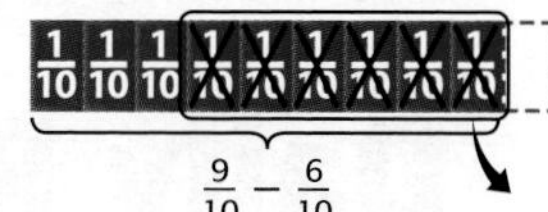

Step 2 **Subtract $\frac{6}{10}$.**

Remove six $\frac{1}{10}$-fraction tiles.

$\frac{9}{10} - \frac{6}{10}$

Step 3 Count the total number of $\frac{1}{10}$-fraction tiles that are left.

$\frac{9}{10} - \frac{6}{10} = \frac{3}{10}$. So, Abbi bought $\frac{3}{10}$ or *three tenths* pound more Swiss cheese.

Think About It

1. Describe how you would model $\frac{4}{5} - \frac{3}{5}$. 1. Use four $\frac{1}{5}$-fraction tiles to show $\frac{4}{5}$. Then take away three $\frac{1}{5}$-fraction tiles to show the subtraction of $\frac{3}{5}$.
2. Describe how you would find the difference $\frac{4}{5} - \frac{3}{5}$. Then find the difference. Count the total number of $\frac{1}{5}$-fraction tiles left; $\frac{1}{5}$

CHECK What You Know

Model each difference using fraction tiles. Then find the difference and write in words. 3–4. See students' work for models.

3. $\frac{2}{4} - \frac{1}{4}$ $\frac{1}{4}$; one fourth

4. $\frac{4}{5} - \frac{2}{5}$ $\frac{2}{5}$; two fifths

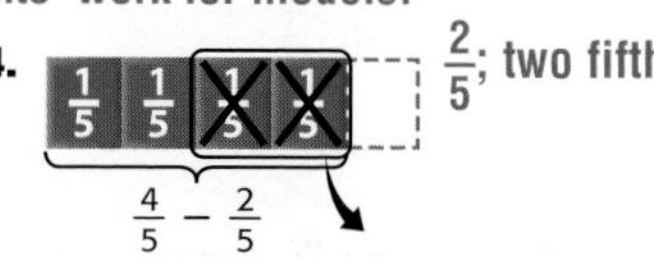

Find each difference. Use fraction tiles if needed. 5–10. See students' work for pictures.

5. $\frac{6}{7} - \frac{4}{7}$ $\frac{2}{7}$
6. $\frac{2}{3} - \frac{1}{3}$ $\frac{1}{3}$
7. $\frac{4}{6} - \frac{3}{6}$ $\frac{1}{6}$
8. $\frac{5}{9} - \frac{3}{9}$ $\frac{2}{9}$
9. $\frac{7}{10} - \frac{4}{10}$ $\frac{3}{10}$
10. $\frac{11}{12} - \frac{6}{12}$ $\frac{5}{12}$
11. **WRITING IN MATH** Look at the numerators and denominators in each exercise. Explain how you could find $\frac{9}{12} - \frac{4}{12}$ without using fraction tiles. See margin.

Additional Answer

11. Sample answer: The numerator is the difference between the numerators of the fractions and the denominator stays the same; subtract 4 from 9 to get the numerator and the denominator is 12.

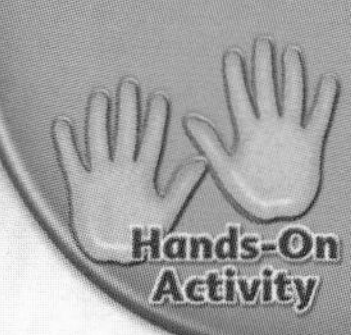

Activity 2 Have students repeat the process for $\frac{9}{10} - \frac{6}{10}$: first model $\frac{9}{10}$ with nine $\frac{1}{10}$-fraction tiles, subtract $\frac{6}{10}$ by removing six $\frac{1}{10}$-fraction tiles, then count the $\frac{1}{10}$-fraction tiles that are left to find the difference.

Think About It

Assign Exercises 1 and 2 to assess student comprehension of the concept presented in the activity.

3 Assess

Formative Assessment

Use **Check What You Know** Exercises 3–11 to assess whether students understand how to use models to subtract fractions with like denominators.

From Concrete to Abstract Use Exercise 11 to bridge the gap between modeling subtraction with fraction tiles and subtracting fractions with like denominators without the use of models or drawings.

Extending the Concept Have students subtract $\frac{5}{6} - \frac{1}{6}$ and write the difference in simplest form.

LESSON

10-2 Subtract Like Fractions

Lesson Planner

Objective

Subtract fractions with like denominators.

Review Vocabulary

greatest common factor (GCF), simplest form

Resources

Materials: dry-erase boards, dry-erase markers
Manipulatives: fraction tiles, fraction circles
Literature Connection: *Gator Pie* by Louise Mathews
Teacher Technology
Interactive Classroom • TeacherWorks

Focus on Math Background

It is also important that students understand why fractions with like denominators can be subtracted by subtracting numerators. The reasoning is similar to that of adding fractions with like denominators. That is, when subtracting fractions, the denominators are left alone because they are identifying the parts that are being combined and just the numerators are subtracted. Hence, 4 *fifths* minus 2 *fifths* must be equal to 2 *fifths*.

Note that the sum or difference of two fractions in simplest form may not be in simplest form. For example, the fractions $\frac{5}{8}$ and $\frac{1}{8}$ are in simplest form, but their sum and difference are not.

$\frac{5}{8} + \frac{1}{8} = \frac{6}{8}$ or $\frac{3}{4}$
sum

$\frac{5}{8} - \frac{1}{8} = \frac{4}{8}$ or $\frac{1}{2}$
difference

Daily Routine

Use these suggestions before beginning the lesson on p. 428.

5-Minute Check

(Reviews Lesson 10-1)

Add. Write each sum in simplest form. Check your answer by using fraction tiles or drawing a picture.

1. $\frac{2}{5} + \frac{1}{5}$ $\frac{3}{5}$

2. $\frac{2}{7} + \frac{3}{7}$ $\frac{5}{7}$

3. $\frac{1}{6} + \frac{3}{6}$ $\frac{2}{3}$

4. $\frac{5}{12} + \frac{4}{12}$ $\frac{3}{4}$

5. $\frac{5}{9} + \frac{4}{9}$ 1

6. $\frac{3}{4} + \frac{3}{4}$ $1\frac{1}{2}$

See students' tiles or pictures.

Problem of the Day

Natalia bought 3 pounds of oranges and 2 pounds of apples. Oranges were on sale for $0.15 less per pound than the apples. The apples cost $0.95 per pound. How much did Natalia spend on fruit? $4.30

Review Math Vocabulary

Write the review vocabulary words and their definitions on the board.

Write $\frac{6}{8}$ on the board. Ask students to identify the greatest common factor of 6 and 8 and explain how to use this number to write $\frac{6}{8}$ in simplest form. Provide additional examples.

Differentiated Instruction

Small Group Options

Option 1 SPATIAL

Below Level BL

Materials: pencil and paper

- Ask students to revisit Example 2 at the beginning of this lesson—Rainfall.
- **How much more rain did Centerville receive than Clarksburg?** $\frac{3}{10}$ inch
- **How much less rain did Spring Valley receive than Brushton?** $\frac{2}{10}$ inch
- **Which two cities receive the same amount combined as Centerville?** Clarksburg and Brushton
- **Now it is your turn. Write another problem that uses this table.** Answers will vary.

Option 2 AUDITORY, LOGICAL

English Language Learners ELL

Materials: paper or plastic dimes, 6–10 per student; paper, pencil; 9 pictures of items on board with price tags of 10¢, 20¢, 30¢, up to 90¢.

Core Vocabulary: spending, choose, what to buy

Common Use Verb: will practice

Hear Math This strategy activates background knowledge to practice subtracting fractions.

- Say: "The value of a dime is 0.1 or $\frac{1}{10}$."
- Say: "We ***will practice*** **spending** money. Start with your dimes. Write that number as a fraction." Sample answer: 6 dimes $= \frac{6}{10}$
- Say: "**Choose what** you want **to buy** from the board. Write that number as a fraction." Sample answer: a 30¢ item $= \frac{3}{10}$
- Ask: "How much did you spend? How much is left over? Write it as a fraction." $\frac{6}{10} - \frac{3}{10} = \frac{3}{10}$
- As students spend money, have them write subtraction sentences to illustrate.

Independent Work Options

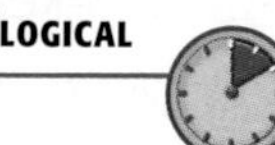

Option 1 VISUAL/LOGICAL

Early Finishers OL

Materials: paper, pencil

- Have students review the inverse relationship between addition and subtraction by writing number sentences with fractions. Ask students to first write five number sentences showing addition of like fractions.
- Next, have students write a related subtraction sentence for each addition sentence they wrote. Ask students to draw a picture to represent each number sentence.

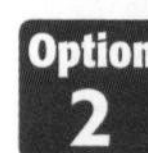

Option 2

Student Technology

Math Online macmillanmh.com

Personal Tutor • Extra Examples

Math Adventures

Option 3

Learning Station: Writing (p. 418I)

Direct students to the Writing Learning Station for opportunities to explore and extend the lesson concept.

Option 4

Problem-Solving Practice

Reinforce problem-solving skills and strategies with the Problem-Solving Practice worksheet.

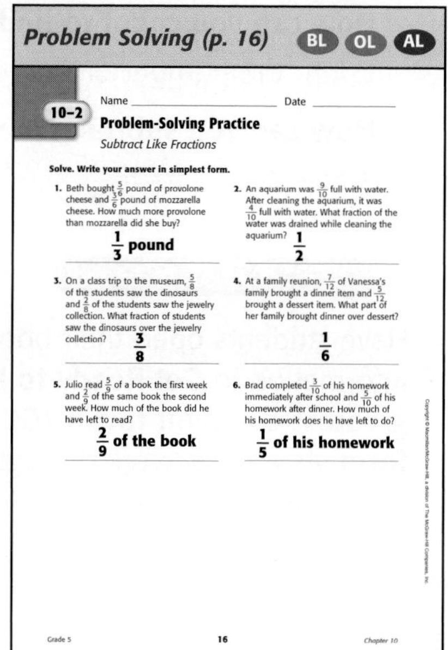

Problem Solving (p. 16) BL OL AL

10–2 Name ________ Date ________

Problem-Solving Practice

Subtract Like Fractions

Solve. Write your answer in simplest form.

1. Beth bought $\frac{5}{6}$ pound of provolone cheese and $\frac{3}{6}$ pound of mozzarella cheese. How much more provolone than mozzarella did she buy? **$\frac{1}{3}$ pound**
2. An aquarium was $\frac{9}{10}$ full with water. After cleaning the aquarium, it was $\frac{4}{10}$ full with water. What fraction of the water was drained while cleaning the aquarium? **$\frac{1}{2}$**
3. On a class trip to the museum, $\frac{5}{8}$ of the students saw the dinosaurs and $\frac{2}{8}$ of the students saw the jewelry collection. What fraction of students saw the dinosaurs over the jewelry collection? **$\frac{3}{8}$**
4. At a family reunion, $\frac{7}{12}$ of Vanessa's family brought a dinner item and $\frac{5}{12}$ brought a dessert item. What part of her family brought dinner over dessert? **$\frac{1}{6}$**
5. Julio read $\frac{5}{9}$ of a book the first week and $\frac{2}{9}$ of the same book the second week. How much of the book did he have left to read? **$\frac{2}{9}$ of the book**
6. Brad completed $\frac{3}{10}$ of his homework immediately after school and $\frac{5}{10}$ of his homework after dinner. How much of his homework does he have left to do? **$\frac{1}{5}$ of his homework**

Grade 5 16 Chapter 10

10-2 Subtract Like Fractions

1 Introduce

Activity Choice 1 • Hands-On 

- Organize students into pairs and provide each pair with a dry-erase board, dry-erase marker, and fraction tiles.
- Write an addition problem with like fractions on the board. Have partners use paper and pencil or the fraction tiles to find the sum.
- Have pairs write the sum on the dry-erase board, then raise their boards to show their answers when you say "responses up."
- Go over the problem, if necessary, and continue with a new addition problem.

Activity Choice 2 • Literature

Introduce the lesson with *Gator Pie* by Louise Mathews. For a related math activity, see p. TR52.

2 Teach

Scaffolding Questions

Have students use fraction tiles to model $\frac{4}{5} - \frac{1}{5}$.

- **What do you do first?** Show $\frac{4}{5}$ by placing four $\frac{1}{5}$ fraction tiles side-by-side.
- **How do you model subtracting $\frac{1}{5}$?** Remove one of the $\frac{1}{5}$ fraction tiles from the group of four tiles.
- **How can you count to find the difference?** Count the number of $\frac{1}{5}$ fraction tiles left.
- **How can you subtract?** 4 tiles − 1 tile = 3 tiles. So $\frac{4}{5} - \frac{1}{5} = \frac{3}{5}$.

GET READY to Learn

Have students open their books and read the information in **Get Ready to Learn**. Review **greatest common factor (GCF)** and **simplest form**. As a class, work through **Examples 1–3**.

10-2 Subtract Like Fractions

MAIN IDEA

I will subtract fractions with like denominators.

Math Online

macmillanmh.com

- Extra Examples
- Personal Tutor
- Self-Check Quiz

GET READY to Learn

Frankie is walking on a nature trail that is $\frac{7}{8}$-mile long. He has already walked $\frac{4}{8}$ mile. How much farther does Frankie have to walk?

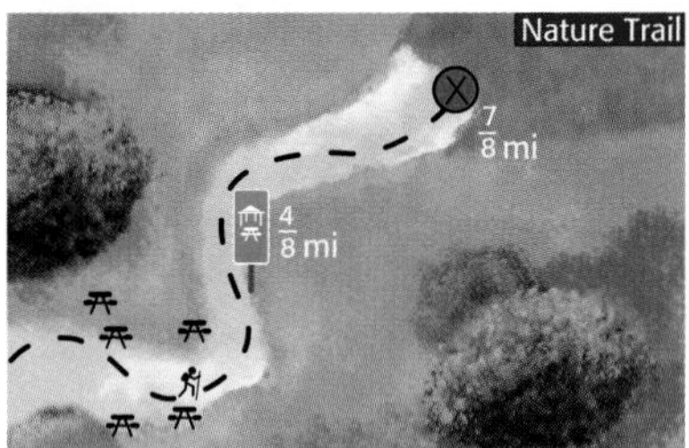

To find how much farther, subtract $\frac{4}{8}$ from $\frac{7}{8}$.

EXAMPLE Subtract Like Fractions

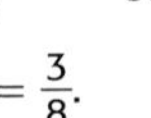

1 Find $\frac{7}{8} - \frac{4}{8}$. Use models to check.

$\frac{7}{8} - \frac{4}{8} = \frac{7-4}{8}$

$= \frac{3}{8}$ Subtract.

So, $\frac{7}{8} - \frac{4}{8} = \frac{3}{8}$.

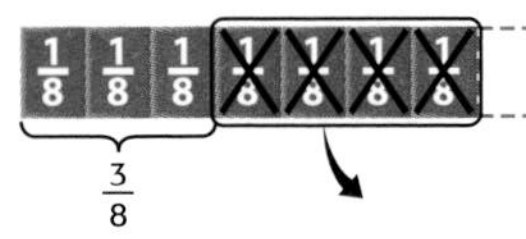

Subtracting like fractions is similar to adding like fractions.

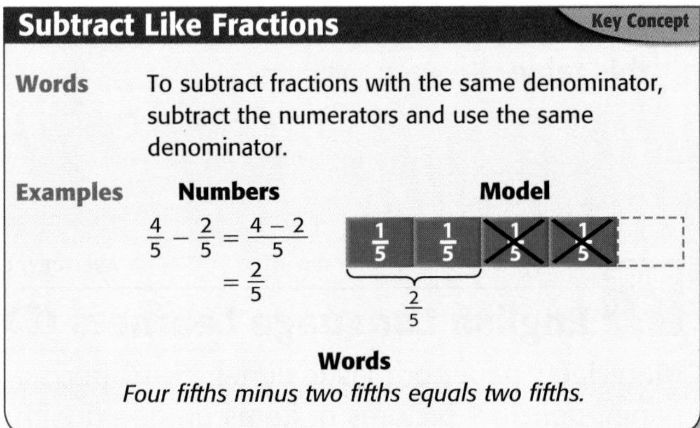

Subtract Like Fractions — Key Concept

Words To subtract fractions with the same denominator, subtract the numerators and use the same denominator.

Examples

Numbers

$\frac{4}{5} - \frac{2}{5} = \frac{4-2}{5}$

$= \frac{2}{5}$

Model

Words

Four fifths minus two fifths equals two fifths.

428 Chapter 10 Add and Subtract Fractions

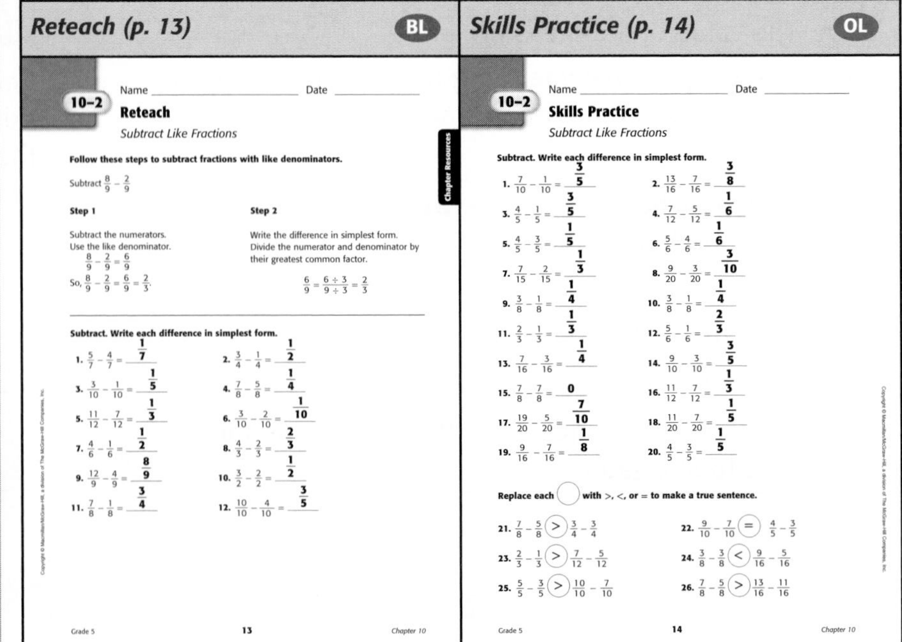

Reteach (p. 13) BL

10-2 Name ______ Date ______

Reteach

Subtract Like Fractions

Follow these steps to subtract fractions with like denominators.

Subtract $\frac{8}{9} - \frac{2}{9}$

Step 1

Subtract the numerators. Use the like denominator.

$\frac{8}{9} - \frac{2}{9} = \frac{6}{9}$

So, $\frac{8}{9} - \frac{2}{9} = \frac{6}{9} = \frac{2}{3}$.

Step 2

Write the difference in simplest form. Divide the numerator and denominator by their greatest common factor.

$\frac{6}{9} = \frac{6 \div 3}{9 \div 3} = \frac{2}{3}$

Subtract. Write each difference in simplest form.

1. $\frac{5}{7} - \frac{4}{7} = \frac{1}{7}$
2. $\frac{3}{4} - \frac{1}{4} = \frac{1}{2}$
3. $\frac{3}{10} - \frac{1}{10} = \frac{1}{5}$
4. $\frac{7}{8} - \frac{5}{8} = \frac{1}{4}$
5. $\frac{11}{12} - \frac{7}{12} = \frac{1}{3}$
6. $\frac{3}{10} - \frac{2}{10} = \frac{1}{10}$
7. $\frac{4}{6} - \frac{1}{6} = \frac{1}{2}$
8. $\frac{4}{3} - \frac{2}{3} = \frac{2}{3}$
9. $\frac{12}{9} - \frac{4}{9} = \frac{8}{9}$
10. $\frac{3}{2} - \frac{2}{2} = \frac{1}{2}$
11. $\frac{7}{8} - \frac{1}{8} = \frac{3}{4}$
12. $\frac{10}{10} - \frac{4}{10} = \frac{3}{5}$

Chapter Resources

Skills Practice (p. 14) OL

10-2 Name ______ Date ______

Skills Practice

Subtract Like Fractions

Subtract. Write each difference in simplest form.

1. $\frac{7}{10} - \frac{1}{10} = \frac{3}{5}$
2. $\frac{13}{16} - \frac{7}{16} = \frac{3}{8}$
3. $\frac{4}{5} - \frac{1}{5} = \frac{3}{5}$
4. $\frac{7}{12} - \frac{5}{12} = \frac{1}{6}$
5. $\frac{4}{5} - \frac{3}{5} = \frac{1}{5}$
6. $\frac{5}{6} - \frac{4}{6} = \frac{1}{6}$
7. $\frac{7}{15} - \frac{2}{15} = \frac{1}{3}$
8. $\frac{9}{20} - \frac{3}{20} = \frac{3}{10}$
9. $\frac{3}{8} - \frac{1}{8} = \frac{1}{4}$
10. $\frac{3}{8} - \frac{1}{8} = \frac{1}{4}$
11. $\frac{2}{3} - \frac{1}{3} = \frac{1}{3}$
12. $\frac{5}{6} - \frac{1}{6} = \frac{2}{3}$
13. $\frac{7}{16} - \frac{3}{16} = \frac{1}{4}$
14. $\frac{9}{10} - \frac{3}{10} = \frac{3}{5}$
15. $\frac{7}{8} - \frac{7}{8} = 0$
16. $\frac{11}{12} - \frac{7}{12} = \frac{1}{3}$
17. $\frac{19}{20} - \frac{5}{20} = \frac{7}{10}$
18. $\frac{11}{20} - \frac{7}{20} = \frac{1}{5}$
19. $\frac{9}{16} - \frac{7}{16} = \frac{1}{8}$
20. $\frac{4}{5} - \frac{3}{5} = \frac{1}{5}$

Replace each ◯ with >, <, or = to make a true sentence.

21. $\frac{7}{8} - \frac{5}{8} > \frac{3}{4} - \frac{3}{4}$
22. $\frac{9}{10} - \frac{7}{10} = \frac{4}{5} - \frac{3}{5}$
23. $\frac{2}{3} - \frac{1}{3} > \frac{7}{12} - \frac{5}{12}$
24. $\frac{3}{8} - \frac{3}{8} < \frac{9}{16} - \frac{5}{16}$
25. $\frac{5}{5} - \frac{3}{5} > \frac{10}{10} - \frac{7}{10}$
26. $\frac{7}{8} - \frac{5}{8} > \frac{13}{16} - \frac{11}{16}$

Real-World EXAMPLES Subtract Like Fractions

WEATHER The table shows the amount of rainfall several cities received in a recent month.

RAINFALL

City	Rainfall (in.)
Spring Valley	$\frac{1}{10}$
Clarksburg	$\frac{6}{10}$
Centerville	$\frac{9}{10}$
Brushton	$\frac{3}{10}$

2 How much more rain did Centerville receive than Brushton? Write in simplest form. Use models to check.

Subtract the amount of rain that fell in Brushton from the amount of rain that fell in Centerville.

$\frac{9}{10} - \frac{3}{10} = \frac{9-3}{10}$ Subtract the numerators.

$= \frac{6}{10}$ Simplify.

$= \frac{6 \div 2}{10 \div 2}$ Divide by the GCF, 2.

$= \frac{3}{5}$ Simplify.

Use models to check.

$\frac{9}{10} - \frac{3}{10}$

So, $\frac{3}{5}$ inch more rain fell in Centerville than in Brushton.

Remember

Divide both the numerator and denominator by the greatest common factor.

3 How many fewer inches of rain did Spring Valley receive than Clarksburg? Write in simplest form. Use models to check.

Subtract the amount of rain that fell in Spring Valley from the amount of rain that fell in Clarksburg.

$\frac{6}{10} - \frac{1}{10} = \frac{6-1}{10}$ Subtract the numerators.

$= \frac{5}{10}$ Simplify.

$= \frac{5 \div 5}{10 \div 5}$ Divide by the GCF, 5.

$= \frac{1}{2}$ Simplify.

Use models to check.

$\frac{6}{10} - \frac{1}{10}$

So, it rained $\frac{1}{2}$ inch less in Spring Valley than in Clarksburg.

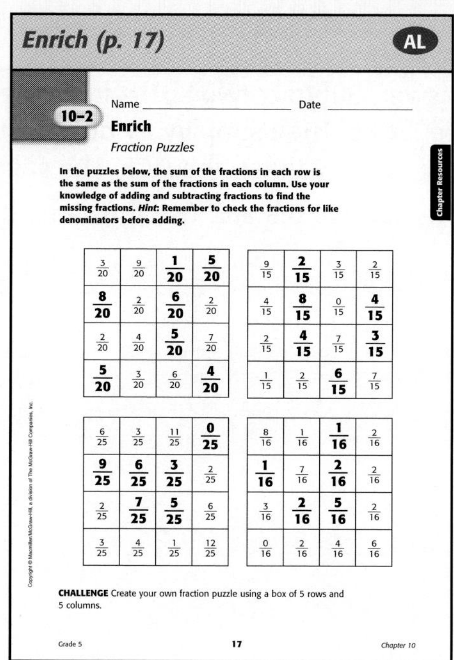

Enrich (p. 17) AL

10–2 Name ____________ Date ________

Enrich

Fraction Puzzles

In the puzzles below, the sum of the fractions in each row is the same as the sum of the fractions in each column. Use your knowledge of adding and subtracting fractions to find the missing fractions. *Hint*: Remember to check the fractions for like denominators before adding.

$\frac{3}{20}$	$\frac{9}{20}$	$\frac{1}{20}$	$\frac{5}{20}$
$\frac{8}{20}$	$\frac{2}{20}$	$\frac{6}{20}$	$\frac{2}{20}$
$\frac{2}{20}$	$\frac{4}{20}$	$\frac{5}{20}$	$\frac{7}{20}$
$\frac{5}{20}$	$\frac{3}{20}$	$\frac{6}{20}$	$\frac{4}{20}$

$\frac{9}{15}$	$\frac{2}{15}$	$\frac{3}{15}$	$\frac{2}{15}$
$\frac{4}{15}$	$\frac{8}{15}$	$\frac{0}{15}$	$\frac{4}{15}$
$\frac{2}{15}$	$\frac{4}{15}$	$\frac{7}{15}$	$\frac{3}{15}$
$\frac{1}{15}$	$\frac{2}{15}$	$\frac{6}{15}$	$\frac{7}{15}$

$\frac{6}{25}$	$\frac{3}{25}$	$\frac{11}{25}$	$\frac{0}{25}$
$\frac{9}{25}$	$\frac{6}{25}$	$\frac{3}{25}$	$\frac{2}{25}$
$\frac{2}{25}$	$\frac{7}{25}$	$\frac{5}{25}$	$\frac{6}{25}$
$\frac{3}{25}$	$\frac{4}{25}$	$\frac{1}{25}$	$\frac{12}{25}$

$\frac{8}{16}$	$\frac{1}{16}$	$\frac{1}{16}$	$\frac{2}{16}$
$\frac{1}{16}$	$\frac{7}{16}$	$\frac{2}{16}$	$\frac{2}{16}$
$\frac{3}{16}$	$\frac{2}{16}$	$\frac{5}{16}$	$\frac{2}{16}$
$\frac{0}{16}$	$\frac{2}{16}$	$\frac{4}{16}$	$\frac{6}{16}$

CHALLENGE Create your own fraction puzzle using a box of 5 rows and 5 columns.

Chapter Resources

Grade 5 17 Chapter 10

Real-World Example

Example 2 Help students read the table and locate the amounts of rainfall for Brushton and Centerville. Have them identify key words in the problem that indicate that they will subtract to solve.

ADDITIONAL EXAMPLES

1 Find $\frac{9}{10} - \frac{6}{10}$. Check by drawing a picture. $\frac{3}{10}$

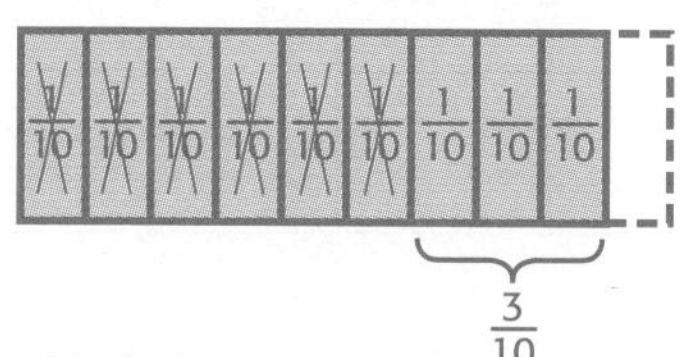

2 Robert used $\frac{3}{4}$ teaspoon of salt and $\frac{1}{4}$ teaspoon of pepper in a recipe. How much more salt did he use than pepper? Write in simplest form. $\frac{1}{2}$ teaspoon

3 Nadia used $\frac{11}{12}$ foot of string for a necklace and Kate used $\frac{8}{12}$ foot of string. How many fewer feet of string did Kate use than Nadia? Write in simplest form. $\frac{1}{4}$ foot

CHECK What You Know

As a class, have students complete Exercises 1–6 in **Check What You Know** as you observe their work.

Exercise 6 Assess student comprehension before assigning practice exercises.

BL Alternate Teaching Strategy

If students have trouble subtracting like fractions by subtracting numerators or drawing pictures to check their answers…

Then use one of these reteach options:

1 CRM **Daily Reteach Worksheet** (p. 13)

2 Have students use fraction circles to model subtraction problems or to check their work. Have them look at the denominators of both fractions in a problem and choose the fraction circle with that number of equal parts. Then have them model the first fraction in the problem with the circle pieces, remove pieces to show subtraction of the second fraction, and count the remaining pieces to find the difference.

3 Practice

Differentiate practice using these leveled assignments for Exercises 7–28.

Level	Assignment
BL Below/ Approaching Level	7–10, 15–16, 19, 21–22
OL On Level	8–14, 16–18, 20, 22–26, 27
AL Above/Beyond Level	8–22 even, 24–28

Have students discuss and complete the Higher Order Thinking problems. For Exercise 24, suggest that students begin by writing an equivalent fraction for $\frac{1}{6}$. They can use that fraction to help them write a subtraction problem.

WRITING IN ▸MATH Have students complete Exercise 28 in their Math Journals. You may choose to use this as an optional formative assessment.

Tips for New Teachers Previous textbook editions may have used the terminology "reduce" to describe the simplest form of a fraction. However, "simplify" is the more accurate instruction. "Reduce" implies that the fractional amount becomes smaller. However, this is not true.

COMMON ERROR!

Students may have trouble deciding if a difference is in simplest form. After they complete the subtraction, have students list all of the factors for the numerator and all of the factors for the denominator. Then have them circle common factors in each list and divide by the greatest common factor (GCF).

CHECK What You Know

Subtract. Write each difference in simplest form. Use models to check. See Examples 1–3 (pp. 428–429) 1–4. See students' model.

1. $\frac{5}{7} - \frac{3}{7}$ $\frac{2}{7}$
2. $\frac{3}{5} - \frac{2}{5}$ $\frac{1}{5}$
3. $\frac{6}{9} - \frac{3}{9}$ $\frac{1}{3}$
4. $\frac{5}{6} - \frac{3}{6}$ $\frac{1}{3}$
5. Ciro spent $\frac{5}{6}$ hour drawing and $\frac{2}{6}$ hour reading. How much more time did he spend drawing than reading? $\frac{1}{2}$ h
6. **Talk About It** Explain how you solved Exercise 5 using words. See margin.

Practice and Problem Solving

EXTRA PRACTICE See page R27.

Subtract. Write each difference in simplest form. Use models to check. See Examples 1–3 (pp. 428–429) 7–14. See students' model.

7. $\frac{2}{3} - \frac{1}{3}$ $\frac{1}{3}$
8. $\frac{3}{5} - \frac{1}{5}$ $\frac{2}{5}$
9. $\frac{6}{7} - \frac{5}{7}$ $\frac{1}{7}$
10. $\frac{3}{6} - \frac{1}{6}$ $\frac{1}{3}$
11. $\frac{5}{9} - \frac{2}{9}$ $\frac{1}{3}$
12. $\frac{6}{8} - \frac{4}{8}$ $\frac{1}{4}$
13. $\frac{3}{4} - \frac{1}{4}$ $\frac{1}{2}$
14. $\frac{9}{12} - \frac{3}{12}$ $\frac{1}{2}$
15. Find the difference between *seven ninths and four ninths.* Write your answer in words. one third
16. What is the difference between *six sevenths and five sevenths?* Write your answer in words. one seventh
17. **Measurement** Roshanda bought $\frac{5}{8}$ pound of ham and $\frac{7}{8}$ pound of roast beef. How much more roast beef than ham did she buy? $\frac{1}{4}$ pound
18. A bucket was $\frac{7}{10}$ full with water. After Vick washed the car, the bucket was only $\frac{3}{10}$ full. What part did Vick use to wash the car? $\frac{2}{5}$ water

For Exercises 19 and 20, use the results of a survey of 28 students and their favorite tourist attractions.

19. What fraction of students prefer Mt. Rushmore over the Grand Canyon? $\frac{3}{14}$

★20. Suppose 4 students change their minds and choose the Statue of Liberty instead of the Grand Canyon. What part of the class now prefers Mt. Rushmore over the Statue of Liberty? $\frac{1}{7}$

Favorite Tourist Attractions

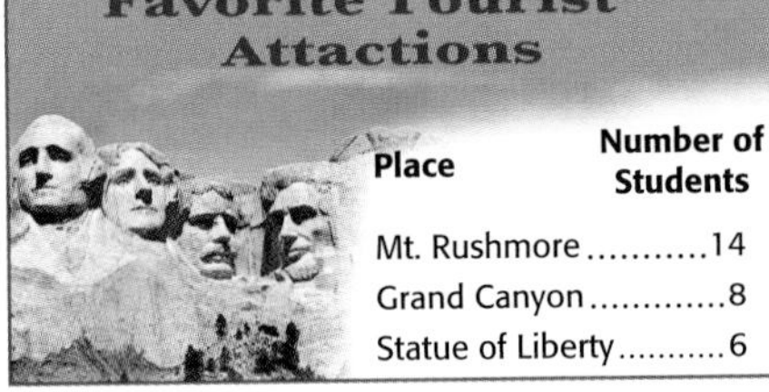

Place	Number of Students
Mt. Rushmore	14
Grand Canyon	8
Statue of Liberty	6

Algebra **Find the value of *x* that makes a true sentence.**

21. $\frac{6}{9} - \frac{x}{9} = \frac{1}{9}$ 5
22. $\frac{x}{8} - \frac{3}{8} = \frac{1}{8}$ 4
23. $\frac{8}{12} - \frac{x}{12} = \frac{1}{4}$ 5

Additional Answers

6. Sample answer: Subtract two sixths from five sixths which equal three sixths. Then simplify by dividing the numerator and denominator by three, the GCF. The solution is one half

28. Subtract the numerators and use the same denominator.

H.O.T. Problems

24. OPEN ENDED Choose two like fractions whose difference is $\frac{1}{6}$ and whose denominators are not 6. $\frac{7}{12} - \frac{5}{12} = \frac{1}{6}$

CHALLENGE Compare. Write >, <, or = to make a true sentence.

25. $\frac{5}{6} - \frac{1}{6} \bullet \frac{3}{6} - \frac{2}{6}$ >
26. $\frac{8}{8} - \frac{8}{8} \bullet \frac{2}{9} - \frac{2}{9}$ =
27. $\frac{3}{4} - \frac{2}{4} \bullet \frac{5}{5} - \frac{1}{5}$ <

28. WRITING IN MATH Write a problem about a real-world situation in which you would find $\frac{3}{4} - \frac{1}{4}$. Then solve. See margin.

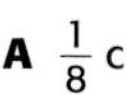

TEST Practice

29. Measurement Paul is making dinner. He uses $\frac{1}{4}$ cup of cheese for a salad and $\frac{2}{4}$ cup of cheese for a casserole. How many cups of cheese does Paul use altogether? (Lesson 10-1) D

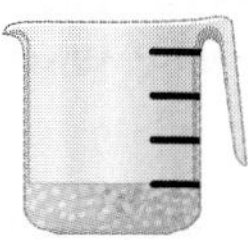

A $\frac{1}{8}$ c
B $\frac{1}{4}$ c
C $\frac{3}{8}$ c
D $\frac{3}{4}$ c

30. The pictures below show how much sausage and pepperoni pizza was left over at the end of one day.

Which fraction represents how much more sausage pizza was left over than pepperoni pizza? (Lesson 10-2) G

F $\frac{3}{16}$
G $\frac{3}{8}$
H $\frac{11}{16}$
J $\frac{11}{8}$

Spiral Review

31. nine elevenths 32. seven thirteenths

Add. Write each sum using words in simplest form. (Lesson 10-1)

31. $\frac{7}{11} + \frac{2}{11}$
32. $\frac{2}{13} + \frac{5}{13}$
33. $\frac{5}{14} + \frac{2}{14}$ one half
34. $\frac{8}{15} + \frac{4}{15}$ four fifths

35. Measurement A recipe for trail mix calls for $\frac{2}{3}$ cup of marshmallows, $\frac{7}{8}$ cup of pretzels, and $\frac{3}{4}$ cup of raisins. Which ingredient is the greatest amount? Which ingredient is the least amount? (Lesson 9-9) pretzels; marshmallows

Write each improper fraction as a mixed number. (Lesson 8-2)

36. $\frac{45}{6}$ $7\frac{1}{2}$
37. $\frac{68}{8}$ $8\frac{1}{2}$
38. $\frac{62}{12}$ $5\frac{1}{6}$
39. $\frac{80}{15}$ $5\frac{1}{3}$

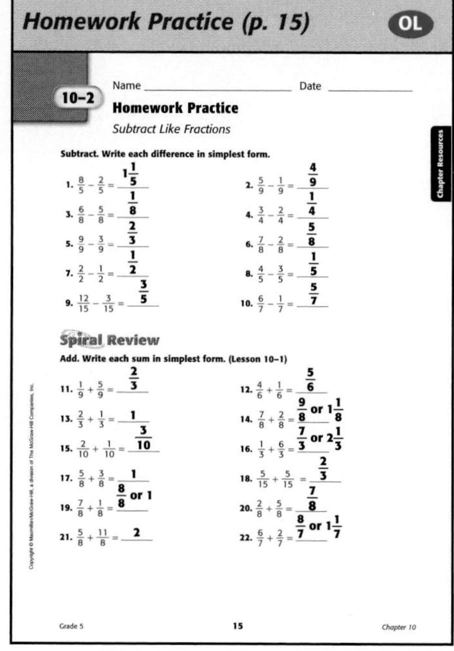

Homework Practice (p. 15) OL

10-2 Name ______________ Date ______________

Homework Practice

Subtract Like Fractions

Subtract. Write each difference in simplest form.

1. $\frac{8}{5} - \frac{2}{5} =$ $1\frac{1}{5}$
2. $\frac{5}{9} - \frac{1}{9} =$ $\frac{4}{9}$
3. $\frac{6}{8} - \frac{5}{8} =$ $\frac{1}{8}$
4. $\frac{3}{4} - \frac{2}{4} =$ $\frac{1}{4}$
5. $\frac{9}{9} - \frac{3}{9} =$ $\frac{2}{3}$
6. $\frac{7}{8} - \frac{2}{8} =$ $\frac{5}{8}$
7. $\frac{2}{2} - \frac{1}{2} =$ $\frac{1}{2}$
8. $\frac{4}{5} - \frac{3}{5} =$ $\frac{1}{5}$
9. $\frac{12}{15} - \frac{3}{15} =$ $\frac{3}{5}$
10. $\frac{6}{7} - \frac{1}{7} =$ $\frac{5}{7}$

Spiral Review

Add. Write each sum in simplest form. (Lesson 10–1)

11. $\frac{1}{9} + \frac{5}{9} =$ $\frac{2}{3}$
12. $\frac{4}{6} + \frac{1}{6} =$ $\frac{5}{6}$
13. $\frac{2}{3} + \frac{1}{3} =$ 1
14. $\frac{7}{8} + \frac{2}{8} =$ $\frac{9}{8}$ or $1\frac{1}{8}$
15. $\frac{2}{10} + \frac{1}{10} =$ $\frac{3}{10}$
16. $\frac{1}{3} + \frac{6}{3} =$ $\frac{7}{3}$ or $2\frac{1}{3}$
17. $\frac{5}{8} + \frac{3}{8} =$ 1
18. $\frac{5}{15} + \frac{5}{15} =$ $\frac{2}{3}$
19. $\frac{7}{8} + \frac{1}{8} =$ $\frac{8}{8}$ or 1
20. $\frac{2}{8} + \frac{5}{8} =$ $\frac{7}{8}$
21. $\frac{5}{8} + \frac{11}{8} =$ 2
22. $\frac{6}{7} + \frac{2}{7} =$ $\frac{8}{7}$ or $1\frac{1}{7}$

Chapter Resources

Grade 5 15 Chapter 10

Assess

Formative Assessment

- **How would you subtract $\frac{7}{8} - \frac{3}{8}$ and write the difference in simplest form? Describe your steps. Then draw a picture to check.** Sample answer: Subtract the numerators: 7 − 3 = 4. So, $\frac{7}{8} - \frac{3}{8} = \frac{4}{8}$. Simplify $\frac{4}{8}$ by dividing the numerator and denominator by the GCF, 4: 4 ÷ 4 = 1 and 8 ÷ 4 = 2. The difference in simplest form is $\frac{1}{2}$.

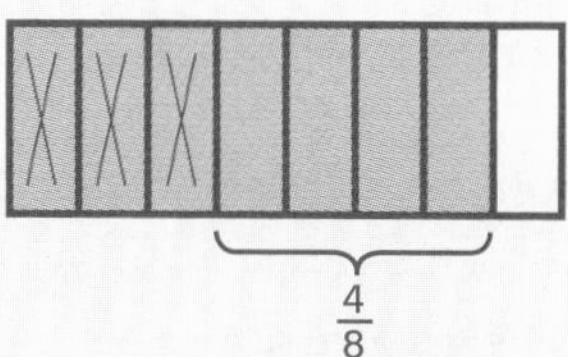

Quick Check **Are students continuing to struggle with subtracting fractions with like denominators?**

If Yes → Small Group Options (p. 428B)

If No → Independent Work Options (p. 428B)
CRM Skills Practice Worksheet (p. 14)
CRM Enrich Worksheet (p. 17)

Yesterday's News Have students write or discuss how addition of fractions with like denominators is similar to subtraction of fractions with like denominators.

TEST Practice

Reviews Lessons 10-1 and 10-2

Assign the Test Practice problems to provide daily reinforcement of test-taking skills.

Spiral Review

Reviews Lessons 8-2, 9-9, and 10-1

Review and assess mastery of skills and concepts from previous chapters.

Math Activity for 10-3

Lesson Planner

Objective

Use models to add unlike fractions.

Resources

Manipulatives: fraction tiles

1 Introduce

Introduce the Concept

- Hand out fraction tiles to pairs of students. Have them place two $\frac{1}{5}$ tiles side by side. **What fraction do these tiles model?** $\frac{2}{5}$
- Have students place four $\frac{1}{10}$ tiles below the $\frac{2}{5}$ tiles to model an equivalent fraction. **What fraction do these tiles model?** $\frac{4}{10}$
- **Why are the two fraction models equivalent?** Sample answer: Both rows of tiles show the same amount.

2 Teach

Activity 1 In Step 2 students can check their equivalent fractions by aligning the tiles below each other. If the tiles do not align, the fractions are not equivalent.

Math Activity for 10-3

Add Unlike Fractions

MAIN IDEA

I will use models to add unlike fractions.

In Lesson 10-1, you learned that like fractions are fractions with the same denominator. Fractions with different denominators are called *unlike fractions.*

Like Fractions	Unlike Fractions
$\frac{3}{8}, \frac{4}{8}$	$\frac{1}{2}, \frac{5}{6}$

You can add fractions that have different denominators using fraction tiles.

1 **To finish building a birdhouse, Jordan uses two boards. One is $\frac{1}{2}$ foot long and the other is $\frac{1}{3}$ foot long. What is the total length of the boards?**

Step 1 Model each fraction using fraction tiles and place them side by side.

$\frac{1}{2}$	$\frac{1}{3}$

Step 2 Find fraction tiles that will match the length of the combined fractions above. Line them up below the model.

$\frac{1}{2}$			$\frac{1}{3}$	
$\frac{1}{6}$	$\frac{1}{6}$	$\frac{1}{6}$	$\frac{1}{6}$	$\frac{1}{6}$

Step 3 Add. There are five of the $\frac{1}{6}$-fraction tiles in all. So, $\frac{1}{2} + \frac{1}{3} = \frac{5}{6}$.

The total length of the boards is $\frac{5}{6}$ foot.

ACTIVITY

Hands-On Activity

2 **Muna bought $\frac{3}{4}$ pound of grapes and $\frac{5}{8}$ pound of cherries. What is the combined weight of the fruit?**

Step 1 Model each fraction using fraction tiles.

Step 2 Find fraction tiles that will match the length of the combined fractions above. Line them up below the model.

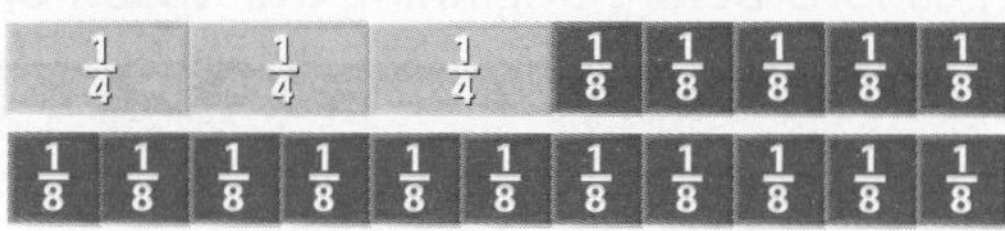

Step 3 Add. There are eleven of the $\frac{1}{8}$-fraction tiles.
So, $\frac{3}{4} + \frac{5}{8} = \frac{11}{8}$ or $1\frac{3}{8}$.

The combined weight of the fruit is $1\frac{3}{8}$ pounds.

Think About It

1. How can finding the multiples of 4 and 12 help you find $\frac{3}{4} + \frac{7}{12}$? Sample answer: Since 12 is a multiple of both 4 and 12, 12 is a common denominator.
2. Describe how you could use fraction tiles to find the sum of $\frac{2}{5}$ and $\frac{1}{10}$. See margin.

Find the sum using fraction tiles.

3. $\frac{2}{3} + \frac{1}{6}$ $\frac{5}{6}$
4. $\frac{3}{4} + \frac{1}{3}$ $\frac{13}{12}$ or $1\frac{1}{12}$
5. $\frac{3}{8} + \frac{1}{4}$ $\frac{5}{8}$
6. $\frac{1}{2} + \frac{5}{6}$ $\frac{8}{6}$ or $1\frac{1}{3}$
7. $\frac{3}{10} + \frac{1}{5}$ $\frac{1}{2}$
8. $\frac{5}{8} + \frac{1}{4}$ $\frac{7}{8}$
9. $\frac{1}{2} + \frac{1}{4}$ $\frac{3}{4}$
10. $\frac{3}{4} + \frac{2}{3}$ $\frac{17}{12}$ or $1\frac{5}{12}$
11. **WRITING IN ▸MATH** Write a real-world problem that can be solved by adding unlike fractions. See margin.

3 Assess

Formative Assessment

Use the **Check What You Know** exercises to assess whether students comprehend how to add fractions with *unlike* denominators.

Extending the Concept Use fraction tiles.

- **Add $\frac{3}{8} + \frac{1}{4}$** $\frac{5}{8}$
- **Explain why the denominator of the difference in the subtraction is 8 instead of 4.** Sample answer: the least common denominator of 4 and 8 is 8, so we have to find equivalent fractions with a denominator of 8. The answer cannot be simplified.

From Concrete to Abstract Use Exercise 11 to link adding unlike fractions with real-world situations.

Additional Answers

2. Sample answer: Place two $\frac{1}{5}$-tiles and one $\frac{1}{10}$-tile side by side. Find tiles that match their length. $\frac{2}{5} + \frac{1}{10} = \frac{1}{2}$
11. Sample answer: One path is $\frac{7}{10}$ mile long and another path is $\frac{3}{4}$ mile long. What is the total length of the paths? $\frac{7}{10} + \frac{3}{4} = \frac{19}{20}$.

LESSON 10-3

Add Unlike Fractions

Lesson Planner

Objective

Add fractions with unlike denominators.

Vocabulary

unlike fractions

Resources

Literature Connection: *How Pizza Came to Queens* by Dayal Kaur Khalsa

Teacher Technology

Interactive Classroom • TeacherWorks • Math Tool Chest

Focus on Math Background

After completing Lesson 10-1, students should understand that when they add fractions with *like* denominators, they are adding or subtracting like units. So, when they add $\frac{1}{7}$ and $\frac{3}{7}$, they understand that they are adding 1 seventh and 3 more sevenths to get 4 sevenths. With this conceptual understanding, it is unlikely that they will add the denominators to produce an incorrect sum of 4 fourteenths. When adding fractions with *unlike* denominators in this lesson, students are often tempted to add the numerators and the denominators. It is very important that they develop understanding through models before moving to paper and pencil. With this understanding and their prior knowledge of equivalent fractions and least common denominators, they are ready to apply what they know to add unlike fractions.

Daily Routine

Use these suggestions before beginning the lesson on p. 434.

5-Minute Check

(Reviews Lesson 10-2)

Subtract. Write each difference in simplest form. Check your answer by using fraction tiles or drawing a picture.

1. $\frac{3}{8} - \frac{1}{8}$ $\frac{1}{4}$
2. $\frac{8}{9} - \frac{4}{9}$ $\frac{4}{9}$
3. $\frac{7}{16} - \frac{3}{16}$ $\frac{1}{4}$

Problem of the Day

One box holds 36 erasers. Reese has to ship 774 erasers. How many boxes does he need to ship all of the erasers? 22 boxes

Building Math Vocabulary

Write the lesson vocabulary word and its definition on the board. Point out to students that musicians use fractions when they read, write, or play music. Have a volunteer who reads music explain what musical notes might be found in one bar of music. Sample answers: half notes, quarter notes, sixteenth notes. Point out that these are all unlike fractions that have to add up to, for example, $\frac{4}{4}$ time.

Visual Vocabulary Cards

Use Visual Vocabulary Card 46 to reinforce the vocabulary introduced in this lesson. (The Define/Example/Ask routine is printed on the back of each card.)

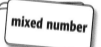

mixed number

Differentiated Instruction

Small Group Options

SPATIAL

Option 1 Below Level BL

Materials: chart paper, markers, fraction tiles

- Write the digits 3 and 9 on the chart paper. Ask students how 3 and 9 are friendly with each other.
- Accept any reasonable answer, but you are looking for a student to say that 9 is a multiple of 3 or 3 goes into 9 three times, or something of that nature.
- **How do $\frac{1}{3}$ and $\frac{1}{9}$ compare on your fraction tiles?** It takes 3 ninths to make $\frac{1}{3}$.
- Repeat this process for 2 and 4 and 4 and 8.

LOGICAL, VISUAL

Option 2 English Language Learners ELL

Materials: index cards (two per student), scissors
Core Vocabulary: agree, different but equal, is the same as
Common Use Verb: to work with

Do Math This strategy allows students to learn about equivalency with unlike denominators.

- Have students cut each index card into two different but equal fractional pieces (for example, one halves and the other thirds) and write the fraction on each piece.
- Have students find examples of two different fractions with unlike denominators they have added together that when combined show a different fraction. For example, $\frac{2}{6} + \frac{3}{9} = \frac{2}{3}$. Partners must agree on the answer.
- Discuss as time permits.

Independent Work Options

SOCIAL, LOGICAL

Option 1 Early Finishers OL

- Assign pairs.
- Have each student write one word problem that involves adding fractions with unlike denominators.
- Students exchange papers and solve each other's problems.
- Students can challenge classmates to solve their problems.

Option 2 Student Technology

Math Online macmillanmh.com

Personal Tutor • Extra Examples

Math Tool Chest Fractions Level 2

Option 3 Learning Station: Health (p. 418J)

Direct students to the Health Learning Station for opportunities to explore and extend the lesson concept.

Option 4 Problem-Solving Daily Practice

Reinforce problem-solving skills and strategies with the Problem-Solving Practice worksheet.

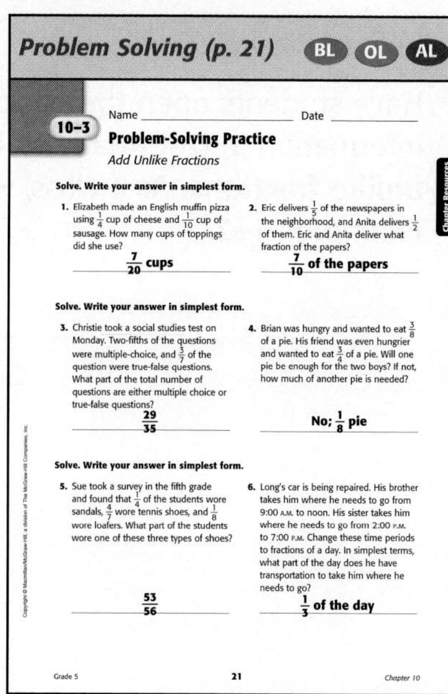

Problem Solving (p. 21) BL OL AL

10–3 Name ____________ Date ____________

Problem-Solving Practice

Add Unlike Fractions

Chapter Resources

Solve. Write your answer in simplest form.

1. Elizabeth made an English muffin pizza using $\frac{1}{4}$ cup of cheese and $\frac{1}{10}$ cup of sausage. How many cups of toppings did she use?
   $\frac{7}{20}$ cups
2. Eric delivers $\frac{1}{5}$ of the newspapers in the neighborhood, and Anita delivers $\frac{1}{2}$ of them. Eric and Anita deliver what fraction of the papers?
   $\frac{7}{10}$ of the papers

Solve. Write your answer in simplest form.

3. Christie took a social studies test on Monday. Two-fifths of the questions were multiple-choice, and $\frac{3}{7}$ of the question were true-false questions. What part of the total number of questions are either multiple choice or true-false questions?
   $\frac{29}{35}$
4. Brian was hungry and wanted to eat $\frac{3}{8}$ of a pie. His friend was even hungrier and wanted to eat $\frac{3}{4}$ of a pie. Will one pie be enough for the two boys? If not, how much of another pie is needed?
   No; $\frac{1}{8}$ pie

Solve. Write your answer in simplest form.

5. Sue took a survey in the fifth grade and found that $\frac{1}{4}$ of the students wore sandals, $\frac{4}{7}$ wore tennis shoes, and $\frac{1}{8}$ wore loafers. What part of the students wore one of these three types of shoes?
   $\frac{53}{56}$
6. Long's car is being repaired. His brother takes him where he needs to go from 9:00 A.M. to noon. His sister takes him where he needs to go from 2:00 P.M. to 7:00 P.M. Change these time periods to fractions of a day. In simplest terms, what part of the day does he have transportation to take him where he needs to go?
   $\frac{1}{3}$ of the day

Grade 5 21 *Chapter 10*

10-3 Add Unlike Fractions

1 Introduce

Activity Choice 1 • Hands-On 

- Ask students to write the first six multiples of 4. Have a volunteer write them on the board. 4, 8, 12, 16, 20, 24
- Next, ask students to write the first six multiples of 6. Have the volunteer record them on the board. 6, 12, 18, 24, 30, 36
- Ask students circle the common multiples of 4 and 6. 12, 24
- Draw a square around the LCM of 4 and 6. 12
- **How are the LCM and the LCD related?** The LCM of two numbers becomes the LCD of those numbers when they are the denominators of two fractions.
- Repeat this activity with other numbers.

Activity Choice 2 • Literature

Introduce the lesson with *How Pizza Came to Queens* by Dayal Kaur Khalsa. For a related math activity, see p. TR52.

2 Teach

Scaffolding Questions

Show $\frac{1}{3}$ and $\frac{1}{4}$ using the twelfths fraction tiles.

- **How many twelfths are equal to $\frac{1}{3}$?** $\frac{4}{12}$
- **How many twelfths are equal to $\frac{1}{4}$?** $\frac{3}{12}$
- $\frac{1}{3} + \frac{1}{4} = \frac{7}{12}$, is already in simplest form.

GET READY to Learn

Have students open their books and read the information in **Get Ready to Learn.** Introduce **unlike fractions.** As a class, work through **Examples 1–2.**

10-3 Add Unlike Fractions

MAIN IDEA

I will add fractions with unlike denominators.

New Vocabulary

unlike fractions

Math Online

macmillanmh.com

- Extra Examples
- Personal Tutor
- Self-Check Quiz

GET READY to Learn

Gene spent $\frac{1}{3}$ hour writing an article for the school paper, and $\frac{1}{4}$ hour proofreading it. How long did Gene spend writing and proofreading his article?

Before you can add two **unlike fractions**, one or both of the fractions must be renamed so that they have a common denominator.

Adding Unlike Fractions — *Key Concept*

To add unlike fractions, perform the following steps:

- Rename the fractions using the least common denominator (LCD).
- Add as with like fractions.
- If necessary, simplify the sum.

EXAMPLE Add Unlike Fractions

1 **Refer to the information above. Find $\frac{1}{3}$ hour + $\frac{1}{4}$ hour.**

The least common denominator of $\frac{1}{3}$ and $\frac{1}{4}$ is 12.

Step 1 Write the problem.		Step 2 Rename using the LCD.		Step 3 Add the like fractions.
$\frac{1}{3}$	→	$\frac{1 \times 4}{3 \times 4} = \frac{4}{12}$	→	$\frac{4}{12}$
$+\frac{1}{4}$	→	$\frac{1 \times 3}{4 \times 3} = \frac{3}{12}$	→	$+\frac{3}{12}$
				$\frac{7}{12}$

So, Gene spent $\frac{7}{12}$ hour writing and proofreading his article.

434 **Chapter 10** Add and Subtract Fractions

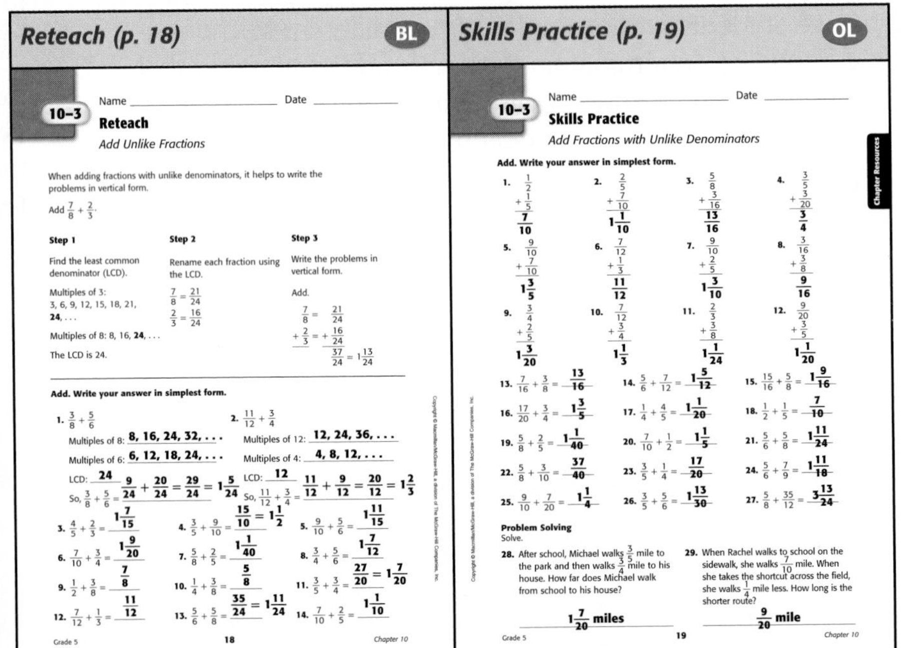

Reteach (p. 18) BL

10-3 Name ______ Date ______

Reteach

Add Unlike Fractions

When adding fractions with unlike denominators, it helps to write the problems in vertical form.

Add $\frac{7}{8} + \frac{2}{3}$.

Step 1 Find the least common denominator (LCD).
Multiples of 3: 3, 6, 9, 12, 15, 18, 21, **24**, . . .
Multiples of 8: 8, 16, **24**, . . .
The LCD is 24.

Step 2 Rename each fraction using the LCD.
$\frac{7}{8} = \frac{21}{24}$
$\frac{2}{3} = \frac{16}{24}$

Step 3 Write the problems in vertical form.
Add.
$\frac{7}{8} = \frac{21}{24}$
$+\frac{2}{3} = +\frac{16}{24}$
$\frac{37}{24} = 1\frac{13}{24}$

Add. Write your answer in simplest form.

1. $\frac{3}{8} + \frac{5}{6}$
Multiples of 8: **8, 16, 24, 32, . . .**
Multiples of 6: **6, 12, 18, 24, . . .**
LCD: **24**
So, $\frac{3}{8} + \frac{5}{6} = \mathbf{\frac{9}{24} + \frac{20}{24} = \frac{29}{24} = 1\frac{5}{24}}$

2. $\frac{11}{12} + \frac{3}{4}$
Multiples of 12: **12, 24, 36, . . .**
Multiples of 4: **4, 8, 12, . . .**
LCD: **12**
So, $\frac{11}{12} + \frac{3}{4} = \mathbf{\frac{11}{12} + \frac{9}{12} = \frac{20}{12} = 1\frac{2}{3}}$

3. $\frac{4}{5} + \frac{2}{3} = \mathbf{1\frac{7}{15}}$
4. $\frac{3}{5} + \frac{9}{10} = \mathbf{\frac{15}{10} = 1\frac{1}{2}}$
5. $\frac{9}{10} + \frac{5}{6} = \mathbf{1\frac{11}{15}}$
6. $\frac{7}{10} + \frac{3}{4} = \mathbf{1\frac{9}{20}}$
7. $\frac{5}{8} + \frac{2}{5} = \mathbf{1\frac{1}{40}}$
8. $\frac{3}{4} + \frac{5}{6} = \mathbf{1\frac{7}{12}}$
9. $\frac{1}{2} + \frac{3}{8} = \mathbf{\frac{7}{8}}$
10. $\frac{1}{4} + \frac{3}{8} = \mathbf{\frac{5}{8}}$
11. $\frac{3}{5} + \frac{3}{4} = \mathbf{\frac{27}{20} = 1\frac{7}{20}}$
12. $\frac{7}{12} + \frac{1}{3} = \mathbf{\frac{11}{12}}$
13. $\frac{5}{6} + \frac{5}{8} = \mathbf{\frac{35}{24} = 1\frac{11}{24}}$
14. $\frac{7}{10} + \frac{2}{5} = \mathbf{1\frac{1}{10}}$

Grade 5 18 Chapter 10

Skills Practice (p. 19) OL

10-3 Name ______ Date ______

Skills Practice

Add Fractions with Unlike Denominators

Add. Write your answer in simplest form.

1. $\frac{1}{2} + \frac{1}{5} = \mathbf{\frac{7}{10}}$
2. $\frac{2}{5} + \frac{7}{10} = \mathbf{1\frac{1}{10}}$
3. $\frac{5}{8} + \frac{3}{16} = \mathbf{\frac{13}{16}}$
4. $\frac{3}{5} + \frac{3}{20} = \mathbf{\frac{3}{4}}$
5. $\frac{9}{10} + \frac{7}{10} = \mathbf{1\frac{3}{5}}$
6. $\frac{7}{12} + \frac{1}{3} = \mathbf{\frac{11}{12}}$
7. $\frac{9}{10} + \frac{2}{5} = \mathbf{1\frac{3}{10}}$
8. $\frac{3}{16} + \frac{3}{8} = \mathbf{\frac{9}{16}}$
9. $\frac{3}{4} + \frac{2}{5} = \mathbf{1\frac{3}{20}}$
10. $\frac{7}{12} + \frac{3}{4} = \mathbf{1\frac{1}{3}}$
11. $\frac{2}{3} + \frac{3}{8} = \mathbf{1\frac{1}{24}}$
12. $\frac{9}{20} + \frac{3}{5} = \mathbf{1\frac{1}{20}}$
13. $\frac{7}{16} + \frac{3}{8} = \mathbf{\frac{13}{16}}$
14. $\frac{5}{6} + \frac{7}{12} = \mathbf{1\frac{5}{12}}$
15. $\frac{15}{16} + \frac{5}{8} = \mathbf{1\frac{9}{16}}$
16. $\frac{17}{20} + \frac{3}{4} = \mathbf{1\frac{3}{5}}$
17. $\frac{1}{4} + \frac{4}{5} = \mathbf{1\frac{1}{20}}$
18. $\frac{1}{2} + \frac{1}{5} = \mathbf{\frac{7}{10}}$
19. $\frac{5}{8} + \frac{2}{5} = \mathbf{1\frac{1}{40}}$
20. $\frac{7}{10} + \frac{1}{2} = \mathbf{1\frac{1}{5}}$
21. $\frac{5}{6} + \frac{5}{8} = \mathbf{1\frac{11}{24}}$
22. $\frac{5}{8} + \frac{3}{10} = \mathbf{\frac{37}{40}}$
23. $\frac{3}{5} + \frac{1}{4} = \mathbf{\frac{17}{20}}$
24. $\frac{5}{6} + \frac{7}{9} = \mathbf{1\frac{11}{18}}$
25. $\frac{9}{10} + \frac{7}{20} = \mathbf{1\frac{1}{4}}$
26. $\frac{3}{5} + \frac{5}{6} = \mathbf{1\frac{13}{30}}$
27. $\frac{5}{8} + \frac{35}{12} = \mathbf{3\frac{13}{24}}$

Problem Solving

Solve.

28. After school, Michael walks $\frac{3}{5}$ mile to the park and then walks $\frac{3}{4}$ mile to his house. How far does Michael walk from school to his house? **$1\frac{7}{20}$ miles**

29. When Rachel walks to school on the sidewalk, she walks $\frac{7}{10}$ mile. When she takes the shortcut across the field, she walks $\frac{1}{4}$ mile less. How long is the shorter route? **$\frac{9}{20}$ mile**

Grade 5 19 Chapter 10

Chapter Resources

Real-World EXAMPLE

2 MUSIC Catalina spent $\frac{1}{6}$ of her free time reading and $\frac{5}{12}$ of her free time practicing her flute. What fraction of her free time did she spend reading and practicing her flute?

Add $\frac{1}{6}$ and $\frac{5}{12}$.

The least common denominator of $\frac{1}{6}$ and $\frac{5}{12}$ is 12.

Remember
You can rename unlike fractions as like fractions by using the LCD.

Step 1		**Step 2**		**Step 3**
Write the problem.		Rename using the LCD.		Add the like fractions.
$\frac{1}{6}$	→	$\frac{1 \times 2}{6 \times 2} = \frac{2}{12}$	→	$\frac{2}{12}$
$+\frac{5}{12}$	→	$\frac{5 \times 1}{12 \times 1} = \frac{5}{12}$	→	$+\frac{5}{12}$
				$\frac{7}{12}$

So, Catalina spent $\frac{7}{12}$ of her free time reading and practicing her flute.

CHECK What You Know

Add. Write in simplest form. See Examples 1, 2 (p. 434–435)

1. $\frac{3}{4} + \frac{1}{8}$ $\frac{7}{8}$
2. $\frac{2}{3} + \frac{1}{9}$ $\frac{7}{9}$
3. $\frac{2}{5} + \frac{1}{2}$ $\frac{9}{10}$
4. $\frac{5}{7} + \frac{2}{14}$ $\frac{6}{7}$
5. $\frac{2}{5} + \frac{3}{10}$ $\frac{7}{10}$
6. $\frac{1}{2} + \frac{3}{7}$ $\frac{13}{14}$
7. $\frac{5}{6} + \frac{3}{4}$ $1\frac{7}{12}$
8. $\frac{2}{5} + \frac{7}{10}$ $1\frac{1}{10}$
9. $\frac{4}{9} + \frac{2}{3}$ $\frac{10}{9}$ or $1\frac{1}{9}$
10. $\frac{5}{12} + \frac{1}{4}$ $\frac{2}{3}$
11. $\frac{4}{7} + \frac{1}{2}$ $\frac{15}{14}$ or $1\frac{1}{14}$
12. $\frac{5}{8} + \frac{2}{3}$ $\frac{31}{24}$ or $1\frac{7}{24}$
13. A farmer harvested $\frac{3}{8}$ of a pecan crop on Friday and $\frac{1}{3}$ of the crop on Saturday. What fraction of the pecan crop was harvested in the two days? $\frac{17}{24}$
14. **Talk About It** Describe the steps for adding the fractions $\frac{5}{12}$ and $\frac{5}{6}$. What is the solution? See Ch. 10 Answer Appendix.

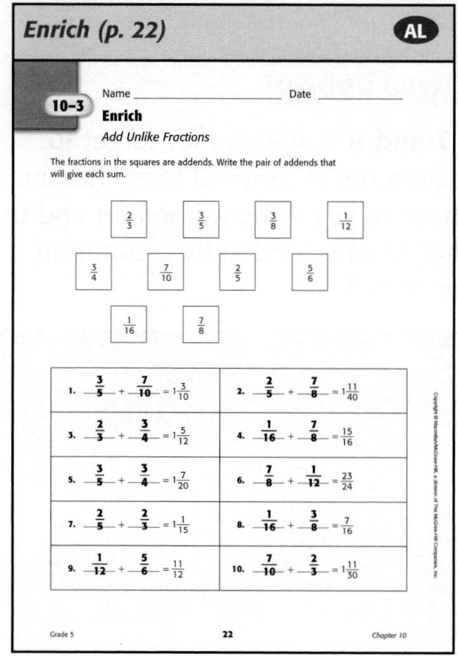

Enrich (p. 22) AL

10–3 Name ______________ Date ________

Enrich

Add Unlike Fractions

The fractions in the squares are addends. Write the pair of addends that will give each sum.

$\frac{2}{3}$ $\frac{3}{5}$ $\frac{3}{8}$ $\frac{1}{12}$

$\frac{3}{4}$ $\frac{7}{10}$ $\frac{2}{5}$ $\frac{5}{6}$

$\frac{1}{16}$ $\frac{7}{8}$

1. $\frac{3}{5} + \frac{7}{10} = 1\frac{3}{10}$	2. $\frac{2}{5} + \frac{7}{8} = 1\frac{11}{40}$
3. $\frac{2}{3} + \frac{3}{4} = 1\frac{5}{12}$	4. $\frac{1}{16} + \frac{7}{8} = \frac{15}{16}$
5. $\frac{3}{5} + \frac{3}{4} = 1\frac{7}{20}$	6. $\frac{7}{8} + \frac{1}{12} = \frac{23}{24}$
7. $\frac{2}{5} + \frac{2}{3} = 1\frac{1}{15}$	8. $\frac{1}{16} + \frac{3}{8} = \frac{7}{16}$
9. $\frac{1}{12} + \frac{5}{6} = \frac{11}{12}$	10. $\frac{7}{10} + \frac{2}{3} = 1\frac{11}{30}$

Grade 5 22 Chapter 10

ADDITIONAL EXAMPLES

1. Find $\frac{4}{7} + \frac{1}{2}$. $1\frac{1}{14}$
2. Emily walked $\frac{1}{7}$ mile to the store and then $\frac{3}{14}$ mile to her friend's house. What is the total distance Emily walked? $\frac{5}{14}$ mile

Before working through the examples, you may wish to have the students practice writing equivalent fractions.

CHECK What You Know

As a class, have students complete Exercises 1–14 in **Check What You Know** as you observe their work.

Exercise 14 Assess students comprehension before assigning practice exercises.

BL Alternate Teaching Strategy

If Students have trouble adding fractions with unlike denominators …

Then use one of these reteach options:

1. CRM **Daily Reteach Worksheet** (p. 18)
2. Tell students they can multiply the denominators of the two fractions to get a *common* denominator to use, even though it will not be the LCD. Then they can simplify the answer.
3. Tech Link Have students use Math Tool Chest to help complete the problem-solving exercises.

Lesson 10-3 Add Unlike Fractions **435**

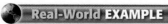

3 Practice

Differentiate practice using these leveled assignments for Exercises 15–33.

Level	Assignment
BL Below/ Approaching Level	15–22, 27–28
OL On Level	16–24, 27, 30, 33
AL Above/Beyond Level	odd 15–29, 31–33

Have students discuss and complete the Higher Order Thinking problems.

WRITING IN ▸MATH Have students complete Exercise 33 in their Math Journals. You may choose to use this exercise as an optional formative assessment.

4 Assess

Formative Assessment

- **Explain how you add unlike fractions.** Sample answer: One or both of the fractions must be renamed so they have a common denominator; add numerators and simplify the answer.
- **Explain how you find the LCD of two or more fractions.** Sample answer: List multiples of each denominator and choose the LCM, the smallest multiple they have in common.

Yesterday's News Have students explain how the earlier lessons on adding and subtracting fractions with like denominators helped them to understand today's lesson.

Quick Check **Are students continuing to struggle with adding and subtracting fractions with unlike denominators?**

If Yes → Small Group Options (p. 434B)

If No → Independent Work Options (p. 434B)
CRM Skills Practice Worksheet (p. 19)
CRM Enrich Worksheet (p. 22)

Practice and Problem Solving

EXTRA PRACTICE See page R27.

Add. Write in simplest form. See Examples 1,2 (pp. 434–435)

15. $\frac{2}{3} + \frac{1}{6}$ $\frac{5}{6}$
16. $\frac{1}{2} + \frac{1}{4}$ $\frac{3}{4}$
17. $\frac{1}{6} + \frac{7}{12}$ $\frac{3}{4}$
18. $\frac{5}{8} + \frac{1}{16}$ $\frac{11}{16}$

19. $\frac{1}{3} + \frac{1}{4}$ $\frac{7}{12}$
20. $\frac{1}{2} + \frac{4}{5}$ $1\frac{3}{10}$
21. $\frac{3}{5} + \frac{3}{10}$ $\frac{9}{10}$
22. $\frac{3}{5} + \frac{3}{6}$ $1\frac{1}{10}$

23. $\frac{2}{16} + \frac{3}{4}$ $\frac{7}{8}$
24. $\frac{7}{8} + \frac{1}{2}$ $1\frac{3}{8}$
25. $\frac{3}{4} + \frac{7}{20}$ $1\frac{1}{10}$
26. $\frac{1}{4} + \frac{3}{8}$ $\frac{5}{8}$

27. Angel has two chores after school. She rakes leaves for $\frac{3}{4}$ hour and spends $\frac{1}{2}$ hour washing the car. How long does Angel spend on her chores? $1\frac{1}{4}$ h

28. **Measurement** One craft project requires $\frac{3}{8}$ yard of ribbon, and another requires $\frac{1}{4}$ yard of ribbon. How much ribbon is needed for both projects? $\frac{5}{8}$ yard

29. Leon walked $\frac{5}{6}$ mile to the store and $\frac{1}{3}$ mile more to the theater. How far did he walk in all? $1\frac{1}{6}$ mi

30. Tashia ate $\frac{1}{3}$ of the pizza and Jay ate $\frac{3}{7}$ of the pizza. What fraction of the pizza did they eat? $\frac{16}{21}$ pizza

31. Sample answer: $\frac{1}{12} + \frac{1}{9} = \frac{7}{36}$

H.O.T. Problems

31. **OPEN ENDED** Write an addition problem involving two unlike fractions. One fraction should have a denominator of 12 and the other fraction should have a denominator of 9. Then, find the sum.

32. **FIND THE ERROR** Kate and Josh are finding the sum of $\frac{3}{4}$ and $\frac{9}{10}$. Who is correct? Explain your reasoning. See Ch. 10 Answer Appendix.

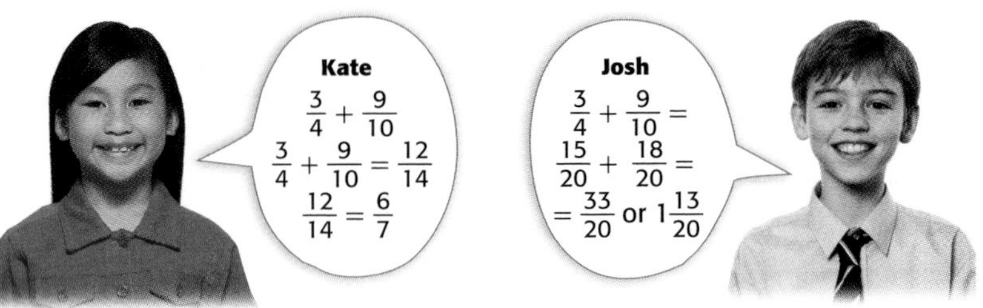

Kate
$\frac{3}{4} + \frac{9}{10}$
$\frac{3}{4} + \frac{9}{10} = \frac{12}{14}$
$\frac{12}{14} = \frac{6}{7}$
Josh
$\frac{3}{4} + \frac{9}{10} =$
$\frac{15}{20} + \frac{18}{20} =$
$= \frac{33}{20}$ or $1\frac{13}{20}$

33. **WRITING IN ▸MATH** Write a real-world problem that can be solved by adding two fractions. Then solve the problem. See Ch. 10 Answer Appendix.

COMMON ERROR!

Exercises 7 and 8 Students may forget to write their answers in simplest form. Remind them to check to see if the numerator and the denominator can be divided by a common factor other than 1.

Math Activity for 10-4
Subtract Unlike Fractions

MAIN IDEA

I will use models to subtract unlike fractions.

You can use fraction tiles to subtract fractions with unlike denominators.

ACTIVITY

1 **Akio lives $\frac{3}{4}$ mile from school. Bianca lives $\frac{1}{6}$ mile from school. How much farther from school does Akio live than Bianca?**

Step 1 Model each fraction using fraction tiles. Place the $\frac{1}{6}$-tiles underneath the $\frac{1}{4}$-tiles.

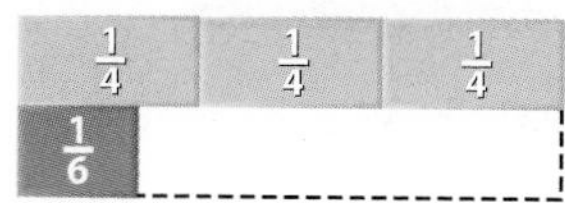

Step 2 Find which fraction will fill in the area of the dotted box.

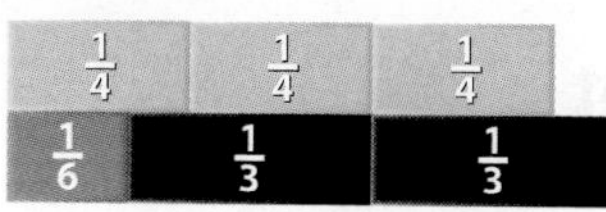

Two of the $\frac{1}{3}$-tiles are too large to fit. Try a different fraction tile.

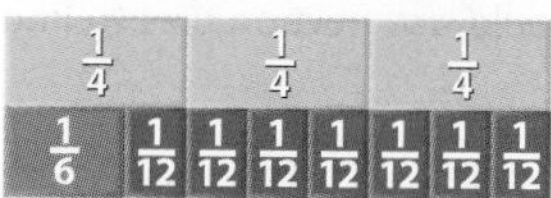

✓ Seven of the $\frac{1}{12}$-tiles fit.

Step 3 Since $\frac{7}{12}$ fills in the area of the dotted box, $\frac{3}{4} - \frac{1}{6} = \frac{7}{12}$.

So, Akio lives $\frac{7}{12}$ mile farther from school than Bianca.

Math Activity for 10-4

Lesson Planner

Objective

Use models to subtract unlike fractions.

Resources

Manipulatives: fraction tiles, index cards

1 Introduce

Introduce the Concept

- Pass out an index card to each student with a fraction written on it.
- Challenge students to circulate around the room and find classmates who have an equivalent fraction to their own. For example, one student may have a $\frac{3}{4}$ card and the other could have the $\frac{6}{8}$ card.
- **How many people did you find with the same fractional amount?**
- **What other fraction cards could be in your group?**

2 Teach

Activity 1 In Step 2 the model shows what might happen if the student first chooses a fraction tile that is not equivalent.

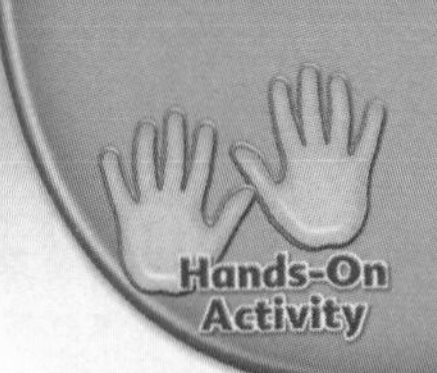

3 Assess

Formative Assessment

Use the **Check What You Know** exercises to assess whether students comprehend how to subtract fractions with *unlike* denominators.

Extending the Concept Use fraction tiles.

- **Subtract $\frac{6}{10} - \frac{1}{2}$.** $\frac{1}{10}$
- **Explain why you must subtract $\frac{1}{2}$ from $\frac{6}{10}$ instead of $\frac{6}{10}$ from $\frac{1}{2}$.** Sample answer: $\frac{6}{10}$ is larger than $\frac{1}{2}$. You must subtract the smaller number from the bigger number, or you will get a negative number.

From Concrete to Abstract Use Exercise 7 to link subtracting unlike fractions with real-world situations.

Additional Answers

2. Sample answer: Line up the $\frac{1}{3}$-fraction tiles underneath the $\frac{1}{2}$-fraction tiles. Use a $\frac{1}{6}$-fraction tile to fill in the remaining space.
7. Sample answer: Manny got $\frac{7}{8}$ of the answers correct on his test. Laura got $\frac{3}{4}$ of the answers correct. How many more answers does Manny have correct? $\frac{1}{8}$

ACTIVITY

2 Lisa and Kofi each bought a small tub of popcorn. Lisa ate $\frac{4}{5}$ of her popcorn and Kofi ate $\frac{3}{10}$ of her popcorn. What fraction more did Lisa eat than Kofi?

Step 1 Model each fraction using fraction tiles. Place the $\frac{1}{10}$-fraction tiles underneath the $\frac{1}{5}$-fraction tiles.

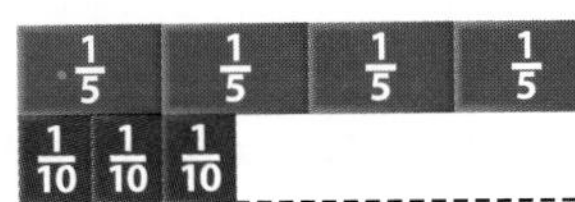

Step 2 Find which fraction will fill in the area of the dotted box.

The $\frac{1}{2}$-fraction tile fits. ✓

Step 3 Since $\frac{1}{2}$ fills in the area of the dotted box, $\frac{4}{5} - \frac{3}{10} = \frac{1}{2}$.

So, Lisa ate $\frac{1}{2}$ tub more popcorn than Kofi.

Think About It

1. Would any of the other fraction tiles fit inside the dotted box for Activity 2? Yes, $\frac{5}{10}$ would work because $\frac{5}{10}$ and $\frac{1}{2}$ are equivalent.
2. Describe how you would use fraction tiles to find $\frac{1}{2} - \frac{1}{3}$. See margin.

CHECK What You Know

Find each difference using fraction tiles.

3. $\frac{2}{3} - \frac{1}{6} = \frac{1}{2}$
4. $\frac{5}{6} - \frac{1}{4} = \frac{7}{12}$
5. $\frac{5}{8} - \frac{1}{4} = \frac{3}{8}$
6. $\frac{4}{5} - \frac{1}{2} = \frac{3}{10}$
7. **WRITING IN ▶MATH** Write a real-world problem that can be solved by subtracting unlike fractions. See margin.

LESSON 10-4

Subtract Unlike Fractions

Lesson Planner

Objective

Subtract fractions with unlike denominators.

Review Vocabulary

unlike fractions

Resources

Literature Connection: *How Pizza Came to Queens* by Dayal Kaur Khalsa

Teacher Technology

Interactive Classroom • TeacherWorks

Focus on Math Background

After completing Lesson 10-3, students should understand that when they add fractions with *unlike* denominators, they must first find the Least Common Denominator. The same skill will be applied to subtracting fractions with unlike denominators. In addition, students will need to recall what they learned in Lesson 9-9 about comparing fractions. As with whole numbers, students must subtract the smaller fraction from the larger fraction and not the other way around.

Daily Routine

Use these suggestions before beginning the lesson on p. 439.

5-Minute Check

(Reviews Lesson 10-3)

Add. Write each sum in simplest form. Check your answer by using fraction tiles or drawing a picture.

1. $\frac{3}{7} + \frac{1}{3}$ $\frac{16}{21}$
2. $\frac{2}{9} + \frac{4}{5}$ $1\frac{1}{45}$
3. $\frac{6}{8} + \frac{3}{16}$ $\frac{15}{16}$

Problem of the Day

Jamel and Rachel each bought 12 bottled waters. Jamel drank $\frac{1}{4}$ of them and Rachel drank $\frac{2}{6}$ of them. How many waters did they drink? 14

Review Math Vocabulary

Write the lesson vocabulary word and its definition on the board. Have students give three or four examples of unlike fractions.

Visual Vocabulary Cards

Use Visual Vocabulary Card 46 to reinforce the vocabulary introduced in this lesson. (The Define/Example/Ask routine is printed on the back of each card.)

Differentiated Instruction

Small Group Options

Option 1 SPATIAL 

Gifted and Talented AL

Materials: grid paper and pencil

- Students can design a floor plan for a dollhouse. Have them use unlike fractions for the room measurements. Next, they should use the given data to choose a wallpaper border.

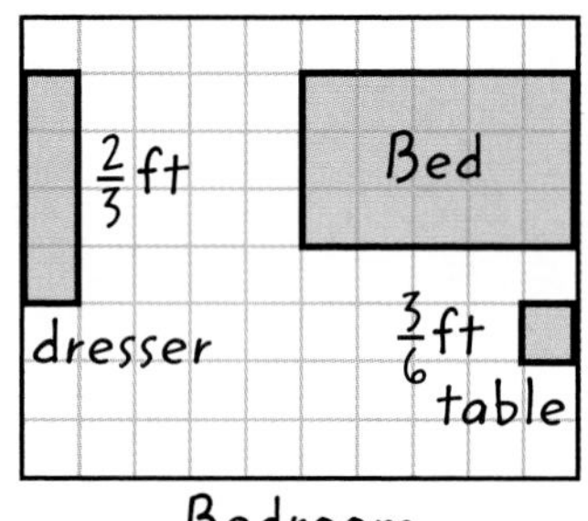

Option 2 VISUAL, LOGICAL 

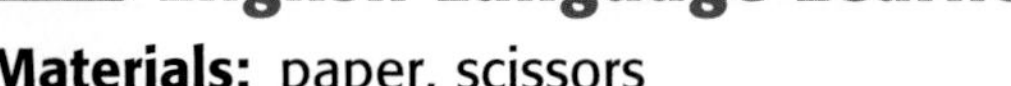

English Language Learners ELL

Materials: paper, scissors
Core Vocabulary: whole, piece, cut apart
Common Use Verb: cover

Do Math This strategy allows students to explore subtracting unlike fractions.

- Write: "$\frac{3}{4} - \frac{1}{2}$"
- Model the problem by folding the paper into fourths and discussing ways to show $\frac{3}{4}$ and then subtract $\frac{1}{2}$, Note that the answer has to be expressed in fourths.
- Repeat for $\frac{3}{4} - \frac{3}{8}$. Allow students to investigate ways to solve the problem in small groups and present their findings.
- Repeat as time permits.
- Allow students to discover changing fractions into a common denominator as they discuss solutions.

Independent Work Options

Option 1 LINGUISTIC/LOGICAL

Early Finishers OL AL

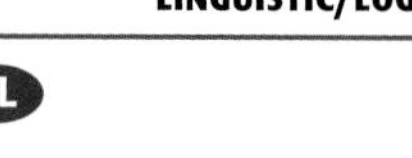

Materials: paper, pencil

- Have the students create drawings of the following fractions:
  $\frac{3}{4}, \frac{5}{6}, \frac{1}{2}, \frac{2}{3}, \frac{1}{4}, \frac{1}{6}$
- Make sure the whole amount of each drawing is the same.

Option 2

Student Technology

macmillanmh.com

Personal Tutor • Extra Examples

Option 3

Learning Station: Reading (p. 418J)

Direct students to the Reading Learning Station for opportunities to explore and extend the lesson concept.

Option 4

Problem-Solving Daily Practice

Reinforce problem-solving skills and strategies with the Problem-Solving Practice worksheet.

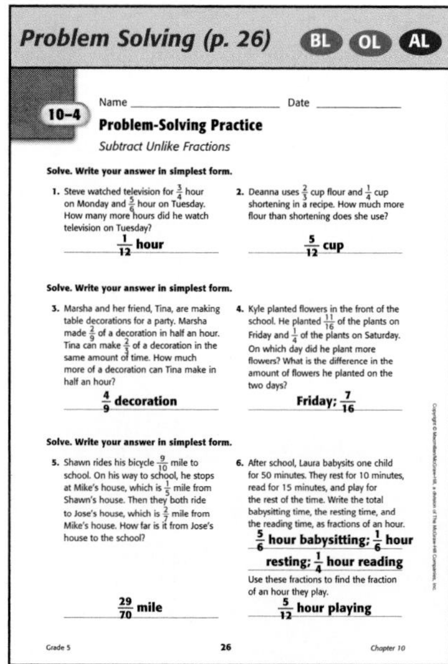

Problem Solving (p. 26) BL OL AL

Name ____________ Date ________

10–4 **Problem-Solving Practice**
Subtract Unlike Fractions

Solve. Write your answer in simplest form.

1. Steve watched television for $\frac{3}{4}$ hour on Monday and $\frac{5}{6}$ hour on Tuesday. How many more hours did he watch television on Tuesday?
   $\frac{1}{12}$ hour
2. Deanna uses $\frac{2}{3}$ cup flour and $\frac{1}{4}$ cup shortening in a recipe. How much more flour than shortening does she use?
   $\frac{5}{12}$ cup

Solve. Write your answer in simplest form.

3. Marsha and her friend, Tina, are making table decorations for a party. Marsha made $\frac{2}{9}$ of a decoration in half an hour. Tina can make $\frac{2}{3}$ of a decoration in the same amount of time. How much more of a decoration can Tina make in half an hour?
   $\frac{4}{9}$ decoration
4. Kyle planted flowers in the front of the school. He planted $\frac{11}{16}$ of the plants on Friday and $\frac{1}{4}$ of the plants on Saturday. On which day did he plant more flowers? What is the difference in the amount of flowers he planted on the two days?
   Friday; $\frac{7}{16}$

Solve. Write your answer in simplest form.

5. Shawn rides his bicycle $\frac{9}{10}$ mile to school. On his way to school, he stops at Mike's house, which is $\frac{1}{5}$ mile from Shawn's house. Then they both ride to Jose's house, which is $\frac{2}{7}$ mile from Mike's house. How far is it from Jose's house to the school?
   $\frac{29}{70}$ mile
6. After school, Laura babysits one child for 50 minutes. They rest for 10 minutes, read for 15 minutes, and play for the rest of the time. Write the total babysitting time, the resting time, and the reading time, as fractions of an hour.
   $\frac{5}{6}$ hour babysitting; $\frac{1}{6}$ hour resting; $\frac{1}{4}$ hour reading
   Use these fractions to find the fraction of an hour they play.
   $\frac{5}{12}$ hour playing

Grade 5 26 *Chapter 10*

10-4 Subtract Unlike Fractions

MAIN IDEA

I will subtract fractions with unlike denominators.

Math Online

macmillanmh.com

- Extra Examples
- Personal Tutor
- Self-Check Quiz

GET READY to Learn

A female Cuban tree frog can be up to $\frac{5}{12}$ foot long. A male Cuban tree frog can be up to $\frac{1}{4}$ foot long. How much longer is the female Cuban tree frog than the male?

Subtracting unlike fractions is similar to adding unlike fractions.

Subtract Unlike Fractions — Key Concept

To subtract unlike fractions, perform the following steps:

- Rename the fractions using the LCD.
- Subtract as with like fractions.
- If necessary, simplify the answer.

EXAMPLE Subtract Unlike Fractions

1 **FROGS How much longer is the female Cuban tree frog than the male Cuban tree frog?**

Find $\frac{5}{12} - \frac{1}{4}$.

The least common denominator of $\frac{5}{12}$ and $\frac{1}{4}$ is 12.

Step 1		Step 2		Step 3
Write the problem.		Rename using the LCD.		Subtract the like fractions.
$\frac{5}{12}$	→	$\frac{5 \times 1}{12 \times 1} = \frac{5}{12}$	→	$\frac{5}{12}$
$-\frac{1}{4}$	→	$\frac{1 \times 3}{4 \times 3} = \frac{3}{12}$	→	$-\frac{3}{12}$
				$\frac{2}{12} = \frac{1}{6}$ Simplify.

A female Cuban tree frog is $\frac{1}{6}$ foot longer than the male.

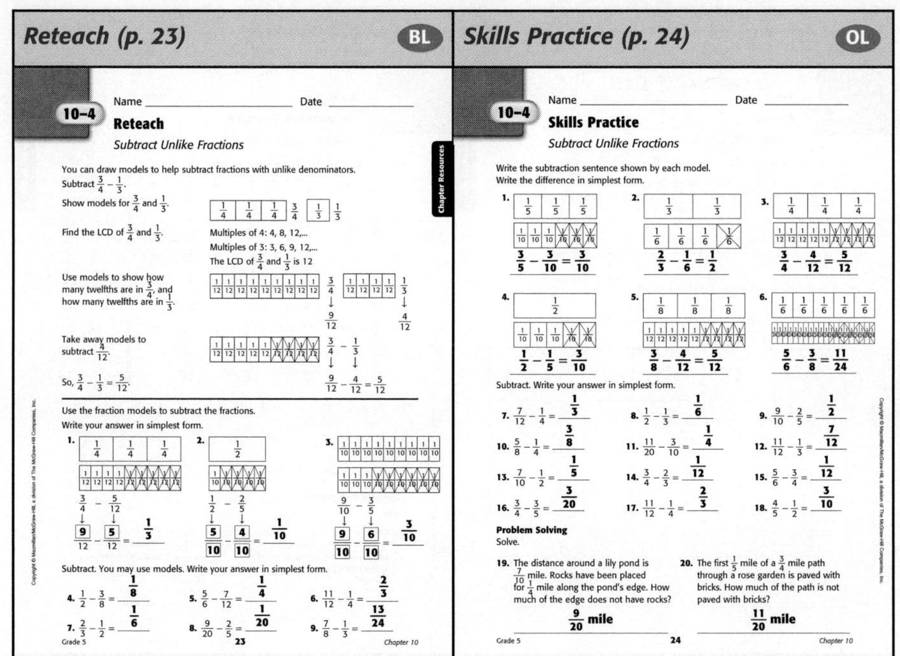

Reteach (p. 23) BL

10–4 Name ______ Date ______

Reteach

Subtract Unlike Fractions

You can draw models to help subtract fractions with unlike denominators.

Subtract $\frac{3}{4} - \frac{1}{3}$.

Show models for $\frac{3}{4}$ and $\frac{1}{3}$.

Find the LCD of $\frac{3}{4}$ and $\frac{1}{3}$. Multiples of 4: 4, 8, 12,... Multiples of 3: 3, 6, 9, 12,... The LCD of $\frac{3}{4}$ and $\frac{1}{3}$ is 12

Use models to show how many twelfths are in $\frac{3}{4}$, and how many twelfths are in $\frac{1}{3}$. $\frac{3}{4} \to \frac{9}{12}$, $\frac{1}{3} \to \frac{4}{12}$

Take away models to subtract $\frac{4}{12}$. $\frac{3}{4} - \frac{1}{3} \to \frac{9}{12} - \frac{4}{12} = \frac{5}{12}$

So, $\frac{3}{4} - \frac{1}{3} = \frac{5}{12}$.

Use the fraction models to subtract the fractions. Write your answer in simplest form.

1. $\frac{3}{4} - \frac{5}{12}$ → $\frac{9}{12} - \frac{5}{12} = \frac{1}{3}$
2. $\frac{1}{2} - \frac{2}{5}$ → $\frac{5}{10} - \frac{4}{10} = \frac{1}{10}$
3. $\frac{9}{10} - \frac{3}{5}$ → $\frac{9}{10} - \frac{6}{10} = \frac{3}{10}$

Subtract. You may use models. Write your answer in simplest form.

4. $\frac{1}{2} - \frac{3}{8} = \frac{1}{8}$
5. $\frac{5}{6} - \frac{7}{12} = \frac{1}{4}$
6. $\frac{11}{12} - \frac{1}{4} = \frac{2}{3}$
7. $\frac{2}{3} - \frac{1}{2} = \frac{1}{6}$
8. $\frac{9}{20} - \frac{2}{5} = \frac{1}{20}$
9. $\frac{7}{8} - \frac{1}{3} = \frac{13}{24}$

Grade 5 23 Chapter 10

Skills Practice (p. 24) OL

10–4 Name ______ Date ______

Skills Practice

Subtract Unlike Fractions

Write the subtraction sentence shown by each model. Write the difference in simplest form.

1. $\frac{3}{5} - \frac{3}{10} = \frac{3}{10}$
2. $\frac{2}{3} - \frac{1}{6} = \frac{1}{2}$
3. $\frac{3}{4} - \frac{4}{12} = \frac{5}{12}$
4. $\frac{1}{2} - \frac{1}{5} = \frac{3}{10}$
5. $\frac{3}{8} - \frac{4}{12} = \frac{5}{12}$
6. $\frac{5}{6} - \frac{3}{8} = \frac{11}{24}$

Subtract. Write your answer in simplest form.

7. $\frac{7}{12} - \frac{1}{4} = \frac{1}{3}$
8. $\frac{1}{2} - \frac{1}{3} = \frac{1}{6}$
9. $\frac{9}{10} - \frac{2}{5} = \frac{1}{2}$
10. $\frac{5}{8} - \frac{1}{4} = \frac{3}{8}$
11. $\frac{11}{20} - \frac{3}{10} = \frac{1}{4}$
12. $\frac{11}{12} - \frac{1}{3} = \frac{7}{12}$
13. $\frac{7}{10} - \frac{1}{2} = \frac{1}{5}$
14. $\frac{3}{4} - \frac{2}{3} = \frac{1}{12}$
15. $\frac{5}{6} - \frac{3}{4} = \frac{1}{12}$
16. $\frac{3}{4} - \frac{3}{5} = \frac{3}{20}$
17. $\frac{11}{12} - \frac{1}{4} = \frac{2}{3}$
18. $\frac{4}{5} - \frac{1}{2} = \frac{3}{10}$

Problem Solving

Solve.

19. The distance around a lily pond is $\frac{7}{10}$ mile. Rocks have been placed for $\frac{1}{4}$ mile along the pond's edge. How much of the edge does not have rocks? $\frac{9}{20}$ **mile**
20. The first $\frac{1}{5}$ mile of a $\frac{3}{4}$ mile path through a rose garden is paved with bricks. How much of the path is not paved with bricks? $\frac{11}{20}$ **mile**

Grade 5 24 Chapter 10

10-4 Subtract Unlike Fractions

1 Introduce

Activity Choice 1 • Hands-On

Assign groups of four and provide each group with fraction pieces. Write these four problems on the board or on an overhead transparency:

$\frac{1}{2} + \frac{3}{10}$ $\frac{5}{6} + \frac{2}{12}$

$\frac{3}{8} + \frac{7}{8}$ $\frac{7}{12} + \frac{2}{3}$

- The first student models the first problem. Once they have completed the problem, they should simplify their answers and model the simplification using fraction pieces. Simplify the answer.
- Students take turns modeling the problems.

Activity Choice 2 • Literature

Introduce the lesson with *How Pizza Came to Queens* by Dayal Kaur Khalsa. For a related math activity, see p. TR52.

2 Teach

Scaffolding Questions

Show $\frac{3}{4}$ and $\frac{2}{8}$ using the eighths fraction tiles.

- **How many eighths are equal to $\frac{3}{4}$?** 6
- **How many eighths are equal to $\frac{2}{8}$?** 2
- Model taking 2 eighths away from 6 **eighths**.
- $\frac{6}{8} - \frac{2}{8} = \frac{4}{8}$ or $\frac{1}{2}$.

GET READY to Learn

Have students open their books and read the information in **Get Ready to Learn.** Introduce **subtracting unlike fractions.** As a class, work through **Examples 1–2.**

ADDITIONAL EXAMPLES

1 Find $\frac{4}{7} - \frac{1}{2}$. $\frac{1}{14}$

2 Eli and Star each have the same amount of collecting cards. Eli gave away $\frac{2}{3}$ of his cards. Star gave away $\frac{1}{4}$ of her cards. What fraction more of his cards did Eli give away than Star? $\frac{5}{12}$

CHECK What You Know

As a class, have students complete Exercises 1–10 in **Check What You Know** as you observe their work.

Exercise 10 Assess student comprehension before assigning practice exercises.

BL Alternate Teaching Strategy

If Students having trouble subtracting fractions with unlike denominators …

Then use one of these reteach options:

1 CRM **Daily Reteach Worksheet** (p. 23)

2 Have students use fraction circles to find equivalents fractions and model Exercises 1-8.

Real-World EXAMPLE — Subtract Unlike Fractions

2 **HOMEWORK** **Jessie finished $\frac{1}{2}$ of her homework. Lakshani finished $\frac{4}{5}$ of her homework. What fraction more of her homework did Lakshani finish than Jessie?**

Subtract $\frac{4}{5} - \frac{1}{2}$.

The least common denominator of $\frac{4}{5}$ and $\frac{1}{2}$ is 10.

Step 1		**Step 2**		**Step 3**
Write the problem.		Rename using the LCD.		Add the like fractions.
$\frac{4}{5}$	→	$\frac{4 \times 2}{5 \times 2} = \frac{8}{10}$	→	$\frac{8}{10}$
$-\frac{1}{2}$	→	$\frac{1 \times 5}{2 \times 5} = \frac{5}{10}$	→	$-\frac{5}{10}$
				$\frac{3}{10}$

Lakshani finished $\frac{3}{10}$ more of her homework than Jessie.

CHECK What You Know

Subtract. Write in simplest form. See Examples 1, 2 (pp. 439–440)

1. $\frac{3}{8} - \frac{1}{4} = \frac{1}{8}$ **2.** $\frac{5}{6} - \frac{1}{2} = \frac{1}{3}$ **3.** $\frac{2}{5} - \frac{1}{4} = \frac{3}{20}$ **4.** $\frac{4}{5} - \frac{1}{6} = \frac{19}{30}$

5. $\frac{7}{8} - \frac{1}{2} = \frac{3}{8}$ **6.** $\frac{7}{12} - \frac{1}{3} = \frac{1}{4}$ **7.** $\frac{5}{6} - \frac{1}{3} = \frac{1}{2}$ **8.** $\frac{2}{3} - \frac{3}{10} = \frac{11}{30}$

9. **Measurement** Danielle poured $\frac{3}{4}$ gallon of water from the full bucket shown at the right. How much water is left in the bucket? $\frac{1}{8}$ gallon

$\frac{7}{8}$ gallon

10. Talk About It Describe the steps you can use to find $\frac{3}{4} - \frac{1}{12}$. Sample answer: Rewrite $\frac{3}{4}$ as $\frac{9}{12}$ so the fractions have like denominators. Then subtract the numerators and simplify; $\frac{2}{3}$.

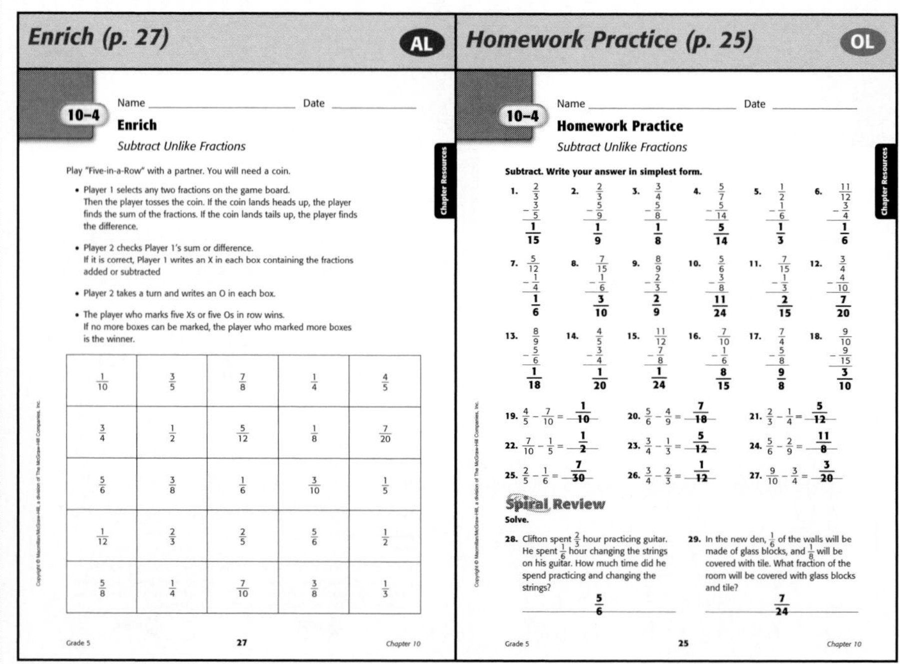

Enrich (p. 27) AL

10–4 Name ________ Date ________

Enrich

Subtract Unlike Fractions

Play "Five-in-a-Row" with a partner. You will need a coin.

- Player 1 selects any two fractions on the game board. Then the player tosses the coin. If the coin lands heads up, the player finds the sum of the fractions. If the coin lands tails up, the player finds the difference.
- Player 2 checks Player 1's sum or difference. If it is correct, Player 1 writes an X in each box containing the fractions added or subtracted
- Player 2 takes a turn and writes an O in each box.
- The player who marks five Xs or five Os in row wins. If no more boxes can be marked, the player who marked more boxes is the winner.

$\frac{1}{10}$	$\frac{3}{5}$	$\frac{7}{8}$	$\frac{1}{4}$	$\frac{4}{5}$
$\frac{3}{4}$	$\frac{1}{2}$	$\frac{5}{12}$	$\frac{1}{8}$	$\frac{7}{20}$
$\frac{5}{6}$	$\frac{3}{8}$	$\frac{1}{6}$	$\frac{3}{10}$	$\frac{1}{5}$
$\frac{1}{12}$	$\frac{2}{3}$	$\frac{2}{5}$	$\frac{5}{6}$	$\frac{1}{2}$
$\frac{5}{8}$	$\frac{1}{4}$	$\frac{7}{10}$	$\frac{3}{8}$	$\frac{1}{3}$

Grade 5 27 Chapter 10

Homework Practice (p. 25) OL

10–4 Name ________ Date ________

Homework Practice

Subtract Unlike Fractions

Subtract. Write your answer in simplest form.

1. $\frac{2}{3} - \frac{3}{5} = \frac{1}{15}$ **2.** $\frac{2}{3} - \frac{5}{9} = \frac{1}{9}$ **3.** $\frac{3}{4} - \frac{5}{8} = \frac{1}{8}$ **4.** $\frac{5}{7} - \frac{5}{14} = \frac{5}{14}$ **5.** $\frac{1}{2} - \frac{1}{6} = \frac{1}{3}$ **6.** $\frac{11}{12} - \frac{3}{4} = \frac{1}{6}$

7. $\frac{5}{12} - \frac{1}{4} = \frac{1}{6}$ **8.** $\frac{7}{15} - \frac{1}{6} = \frac{3}{10}$ **9.** $\frac{8}{9} - \frac{2}{3} = \frac{2}{9}$ **10.** $\frac{5}{6} - \frac{3}{8} = \frac{11}{24}$ **11.** $\frac{7}{15} - \frac{1}{3} = \frac{2}{15}$ **12.** $\frac{3}{4} - \frac{4}{10} = \frac{7}{20}$

13. $\frac{8}{9} - \frac{5}{6} = \frac{1}{18}$ **14.** $\frac{4}{5} - \frac{3}{4} = \frac{1}{20}$ **15.** $\frac{11}{12} - \frac{7}{8} = \frac{1}{24}$ **16.** $\frac{7}{10} - \frac{1}{6} = \frac{8}{15}$ **17.** $\frac{7}{4} - \frac{5}{8} = \frac{9}{8}$ **18.** $\frac{9}{10} - \frac{9}{15} = \frac{3}{10}$

19. $\frac{4}{5} - \frac{7}{10} = \frac{1}{10}$ **20.** $\frac{5}{6} - \frac{4}{9} = \frac{7}{18}$ **21.** $\frac{2}{3} - \frac{1}{4} = \frac{5}{12}$

22. $\frac{7}{10} - \frac{1}{5} = \frac{1}{2}$ **23.** $\frac{3}{4} - \frac{1}{3} = \frac{5}{12}$ **24.** $\frac{5}{6} - \frac{2}{9} = \frac{11}{8}$

25. $\frac{2}{5} - \frac{1}{6} = \frac{7}{30}$ **26.** $\frac{3}{4} - \frac{2}{3} = \frac{1}{12}$ **27.** $\frac{9}{10} - \frac{3}{4} = \frac{3}{20}$

Spiral Review

Solve.

28. Clifton spent $\frac{2}{3}$ hour practicing guitar. He spent $\frac{1}{6}$ hour changing the strings on his guitar. How much time did he spend practicing and changing the strings? $\frac{5}{6}$

29. In the new den, $\frac{1}{6}$ of the walls will be made of glass blocks, and $\frac{1}{8}$ will be covered with tile. What fraction of the room will be covered with glass blocks and tile? $\frac{7}{24}$

Grade 5 25 Chapter 10

★ indicates multi-step problem

Practice and Problem Solving

EXTRA PRACTICE See page R27.

Subtract. Write in simplest form. See Examples 1,2 (pp. 439–440)

11. $\frac{5}{8} - \frac{1}{2}$ $\frac{1}{8}$ **12.** $\frac{2}{5} - \frac{1}{10}$ $\frac{3}{10}$ **13.** $\frac{1}{2} - \frac{1}{4}$ $\frac{1}{4}$ **14.** $\frac{4}{5} - \frac{2}{15}$ $\frac{2}{3}$

15. $\frac{5}{12} - \frac{1}{6}$ $\frac{1}{4}$ **16.** $\frac{7}{10} - \frac{1}{4}$ $\frac{9}{20}$ **17.** $\frac{5}{6} - \frac{3}{4}$ $\frac{1}{12}$ **18.** $\frac{2}{3} - \frac{3}{5}$ $\frac{1}{15}$

19. $\frac{7}{8} - \frac{1}{4}$ $\frac{5}{8}$ **20.** $\frac{7}{10} - \frac{1}{2}$ $\frac{1}{5}$ **21.** $\frac{5}{8} - \frac{1}{6}$ $\frac{11}{24}$ **22.** $\frac{7}{12} - \frac{1}{3}$ $\frac{1}{4}$

23. Denelle rides her bicycle $\frac{2}{3}$ mile to school. On Friday, she took a shortcut so that the ride to school was $\frac{1}{9}$ mile shorter. How long was Denelle's bicycle ride on Friday? $\frac{5}{9}$ mi

24. **Measurement** The average snowfall in April and October for Springfield is shown in the table at the right. How much more snow falls on average in April than in October? $\frac{1}{2}$ in.

Average Snowfall for Springfield	
Month	Snowfall (in.)
April	$\frac{4}{5}$
October	$\frac{3}{10}$

25. Wyatt is hiking a trail that is $\frac{11}{12}$ mile long. After hiking $\frac{1}{4}$ mile, he stops for water. How much farther must he hike to finish the trail? $\frac{2}{3}$ mile

26. Lavell has $\frac{7}{10}$ of his homework finished. Jaclyn has $\frac{4}{9}$ of her homework finished. How much more of his homework does Lavell have finished than Jaclyn? $\frac{23}{90}$

★**27.** A mosaic design is $\frac{7}{15}$ red, $\frac{1}{5}$ blue, and $\frac{1}{3}$ yellow. What fraction more of the mosaic is blue and yellow than red? $\frac{1}{15}$

H.O.T. Problems

28. **OPEN ENDED** Write a subtraction problem involving fractions with the denominators 8 and 24. Then find the difference. Include the steps you used. Sample answer: $\frac{1}{8} - \frac{1}{24} = \frac{3}{24} - \frac{1}{24} = \frac{2}{24}$ or $\frac{1}{12}$

29. **CHALLENGE** Evaluate $x - y$ if $x = \frac{5}{6}$ and $y = \frac{7}{10}$. $\frac{2}{15}$

30. WRITING IN ► MATH Describe the difference between subtracting fractions with like denominators and subtracting fractions with unlike denominators. See Ch. 10 Answer Appendix.

3 Practice

Differentiate practice using these leveled assignments for Exercises 11–30.

Level	Assignment
BL Below/Approaching Level	11–18, 23–24
OL On Level	12–20, 24–27, 30
AL Above/Beyond Level	12–22 even, 23–27, 28–30

Have students discuss and complete the Higher Order Thinking problems.

WRITING IN ► MATH Have students complete Exercise 30 in their Math Journals. You may choose to use this exercise as an optional formative assessment.

4 Assess

Formative Assessment

- **Explain how you subtract unlike fractions.** Sample answer: One or both of the fractions must be renamed so they have a common denominator; subtract the numerators and simplify the answer.

Yesterday's News Have students explain how the earlier lesson on adding unlike fractions helped them to understand today's lesson.

Quick Check **Are students continuing to struggle with subtracting fractions with unlike denominators?**

If Yes → Small Group Options (p. 434B)

If No → Independent Work Options (p. 439B)
CRM Skills Practice Worksheet (p. 24)
CRM Enrich Worksheet (p. 27)

COMMON ERROR!

Exercises 16–18, and 21 Students may forget to change both of their fractions to an equivalent fraction.

10-5 Problem-Solving Skill
Determine Reasonable Answers

Lesson Planner

Objective

Solve problems by determining reasonable answers.

Resources

Literature Connection: *Minnie's Diner: A Multiplying Menu* by Dayle Ann Dodds

Teacher Technology

Interactive Classroom • TeacherWorks

Real-World Problem Solving Library
Math and Social Studies: *Life in Colonial America*

Use these leveled books to reinforce and extend problem-solving skills and strategies.

Leveled for:

- OL On Level
- ELL Sheltered English
- SP Spanish

For additional support, see the Real-World Problem Solving Teacher Guide.

Daily Routine

Use these suggestions before beginning the lesson on p. 442.

5-Minute Check

(Reviews Lesson 10-4)

Subtract. Write each difference in simplest form. Check your answer by using fraction tiles or drawing a picture.

1. $\frac{4}{5} - \frac{1}{3}$ $\frac{7}{15}$
2. $\frac{6}{7} - \frac{2}{3}$ $\frac{4}{21}$
3. $\frac{7}{8} - \frac{1}{2}$ $\frac{3}{8}$
4. $\frac{4}{6} - \frac{1}{4}$ $\frac{5}{12}$
5. $\frac{8}{9} - \frac{3}{4}$ $\frac{5}{36}$
6. $\frac{11}{12} - \frac{7}{24}$ $\frac{15}{24}$

See students' tiles or pictures.

Problem of the Day

Leela, Juan, and Andy are reading the same book. Leela finished $\frac{5}{6}$ of the book, Juan finished $\frac{24}{30}$, and Andy finished $\frac{11}{15}$. Who finished the most? the least? most: Leela; least: Andy

Differentiated Instruction

Small Group Options

LOGICAL

Option 1 Gifted and Talented AL

Materials: pencil and paper

- Hand students this problem:

  Esteban and his brother each take two sandwiches for lunch every weekday. Their mother can buy either 20-slice or 30-slice loaves of bread. If she wants no leftover bread for the weekend, what size loaves should she buy? two 20 slices loaves of bread
- **Is it reasonable for their mother to buy one 20-slice loaf for the week? Why?** No, because that is not enough bread. She should buy two 20-slice loaves.
- Have students write another question to go with this problem and share it with other students.

LINGUISTIC

Option 2 English Language Learners ELL

Core Vocabulary: exact/estimate, list of events, enough
Common Use Verb: brainstorm

Talk Math This strategy allows students to use background knowledge to vocalize math skills.

- Say: "Sometimes we need **exact** numbers and sometimes we only need an **estimate**. Let us make a **list of events** and ***brainstorm*** if we need **exact** numbers or **estimated** numbers."
- List and discuss the following:

  How long does it take you to get dressed?

  How long does it take you to boil an egg?

  How many eggs do I put in my cake?
- Students brainstorm lists of other events and decide as a class if exact numbers or estimates are called for.

Independent Work Options

LINGUISTIC, LOGICAL

Option 1 Early Finishers OL AL

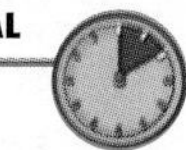

Materials: calculators

- Ask students to write four addition word problems that can each be solved using a different method: calculator, paper and pencil, estimation, and mental math.
- Have students exchange problems with a classmate, solve the problems, and tell which method they used and why.

Option 2 Student Technology

Math Online macmillanmh.com

Personal Tutor • Extra Examples

Option 3 Learning Station: Reading (p. 418J)

Direct students to the Reading Learning Station for opportunities to explore and extend the lesson concept.

10-5 Problem-Solving Skill

1 Introduce

Activity Choice 1 • Review

- Present students with the following problem:
  Benita places 4 square tables end-to-end to make one large rectangular table. One square table can seat two people on each side. How many people can sit around the new large table?
- **What problem-solving strategy could you use to solve the problem?** draw a picture
- Discuss how to use the *draw a picture* strategy. Ask a volunteer to *draw a picture* on the board and solve the problem. 20 people

Activity Choice 2 • Literature

Introduce the lesson with *Minnie's Diner: A Multiplying Menu* by Dayle Ann Dodds. For a related math activity, see p. TR52.

2 Teach

Have students read the problem on feeding a rabbit. Guide them through the problem-solving steps.

Understand Using the questions, review what students know and need to find.

Plan Have them discuss their strategy.

Solve Guide students to use the *find a reasonable answer* strategy to solve the problem.

- **What key word in this problem tells you that an estimate, not an exact answer, is needed?** about
- **How do you know that $\frac{3}{4}$ rounds up to 1?** Sample answer: It is closer to 1 than 0 on a number line.

Check Have students look back at the problem to make sure that the answer fits the facts given.

COMMON ERROR!

Exercise 8 Students may try to add to find the estimate. Have students reread the problem and circle any key words that may indicate addition or subtraction.

10-5 Problem-Solving Skill

MAIN IDEA I will solve problems by determining reasonable answers.

Leandra feeds her pet rabbit Bounce the same amount of food each day. Bounce eats three times a day. *About* how much food does Leandra feed Bounce in a week?

Time	Food (cups)
Morning	$\frac{3}{4}$
Afternoon	$\frac{3}{4}$
Evening	$\frac{1}{4}$

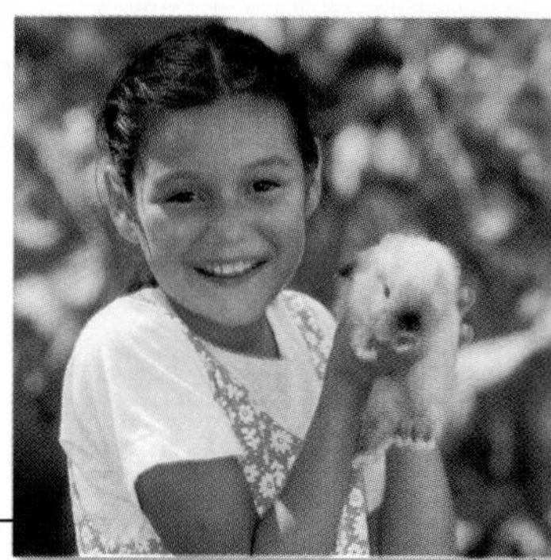

Understand **What facts do you know?**

- Leandra feeds the rabbit the same amount every day.

What do you need to find?

- About how much food she feeds her rabbit each week.

Plan You can use estimation to find a reasonable answer.

Solve Round each amount of food to the nearest whole number.

Morning	Afternoon	Evening
$\frac{3}{4} \rightarrow 1$	$\frac{3}{4} \rightarrow 1$	$\frac{1}{4} \rightarrow 0$

In one day, she feeds Bounce about 1 + 1 + 0 or 2 cups of food.

Multiply by the number of days in a week.

days in 1 week ↓ ↓ cups of food each day

$7 \times 2 = 14$ ← cups of food in 7 days or 1 week

Leandra feeds Bounce about 14 cups of food in a week.

Check Look back. Since there are 7 days in a week, multiply each amount by 7.

$(7 \times 1) + (7 \times 1) + (7 \times 0) = 14$

So, the answer is reasonable.

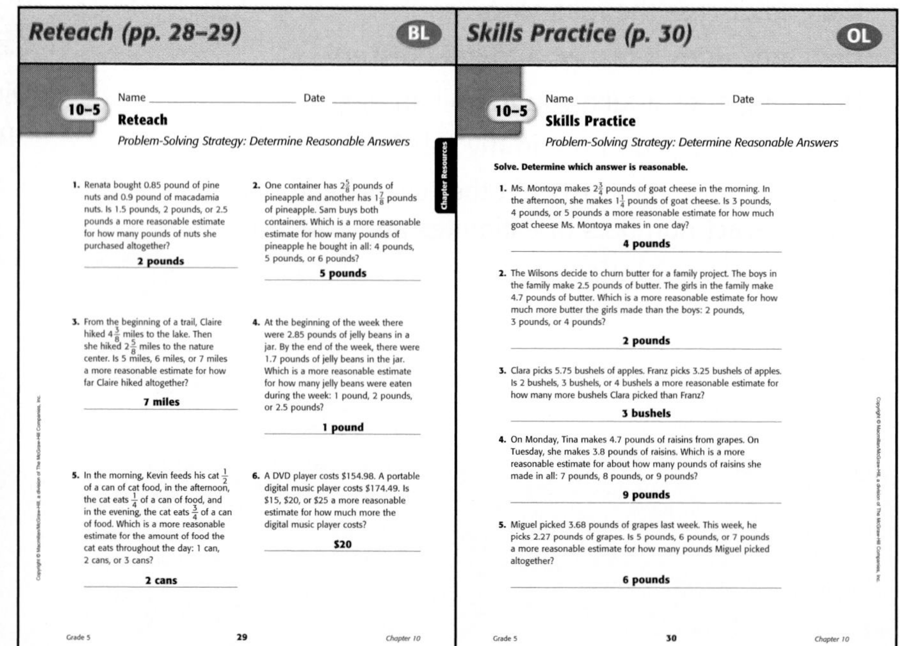

Reteach (pp. 28–29) BL

10-5 Name ______ Date ______

Reteach

Problem-Solving Strategy: Determine Reasonable Answers

1. Renata bought 0.85 pound of pine nuts and 0.9 pound of macadamia nuts. Is 1.5 pounds, 2 pounds, or 2.5 pounds a more reasonable estimate for how many pounds of nuts she purchased altogether? **2 pounds**
2. One container has $2\frac{5}{8}$ pounds of pineapple and another has $1\frac{7}{8}$ pounds of pineapple. Sam buys both containers. Which is a more reasonable estimate for how many pounds of pineapple he bought in all: 4 pounds, 5 pounds, or 6 pounds? **5 pounds**
3. From the beginning of a trail, Claire hiked $4\frac{3}{8}$ miles to the lake. Then she hiked $2\frac{5}{8}$ miles to the nature center. Is 5 miles, 6 miles, or 7 miles a more reasonable estimate for how far Claire hiked altogether? **7 miles**
4. At the beginning of the week there were 2.85 pounds of jelly beans in a jar. By the end of the week, there were 1.7 pounds of jelly beans in the jar. Which is a more reasonable estimate for how many jelly beans were eaten during the week: 1 pound, 2 pounds, or 2.5 pounds? **1 pound**
5. In the morning, Kevin feeds his cat $\frac{1}{2}$ of a can of cat food, in the afternoon, the cat eats $\frac{1}{4}$ of a can of food, and in the evening, the cat eats $\frac{3}{4}$ of a can of food. Which is a more reasonable estimate for the amount of food the cat eats throughout the day: 1 can, 2 cans, or 3 cans? **2 cans**
6. A DVD player costs $154.98. A portable digital music player costs $174.49. Is $15, $20, or $25 a more reasonable estimate for how much more the digital music player costs? **$20**

Chapter Resources

Grade 5 29 Chapter 10

Skills Practice (p. 30) OL

10-5 Name ______ Date ______

Skills Practice

Problem-Solving Strategy: Determine Reasonable Answers

Solve. Determine which answer is reasonable.

1. Ms. Montoya makes $2\frac{3}{4}$ pounds of goat cheese in the morning. In the afternoon, she makes $1\frac{1}{4}$ pounds of goat cheese. Is 3 pounds, 4 pounds, or 5 pounds a more reasonable estimate for how much goat cheese Ms. Montoya makes in one day? **4 pounds**
2. The Wilsons decide to churn butter for a family project. The boys in the family make 2.5 pounds of butter. The girls in the family make 4.7 pounds of butter. Which is a more reasonable estimate for how much more butter the girls made than the boys: 2 pounds, 3 pounds, or 4 pounds? **2 pounds**
3. Clara picks 5.75 bushels of apples. Franz picks 3.25 bushels of apples. Is 2 bushels, 3 bushels, or 4 bushels a more reasonable estimate for how many more bushels Clara picked than Franz? **3 bushels**
4. On Monday, Tina makes 4.7 pounds of raisins from grapes. On Tuesday, she makes 3.8 pounds of raisins. Which is a more reasonable estimate for about how many pounds of raisins she made in all: 7 pounds, 8 pounds, or 9 pounds? **9 pounds**
5. Miguel picked 3.68 pounds of grapes last week. This week, he picks 2.27 pounds of grapes. Is 5 pounds, 6 pounds, or 7 pounds a more reasonable estimate for how many pounds Miguel picked altogether? **6 pounds**

Grade 5 30 Chapter 10

ANALYZE the Strategy

Refer to the problem on the previous page. 1–2, 4. See Ch. 10 Answer Appendix.

1. Explain why estimation is often the best way to find reasonable answers.
2. What other methods of computation could you use to solve the problem? Explain.
3. Find how much more food Leandra feeds her rabbit in the morning than in the evening. $\frac{1}{2}$ c
4. What method of computation did you use to solve Exercise 3? Explain your reasoning.

PRACTICE the Strategy

See page R28.

Solve. Determine which answer is reasonable.

5. Thirty students from the Netherlands set up a record 1,500,000 dominoes. Of these, 1,138,101 were toppled by one push. Which is a more reasonable estimate for how many dominoes remained standing after that push: 350,000 or 400,000? 350,000
6. Use the graph below. Is 20 inches, 23 inches, or 215 inches a reasonable total amount of rain that fell in May, June, and July? 20 in.

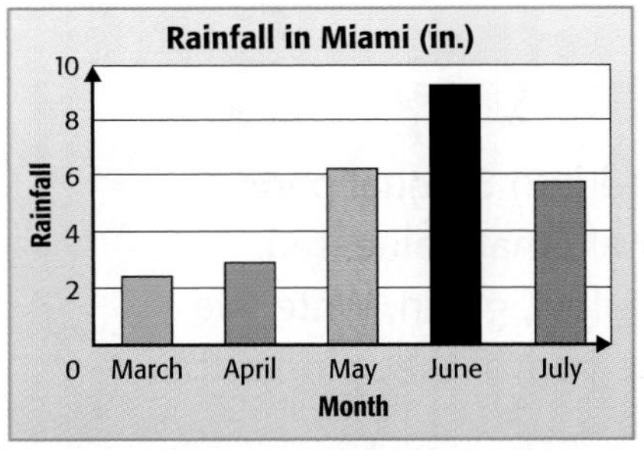

7. A puzzle book costs $4.25. A novel costs $9.70 more than the puzzle book. Which is a more reasonable estimate for the total cost of both items: $14, $16, or $18? $18
8. Use the table to determine whether 245 pounds, 260 pounds, or 263 pounds is a reasonable estimate for how much more the ostrich weighs than the flamingo. Explain. 245 lb

Bird	Weight (lb)
Flamingo	$9\frac{1}{10}$
Ostrich	$253\frac{1}{2}$

8–9. See Ch. 10 Answer Appendix for explanations.

9. **Measurement** A grocer sells 12 pounds of apples. Of those, $5\frac{3}{4}$ pounds are green and $3\frac{1}{4}$ pounds are golden. The rest are red. Which is a more reasonable estimate for how many pounds of red apples the grocer sold: 3 pounds or 5 pounds? Explain. 3 lb
10. **WRITING IN ▶MATH** Write an addition or subtraction problem involving fractions with like denominators. Ask a classmate to determine a reasonable answer for the problem. See Ch. 10 Answer Appendix.

Analyze the Strategy Use Exercises 1–4 to analyze and discuss the problem-solving strategy.

BL Alternate Teaching Strategy

If students have trouble rounding fractions to estimate...

Then use one of these reteach options:

1 CRM **Daily Reteach Worksheet** (pp. 28–29)

2 Guide students to draw a number line from 0 to 1, divide it into fourths, and label it 0, $\frac{1}{4}$, $\frac{2}{4}$, $\frac{3}{4}$, and 1. Have students use the number line to help them round $\frac{3}{4}$ and $\frac{1}{4}$ to the nearest whole number, 0 or 1.

3 Practice

Using the Exercises

Exercises 5–10 give students the opportunity to practice finding reasonable answers.

Exercise 7 Students may read the problem quickly and add $4 and $10 using mental math instead of adding $4 + ($4 + $10). Encourage students to read problems carefully to make sure they understand the facts before solving.

4 Assess

Formative Assessment

Present students with the following problem:

Yoo Ki is saving his money to buy a bike and accessories. The prices are: a bike for $289.99; a helmet for $25.99, a headlight for $21.50, and a rear light for $16.50. Is it reasonable to say that he needs to save $300 to buy the items? No. Rounding each price gives you $290 + 30 + 20 + 20 = $360, so $300 is not enough.

Quick Check **Are students continuing to struggle with solving problems by finding reasonable answers?**

If Yes → CRM Reteach Worksheet (pp. 28–29)

If No → Independent Work Options (p. 442B)
CRM Skills Practice Worksheet (p. 30)
CRM Enrich Worksheet (p. 32)

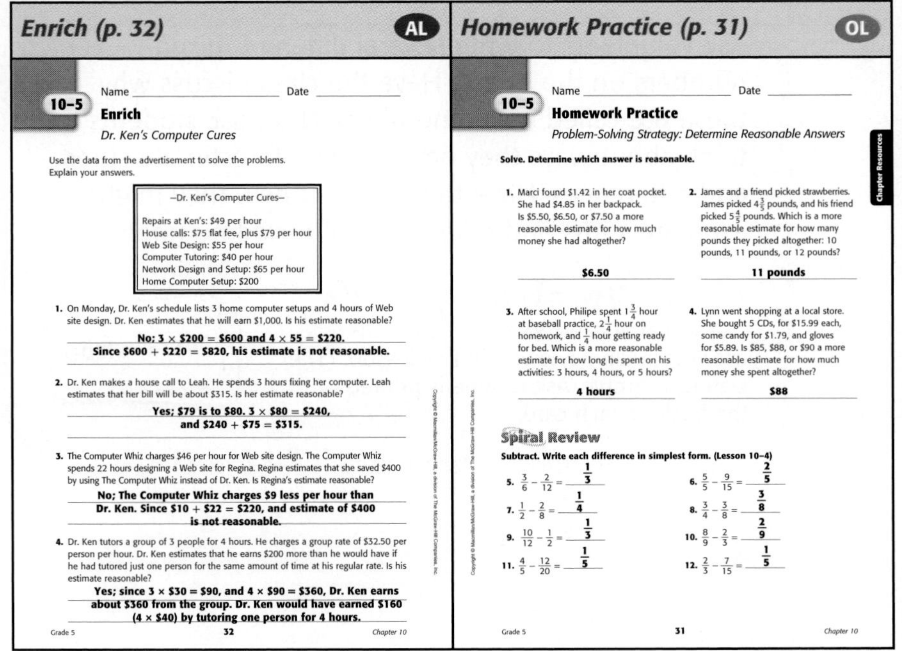

Enrich (p. 32) AL

10-5 Name ______ Date ______

Enrich

Dr. Ken's Computer Cures

Use the data from the advertisement to solve the problems. Explain your answers.

–Dr. Ken's Computer Cures–

Repairs at Ken's: $49 per hour
House calls: $75 flat fee, plus $79 per hour
Web Site Design: $55 per hour
Computer Tutoring: $40 per hour
Network Design and Setup: $65 per hour
Home Computer Setup: $200

1. On Monday, Dr. Ken's schedule lists 3 home computer setups and 4 hours of Web site design. Dr. Ken estimates that he will earn $1,000. Is his estimate reasonable?
No; 3 × $200 = $600 and 4 × 55 = $220. Since $600 + $220 = $820, his estimate is not reasonable.
2. Dr. Ken makes a house call to Leah. He spends 3 hours fixing her computer. Leah estimates that her bill will be about $315. Is her estimate reasonable?
Yes; $79 is to $80. 3 × $80 = $240, and $240 + $75 = $315.
3. The Computer Whiz charges $46 per hour for Web site design. The Computer Whiz spends 22 hours designing a Web site for Regina. Regina estimates that she saved $400 by using The Computer Whiz instead of Dr. Ken. Is Regina's estimate reasonable?
No; The Computer Whiz charges $9 less per hour than Dr. Ken. Since $10 + $22 = $220, and estimate of $400 is not reasonable.
4. Dr. Ken tutors a group of 3 people for 4 hours. He charges a group rate of $32.50 per person per hour. Dr. Ken estimates that he earns $200 more than he would have if he had tutored just one person for the same amount of time at his regular rate. Is his estimate reasonable?
Yes; since 3 × $30 = $90, and 4 × $90 = $360, Dr. Ken earns about $360 from the group. Dr. Ken would have earned $160 (4 × $40) by tutoring one person for 4 hours.

Grade 5 32 Chapter 10

Homework Practice (p. 31) OL

10-5 Name ______ Date ______

Homework Practice

Problem-Solving Strategy: Determine Reasonable Answers

Chapter Resources

Solve. Determine which answer is reasonable.

1. Marci found $1.42 in her coat pocket. She had $4.85 in her backpack. Is $5.50, $6.50, or $7.50 a more reasonable estimate for how much money she had altogether? **$6.50**
2. James and a friend picked strawberries. James picked $4\frac{3}{5}$ pounds, and his friend picked $5\frac{4}{5}$ pounds. Which is a more reasonable estimate for how many pounds they picked altogether: 10 pounds, 11 pounds, or 12 pounds? **11 pounds**
3. After school, Philipe spent $1\frac{3}{4}$ hour at baseball practice, $2\frac{1}{4}$ hour on homework, and $\frac{1}{4}$ hour getting ready for bed. Which is a more reasonable estimate for how long he spent on his activities: 3 hours, 4 hours, or 5 hours? **4 hours**
4. Lynn went shopping at a local store. She bought 5 CDs, for $15.99 each, some candy for $1.79, and gloves for $5.89. Is $85, $88, or $90 a more reasonable estimate for how much money she spent altogether? **$88**

Spiral Review

Subtract. Write each difference in simplest form. (Lesson 10–4)

5. $\frac{3}{6} - \frac{2}{12} = \frac{1}{3}$
6. $\frac{5}{5} - \frac{9}{15} = \frac{2}{5}$
7. $\frac{1}{2} - \frac{2}{8} = \frac{1}{4}$
8. $\frac{3}{4} - \frac{3}{8} = \frac{3}{8}$
9. $\frac{10}{12} - \frac{1}{2} = \frac{1}{3}$
10. $\frac{8}{9} - \frac{2}{3} = \frac{2}{9}$
11. $\frac{4}{5} - \frac{12}{20} = \frac{1}{5}$
12. $\frac{2}{3} - \frac{7}{15} = \frac{1}{5}$

Grade 5 31 Chapter 10

LESSON 10-6

Estimate Sums and Differences

Lesson Planner

Objective

Estimate sums and differences of mixed numbers.

Review Vocabulary

mixed number, estimate

Resources

Materials: masking tape, index cards
Manipulatives: fraction tiles
Literature Connection: *Let's Investigate Estimating* by Marion Smoothy
Teacher Technology
Interactive Classroom • TeacherWorks

Focus on Math Background

Estimation is an important skill for students to master because often an approximation is all that is needed in a real-world situation. Also, students can use estimation to check the reasonableness of an answer. In previous lessons, students learned about mixed numbers and also learned how to round fractions to the nearest half. Estimates in this lesson are based on rounding mixed numbers to the nearest whole number. That is, mixed numbers are rounded down if the fractional part of the mixed number is less than one-half and rounded up if the fractional part is greater than one-half. However, in real life, sometimes rounding all numbers up may be necessary. For example, a measurement problem where students are asked to estimate a minimum amount of fencing needed for a rectangular yard calls for an overestimate. In this case, students should round all measurements up.

Daily Routine

Use these suggestions before beginning the lesson on p. 444.

5-Minute Check 

(Reviews Lesson 10-5)

Solve. Determine which answer is reasonable.
Ali bought lunch at a restaurant. She spent $5.75 for a sandwich, $1.99 for a cup of soup, and $1.29 for milk. Which is a more reasonable estimate for the amount of money Ali spent on lunch, $9.00 or $10.00? $9.00

Problem of the Day 

A circular spinner is divided into 8 equal parts. The colors on the spinner alternate blue, red, yellow, green, blue, red, yellow, green. Write five equivalent fractions for the part of the spinner that is red. Sample answers: $\frac{1}{4}, \frac{2}{8}, \frac{3}{12}, \frac{4}{16}, \frac{5}{20}$

Review Math Vocabulary

Write the review vocabulary words and their definitions on the board.

Ask volunteers to write several different mixed numbers on the board. Have the class discuss why these are called mixed numbers. Next, ask students to think about ways they have learned to estimate sums and differences. Have them predict how they might estimate sums and differences of mixed numbers.

Visual Vocabulary Cards

Use Visual Vocabulary Card 24 to reinforce the vocabulary reviewed in this lesson. (The Define/Example/Ask routine is printed on the back of each card.)

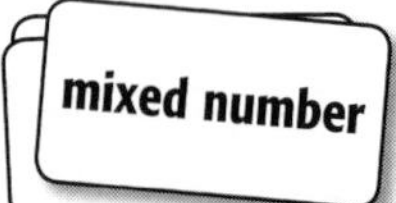

Differentiated Instruction

Small Group Options

Option 1 Gifted and Talented AL

SPATIAL

Materials: paper, pencils

- Have pairs of students take turns calling out mixed numbers while the other student rounds it to the nearest whole number.
- Have pairs pick a goal number to try to reach and ask them to record the number of times they think it will take them to reach it. For example, if the goal is 12, students may say that they will get to 12 in three tries:

Try 1: $4\frac{3}{4} \rightarrow$ 5

Try 2: $3\frac{1}{7} \rightarrow$ 3

Try 3: $4\frac{2}{8} \rightarrow$ $\underline{+\ 4}$

Option 2 English Language Learners ELL

INTERPERSONAL, KINESTHETIC

Materials: construction paper, number cubes

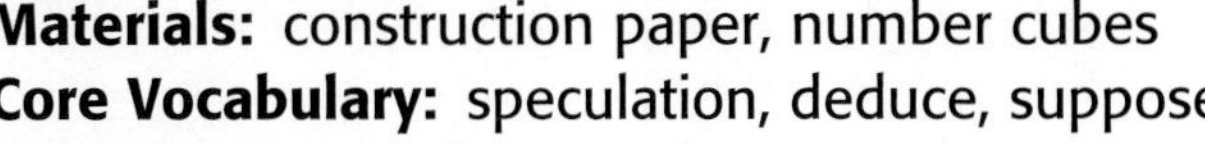

Core Vocabulary: speculation, deduce, suppose

Common Use Verb: speculate

Do Math This strategy activates background knowledge and estimation skills to practice adding and subtracting decimals.

- Roll two number cubes and use to make a fraction, for example, $\frac{2}{5}$.
- Say: "My roll rounds down to ________. (ex. $\frac{1}{2}$) Give me a decimal that might make one whole."
- As students speculate, discuss deductive reasoning using the core vocabulary. They can presume it is not less than $\frac{1}{2}$, etc.
- Have students call out their speculations; the one that is closest to a whole wins.
- Repeat as time permits. When a 10, 11, or 12 is rolled, students will have to estimate down.

Independent Work Options

Option 1 Early Finishers OL

SOCIAL, LOGICAL

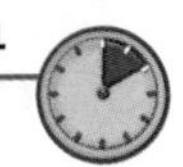

Materials: ten index cards

- Have students think of ten different mixed numbers between 1 and 10 and write each number on a separate index card.
- Ask students to choose two index cards and estimate the sum of the numbers shown. Then have them estimate the difference between the larger number and the smaller number.
- Have students continue picking cards and estimating sums and differences until all cards have been chosen.

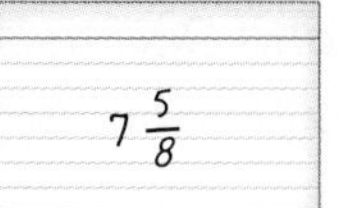

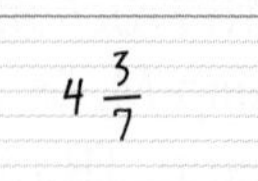

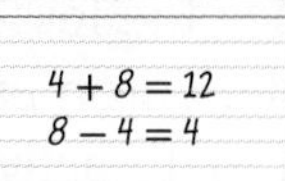

Option 2 Student Technology

Tech Link

macmillanmh.com

Personal Tutor • Extra Examples

Math Adventures

Option 3 Learning Station: Health (p. 418J)

Direct students to the Health Learning Station for opportunities to explore and extend the lesson concept.

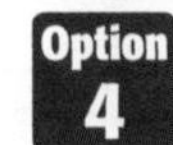

Option 4 Problem-Solving Practice

Reinforce problem-solving skills and strategies with the Problem-Solving Practice worksheet.

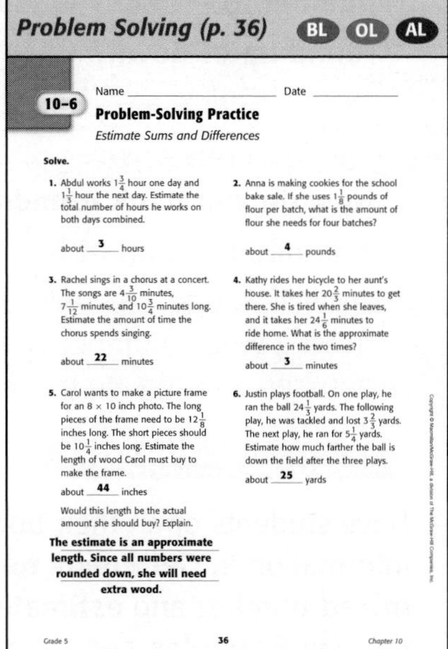

Problem Solving (p. 36) BL OL AL

10–6 Name ____________ Date ________

Problem-Solving Practice

Estimate Sums and Differences

Solve.

1. Abdul works $1\frac{3}{4}$ hour one day and $1\frac{1}{3}$ hour the next day. Estimate the total number of hours he works on both days combined.

   about **3** hours

2. Anna is making cookies for the school bake sale. If she uses $1\frac{1}{8}$ pounds of flour per batch, what is the amount of flour she needs for four batches?

   about **4** pounds

3. Rachel sings in a chorus at a concert. The songs are $4\frac{3}{10}$ minutes, $7\frac{1}{12}$ minutes, and $10\frac{3}{4}$ minutes long. Estimate the amount of time the chorus spends singing.

   about **22** minutes

4. Kathy rides her bicycle to her aunt's house. It takes her $20\frac{2}{3}$ minutes to get there. She is tired when she leaves, and it takes her $24\frac{1}{6}$ minutes to ride home. What is the approximate difference in the two times?

   about **3** minutes

5. Carol wants to make a picture frame for an 8 × 10 inch photo. The long pieces of the frame need to be $12\frac{1}{8}$ inches long. The short pieces should be $10\frac{1}{4}$ inches long. Estimate the length of wood Carol must buy to make the frame.

   about **44** inches

   Would this length be the actual amount she should buy? Explain.

   The estimate is an approximate length. Since all numbers were rounded down, she will need extra wood.

6. Justin plays football. On one play, he ran the ball $24\frac{1}{3}$ yards. The following play, he was tackled and lost $3\frac{2}{3}$ yards. The next play, he ran for $5\frac{1}{4}$ yards. Estimate how much farther the ball is down the field after the three plays.

   about **25** yards

Grade 5 36 Chapter 10

10-6 Estimate Sums and Differences

1 Introduce

Activity Choice 1 • Hands-On 

- Make a number line showing whole numbers from 1 to 10 with masking tape on the floor or draw it on the board.
- Organize students into pairs and give each pair an index card labeled with a different mixed number between 1 and 10, for example, $2\frac{2}{3}$, $5\frac{1}{12}$, $8\frac{5}{8}$, etc.
- Ask partners to work together to decide where their number should be placed.
- Have one pair place their card on the number line and justify the placement to the class. Once the class agrees with the placement, continue until all cards are placed on the line.

Activity Choice 2 • Literature

Introduce the lesson with *Fractions and Decimals* by Lucille Caron and Philip M. St. Jacques. For a related math activity, see p. TR53.

2 Teach

Scaffolding Questions

Guide students to use the number line to help them round each mixed number to the nearest whole number. Ask questions about the rounded numbers.

- **Does $2\frac{2}{3}$ round to 2 or to 3? How do you know?** 3; $\frac{2}{3}$ is closer to 3 than to 2 on the number line.
- **How can comparing the fraction in a mixed number to $\frac{1}{2}$ help you know whether to round up or down?** If the fraction is equal to or greater than $\frac{1}{2}$, round up. If it is less than $\frac{1}{2}$, round down.
- **How do you think rounding could help you estimate the sum of $5\frac{1}{12}$ and $8\frac{5}{8}$?** Sample answer: Round each mixed number to the nearest whole number and add the whole numbers to estimate the sum.

GET READY to Learn

Have students open their books and read the information in **Get Ready to Learn.** Review **mixed number** and **estimate**. As a class, work through **Examples 1–4**.

10-6 Estimate Sums and Differences

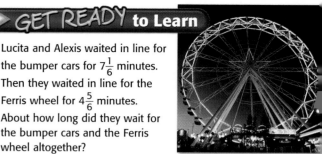

MAIN IDEA

I will estimate sums and differences of mixed numbers.

Math Online

macmillanmh.com

- Extra Examples
- Personal Tutor
- Self-Check Quiz

GET READY to Learn

Lucita and Alexis waited in line for the bumper cars for $7\frac{1}{6}$ minutes. Then they waited in line for the Ferris wheel for $4\frac{5}{6}$ minutes. About how long did they wait for the bumper cars and the Ferris wheel altogether?

To estimate the sum of $7\frac{1}{6}$ and $4\frac{5}{6}$, round each mixed number to the nearest whole number. Then add.

EXAMPLE Estimate Sums

1 **Estimate $7\frac{1}{6} + 4\frac{5}{6}$ to answer the problem above.**

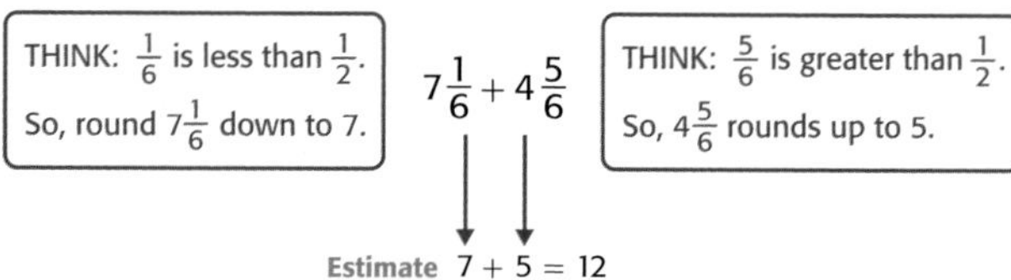

THINK: $\frac{1}{6}$ is less than $\frac{1}{2}$.
So, round $7\frac{1}{6}$ down to 7.
$7\frac{1}{6} + 4\frac{5}{6}$
THINK: $\frac{5}{6}$ is greater than $\frac{1}{2}$.
So, $4\frac{5}{6}$ rounds up to 5.
Estimate $7 + 5 = 12$

So, Lucita and Alexis waited about 12 minutes altogether.

Estimate Differences

2 **Estimate $3\frac{5}{8} - 1\frac{1}{8}$.**

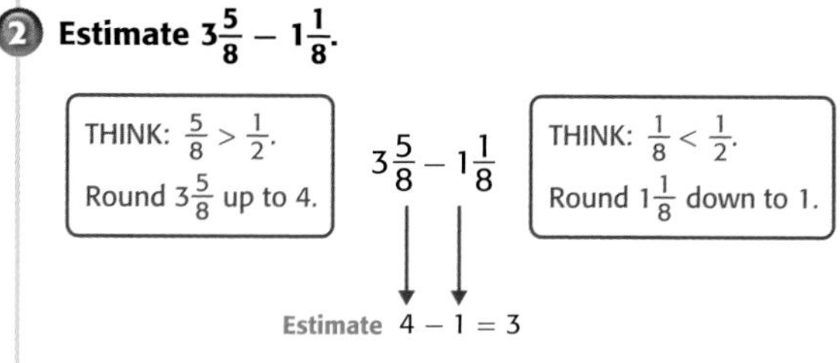

THINK: $\frac{5}{8} > \frac{1}{2}$.
Round $3\frac{5}{8}$ up to 4.
$3\frac{5}{8} - 1\frac{1}{8}$
THINK: $\frac{1}{8} < \frac{1}{2}$.
Round $1\frac{1}{8}$ down to 1.
Estimate $4 - 1 = 3$

So, $3\frac{5}{8} - 1\frac{1}{8}$ is about 3.

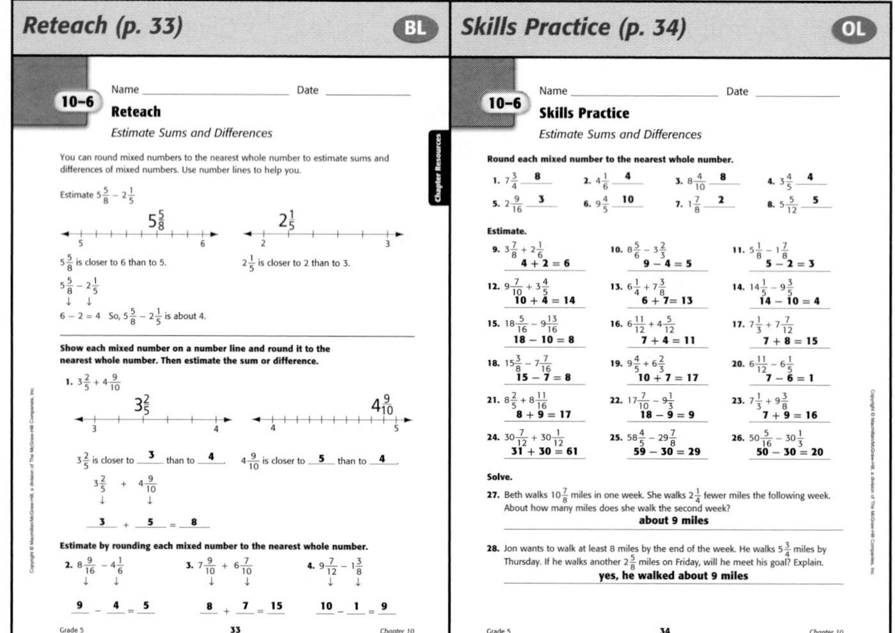

Reteach (p. 33) BL

10-6 Name ________ Date ________

Reteach

Estimate Sums and Differences

You can round mixed numbers to the nearest whole number to estimate sums and differences of mixed numbers. Use number lines to help you.

Estimate $5\frac{5}{8} - 2\frac{1}{5}$

$5\frac{5}{8}$ is closer to 6 than to 5. $2\frac{1}{5}$ is closer to 2 than to 3.

$5\frac{5}{8} - 2\frac{1}{5}$

$6 - 2 = 4$ So, $5\frac{5}{8} - 2\frac{1}{5}$ is about 4.

Show each mixed number on a number line and round it to the nearest whole number. Then estimate the sum or difference.

1. $3\frac{2}{5} + 4\frac{9}{10}$

$3\frac{2}{5}$ is closer to **3** than to **4**. $4\frac{9}{10}$ is closer to **5** than to **4**.

$3\frac{2}{5} + 4\frac{9}{10}$

3 + **5** = **8**

Estimate by rounding each mixed number to the nearest whole number.

2. $8\frac{9}{16} - 4\frac{1}{6}$ **9** − **4** = **5**
3. $7\frac{9}{10} + 6\frac{7}{10}$ **8** + **7** = **15**
4. $9\frac{7}{12} - 1\frac{3}{8}$ **10** − **1** = **9**

Grade 5 33 Chapter 10

Skills Practice (p. 34) OL

10-6 Name ________ Date ________

Skills Practice

Estimate Sums and Differences

Round each mixed number to the nearest whole number.

1. $7\frac{3}{4}$ **8**
2. $4\frac{1}{6}$ **4**
3. $8\frac{4}{10}$ **8**
4. $3\frac{4}{5}$ **4**
5. $2\frac{9}{16}$ **3**
6. $9\frac{4}{5}$ **10**
7. $1\frac{7}{8}$ **2**
8. $5\frac{5}{12}$ **5**

Estimate.

9. $3\frac{7}{8} + 2\frac{1}{6}$ **4 + 2 = 6**
10. $8\frac{5}{6} - 3\frac{2}{3}$ **9 − 4 = 5**
11. $5\frac{1}{8} - 1\frac{7}{8}$ **5 − 2 = 3**
12. $9\frac{7}{10} + 3\frac{4}{5}$ **10 + 4 = 14**
13. $6\frac{1}{4} + 7\frac{3}{8}$ **6 + 7 = 13**
14. $14\frac{1}{5} - 9\frac{3}{5}$ **14 − 10 = 4**
15. $18\frac{5}{16} - 9\frac{13}{16}$ **18 − 10 = 8**
16. $6\frac{11}{12} + 4\frac{5}{12}$ **7 + 4 = 11**
17. $7\frac{1}{3} + 7\frac{7}{12}$ **7 + 8 = 15**
18. $15\frac{3}{8} - 7\frac{7}{16}$ **15 − 7 = 8**
19. $9\frac{4}{5} + 6\frac{2}{3}$ **10 + 7 = 17**
20. $6\frac{11}{12} - 6\frac{1}{5}$ **7 − 6 = 1**
21. $8\frac{2}{5} + 8\frac{11}{16}$ **8 + 9 = 17**
22. $17\frac{7}{10} - 9\frac{1}{3}$ **18 − 9 = 9**
23. $7\frac{1}{3} + 9\frac{3}{8}$ **7 + 9 = 16**
24. $30\frac{7}{12} + 30\frac{1}{12}$ **31 + 30 = 61**
25. $58\frac{4}{5} - 29\frac{7}{8}$ **59 − 30 = 29**
26. $50\frac{5}{16} - 30\frac{1}{3}$ **50 − 30 = 20**

Solve.

27. Beth walks $10\frac{7}{8}$ miles in one week. She walks $2\frac{1}{4}$ fewer miles the following week. About how many miles does she walk the second week? **about 9 miles**
28. Jon wants to walk at least 8 miles by the end of the week. He walks $5\frac{3}{4}$ miles by Thursday. If he walks another $2\frac{5}{8}$ miles on Friday, will he meet his goal? Explain. **yes, he walked about 9 miles**

Grade 5 34 Chapter 10

Real-World EXAMPLE

3 SWIMMING The table shows how many hours Alfie swam in two weeks. About how many hours did he swim altogether?

Day	Length (hours)
Week 1	$4\frac{1}{3}$
Week 2	$2\frac{5}{6}$

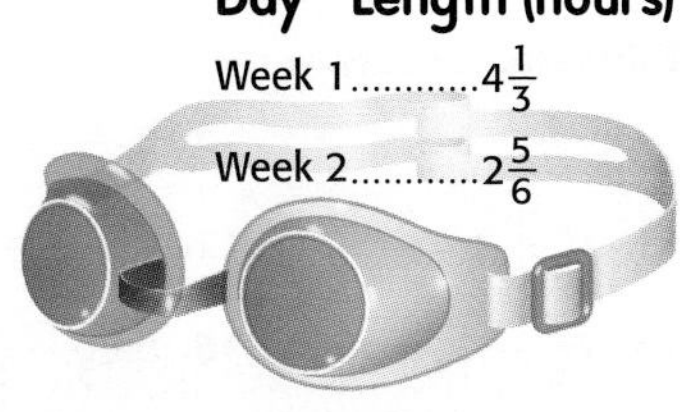

Round each mixed number to the nearest whole number. Then add.

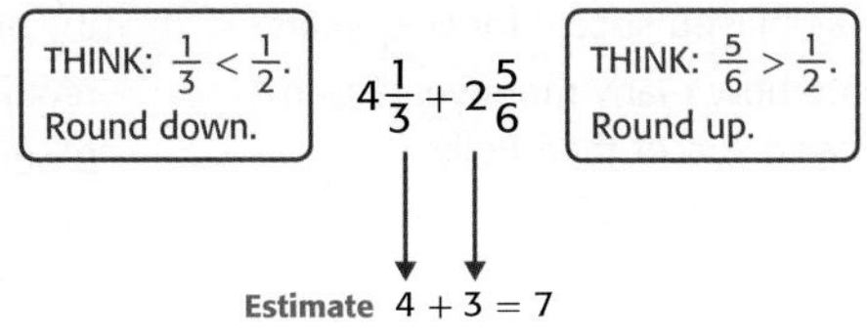

THINK: $\frac{1}{3} < \frac{1}{2}$. Round down. $4\frac{1}{3} + 2\frac{5}{6}$ THINK: $\frac{5}{6} > \frac{1}{2}$. Round up.

Estimate $4 + 3 = 7$

So, Alfie swam for about 7 hours.

Real-World EXAMPLE

4 MEASUREMENT A fish tank can hold $10\frac{2}{5}$ gallons of water. Suppose the tank has $6\frac{1}{10}$ gallons of water. About how much more water is needed to fill the tank?

Round $10\frac{2}{5}$ to 10 and $6\frac{1}{10}$ to 6.

Estimate $10 - 6 = 4$

So, about 4 more gallons are needed to fill the tank.

CHECK What You Know

Estimate by rounding each mixed number to the nearest whole number. See Examples 1–4 (pp. 444–445) **1–5. See Ch. 10 Answer Appendix.**

1. $2\frac{1}{8} + 3\frac{5}{8}$
2. $3\frac{3}{5} + 1\frac{1}{5}$
3. $5\frac{2}{9} - 3\frac{2}{3}$
4. $7\frac{4}{6} - 4\frac{3}{12}$
5. Liam spent $1\frac{3}{4}$ hours playing board games and $2\frac{1}{4}$ hours watching a movie. About how much time did Liam spend on these two activities?
6. Talk About It Write at least two sentences to explain how you would estimate $8\frac{4}{7} - 4\frac{2}{7}$.

Sample answer: Round $8\frac{4}{7}$ up to 9. Round $4\frac{2}{7}$ down to 4. Then subtract. So, 9 − 4 is 5.

Enrich (p. 37) AL

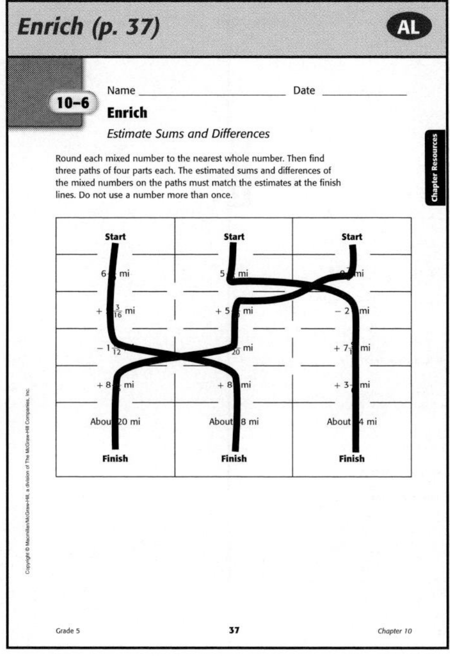
10-6 Name ______ Date ______

Enrich

Estimate Sums and Differences

Round each mixed number to the nearest whole number. Then find three paths of four parts each. The estimated sums and differences of the mixed numbers on the paths must match the estimates at the finish lines. Do not use a number more than once.

Grade 5 37 Chapter 10

Estimate Sums

Example 1 Students may have difficulty comparing the fractional part of each mixed number to $\frac{1}{2}$ to round. Have students write an equivalent fraction for $\frac{1}{2}$ using the denominator of the fractions in the problem.

ADDITIONAL EXAMPLES

1. Estimate $2\frac{4}{6} + 3\frac{1}{6}$. 6
2. Estimate $8\frac{3}{8} - 3\frac{7}{8}$. 4
3. Javier walked $2\frac{3}{5}$ miles on Saturday and $1\frac{7}{10}$ miles on Sunday. About how many miles did he walk in all? about 5 miles
4. A punch recipe calls for $9\frac{2}{3}$ cups of juice. Angie has used $6\frac{2}{6}$ cups of juice in the mixture. About how much more juice does Angie need to finish making the punch? about 4 more cups

CHECK What You Know

As a class, have students complete Exercises 1–6 in **Check What You Know** as you observe their work.

Exercise 6 Assess student comprehension before assigning practice exercises.

BL Alternate Teaching Strategy

If students have trouble rounding mixed numbers to estimate sums and differences…

Then use one of these reteach options:

1. CRM **Daily Reteach Worksheet** (p. 33)
2. Have students use one $\frac{1}{2}$-fraction tile as a benchmark. Have them model the fractional part of a mixed number. They can visually compare the fraction to $\frac{1}{2}$ to decide if a number should be rounded up or down.

COMMON ERROR!

Students may round down too far when rounding mixed numbers. For every mixed number, have students write the two whole numbers it is located between. Remind students that they will round to one of those two numbers.

3 Practice

Differentiate practice using these leveled assignments for Exercises 7–31.

Level	Assignment
BL Below/ Approaching Level	7–11, 13, 19, 21, 23–25, 31
OL On Level	7–15, 17, 19, 21–26, 31
AL Above/Beyond Level	7–25 odd, 27–31

Have students discuss and complete the Higher Order Thinking problems. For Exercises 28–30, have students round each mixed number and estimate the sum or difference, then compare.

MATH Have students complete Exercise 31 in their Math Journals. You may choose to use this exercise as an optional formative assessment.

4 Assess

Formative Assessment

- **How is estimating sums and differences of mixed numbers similar to estimating sums and differences of decimals?** You round each number to the nearest whole number first, then add or subtract the rounded numbers.

Quick Check **Are students continuing to struggle with estimating sums and differences of mixed numbers?**

If Yes → CRM Reteach Worksheet (p. 33)

If No → Independent Work Options (p. 444B)
CRM Skills Practice Worksheet (p. 34)
CRM Enrich Worksheet (p. 37)

Name the Math Write $11\frac{4}{5} - 6\frac{2}{5}$ on the board. Have students explain the steps they would take to estimate the difference.

★ indicates multi-step problem

Practice and Problem Solving

See page R28.

Estimate. See Examples 1–4 (pp. 444–445) 7–20. See Ch. 10 Answer Appendix.

7. $9\frac{1}{7} - 5\frac{6}{7}$ **8.** $6\frac{7}{10} - 1\frac{2}{10}$ **9.** $5\frac{3}{9} + 3\frac{7}{9}$ **10.** $8\frac{11}{12} + 4\frac{4}{12}$

11. $10\frac{2}{7} + 7\frac{5}{7}$ **12.** $12\frac{5}{10} + 9\frac{6}{10}$ **13.** $15\frac{6}{14} - 3\frac{4}{7}$ **14.** $13\frac{4}{11} - 4\frac{1}{4}$

15. $7\frac{7}{9} - \frac{15}{18}$ **16.** $8\frac{9}{15} - \frac{4}{5}$ **17.** $19\frac{3}{7} + \frac{13}{14}$ **18.** $\frac{9}{16} + 16\frac{5}{8}$

19. Polly has played soccer for $3\frac{5}{6}$ years. Gen has played soccer for $6\frac{1}{12}$ years. Estimate how many more years Gen has played soccer than Polly.

★**20.** To clean a large painting, you need $3\frac{1}{4}$ ounces of cleaner. A small painting requires only $2\frac{3}{4}$ ounces. You have 8 ounces of cleaner. About how many ounces of cleaner will you have left if you clean a large and a small painting?

Measurement **For Exercises 21 and 22, use the picture shown.**

★**21.** About how much taller is the birdhouse than the tree house? See Ch. 10 Answer Appendix.

★**22.** Find the height difference between the birdhouse and the tree house. Is it greater than or less than the difference in height between the swing set and the tree house? Use estimation. 1 ft less than

Algebra **Estimate the value of each expression if $n = 2\frac{7}{8}$.**

23. $n + 2\frac{5}{8}$ 6 **24.** $n - \frac{6}{8}$ 2 **25.** $15 - n$ 12 **26.** $n + 18$ 21

H.O.T. Problems

27. OPEN ENDED Select two mixed numbers whose estimated difference is 1. Justify your selection. 27–31. See Ch. 10 Answer Appendix.

CHALLENGE **Without calculating, replace ● with < or > to make a true sentence. Explain your reasoning.**

28. $3\frac{7}{8} + 4\frac{1}{8}$ ● 9 < **29.** $6\frac{7}{9} - 5\frac{3}{9}$ ● 1 > **30.** 3 ● $4\frac{8}{10} - 3\frac{1}{10}$ >

31. WRITING IN MATH Describe a real-world situation where it makes sense to round two numbers up even though one number could be rounded down.

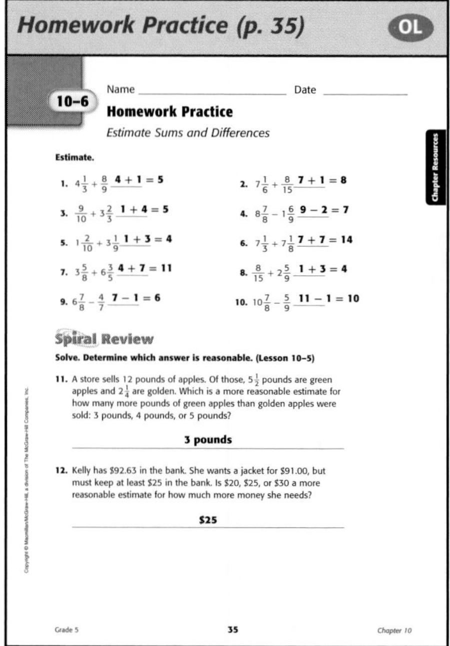

Homework Practice (p. 35) OL

10–6 Name ______ Date ______

Homework Practice

Estimate Sums and Differences

Estimate.

1. $4\frac{1}{3} + \frac{8}{9}$ **4 + 1 = 5**
2. $7\frac{1}{6} + \frac{8}{15}$ **7 + 1 = 8**
3. $\frac{9}{10} + 3\frac{2}{3}$ **1 + 4 = 5**
4. $8\frac{7}{8} - 1\frac{6}{9}$ **9 − 2 = 7**
5. $1\frac{2}{10} + 3\frac{1}{9}$ **1 + 3 = 4**
6. $7\frac{1}{3} + 7\frac{1}{8}$ **7 + 7 = 14**
7. $3\frac{5}{8} + 6\frac{3}{5}$ **4 + 7 = 11**
8. $\frac{8}{15} + 2\frac{5}{9}$ **1 + 3 = 4**
9. $6\frac{7}{8} - \frac{4}{7}$ **7 − 1 = 6**
10. $10\frac{7}{8} - \frac{5}{9}$ **11 − 1 = 10**

Spiral Review

Solve. Determine which answer is reasonable. (Lesson 10–5)

11. A store sells 12 pounds of apples. Of those, $5\frac{1}{2}$ pounds are green apples and $2\frac{1}{4}$ are golden. Which is a more reasonable estimate for how many more pounds of green apples than golden apples were sold: 3 pounds, 4 pounds, or 5 pounds?

3 pounds

12. Kelly has $92.63 in the bank. She wants a jacket for $91.00, but must keep at least $25 in the bank. Is $20, $25, or $30 a more reasonable estimate for how much more money she needs?

$25

Chapter Resources

Grade 5 35 Chapter 10

CHAPTER 10

Mid-Chapter Check

Lessons 10-1 through 10-6

Add. Write each sum in simplest form. (Lesson 10-1)

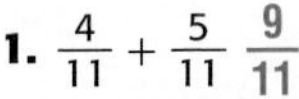

1. $\frac{4}{11} + \frac{5}{11}$ $\frac{9}{11}$ **2.** $\frac{9}{13} + \frac{3}{13}$ $\frac{12}{13}$

3. MULTIPLE CHOICE A family bought two pizzas and ate only part of each pizza. The pictures show how much of the pizzas were left. How much of one whole pizza was left over? (Lesson 10-1) B

A $\frac{7}{8}$ **C** $\frac{1}{5}$

B $\frac{5}{8}$ **D** $\frac{1}{8}$

Subtract. Write each difference in simplest form. (Lesson 10-2)

4. $\frac{6}{7} - \frac{4}{7}$ $\frac{2}{7}$ **5.** $\frac{7}{11} - \frac{6}{11}$ $\frac{1}{11}$

Add. Write in simplest form. (Lesson 10-3)

6. $\frac{2}{3} + \frac{1}{6}$ $\frac{5}{6}$ **7.** $\frac{2}{7} + \frac{1}{2}$ $\frac{11}{14}$

8. Sasha ran $\frac{2}{4}$ mile on Monday and $\frac{5}{12}$ mile on Tuesday. What is the total distance Sasha ran? $\frac{11}{12}$ mi

Subtract. Write in simplest form. (Lesson 10-4)

9. $\frac{6}{7} - \frac{1}{3}$ $\frac{11}{21}$ **10.** $\frac{2}{3} - \frac{1}{2}$ $\frac{1}{6}$

Algebra Find the value of *x* that makes a true sentence. (Lesson 10-4)

11. $\frac{x}{12} - \frac{5}{12} = \frac{1}{12}$ 6 **12.** $\frac{3}{16} + \frac{x}{4} = \frac{7}{16}$ 1

13. An \$156.99 electric scooter has been discounted by \$19.99. Which is a more reasonable estimate for the discounted price: \$130, \$137, or \$140? Explain. (Lesson 10-5) \$137, See Ch. 10 Answer Appendix for explanation.

14. Measurement Mr. Nair bought $3\frac{1}{4}$ pounds of oranges. He bought $\frac{3}{4}$ pound more of bananas than oranges. *About* how many pounds of oranges and bananas did he buy? (Lesson 10-6) 7 lb

Estimate by rounding each mixed number to the nearest whole number. (Lesson 10-6)

15. $11\frac{1}{6} - 2\frac{5}{6}$ 8 **16.** $9\frac{7}{10} + 3\frac{6}{10}$ 14

17. $7\frac{2}{7} + 6\frac{5}{7}$ 14 **18.** $14\frac{3}{16} - 11\frac{9}{16}$ 2

19. MULTIPLE CHOICE Mrs. Orta used $5\frac{3}{4}$ gallons of blue paint and $2\frac{1}{4}$ gallons of yellow paint. About how many gallons of paint did she use? (Lesson 10-6) J

F 2 gal **H** 6 gal

G 4 gal **J** 8 gal

20. WRITING IN MATH Write an addition problem using words for the following model. Then find the sum. (Lesson 10-1) See Ch. 10 Answer Appendix.

CHAPTER 10

Mid-Chapter Check

Lessons 10-1 through 10-6

Formative Assessment

Use the Mid-Chapter Check to assess students' progress in the first half of the chapter.

Customize and create multiple versions of your Mid-Chapter Check and the test answer keys.

FOLDABLES Dinah Zike's Foldables

Use these lesson suggestions to incorporate the Foldables during the chapter.

Lessons 10-1, 10-2 Students use the left column of the Pocket Chart Foldable to list steps and define terms related to adding and subtracting like fractions. Examples of student work on quarter sheets of paper or index cards should be stored in the left, side pocket.

Lessons 10-3, 10-4 Students use the right column of the Pocket Chart Foldable to list steps and define terms related to adding and subtracting unlike fractions. Examples of student work on quarter sheets of paper or index cards should be stored in the left, side pocket.

Data-Driven Decision Making

Based on the results of the Mid-Chapter Check, use the following resources to review concepts that continue to give students problems.

Exercises	State/Local Standards	What's the Math?	Error Analysis	Resources for Review
1–5, 11, 20 Lesson 10-1 Lesson 10-2		Add and subtract fractions with like denominators.	Does not write answers in simplest form or know how to reduce. Adds or subtracts denominators in fractions. Does not understand "sum or difference."	CRM Chapter 10 Resource Masters (Reteach Worksheets) Math Adventures My Math Zone Chapter 10 Math Online Extra Examples • Concepts in Motion
6–10, 12 Lesson 10-3 Lesson 10-4		Add and subtract unlike fractions.	Does not write answers in simplest form. Does not find the least common denominator (LCD).	
13–19 Lesson 10-6		Estimate sums and differences of mixed numbers.	Adds all numbers. Does not understand "discounted," "mixed numbers" or how to compute with them. Adds denominators.	

LESSON

10-7 Add Mixed Numbers

Lesson Planner

Objective

Add mixed numbers.

Review Vocabulary

whole number, fraction

Resources

Manipulatives: clocks, fraction models
Literature Connection: *Fraction Action* by Loreen Leedy
Teacher Technology
Interactive Classroom • TeacherWorks
Alternate Lesson: Use *IMPACT Mathematics*: Unit F to provide practice with adding mixed numbers.

Focus on Math Background

At this point, students understand the relationship between mixed numbers and improper fractions and can write improper fractions as mixed numbers and mixed numbers as improper fractions. They also know how to add and subtract fractions with like denominators. In this lesson, students use these skills as they add mixed numbers with fractions that have like denominators. When adding mixed numbers, regrouping may be necessary. For example:

$$\begin{array}{r} 4\frac{2}{5} \\ +\ 1\frac{4}{5} \\ \hline 5\frac{6}{5} \end{array} = 5 + 1\frac{1}{5} = 6\frac{1}{5}$$

Daily Routine

Use these suggestions before beginning the lesson on p. 448.

5-Minute Check

(Reviews Lesson 10-6)

Estimate.

1. $5\frac{1}{5} - 1\frac{4}{5}$ 3

2. $8\frac{11}{12} - 4\frac{9}{12}$ 4

3. $2\frac{1}{4} + 6\frac{2}{4}$ 9

4. $11\frac{3}{11} + 8\frac{2}{11}$ 19

5. $8\frac{4}{7} - \frac{6}{7}$ 8

6. $\frac{9}{14} + 15\frac{3}{14}$ 16

Problem of the Day

Hilary deposited $40 in a savings account every month for 8 months. For each month of the next 4 months, she deposited $7 more than the previous month. How much did she deposit in the savings account in the 12 months?

$40 × 8 = $320;
$47 × 4 = $188;
$320 + $188 = $508

Review Math Vocabulary

Write the review vocabulary words and their definitions on the board.

Write the mixed number $6\frac{1}{2}$ on the board. Have students identify the whole number and the fraction. Then ask them which two whole numbers the mixed number is between. Have them explain how the fraction tells them which whole number the mixed number will round to.

Differentiated Instruction

Small Group Options

Option 1 Below Level BL

SPATIAL

Materials: paper and pencil

- Hand this problem to students:
- *Mrs. Martinez has 9 cups of flour in a container. She wants to make muffins using $2\frac{1}{4}$ cups of flour, banana bread using $3\frac{1}{4}$ cups of flour and whole wheat bread using $2\frac{3}{4}$ cups of flour. Can she bake all 3 of these recipes with the flour she has or must she go to the store for more?* Find a way to illustrate this problem. She can bake all three recipes and still have $\frac{3}{4}$ cup left over.

Option 2 English Language Learners ELL

VISUAL, LINGUISTIC

Materials: 4 sheets of construction paper for teacher, 10 index cards per group

Core Vocabulary: cut, in all, equation

Common Use Verb: to show

Do Math This strategy helps students visualize adding mixed numbers.

- Hold one sheet of paper. Ask: "How can I ***show*** sixths?" Cut the paper into sixths.
- Ask: "How many sixths do I have?" 6
- Hold up three other sheets. Ask: "How many sixths **in all**?" $\frac{24}{6}$
- Hold up two sheets and 2 sixths. Ask: "What number is this?" $2\frac{2}{6}$ or $\frac{14}{6}$
- Ask: "If I add $1\frac{3}{6}$ to it, how much will I have?" Model. Write: "$2\frac{2}{6} + 1\frac{3}{6} = 3\frac{5}{6}$"
- Say: "Use your cards to show me $2\frac{2}{4} + 1\frac{1}{2}$; then write an **equation** to show your work."

Independent Work Options

Option 1 Early Finishers OL

VISUAL/SPATIAL

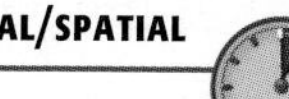

Materials: paper, pencils

- Have students draw pictures to model the addition in Exercises 1–6 on p. 449 of their books.
- Encourage students to draw shapes such as circles or rectangles to show each mixed number addend, then combine the fractions and whole numbers to illustrate the sum.

Option 2 Student Technology

Math Online macmillanmh.com

Personal Tutor • Extra Examples

Math Adventures

Option 3 Learning Station: Art (p. 418I)

Direct students to the Art Learning Station for opportunities to explore and extend the lesson concept.

Option 4 Problem-Solving Practice

Reinforce problem-solving skills and strategies with the Problem-Solving Practice worksheet.

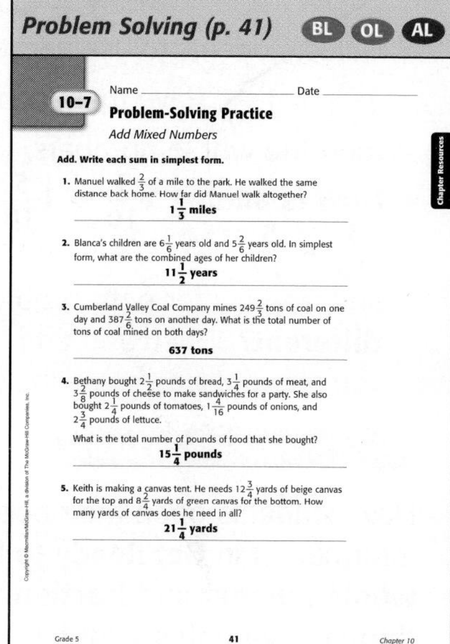

Problem Solving (p. 41) BL OL AL

10–7 Name ______ Date ______

Problem-Solving Practice

Add Mixed Numbers

Chapter Resources

Add. Write each sum in simplest form.

1. Manuel walked $\frac{2}{3}$ of a mile to the park. He walked the same distance back home. How far did Manuel walk altogether?
   $1\frac{1}{3}$ miles
2. Blanca's children are $6\frac{1}{6}$ years old and $5\frac{2}{6}$ years old. In simplest form, what are the combined ages of her children?
   $11\frac{1}{2}$ years
3. Cumberland Valley Coal Company mines $249\frac{2}{3}$ tons of coal on one day and $387\frac{2}{6}$ tons on another day. What is the total number of tons of coal mined on both days?
   637 tons
4. Bethany bought $2\frac{1}{2}$ pounds of bread, $3\frac{1}{4}$ pounds of meat, and $3\frac{2}{8}$ pounds of cheese to make sandwiches for a party. She also bought $2\frac{1}{4}$ pounds of tomatoes, $1\frac{4}{16}$ pounds of onions, and $2\frac{3}{4}$ pounds of lettuce.
   What is the total number of pounds of food that she bought?
   $15\frac{1}{4}$ pounds
5. Keith is making a canvas tent. He needs $12\frac{3}{4}$ yards of beige canvas for the top and $8\frac{2}{4}$ yards of green canvas for the bottom. How many yards of canvas does he need in all?
   $21\frac{1}{4}$ yards

Grade 5 41 Chapter 10

Add Mixed Numbers

1 Introduce

Activity Choice 1 • Hands-On 

- Relate time concepts to fractions and review adding fractions with like denominators.
- Write $\frac{1}{4}$ on the board. **How many minutes are in one quarter of an hour?** 15 minutes Have students model the passing of one quarter hour on a clock.
- Ask students to use their clocks or paper and pencil to solve the following problem:

  Huyana spent one quarter of an hour walking from her house to the bus stop. She spent another quarter of an hour riding the bus to school. What fraction of an hour did Huyana spend traveling? $\frac{1}{2}$ hour
- **How many minutes is that?** 30

Activity Choice 2 • Literature

Introduce the lesson with *Fraction Action* by Loreen Leedy. For a related math activity, see p. TR53.

2 Teach

Scaffolding Questions

Have students use fraction models to show $\frac{3}{10} + \frac{1}{2}$.

- **What is the sum in simplest form?** $\frac{4}{5}$
- **How do you simplify the sum?** Sample answer: Divide the numerator and denominator of the sum, $\frac{8}{10}$, by their greatest common factor, 2.
- Guide students to use fraction models to show $2\frac{3}{10} + 1\frac{5}{10}$. Have them combine the fractions, then the whole numbers, to find the sum.
- **How is adding $2\frac{3}{10} + 1\frac{5}{10}$ like adding $\frac{3}{10} + \frac{5}{10}$?** You combine the fraction models and simplify for both problems. **How is it different?** When you add the mixed numbers, you also must combine the whole number parts.

GET READY to Learn

Have students open their books and read the information in **Get Ready to Learn**. Review **whole number** and **fraction**. As a class, work through **Examples 1 and 2.**

10-7 Add Mixed Numbers

MAIN IDEA

I will add mixed numbers.

Math Online

macmillanmh.com
- Extra Examples
- Personal Tutor
- Self-Check Quiz

GET READY to Learn

One day Emma gathered $2\frac{1}{4}$ dozen eggs. The next day, she gathered $1\frac{1}{4}$ dozen eggs. How many dozen eggs did she gather in all?

You can find an exact answer by adding the mixed numbers.

Real-World EXAMPLE Add Mixed Numbers

1 FOOD Refer to the information above. How many dozen eggs did Emma gather?

Find $2\frac{1}{4} + 1\frac{1}{4}$. Estimate $2 + 1 = 3$

Step 1 Add the fractions.

$$\begin{array}{r} 2\frac{1}{4} \\ +\ 1\frac{1}{4} \\ \hline \frac{2}{4} \end{array} \qquad \frac{1}{4} + \frac{1}{4} = \frac{2}{4}$$

Step 2 Add the whole numbers.

$$\begin{array}{r} 2\frac{1}{4} \\ +\ 1\frac{1}{4} \\ \hline 3\frac{2}{4} \end{array}$$

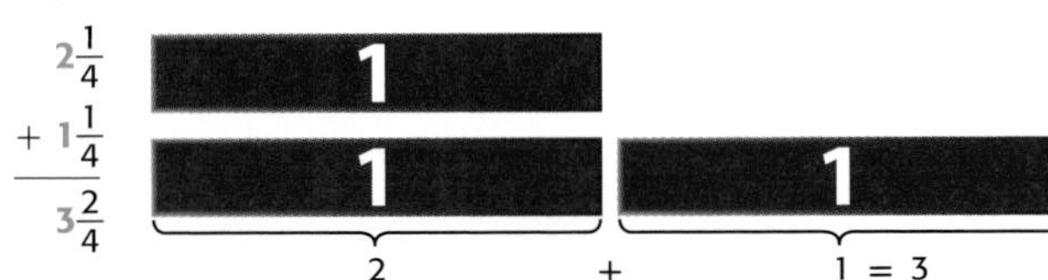

Step 3 Simplify.

$3\frac{2}{4} = 3\frac{1}{2}$ Divide the numerator and denominator by the GCF, 2.

Check for Reasonableness $3\frac{1}{2} \approx 3$ ✓

So, Emma gathered $3\frac{1}{2}$ dozen eggs.

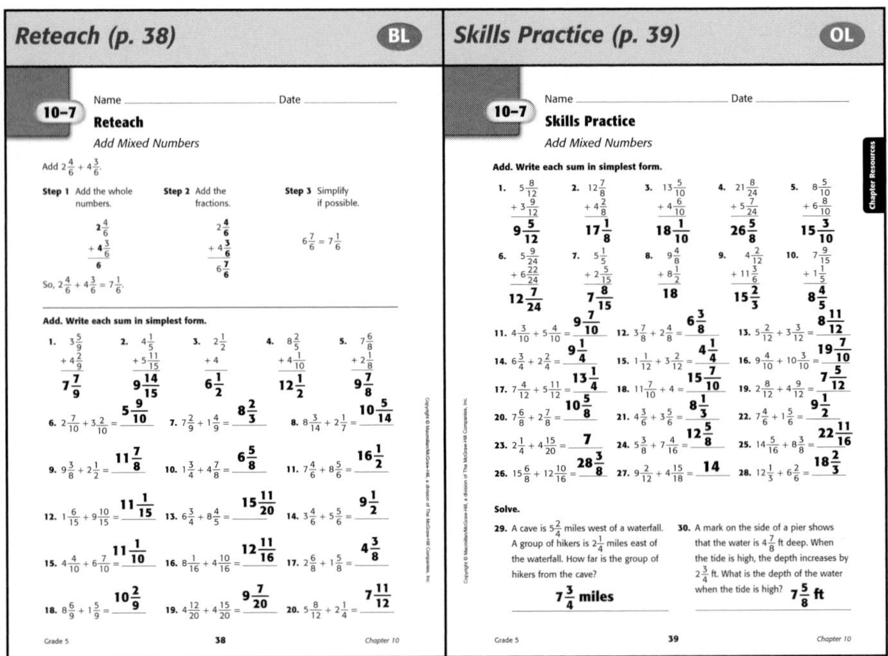

Reteach (p. 38) BL

10-7 Name ______ Date ______

Reteach

Add Mixed Numbers

Add $2\frac{4}{6} + 4\frac{3}{6}$.

Step 1 Add the whole numbers. $2\frac{4}{6} + 4\frac{3}{6}$: 6

Step 2 Add the fractions. $2\frac{4}{6} + 4\frac{3}{6} = 6\frac{7}{6}$

Step 3 Simplify if possible. $6\frac{7}{6} = 7\frac{1}{6}$

So, $2\frac{4}{6} + 4\frac{3}{6} = 7\frac{1}{6}$.

Add. Write each sum in simplest form.

1. $3\frac{5}{9} + 4\frac{2}{9}$ **$7\frac{7}{9}$**
2. $4\frac{1}{5} + 5\frac{11}{15}$ **$9\frac{14}{15}$**
3. $2\frac{1}{2} + 4$ **$6\frac{1}{2}$**
4. $8\frac{2}{5} + 4\frac{1}{10}$ **$12\frac{1}{2}$**
5. $7\frac{6}{8} + 2\frac{1}{8}$ **$9\frac{7}{8}$**
6. $2\frac{7}{10} + 3\frac{2}{10} =$ **$5\frac{9}{10}$**
7. $7\frac{2}{9} + 1\frac{4}{9} =$ **$8\frac{2}{3}$**
8. $8\frac{3}{14} + 2\frac{1}{7} =$ **$10\frac{5}{14}$**
9. $9\frac{3}{8} + 2\frac{1}{2} =$ **$11\frac{7}{8}$**
10. $1\frac{3}{4} + 4\frac{7}{8} =$ **$6\frac{5}{8}$**
11. $7\frac{4}{6} + 8\frac{5}{6} =$ **$16\frac{1}{2}$**
12. $1\frac{6}{15} + 9\frac{10}{15} =$ **$11\frac{1}{15}$**
13. $6\frac{3}{4} + 8\frac{4}{5} =$ **$15\frac{11}{20}$**
14. $3\frac{4}{6} + 5\frac{5}{6} =$ **$9\frac{1}{2}$**
15. $4\frac{4}{10} + 6\frac{7}{10} =$ **$11\frac{1}{10}$**
16. $8\frac{1}{16} + 4\frac{10}{16} =$ **$12\frac{11}{16}$**
17. $2\frac{6}{8} + 1\frac{5}{8} =$ **$4\frac{3}{8}$**
18. $8\frac{6}{9} + 1\frac{5}{9} =$ **$10\frac{2}{9}$**
19. $4\frac{12}{20} + 4\frac{15}{20} =$ **$9\frac{7}{20}$**
20. $5\frac{8}{12} + 2\frac{1}{4} =$ **$7\frac{11}{12}$**

Grade 5 38 Chapter 10

Skills Practice (p. 39) OL

10-7 Name ______ Date ______

Skills Practice

Add Mixed Numbers

Add. Write each sum in simplest form.

1. $5\frac{8}{12} + 3\frac{9}{12}$ **$9\frac{5}{12}$**
2. $12\frac{7}{8} + 4\frac{2}{8}$ **$17\frac{1}{8}$**
3. $13\frac{5}{10} + 4\frac{6}{10}$ **$18\frac{1}{10}$**
4. $21\frac{8}{24} + 5\frac{7}{24}$ **$26\frac{5}{8}$**
5. $8\frac{5}{10} + 6\frac{8}{10}$ **$15\frac{3}{10}$**
6. $5\frac{9}{24} + 6\frac{22}{24}$ **$12\frac{7}{24}$**
7. $5\frac{1}{5} + 2\frac{5}{15}$ **$7\frac{8}{15}$**
8. $9\frac{4}{8} + 8\frac{1}{2}$ **18**
9. $4\frac{2}{12} + 11\frac{3}{6}$ **$15\frac{2}{3}$**
10. $7\frac{9}{15} + 1\frac{1}{5}$ **$8\frac{4}{5}$**
11. $4\frac{3}{10} + 5\frac{4}{10} =$ **$9\frac{7}{10}$**
12. $3\frac{7}{8} + 2\frac{4}{8} =$ **$6\frac{3}{8}$**
13. $5\frac{2}{12} + 3\frac{3}{12} =$ **$8\frac{11}{12}$**
14. $6\frac{3}{4} + 2\frac{2}{4} =$ **$9\frac{1}{4}$**
15. $1\frac{1}{12} + 3\frac{2}{12} =$ **$4\frac{1}{4}$**
16. $9\frac{4}{10} + 10\frac{3}{10} =$ **$19\frac{7}{10}$**
17. $7\frac{4}{12} + 5\frac{11}{12} =$ **$13\frac{1}{4}$**
18. $11\frac{7}{10} + 4 =$ **$15\frac{7}{10}$**
19. $2\frac{8}{12} + 4\frac{9}{12} =$ **$7\frac{5}{12}$**
20. $7\frac{6}{8} + 2\frac{7}{8} =$ **$10\frac{5}{8}$**
21. $4\frac{3}{6} + 3\frac{5}{6} =$ **$8\frac{1}{3}$**
22. $7\frac{4}{6} + 1\frac{5}{6} =$ **$9\frac{1}{2}$**
23. $2\frac{1}{4} + 4\frac{15}{20} =$ **7**
24. $5\frac{3}{8} + 7\frac{4}{16} =$ **$12\frac{5}{8}$**
25. $14\frac{5}{16} + 8\frac{3}{8} =$ **$22\frac{11}{16}$**
26. $15\frac{6}{8} + 12\frac{10}{16} =$ **$28\frac{3}{8}$**
27. $9\frac{2}{12} + 4\frac{15}{18} =$ **14**
28. $12\frac{1}{3} + 6\frac{2}{6} =$ **$18\frac{2}{3}$**

Solve.

29. A cave is $5\frac{2}{4}$ miles west of a waterfall. A group of hikers is $2\frac{1}{4}$ miles east of the waterfall. How far is the group of hikers from the cave? **$7\frac{3}{4}$ miles**
30. A mark on the side of a pier shows that the water is $4\frac{7}{8}$ ft deep. When the tide is high, the depth increases by $2\frac{3}{4}$ ft. What is the depth of the water when the tide is high? **$7\frac{5}{8}$ ft**

Grade 5 39 Chapter 10

Chapter Resources

2 **REPTILES The diagram shows the length of a sea turtle. What is the total length of the sea turtle?**

Remember

Estimate first. Then compare your answer with the estimate.

Find $\frac{7}{8} + 3\frac{1}{4} + 1\frac{1}{8}$.

Step 1 Write the problem.

$$\frac{7}{8} \quad 3\frac{1}{4} \quad +1\frac{1}{8}$$

Step 2 Rename the fractions using the LCD.

$$\frac{7}{8} = \frac{7}{8} \quad 3\frac{1 \times 2}{4 \times 2} = 3\frac{2}{8} \quad +1\frac{1}{8} = 1\frac{1}{8}$$

Step 3 Add the fractions and whole numbers.

$$\frac{7}{8} \quad 3\frac{2}{8} \quad +1\frac{1}{8} \quad 4\frac{10}{8}$$

Step 4 Simplify.

$4\frac{10}{8} = 4 + 1\frac{2}{8} = 5\frac{2}{8} = 5\frac{1}{4}$

The total length of the sea turtle is $5\frac{1}{4}$ feet.

Add Mixed Numbers — Key Concepts

- Rename the fraction using the LCD.
- Add the fractions and then the whole numbers.
- Simplify if needed.

★ indicates multi-step problem

CHECK What You Know

Add. Write each sum in simplest form. See Examples 1, 2 (pp. 448–449)

1. $3\frac{3}{8} + 2\frac{4}{8}$ $5\frac{7}{8}$
2. $4\frac{4}{6} + 2\frac{1}{6}$ $6\frac{5}{6}$
3. $5\frac{1}{10} + 5\frac{3}{10}$ $10\frac{2}{5}$
4. $3\frac{4}{9} + 4\frac{2}{3}$ $8\frac{1}{9}$
5. $6\frac{3}{4} + 3\frac{1}{8}$ $9\frac{7}{8}$
6. $4\frac{3}{7} + 7\frac{1}{2}$ $11\frac{13}{14}$
7. Yushua worked $5\frac{1}{2}$ hours on Monday, $7\frac{1}{2}$ hours on Tuesday, and $6\frac{1}{2}$ hours on Wednesday. How many hours did he work in all? $19\frac{1}{2}$ h
8. Talk About It — Explain how to simplify $3\frac{6}{4}$. See margin.

Additional Answer

8. Sample answer: Change $\frac{6}{4}$ to a mixed number by dividing the numerator, 6, by the denominator, 4. Write the remainder of 2 as a fraction with the divisor as the denominator. Then add the mixed number $1\frac{2}{4}$ to 3 or $4\frac{2}{4}$. Then simplify $\frac{2}{4}$ by dividing the numerator and denominator by the GCF, 2. So, $3\frac{6}{4}$ simplified is $4\frac{1}{2}$.

Real-World Example

Example 2 Go over the steps for solving the problem carefully with students, paying particular attention to Step 4. Point out that the fraction part of the answer is an improper fraction that must be converted to a mixed number to solve. Make sure students understand that they must add the whole number part of the new mixed number to the whole number part of the sum and write the new sum in simplest form.

ADDITIONAL EXAMPLES

1. A pizzeria divides their pizzas into tenths. At the end of one day, the pizzeria had $1\frac{3}{10}$ cheese pizzas and $3\frac{1}{10}$ pepperoni pizzas left. How many pizzas were left in all? $4\frac{2}{5}$
2. Adia tied three pieces of ribbon together to decorate a tree in her yard. She tied $2\frac{2}{3}$ feet of yellow ribbon, $1\frac{2}{6}$ feet of blue ribbon, and $\frac{2}{3}$ feet of red ribbon together. How much ribbon did she use in all? $4\frac{2}{3}$ feet

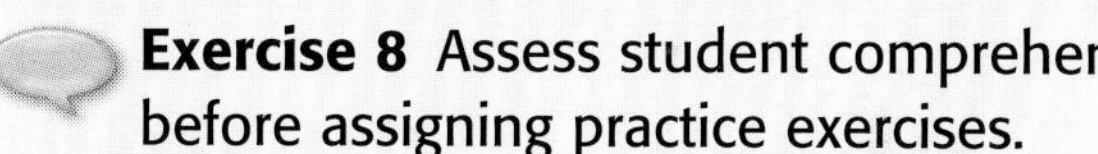

As a class, have students complete Exercises 1–8 in **Check What You Know** as you observe their work.

Exercise 8 Assess student comprehension before assigning practice exercises.

BL Alternate Teaching Strategy

If students have trouble adding mixed numbers using paper and pencil…

Then use one of these reteach options:

1. CRM **Daily Reteach Worksheet** (p. 38)
2. Have students model each mixed number addend with fraction circles. Have them combine the fraction pieces first, then the whole circles to add. When necessary, have them trade fraction pieces for whole circles to rename improper fractions. Then have them count wholes and fraction pieces to find the sum.

3 Practice

Differentiate practice using these leveled assignments for Exercises 9–25.

Level	Assignment
BL Below/ Approaching Level	9–12, 17–19
OL On Level	10–15, 17–21, 24
AL Above/Beyond Level	10–22 even, 23–25

Have students discuss and complete the Higher Order Thinking problems. For Exercise 24, suggest that students first solve the addition problem themselves. They can use their answer to help them choose the correct answer and explain why the other answer is incorrect.

WRITING IN ▸MATH Have students complete Exercise 25 in their Math Journals. You may choose to use this as an optional formative assessment.

Additional Answers

19. $3\frac{1}{2}$ quarts;

1	1

$\frac{1}{8}$ $\frac{1}{8}$ $\frac{1}{8}$ $\frac{1}{8}$ $\frac{1}{8}$ $\frac{1}{8}$ $\frac{1}{8}$ $\frac{1}{8}$ $\frac{1}{8}$ $\frac{1}{8}$ $\frac{1}{8}$ $\frac{1}{8}$

$\frac{5}{8}$ + $\frac{7}{8}$ = $3\frac{1}{2}$

22. Sample answer: yes; he carried $10\frac{5}{8}$ gallons after 3 trips. So, 5 more gallons would fill the pool.

23. Sample answer: A painter uses $2\frac{3}{4}$ gallons of white paint and $2\frac{2}{4}$ gallons of tan paint to paint a house. How many gallons of paint did the painter use altogether?; $5\frac{1}{4}$ gallons of paint

24. Urbano: Brandy added the denominators.

25. sometimes; $1\frac{1}{2} + 1\frac{1}{2} = 3$; $1\frac{1}{4} + 1\frac{1}{4} = 2\frac{1}{2}$

! COMMON ERROR!

Exercises 13–17 and 19–22 When the fraction part of the sum is an improper fraction, students may forget to rename the improper fraction and add the additional whole number to the sum. Have students check their sums to see if the numerator is greater than or equal to the denominator. If it is, they must rename it as a mixed number and then simplify.

Practice and Problem Solving

Add. Write each sum in simplest form. See Examples 1, 2 (pp. 448–449)

9. $4\frac{3}{5} + 3\frac{1}{5}$ $7\frac{4}{5}$ **10.** $7\frac{4}{11} + 2\frac{6}{11}$ $9\frac{10}{11}$ **11.** $5\frac{1}{12} + 6\frac{3}{12}$ $11\frac{1}{3}$ **12.** $8\frac{4}{15} + 3\frac{2}{15}$ $11\frac{2}{5}$

13. $6\frac{1}{9} + 2\frac{1}{3}$ $8\frac{4}{9}$ **14.** $5\frac{3}{9} + 6\frac{1}{2}$ $11\frac{5}{6}$ **15.** $9\frac{9}{10} + 7\frac{3}{5}$ $17\frac{1}{2}$ **16.** $14\frac{19}{20} + 8\frac{1}{4}$ $23\frac{1}{5}$

17. Find *five and two eighths plus three and six eighths*. Write in words. nine

18. Find *ten and three sevenths plus eighteen and two sevenths*. Write in words. twenty-eight and five sevenths

19. Measurement Zita made $1\frac{5}{8}$ quarts of punch. Then she made $1\frac{7}{8}$ more quarts. How much punch did she make in all? See margin.

20. A flower is $9\frac{3}{4}$ inches tall. In one week, it grew $1\frac{1}{8}$ inches. How tall is the flower at the end of the week? $10\frac{7}{8}$ in.

21. Pati made fruit salad using the recipe. How many cups of fruit are needed? $8\frac{3}{4}$ c

Recipe for Fruit Salad
$3\frac{2}{4}$ c Apple
$1\frac{1}{4}$ c Grapefruit
$1\frac{3}{4}$ c Orange
$2\frac{1}{4}$ c Pear

★22. Measurement Connor is filling a 15-gallon wading pool. On his first trip, he carried $3\frac{1}{12}$ gallons of water. He carried $3\frac{5}{6}$ gallons on his second trip and $3\frac{1}{2}$ gallons on his third trip. Suppose he carries 5 gallons on his next trip. Will the pool be filled? Explain. See margin.

H.O.T. Problems

23. OPEN ENDED Write a real-world problem involving the addition of two mixed numbers whose sum is $5\frac{1}{4}$. Then solve the problem.

24. FIND THE ERROR Urbano and Brandy are finding $4\frac{1}{5} + 2\frac{3}{5}$. Who is correct? Explain your reasoning. 23–25. See margin.

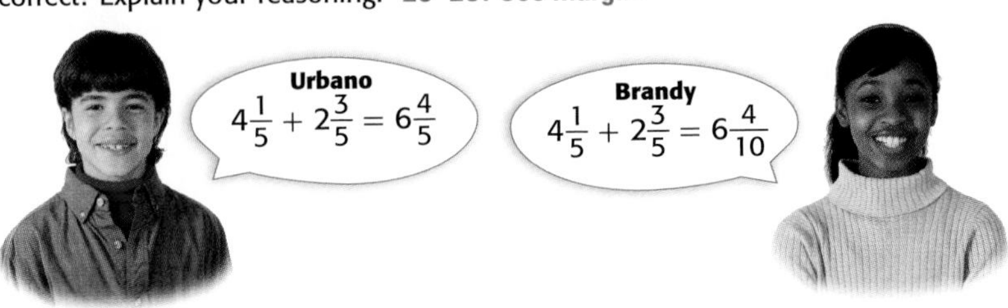

Urbano
$4\frac{1}{5} + 2\frac{3}{5} = 6\frac{4}{5}$
Brandy
$4\frac{1}{5} + 2\frac{3}{5} = 6\frac{4}{10}$

25. **WRITING IN ▸MATH** Is the sum of two mixed numbers *always*, *sometimes*, or *never* a mixed number? Use an example to explain.

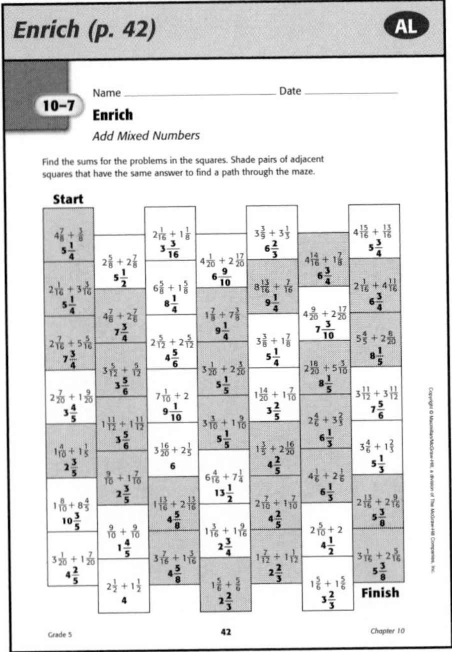

Enrich (p. 42) AL

10-7 Name ________ Date ________

Enrich

Add Mixed Numbers

Find the sums for the problems in the squares. Shade pairs of adjacent squares that have the same answer to find a path through the maze.

Start

$4\frac{7}{8} + \frac{3}{8}$ $5\frac{1}{4}$; $2\frac{1}{16} + 3\frac{3}{16}$ $5\frac{1}{4}$; $2\frac{7}{16} + 5\frac{5}{16}$ $7\frac{3}{4}$; $2\frac{7}{20} + 1\frac{9}{20}$ $3\frac{4}{5}$; $1\frac{4}{10} + 1\frac{1}{5}$ $2\frac{3}{5}$; $1\frac{8}{10} + 8\frac{4}{5}$ $10\frac{3}{5}$; $3\frac{1}{20} + 1\frac{7}{20}$ $4\frac{2}{5}$

$2\frac{5}{8} + 2\frac{7}{8}$ $5\frac{1}{2}$; $4\frac{7}{8} + 2\frac{7}{8}$ $7\frac{3}{4}$; $3\frac{5}{12} + \frac{5}{12}$ $3\frac{5}{6}$; $1\frac{11}{12} + 1\frac{11}{12}$ $3\frac{5}{6}$; $\frac{9}{10} + 1\frac{7}{10}$ $2\frac{3}{5}$; $\frac{9}{10} + \frac{9}{10}$ $1\frac{4}{5}$; $2\frac{1}{2} + 1\frac{1}{2}$ 4

$2\frac{1}{16} + 1\frac{1}{8}$ $3\frac{3}{16}$; $6\frac{5}{8} + 1\frac{5}{8}$ $8\frac{1}{4}$; $2\frac{5}{12} + 2\frac{5}{12}$ $4\frac{5}{6}$; $7\frac{1}{10} + 2$ $9\frac{1}{10}$; $3\frac{16}{20} + 2\frac{1}{5}$ 6; $1\frac{13}{16} + 2\frac{13}{16}$ $4\frac{5}{8}$; $3\frac{7}{16} + 1\frac{3}{16}$ $4\frac{5}{8}$

$4\frac{1}{20} + 2\frac{17}{20}$ $6\frac{9}{10}$; $1\frac{7}{8} + 7\frac{3}{8}$ $9\frac{1}{4}$; $3\frac{1}{20} + 2\frac{3}{20}$ $5\frac{1}{5}$; $3\frac{3}{10} + 1\frac{9}{10}$ $5\frac{1}{5}$; $6\frac{4}{16} + 7\frac{1}{4}$ $13\frac{1}{2}$; $1\frac{3}{16} + 1\frac{9}{16}$ $2\frac{3}{4}$; $1\frac{5}{6} + \frac{5}{6}$ $2\frac{2}{3}$

$3\frac{3}{9} + 3\frac{1}{3}$ $6\frac{2}{3}$; $8\frac{13}{16} + \frac{7}{16}$ $9\frac{1}{4}$; $3\frac{3}{8} + 1\frac{7}{8}$ $5\frac{1}{4}$; $1\frac{14}{20} + 1\frac{7}{10}$ $3\frac{2}{5}$; $1\frac{3}{5} + 2\frac{16}{20}$ $4\frac{2}{5}$; $2\frac{7}{10} + 1\frac{7}{10}$ $4\frac{2}{5}$; $1\frac{7}{12} + 1\frac{1}{12}$ $2\frac{2}{3}$

$4\frac{14}{16} + 1\frac{7}{8}$ $6\frac{3}{4}$; $4\frac{9}{20} + 2\frac{17}{20}$ $7\frac{3}{10}$; $2\frac{18}{20} + 5\frac{3}{10}$ $8\frac{1}{5}$; $2\frac{4}{6} + 3\frac{2}{3}$ $6\frac{1}{3}$; $4\frac{1}{6} + 2\frac{1}{6}$ $6\frac{1}{3}$; $2\frac{5}{10} + 2$ $4\frac{1}{2}$; $1\frac{5}{6} + 1\frac{5}{6}$ $3\frac{2}{3}$

$4\frac{15}{16} + \frac{13}{16}$ $5\frac{3}{4}$; $2\frac{1}{16} + 4\frac{11}{16}$ $6\frac{3}{4}$; $5\frac{4}{5} + 2\frac{8}{20}$ $8\frac{1}{5}$; $3\frac{11}{12} + 3\frac{11}{12}$ $7\frac{5}{6}$; $3\frac{4}{6} + 1\frac{2}{3}$ $5\frac{1}{3}$; $2\frac{13}{16} + 2\frac{9}{16}$ $5\frac{3}{8}$; $3\frac{1}{16} + 2\frac{5}{16}$ $5\frac{3}{8}$

Finish

Grade 5 42 Chapter 10

Practice

26. Marie bought $4\frac{1}{2}$ pints of ice cream for her birthday party. Her mother also bought $2\frac{1}{4}$ pints of ice cream for the party. How many pints of ice cream did Marie have for her birthday party? **(Lesson 10-5)** D

A $2\frac{1}{4}$ pt

B $2\frac{3}{4}$ pt

C $6\frac{3}{8}$ pt

D $6\frac{3}{4}$ pt

27. The length and the width of Samson's swimming pool is shown.

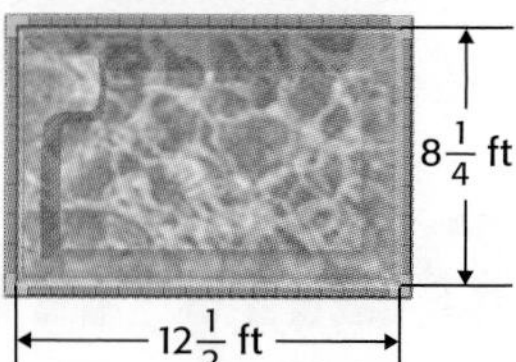

About how much longer is the length of the pool than the width of the pool? **(Lesson 10-4)** G

F 3 ft **H** 20 ft

G 5 ft **J** 21 ft

Spiral Review

28. Nestor and Tanya rode two different rides at the fair. Nestor rode the Roller Express. The ride lasted about $1\frac{1}{3}$ minutes. Tanya rode the Rattler, which lasted about $2\frac{2}{3}$ minutes. About how much longer did the Rattler last than the Roller Express? **(Lesson 10-6)** about 2 min

29. Measurement The distance around Saturn is 235,298 miles. The distance around Jupiter is 279,118 miles. Is 45,000 miles or 55,000 miles a more reasonable estimate for the difference between the distance around Jupiter and the distance around Saturn? Explain. **(Lesson 10-5)** 45,000 mi; Round 279,118 to 279,000 and 235,298 to 235,000. 279,000 − 235,000 = 44,000

Write each decimal as a fraction in simplest form. (Lesson 9-5)

30. 0.8 $\frac{4}{5}$ **31.** 0.9 $\frac{9}{10}$ **32.** 0.29 $\frac{29}{100}$ **33.** 0.11 $\frac{11}{100}$

Write each mixed number as an improper fraction. (Lesson 8-4)

34. $3\frac{5}{6}$ $\frac{23}{6}$ **35.** $6\frac{1}{4}$ $\frac{25}{4}$ **36.** $4\frac{1}{3}$ $\frac{13}{3}$ **37.** $5\frac{2}{5}$ $\frac{27}{5}$

38. Ginny's basketball team scored 44 points in one game. If Ginny scored 16 points, how many points did the rest of team score? Write and solve an addition equation. **(Lesson 6-2)** $16 + x = 44$; 28

Divide. (Lesson 4-3)

39. 48 ÷ 5 9 R3 **40.** 48 ÷ 3 16 **41.** 172 ÷ 4 43 **42.** 264 ÷ 6 44

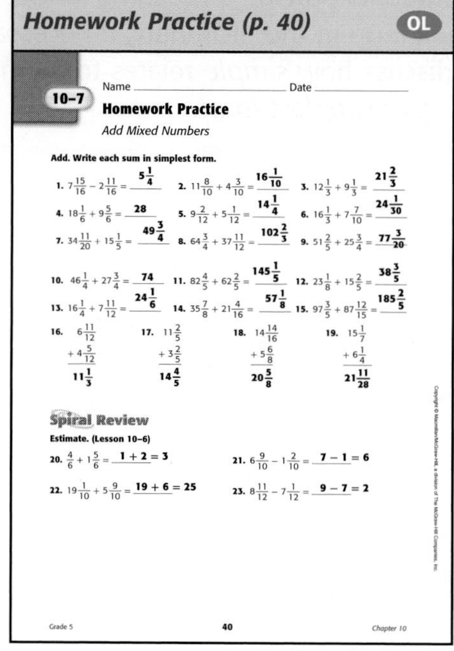

Homework Practice (p. 40) OL

10-7 Name ________ Date ________

Homework Practice

Add Mixed Numbers

Add. Write each sum in simplest form.

1. $7\frac{15}{16} - 2\frac{11}{16} =$ **$5\frac{1}{4}$**
2. $11\frac{8}{10} + 4\frac{3}{10} =$ **$16\frac{1}{10}$**
3. $12\frac{1}{3} + 9\frac{1}{3} =$ **$21\frac{2}{3}$**
4. $18\frac{1}{6} + 9\frac{5}{6} =$ **28**
5. $9\frac{2}{12} + 5\frac{1}{12} =$ **$14\frac{1}{4}$**
6. $16\frac{1}{3} + 7\frac{7}{10} =$ **$24\frac{1}{30}$**
7. $34\frac{11}{20} + 15\frac{1}{5} =$ **$49\frac{3}{4}$**
8. $64\frac{3}{4} + 37\frac{11}{12} =$ **$102\frac{2}{3}$**
9. $51\frac{2}{5} + 25\frac{3}{4} =$ **$77\frac{3}{20}$**
10. $46\frac{1}{4} + 27\frac{3}{4} =$ **74**
11. $82\frac{4}{5} + 62\frac{2}{5} =$ **$145\frac{1}{5}$**
12. $23\frac{1}{8} + 15\frac{2}{5} =$ **$38\frac{3}{5}$**
13. $16\frac{1}{4} + 7\frac{11}{12} =$ **$24\frac{1}{6}$**
14. $35\frac{7}{8} + 21\frac{4}{16} =$ **$57\frac{1}{8}$**
15. $97\frac{3}{5} + 87\frac{12}{15} =$ **$185\frac{2}{5}$**
16. $6\frac{11}{12} + 4\frac{5}{12}$ = **$11\frac{1}{3}$**
17. $11\frac{2}{5} + 3\frac{2}{5}$ = **$14\frac{4}{5}$**
18. $14\frac{14}{16} + 5\frac{6}{8}$ = **$20\frac{5}{8}$**
19. $15\frac{1}{7} + 6\frac{1}{4}$ = **$21\frac{11}{28}$**

Spiral Review

Estimate. (Lesson 10-6)

20. $\frac{4}{6} + 1\frac{5}{6} =$ **1 + 2 = 3**
21. $6\frac{9}{10} - 1\frac{2}{10} =$ **7 − 1 = 6**
22. $19\frac{1}{10} + 5\frac{9}{10} =$ **19 + 6 = 25**
23. $8\frac{11}{12} - 7\frac{1}{12} =$ **9 − 7 = 2**

Grade 5 40 Chapter 10

4 Assess

Formative Assessment

- **If the sum of two mixed numbers is $5\frac{11}{9}$, is there another step needed to solve the problem? Explain.** Yes; since $\frac{11}{9}$ is an improper fraction, it needs to be renamed as a mixed number, $1\frac{2}{9}$, and then simplified: $5 + 1\frac{2}{9} = 6\frac{2}{9}$.

Quick Check **Are students continuing to struggle with adding mixed numbers?**

If Yes → Small Group Options (p. 448B)

If No → Independent Work Options (p. 448B)
CRM Skills Practice Worksheet (p. 39)
CRM Enrich Worksheet (p. 42)

Ticket Out the Door Write $10\frac{4}{5} + 2\frac{3}{5}$ on the board. Have students find the sum and write it on a slip of paper to give to you as they leave class for the day.

Practice

Reviews Lessons 10-6 and 10-7

Assign the Test Practice problems to provide daily reinforcement of test-taking skills.

Spiral Review

Reviews Lessons 4-3, 6-2, 8-4, 9-5, 10-5, and 10-6

Review and assess mastery of skills and concepts from previous chapters.

LESSON 10-8

Subtract Mixed Numbers

Lesson Planner

Objective

Subtract mixed numbers.

Review Vocabulary

simplest form

Resources

Manipulatives: play money, fraction models
Literature Connection: *The Missing Piece* by Shel Silverstein
Teacher Technology
Interactive Classroom • TeacherWorks
Alternate Lesson: Use *IMPACT Mathematics*: Unit F to provide practice with subtracting mixed numbers.

Focus on Math Background

In this lesson, the skills learned in Lesson 10-5 are extended to subtraction, that is, rather than adding the mixed number the mixed numbers are subtracted. Note that subtraction of mixed numbers that require regrouping is not introduced until the next lesson.

In summary, to add or subtract mixed numbers:

- the fractions are added or subtracted,
- the whole numbers are added or subtracted,
- the two parts are added together to show the sum or difference,
- the result is simplified if necessary.

Daily Routine

Use these suggestions before beginning the lesson on p. 452.

5-Minute Check

(Reviews Lesson 10-7)

Add. Write each sum in simplest form.

1. $3\frac{1}{7} + 2\frac{4}{7}$ $5\frac{5}{7}$

2. $4\frac{1}{4} + 5\frac{4}{8}$ $9\frac{3}{4}$

3. $1\frac{5}{9} + 8\frac{1}{9}$ $9\frac{2}{3}$

4. $6\frac{2}{8} + 5\frac{3}{4}$ 12

5. $10\frac{3}{5} + 4\frac{4}{5}$ $15\frac{2}{5}$

6. $15\frac{11}{12} + 8\frac{1}{3}$ $24\frac{1}{4}$

Problem of the Day

One small box holds 8 books. There are 254 books. How many boxes are needed to store all of the books? How many books will be in the last box? 32; 6 books

Building Math Vocabulary

Write the review vocabulary word and its definition on the board.

Have students provide a meaning for the term *simple* and look it up in the dictionary, if necessary. Then have them discuss how *simple* relates to the mathematical meaning of *simplest form*.

Differentiated Instruction

Small Group Options

Option 1 Below Level BL

LOGICAL

Materials: fraction circles, paper and pencil

- Present this problem to students:

  Alejandro and Kyle want to paint the decks on their houses. Alejandro says he needs $2\frac{7}{8}$ gallons of paint for his deck. Kyle says his deck will need $2\frac{1}{8}$ gallons of paint. How much more paint does Alejandro need than Kyle needs for the job? Jim needs $\frac{6}{8}$ or $\frac{3}{4}$ more gallons of paint.

Option 2 English Language Learners ELL

AUDITORY, LOGICAL

Materials: play money (dollars, dimes), paper, pencil
Core Vocabulary: dimes, change, predict
Common Use Verb: compare

Hear Math This strategy connects background knowledge about money, decimals and fractions to help students subtract mixed numbers. Write \$9.70 – \$3.40. Students use manipulatives to show their answer \$6.30

- Write: "$9\frac{7}{10} - 3\frac{4}{10} = ?$" Ask students how this problem is like the first one. Ask them to predict the answer. $6\frac{3}{10}$
- Have students write numbers as mixed numbers and subtract. Compare both answers. When answers are read out loud they will sound the same.

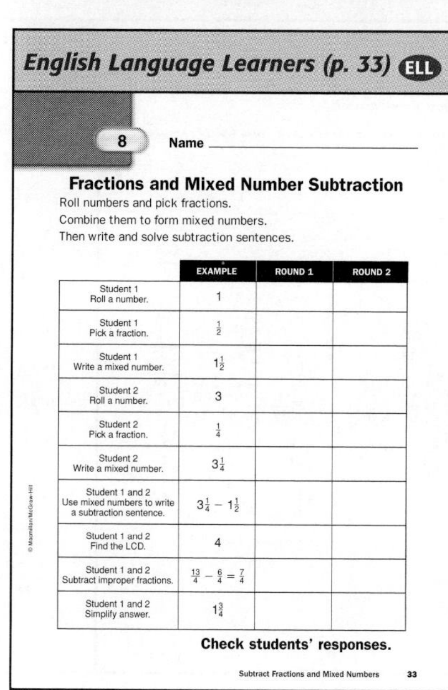

English Language Learners (p. 33) ELL

8 Name ____________

Fractions and Mixed Number Subtraction

Roll numbers and pick fractions.
Combine them to form mixed numbers.
Then write and solve subtraction sentences.

	EXAMPLE	ROUND 1	ROUND 2
Student 1 Roll a number.	1		
Student 1 Pick a fraction.	$\frac{1}{2}$		
Student 1 Write a mixed number.	$1\frac{1}{2}$		
Student 2 Roll a number.	3		
Student 2 Pick a fraction.	$\frac{1}{4}$		
Student 2 Write a mixed number.	$3\frac{1}{4}$		
Student 1 and 2 Use mixed numbers to write a subtraction sentence.	$3\frac{1}{4} - 1\frac{1}{2}$		
Student 1 and 2 Find the LCD.	4		
Student 1 and 2 Subtract improper fractions.	$\frac{13}{4} - \frac{6}{4} = \frac{7}{4}$		
Student 1 and 2 Simplify answer.	$1\frac{3}{4}$		

Check students' responses.

Subtract Fractions and Mixed Numbers 33

Use this worksheet to provide additional support for English Language Learners.

Independent Work Options

Option 1 Early Finishers OL AL

LOGICAL/INTRAPERSONAL

Materials: paper, pencils

- Have students check their answers to Exercises 1–6 and 9–16 on pp. 453–454 in two ways.
- First, have students add the difference to the number being subtracted to get the first number.
- Next, have students subtract the difference from the first number to get the second number.

Option 2 Student Technology

Math Online macmillanmh.com

Personal Tutor • Extra Examples

Math Adventures

Option 3 Learning Station: Social Studies (p. 418J)

Direct students to the Social Studies Learning Station for opportunities to explore and extend the lesson concept.

Option 4 Problem-Solving Practice

Reinforce problem-solving skills and strategies with the Problem-Solving Practice worksheet.

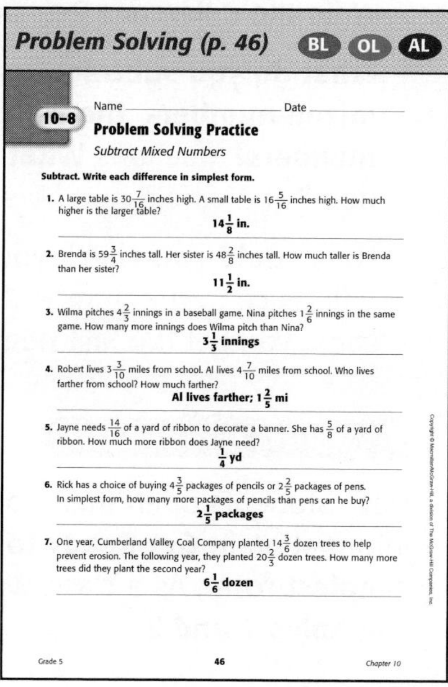

Problem Solving (p. 46) BL OL AL

10–8 Name ____________ Date ____________

Problem Solving Practice

Subtract Mixed Numbers

Subtract. Write each difference in simplest form.

1. A large table is $30\frac{7}{16}$ inches high. A small table is $16\frac{5}{16}$ inches high. How much higher is the larger table?
   $14\frac{1}{8}$ in.
2. Brenda is $59\frac{3}{4}$ inches tall. Her sister is $48\frac{2}{8}$ inches tall. How much taller is Brenda than her sister?
   $11\frac{1}{2}$ in.
3. Wilma pitches $4\frac{2}{3}$ innings in a baseball game. Nina pitches $1\frac{2}{6}$ innings in the same game. How many more innings does Wilma pitch than Nina?
   $3\frac{1}{3}$ innings
4. Robert lives $3\frac{3}{10}$ miles from school. Al lives $4\frac{7}{10}$ miles from school. Who lives farther from school? How much farther?
   Al lives farther; $1\frac{2}{5}$ mi
5. Jayne needs $\frac{14}{16}$ of a yard of ribbon to decorate a banner. She has $\frac{5}{8}$ of a yard of ribbon. How much more ribbon does Jayne need?
   $\frac{1}{4}$ yd
6. Rick has a choice of buying $4\frac{3}{5}$ packages of pencils or $2\frac{2}{5}$ packages of pens. In simplest form, how many more packages of pencils than pens can he buy?
   $2\frac{1}{5}$ packages
7. One year, Cumberland Valley Coal Company planted $14\frac{3}{6}$ dozen trees to help prevent erosion. The following year, they planted $20\frac{2}{3}$ dozen trees. How many more trees did they plant the second year?
   $6\frac{1}{6}$ dozen

Grade 5 46 Chapter 10

10-8 Subtract Mixed Numbers

1 Introduce

Activity Choice 1 • Hands-On 

- Provide students with play dollars and coins.
- Show students a dollar. **If this dollar is a whole, what are some names for its fractional parts?** Sample answers: $10¢ = \frac{1}{10}$, $25¢ = \frac{1}{4}$, $50¢ = \frac{1}{2}$, $75¢ = \frac{3}{4}$
- Show students 2 dollars and 25 cents. **Write this amount as a mixed number.** $2\frac{1}{4}$
- Repeat with different combinations of bills and coins.

Activity Choice 2 • Literature

Introduce the lesson with *The Missing Piece* by Shel Silverstein. For a related math activity, see p. TR53.

2 Teach

Scaffolding Questions

Model $3.40 with play dollar bills and dimes.

- **Write $3.40 as a mixed number.** $3\frac{4}{10}$
- Write $3\frac{4}{10} - 1\frac{1}{10}$ on the board. **Suppose you spent $1\frac{1}{10}$ of a dollar on a snack. How much money would you have left?** $2\frac{3}{10}$ or $2.30
- Model how to first take away $\frac{1}{10}$, or 1 dime, from $3.40. Then take away 1 whole, or 1 dollar, so there is $2\frac{3}{10}$ dollars or $2.30 left. Write the difference $2\frac{3}{10}$ on the board.
- **What do you subtract first when subtracting mixed numbers, the fractions or the whole numbers?** fractions **What do you subtract next?** the whole numbers
- **How could you check your answer?** Add the difference to the number being subtracted to see if you get the first number.

GET READY to Learn

Have students open their books and read the information in **Get Ready to Learn**. Review **simplest form**. As a class, work through **Examples 1 and 2**.

10-8 Subtract Mixed Numbers

MAIN IDEA

I will subtract mixed numbers.

Math Online

macmillanmh.com

- Extra Examples
- Personal Tutor
- Self-Check Quiz

GET READY to Learn

Payat has a $2\frac{3}{4}$ cup package of cheese. He uses $1\frac{1}{4}$ cups to make a pizza. How much cheese is left?

You can find an exact answer by subtracting $1\frac{1}{4}$ from $2\frac{3}{4}$.

Real-World EXAMPLE — Subtract Mixed Numbers

1 FOOD Refer to the information above. How many cups of cheese are left? Check by using fraction tiles.

Find $2\frac{3}{4} - 1\frac{1}{4}$. **Estimate** $3 - 1 = 2$

Step 1 Subtract the fractions.

$$\begin{array}{r} 2\frac{3}{4} \\ -\,1\frac{1}{4} \\ \hline \frac{2}{4} \end{array}$$

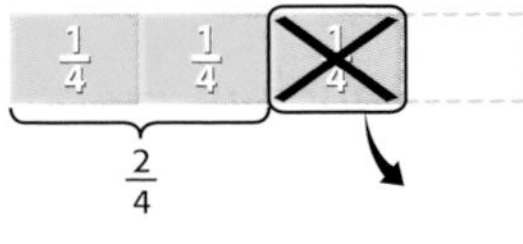

Step 2 Subtract the whole numbers.

$$\begin{array}{r} 2\frac{3}{4} \\ -\,1\frac{1}{4} \\ \hline 1\frac{2}{4} \end{array}$$

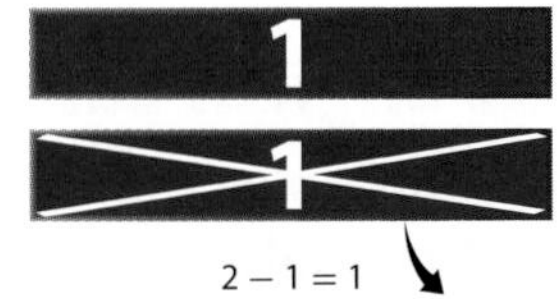

Step 3 Simplify $1\frac{2}{4}$.

$1\frac{2}{4} = 1\frac{1}{2}$ Divide the numerator and denominator by the GCF, 2.

Check for reasonableness $1\frac{1}{2} \approx 2$ ✓

So, $1\frac{1}{2}$ cups of cheese were left.

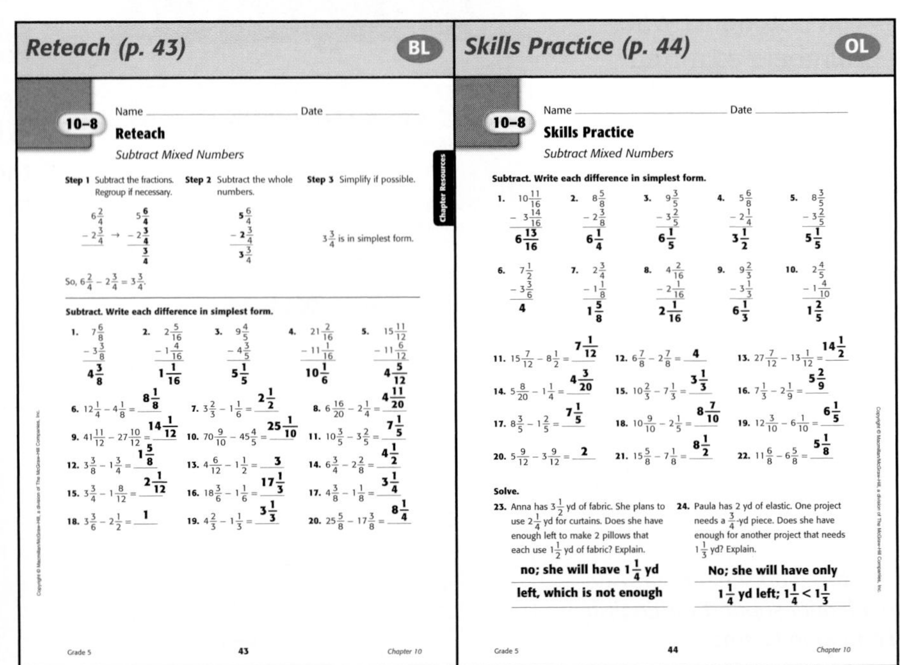

Reteach (p. 43) BL

10-8 Name ________ Date ________

Reteach

Subtract Mixed Numbers

Step 1 Subtract the fractions. Regroup if necessary.

$$\begin{array}{r} 6\frac{2}{4} \\ -\,2\frac{3}{4} \\ \hline \end{array} \rightarrow \begin{array}{r} 5\frac{6}{4} \\ -\,2\frac{3}{4} \\ \hline \frac{3}{4} \end{array}$$

Step 2 Subtract the whole numbers.

$$\begin{array}{r} 5\frac{6}{4} \\ -\,2\frac{3}{4} \\ \hline 3\frac{3}{4} \end{array}$$

Step 3 Simplify if possible.

$3\frac{3}{4}$ is in simplest form.

So, $6\frac{2}{4} - 2\frac{3}{4} = 3\frac{3}{4}$.

Subtract. Write each difference in simplest form.

1. $7\frac{6}{8} - 3\frac{3}{8}$ = **$4\frac{3}{8}$**
2. $2\frac{5}{16} - 1\frac{4}{16}$ = **$1\frac{1}{16}$**
3. $9\frac{4}{5} - 4\frac{3}{5}$ = **$5\frac{1}{5}$**
4. $21\frac{2}{16} - 11\frac{1}{16}$ = **$10\frac{1}{6}$**
5. $15\frac{11}{12} - 11\frac{6}{12}$ = **$4\frac{5}{12}$**
6. $12\frac{1}{4} - 4\frac{1}{8}$ = **$8\frac{1}{8}$**
7. $3\frac{2}{3} - 1\frac{1}{6}$ = **$2\frac{1}{2}$**
8. $6\frac{16}{20} - 2\frac{1}{4}$ = **$4\frac{11}{20}$**
9. $41\frac{11}{12} - 27\frac{10}{12}$ = **$14\frac{1}{12}$**
10. $70\frac{9}{10} - 45\frac{4}{5}$ = **$25\frac{1}{10}$**
11. $10\frac{3}{5} - 3\frac{2}{5}$ = **$7\frac{1}{5}$**
12. $3\frac{3}{8} - 1\frac{3}{4}$ = **$1\frac{5}{8}$**
13. $4\frac{6}{12} - 1\frac{1}{2}$ = **3**
14. $6\frac{3}{4} - 2\frac{2}{8}$ = **$4\frac{1}{2}$**
15. $3\frac{3}{4} - 1\frac{8}{12}$ = **$2\frac{1}{12}$**
16. $18\frac{3}{6} - 1\frac{1}{6}$ = **$17\frac{1}{3}$**
17. $4\frac{3}{8} - 1\frac{1}{8}$ = **$3\frac{1}{4}$**
18. $3\frac{3}{6} - 2\frac{1}{2}$ = **1**
19. $4\frac{2}{3} - 1\frac{1}{3}$ = **$3\frac{1}{3}$**
20. $25\frac{5}{8} - 17\frac{3}{8}$ = **$8\frac{1}{4}$**

Grade 5 43 Chapter 10

Skills Practice (p. 44) OL

10-8 Name ________ Date ________

Skills Practice

Subtract Mixed Numbers

Subtract. Write each difference in simplest form.

1. $10\frac{11}{16} - 3\frac{14}{16}$ = **$6\frac{13}{16}$**
2. $8\frac{5}{8} - 2\frac{3}{8}$ = **$6\frac{1}{4}$**
3. $9\frac{3}{5} - 3\frac{2}{5}$ = **$6\frac{1}{5}$**
4. $5\frac{6}{8} - 2\frac{1}{4}$ = **$3\frac{1}{2}$**
5. $8\frac{3}{5} - 3\frac{2}{5}$ = **$5\frac{1}{5}$**
6. $7\frac{1}{2} - 3\frac{3}{6}$ = **4**
7. $2\frac{3}{4} - 1\frac{1}{8}$ = **$1\frac{5}{8}$**
8. $4\frac{2}{16} - 2\frac{1}{16}$ = **$2\frac{1}{16}$**
9. $9\frac{2}{3} - 3\frac{1}{3}$ = **$6\frac{1}{3}$**
10. $2\frac{4}{5} - 1\frac{4}{10}$ = **$1\frac{2}{5}$**
11. $15\frac{7}{12} - 8\frac{1}{2}$ = **$7\frac{1}{12}$**
12. $6\frac{7}{8} - 2\frac{7}{8}$ = **4**
13. $27\frac{7}{12} - 13\frac{1}{12}$ = **$14\frac{1}{2}$**
14. $5\frac{8}{20} - 1\frac{1}{4}$ = **$4\frac{3}{20}$**
15. $10\frac{2}{3} - 7\frac{1}{3}$ = **$3\frac{1}{3}$**
16. $7\frac{1}{3} - 2\frac{1}{9}$ = **$5\frac{2}{9}$**
17. $8\frac{3}{5} - 1\frac{2}{5}$ = **$7\frac{1}{5}$**
18. $10\frac{9}{10} - 2\frac{1}{5}$ = **$8\frac{7}{10}$**
19. $12\frac{3}{10} - 6\frac{1}{10}$ = **$6\frac{1}{5}$**
20. $5\frac{9}{12} - 3\frac{9}{12}$ = **2**
21. $15\frac{5}{8} - 7\frac{1}{8}$ = **$8\frac{1}{2}$**
22. $11\frac{6}{8} - 6\frac{5}{8}$ = **$5\frac{1}{8}$**

Solve.

23. Anna has $3\frac{1}{2}$ yd of fabric. She plans to use $2\frac{1}{4}$ yd for curtains. Does she have enough left to make 2 pillows that each use $1\frac{1}{2}$ yd of fabric? Explain.
no; she will have $1\frac{1}{4}$ yd left, which is not enough

24. Paula has 2 yd of elastic. One project needs a $\frac{3}{4}$-yd piece. Does she have enough for another project that needs $1\frac{1}{3}$ yd? Explain.
No; she will have only $1\frac{1}{4}$ yd left; $1\frac{1}{4} < 1\frac{1}{3}$

Grade 5 44 Chapter 10

Real-World EXAMPLE Subtract Mixed Numbers

2 **FISH A Pigfish and a Shiner are shown below. How much longer is the Pigfish than the Shiner?**

Find $6\frac{11}{16} - 2\frac{5}{8}$ **Estimate** $7 - 3 = 4$

Step 1 Write the problem.

$$\begin{array}{r} 6\frac{11}{16} \\ -\ 2\frac{5}{8} \\ \hline \end{array}$$

Step 2 Rename the fractions using the LCD.

$$\begin{array}{rl} 6\frac{11}{16} & = 6\frac{11}{16} \\ -\ 2\frac{5 \times 2}{8 \times 2} & = 2\frac{10}{16} \\ \hline \end{array}$$

Step 3 Subtract the fractions and mixed numbers.

$$\begin{array}{r} 6\frac{11}{16} \\ -\ 2\frac{10}{16} \\ \hline 4\frac{1}{16} \end{array}$$

So, the Pigfish is $4\frac{1}{16}$ inches longer than the Shiner.

Remember

Always check for reasonableness.

$4\frac{1}{16} \approx 4$ ✓

Subtract Mixed Numbers

Key Concept

- If needed, rename the fractions using the LCD.
- Subtract the fractions.
- Then subtract the whole numbers.
- Simplify if needed.

CHECK What You Know

Subtract. Write each difference in simplest form. See Examples 1, 2 (pp. 452–453)

1. $4\frac{2}{3} - 2\frac{1}{3}$ $2\frac{1}{3}$

2. $5\frac{4}{5} - 3\frac{2}{5}$ $2\frac{2}{5}$

3. $6\frac{5}{6} - 5\frac{2}{6}$ $1\frac{1}{2}$

4. $7\frac{7}{8} - 4\frac{1}{2}$ $3\frac{3}{8}$

5. $12\frac{7}{10} - 7\frac{2}{5}$ $5\frac{3}{10}$

6. $15\frac{11}{12} - 4\frac{1}{3}$ $11\frac{7}{12}$

7. Bella is $10\frac{5}{12}$ years old. Franco is $12\frac{7}{12}$ years old. What is the difference in their ages? $2\frac{1}{6}$ yr

8. Talk About It Describe the steps you would take to find $3\frac{5}{8} - 2\frac{3}{8}$. See Ch. 10 Answer Appendix.

Subtract Mixed Numbers

Example 1 Model the problem with fraction tiles. Show $2\frac{3}{4}$. First remove one $\frac{1}{4}$-fraction tile, then 1 whole unit tile to show subtraction of $1\frac{1}{4}$.

ADDITIONAL EXAMPLES

1 Omar has $3\frac{7}{8}$ cups of milk in a container. He drinks $1\frac{5}{8}$ cup. How much milk is left? $2\frac{1}{4}$ cup

2 Elm Street is $4\frac{9}{10}$ miles long and Oak Street is $2\frac{2}{5}$ miles long. How much longer is Elm Street than Oak Street? $2\frac{1}{2}$ miles longer

CHECK What You Know

As a class, have students complete Exercises 1–8 in **Check What You Know** as you observe their work.

Exercise 8 Assess student comprehension before assigning practice exercises.

BL Alternate Teaching Strategy

If students have trouble subtracting mixed numbers using paper and pencil...

Then Use one of these reteach options:

1. CRM **Daily Reteach Worksheet** (p. 43)
2. Have students use fraction circles. Have them model the first mixed number in a subtraction problem with whole circles and fraction pieces. Then have them remove fraction pieces, then wholes, to show the subtraction. The remaining pieces show the difference.

COMMON ERROR!

Students may not write their answers in simplest form. Have students look at the numerator and denominator of the fraction part of their answer and ask themselves: Can both numbers be divided by 2? Can both numbers be divided by 3? Can both numbers be divided by 5? If the answer to any of these questions is yes, then the fraction can be simplified.

Enrich (p. 47) AL

10–8

Name ______________________ Date ______________

Enrich

Subtract Mixed Numbers

Play this game with a partner. You will need a counter.

- Together choose a whole number from 5 through 10. Write it in the square at that bottom right of the game board. Place your counter on Start. Then move it one square in any direction. Find the sum or difference of the numbers in the starting square and the square you moved to. If fractions don't have like denominators, try using an equivalent fraction to find the sum or difference. Record it on a separate sheet of paper.
- Players alternate turns. On each turn, move one square. Add or subtract the number in that square to or from your previous sum or difference and record your answer. You cannot return to a square.
- The winner is the first player who reaches the target square with a sum or difference equal to the target number.

Start

$2\frac{1}{2}$	$1\frac{1}{6}$	$3\frac{5}{8}$	$2\frac{1}{8}$	$4\frac{1}{2}$	$1\frac{1}{3}$
$3\frac{1}{4}$	$2\frac{2}{5}$	$1\frac{2}{3}$	$1\frac{1}{4}$	$1\frac{4}{5}$	$2\frac{1}{4}$
$3\frac{2}{3}$	$1\frac{7}{8}$	$3\frac{1}{2}$	$1\frac{7}{10}$	$1\frac{1}{2}$	$2\frac{5}{6}$
$1\frac{3}{4}$	$1\frac{3}{8}$	$\frac{2}{3}$	$\frac{5}{8}$	$\frac{3}{5}$	$\frac{3}{8}$
$1\frac{1}{2}$	$2\frac{3}{10}$	$\frac{1}{4}$	$\frac{1}{5}$	$\frac{1}{2}$	$\frac{3}{4}$
$5\frac{1}{4}$	$2\frac{3}{4}$	$\frac{1}{8}$	$\frac{1}{6}$	$\frac{1}{3}$	Target Number ______

Grade 5 47 Chapter 10

Chapter Resources

3 Practice

Differentiate practice using these leveled assignments for Exercises 9–32.

Level	Assignment
BL Below/ Approaching Level	9–14, 21–23
OL On Level	11–19, 21–25, 31
AL Above/Beyond Level	10–26 even, 27–32

Have students discuss and complete the Higher Order Thinking problems. For Exercises 27 and 32, encourage students to brainstorm different situations where subtraction of mixed numbers occurs. For example, comparing two lengths or other measurements.

WRITING IN ▶MATH Have students complete Exercise 32 in their Math Journals. You may choose to use this exercise as an optional formative assessment.

4 Assess

Formative Assessment

Write $5\frac{5}{12} - 2\frac{4}{12}$ on the board.

- **How would you find the difference using fraction tiles? Show your work.** Show 5 whole units and five $\frac{1}{12}$-fraction pieces. Take away four twelfths and two whole units. There are $3\frac{1}{12}$ left.
- **How would you find the difference using paper and pencil?** First subtract the fractions to get $\frac{1}{12}$. Next subtract the whole numbers to get 3. The answer is $3\frac{1}{12}$.

Quick Check **Are students continuing to struggle with subtracting mixed numbers?**

If Yes → Small Group Options (p. 452B)

If No → Independent Work Options (p. 452B)
CRM Skills Practice Worksheet (p. 44)
CRM Enrich Worksheet (p. 47)

Yesterday's News Have students discuss or write about how adding mixed numbers is similar to subtracting mixed numbers.

Practice and Problem Solving

Subtract. Write each difference in simplest form. See Examples 1, 2 (pp. 452–453)

9. $5\frac{3}{4} - 2\frac{2}{4}$ $3\frac{1}{4}$ **10.** $6\frac{5}{7} - 3\frac{3}{7}$ $3\frac{2}{7}$ **11.** $7\frac{8}{9} - 5\frac{3}{9}$ $2\frac{5}{9}$ **12.** $8\frac{3}{8} - 2\frac{2}{8}$ $6\frac{1}{8}$

13. $13\frac{9}{10} - 4\frac{4}{10}$ $9\frac{1}{2}$ **14.** $12\frac{5}{6} - 7\frac{2}{6}$ $5\frac{1}{2}$ **15.** $11\frac{11}{12} - 2\frac{1}{6}$ $9\frac{3}{4}$ **16.** $14\frac{9}{14} - 5\frac{2}{7}$ $9\frac{5}{14}$

17. $18\frac{11}{15} - 9\frac{2}{5}$ $9\frac{1}{3}$ **18.** $17\frac{15}{16} - 9\frac{3}{4}$ $8\frac{3}{16}$ **19.** $35\frac{7}{8} - 18\frac{5}{12}$ $17\frac{11}{24}$ **20.** $44\frac{6}{7} - 21\frac{3}{4}$ $23\frac{3}{28}$

21. Find *ten and seven tenths minus three and four tenths*. Write in words. seven and three tenths

22. Find *twelve and five ninths minus five and two ninths*. Write in words. seven and one third

23. Measurement The length of Mr. Cho's garden is $8\frac{5}{6}$ feet. Find the width of Mr. Cho's garden if it is $3\frac{1}{6}$ feet less than the length. $5\frac{2}{3}$ ft

24. Mrs. Gabel bought $7\frac{5}{6}$ gallons of punch for the class party. The students drank $4\frac{3}{6}$ gallons of punch. How much punch was left at the end of the party? $3\frac{1}{3}$ gal

25. Warner lives $9\frac{2}{3}$ blocks away from school. Shelly lives $12\frac{7}{8}$ blocks away from school. How many more blocks does Shelly live away from school than Warner? $3\frac{5}{24}$

26. A snack mix recipe calls for $5\frac{3}{4}$ cups of cereal and $3\frac{5}{12}$ cups less raisins. How many cups of raisins are needed? $2\frac{1}{3}$ c

H.O.T. Problems

27. See Ch. 10 Answer Appendix.

27. OPEN ENDED Write a real-world problem involving the subtraction of two mixed numbers whose difference is less than $2\frac{1}{2}$. Then solve.

CHALLENGE Find the value of each variable that makes a true sentence.

28. $n + 2\frac{1}{2} = 6\frac{3}{10}$ $3\frac{8}{10}$ **29.** $k + 3\frac{2}{8} = 7\frac{5}{8}$ $4\frac{3}{8}$ **30.** $4\frac{1}{6} + t = 13\frac{5}{6}$ $9\frac{4}{6}$

31. WHICH ONE DOESN'T BELONG? Identify the expression that does not belong with the other three. Explain your reasoning. See Ch. 10 Answer Appendix.

$5\frac{7}{10} - 3\frac{2}{10}$ | $11\frac{6}{8} - 9\frac{2}{8}$ | $8\frac{5}{6} - 6\frac{2}{6}$ | $7\frac{3}{4} - 5\frac{2}{4}$

32. WRITING IN ▶MATH Write a real-word problem involving subtraction of mixed numbers with unlike denominators. Then solve. Use fraction tiles to justify your solution. See Ch. 10 Answer Appendix.

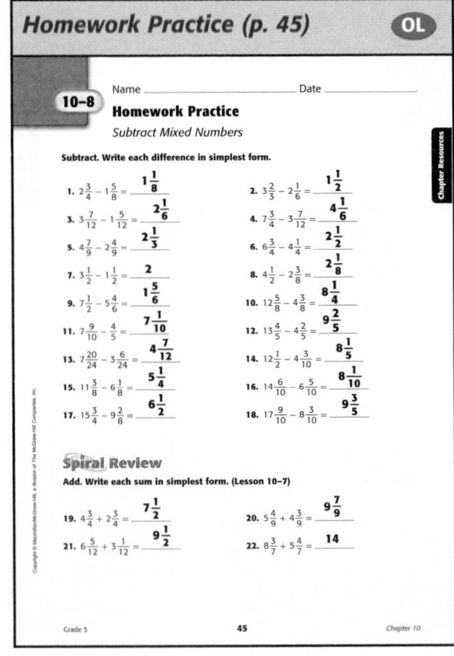
Homework Practice (p. 45) OL

10-8 Name ______ Date ______

Homework Practice

Subtract Mixed Numbers

Subtract. Write each difference in simplest form.

1. $2\frac{3}{4} - 1\frac{5}{8} =$ $1\frac{1}{8}$
2. $3\frac{2}{3} - 2\frac{1}{6} =$ $1\frac{1}{2}$
3. $3\frac{7}{12} - 1\frac{5}{12} =$ $2\frac{1}{6}$
4. $7\frac{3}{4} - 3\frac{7}{12} =$ $4\frac{1}{6}$
5. $4\frac{7}{9} - 2\frac{4}{9} =$ $2\frac{1}{3}$
6. $6\frac{3}{4} - 4\frac{1}{4} =$ $2\frac{1}{2}$
7. $3\frac{1}{2} - 1\frac{1}{2} =$ 2
8. $4\frac{1}{2} - 2\frac{3}{8} =$ $2\frac{1}{8}$
9. $7\frac{1}{2} - 5\frac{4}{6} =$ $1\frac{5}{6}$
10. $12\frac{5}{8} - 4\frac{3}{8} =$ $8\frac{1}{4}$
11. $7\frac{9}{10} - \frac{4}{5} =$ $7\frac{1}{10}$
12. $13\frac{4}{5} - 4\frac{2}{5} =$ $9\frac{2}{5}$
13. $7\frac{20}{24} - 3\frac{6}{24} =$ $4\frac{7}{12}$
14. $12\frac{1}{2} - 4\frac{3}{10} =$ $8\frac{1}{5}$
15. $11\frac{3}{8} - 6\frac{1}{8} =$ $5\frac{1}{4}$
16. $14\frac{6}{10} - 6\frac{5}{10} =$ $8\frac{1}{10}$
17. $15\frac{3}{4} - 9\frac{2}{8} =$ $6\frac{1}{2}$
18. $17\frac{9}{10} - 8\frac{3}{10} =$ $9\frac{3}{5}$

Spiral Review

Add. Write each sum in simplest form. (Lesson 10–7)

19. $4\frac{3}{4} + 2\frac{3}{4} =$ $7\frac{1}{2}$
20. $5\frac{4}{9} + 4\frac{3}{9} =$ $9\frac{7}{9}$
21. $6\frac{5}{12} + 3\frac{1}{12} =$ $9\frac{1}{2}$
22. $8\frac{3}{7} + 5\frac{4}{7} =$ 14

Chapter Resources

Grade 5 45 Chapter 10

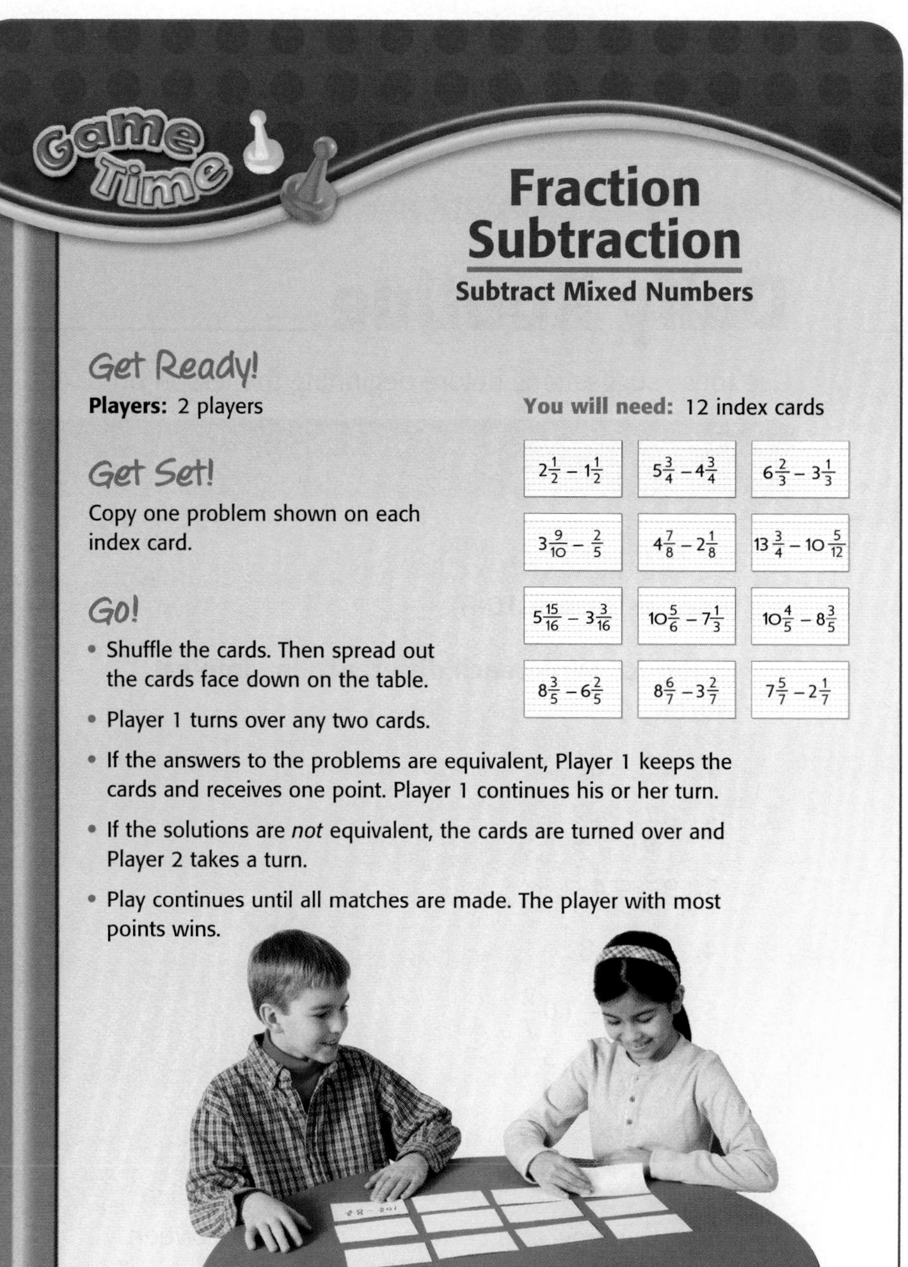

Fraction Subtraction

Subtract Mixed Numbers

Get Ready!

Players: 2 players

You will need: 12 index cards

Get Set!

Copy one problem shown on each index card.

$2\frac{1}{2} - 1\frac{1}{2}$	$5\frac{3}{4} - 4\frac{3}{4}$	$6\frac{2}{3} - 3\frac{1}{3}$
$3\frac{9}{10} - \frac{2}{5}$	$4\frac{7}{8} - 2\frac{1}{8}$	$13\frac{3}{4} - 10\frac{5}{12}$
$5\frac{15}{16} - 3\frac{3}{16}$	$10\frac{5}{6} - 7\frac{1}{3}$	$10\frac{4}{5} - 8\frac{3}{5}$
$8\frac{3}{5} - 6\frac{2}{5}$	$8\frac{6}{7} - 3\frac{2}{7}$	$7\frac{5}{7} - 2\frac{1}{7}$

Go!

- Shuffle the cards. Then spread out the cards face down on the table.
- Player 1 turns over any two cards.
- If the answers to the problems are equivalent, Player 1 keeps the cards and receives one point. Player 1 continues his or her turn.
- If the solutions are *not* equivalent, the cards are turned over and Player 2 takes a turn.
- Play continues until all matches are made. The player with most points wins.

Game Time Fraction Subtraction **455**

Differentiated Practice

Use these leveled suggestions to differentiate the game for all learners.

Level	Assignment
BL Below/ Approaching Level	Students rename the unlike fractions as like fractions before the game begins.
OL On Level	Have students play the game with the rules as written.
AL Above/Beyond Level	Students have to express the answer to their pair as not only mixed numbers but improper fractions as well in order to get a point for the equivalent pair.

Fraction Subtraction

Math Concept: Subtract Mixed Numbers

Materials: 12 index cards, paper, pencils

Introduce the game on p. 455 to your students to play as a class, in small groups, or at a learning workstation to review concepts introduced in this chapter.

Instructions

- Students play in pairs. They copy one mixed number subtraction problem on each card, as shown on p. 455.
- Students spread the cards out, face down, on the table. Player 1 turns over any two cards. If the solutions to the problems on both cards are equivalent, Player 1 keeps the cards and receives one point. Player 1 takes another turn. If the solutions are not equivalent, the cards are turned back over and Player 2 takes a turn.
- Play continues until all matches are made. Players add up how many equivalent pairs they've made and get a point for each one. The player with the most points wins.

Extend the Game

Have students make the game using mixed-number problem pairs they make up themselves.

10-9 Problem-Solving Investigation Choose a Strategy

Lesson Planner

Objective

Choose the best strategy to solve a problem.

Resources

Materials: yard stick, masking tape, ruler
Manipulatives: play money
Teacher Technology
Interactive Classroom • TeacherWorks

Real-World Problem Solving Library
Math and Social Studies: ***Life in Colonial America***
Use these leveled books to reinforce and extend problem-solving skills and strategies.

Leveled for:

- OL On Level
- ELL Sheltered English
- SP Spanish

For additional support, see the Real-World Problem Solving Teacher Guide.

Daily Routine

Use these suggestions before beginning the lesson on p. 456.

5-Minute Check

(Reviews Lesson 10-8)

Subtract. Write each difference in simplest form.

1. $4\frac{2}{3} - 2\frac{1}{3}$ $2\frac{1}{3}$
2. $8\frac{7}{9} - 3\frac{2}{9}$ $5\frac{5}{9}$
3. $9\frac{3}{4} - 4\frac{1}{4}$ $5\frac{1}{2}$
4. $11\frac{7}{8} - 8\frac{1}{2}$ $3\frac{3}{8}$
5. $15\frac{9}{14} - 10\frac{2}{7}$ $5\frac{5}{14}$
6. $21\frac{15}{16} - 8\frac{3}{4}$ $13\frac{3}{16}$

Problem of the Day

Jon is thinking of a composite number between 20 and 60 that is divisible by 3, 6, and 9, as well as other numbers. The digit in the tens place is twice the digit in the ones place. What number is he thinking of? 36

Differentiated Instruction

Small Group Options

Option 1 Gifted and Talented AL

VISUAL, PAIR

Materials: chart paper, markers, pencils, paper

- Write the following problem on the chart paper:

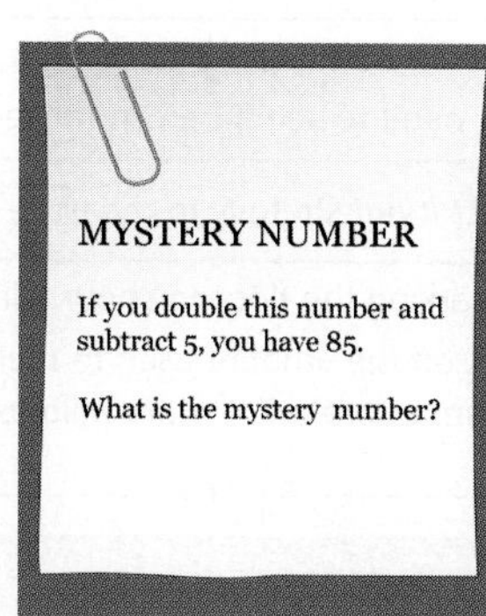

MYSTERY NUMBER

If you double this number and subtract 5, you have 85.

What is the mystery number?

- Ask the students to solve the problem and show all their work.
- Upon solving the problem, ask the students to share their strategy with the others in the group. Solicit different methods of solving this problem.

Option 2 English Language Learners ELL

SOCIAL

Materials: paper, pencil
Core Vocabulary: report, steps, process
Common Use Verb: was
Write Math This strategy helps peers learn from each other and activates acquired language.

- Divide the class into four groups.
- Give each group a different strategy to use to solve Exercise 3.
- Post the problem on the board.
- Ask students to solve the problem using the strategy assigned.
- Have each group write a report that explains the steps they took to solve the problem.
- After writing the report, ask the students to present their report to the class.

Independent Work Options

Option 1 Early Finishers OL AL

SPATIAL/LINGUISTIC

Materials: ruler, yard stick, and other common measurement tools (optional), play money, two-color counters

- Have students choose a manipulative, such as play money or counters, and write a word problem that can be solved by using their manipulative to model the problem.
- Next have students choose a measurement tool, such as a ruler or yard stick, and write a second problem that can be solved using the tool.

Option 2 Student Technology

Math Online macmillanmh.com

Personal Tutor • Extra Examples

Option 3 Learning Station: Writing (p. 418J)

Direct students to the Writing Learning Station for opportunities to explore and extend the lesson concept.

10-9 Problem-Solving Investigation

1 Introduce

Activity Choice • Review

- Present students with the following problem: *Marta has $4\frac{3}{4}$ gallons of apple juice and $3\frac{1}{8}$ gallons of grape juice. Is it reasonable to say that she has 8 gallons of juice total?*
- **What problem-solving strategy could you use?** *find a reasonable answer*
- **Solve.** Yes, it is reasonable to say she has about 8 gallons of juice. Round $4\frac{3}{4}$ to 5 and $3\frac{1}{8}$ to 3. $5 + 3 = 8$.

2 Teach

Have students read the problem on making pillows. Guide them through the problem-solving steps.

Understand Using the questions, review what students know and need to find.

Plan Have them discuss their strategy.

Solve Guide students to use *act it out* to solve the problem.

- **Use a yardstick and tape to measure and mark the beginning and end of $6\frac{1}{4}$ yards on the floor. How did you find $\frac{1}{4}$ yard on the yardstick?** Possible answer: 1 yard = 36 inches, and $\frac{1}{4}$ of 36 inches is 9 inches.
- **What will you measure and mark next?** Start at the first tape mark and measure and mark $1\frac{3}{8}$ yard.
- **How do you know there is not enough material to make 5 pillows?** The fifth measurement of $1\frac{3}{8}$ yards goes past the $6\frac{1}{4}$ yard mark.

Check Have students look back at the problem to make sure that the answer fits the facts given.

COMMON ERROR!

Exercise 8 Students may try to use estimation to solve this problem and get an incorrect answer. Guide students to use a yard stick or ruler to act out the problem, or use paper and pencil to add $1\frac{3}{4}$ five times and compare the sum to $9\frac{1}{4}$.

10-9 Problem-Solving Investigation

MAIN IDEA I will choose the best strategy to solve a problem.

P.S.I. TEAM +

JACOBO: I have a bolt of material that has $6\frac{1}{4}$ yards of material on it. I have used $1\frac{3}{8}$ yards to make a large pillow. Do I have enough material to make four more pillows just like the first one?

YOUR MISSION: Find out whether Jacobo has enough material for four more pillows.

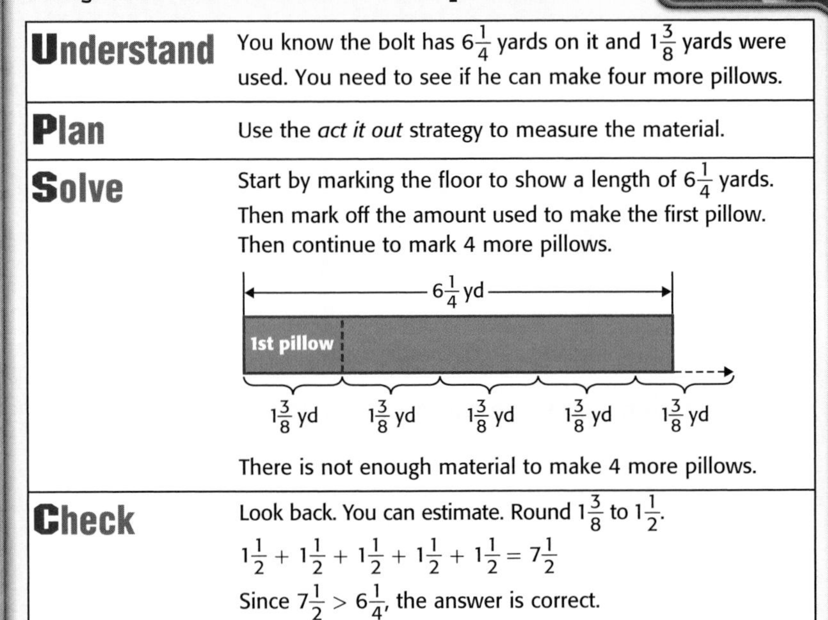

Understand You know the bolt has $6\frac{1}{4}$ yards on it and $1\frac{3}{8}$ yards were used. You need to see if he can make four more pillows.

Plan Use the *act it out* strategy to measure the material.

Solve Start by marking the floor to show a length of $6\frac{1}{4}$ yards. Then mark off the amount used to make the first pillow. Then continue to mark 4 more pillows.

There is not enough material to make 4 more pillows.

Check Look back. You can estimate. Round $1\frac{3}{8}$ to $1\frac{1}{2}$.

$1\frac{1}{2} + 1\frac{1}{2} + 1\frac{1}{2} + 1\frac{1}{2} + 1\frac{1}{2} = 7\frac{1}{2}$

Since $7\frac{1}{2} > 6\frac{1}{4}$, the answer is correct.

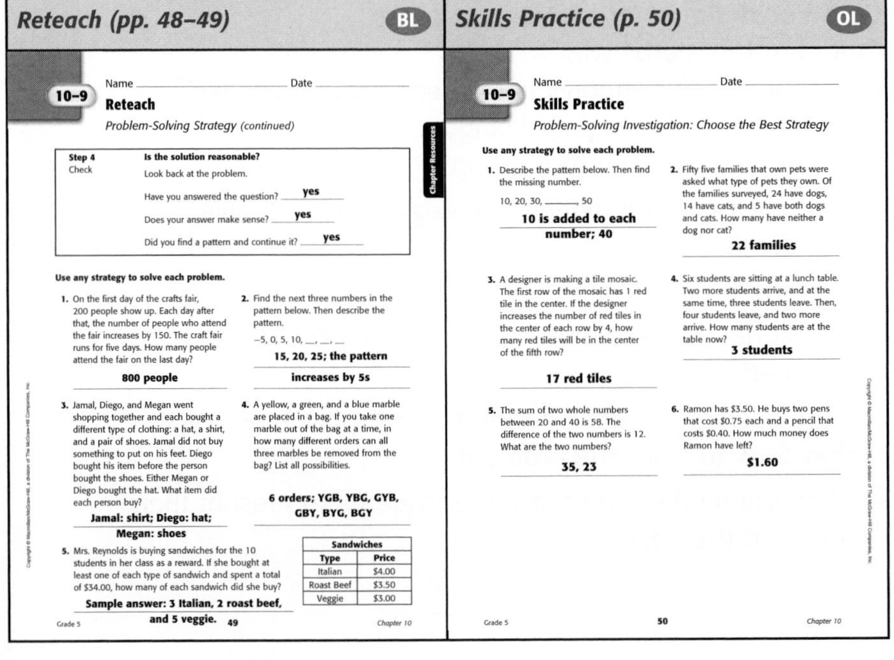

Reteach (pp. 48–49) BL

Name ____ Date ____

10-9 **Reteach**

Problem-Solving Strategy (continued)

Chapter Resources

Step 4 Check	Is the solution reasonable?
	Look back at the problem.
	Have you answered the question? **yes**
	Does your answer make sense? **yes**
	Did you find a pattern and continue it? **yes**

Use any strategy to solve each problem.

1. On the first day of the crafts fair, 200 people show up. Each day after that, the number of people who attend the fair increases by 150. The craft fair runs for five days. How many people attend the fair on the last day?
   800 people
2. Find the next three numbers in the pattern below. Then describe the pattern.
   −5, 0, 5, 10, __, __, __
   15, 20, 25; the pattern increases by 5s
3. Jamal, Diego, and Megan went shopping together and each bought a different type of clothing: a hat, a shirt, and a pair of shoes. Jamal did not buy something to put on his feet. Diego bought his item before the person bought the shoes. Either Megan or Diego bought the hat. What item did each person buy?
   Jamal: shirt; Diego: hat; Megan: shoes
4. A yellow, a green, and a blue marble are placed in a bag. If you take one marble out of the bag at a time, in how many different orders can all three marbles be removed from the bag? List all possibilities.
   6 orders; YGB, YBG, GYB, GBY, BYG, BGY
5. Mrs. Reynolds is buying sandwiches for the 10 students in her class as a reward. If she bought at least one of each type of sandwich and spent a total of $34.00, how many of each sandwich did she buy?
   Sample answer: 3 Italian, 2 roast beef, and 5 veggie.

Sandwiches	
Type	Price
Italian	$4.00
Roast Beef	$3.50
Veggie	$3.00

Grade 5 49 Chapter 10

Skills Practice (p. 50) OL

Name ____ Date ____

10-9 **Skills Practice**

Problem-Solving Investigation: Choose the Best Strategy

Use any strategy to solve each problem.

1. Describe the pattern below. Then find the missing number.
   10, 20, 30, ____, 50
   10 is added to each number; 40
2. Fifty five families that own pets were asked what type of pets they own. Of the families surveyed, 24 have dogs, 14 have cats, and 5 have both dogs and cats. How many have neither a dog nor cat?
   22 families
3. A designer is making a tile mosaic. The first row of the mosaic has 1 red tile in the center. If the designer increases the number of red tiles in the center of each row by 4, how many red tiles will be in the center of the fifth row?
   17 red tiles
4. Six students are sitting at a lunch table. Two more students arrive, and at the same time, three students leave. Then, four students leave, and two more arrive. How many students are at the table now?
   3 students
5. The sum of two whole numbers between 20 and 40 is 58. The difference of the two numbers is 12. What are the two numbers?
   35, 23
6. Ramon has $3.50. He buys two pens that cost $0.75 each and a pencil that costs $0.40. How much money does Ramon have left?
   $1.60

Grade 5 50 Chapter 10

★ indicates multi-step problem

Mixed Problem Solving

See page R29.

Use any strategy shown below to solve each problem.

★**1.** Alyssa needs $7\frac{5}{8}$ inches of ribbon for one project and $4\frac{7}{8}$ inches of ribbon for another project. If she has 12 inches of ribbon, will she have enough to complete both projects? Explain. See Ch. 10 Answer Appendix.

2. Berto surveyed his classmates about their favorite type of movie. He used C for comedy, A for Action, and S for scary. How many more people favored comedies than action movies? 4

FAVORITE MOVIES

S	C	A	C	C
A	C	S	A	A
C	A	C	C	S
A	C	S	A	C
C	S	A	C	C

3. **Measurement** A high jumper starts the bar at 48 inches and raises the bar $\frac{1}{2}$ inch after each jump. How high will the bar be on the seventh jump? 51 in.

4. Max, Aleta, Digna, and Tom won the first four prizes in the spelling bee. Max placed second. Aleta did not place third. Tom placed fourth. What did Digna place? third

5. Shanté has eight coins in her pocket that total \$1.32. What are the eight coins that she has in her pocket? See Ch. 10 Answer Appendix.

★**6.** Gift boxes come in five different sizes. The length of the gift boxes decreases by $2\frac{1}{2}$ inches. For each $2\frac{1}{2}$-inch decrease, the price decreases by \$0.75. The length of the largest box is 22 inches and costs \$3.75. Find the length and cost of the smallest box. 12 in.; \$0.75

7. What is the next figure in the pattern?

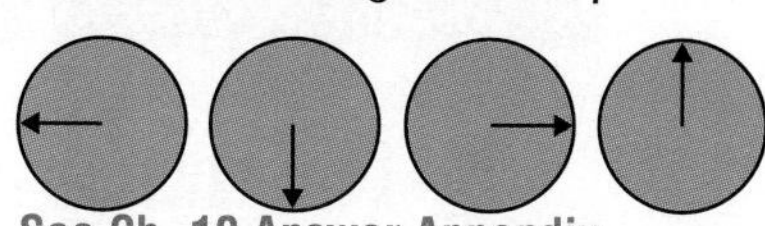

See Ch. 10 Answer Appendix.

8. **Measurement** Josiah has a piece of wood that measures $9\frac{3}{8}$ feet. He wants to make 5 shelves. If each shelf is $1\frac{3}{4}$ feet long, does he have enough to make 5 shelves? yes

9. Franklin leaves home at 10:00 A.M. He rides his bike an average of 14 miles each hour. By 2:00 P.M., how many miles will Franklin have biked?

9–11. See Ch. 10 Answer Appendix.

10. The number of siblings each student in Ms. Kennedy's class has is shown below. How many more students have two or more siblings than students who have only one sibling?

Number of Siblings					
2	1	4	2	1	0
3	2	1	1	2	3
1	1	2	0	3	1

11. **WRITING IN MATH** Refer to Exercise 4. Which strategy did you use to solve this problem? Why?

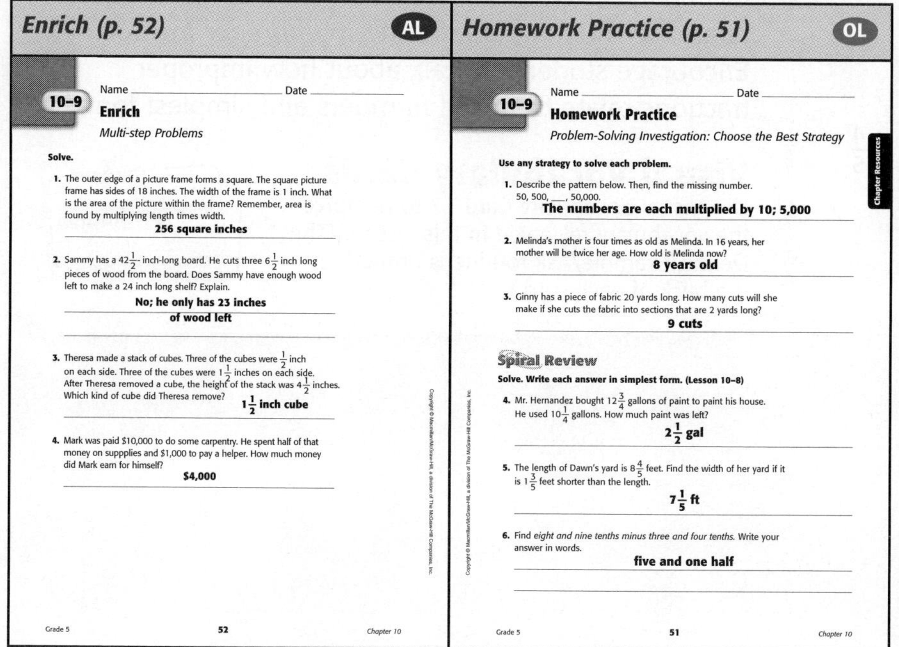

Enrich (p. 52) AL

10–9 Name ______ Date ______

Enrich

Multi-step Problems

Solve.

1. The outer edge of a picture frame forms a square. The square picture frame has sides of 18 inches. The width of the frame is 1 inch. What is the area of the picture within the frame? Remember, area is found by multiplying length times width. **256 square inches**

2. Sammy has a $42\frac{1}{2}$- inch-long board. He cuts three $6\frac{1}{2}$ inch long pieces of wood from the board. Does Sammy have enough wood left to make a 24 inch long shelf? Explain. **No; he only has 23 inches of wood left**

3. Theresa made a stack of cubes. Three of the cubes were $\frac{1}{2}$ inch on each side. Three of the cubes were $1\frac{1}{2}$ inches on each side. After Theresa removed a cube, the height of the stack was $4\frac{1}{2}$ inches. Which kind of cube did Theresa remove? **$1\frac{1}{2}$ inch cube**

4. Mark was paid \$10,000 to do some carpentry. He spent half of that money on suppplies and \$1,000 to pay a helper. How much money did Mark earn for himself? **\$4,000**

Grade 5 52 Chapter 10

Homework Practice (p. 51) OL

10–9 Name ______ Date ______

Homework Practice

Problem-Solving Investigation: Choose the Best Strategy

Chapter Resources

Use any strategy to solve each problem.

1. Describe the pattern below. Then, find the missing number. 50, 500, ___, 50,000. **The numbers are each multiplied by 10; 5,000**

2. Melinda's mother is four times as old as Melinda. In 16 years, her mother will be twice her age. How old is Melinda now? **8 years old**

3. Ginny has a piece of fabric 20 yards long. How many cuts will she make if she cuts the fabric into sections that are 2 yards long? **9 cuts**

Spiral Review

Solve. Write each answer in simplest form. (Lesson 10–8)

4. Mr. Hernandez bought $12\frac{3}{4}$ gallons of paint to paint his house. He used $10\frac{1}{4}$ gallons. How much paint was left? **$2\frac{1}{2}$ gal**

5. The length of Dawn's yard is $8\frac{4}{5}$ feet. Find the width of her yard if it is $1\frac{3}{5}$ feet shorter than the length. **$7\frac{1}{5}$ ft**

6. Find *eight and nine tenths minus three and four tenths.* Write your answer in words. **five and one half**

Grade 5 51 Chapter 10

BL Alternate Teaching Strategy

If students have trouble choosing the best strategy to solve a problem…

Then use one of these reteach options:

1 CRM **Daily Reteach Worksheet** (pp. 48–49)

2 Present students with four problems that can be solved using different strategies, such as *act it out, look for a pattern, use logical reasoning,* or *make a graph.*

- Write the four strategies on the board and have pairs or small groups of students work together to match each strategy to a problem. Have students present their answers and explain their choices of strategies.

3 Practice

Using the Exercises

Exercises 2 and 10 Students may make a frequency table or graph to solve these problems.

Exercise 4 You may have groups of four students work together to act out and solve this problem.

Exercise 5 You may choose to provide students with play money and have them act out the problem to solve.

4 Assess

Formative Assessment

- **When might you use the *act it out* strategy to solve a word problem?** Sample answer: when the problem involves measurements or money

Quick Check

Are students continuing to struggle with choosing a strategy to solve a problem?

If Yes → CRM Reteach Worksheet (pp. 48–49)

If No → Independent Work Options (p. 456B)
CRM Skills Practice Worksheet (p. 50)
CRM Enrich Worksheet (p. 52)

LESSON

10-10 Subtraction with Renaming

Lesson Planner

Objective

Subtract mixed numbers.

Review Vocabulary

improper fraction

Resources

Manipulatives: play money, fraction models
Literature Connection: *Fractions and Decimals* by Lucille Caron and Philip M. St. Jacques
Teacher Technology
Interactive Classroom • TeacherWorks
Alternate Lesson: Use *IMPACT Mathematics*: Unit F to provide practice with subtracting mixed numbers.

Focus on Math Background

In the previous lesson, students learned to subtract mixed numbers by first subtracting the fractions, and then subtracting the whole numbers. However, in cases when the minuend (first number) is a whole number or the fraction in the minuend is less than the fraction in the subtrahend (second number), it is necessary to rename the minuend as an improper fraction before subtracting. Below are two examples of subtracting with renaming:

$$4 \rightarrow 3\frac{8}{8}$$
$$-1\frac{5}{8} \rightarrow -1\frac{5}{8}$$
$$2\frac{3}{8}$$

minuend is a whole number

$$5\frac{3}{10} = 4\frac{10}{10} + \frac{3}{10} = 4\frac{13}{10}$$
$$-2\frac{5}{10} \qquad -2\frac{5}{10}$$
$$2\frac{8}{10} = 2\frac{4}{5}$$

minuend is a mixed number

Daily Routine

Use these suggestions before beginning the lesson on p. 458.

5-Minute Check

(Reviews Lesson 10-9)

Use any problem-solving strategy to solve.
Jamala has nine coins in her pocket that total \$1.26. What are the nine coins? 3 quarters, 5 dimes, 1 penny

Problem of the Day

A salad costs \$2.59. A soup costs \$0.98 less than a salad, and a glass of milk costs \$0.27 less than a soup. How much do a salad, a soup, and a milk cost altogether? \$5.54

Review Math Vocabulary

Write the review vocabulary word and its definition on the board.

Have a volunteer look up the term *improper* in the dictionary. Have students discuss how this definition relates to the mathematical term *improper fraction*. Encourage students to talk about how improper fractions relate to mixed numbers and simplest form.

Visual Vocabulary Cards

Use Visual Vocabulary Card 17 to reinforce the vocabulary reviewed in this lesson. (The Define/Example/Ask routine is printed on the back of each card.)

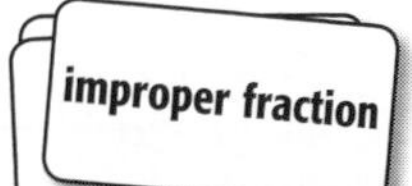

Differentiated Instruction

Small Group Options

Option 1 Below Level (BL)

SPATIAL

Materials: yarn, paper and pencil

- Present this problem to students:

  Mr. Nelson needs some rope for a fence project. He has one piece that is $1\frac{2}{3}$ yards long and another piece that is $2\frac{1}{3}$ yards long. What is the difference in the two pieces of rope? $\frac{2}{3}$ yard
- *He decides to tie the two pieces of rope together using a square knot which takes up $\frac{1}{3}$ yard of rope. Now how long is the whole piece of rope? Find a way to show your work.* $3\frac{2}{3}$ yards
- Have students act out the problem using the yarn.

Option 2 English Language Learners (ELL)

TACTILE

Materials: 5 tens and 5 ones base ten manipulatives per student, index cards, scissors

Core Vocabulary: separate, from, rename

Common Use Verb: can be done

See Math This strategy connects subtraction with renaming to background knowledge of regrouping and place value.

- Give students work with listed manipulatives. Write 15 – 2. Students should model the answer using their manipulatives.
- Write 23 – 8. Have students *try* to use manipulatives. (They cannot take 8 from 3.) Discuss what can be done. Change a 10 for 10 ones.
- Write $2\frac{1}{4} - 1\frac{2}{4}$ on the board.
- Explain that just as you cannot take 8 from 3 in the problem 23 – 8, you cannot take $\frac{2}{4}$ from $\frac{1}{4}$.
- Now demonstrate how to rename the fraction using fraction circles.
- Have students try with the problem $3\frac{2}{5} - 1\frac{3}{5}$.

Independent Work Options

Option 1 Early Finishers (OL)

VISUAL/SPATIAL

Materials: fraction tiles

- Ask students to write five subtraction exercises with mixed numbers that require renaming before subtracting.
- Have students exchange problems with a partner and model the subtraction with fraction tiles to solve.

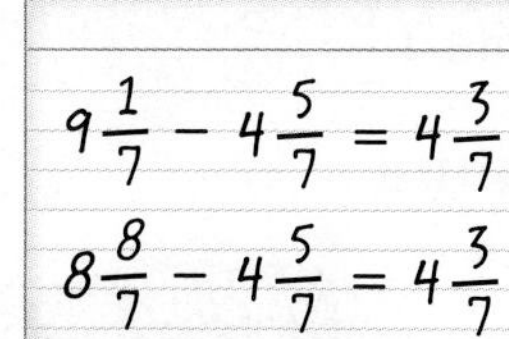

$9\frac{1}{7} - 4\frac{5}{7} = 4\frac{3}{7}$
$8\frac{8}{7} - 4\frac{5}{7} = 4\frac{3}{7}$

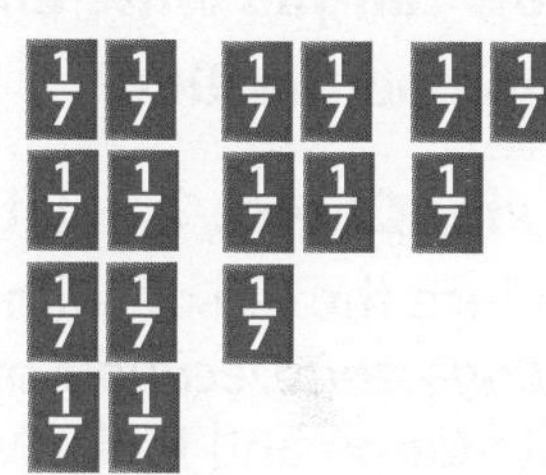

$\frac{8}{7} - \frac{5}{7} = \frac{3}{7}$

Option 2 Student Technology

macmillanmh.com

Personal Tutor • Extra Examples

Option 3 Learning Station: Social Studies (p. 418H)

Direct students to the Social Studies Learning Station for opportunities to explore and extend the lesson concept.

Option 4 Problem-Solving Practice

Reinforce problem-solving skills and strategies with the Problem-Solving Practice worksheet.

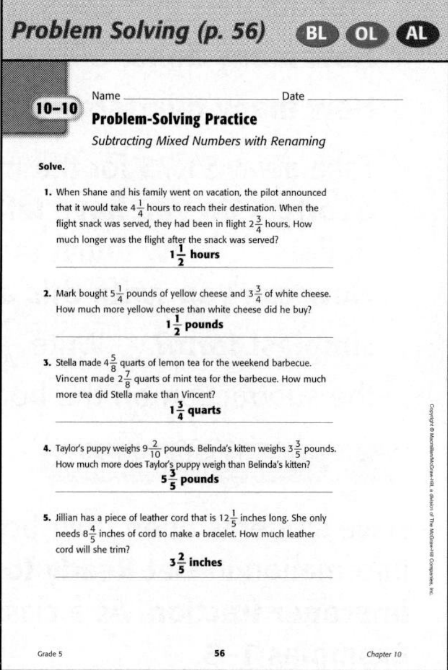

Problem Solving (p. 56) BL OL AL

10–10 Name ____________ Date ________

Problem-Solving Practice

Subtracting Mixed Numbers with Renaming

Solve.

1. When Shane and his family went on vacation, the pilot announced that it would take $4\frac{1}{4}$ hours to reach their destination. When the flight snack was served, they had been in flight $2\frac{3}{4}$ hours. How much longer was the flight after the snack was served?
   $1\frac{1}{2}$ hours
2. Mark bought $5\frac{1}{4}$ pounds of yellow cheese and $3\frac{3}{4}$ of white cheese. How much more yellow cheese than white cheese did he buy?
   $1\frac{1}{2}$ pounds
3. Stella made $4\frac{5}{8}$ quarts of lemon tea for the weekend barbecue. Vincent made $2\frac{7}{8}$ quarts of mint tea for the barbecue. How much more tea did Stella make than Vincent?
   $1\frac{3}{4}$ quarts
4. Taylor's puppy weighs $9\frac{2}{10}$ pounds. Belinda's kitten weighs $3\frac{3}{5}$ pounds. How much more does Taylor's puppy weigh than Belinda's kitten?
   $5\frac{3}{5}$ pounds
5. Jillian has a piece of leather cord that is $12\frac{1}{5}$ inches long. She only needs $8\frac{4}{5}$ inches of cord to make a bracelet. How much leather cord will she trim?
   $3\frac{2}{5}$ inches

Grade 5 56 Chapter 10

10-10 Subtracting with Renaming

1 Introduce

Activity Choice 1 • Hands-On 

- Review renaming mixed numbers as improper fractions and relate this concept to money.
- Write \$1.25 on the board and give students one play dollar and one play quarter. **If one dollar is a whole, how can we write \$1.25 as a mixed number?** $1\frac{1}{4}$
- **How many quarters equal \$1?** four Have students trade one dollar bill for four quarters.
- **How much money do you have now?** \$1.25
- **How can you write this amount as an improper fraction?** $\frac{5}{4}$ Write $1\frac{1}{4} = \frac{5}{4}$.

Activity Choice 2 • Literature

Introduce the lesson with *Fractions and Decimals* by Lucille Caron and Philip M. St. Jacques. For a related math activity, see p. TR53.

2 Teach

Scaffolding Questions

Give students two dollars and one quarter. Tell them they have \$2.25 and will spend \$1.75.

- **How can you write \$2.25 as a mixed number?** $2\frac{1}{4}$ **How can you write \$1.75?** $1\frac{3}{4}$ Write $2\frac{1}{4} - 1\frac{3}{4}$ on the board.
- **Can you take away 3 quarters from 1 quarter?** no Guide students to understand that they must trade one of their dollars for four quarters in order to be able to subtract.
- **How many dollar bills do you have now?** 1 **How many quarters?** 5 Write $1\frac{5}{4} - 1\frac{3}{4}$.
- Take away \$1.75 for the muffin. **How many quarters do you have left?** 2 **How many dollars?** 0 **How much money is that?** \$0.50 **How can you write this as a fraction in simplest form?** $\frac{1}{2}$ Write $\frac{2}{4} = \frac{1}{2}$ to complete the subtraction on the board.

GET READY to Learn

Have students open their books and read the information in **Get Ready to Learn**. Review **improper fraction**. As a class, work through **Examples 1–3**.

10-10 Subtraction with Renaming

MAIN IDEA

I will subtract mixed numbers.

Math Online

macmillanmh.com
- Extra Examples
- Personal Tutor
- Self-Check Quiz

GET READY to Learn

The black-tailed jackrabbit and the swamp rabbit are two mammals common to the Southern United States. A black-tailed jackrabbit weighs about $2\frac{1}{3}$ pounds. A swamp rabbit weighs about $1\frac{2}{3}$ pounds.

Sometimes the fraction in the first mixed number is less than the fraction in the second mixed number. In this case, the first mixed number needs to be renamed.

Real-World EXAMPLE Rename Mixed Numbers to Subtract

1 ANIMALS How much more does the black-tailed jackrabbit weigh than the swamp rabbit?

You need to find $2\frac{1}{3} - 1\frac{2}{3}$.

Since $\frac{1}{3}$ is less than $\frac{2}{3}$, rename $2\frac{1}{3}$ before subtracting.

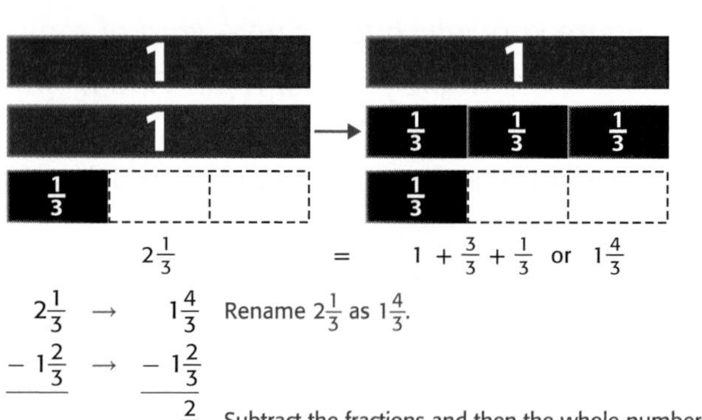

$$2\frac{1}{3} = 1 + \frac{3}{3} + \frac{1}{3} \text{ or } 1\frac{4}{3}$$

$$\begin{array}{r} 2\frac{1}{3} \\ -\,1\frac{2}{3} \\ \hline \end{array} \rightarrow \begin{array}{r} 1\frac{4}{3} \\ -\,1\frac{2}{3} \\ \hline \frac{2}{3} \end{array}$$

Rename $2\frac{1}{3}$ as $1\frac{4}{3}$.

Subtract the fractions and then the whole numbers.

So, a black-tailed jackrabbit weighs about $\frac{2}{3}$ pound more than a swamp rabbit.

458 **Chapter 10** Add and Subtract Fractions

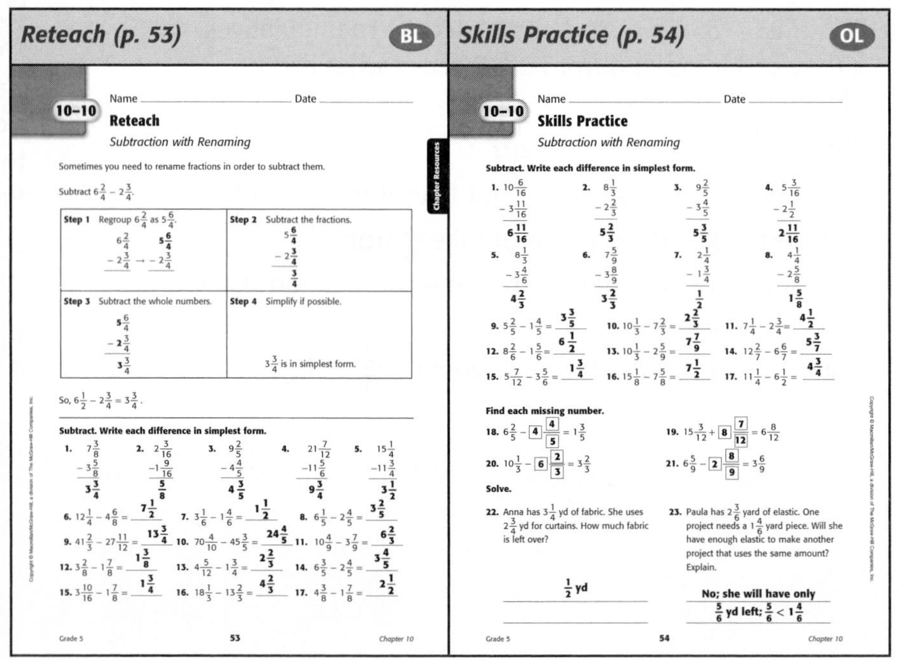

Reteach (p. 53) BL

10-10 Name ______ Date ______

Reteach

Subtraction with Renaming

Sometimes you need to rename fractions in order to subtract them.

Subtract $6\frac{2}{4} - 2\frac{3}{4}$.

Step 1 Regroup $6\frac{2}{4}$ as $5\frac{6}{4}$. $6\frac{2}{4} - 2\frac{3}{4} \rightarrow 5\frac{6}{4} - 2\frac{3}{4}$	**Step 2** Subtract the fractions. $5\frac{6}{4} - 2\frac{3}{4}$: $\frac{3}{4}$
Step 3 Subtract the whole numbers. $5\frac{6}{4} - 2\frac{3}{4} = 3\frac{3}{4}$	**Step 4** Simplify if possible. $3\frac{3}{4}$ is in simplest form.

So, $6\frac{1}{2} - 2\frac{3}{4} = 3\frac{3}{4}$.

Subtract. Write each difference in simplest form.

1. $7\frac{3}{8} - 3\frac{5}{8}$ **$3\frac{3}{4}$**
2. $2\frac{3}{16} - 1\frac{9}{16}$ **$\frac{5}{8}$**
3. $9\frac{2}{5} - 4\frac{4}{5}$ **$4\frac{3}{5}$**
4. $21\frac{7}{12} - 11\frac{5}{6}$ **$9\frac{3}{4}$**
5. $15\frac{1}{4} - 11\frac{3}{4}$ **$3\frac{1}{2}$**
6. $12\frac{1}{4} - 4\frac{6}{8} =$ **$7\frac{1}{2}$**
7. $3\frac{1}{6} - 1\frac{4}{6} =$ **$1\frac{1}{2}$**
8. $6\frac{1}{5} - 2\frac{4}{5} =$ **$3\frac{2}{5}$**
9. $41\frac{2}{3} - 27\frac{11}{12} =$ **$13\frac{3}{4}$**
10. $70\frac{4}{10} - 45\frac{3}{5} =$ **$24\frac{4}{5}$**
11. $10\frac{4}{9} - 3\frac{7}{9} =$ **$6\frac{2}{3}$**
12. $3\frac{2}{8} - 1\frac{7}{8} =$ **$1\frac{3}{8}$**
13. $4\frac{5}{12} - 1\frac{3}{4} =$ **$2\frac{2}{3}$**
14. $6\frac{3}{5} - 2\frac{4}{5} =$ **$3\frac{4}{5}$**
15. $3\frac{10}{16} - 1\frac{7}{8} =$ **$1\frac{3}{4}$**
16. $18\frac{1}{3} - 13\frac{2}{3} =$ **$4\frac{2}{3}$**
17. $4\frac{3}{8} - 1\frac{7}{8} =$ **$2\frac{1}{2}$**

Grade 5 53 Chapter 10

Chapter Resources

Skills Practice (p. 54) OL

10-10 Name ______ Date ______

Skills Practice

Subtraction with Renaming

Subtract. Write each difference in simplest form.

1. $10\frac{6}{16} - 3\frac{11}{16}$ **$6\frac{11}{16}$**
2. $8\frac{1}{3} - 2\frac{2}{3}$ **$5\frac{2}{3}$**
3. $9\frac{2}{5} - 3\frac{4}{5}$ **$5\frac{3}{5}$**
4. $5\frac{3}{16} - 2\frac{1}{2}$ **$2\frac{11}{16}$**
5. $8\frac{1}{3} - 3\frac{4}{6}$ **$4\frac{2}{3}$**
6. $7\frac{5}{9} - 3\frac{8}{9}$ **$3\frac{2}{3}$**
7. $2\frac{1}{4} - 1\frac{3}{4}$ **$\frac{1}{2}$**
8. $4\frac{1}{4} - 2\frac{5}{8}$ **$1\frac{5}{8}$**
9. $5\frac{2}{5} - 1\frac{4}{5} =$ **$3\frac{3}{5}$**
10. $10\frac{1}{3} - 7\frac{2}{3} =$ **$2\frac{2}{3}$**
11. $7\frac{1}{4} - 2\frac{3}{4} =$ **$4\frac{1}{2}$**
12. $8\frac{2}{6} - 1\frac{5}{6} =$ **$6\frac{1}{2}$**
13. $10\frac{1}{3} - 2\frac{5}{9} =$ **$7\frac{7}{9}$**
14. $12\frac{2}{7} - 6\frac{6}{7} =$ **$5\frac{3}{7}$**
15. $5\frac{7}{12} - 3\frac{5}{6} =$ **$1\frac{3}{4}$**
16. $15\frac{1}{8} - 7\frac{5}{8} =$ **$7\frac{1}{2}$**
17. $11\frac{1}{4} - 6\frac{1}{2} =$ **$4\frac{3}{4}$**

Find each missing number.

18. $6\frac{2}{5} - \boxed{4}\frac{\boxed{4}}{\boxed{5}} = 1\frac{3}{5}$
19. $15\frac{3}{12} + \boxed{8}\frac{\boxed{7}}{\boxed{12}} = 6\frac{8}{12}$
20. $10\frac{1}{3} - \boxed{6}\frac{\boxed{2}}{\boxed{3}} = 3\frac{2}{3}$
21. $6\frac{5}{9} - \boxed{2}\frac{\boxed{8}}{\boxed{9}} = 3\frac{6}{9}$

Solve.

22. Anna has $3\frac{1}{4}$ yd of fabric. She uses $2\frac{3}{4}$ yd for curtains. How much fabric is left over?

$\frac{1}{2}$ yd

23. Paula has $2\frac{3}{6}$ yard of elastic. One project needs a $1\frac{4}{6}$ yard piece. Will she have enough elastic to make another project that uses the same amount? Explain.

No; she will have only $\frac{5}{6}$ yd left; $\frac{5}{6} < 1\frac{4}{6}$

Grade 5 54 Chapter 10

EXAMPLE Rename Mixed Numbers to Subtract

2 **Find $4\frac{1}{4} - 2\frac{5}{8}$.**

Rename $4\frac{1}{4}$ as $4\frac{2}{8}$ to make like fractions.

Since $\frac{2}{8}$ is less than $\frac{5}{8}$, rename $4\frac{2}{8}$ before subtracting.

THINK $4\frac{2}{8} = 3 + 1 + \frac{2}{8}$

$= 3 + \frac{8}{8} + \frac{2}{8}$ or $3\frac{10}{8}$ Rename 1 as $\frac{8}{8}$.

$4\frac{2}{8} \rightarrow 3\frac{10}{8}$ Rename $4\frac{2}{8}$ as $3\frac{10}{8}$.

$-2\frac{5}{8} \rightarrow -2\frac{5}{8}$

$1\frac{5}{8}$ Subtract the fractions and then the whole numbers.

So, $4\frac{2}{8} - 2\frac{5}{8} = 1\frac{5}{8}$. Check your answer by drawing a picture.

Remember

You can always check by using fraction tiles or drawing a picture.

Real-World EXAMPLE Rename Mixed Numbers to Subtract

3 **Measurement** **Sally is making a flag. She has 2 yards of fabric. The sewing pattern calls for $1\frac{1}{4}$ yards. How much fabric will be left?**

Rename 2 as a mixed number before subtracting.

1	1
1 →	$\frac{1}{4}$ $\frac{1}{4}$ $\frac{1}{4}$ $\frac{1}{4}$

2 = 1 + $\frac{1}{4}$ or $1\frac{4}{4}$

$2 \rightarrow 1\frac{4}{4}$ Rename 2 as $1\frac{4}{4}$.

$-1\frac{1}{4} \rightarrow -1\frac{1}{4}$

$\frac{3}{4}$ Subtract the fractions and then the whole numbers.

So, Sally will have $\frac{3}{4}$ yard of fabric left.

Enrich (p. 57) AL

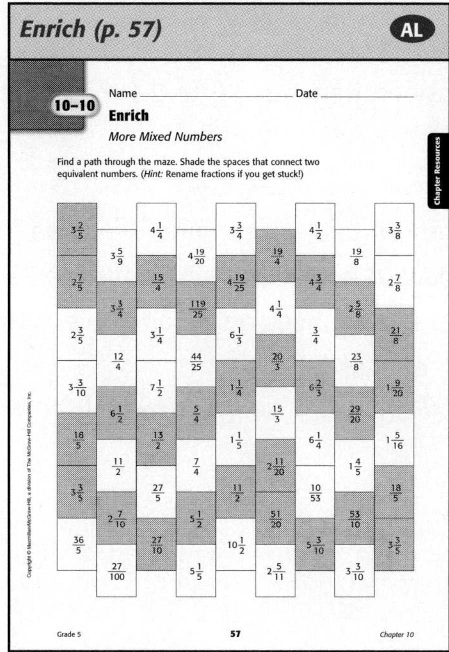

Rename Mixed Numbers to Subtract

Real-World Example 1 Have students model the problem with fraction tiles. Have them trade one whole tile for three $\frac{1}{3}$-tiles to show the renaming, then remove tiles to subtract. Remind students to first subtract the fractions, then the whole numbers.

ADDITIONAL EXAMPLES

1. A bag of potatoes weighs $3\frac{1}{5}$ pounds. A bag of onions weighs $2\frac{4}{5}$ pounds. How much more do the potatoes weigh than the onions? $\frac{2}{5}$ pounds
2. Find $6\frac{1}{2} - 3\frac{2}{3}$. $2\frac{5}{6}$
3. Bradley has 4 yards of fencing. He is making a fence that is $3\frac{3}{4}$ yards long. How much fencing material will be left? $\frac{1}{4}$ yard

COMMON ERROR!

Students may forget to change the whole number when renaming. Have students cross out the original whole number and write the new whole number (the original minus one) above it before they write the improper fraction. Point out that this is similar to what they do when they regroup when subtracting whole numbers.

As a class, have students complete Exercises 1–5 in **Check What You Know** as you observe their work.

Exercise 5 Assess student comprehension before assigning practice exercises.

BL Alternate Teaching Strategy

If students have trouble using paper and pencil to subtract mixed numbers with renaming…

Then use one of these reteach options:

1 CRM **Daily Reteach Worksheet** (p. 53)

2 Have students either draw pictures or use fraction circles to show the first mixed number in a subtraction problem. Guide them to trade wholes for fraction pieces to show renaming, then take away (or cross out) fractions and wholes to show the subtraction.

3 Practice

Differentiate practice using these leveled assignments for Exercises 6–23.

Level	Assignment
BL Below/ Approaching Level	6–11, 15, 17, 19, 23
OL On Level	6–13, 15–20, 23
AL Above/Beyond Level	7–19 odd, 21–23

Have students discuss and complete the Higher Order Thinking problems. For Exercise 22, suggest that students solve the subtraction problem themselves first. Have them use their work to help them decide which student is correct and identify the other student's error.

WRITING IN MATH Have students complete Exercise 23 in their Math Journals. You may choose to use this as an optional formative assessment.

★ indicates multi-step problem

CHECK What You Know

Subtract. Write each difference in simplest form. See Examples 1–3 (pp. 458–459)

1. $3\frac{1}{6} - 1\frac{1}{3}$ $1\frac{5}{6}$
2. $5\frac{2}{5} - 3\frac{4}{5}$ $1\frac{3}{5}$
3. $6\frac{2}{9} - 2\frac{8}{9}$ $3\frac{1}{3}$
4. **Measurement** Arlo had 5 gallons of paint. He used $2\frac{10}{16}$ gallons. How much paint does he have left? $2\frac{3}{8}$ gal
5. **Talk About It** Describe the steps you would use to solve $3\frac{2}{7} - 1\frac{4}{7}$. Then solve. See margin.

Practice and Problem Solving

EXTRA PRACTICE See page R29.

Subtract. Write each difference in simplest form. See Examples 1–3 (pp. 458–459)

6. $4\frac{3}{8} - 1\frac{5}{8}$ $2\frac{3}{4}$
7. $5\frac{1}{4} - 4\frac{1}{2}$ $\frac{3}{4}$
8. $7\frac{2}{7} - 6\frac{4}{7}$ $\frac{5}{7}$
9. $9\frac{3}{10} - 5\frac{7}{10}$ $3\frac{3}{5}$
10. $10\frac{1}{3} - 3\frac{6}{9}$ $6\frac{2}{3}$
11. $13 - 4\frac{1}{3}$ $8\frac{2}{3}$
12. $12 - 5\frac{1}{6}$ $6\frac{5}{6}$
13. $18 - 9\frac{2}{8}$ $8\frac{3}{4}$
14. $17 - 7\frac{3}{12}$ $9\frac{3}{4}$
15. Find *ten and one fourth minus three and two fourths*. Write in words. six and three fourths
16. Find *nine minus four and six tenths*. Write in words. four and two fifths
17. Sherman's backpack weighs $6\frac{1}{4}$ pounds. Brie's backpack weighs $5\frac{3}{4}$ pounds. How much heavier is Sherman's backpack than Brie's backpack? $\frac{1}{2}$ lb
18. Rosa jogged $10\frac{3}{16}$ miles in one week. The next week she jogged $8\frac{7}{16}$ miles. How many more miles did she jog the first week? $1\frac{3}{4}$ mi

Real-World PROBLEM SOLVING

Science The table shows the average lengths of common United States insects.

Insect	Length (in.)
Monarch Butterfly	$3\frac{4}{8}$
Walking Stick	4
Grasshopper	$1\frac{6}{8}$
Bumble Bee	$\frac{5}{8}$

Source: Natural Wildlife Federation

19. Find the difference in length between a walking stick and a bumble bee. $3\frac{3}{8}$ in.
20. ★ Is the difference in length between a monarch butterfly and a bumble bee greater or less than the difference in length between a walking stick and grasshopper? Explain your reasoning. greater than; $2\frac{7}{8} > 2\frac{1}{4}$

Additional Answers

5. Sample answer: Rename $3\frac{2}{7}$ to $2\frac{9}{7}$ then subtract $1\frac{4}{7}$ from $2\frac{9}{7}$. $1\frac{5}{7}$.
21. Sample answer: $7\frac{1}{6} - 2\frac{2}{6}$; $3\frac{5}{6}$
22. Rachel; Brandon did not rename $3\frac{1}{5}$ as an improper fraction.
23. Sample answer: A bottle of glue contains $3\frac{1}{4}$ ounces. A student uses $1\frac{3}{4}$ ounces on an art project. How much glue is left?; $1\frac{1}{2}$ ounces left
31. $\frac{1}{2}$ pizza; See students' work for models.

H.O.T. Problems

21–23. See margin.

21. **OPEN ENDED** Write a subtraction problem in which you have to rename a fraction and whose solution is between 3 and 4.

22. **FIND THE ERROR** Rachel and Brandon are finding $3\frac{1}{5} - 2\frac{3}{5}$. Who is correct? Explain.

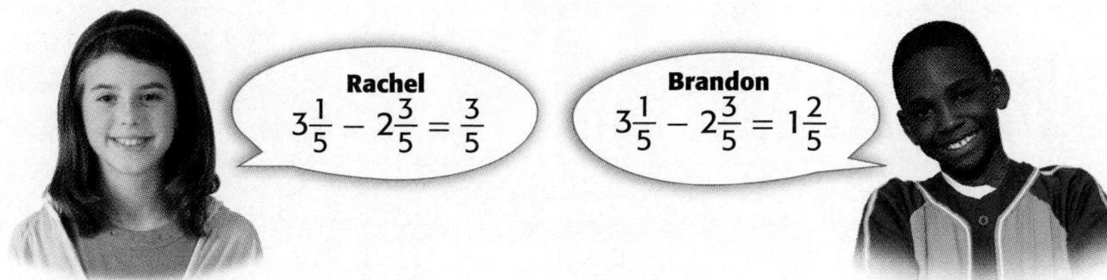

Rachel
$3\frac{1}{5} - 2\frac{3}{5} = \frac{3}{5}$
Brandon
$3\frac{1}{5} - 2\frac{3}{5} = 1\frac{2}{5}$

23. **WRITING IN MATH** Write a real-world problem involving subtraction in which you have to rename a fraction.

TEST Practice

24. Ross has 6 yards of material. He uses $2\frac{1}{3}$ yards. How many yards of material does he have left? (Lesson 10-8) C

A $2\frac{2}{3}$ yd **C** $3\frac{2}{3}$ yd
B $3\frac{1}{3}$ yd **D** $8\frac{1}{3}$ yd

25. Careta swam $7\frac{5}{8}$ miles. Joey swam $5\frac{1}{8}$ miles. How many more miles did Careta swim than Joey? (Lesson 10-8) H

F $13\frac{3}{4}$ mi **H** $2\frac{1}{2}$ mi
G $2\frac{6}{8}$ mi **J** $2\frac{1}{4}$ mi

Spiral Review

26. Kendra buys a sandwich for \$2.79, a carton of milk for \$0.65, and a bag of pretzels for \$0.99. How much more can she spend without going over \$6? (Lesson 10-9) \$1.57

Subtract. Write each difference in simplest form. (Lesson 10-8)

27. $5\frac{3}{10} - 2\frac{2}{10}$ $3\frac{1}{10}$ 28. $6\frac{9}{11} - 5\frac{2}{11}$ $1\frac{7}{11}$ 29. $14\frac{7}{9} - 12\frac{1}{9}$ $2\frac{2}{3}$ 30. $15\frac{6}{8} - 12\frac{1}{4}$ $3\frac{1}{2}$

31. Kira and Justin are sharing a pizza. Kira eats $\frac{2}{6}$ of the pizza, and Justin eats $\frac{1}{6}$ of the pizza. What part of the pizza did they eat in all? Support your answer with a model. (Lesson 10-1) See margin.

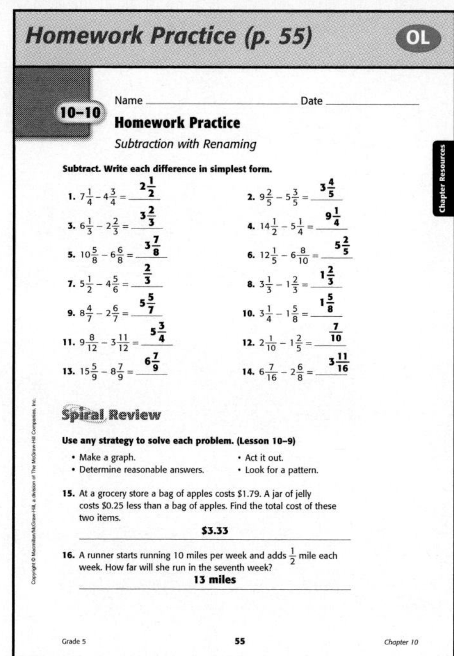
Homework Practice (p. 55) OL

10-10 Name ____________ Date ____________

Homework Practice

Subtraction with Renaming

Subtract. Write each difference in simplest form.

1. $7\frac{1}{4} - 4\frac{3}{4} =$ $2\frac{1}{2}$
2. $9\frac{2}{5} - 5\frac{3}{5} =$ $3\frac{4}{5}$
3. $6\frac{1}{3} - 2\frac{2}{3} =$ $3\frac{2}{3}$
4. $14\frac{1}{2} - 5\frac{1}{4} =$ $9\frac{1}{4}$
5. $10\frac{5}{8} - 6\frac{6}{8} =$ $3\frac{7}{8}$
6. $12\frac{1}{5} - 6\frac{8}{10} =$ $5\frac{2}{5}$
7. $5\frac{1}{2} - 4\frac{5}{6} =$ $\frac{2}{3}$
8. $3\frac{1}{3} - 1\frac{2}{3} =$ $1\frac{2}{3}$
9. $8\frac{4}{7} - 2\frac{6}{7} =$ $5\frac{5}{7}$
10. $3\frac{1}{4} - 1\frac{5}{8} =$ $1\frac{5}{8}$
11. $9\frac{8}{12} - 3\frac{11}{12} =$ $5\frac{3}{4}$
12. $2\frac{1}{10} - 1\frac{2}{5} =$ $\frac{7}{10}$
13. $15\frac{5}{9} - 8\frac{7}{9} =$ $6\frac{7}{9}$
14. $6\frac{7}{16} - 2\frac{6}{8} =$ $3\frac{11}{16}$

Chapter Resources

Spiral Review

Use any strategy to solve each problem. (Lesson 10–9)

- Make a graph.
- Determine reasonable answers.
- Act it out.
- Look for a pattern.

15. At a grocery store a bag of apples costs \$1.79. A jar of jelly costs \$0.25 less than a bag of apples. Find the total cost of these two items.

\$3.33

16. A runner starts running 10 miles per week and adds $\frac{1}{2}$ mile each week. How far will she run in the seventh week?

13 miles

Grade 5 55 *Chapter 10*

4 Assess

Formative Assessment

Write $9\frac{3}{10} - 5\frac{9}{10}$ on the board.

- **Do you need to rename $9\frac{3}{10}$ to subtract? Why or why not?** yes, because you cannot subtract $\frac{9}{10}$ from $\frac{3}{10}$
- **Explain how to rename and subtract. What is the difference in simplest form?** Rename $9\frac{3}{10}$ as $8\frac{13}{10}$. Subtract the fractions: $\frac{13}{10} - \frac{9}{10} = \frac{4}{10}$. Subtract the whole numbers: $8 - 5 = 3$. The difference is $3\frac{4}{10}$, which can be simplified to $3\frac{2}{5}$.

Quick Check **Are students continuing to struggle with subtracting mixed numbers with renaming?**

If Yes → Small Group Options (p. 458B)

If No → Independent Work Options (p. 458B)
CRM Skills Practice Worksheet (p. 54)
CRM Enrich Worksheet (p. 57)

Ticket Out the Door Write $11\frac{2}{8} - 4\frac{5}{8}$ on the board. Have students find the difference in simplest form and write it on a slip of paper to give to you as they leave class for the day.

TEST Practice

Reviews Lesson 10-8

Assign the Test Practice problems to provide daily reinforcement of test-taking skills.

Spiral Review

Reviews Lessons 10-1, 10-8, and 10-9

Review and assess mastery of skills and concepts from previous chapters.

Lesson Planner

Objective

Interpret information and data from science to solve problems.

National Standard 

Students will learn properties and changes of properties in matter.

Resources

Materials: paper, pencils

Activate Prior Knowledge

Before you turn students' attention to the pages, ask them to discuss mixtures.

- **What mixtures do you know of?** clay, paint
- **What do all mixtures have in common?** The substances in them can be physically separated.

Use the Student Page

Ask students to read the information on pp. 462–463 and answer these questions:

- **How many teaspoons of oil and food coloring do you need for one batch of clay?** $2\frac{1}{3}$ teaspoons
- **How much more water than glycerin do you need to make bubble-blowing liquid?** 4 cups

Making Mixtures

Mixtures are all around you. Rocks, air, and ocean water are all mixtures. So are paints, clay, and chalk. The substances in mixtures are combined physically, not chemically. Although some substances seem to dissolve in others, each substance in a mixture keeps its own physical properties. This means that the substances in mixtures can be physically separated.

You can make some fun mixtures by using specific amounts of substances. For example, to make one type of invisible ink, you use $\frac{1}{2}$ as much baking soda as water. If you use $\frac{1}{2}$ of a cup of water, you use $\frac{1}{4}$ of a cup of baking soda. You can use other recipes to make mixtures such as sculpting clay and bubble-blowing liquid.

Real-World Math

Use the information on page 463 to solve each problem.

1. How much water do you need to make a batch of clay? $1\frac{1}{4}$ c
2. How much more salt than cornstarch do you need to make a batch of clay? $\frac{2}{3}$ c
3. What amount of solid ingredients do you need to make a batch of clay? 4 c
4. How much liquid do you need to make bubble-blowing liquid? (*Hint:* Glycerin is a liquid.) $4\frac{1}{2}$ c
5. If you make three batches of clay, how much food coloring will you need? 2 tsp
6. If you make two batches of bubble-blowing liquid, how much water will you need? $8\frac{1}{2}$ c
7. If you make two batches of bubble-blowing liquid, how much soap will you need? $3\frac{1}{2}$ oz
8. How many teaspoons of oil and food coloring do you need to make one batch of clay? $2\frac{1}{3}$ tsp

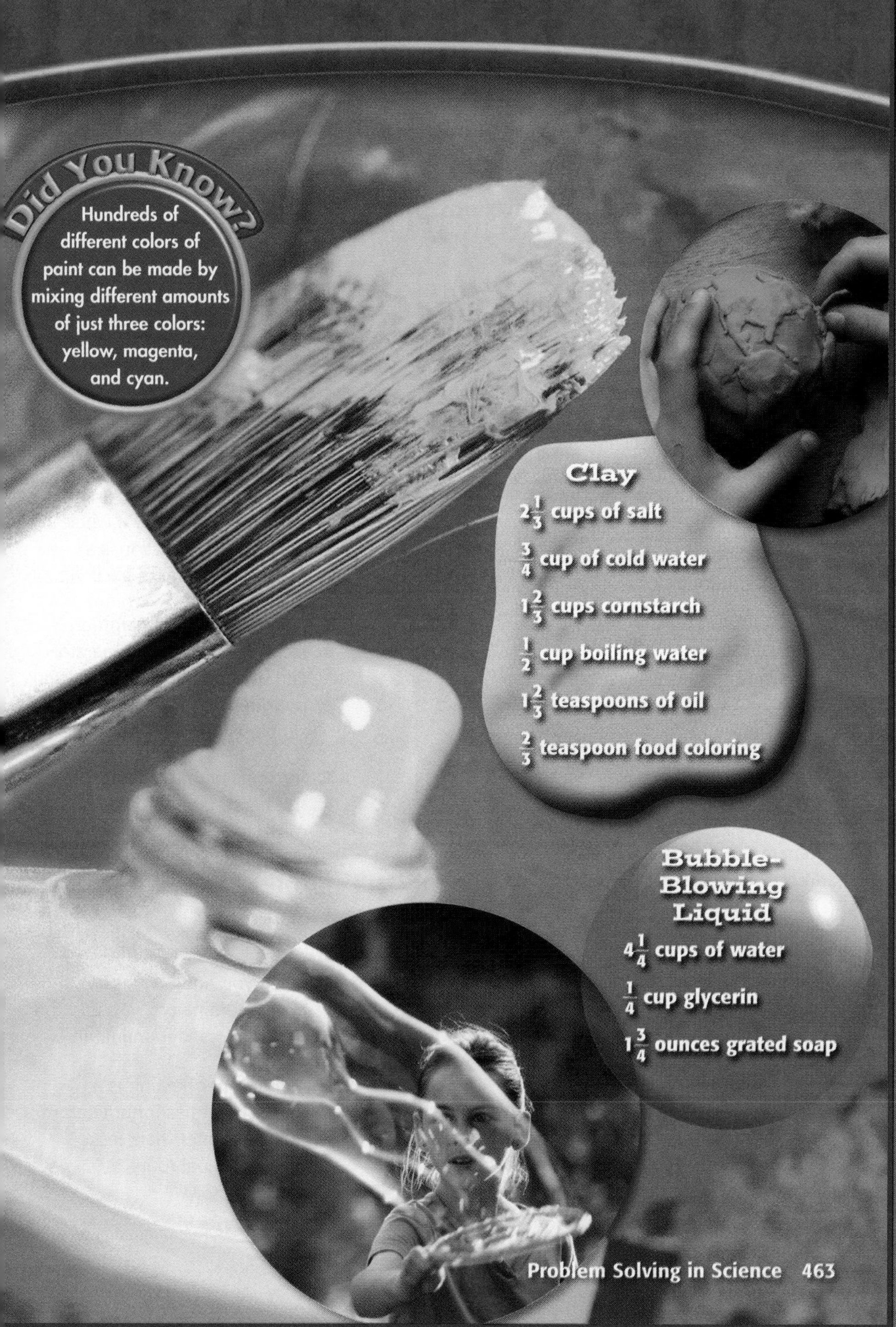
Did You Know?
Hundreds of different colors of paint can be made by mixing different amounts of just three colors: yellow, magenta, and cyan.
Clay
$2\frac{1}{3}$ cups of salt
$\frac{3}{4}$ cup of cold water
$1\frac{2}{3}$ cups cornstarch
$\frac{1}{2}$ cup boiling water
$1\frac{2}{3}$ teaspoons of oil
$\frac{2}{3}$ teaspoon food coloring
Bubble-Blowing Liquid
$4\frac{1}{4}$ cups of water
$\frac{1}{4}$ cup glycerin
$1\frac{3}{4}$ ounces grated soap
Problem Solving in Science 463

Real-World Math

Assign the exercises on p. 462. Encourage students to choose a problem-solving strategy before beginning each exercise. If necessary, review the strategies suggested in Lesson 10-9, p. 457.

Exercise 1 Point out to students that water appears twice in the list of ingredients for clay.

Exercise 4 Tell students that glycerin is a liquid.

Exercise 8 Tell students that they do not need to include the ingredients measured in teaspoons.

WRITING IN ▸MATH Have students create a word problem that uses the information found in the text and in the chart on p. 462.

Extend the Activity

Have students figure out how much of each ingredient they will need if they make one batch of clay and bubble-blowing liquid for each student in the class.

CHAPTER 10 Study Guide and Review

FOLDABLES Dinah Zike's Foldables

Use these lesson suggestions to incorporate the Foldable during the chapter. Students can then use their Foldables to review for the test.

Lesson 10-7, 10-8 Students use the left column of the Pocket Chart Foldable to list steps and define terms related to adding and subtracting like fractions and mixed numbers. Examples of student work on quarter sheets of paper or index cards should be stored in the left side pocket.

Lessons 10-7, 10-8 Students use the right column of the Pocket Chart Foldable to list steps and define terms related to adding and subtracting unlike fractions and mixed numbers. Examples of student work on quarter sheets of paper or index cards should be stored in the right side pocket.

Key Vocabulary

The page references after each word denote where that term was first introduced. If students have difficulty answering Exercises 1–6, remind them they can use the page references to review the vocabulary terms.

Vocabulary Review

Review chapter vocabulary using one of the following options.

- **Visual Vocabulary Cards** (17, 24)
- **eGlossary** at macmillanmh.com

CHAPTER 10 Study Guide and Review

FOLDABLES Study Organizer GET READY to Study

Be sure the following Big Ideas are written in your Foldable.

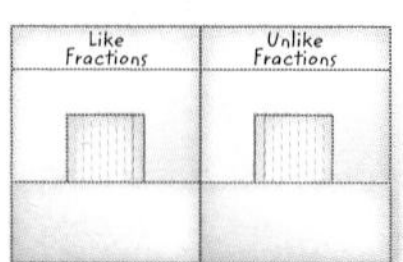

Key Concepts

Add and Subtract Like Fractions
(pp. 423, 424)

- Add or subtract the numerators. Use the same denominator.

$$\begin{array}{r} \frac{1}{4} \\ +\frac{2}{4} \\ \hline \frac{3}{4} \end{array} \qquad \begin{array}{r} \frac{5}{8} \\ -\frac{2}{8} \\ \hline \frac{3}{8} \end{array}$$

Add and Subtract Unlike Fractions
(pp. 434, 437)

- Rename the fraction using the LCD. Then add or subtract as with **like fractions**.

Estimation (p. 444)

- Estimate sums and differences of mixed numbers by rounding to the nearest whole number.

Add and Subtract Mixed Fractions
(pp. 448, 452)

- Add or subtract the fractions. Then add or subtract the whole numbers.

Key Vocabulary

like fractions (p. 421)
unlike fractions (p. 432)

Vocabulary Check

Choose the correct word or number that completes each sentence.

1. A number formed by a whole number and a fraction is a (mixed number, like fraction).
2. When the greatest common factor (GCF) of the numerator and denominator is 1, a fraction is written in (improper form, simplest form).
3. Fractions with the same (numerator, denominator) are called like fractions.
4. Fractions with different (numerators, denominators) are called unlike fractions.
5. When you add fractions with like denominators, you add the (numerators, denominators).
6. An improper fraction is a fraction that has a numerator that is (greater than, less than) or equal to its denominator.

Chapter 10 Project

Number Line Rounding Race

Alone, in pairs, or in small groups, have students discuss the results of their completed chapter project with the class. Assess their work using the Chapter Project rubric found in Chapter 10 Resource Masters, p. 68.

Lesson-by-Lesson Review

10-1 Add Like Fractions (pp. 423–425) 7–8. See students' work for models.

Example 1

Find $\frac{4}{10} + \frac{4}{10}$. Estimate $\frac{1}{2} + \frac{1}{2} = 1$

$\frac{4}{10} + \frac{4}{10} = \frac{4+4}{10}$ Add the numerators.

$= \frac{8}{10}$ Simplify.

$= \frac{8 \div 2}{10 \div 2}$ Divide by the GCF, 2.

$= \frac{4}{5}$ Simplify.

Add. Write each sum in simplest form. Check your answer by using models.

7. $\frac{3}{9} + \frac{6}{9}$ 1

8. $\frac{1}{6} + \frac{4}{6}$ $\frac{5}{6}$

9. What fraction of flowers in the table are either pansies or tulips? $\frac{5}{6}$

Flower	Number
Mums	3
Pansies	7
Tulips	8

10-2 Subtract Like Fractions (pp. 428–431) 10–11. See students' work for models.

Example 2

Find $\frac{11}{12} - \frac{5}{12}$. Estimate $1 - \frac{1}{2} = \frac{1}{2}$

$\frac{11}{12} - \frac{5}{12} = \frac{11-5}{12}$ Subtract the numerators.

$= \frac{6}{12}$ Simplify.

$= \frac{6 \div 6}{12 \div 6}$ Divide by the GCF, 6.

$= \frac{1}{2}$ Simplify.

Subtract. Write each difference in simplest form. Check your answer by using models.

10. $\frac{2}{9} - \frac{1}{9}$ $\frac{1}{9}$

11. $\frac{11}{14} - \frac{4}{14}$ $\frac{1}{2}$

12. A class is surveyed to find out their favorite color. Of the class, $\frac{7}{24}$ prefers red, $\frac{4}{24}$ prefers green, and $\frac{13}{24}$ prefers blue. What fraction of the class prefers blue over red? $\frac{6}{24}$ or $\frac{1}{4}$

10-3 Add Unlike Fractions (pp. 434–436)

Example 3

Find $\frac{2}{3} + \frac{1}{2}$.

$\frac{2 \times 2}{3 \times 2} = \frac{4}{6}$ Rename the fractions using the LCD.

$+\frac{1 \times 3}{2 \times 3} = \frac{3}{6}$ Add as with like fractions.

$= \frac{7}{6} = 1\frac{1}{6}$ Simplify.

Add. Write each sum in simplest form.

13. $\frac{1}{4} + \frac{3}{8}$ $\frac{5}{8}$

14. $\frac{1}{2} + \frac{2}{7}$ $\frac{11}{14}$

15. On Monday, Matt ran $\frac{4}{9}$ mile. On Tuesday, he ran $\frac{1}{3}$ mile. How far did he run in all? $\frac{7}{9}$

Lesson-by-Lesson Review

Have students complete the Lesson-by-Lesson Review on pp. 465–469. Then you can use ExamView® Assessment Suite to customize another review worksheet that practices all the objectives of this chapter or only the objectives on which your students need more help.

Intervention If the given examples are not sufficient to review the topics covered by the questions, remind students that the page references tell them where to review that topic in their textbook.

CHAPTER 10 Study Guide and Review

CHAPTER 10 Study Guide and Review

10-4 Subtract Unlike Fractions (pp. 439–441)

Example 4

Find $\frac{4}{5} - \frac{1}{4}$.

$$\frac{4 \times 4}{5 \times 4} = \frac{16}{20}$$

Rename the fractions using the LCD.

$$-\frac{1 \times 5}{4 \times 5} = \frac{5}{20}$$

Add as with like fractions.

$$= \frac{11}{20}$$

Subtract. Write each difference in simplest form.

16. $\frac{4}{6} - \frac{1}{2}$ $\frac{1}{6}$

17. $\frac{11}{12} - \frac{2}{3}$ $\frac{1}{4}$

18. Jada cleaned $\frac{7}{9}$ of her room. Trent cleaned $\frac{1}{2}$ of his room. How much more of her room did Jada clean? $\frac{5}{18}$

10-5 Problem-Solving Skill: Determine Reasonable Answers (pp. 442–443)

Example 5

Ted Hoz has the world's largest collection of golf balls. He has 74,849 golf balls. He estimates that he has room for 95,000 golf balls. Is 20,000 or 25,000 a more reasonable estimate for how many more golf balls he can collect?

Estimate 95,000–74,849.

Step 1 Round 74,849 to the nearest thousand.

$$74{,}849 \rightarrow 75{,}000$$

Step 2 Subtract.

$$\begin{array}{r} 95{,}000 \\ -\ 75{,}000 \\ \hline 20{,}000 \end{array}$$

So, Ted Hoz can collect about 20,000 more golf balls.

Solve. Determine which answer is reasonable. Explain your answer.

19. A footbag is a small bean bag controlled by the feet. The table shows how many times the male and female world record holders kicked a footbag.

Record Holder	Number of Times Kicking Footbag
Constance Constable	24,713
Ted Martin	63,326

Which is a more reasonable estimate for how many more times Ted Martin kicked the footbag than Constance Constable: 38,000 or 45,000? 38,000

20. Measurement Susan is $5\frac{5}{6}$ feet tall and her brother Nick is $4\frac{1}{6}$ feet tall. Which is a more reasonable estimate for how much taller Susan is than her brother: $1\frac{1}{2}$ feet, 2 feet, or 3 feet? 2 ft

466 Chapter 10 Add and Subtract Fractions

10-6 Estimate Sums and Differences (pp. 444–446)

Example 6

Estimate $8\frac{7}{9} - 5\frac{1}{9}$.

$$8\frac{7}{9} - 5\frac{1}{9}$$

$$\downarrow \quad \downarrow$$

Estimate $9 - 5 = 4$

So, $8\frac{7}{9} - 5\frac{1}{9}$ is about 4.

Estimate by rounding the mixed number to a whole number.

21. $4\frac{1}{3} + 3\frac{5}{6}$ 8 **22.** $8\frac{2}{3} - 3\frac{7}{9}$ 5

23. $14\frac{5}{12} - 8\frac{7}{12}$ 5 **24.** $12\frac{8}{15} + 9\frac{4}{15}$ 22

25. Darnell is $13\frac{3}{4}$ years old. His younger sister is $9\frac{1}{4}$ years old. About how many years older is Darnell? 5 yrs

10-7 Add Mixed Numbers (pp. 448–451) 30. $9\frac{1}{2}$ mi

Example 7

Find $5\frac{3}{6} + 2\frac{2}{6}$.

Step 1 Add the fractions.

$$\begin{array}{r} 5\frac{3}{6} \\ +\ 2\frac{2}{6} \\ \hline \frac{5}{6} \end{array}$$

Step 2 Add the whole numbers.

$$\begin{array}{r} 5\frac{3}{6} \\ +\ 2\frac{2}{6} \\ \hline 7\frac{5}{6} \end{array}$$

Add. Write each sum in simplest form.

26. $1\frac{1}{5} + 2\frac{3}{5}$ $3\frac{4}{5}$ **27.** $2\frac{3}{9} + 6\frac{1}{3}$ $8\frac{2}{3}$

28. $3\frac{3}{10} + 7\frac{7}{10}$ 11 **29.** $8\frac{7}{12} + 7\frac{2}{3}$ $16\frac{1}{4}$

30. Vera and Sonia went canoeing. They traveled $5\frac{3}{8}$ miles in the morning and $4\frac{1}{8}$ miles in the afternoon. How many miles did they canoe altogether?

10-8 Subtract Mixed Numbers (pp. 452–454)

Example 8

Find $4\frac{5}{6} - 3\frac{2}{6}$.

Step 1 Subtract the fractions.

$$\begin{array}{r} 4\frac{5}{6} \\ -\ 3\frac{2}{6} \\ \hline \frac{3}{6} \end{array}$$

Step 2 Subtract the whole numbers.

$$\begin{array}{r} 4\frac{5}{6} \\ -\ 3\frac{2}{6} \\ \hline 1\frac{3}{6} = 1\frac{1}{2} \end{array}$$

Subtract. Write each difference in simplest form.

31. $3\frac{4}{5} - 1\frac{3}{5}$ $2\frac{1}{5}$ **32.** $5\frac{8}{9} - 3\frac{5}{9}$ $2\frac{1}{3}$

33. $14\frac{11}{12} - 8\frac{7}{12}$ $6\frac{1}{3}$ **34.** $19\frac{14}{15} - 12\frac{1}{5}$ $7\frac{11}{15}$

35. In one week, the fifth grade class recycled $9\frac{2}{3}$ pounds of glass, and $12\frac{3}{4}$ pounds of newspaper. How many more pounds of newspaper than glass did the class recycle? $3\frac{1}{12}$

Chapter 10 Study Guide and Review **467**

CHAPTER 10 Study Guide and Review

10-9 Problem-Solving Investigation: Choose a Strategy (pp. 456–457)

Example 9

After one month, Migina had saved \$25. After 2 months, she had saved \$40. After 3 months, she had saved \$55. Suppose she continues saving at this rate. How long will it take Migina to save enough money to buy a satellite radio that costs \$90?

To solve the problem, you can use the *look for a pattern* strategy.

\$25 → \$40 → \$55 → \$70 → \$85 → \$100 (each step +15)

She will have saved enough money in 6 months.

Solve.

36. **Measurement** Frank is building steps for a porch. He has $12\frac{5}{6}$ feet of wood. He needs to build 4 steps. If each step uses $3\frac{1}{3}$ feet of wood, does he have enough to make 4 steps? Explain.
No, $3\frac{1}{3} + 3\frac{1}{3} + 3\frac{1}{3} + 3\frac{1}{3} = 13\frac{1}{3}$

37. Mrs. Orta is making candles for the school craft show. The supplies needed to make a dozen candles cost \$5.25. How much profit will Mrs. Orta make if she sells all the candles for \$4.25 each? \$45.75

10-10 Subtraction with Renaming (pp. 458–461)

Example 10

Find $7\frac{1}{5} - 2\frac{4}{5}$. Estimate $7 - 3 = 4$

Since $\frac{1}{5}$ is less than $\frac{4}{5}$, rename $7\frac{1}{5}$.

THINK $7\frac{1}{5} = 6 + \frac{5}{5} + \frac{1}{5} = 6\frac{6}{5}$

$7\frac{1}{5} \rightarrow 6\frac{6}{5}$ Rename $7\frac{1}{5}$ as $6\frac{6}{5}$.

$-2\frac{4}{5} \rightarrow -2\frac{4}{5}$ Subtract.

$4\frac{2}{5}$

So, $7\frac{1}{5} - 2\frac{4}{5} = 4\frac{2}{5}$.

38–41. See students' work for models.

Subtract. Write each difference in simplest form. Check your answer by using models. 42. $3\frac{2}{3}$ mi

38. $5\frac{1}{8} - 2\frac{6}{8}$ $2\frac{3}{8}$
39. $8\frac{3}{7} - 3\frac{6}{7}$ $4\frac{4}{7}$
40. $9\frac{4}{9} - 8\frac{7}{9}$ $\frac{2}{3}$
41. $15\frac{6}{10} - 8\frac{4}{5}$ $6\frac{4}{5}$
42. Jin lives 10 miles from the beach. Her friend lives $6\frac{1}{3}$ miles from the beach. How much farther does Jin live from the beach than her friend?

Chapter Test

Math Online macmillanmh.com
• Chapter Test

Add or subtract. Write each sum or difference in simplest form.

1. $\frac{9}{11} + \frac{1}{11}$ $\frac{10}{11}$

2. $\frac{9}{13} - \frac{7}{13}$ $\frac{2}{13}$

3. $\frac{4}{7} - \frac{1}{3}$ $\frac{5}{21}$

4. $\frac{4}{15} + \frac{3}{5}$ $\frac{13}{15}$

5. MULTIPLE CHOICE Zacharias has $\frac{2}{3}$ cup of pasta. He uses $\frac{1}{3}$ cup for a salad as shown in the measuring cups below. C

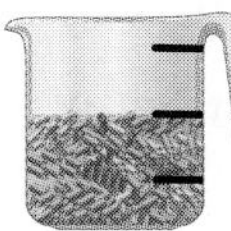
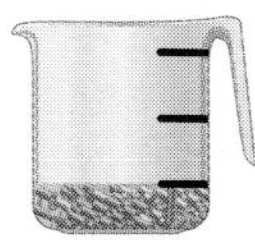

How much pasta does he have left?

A 1 c **C** $\frac{1}{3}$ c

B $\frac{1}{2}$ c **D** 0 c

6. Measurement On a recent trip around Kentucky, Mr. Chavez drove 83 miles from Newport to Lexington and then 77 miles from Lexington to Louisville. Which is a reasonable estimate for the total number of miles he drove: 100 miles, 160 miles, or 180 miles? 160 mi

7. A sea otter remained underwater for $\frac{6}{8}$ minute. Then it came back to the surface for air. It dove a second time and stayed underwater for $\frac{3}{4}$ minute. About how long was the sea otter underwater altogether? $\frac{12}{8}$ or $1\frac{1}{2}$ minutes

Estimate by rounding the mixed number to a whole number.

8. $6\frac{1}{5} - 4\frac{3}{5}$ 1

9. $9\frac{4}{5} + 1\frac{3}{10}$ 11

10. $8\frac{3}{11} + 3\frac{6}{11}$ 12

11. $12\frac{8}{15} - 7\frac{1}{3}$ 6

Add or subtract. Write each sum or difference in simplest form.

12. $9\frac{4}{6} - 5\frac{1}{2}$ $4\frac{1}{6}$

13. $3\frac{1}{9} + 7\frac{6}{9}$ $10\frac{7}{9}$

14. $14\frac{9}{12} - 8\frac{1}{4}$ $6\frac{1}{2}$

15. $9\frac{5}{16} + 11\frac{7}{16}$ $20\frac{3}{4}$

16. MULTIPLE CHOICE On Saturday, Phoebe biked $5\frac{2}{10}$ miles. Then she biked $6\frac{6}{10}$ miles on Sunday. How many miles did she bike altogether? G

F $12\frac{8}{10}$ mi **H** $11\frac{8}{20}$ mi

G $11\frac{4}{5}$ mi **J** $1\frac{2}{5}$ mi

17. Algebra What is the next figure in the pattern?

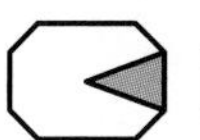
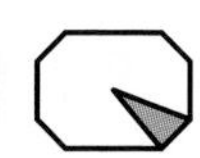

See Ch. 10 Answer Appendix.

Subtract. Write each difference in simplest form.

18. $16\frac{1}{10} - 7\frac{3}{10}$ $8\frac{4}{5}$

19. $20\frac{1}{3} - 5\frac{5}{6}$ $14\frac{1}{2}$

20. WRITING IN MATH Explain how you would find $4 - 3\frac{5}{6}$. Justify your steps by using a model. See Ch. 10 Answer Appendix.

Chapter 10 Chapter Test

Summative Assessment

Use these alternate leveled chapter tests to differentiate assessment for the specific needs of your students.

Leveled Chapter 10 Tests			
Form	**Type**	**Level**	**CRM Pages**
1	Multiple Choice	BL	70–71
2A	Multiple Choice	OL	72–73
2B	Multiple Choice	OL	74–75
2C	Free Response	AL	76–77
2D	Free Response	AL	78–79
3	Free Response	AL	80–81

BL = below/approaching grade level
OL = on grade level
AL = above/beyond grade level

Vocabulary Test

CRM **Chapter 10 Resource Masters** (p. 65)

ExamView Assessment Suite Customize and create multiple versions of your Chapter Test and the test answer keys.

Data-Driven Decision Making

Based on the results of the Chapter Test, use the following to review concepts that continue to present students with problems.

Exercises	State/Local Standards	What's the Math?	Error Analysis	Resources for Review
1–5, 12–16, 18–19		Add or subtract fractions and mixed numbers and write answers in simplest form.	Does not add or subtract accurately. Does not know how to reduce fractions to simplest form. Does not understand "sum," "difference," "justify your steps."	CRM Chapter 10 Resource Masters (Reteach Worksheets) Math Adventures My Math Zone Chapter 10 Math Online Extra Examples • Concepts in Motion
6–7, 17, 20		Choose a strategy to solve a problem.	Does not know what information to use to solve word problems. Does not choose correct process to compute answers.	
8–11		Estimate by rounding mixed number to a whole number.	Does not estimate to find answer. Does not understand "estimate by rounding," "whole number."	

Chapter 10 Test Practice

Formative Assessment

- Use Student Edition pp. 470–471 as practice and cumulative review. The questions are written in the same style as many state tests.
- You can also use these two pages to benchmark student progress, or as an alternate homework assignment.

Additional practice pages can be found in the Chapter 10 Resource Masters.

CRM Chapter 10 Resource Masters
Cumulative Test Practice

- Multiple Choice format
- Free Response format

Create practice worksheets or tests that align to your state standards.

Math Online Have students visit macmillanmh.com for additional practice to reinforce your state standards.

Test Practice

Cumulative, Chapters 1–10

Math Online macmillanmh.com
• Test Practice

PART I Multiple Choice

Read each question. Then fill in the correct answer on the answer sheet provided by your teacher or on a sheet of paper.

1. Hakeem ate $\frac{1}{4}$ of a pie. His two brothers each ate $\frac{1}{8}$ of the pie. How much of the pie did Hakeem and his brothers eat altogether? C

A $\frac{1}{3}$

B $\frac{2}{8}$

C $\frac{1}{2}$

D $\frac{5}{8}$

2. Last school week, it rained 2 out of 5 days. Which fraction is greater than $\frac{2}{5}$? F

F $\frac{1}{2}$ **H** $\frac{1}{4}$

G $\frac{1}{3}$ **J** $\frac{3}{16}$

3. Javier made a pan of brownies to share with his classmates. The pan was divided evenly into 30 brownies. Javier gave away 20 brownies. What fraction of the brownies did he have left? B

A $\frac{1}{4}$ **C** $\frac{2}{3}$

B $\frac{1}{3}$ **D** $\frac{3}{4}$

4. The graph shows some areas around Anica's home town.

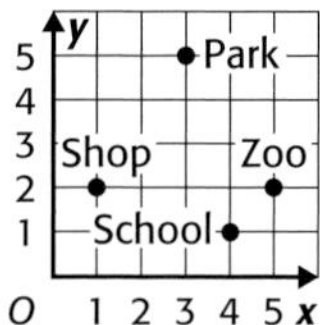

Which ordered pair best represents the point on the graph labeled "School"? G

F (1, 2) **H** (5, 2)

G (4, 1) **J** (1, 4)

5. Enrique and Sydney are making oatmeal raisin cookies. Enrique's recipe calls for $\frac{1}{2}$ cup of raisins per dozen, and Sydney's recipe calls for $\frac{5}{8}$ cup of raisins per dozen. How many raisins do they need in all? B

A 1

B $1\frac{1}{8}$

C $1\frac{1}{2}$

D 2

6. Malak's family bought a bag of apples at a farmer's market. If they ate $\frac{7}{12}$ of the apples, what fraction of the apples remained? G

F $\frac{1}{3}$ **H** $\frac{1}{2}$

G $\frac{5}{12}$ **J** $\frac{2}{3}$

Test-Taking Tip

Remind students to be sure that they are answering the question that is being asked.

7. Agustin has completed $\frac{5}{12}$ of his project, and Evelina has completed $\frac{2}{6}$ of her project. How much more of the project does Agustin have finished than Evelina? **A**

A $\frac{1}{12}$ **C** $\frac{3}{4}$

B $\frac{2}{6}$ **D** $\frac{11}{12}$

8. Myron gives his cat $\frac{2}{5}$ cup of dry food in the morning and $\frac{1}{5}$ cup of dry food in the afternoon, as shown below. How much dry food does he give his cat each day? **G**

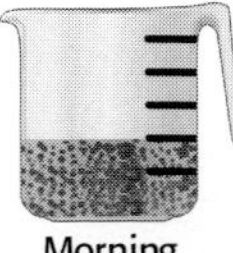
Morning

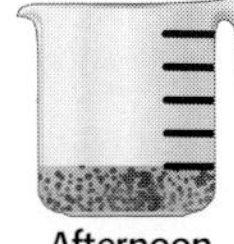
Afternoon

F $\frac{2}{5}$ cup **H** $\frac{4}{5}$ cup

G $\frac{3}{5}$ cup **J** 1 cup

9. Which fraction is greater than $\frac{3}{4}$? **B**

A $\frac{1}{2}$ **C** $\frac{1}{3}$

B $\frac{6}{7}$ **D** $\frac{3}{8}$

PART 2 Short Response

Record your answers on the sheet provided by your teacher or on a sheet of paper.

10. Explain how to find the *x*-coordinate of point *P* shown below. **See margin.**

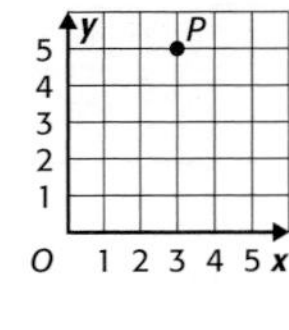

11. Malcom delivered $\frac{1}{3}$ of the newspapers. Angela delivered $\frac{2}{3}$ of the newspapers. Are there any newspapers that still need to be delivered? Explain. **See margin.**

PART 3 Extended Response

Record your answers on the answer sheet provided by your teacher or on a sheet of paper. Show your work.

12. Compare $\frac{2}{3}$ and $\frac{1}{8}$ using a drawing. **See margin.**

13. Explain how to find $5\frac{1}{8} + 6\frac{2}{4}$. **See margin.**

NEED EXTRA HELP?													
If You Missed Question...	1	2	3	4	5	6	7	8	9	10	11	12	13
Go to Lesson...	10-3	9-9	10-2	6-4	10-7	10-2	10-8	10-1	9-9	6-4	10-3	9-9	10-7

Answer Sheet Practice

Have students simulate taking a state test by recording their answers on a practice recording sheet.

CRM Chapter 10 Resource Masters
Student Recording Sheet (p. 86)

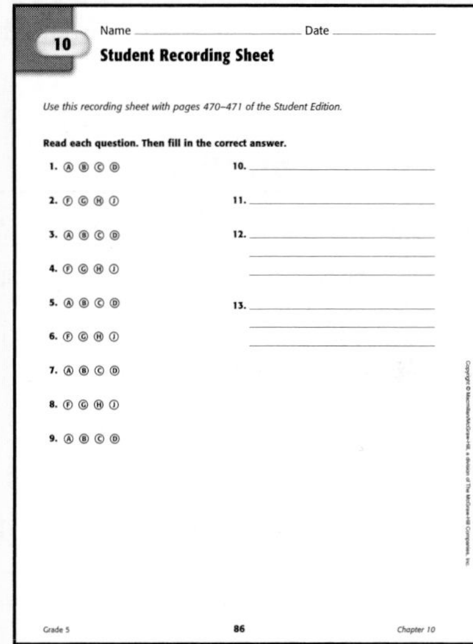
10 Name ______ Date ______
Student Recording Sheet

Use this recording sheet with pages 470–471 of the Student Edition.

Read each question. Then fill in the correct answer.

1. Ⓐ Ⓑ Ⓒ Ⓓ
2. Ⓕ Ⓖ Ⓗ Ⓙ
3. Ⓐ Ⓑ Ⓒ Ⓓ
4. Ⓕ Ⓖ Ⓗ Ⓙ
5. Ⓐ Ⓑ Ⓒ Ⓓ
6. Ⓕ Ⓖ Ⓗ Ⓙ
7. Ⓐ Ⓑ Ⓒ Ⓓ
8. Ⓕ Ⓖ Ⓗ Ⓙ
9. Ⓐ Ⓑ Ⓒ Ⓓ

10. ______
11. ______
12. ______
13. ______

Grade 5 86 Chapter 10

Additional Answers

10. Move three spaces to the right. The *x*-coodinate is 3.

11. No; $\frac{1}{3} + \frac{2}{3} = 1$; all of the newspapers have been delivered.

12.

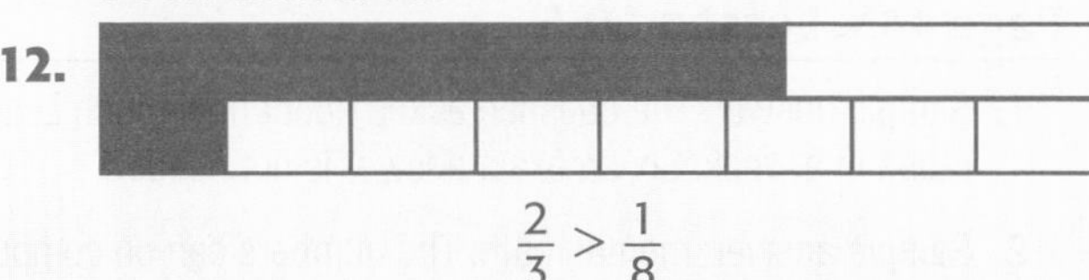

$$\frac{2}{3} > \frac{1}{8}$$

13. Sample answer: Add the whole numbers 5 + 6. Rename the fractions using a common denominator. This changes the fraction $\frac{2}{4}$ to $\frac{4}{8}$. Add the fractions. The answer is $11\frac{5}{8}$.

Pages 424–425, Lesson 10-1

8. Add five twelfths and 4 twelfths which equal nine twelfths. Then divide the numerator and the denominator by three, the GCF, to simplify the answer.

19. $1\frac{4}{5}$ mi;

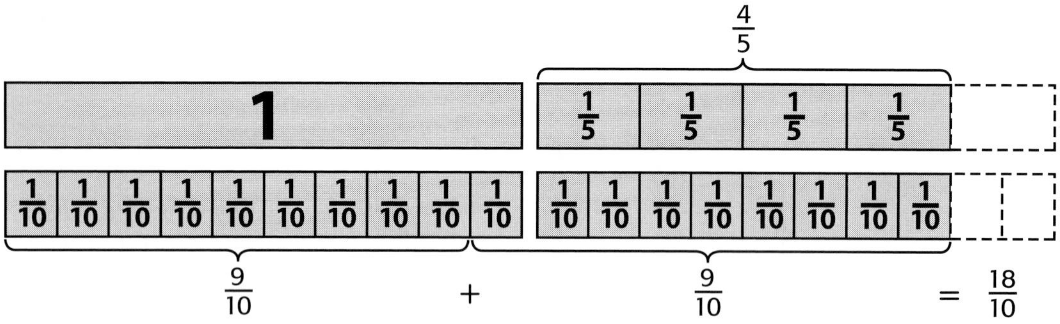

$\frac{4}{5}$

1 | $\frac{1}{5}$ | $\frac{1}{5}$ | $\frac{1}{5}$ | $\frac{1}{5}$

$\frac{1}{10}$ | $\frac{1}{10}$ | $\frac{1}{10}$ | $\frac{1}{10}$ | $\frac{1}{10}$ | $\frac{1}{10}$ | $\frac{1}{10}$ | $\frac{1}{10}$ | $\frac{1}{10}$ | $\frac{1}{10}$ | $\frac{1}{10}$ | $\frac{1}{10}$ | $\frac{1}{10}$ | $\frac{1}{10}$ | $\frac{1}{10}$ | $\frac{1}{10}$ | $\frac{1}{10}$ | $\frac{1}{10}$

$\frac{9}{10} + \frac{9}{10} = \frac{18}{10}$

28. Sample answer: $\frac{8}{16}$ and $\frac{4}{16}$; $\frac{8}{16} + \frac{4}{16} = \frac{12}{16}$ or $\frac{3}{4}$

29. Sample answer: Geoff planted tomato plants in $\frac{3}{10}$ of his garden. He planted roses in $\frac{2}{10}$ of the garden. What fraction of his garden has he planted?; $\frac{1}{2}$

Page 435-436, Lesson 10-3

14. Sample answer: Rename $\frac{5}{6}$ as $\frac{10}{12}$ so that the fractions have like denominators. Then add the numerators and simplify the answer; $\frac{11}{4}$.

32. Josh; Kate did not rename fractions using the LCD. She incorrectly added the numerators and added the denominators.

33. Sample answer: One group of volunteers picked up litter along a section of highway $\frac{5}{6}$ mile long. Another group picked up litter along a section $\frac{1}{4}$ mile long. What was the total length of highway that was cleaned up? Answer: $\frac{11}{12}$ mi

Page 441, Lesson 10-4

30. Sample answer: When fractions have like denominators, subtract the numerators and write the answer over the common denominator. When fractions have unlike denominators, first find a common denominator and rename one or both of the fractions. Then subtract the numerators and write the answer over the common denominator.

Page 443, Lesson 10-5

1. Sample answer: The question asked about how much Leandra feeds his rabbit in a week. So, an exact answer is not needed.

2. Sample answer: mental math; The numbers can be computed "in my head"

4. Sample answer: paper and pencil; An exact answer was needed and the calculations were simple.

8. Sample answer: Round $9\frac{1}{10}$ down to 9 and round $253\frac{1}{2}$ up to 254. So, 9 lb + 254 lb is 263 lb.

9. Sample answer: Round $5\frac{3}{4}$ up to 6 and round $3\frac{1}{4}$ down to 3. So, 6 lb − 3 lb is 3 lb.

10. Sample answer: A television stand is $46\frac{3}{8}$ inches tall. A television is $35\frac{1}{8}$ inches tall. What is the combined height of the television and stand?; paper and pencil; $81\frac{1}{2}$ in.

Pages 445–446, Lesson 10-6

1. Sample answer: 2 + 4 = 6 **2.** Sample answer: 4 + 1 = 5

3. Sample answer: 5 - 4 = 1 **4.** Sample answer: 8 - 4 = 4

5. Sample answer: 2 + 2 = 4; 4 h

7. Sample answer: 9 - 6 = 3 **8.** Sample answer: 7 - 1 = 6

9. Sample answer: 5 + 4 = 9

10. Sample answer: 9 + 4 = 13

11. Sample answer: 10 + 8 = 18

12. Sample answer: 13 + 10 = 23

13. Sample answer: 15 − 4 = 11

14. Sample answer: 13 − 4 = 9

15. Sample answer: 8 - 1 = 7 **16.** Sample answer: 9 - 1 = 8

17. Sample answer: 19 + 1 = 20

18. Sample answer: 1 + 17 = 18

19. Sample answer: 6 − 4 = 2; 2 yr

20. Sample answer: 3 + 3 = 6; 8 − 6 = 2; 2 oz

21. Sample answer: 9 + 3 = 12; 15 − 12 = 3; 3 ft

27. Sample answer: $2\frac{9}{10}$, $2\frac{1}{3}$; Round $2\frac{9}{10}$ up to 3. Round $2\frac{1}{3}$ down to 2. So, 3 − 2 = 1.

28. Sample answer: <; $3\frac{7}{8}$ is almost 4 and $4\frac{5}{11} < 5$. So, $3\frac{7}{8} + 4\frac{5}{11}$ is about 4 + 4 or 8.

29. Sample answer: >; $6\frac{7}{9}$ is almost 7 and $5\frac{3}{8} < 6$. So, $6\frac{7}{9} - 5\frac{3}{8}$ is about 7 − 5 or 2.

30. Sample answer: >; $4\frac{8}{10}$ is almost 5 and $3\frac{1}{5} < 4$. So, $4\frac{8}{10} - 3\frac{1}{5}$ is about 5 − 3 or 2.

31. Sample answer: Suppose you are building a sandbox that is $5\frac{2}{6}$ inches wide and $8\frac{5}{6}$ inches long. Estimate how much wood you will need. You would want to round both numbers up, so that you would have enough wood to build the sand box

Page 447, Mid-Chapter Check

13. Sample answer: Round 156.99 up to 160 and round 19.99 up to 20. So, $156 − $20 = $136.

20. Sample answer: three sixths plus two sixths equal five sixths; $\frac{5}{6}$

Pages 453–454, Lesson 10-8

8. Sample answer: First, subtract the fraction. Then subtract the whole numbers. Simplify if needed.

27. Sample answer: A baker had $5\frac{3}{4}$ cups of flour. He used $4\frac{1}{4}$ cups for two different recipes. How many cups of flour does he have left?; $1\frac{1}{2}$ c

31. $7\frac{3}{4} - 5\frac{2}{4}$; because its value is $2\frac{1}{4}$; the other three expressions have values of $2\frac{1}{2}$.

32. Sample answer: Joe has $3\frac{5}{8}$ cups of sugar. He used $1\frac{1}{4}$ cups. How much sugar does he have left? $2\frac{3}{8}$

Page 457, Lesson 10-9

1. No; Sample answer: $7\frac{5}{8} + 4\frac{7}{8} = 12\frac{1}{2}$; since $12\frac{1}{2} > 12$, she does not have enough ribbon.

5. 5 quarters, 1 nickel, 2 pennies

7.

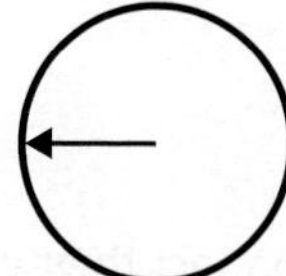

9. 56 mi

10. 2 students

11. Act it out because by acting out the order of the people, you can easily see what place each person finished.

Page 469, Chapter Test

17.

20. Sample answer:

Step 1: Rename 4 as $3\frac{6}{6}$.

Step 2: Then find $3\frac{6}{6} - 3\frac{5}{6}$.

Step 3: $3\frac{6}{6} - 3\frac{5}{6} = \frac{1}{6}$. See student work for models.

Chapter Overview

Chapter-at-a-Glance

In Chapter 11, the emphasis is on using customary units of length, weight, capacity, and time.

Lesson	Math Objective	State/Local Standards
EXPLORE 11-1 **Measure With a Ruler** (pp. 475–476)	Measure length to the nearest half inch and quarter inch.	
11-1 **Units of Length** (pp. 477–478)	Choose an appropriate customary unit for measuring length and convert customary units of length.	
11-2 **Problem-Solving Strategy: Draw a Diagram** (pp. 482–483)	Solve problems by drawing a diagram.	
11-3 **Units of Weight** (pp. 484–487)	Convert customary units of weight.	
11-4 **Units of Capacity** (pp. 488–490)	Convert customary units of capacity.	
11-5 **Units of Time** (pp. 492–495)	Convert units of time.	
11-6 **Problem-Solving Investigation: Choose a Strategy** (pp. 496–497)	Choose the best strategy to solve a problem.	
11-7 **Elapsed Time** (pp. 498–501)	Add and subtract measures of time.	

Use Measures in the Customary System

BIG Idea Measurement is one of the most practical real-life experiences that students learn in mathematics. It is important that students can explain what measurable attributes are associated with different objects or situations. It is necessary to not only teach conversion of measurements, but we must provide students with opportunities to measure using a variety of tools. Taking advantage of cross-curricular instruction in science, physical education, and art will give students practical applications with measurement.

Measurement Students measure and use units of length. This concept will help prepare them for measurement concepts, such as finding perimeter and area. (Lesson 11-1)

G5-FP5C Measurement: Students' experiences connect their work with solids and volume to their earlier work with capacity and weight or mass. They solve problems that require attention to both approximation and percision of measurement.

Skills Trace

Vertical Alignment

Fourth Grade

In fourth grade, students learned to:

- Estimate, measure and convert customary units of length, capacity, weight, and volume.
- Measure temperature and calculate changes in temperature.

Fifth Grade

During this chapter, students learn to:

- Convert customary units of length, weight, capacity, and time.
- Choose an appropriate customary unit for measuring length.
- Add and subtract measures.

After this chapter, students learn to:

- Convert metric units of length, mass, and capacity.
- Choose appropriate temperatures in degrees Fahrenheit and Celsius for real-life situations.

Sixth Grade

In sixth grade, students learn to:

- Change units of length and measure length, capacity, weight, and time in the customary system.

Backmapping and Vertical Alignment McGraw-Hill's *Math Connects* program was conceived and developed with the final results in mind: student success in Algebra 1 and beyond. The authors, using the **NCTM Focal Points and Focal Connections** as their guide, developed this brand new series by backmapping from Algebra 1 concepts, and vertically aligning the topics so that they build upon prior skills and concepts and serve as a foundation for future topics.

Math Vocabulary

The following math vocabulary words for Chapter 11 are listed in the glossary of the ***Student Edition***. You can find interactive definitions in 13 languages in the ***eGlossary*** at macmillanmh.com.

capacity The amount a container can hold, measured in units of dry or liquid measure. (p. 488A)

cup A customary unit of capacity equal to 8 fluid ounces. (p. 488A)

customary units The measurement system that includes units such as foot, pound, quart, and degrees Fahrenheit. See Table of Measures. Also called standard measurement. (p. 477A)

elapsed time The amount of time between the beginning and end of an activity. (p. 500A)

fluid ounce A customary unit of capacity. (p. 488A)

foot A customary unit for measuring length. The plural is feet. 1 foot = 12 inches (p. 477A)

gallon A customary unit for measuring capacity for unit liquids. 1 gallon = 4 quarts (p. 488A)

mile A customary unit of measure for distance. 1 mile = 5280 feet. (p. 477A)

ounce A customary unit for measuring weight or capacity. (p. 484A)

pound A customary unit for measuring weight or mass. 1 pound = 16 ounces (p. 484A)

ton A customary unit to measure weight. 1 ton = 2000 pounds (p. 484A)

weight A measurement that tells how heavy an object is. (p. 484A)

Chapter Planner

Suggested Pacing		
Instruction	Review & Assessment	TOTAL
8 days	1 day	**9 days**

Diagnostic Assessment
Quick Check (p. 474)

	Explore 11-1 (Pacing: 1 day)	Lesson 11-1 (Pacing: 1 day)	Lesson 11-2 (Pacing: 1 day)
Lesson/ Objective	**Measure with a Ruler** (pp. 475–476) **Objective:** Measure length to the nearest half inch and quarter inch.	**Units of Length** (pp. 477–480) **Objective:** Choose an appropriate customary unit for measuring length and convert customary units of length.	**Problem-Solving Strategy Draw a Diagram** (pp. 482–483) **Objective:** Solve problems by drawing a diagram.
State/Local Standards			
Math Vocabulary	**length**	**customary units, foot, inch, yard, mile, convert**	
Lesson Resources	**Manipulatives** rulers	**Materials** index cards **Manipulatives** ruler **Other Resources** CRM Leveled Worksheets (pp. 8–12) Daily Reteach • 5-Minute Check • Problem of the Day	**Other Resources** CRM Leveled Worksheets (pp. 13–17) Daily Reteach • 5-Minute Check • Problem of the Day *City Planning*
Technology		Math Adventures	
Math Online	Concepts in Motion	Personal Tutor	
Reaching All Learners		English Learners, p. 477B ELL Gifted and Talented, p. 477B AL Early Finishers, p. 477B OL AL	English Learners, p. 482B ELL Below Level, p. 482B BL Early Finishers, p. 482B OL AL
Alternate Lesson		*IMPACT Mathematics:* Unit H	

Game Time
Mystery Measurements (p. 481)

Use Measures in the Customary System

	Lesson 11-3 (Pacing: 1 day)	Lesson 11-4 (Pacing: 1 day)	Lesson 11-5 (Pacing: 1 day)
Lesson/ Objective	**Units of Weight** (pp. 484–487) **Objective:** Convert customary units of weight.	**Units of Capacity** (pp. 488–490) **Objective:** Convert customary units of capacity.	**Units of Time** (pp. 492–495) **Objective:** Convert units of time.
State/Local Standards			
Math Vocabulary	**weight, pound, ounce, ton**	**capacity, cup, fluid ounce, pint, quart, gallon**	
Lesson Resources	**Materials** art paper, index cards **Other Resources** CRM Leveled Worksheets (pp. 18–22) Daily Reteach • 5-Minute Check • Problem of the Day	**Materials** water **Manipulatives** capacity containers **Other Resources** CRM Leveled Worksheets (pp. 23–27) Daily Reteach • 5-Minute Check • Problem of the Day	**Materials** chart paper **Other Resources** CRM Leveled Worksheets (pp. 28–32) Daily Reteach • 5-Minute Check • Problem of the Day
Technology **Math Online**	Math Adventures Personal Tutor	Math Adventures Personal Tutor	Math Adventures Personal Tutor
Reaching All Learners	English Learners, p. 484B ELL Gifted and Talented, p. 484B AL Early Finishers, p. 484B AL	English Learners, p. 488B ELL Below Level, p. 488B BL Early Finishers, p. 488B AL	English Learners, p. 492B ELL Gifted and Talented, p. 492B AL Early Finishers, p. 492B AL
Alternate Lesson			*IMPACT Mathematics:* Unit H

Formative Assessment
Mid-Chapter Check (p. 491)

Chapter Planner

	Lesson 11-6 (Pacing: 1 day)	Lesson 11-7 (Pacing: 1 day)
Lesson/ Objective	**Problem-Solving Investigation** **Choose a Strategy** (pp. 496–497) **Objective:** Choose the best strategy to solve a problem.	**Elapsed Time** (pp. 500–503) **Objective:** Add and subtract measures of time.
State/Local Standards		
Math Vocabulary		**elapsed time**
Lesson Resources	**Other Resources** CRM Leveled Worksheets (pp. 33–37) Daily Reteach • 5-Minute Check • Problem of the Day *City Planning*	**Manipulatives** demonstration clock **Other Resources** CRM Leveled Worksheets (pp. 38–42) Daily Reteach • 5-Minute Check • Problem of the Day
Technology		Math Adventures
Math Online		Personal Tutor
Reaching All Learners	English Learners, p. 496B ELL Below Level, p. 496B BL Early Finishers, p. 496B OL AL	English Learners, p. 500B ELL Below Level, p. 500B BL Early Finishers, p. 500B AL
Alternate Lesson		*IMPACT Mathematics:* Unit H
	Problem Solving in Health (p. 498)	**Summative Assessment** • Study Guide and Review (p. 504) • Chapter Test (p. 509) • Test Practice (p. 510)

Assessment Options

Diagnostic Assessment

- SE *Option 1:* Quick Check (p. 574)
- *Option 2:* Online Quiz macmillanmh.com
- CRM *Option 3:* Diagnostic Test (p. 44)
- CRM *Option 4:* Chapter pretest (p. 45)

Formative Assessment

- TE Alternate Teaching Strategies (every lesson)
- SE Talk About It (every lesson)
- SE Writing in Math (every lesson)
- SE Check What You Know (every lesson)
- TE Into the Future (p. 480)
- TE Name the Math (pp. 490, 503)
- SE Mid-Chapter Check (p. 491)
- CRM Lesson Quizzes (pp. 46–48)
- CRM Mid-Chapter Test (p. 49)

Summative Assessment

- SE Chapter Test (p. 509)
- SE Test Practice (p.510)
- CRM Vocabulary Test (p. 50)
- CRM Leveled Chapter Tests (pp. 55–66)
- CRM Cumulative Test Practice (pp. 69–71)
- CRM Oral Assessment (pp. 51–52)
- ExamView® Assessment Suite
- Advance Tracker

Mc Graw Hill Professional Development

Targeted professional development has been articulated throughout **McGraw-Hill's *Math Connects*** program. The **McGraw-Hill Professional Development Video Library** provides short videos that support the **NCTM Focal Points and Focal Connections.** For more information, visit macmillanmh.com.

Model Lessons

Instructional Strategies

Assessment Tips

Measurement concepts can be difficult for students to grasp so be very clear regarding the objectives you want them to master.

- Come up with four or five specific objectives you want to observe during this chapter.
- Create a class checklist, which includes these four or five objectives.
- When students master a specific objective, check it off.
- Add comments where appropriate.

Teacher Notes

Learning Stations
Cross-Curricular Links

individual | SPATIAL

Is That Right?

See if the capacity label on different containers is correct.

- Fill containers marked for capacity, such as a juice bottle, with water.
- Then test the measurements marked on the containers. Measure the water from each container into a liquid measuring cup to see if there is really the same amount of liquid as the container says there is.
- Did you find any labeling mistakes?

Materials:
- containers of different sizes, such as empty juice bottles
- liquid measuring cups of different sizes
- access to water

pair | SPATIAL

Measuring Mosaics

- Cut colored paper into $\frac{1}{2}$-inch squares (the length and width of the square should both measure $\frac{1}{2}$ inch).
- Make a mosaic picture out of your squares. Keep track of how many squares you use.
- How long would your total number of squares be if you laid them end to end? What about your partner's squares? What is the difference in length between your imaginary line of mosaic squares and that of your partner?

Total Length = ?

Materials:
- colored paper
- glue
- scissors
- ruler
- paper

individual | LOGICAL

Measure a Mystery

- Write a mystery story in which all of the clues are found using measurements. But what kind of units should the main character use to find the measurements? That is part of the mystery.
- For each clue, your main character should try to figure out what unit of measurement would make sense to use. You may use weight, capacity, length, and even time measurements to help your measurement detective solve the mystery.

Detective Solano knew that the distance would have to be measured in miles...

Materials:
- paper
- pencils

Use Measures in the Customary System

Health

Customary Limbo

Play the limbo game and practice using the customary system at the same time.

- Start your game with the limbo bar held 1 yard high. Everyone in the group should have a chance to limbo under the bar. Do not touch the bar, and try not to fall down.
- Lower the limbo bar by 6 inches. How low is it now?
- Keep lowering the bar by six inches each time. See how low you can go without falling.

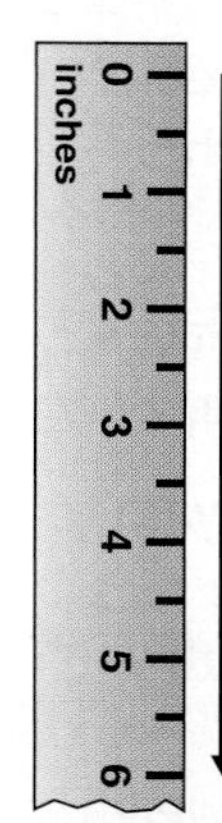

Materials:
- limbo bar (bamboo rod or broomstick)
- yardstick

Music

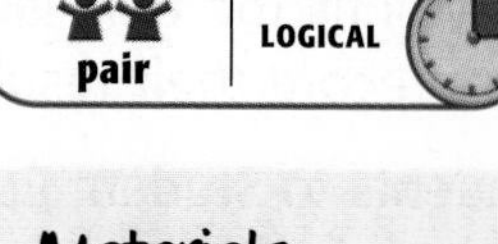

How Long Is That Song?

- Take turns listening to and estimating the length of a song on a music CD.
- Check the CD player or CD label to see the actual time. Subtract the larger time from the smaller time.
- Compare estimates.
- Using the length of time for each song, estimate how long the CD's playing time is. What is the difference between your estimate and your partner's estimate?
- Now, check the CD label to see what the total playing time for the CD is. How close did each of your estimates come to the real total time?

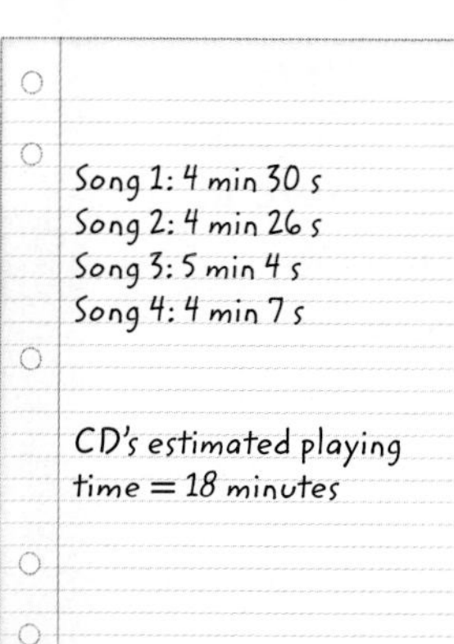

Song 1: 4 min 30 s
Song 2: 4 min 26 s
Song 3: 5 min 4 s
Song 4: 4 min 7 s
CD's estimated playing time = 18 minutes

Materials:
- music CDs
- CD player
- stopwatch
- paper
- pencils
- headphones

Social Studies

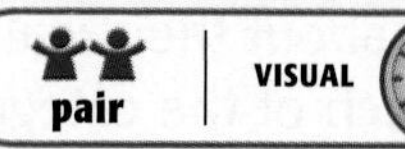

Hop Across Town

Who is going to make it across your town first?

- Imagine that your graph paper represents your town. Each square on your graph paper represents $\frac{1}{10}$ of a mile. Start at the bottom of your town and head north. Take turns rolling a number cube to figure out how many tenths of a mile you will travel.
  Bonus: how many feet do you travel in $\frac{1}{10}$ of a mile?
- Each time you roll and travel, you have to add up the tenths of a mile to see how far you have come from the very beginning.
  Bonus: How many feet is that?

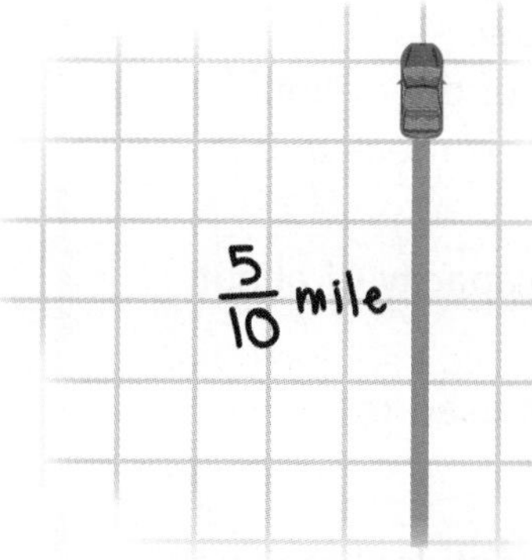

Materials:
- number cube
- graph paper
- pencils

CHAPTER 11

Introduce the Chapter

 Real World: Measuring Up

Materials: rulers, yardsticks, yarn, pound and ounce scales, fluid ounce, cup, pint, quart and gallon measures

Share with students that they are going to learn about customary units of measurement in this chapter.

Divide students into small groups. Provide places for groups to measure length, weight, and capacity.

For measuring length, provide 5 lengths of yarn that range from 5 inches to 3 yards and are labeled A–E. Students measure and record the length for each. For weight, provide several objects from light to heavy. Have students weigh each and record in ounces and pounds. For capacity, students can fill the containers with water and discover how many of a smaller container will fill the next larger size container. Have them record their results.

Direct students to Student Edition p. 472. Have students read the paragraph at the top of the page.

- **Name something that you might measure in feet.** your height, the length of your desk, etc.
- **Name something you might measure in yards.** a football field, material from a fabric store, etc.

WRITING IN ►MATH

Starting the Chapter
Have students write a paragraph in their Math Journals telling about their experiences with measuring length, weight, and capacity. Encourage them to tell about their real world experiences related to each of the categories of measurement.

Key Vocabulary Introduce the key vocabulary in the chapter using the routine below.

Define: Capacity is the amount of dry or liquid material a container can hold. It is measured in units.

Example: A mop bucket has a capacity of about 6 gallons.
Ask: What are some other units used to measure capacity?

Read-Aloud Anthology For an optional reading activity to introduce this chapter's math concepts, see the Read-Aloud Anthology on p. TR31.

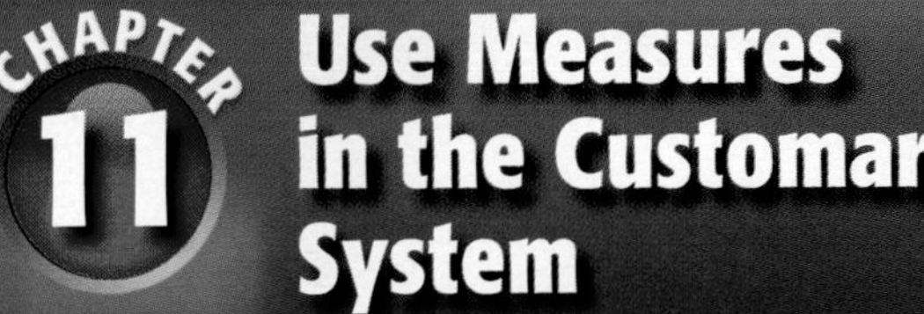

CHAPTER 11 Use Measures in the Customary System

BIG Idea **How do you convert among customary units?**

You can use multiplication or division to convert among customary units.

Example The Manhattan Bridge in New York City connects Manhattan to Brooklyn. The bridge is 1,470 feet long. This is 1,470 ÷ 3, or 490 yards.

What will I learn in this chapter?

- Choose appropriate customary units for measuring length.
- Convert customary units of length, weight, and capacity.
- Convert units of time.
- Solve problems involving elapsed time.
- Solve problems by using the *draw a diagram* strategy.

Key Vocabulary

length
customary units
weight
capacity
elapsed time

Math Online **Student Study Tools** at macmillanmh.com

 Chapter 11 Project

Stepping It Up

Students use a known length to measure places in the school.

- Students use the length of their feet to measure the hallways, cafeteria, gymnasium, and classroom.
- Students first estimate how many heel-to-toe steps they would take for each distance they want to measure and put this estimate in one column of a chart. They each write the measurement of their foot to calculate the real distance. Then they calculate the distances using the heel-to-toe stepping technique. They write the exact measurements next to the estimates on the chart.
- Challenge students to think of other known lengths they might use to estimate these distances.

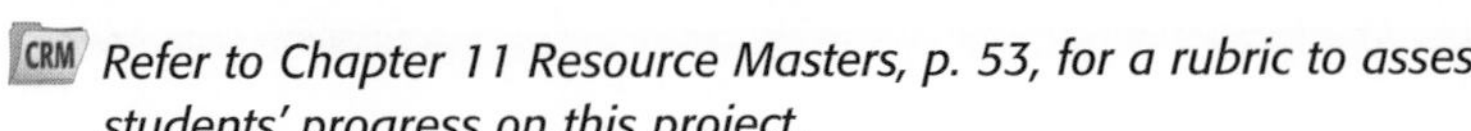

CRM *Refer to Chapter 11 Resource Masters, p. 53, for a rubric to assess students' progress on this project.*

FOLDABLES® Study Organizer Make this Foldable to help you organize information about the customary system. Begin with a sheet of $8\frac{1}{2}''$ by $11''$ paper.

1. **Fold** the short sides toward the middle.
2. **Fold** the top to the bottom.
3. **Open.** Cut along the second fold to make four tabs.
4. **Label** each of the tabs as shown.

Lesson, Page	ESL Standards	Modality	Level
11-1, p. 477B	Goal 2, Standard 3, e	Spatial, Linguistic	Intermediate
11-2, p. 482B	Goal 2, Standard 1, c	Logical	Advanced
11-3, p. 484B	Goal 2, Standard 2, a	Linguistic	Beginning
11-4, p. 488B	Goal 1, Standard 3, c	Kinesthetic, Visual	Intermediate
11-5, p. 492B	Goal 2, Standard 2, d	Auditory	Intermediate
11-6, p. 496B	Goal 2, Standard 2, g	Linguistic, Logical	Advanced
11-7, p. 500B	Goal 1, Standard 3, l	Spatial, Logical	Intermediate

Table title: ELL National ESL Standards Alignment for Chapter 11

The National ESL Standards can be found in the Teacher Reference Handbook.

FOLDABLES® Dinah Zike's Foldables

Guide students through the directions on Student Edition p. 473 to create their own Foldable graphic organizers for the customary system. Students may also use their Foldables to study and review for chapter assessments.

When to Use It Lessons 11-1, 11-3, 11-4, and 11-5. (Additional instructions for using the Foldables with these lessons are found on pp. 491 and 504.)

Chapter 11 Literature List

Lesson	Book Title
11-1	**Measuring Penny** Loreen Leedy
11-2	**Zachary Zormer: Shape Transformer** Joanne Reisberg
11-3	**Measuring Up!** Sandra Markle
11-4	**Millions to Measure** David M. Schwartz
11-5	**Measuring Penny** Loreen Leedy
11-7	**Telling Time With Big Mama Cat** Dan Harper
Any	**The Mitten** Jan Brett

- Read the Math at Home letter found on Chapter 11 Resource Masters, p. 4, with the class and have each student sign it. (A Spanish version is found on p. 5.)
- Send home copies of the Math at Home letter with each student.

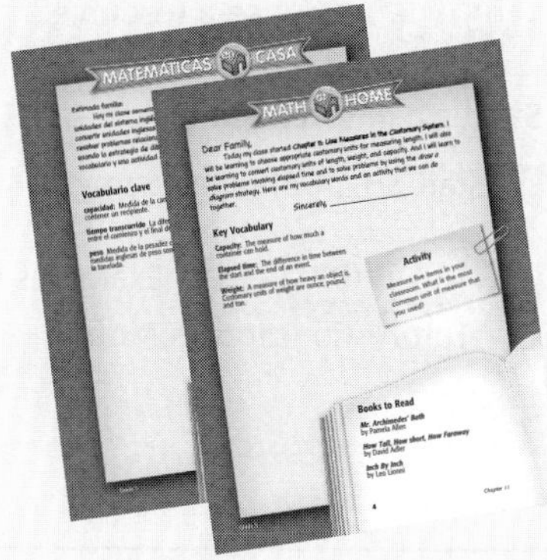

Diagnostic Assessment

Check for students' prerequisite skills before beginning the chapter.

- **Option 1:** ***Quick Check***
  SE Student Edition, p. 474
- **Option 2:** ***Online Assessment***
  Math Online macmillanmh.com
- **Option 3:** ***Diagnostic Tests***
  CRM Chapter 11 Resource Masters, p. 44 - 45

RTI (Response to Intervention)

Apply the Results Based on the results of the diagnostics assessment on Student Edition p. 474, use the chart below to address individual needs before beginning the chapter.

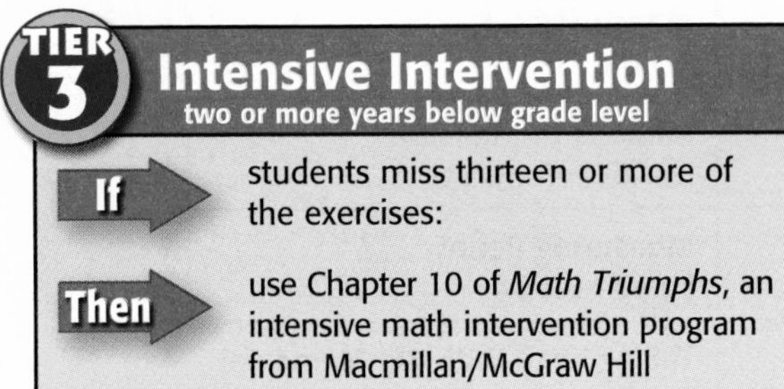

TIER 3 Intensive Intervention
two or more years below grade level

If students miss thirteen or more of the exercises:

Then use Chapter 10 of *Math Triumphs*, an intensive math intervention program from Macmillan/McGraw Hill

ARE YOU READY for Chapter 11?

You have two ways to check prerequisite skills for this chapter.

Option 2
Math Online Take the Chapter Readiness Quiz at macmillanmh.com.

Option 1
Complete the Quick Check below.

QUICK Check

Multiply. (Lesson 3-6) (Used in Lessons 11-1 through 11-5)

1. 14×3 42 **2.** 36×5 180 **3.** 760×2 1,520

4. 15×12 180 **5.** 16×14 224 **6.** 280×4 1,120

7. A musical was sold out for three straight shows. If 825 tickets were sold at each performance, how many tickets were sold in all? 2,475

Divide. Write any remainders as fractions in simplest form. (Lessons 4-4 and 8-1) (Used in Lessons 11-1 through 11-5)

8. $45 \div 3$ 15 **9.** $112 \div 16$ 7 **10.** $39 \div 4$ $9\frac{3}{4}$

11. $52 \div 12$ $4\frac{1}{3}$ **12.** $950 \div 20$ $47\frac{1}{2}$ **13.** $220 \div 8$ $27\frac{1}{2}$

14. A box has 144 ounces of grapes. How many 16-ounce packages of grapes can be made? 9 packages

Find how much time has passed. (Prior Grade) (Used in Lesson 11-7)

15. 20 min

8:10 A.M.

8:30 A.M.

16. 15 min

7:35 P.M.

7:50 P.M.

17. 6:05 A.M. to 6:45 A.M. 40 min **18.** 12:25 A.M. to 12:50 A.M. 25 min

19. April walked her dog from 11:05 A.M. to 11:25 A.M. For how many minutes did she walk her dog? 20 min

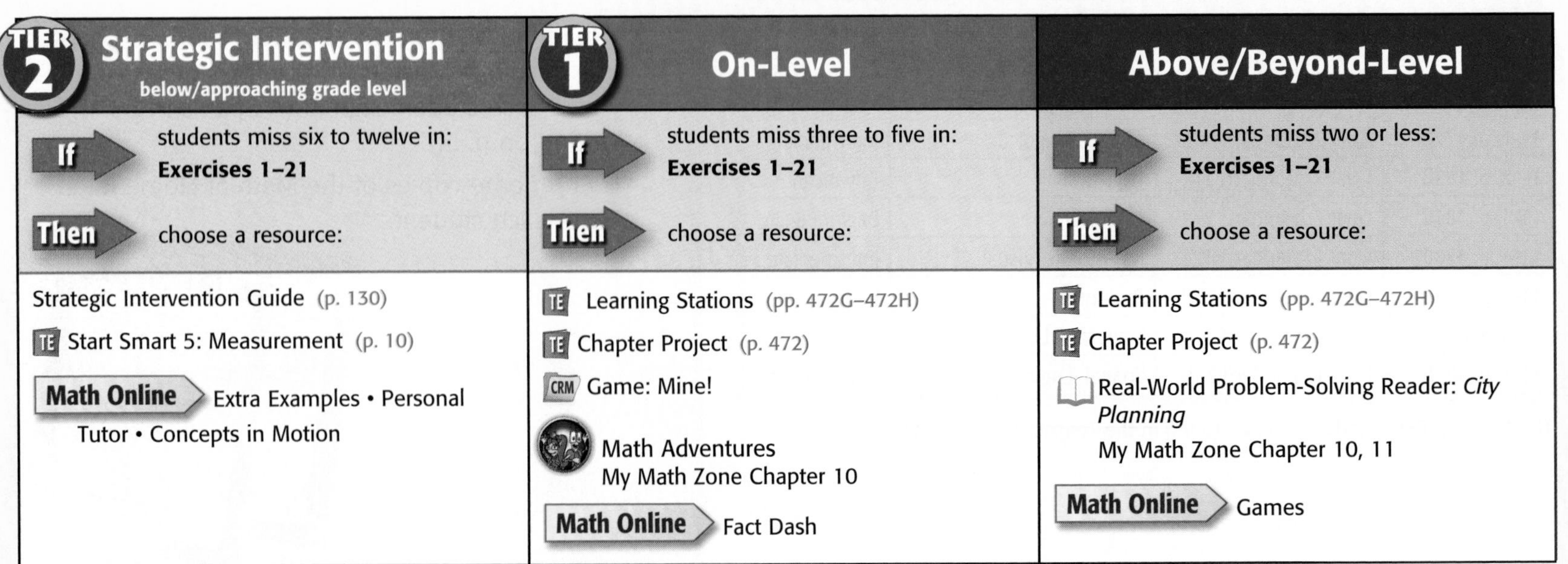

TIER 2 Strategic Intervention below/approaching grade level	TIER 1 On-Level	Above/Beyond-Level
If students miss six to twelve in: **Exercises 1–21**	**If** students miss three to five in: **Exercises 1–21**	**If** students miss two or less: **Exercises 1–21**
Then choose a resource:	**Then** choose a resource:	**Then** choose a resource:
Strategic Intervention Guide (p. 130) TE Start Smart 5: Measurement (p. 10) Math Online Extra Examples • Personal Tutor • Concepts in Motion	TE Learning Stations (pp. 472G–472H) TE Chapter Project (p. 472) CRM Game: Mine! Math Adventures My Math Zone Chapter 10 Math Online Fact Dash	TE Learning Stations (pp. 472G–472H) TE Chapter Project (p. 472) Real-World Problem-Solving Reader: *City Planning* My Math Zone Chapter 10, 11 Math Online Games

Measure with a Ruler

MAIN IDEA
I will measure length to the nearest half inch and quarter inch.
You Will Need
a ruler
Math Online
macmillanmh.com
• Concepts in Motion

Length is the measurement of distance between two points. You can use a ruler like the one at the right to measure the length of objects to the nearest half inch or quarter inch.

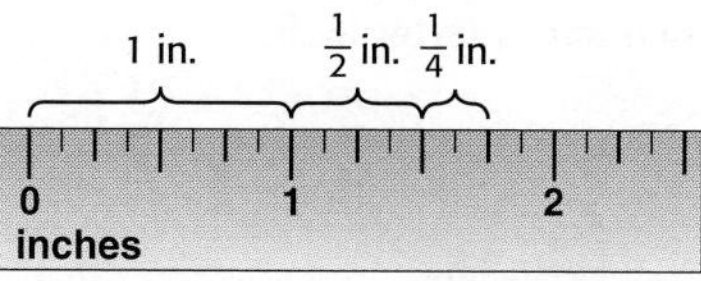

ACTIVITY

1 Find the length of the button to the nearest half inch and quarter inch.

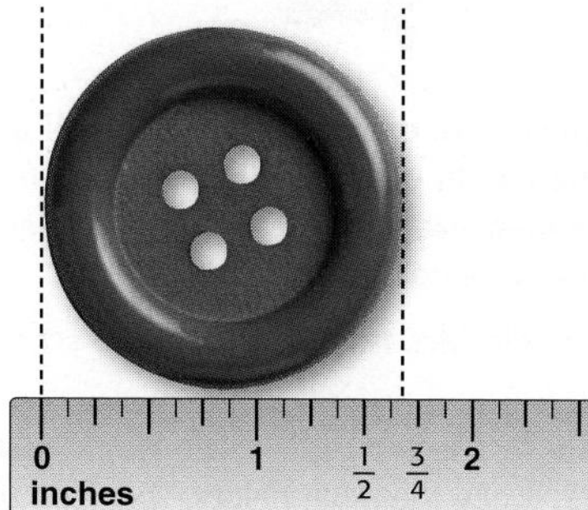

Step 1 Place the ruler against one edge of the object. Line up the zero on the ruler with the end of the object.

Step 2 Find the half inch mark that is closest to the other end. Repeat for the quarter inch mark.

To the nearest half inch, the button is $1\frac{1}{2}$ inches long. To the nearest quarter inch, it is $1\frac{3}{4}$ inches long.

Think About It

1. Explain how you can tell the difference between the half inch and quarter inch marks when measuring an object with a ruler. **See margin.**
2. Will you ever have the same answer when measuring to the nearest half inch and measuring to the nearest quarter inch? Explain your reasoning. **See margin.**

Additional Answers

1. The half inch line is halfway between the inch marks. The quarter inch marks divide an inch into fourths. The half inch marks are longer than the quarter inch marks.
2. Yes, $\frac{2}{4}$ is the same as $\frac{1}{2}$.

Measurement Activity for 11-1

Lesson Planner

Objective

Measure length to the nearest half inch and quarter inch.

Vocabulary

length

Resources

Manipulatives: rulers

1 Introduce

- Before beginning the activity, have students examine the inch side of their rulers. **Into what fractional parts is 1 inch divided?** eighths, fourths, halves, and whole inches
- Ask students to draw two 3-inch lines, one below the other. Label whole inches on each. Mark half inches on the first line and quarter inches on the second line. **Which line would measure the most precisely?** the line marked in fourths (quarters)
- Tell students that in some situations, precise measurement is needed more than in others. **Can you name some measurement situations and tell what kind of precision may be needed?** Answers will vary.

2 Teach

Activity 1 When measuring to the nearest $\frac{1}{4}$ inch, students use the $\frac{1}{8}$ inch marks on the ruler as halfway points to judge which fourth is closer.

Think About It

Assign Exercises 1–2 to assess student comprehension of the concept presented in the activity.

Assess

Formative Assessment

Use **Check What You Know** Exercises 3–6 to assess whether students understand how to measure to the nearest half inch and quarter inch.

From Concrete to Abstract Use Exercises 13–15 to bridge the gap between using inches to measure and choosing a more appropriate unit of measure to measure larger objects.

Extending the Concept Ask students what fractional part of an inch would give an even more precise measure than $\frac{1}{4}$ inch. $\frac{1}{8}$ inch

CHECK What You Know

Measure the length of each of the following to the nearest half inch and quarter inch.

3. 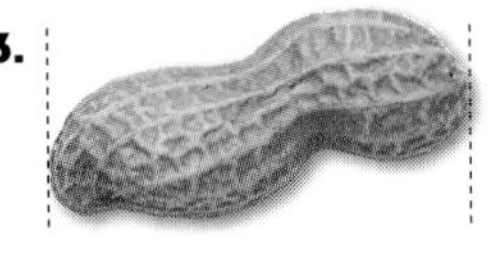 $1\frac{1}{2}$ in., $1\frac{3}{4}$ in.

4.  $2\frac{1}{2}$ in., $2\frac{1}{2}$ in.

5.  1 in., $1\frac{1}{4}$ in.

6. 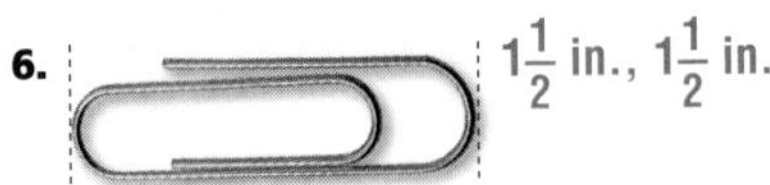 $1\frac{1}{2}$ in., $1\frac{1}{2}$ in.

***Inches* are used to measure small objects. You can measure the length of larger objects using *feet* or *yards*. *Miles* are used to measure very great lengths. Select an appropriate unit to measure each of the following.**

7. distance from your home to school mi

8. length of your classroom ft or yd

9. width of a cell phone in.

10. height of a classmate in. or ft

11. Copy the table below. Then complete the table using ten objects found in your classroom. The first one is done for you. See students' work.

Object	Unit of Measure	Estimate	Actual Length
Height of classroom door	feet	6 feet	8 feet

12–15. Sample answers are given. 15. distance across my state

Name an object that you would measure using each unit.

12. inch DVD case **13.** yard football field **14.** foot height of a building **15.** mile

16. Draw a line that is between 4 and 5 inches long. Measure the length to the nearest quarter inch. See students' work.

17. Draw a line that is $2\frac{1}{2}$ inches long when measured to the nearest half inch and nearest quarter inch. See students' work.

18. WRITING IN MATH Suppose you know that a line is 3 inches long when measured to the nearest inch. What do you know about the actual length of the line? It is between $2\frac{1}{2}$ and $3\frac{1}{2}$ inches long.

LESSON 11-1

Units of Length

Lesson Planner

Objective

Choose an appropriate customary unit for measuring length and convert customary units of length.

Vocabulary

customary units, foot, inch, yard, mile, convert

Resources

Materials: index cards
Manipulatives: ruler
Literature Connection: *Measuring Penny* by Loreen Leedy
Alternate Lesson: Use *IMPACT Mathematics:* Unit C to provide practice with length.
Teacher Technology
TeacherWorks • Interactive Classroom

Focus on Math Background

In Grade 4, students found the perimeter and area of figures whose dimensions were given in units belonging to the *U.S. Customary System*. This is a system of measure used in the United States. When learning to change from one unit to another, students must make use of their background in fractions. Students need to understand that each unit of length can be divided into smaller units. The precision of a measurement depends on the units of measure used. The smaller the unit of measure used, the greater the precision.

When writing abbreviations for units of length, notice that ft, yd, and mi do not have periods. The one exception is the abbreviation for inches *(in.)* for which a period is used to make sure the word *in* is not confused with the abbreviation for inch.

Daily Routine

Use these suggestions before beginning the lesson on p. 477.

5-Minute Check

(Reviews Lesson 10-10)

Subtract. Write each difference in simplest form. Check your answer by using fraction tiles or drawing a picture.

1. $6\frac{2}{8} - 2\frac{3}{4}$ $3\frac{1}{2}$
2. $9\frac{3}{5} - 5\frac{4}{5}$ $3\frac{4}{5}$
3. $14\frac{3}{10} - 12\frac{9}{10}$ $1\frac{2}{5}$
4. $16 - 11\frac{4}{12}$ $4\frac{2}{3}$
5. $13 - 6\frac{1}{8}$ $6\frac{7}{8}$
6. $14\frac{4}{14} - 13\frac{5}{7}$ $\frac{4}{7}$

Problem of the Day

How many five-dollar bills are equal to 50,000 pennies? Explain how you found your answer. 100 five dollar bills; $5 = 500 pennies and 500 × 100 = 50,000 pennies.

Building Math Vocabulary

Write the lesson vocabulary words and their definitions on the board.

Have students write each word and its definition in their notes. Discuss customary units. Then ask students to write a sentence telling what they would measure using each of the units of measure.

Differentiated Instruction

Small Group Options

Option 1 Gifted and Talented AL

SPATIAL

Materials: paper and pencil

- Have students work with a partner to make a list of 10 items that can be easily measured.
- Ask them to list 4 measurement estimates, one of which is reasonable, for each of the 10 items.
- Have students exchange papers with another student pair to determine the most reasonable estimate.

Option 2 English Language Learners ELL

SPATIAL, LINGUISTIC

Materials: poster board, markers
Core Vocabulary: foot, yard, unit
Common Use Verb: measure by

Do Math This strategy helps students choose appropriate measurement units.

- Create four posters with the information in the boxes headed with inch, foot and yard.
- Ask students to identify 2–3 items in the classroom that could be measured by each unit. For the mile, post pictures of large distances.
- Have students test choices by using their bodies as measuring tools; bent knuckle is about an inch, elbow to fingers (on a fifth grader) is about a foot, and hand to chest is about a yard.
- Write items that could be measured by each unit on the posters.

Use this worksheet to provide additional support for English Language Learners.

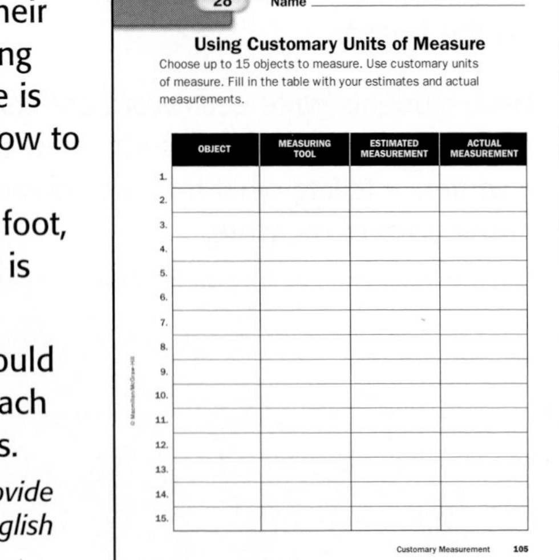
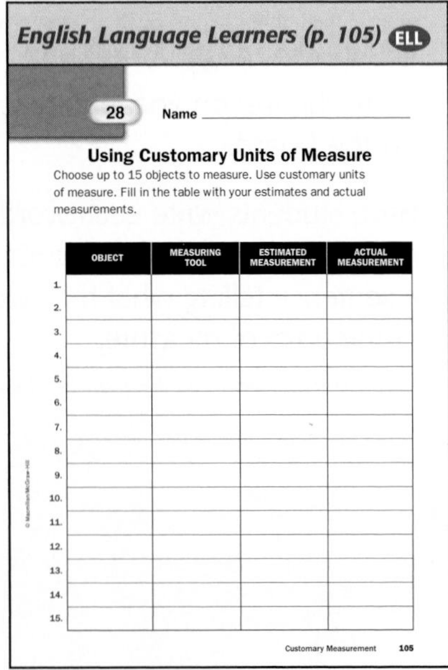

English Language Learners (p. 105) ELL

28 Name ________

Using Customary Units of Measure

Choose up to 15 objects to measure. Use customary units of measure. Fill in the table with your estimates and actual measurements.

	OBJECT	MEASURING TOOL	ESTIMATED MEASUREMENT	ACTUAL MEASUREMENT
1.				
2.				
3.				
4.				
5.				
6.				
7.				
8.				
9.				
10.				
11.				
12.				
13.				
14.				
15.				

Customary Measurement 105

Independent Work Options

Option 1 Early Finishers OL AL

INTRAPERSONAL

Materials: number cube, pencil and paper

- Have students draw and label a table with the headings Inch, Foot, and Yard.
- Students roll the number cube and write the number rolled in the Yard column of the table.
- Ask students to convert the number of yards they wrote to fill in the remaining columns of their table. If time allows, students may roll again and repeat the activity.

Option 2 Student Technology

Tech Link

Math Online macmillanmh.com

Personal Tutor • Extra Examples

Math Adventures

Option 3 Learning Station: Music (p. 472G)

Direct students to the Music Learning Station for opportunities to explore and extend the lesson concept.

Option 4 Problem-Solving Practice

Reinforce problem-solving skills and strategies with the Problem-Solving Practice worksheet.

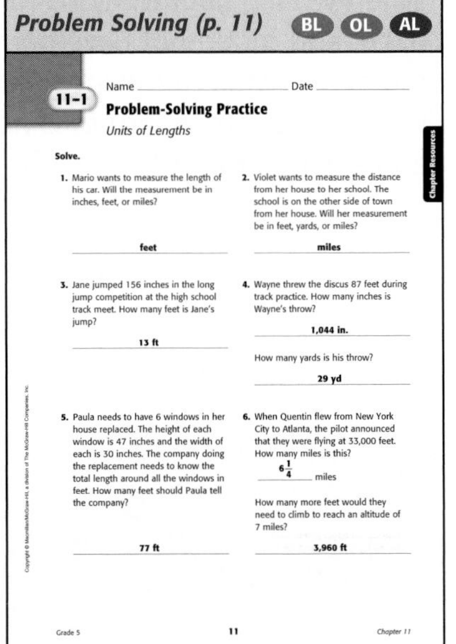

Problem Solving (p. 11) BL OL AL

11-1 Name ________ Date ________

Problem-Solving Practice

Units of Lengths

Chapter Resources

Solve.

1. Mario wants to measure the length of his car. Will the measurement be in inches, feet, or miles?
   feet

2. Violet wants to measure the distance from her house to her school. The school is on the other side of town from her house. Will her measurement be in feet, yards, or miles?
   miles

3. Jane jumped 156 inches in the long jump competition at the high school track meet. How many feet is Jane's jump?
   13 ft

4. Wayne threw the discus 87 feet during track practice. How many inches is Wayne's throw?
   1,044 in.
   How many yards is his throw?
   29 yd

5. Paula needs to have 6 windows in her house replaced. The height of each window is 47 inches and the width of each is 30 inches. The company doing the replacement needs to know the total length around all the windows in feet. How many feet should Paula tell the company?
   77 ft

6. When Quentin flew from New York City to Atlanta, the pilot announced that they were flying at 33,000 feet. How many miles is this?
   $6\frac{1}{4}$ miles
   How many more feet would they need to climb to reach an altitude of 7 miles?
   3,960 ft

Grade 5 11 Chapter 11

11-1 Units of Length

GET READY to Learn

For many of the thrill rides at amusement parks, riders must be at least 48 inches tall.

MAIN IDEA

I will choose an appropriate customary unit for measuring length and convert customary units of length.

New Vocabulary

- length
- customary units
- foot
- inch
- yard
- mile
- convert

Math Online

macmillanmh.com

- Extra Examples
- Personal Tutor
- Self-Check Quiz

The units of **length** most often used in the United States are the inch, foot, yard, and mile. These units are called **customary units**.

Customary Units of Length — Key Concepts

1 **foot** (ft) = 12 **inches** (in.)
1 **yard** (yd) = 3 ft or 36 in.
1 **mile** (mi) = 5,280 ft or 1,760 yd

When you **convert** measurements, you change from one unit to another. To convert a larger unit to a smaller unit, *multiply*.

Real-World EXAMPLE — Convert Larger Units to Smaller Units

1 **RIDES Refer to the information above. Cheng is 4 feet tall. Is he tall enough to ride a thrill ride at an amusement park?**

4 ft = ■ in. Larger units (feet) are being converted to smaller units (inches).

Since 1 foot = 12 inches, multiply 4 by 12.

4 × 12 = 48

12 in.	
12 in.	4 ft
12 in.	
12 in.	

So, 4 ft = 48 in. Since 4 feet equals 48 inches, Cheng is tall enough to ride the thrill rides.

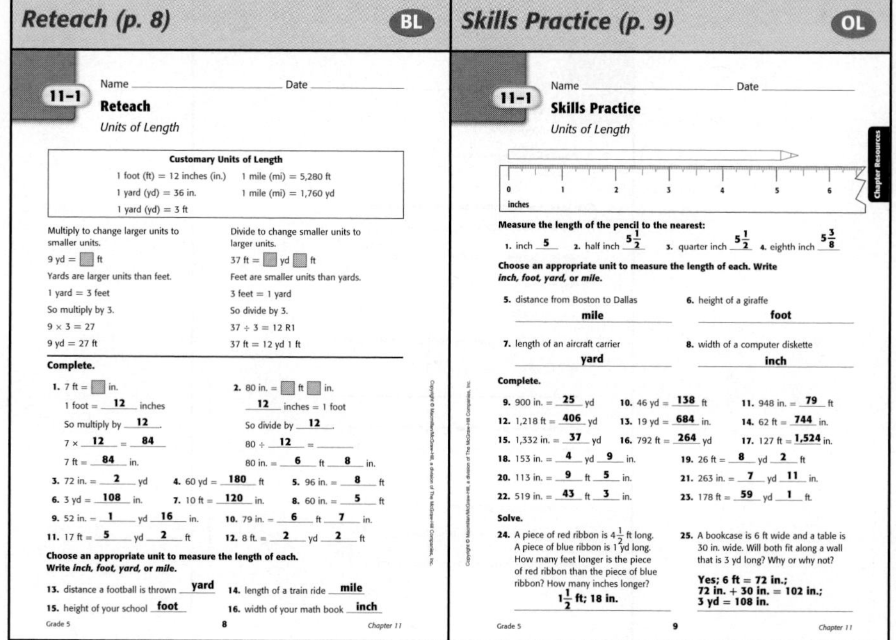

Reteach (p. 8) BL

11-1 Name ______ Date ______

Reteach

Units of Length

Customary Units of Length

1 foot (ft) = 12 inches (in.) 1 mile (mi) = 5,280 ft
1 yard (yd) = 36 in. 1 mile (mi) = 1,760 yd
1 yard (yd) = 3 ft

Multiply to change larger units to smaller units.
9 yd = ■ ft
Yards are larger units than feet.
1 yard = 3 feet
So multiply by 3.
9 × 3 = 27
9 yd = 27 ft

Divide to change smaller units to larger units.
37 ft = ■ yd ■ ft
Feet are smaller units than yards.
3 feet = 1 yard
So divide by 3.
37 ÷ 3 = 12 R1
37 ft = 12 yd 1 ft

Complete.

1. 7 ft = ■ in.
 1 foot = **12** inches
 So multiply by **12**.
 7 × **12** = **84**
 7 ft = **84** in.
2. 80 in. = ■ ft ■ in.
 12 inches = 1 foot
 So divide by **12**.
 80 ÷ **12** = ____
 80 in. = **6** ft **8** in.
3. 72 in. = **2** yd
4. 60 yd = **180** ft
5. 96 in. = **8** ft
6. 3 yd = **108** in.
7. 10 ft = **120** in.
8. 60 in. = **5** ft
9. 52 in. = **1** yd **16** in.
10. 79 in. = **6** ft **7** in.
11. 17 ft = **5** yd **2** ft
12. 8 ft. = **2** yd **2** ft

Choose an appropriate unit to measure the length of each. Write *inch, foot, yard,* or *mile*.

13. distance a football is thrown **yard**
14. length of a train ride **mile**
15. height of your school **foot**
16. width of your math book **inch**

Grade 5 8 Chapter 11

Skills Practice (p. 9) OL

11-1 Name ______ Date ______

Skills Practice

Units of Length

inches 0 1 2 3 4 5 6

Measure the length of the pencil to the nearest:

1. inch **5**
2. half inch $5\frac{1}{2}$
3. quarter inch $5\frac{1}{2}$
4. eighth inch $5\frac{3}{8}$

Choose an appropriate unit to measure the length of each. Write *inch, foot, yard,* or *mile*.

5. distance from Boston to Dallas **mile**
6. height of a giraffe **foot**
7. length of an aircraft carrier **yard**
8. width of a computer diskette **inch**

Complete.

9. 900 in. = **25** yd
10. 46 yd = **138** ft
11. 948 in. = **79** ft
12. 1,218 ft = **406** yd
13. 19 yd = **684** in.
14. 62 ft = **744** in.
15. 1,332 in. = **37** yd
16. 792 ft = **264** yd
17. 127 ft = **1,524** in.
18. 153 in. = **4** yd **9** in.
19. 26 ft = **8** yd **2** ft
20. 113 in. = **9** ft **5** in.
21. 263 in. = **7** yd **11** in.
22. 519 in. = **43** ft **3** in.
23. 178 ft = **59** yd **1** ft.

Solve.

24. A piece of red ribbon is $4\frac{1}{2}$ ft long. A piece of blue ribbon is 1 yd long. How many feet longer is the piece of red ribbon than the piece of blue ribbon? How many inches longer?
 $1\frac{1}{2}$ ft; 18 in.
25. A bookcase is 6 ft wide and a table is 30 in. wide. Will both fit along a wall that is 3 yd long? Why or why not?
 Yes; 6 ft = 72 in.; 72 in. + 30 in. = 102 in.; 3 yd = 108 in.

Grade 5 9 Chapter 11

Chapter Resources

11-1 Units of Length

1 Introduce

Activity Choice 1 • Hands-On

- Have students meet briefly in small groups to generate lists of items that would be measured in inches, feet, yards, and miles.
- Ask students to present their lists to the class. **What is a possible rule for choosing a unit of measure?** Choose a larger unit of measure for larger items.
- Tell students that there are times when a smaller unit of measure might be required to measure more precisely. **When would using inches be more appropriate than using feet to measure?** measuring the height of a small plant or animal
- Discuss with students the idea that sometimes two different units are used to measure. Have them use a ruler to measure their desktop and use feet and inches to tell the length and width measurements.

Activity Choice 2 • Literature

Introduce the lesson with *Measuring Penny* by Loreen Leedy. For a related math activity, see p. TR54.

2 Teach

Scaffolding Questions

Write the following on the board: 1 ft = 12 in., 1 yd = 3 ft, 1 mile = 5,280 ft

- **What equation would show how many inches are in a yard?** 12 × 3 = 36 in.
- **How would you find the number of inches in 4 yards?** 12 × 3 × 4 = 144 in.
- **Are there more feet or yards in a mile? Explain.** More feet; since yards are a larger unit of measure, there are fewer in a mile.
- **How would you find the number of yards in one mile?** Divide the number of feet in a mile by 3 since there are 3 feet per yard.

GET READY to Learn

Have students open their books and read the information in **Get Ready to Learn.** Introduce **customary units, foot, inch, yard, mile,** and **convert**. As a class, work through **Examples 1–3.**

Parts of Units

Example 3 Make sure that students understand that there may be two ways to write an answer when there is a remainder in a conversion problem.

ADDITIONAL EXAMPLES

1. Leah is 5 feet tall. She must be 60 inches tall to ride one of the rides. Is she tall enough? Leah is 60 in. tall. She is tall enough to ride.
2. A fence is 240 inches long. How many feet long is it? 20 ft long
3. Convert 8 feet to yards. 2 yd 2 ft or $2\frac{2}{3}$ yd

CHECK What You Know

As a class, have students complete Exercises 1–8 in **Check What You Know** as you observe their work.

Exercise 8 Assess student comprehension before assigning practice exercises.

BL Alternate Teaching Strategy

If students have trouble converting units of length...

Then use one of these reteach options:

1. CRM **Daily Reteach Worksheet** (p. 8)
2. Have them use an index card to write the conversions from smaller units to larger units on one side and larger units to smaller units on the other side. Help students to write a list of conversions for the various units. Students can then use their cards to identify if the unit is changing from smaller to larger or from larger to smaller.

In Example 3, some students may confuse the 6-inch remainder with a decimal and write 3.6 feet. Work with students to clarify that the remainders are the same units as the divisor.

To convert a smaller unit to a larger unit, *divide*.

Real-World EXAMPLE Convert Smaller Units to Larger Units

2 **SPORTS A basketball court is 84 feet long. How many yards long is it?**

84 ft = ■ yd Smaller units (feet) are being converted to larger units (yards).

Since 3 feet = 1 yard, divide 84 by 3.

84 ÷ 3 = 28

So, 84 ft = 28 yd. The basketball court is 28 yards long.

Vocabulary Link

Customary

Everyday Use commonly practiced, used, or observed

Math Use system of measurement

Units of length in the customary system can also be expressed using different units of measure or as fractions.

EXAMPLE Parts of Units

3 **Convert 42 inches to feet.**

One Way: **Use feet and inches.**

Since you are changing a smaller unit to a larger unit, divide.

42 ÷ 12 = 3 R6 12 in. = 1 ft

The remainder 6 means there are 6 inches left over.

42 in. = 3 ft 6 in.

Remember

All measurements are approximations. However, if you use smaller units, you will get a more *precise* measure, or a measure that is closer to the exact measure.

Another Way: **Use fractions.**

42 ÷ 12 = 3 R6 3 R6 means 42 inches = 3 feet 6 inches.

The remainder 6 means there are 6 inches out of a foot left over.

The fraction of a foot is $\frac{6}{12}$ or $\frac{1}{2}$.

42 in. = $3\frac{1}{2}$ ft

12 in.
12 in.
12 in.
6 in.
} $3\frac{1}{2}$ ft

So, 42 inches is equal to 3 feet 6 inches or $3\frac{1}{2}$ feet.

478 **Chapter 11** Use Measures in the Customary System

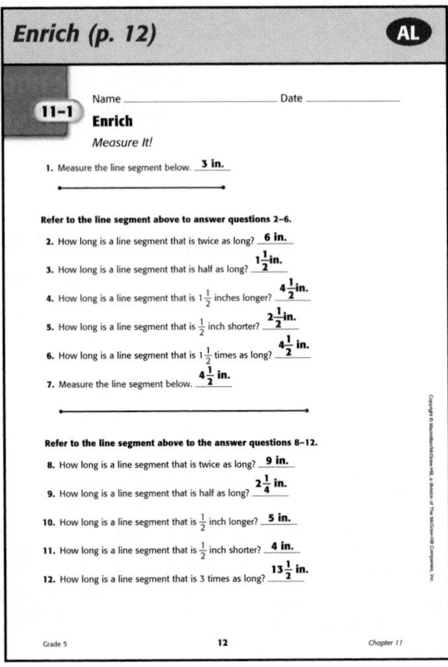

Enrich (p. 12) AL

Name ______ Date ______

11-1 **Enrich**

Measure It!

1. Measure the line segment below. **3 in.**

Refer to the line segment above to answer questions 2–6.

2. How long is a line segment that is twice as long? **6 in.**
3. How long is a line segment that is half as long? **$1\frac{1}{2}$ in.**
4. How long is a line segment that is $1\frac{1}{2}$ inches longer? **$4\frac{1}{2}$ in.**
5. How long is a line segment that is $\frac{1}{2}$ inch shorter? **$2\frac{1}{2}$ in.**
6. How long is a line segment that is $1\frac{1}{2}$ times as long? **$4\frac{1}{2}$ in.**
7. Measure the line segment below. **$4\frac{1}{2}$ in.**

Refer to the line segment above to the answer questions 8–12.

8. How long is a line segment that is twice as long? **9 in.**
9. How long is a line segment that is half as long? **$2\frac{1}{4}$ in.**
10. How long is a line segment that is $\frac{1}{2}$ inch longer? **5 in.**
11. How long is a line segment that is $\frac{1}{2}$ inch shorter? **4 in.**
12. How long is a line segment that is 3 times as long? **$13\frac{1}{2}$ in.**

Grade 5 12 Chapter 11

★ indicates multi-step problem

CHECK What You Know

Complete. See Examples 1–3 (pp. 477–478)

1. 60 in. = ■ ft 5
2. 5,280 ft = ■ mi 1
3. 9 ft = ■ in. 108
4. 6 yd = ■ in. 216
5. 22 ft = ■ yd ■ ft 7; 1
6. 40 in. = ■ ft $3\frac{1}{3}$
7. Carlos is 63 inches tall. What is his height in feet? 5 ft 3 in. or $5\frac{1}{4}$ ft
8. 

Explain how to convert units from feet to inches. See margin.

Practice and Problem Solving

EXTRA PRACTICE See page R29.

Complete. See Examples 1–3 (pp. 477–478) 15. 8 ft 2 in.; $8\frac{1}{6}$ ft

9. 19 yd = ■ in. 684
10. 26,400 ft = ■ mi 5
11. 5 mi = ■ yd 8,800
12. 105 in. = ■ yd ■ in. 2; 33
13. 15 ft 8 in. = ■ in. 188
14. 150 in. = ■ yd $4\frac{1}{6}$
15. **Measurement** A bull had horns that measured 98 inches across. What is this length in feet and inches? in feet?
16. ★ Ty has two pieces of wood. Which piece of wood is longer? piece 1

Piece	Length
1	1 yd 9 in.
2	44 in.

17. The *U.S.S. Harry Truman* is an aircraft carrier that is 1,092 feet long. Find the length in yards. 364 yd
18. ★ Dana ran $\frac{1}{4}$ mile. Trish ran 445 yards. Who ran the greater distance? Explain. Trish; $\frac{1}{4}$ mi equals 440 yd and $445 > 440$.

Choose an appropriate unit to measure each of the following.

19. length of a cellular phone in.
20. length of a kitchen ft or yd
21. width of a television in.
22. length of community swimming pool yd
23. distance between two cities mi
24. height of soccer goal posts ft

Real-World PROBLEM SOLVING

Social Studies Around 3000 B.C., the Egyptians developed units of length based on parts of the body.

Choose the appropriate measure to find each distance.

25. width of your desk hand
26. width of a sheet of paper digit
27. your height hand
28. width of the classroom cubit

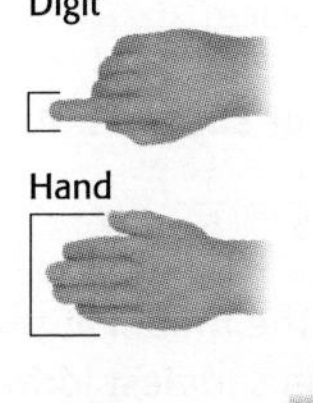

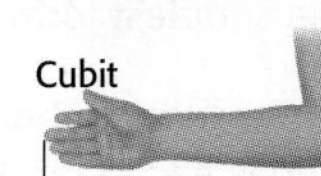

Additional Answers

8. Sample answer: Multiply the number of feet by 12. There will be more inches than feet because inches are smaller units than feet.

3 Practice

Differentiate practice using these leveled assignments for Exercises 9–31.

Level	Assignment
BL Below/ Approaching Level	9–14, 16, 25–27
OL On Level	9–18, 21–24, 27–29, 31
AL Above/Beyond Level	9–27 odd, 29–31

Have students discuss and complete the Higher Order Thinking problems. For Exercise 30, help students understand that, because 320 rods = 1 mile, it is also true that 320 rods = 5,280 feet.

WRITING IN ▸MATH Have students complete Exercise 31 in their Math Journals. You may choose to use this exercise as an optional formative assessment.

COMMON ERROR!

Exercises 9–14 Students may have trouble deciding if they should multiply or divide to convert units. If larger units are converted to smaller units, there will be more of the smaller units, so multiplication is needed to convert correctly. If smaller units are converted to larger units, there will be fewer of the larger units, so division will be needed.

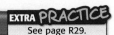

4 Assess

Formative Assessment

Write the following on the board: 16 feet.

- **How would you convert 16 feet to inches?** multiply 16 × 12, 16 feet = 192 inches
- **How would you convert 16 feet to yards?** divide 16 by 3 **What are two ways to state 16 feet as yards?** 5 yds 1 ft and $5\frac{1}{3}$ yards

Quick Check

Are students continuing to struggle with choosing an appropriate unit of measure and converting customary units of length?

If Yes → Strategic Interventioin Guide (p. 130)

If No → Independent Work Options (p. 477B)
CRM Skills Practice Worksheet (p. 9)
CRM Enrich Worksheet (p. 12)

Into the Future Have students write how they think what they learned about converting units of measure in this lesson will help them in the future as they convert units of measure in weight, capacity, and time.

TEST Practice

Reviews Lesson 11-1

Assign the Test Practice problems to provide daily reinforcement of test-taking skills.

Spiral Review

Reviews Lessons 8-1, 9-5, 10-1, 10-2, 10-9, and 10-10

Review and assess mastery of skills and concepts from previous chapters.

H.O.T. Problems

29. OPEN ENDED Estimate the width of a window in your school. Then measure the width in feet and inches. See students' work.

30. CHALLENGE There are 320 *rods* in a mile. Find the length of a *rod* in feet. $16\frac{1}{2}$ ft

31. WRITING IN MATH Write a real-world problem that can be solved by converting yards to feet. Then solve. Sample answer: The length of a hallway is 6 yards. Carpet is sold by the foot. How many feet of carpet are needed?; 18 ft

TEST Practice

32. Which relationship between units of length is correct? (Lesson 11-1) C

A One foot is $\frac{1}{12}$ of one yard.

B One yard is $\frac{1}{4}$ of one mile.

C One foot is $\frac{1}{3}$ of one yard.

D One inch is $\frac{1}{3}$ of one foot.

33. The picture shows the height of a statue. What is the height of the statue in inches? (Lesson 11-1) J

F 13 inches

G 22 inches

H 36 inches

J 40 inches

Spiral Review

34. A full bag contains $7\frac{2}{4}$ cups of flour. There are $1\frac{3}{4}$ cups left in a bag. How many cups have been used? (Lesson 10-8) $5\frac{3}{4}$ c

35. The softball team has ten players. Suppose each player shakes hands with every other player. How many handshakes take place? (Lesson 10-7) 45

Add or subtract. (Lessons 10-1 and 10-2)

36. $\frac{3}{5} - \frac{1}{5}$ $\frac{2}{5}$

37. $\frac{1}{10} + \frac{3}{10}$ $\frac{2}{5}$

38. $\frac{2}{9} + \frac{8}{9}$ $1\frac{1}{9}$

39. $\frac{7}{9} - \frac{4}{9}$ $\frac{1}{3}$

40. The model at the right shows 0.004. Write 0.004 as a fraction in simplest form. (Lesson 9-5) $\frac{1}{250}$

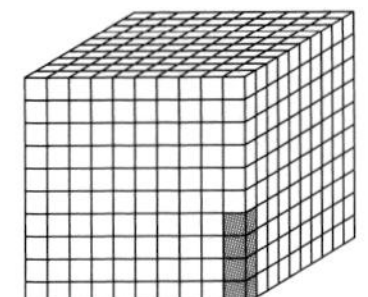

41. Four friends share three brownies equally. How many brownies does each friend get? (Lesson 8-1) $1\frac{1}{3}$ brownies

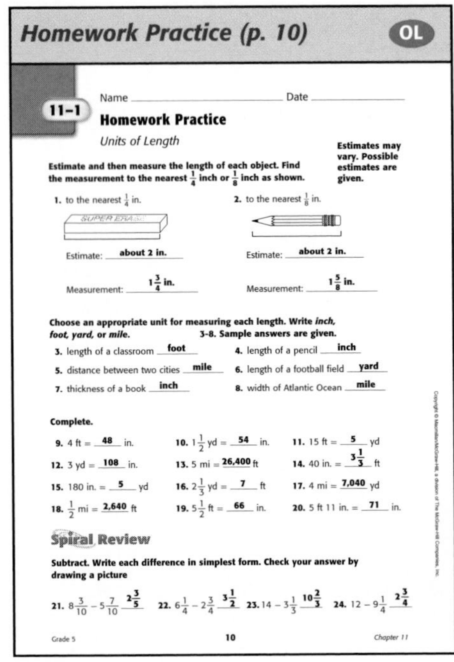

Homework Practice (p. 10) OL

11-1 Name ________ Date ________

Homework Practice

Units of Length

Estimate and then measure the length of each object. Find the measurement to the nearest $\frac{1}{4}$ inch or $\frac{1}{8}$ inch as shown. **Estimates may vary. Possible estimates are given.**

1. to the nearest $\frac{1}{4}$ in.

Estimate: **about 2 in.**

Measurement: $1\frac{3}{4}$ **in.**

2. to the nearest $\frac{1}{8}$ in.

Estimate: **about 2 in.**

Measurement: $1\frac{5}{8}$ **in.**

Choose an appropriate unit for measuring each length. Write *inch*, *foot*, *yard*, or *mile*. **3-8. Sample answers are given.**

3. length of a classroom **foot**
4. length of a pencil **inch**
5. distance between two cities **mile**
6. length of a football field **yard**
7. thickness of a book **inch**
8. width of Atlantic Ocean **mile**

Complete.

9. 4 ft = **48** in.
10. $1\frac{1}{2}$ yd = **54** in.
11. 15 ft = **5** yd
12. 3 yd = **108** in.
13. 5 mi = **26,400** ft
14. 40 in. = $3\frac{1}{3}$ ft
15. 180 in. = **5** yd
16. $2\frac{1}{3}$ yd = **7** ft
17. 4 mi = **7,040** yd
18. $\frac{1}{2}$ mi = **2,640** ft
19. $5\frac{1}{2}$ ft = **66** in.
20. 5 ft 11 in. = **71** in.

Spiral Review

Subtract. Write each difference in simplest form. Check your answer by drawing a picture

21. $8\frac{3}{10} - 5\frac{7}{10}$ $2\frac{3}{5}$
22. $6\frac{1}{4} - 2\frac{3}{4}$ $3\frac{1}{2}$
23. $14 - 3\frac{1}{3}$ $10\frac{2}{3}$
24. $12 - 9\frac{1}{4}$ $2\frac{3}{4}$

Grade 5 10 Chapter 11

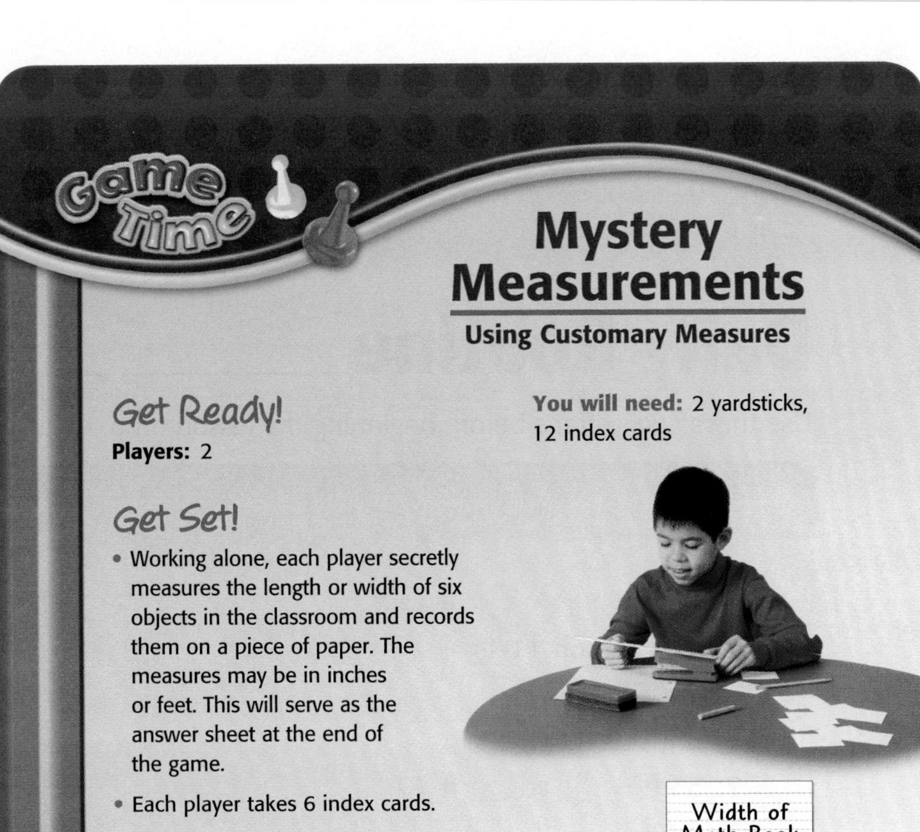

Mystery Measurements

Using Customary Measures

Get Ready!

Players: 2

You will need: 2 yardsticks, 12 index cards

Get Set!

- Working alone, each player secretly measures the length or width of six objects in the classroom and records them on a piece of paper. The measures may be in inches or feet. This will serve as the answer sheet at the end of the game.
- Each player takes 6 index cards.
- For each object, the measurement is recorded on one card. A description of what was measured is recorded on another card. Make sure each measurement is different.

Go!

- Each player shuffles his or her cards.
- Keeping the cards facedown, players exchange cards.
- At the same time, players turn over all the cards given to them.
- Each player attempts to match each object with its measure.
- The player with more correct matches after 1 minute is the winner.

Game Time Mystery Measurements **481**

Differentiated Practice

Use these leveled suggestions to differentiate the game for all learners.

Level	Assignment
BL Below/ Approaching Level	Students work in teams of two and help each other pair up the cards. They get seven to ten minutes to match up the card pairs.
OL On Level	Have students play the game with the rules as written.
AL Above/Beyond Level	Students create larger decks with more objects to pair up in five minutes.

Mystery Measurements

Math Concept:
Using Customary Measures

Materials: 12 index cards, 2 yardsticks, pencils

Introduce the game on p. 481 to your students to play as a class, in small groups, or at a learning workstation to review concepts introduced in this chapter.

Instructions

- Students play in pairs. Each player secretly measures the length of six objects in the classroom and records the measurements on a piece of paper, to be used as an answer sheet at the end of the game.
- Each player takes 6 index cards and cuts them in half, making 12 cards. He or she records the measurement of each of their objects on one card and the object description on another card. They make sure that each measurement is different.
- Each player shuffles his or her cards. Keeping the cards facedown, the players exchange piles of cards.
- All players turn over the cards given to them. They each try to match up objects with their correct measurements as fast as they can.
- The player who has the most correct matches after 1 minute wins the game.

Extend the Game

Have students play the game using weight measurements and familiar objects around the classroom.

11-2 Problem-Solving Strategy
Draw a Diagram

Lesson Planner

Objective
Solve problems by drawing a diagram.

Resources
Literature Connection: *Zachary Zormer: Shape Transformer* by Joanne Reisberg
Teacher Technology
TeacherWorks • Interactive Classroom

Real-World Problem Solving Library
Math and Social Studies: ***City Planning***

Use these leveled books to reinforce and extend problem-solving skills and strategies.

Leveled for:
- OL On Level
- ELL Sheltered English
- SP Spanish

For additional support, see the Real-World Problem Solving Teacher Guide.

Daily Routine

Use these suggestions before beginning the lesson on p. 482.

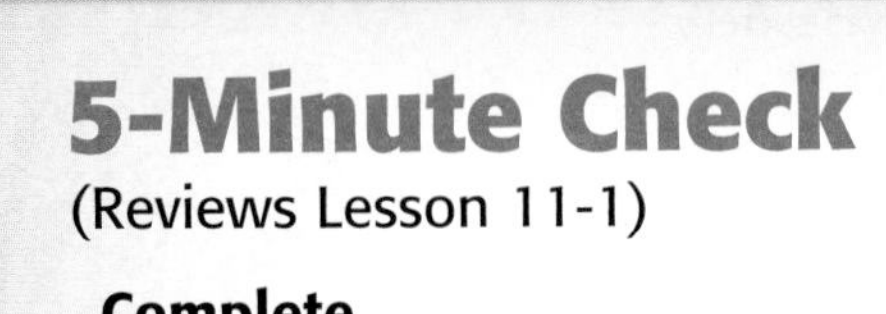

5-Minute Check

(Reviews Lesson 11-1)

Complete.

1. 4 mi = ___ yd 7,040
2. 53 ft = ___ yd ___ ft 17; 2
3. 3 mi = ___ ft 15,840
4. 13 ft = ___ in. 156
5. 172 in. = ___ ft $14\frac{4}{12}$ or $14\frac{1}{3}$

Problem of the Day

A number is divided by 12. When the quotient is multiplied by 15, the product is 270. What is the number? Tell how you found the answer. 216; explanations will vary.

Differentiated Instruction

Small Group Options

Option 1 Below Level BL

VISUAL, PAIR

Materials: pencil and paper

- Hand students this problem written on paper:

  Tom has 252 feet of rope. He wants to cut it into 9-foot long sections. How many 9 foot pieces will he have and how many cuts will he have to make? Draw a diagram to solve. He will have 28 9-foot sections and he will have to make 27 cuts.

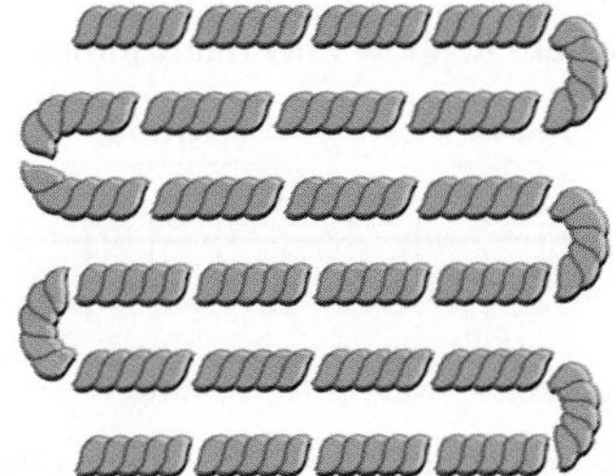

Option 2 English Language Learners ELL

SPATIAL, LINGUISTIC

Core Vocabulary: the size, draw to size, measurement
Common Use Verb: size

Do Math This strategy helps students use drawing to practice measurement and clarify vocabulary.

- Show a stapler and measure it. Write: "The size of the stapler is 7 inches."
- Discuss the way the word "size" can be used (dimension, mass, magnitude, volume) and how it is used idiomatically (to size up, draw to size).
- Have students draw the object "to size" on regular notebook paper.
- Allow students to measure their drawing. Say: "This measurement is **the size** of your drawing. You tried to draw the stapler **to size**, which is 7 inches."
- Have students cut out their drawing and compare it to others.
- Discuss the differences in sizes, restate student language as needed.

Independent Work Options

Option 1 Early Finishers OL AL

SOCIAL, LINGUISTIC

Materials: magazines, newspapers, scissors, paper

- Have students find an interesting photo and write a word problem to go with the photo.
- Have students cut out the photo; paste it on paper; and write the problem and a four-step solution below the photo.
- Post the problems for other students to read and solve.

Option 2 Student Technology

Math Online macmillanmh.com

Personal Tutor • Extra Examples

Option 3 Learning Station: Health (p. 472H)

Direct students to the Health Learning Station for opportunities to explore and extend the lesson concept.

Problem-Solving Strategy

1 Introduce

Activity Choice 1 • Review

- Pose the following problem:

  Josephina saw some chickens and goats at the zoo. There were 3 more chickens than goats but 18 more goat legs than chicken legs. How many chickens and goats were there?
- **What strategy could be used to solve the problem?** guess and check
- **How many of each animal are there?** 15 chickens and 12 goats

Activity Choice 2 • Literature

Introduce the lesson with *Zachary Zormer: Shape Transformer* by Joanne Reisberg. For a related math activity, see p. TR54.

2 Teach

Have students read the problem. Guide them through the problem-solving steps.

Understand Using the questions, review what students know and need to find.

Plan Have them discuss their strategy.

Solve Guide students to draw a diagram to solve the problem.

- **What should your diagram show?** Sample answer: a line showing distances, the jumps of the frog, and the jumps of the cricket
- **What are you looking for on your diagram?** when the frog and cricket land at the same place
- Have students complete their diagrams and find the solution.

Check Have students look back at the problem to make sure that the answer fits the facts given.

COMMON ERROR!

Exercise 5 Some students may have problems with directions. Remind them that north is usually drawn upward, south downward, east to the right, and west to the left. Provide students with grid paper.

Problem-Solving Strategy

MAIN IDEA I will solve problems by drawing a diagram.

A frog and a cricket start at the same place and jump in the same direction. The table shows the distance they jump each time.

Animal	Length of Jump
frog	5 feet
cricket	3 feet

If the frog jumps 15 times and the cricket jumps 25 times, how many times will they land in the same place?

Understand **What facts do you know?**

- The distance each animal jumps.

What do you need to find?

- The number of jumps each animal will make before landing in the same place.

Plan Solve the problem by drawing a diagram.

Solve **Use your plan to solve the problem.**

Draw a diagram to show how many jumps each animal makes.

1 jump 1 jump 1 jump

0 ft 2 ft 4 ft 6 ft 8 ft 10 ft 12 ft 14 ft 16 ft

1 jump 1 jump 1 jump 1 jump 1 jump

The animals meet after every 3 jumps by the frog and every 5 jumps by the cricket. The animals will land in the same place after the frog jumps three, six, nine, twelve, and fifteen times.

So, the animals will land in the same place 5 times.

Check Look back. Divide the total number of feet jumped by the LCM of 3 and 5 to find how many times the animals are in the same place. Since 75 ÷ 15 is 5, the answer is correct.

482 Chapter 11 Use Measures in the Customary System

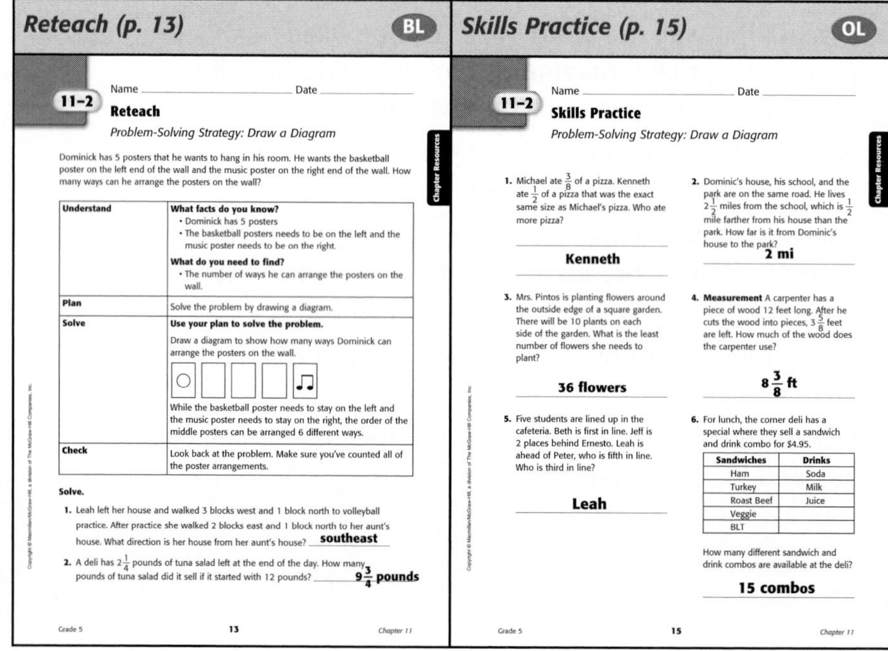

Reteach (p. 13) BL

11-2 Name ______ Date ______

Reteach

Problem-Solving Strategy: Draw a Diagram

Dominick has 5 posters that he wants to hang in his room. He wants the basketball poster on the left end of the wall and the music poster on the right end of the wall. How many ways can he arrange the posters on the wall?

Understand	**What facts do you know?** • Dominick has 5 posters • The basketball posters needs to be on the left and the music poster needs to be on the right. **What do you need to find?** • The number of ways he can arrange the posters on the wall.
Plan	Solve the problem by drawing a diagram.
Solve	**Use your plan to solve the problem.** Draw a diagram to show how many ways Dominick can arrange the posters on the wall. While the basketball poster needs to stay on the left and the music poster needs to stay on the right, the order of the middle posters can be arranged 6 different ways.
Check	Look back at the problem. Make sure you've counted all of the poster arrangements.

Solve.

1. Leah left her house and walked 3 blocks west and 1 block north to volleyball practice. After practice she walked 2 blocks east and 1 block north to her aunt's house. What direction is her house from her aunt's house? **southeast**
2. A deli has $2\frac{1}{4}$ pounds of tuna salad left at the end of the day. How many pounds of tuna salad did it sell if it started with 12 pounds? **$9\frac{3}{4}$ pounds**

Grade 5 13 Chapter 11

Chapter Resources

Skills Practice (p. 15) OL

11-2 Name ______ Date ______

Skills Practice

Problem-Solving Strategy: Draw a Diagram

1. Michael ate $\frac{3}{8}$ of a pizza. Kenneth ate $\frac{1}{2}$ of a pizza that was the exact same size as Michael's pizza. Who ate more pizza? **Kenneth**
2. Dominic's house, his school, and the park are on the same road. He lives $2\frac{1}{2}$ miles from the school, which is $\frac{1}{2}$ mile farther from his house than the park. How far is it from Dominic's house to the park? **2 mi**
3. Mrs. Pintos is planting flowers around the outside edge of a square garden. There will be 10 plants on each side of the garden. What is the least number of flowers she needs to plant? **36 flowers**
4. **Measurement** A carpenter has a piece of wood 12 feet long. After he cuts the wood into pieces, $3\frac{5}{8}$ feet are left. How much of the wood does the carpenter use? **$8\frac{3}{8}$ ft**
5. Five students are lined up in the cafeteria. Beth is first in line. Jeff is 2 places behind Ernesto. Leah is ahead of Peter, who is fifth in line. Who is third in line? **Leah**
6. For lunch, the corner deli has a special where they sell a sandwich and drink combo for $4.95.

Sandwiches	Drinks
Ham	Soda
Turkey	Milk
Roast Beef	Juice
Veggie	
BLT	

How many different sandwich and drink combos are available at the deli? **15 combos**

Grade 5 15 Chapter 11

Chapter Resources

ANALYZE the Strategy

Refer to the problem on the previous page.

1. If the frog jumped 4 feet each time and the cricket jumped 3 feet each time, after how many jumps would they meet? **12 jumps**
2. Why did it help to draw a diagram of the situation to solve the problem? **See Ch. 11 Answer Appendix.**
3. Can you think of a time when drawing a diagram was helpful to you? **See students' work.**
4. Is there another strategy you could use to solve this problem? **Sample answer: Use the *look for a pattern* strategy.**

PRACTICE the Strategy

EXTRA PRACTICE See page R30.

Solve. Use the *draw a diagram* strategy.

5. On her way home from school, Becky walked 2 blocks south to the corner store, 3 blocks east to visit a friend, and then 5 blocks north to go home. What direction is her home from the school? **northeast**
6. **Measurement** Mr. Blackmon is building a fence around his garden. He wants to put fence posts every 3 feet, including each corner. How many total posts will be around the outside of the garden? **14 posts**

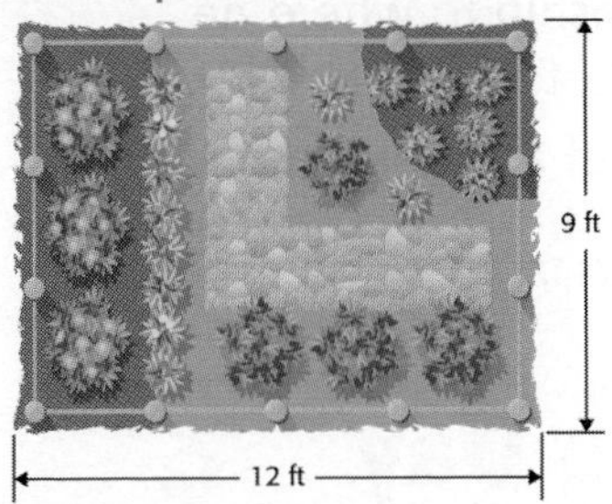

7. There are four booths in a row at the school carnival: face painting, ring toss, the dunk tank, and a cupcake walk. The dunk tank is on the far left. The ring toss is in between the face painting booth and the cupcake walk. The cupcake walk has only one neighbor. List the order of the booths from left to right. **See Ch. 11 Answer Appendix.**
8. For a school lunch, students must choose one entrée, one side dish, and one drink from the table shown. How many different school lunches can be purchased? **18 lunches**

Entrée	Side dish	Drink
spaghetti	potatoes	milk
chicken	fruit cup	juice
hamburger	salad	

9. To score a touchdown, a football team needed to gain 35 yards. On their next five plays, the team gained 10 yards, lost 5 yards, lost 3 yards, gained 15 yards, and gained 10 yards. Did they score a touchdown? If not, how many more yards did they need to gain? **no; 8 yards**
10. Kylie has 5 pictures to display on a shelf. She wants the picture of her family on the right end and the picture of her dog on the left end. How many ways can she arrange the pictures? **6 ways**
11. **WRITING IN MATH** Refer to Exercise 7. How did you use the *draw a diagram* strategy to solve this problem? **See Ch. 11 Answer Appendix.**

Enrich (p. 17) AL

11–2 Name ______ Date ______

Enrich

Another Customary Unit

The inch, foot, yard, and mile are the most commonly used customary units of length. Another customary unit of length is called a *rod*.

Customary Units of Length
1 rod (rd) = 16.5 feet
1 rod = 5.5 yards
1 mile = 320 rods

Complete.

1. 6 rd = ☐ yd **33**
2. 9 rd = ☐ ft **$148\frac{1}{2}$**
3. 22 yd = ☐ rd **4**
4. 165 ft = ☐ rd **10**
5. 2 mi = ☐ rd **640**
6. 880 rd = ☐ mi **$2\frac{3}{4}$**
7. 750 rd = ☐ mi ☐ rd **2; 110**
8. 20 ft = ☐ rd ☐ ft **$1; 3\frac{1}{2}$**
9. 645 rd = ☐ mi ☐ ft **$2; 82\frac{1}{2}$**
10. 8 rd 3 ft = ☐ ft **135**
11. For which object listed below could you use a rod to measure the length? Explain your reasoning.
    - big-screen T.V.
    - cruise ship
    - dog house

    Cruise ship; a T.V. and dog house are both less than 16.5 feet, or 1 rod long.
12. Which is a more reasonable estimate for the length of a bedroom: 1 rod or 4 rods? Explain.
    1 rod, because it equals 16.5 ft; 4 rods equals 66 ft, which is too long for a bedroom.
13. The lengths of two skateboard ramps are shown in the table. Which ramp is the longer one? **Ramp B**

Ramp	Length
A	2 rd 5 ft
B	40 ft

14. How many inches is 2.4 rods? **$475\frac{1}{5}$ in.**

Grade 5 17 Chapter 11

Chapter Resources

Homework Practice (p. 16) OL

11–2 Name ______ Date ______

Homework Practice

Problem-Solving Strategy: Draw a Diagram

Solve. Use the *draw a diagram* strategy.

1. At a party, everyone shook hands with everyone else exactly once. There were a total of 36 handshakes. How many people were at the party? **9 people**
2. Joey ate $2\frac{1}{4}$ eggs for breakfast on Monday. If he has eaten $13\frac{1}{2}$ eggs by the end of the week, how many eggs did he eat from Tuesday through Sunday? Write an equation and solve. **$13\frac{1}{2} - 2\frac{1}{4} = 11\frac{1}{4}$ eggs**
3. On the way to school, Zoe walks 3 blocks east, 2 blocks south, and 1 block west. What direction is the school from Zoe's home? **southeast**
4. The Robinson family is having their portrait taken sitting on a bench. If Mr. and Mrs. Robinson sit on either end, how many different ways can their 3 children sit between them? **6 ways**

Spiral Review

Choose an appropriate unit to measure the length of each. Write *inch, foot, yard,* or *mile.* (Lesson 11–2)

5. distance between two countries **mile**
6. length of a football field **yard**
7. length of a necklace **inch**
8. width of a dresser **inch**
9. height of a 5th grader **foot**
10. width of computer **inch**

Grade 5 16 Chapter 11

Analyze the Strategy Use Exercises 1–4 to analyze and discuss the problem-solving strategy.

BL Alternate Teaching Strategy

If students have trouble drawing a diagram…

Then use one of these reteach options:

1 CRM **Daily Reteach Worksheet** (p. 13)

2 Pose this problem: *A softball league with 8 teams is planning a single-elimination, end-of-the-year tournament*
- **How many games will be played in all?** 4 + 2 + 1 = 7 games
- Help students use the *draw a diagram* strategy to solve the problem.

3 Practice

Using the Exercises

Exercise 6 Point out that only one post will be needed at the corners.

Exercise 9 Suggest that students draw a number line.

4 Assess

Formative Assessment

Pose this problem: *Four students are in line by height. Amy is taller than Jim and Ping; Jim is shorter than Ping; the tallest, Rafi, is the last in line. In what order are the students lined up, shortest to tallest?* Jim, Ping, Amy, Rafi

- **How can you draw a diagram to represent this situation?** Sample answer: Draw four blank boxes; start by writing "R" in the last box and working through the other hints.

Quick Check **Are students continuing to struggle with writing equations to solve problems?**

If Yes → Small Group Options (p. 482B)
Strategic Intervention Guide (p. 130)

If No → Independent Work Options (p. 482B)
CRM Skills Practice Worksheet (p. 15)
CRM Enrich Worksheet (p. 17)

LESSON 11-3 Units of Weight

Lesson Planner

Objective

Convert customary units of weight.

Vocabulary

weight, pound, ounce, ton

Resources

Materials: chart paper, index cards
Literature Connection: *Measuring Up!* by Sandra Markle
Teacher Technology
TeacherWorks • Interactive Classroom

Focus on Math Background

The weight of an object is the force with which the object is pulled vertically downward by gravity. Hence, the weight of an object varies depending on how far it is from the center of Earth; e.g., the weight of an object at the top of a mountain is less than the weight of the same object at sea level because the force that Earth's gravity exerts is less.

Smaller unit to larger unit: divide.

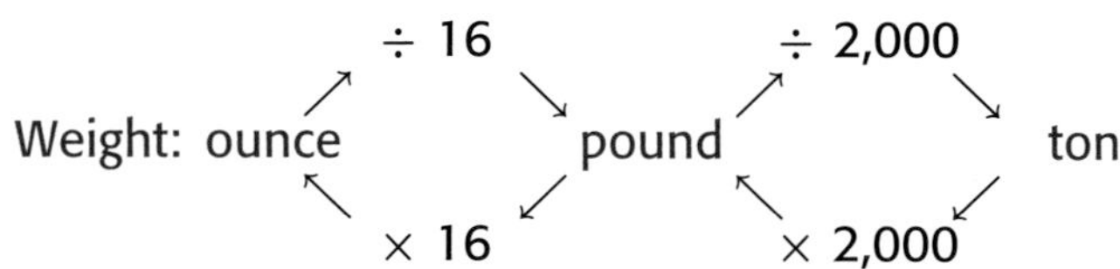

Larger unit to smaller unit: multiply.

Note: The customary units of weight are based on the old British system called *avoirdupois*.

Daily Routine

Use these suggestions before beginning the lesson on p. 484.

5-Minute Check

(Reviews Lesson 11-2)

Solve. Use the draw a diagram strategy.

1. Jay walks north 3 blocks; turns right and walks 2 blocks; turns right and walks 4 blocks; then turns right and walks 2 blocks. Where is Jay in relationship to where he started? 1 block south of his starting point
2. What is the perimeter of a square pool with an area of 400 ft^2? 80 ft

Problem of the Day

What is the least three-digit number that is divisible by 9? What is the greatest three digit number that is divisible by 9? Show your work. 108; 999

Building Math Vocabulary

Write the lesson vocabulary words and their definitions on the board.

Ask students to write the words and definitions in their Math Journals. Have them write sentences to tell what might be measured for each of the units of measure.

Differentiated Instruction

Small Group Options

Option 1 Gifted and Talented AL

SPATIAL

Materials: popcorn kernel, scales

- Have students devise a method for estimating the weight of a popcorn kernel.

Option 2 English Language Learners

LINGUISTIC

Materials: classroom objects, scale

Core Vocabulary: 1-pound, less than, about

Common Use Verb: weigh

Do Math This strategy teaches students about units of weight and how to estimate approximate weight.

- Head three pieces of poster paper with *less than a pound, more than a pound, and 1 pound.*
- Pass around things that weigh more than, less than, and about 1 pound.
- Write the name of the item on the board, have students decide what poster it belongs on, and write it on the appropriate poster.
- Check the weight of objects by using a scale.

Independent Work Options

Option 1 Early Finishers AL

LOGICAL

Materials: product packages with weights marked in pounds and ounces, pencils, paper

- Have students draw a table with the following headings: Product, Weight as Written, Weight in Ounces, Weight in Pounds.
- For each product, ask students to fill in the columns of their table correctly by writing the name of the product, the stated weight, and their own conversions to ounces and to pounds.

Option 2 Student Technology

Tech Link

Math Online macmillanmh.com

Personal Tutor • Extra Examples

Math Adventures

Option 3 Learning Station: Science (p. 472H)

Direct students to the Science Learning Station for opportunities to explore and extend the lesson concept.

Option 4 Problem-Solving Practice

Reinforce problem-solving skills and strategies with the Problem-Solving Practice worksheet.

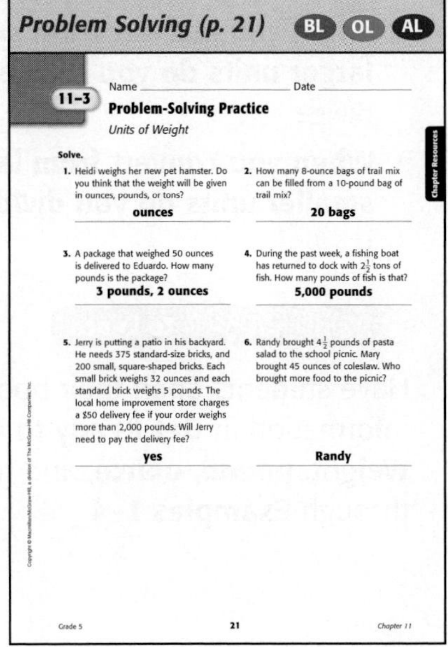
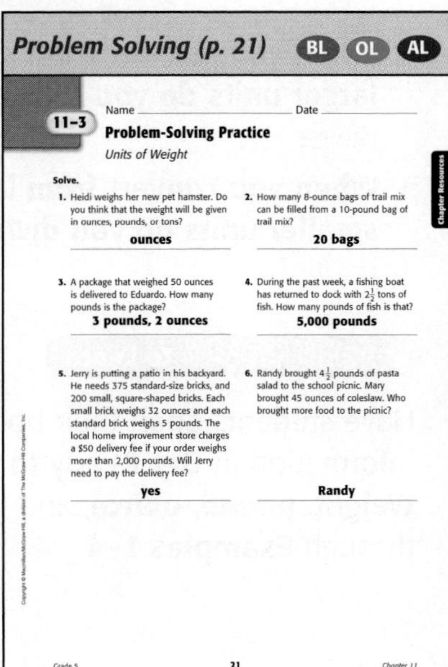

Problem Solving (p. 21) BL OL AL

11-3 Name ______ Date ______

Problem-Solving Practice

Units of Weight

Solve.

1. Heidi weighs her new pet hamster. Do you think that the weight will be given in ounces, pounds, or tons? **ounces**
2. How many 8-ounce bags of trail mix can be filled from a 10-pound bag of trail mix? **20 bags**
3. A package that weighed 50 ounces is delivered to Eduardo. How many pounds is the package? **3 pounds, 2 ounces**
4. During the past week, a fishing boat has returned to dock with $2\frac{1}{2}$ tons of fish. How many pounds of fish is that? **5,000 pounds**
5. Jerry is putting a patio in his backyard. He needs 375 standard-size bricks, and 200 small, square-shaped bricks. Each small brick weighs 32 ounces and each standard brick weighs 5 pounds. The local home improvement store charges a $50 delivery fee if your order weighs more than 2,000 pounds. Will Jerry need to pay the delivery fee? **yes**
6. Randy brought $4\frac{1}{2}$ pounds of pasta salad to the school picnic. Mary brought 45 ounces of coleslaw. Who brought more food to the picnic? **Randy**

Chapter Resources

Grade 5 21 Chapter 11

11-3 Units of Weight

1 Introduce

Activity Choice 1 • Hands-On

- Have students work in small groups. Distribute one sheet of paper to each group and have them create a table with three columns labeled Ounces, Pounds, and Tons.
- Have students create a list of items that are weighed in ounces, in pounds, and in tons.
- Ask students to share their lists with the class.
- Review with the students the abbreviations for ounces (oz), pounds (lb) and tons (T).

Activity Choice 2 • Literature

Introduce the lesson with *Measuring Up!* by Sandra Markle. For a related math activity, see p. TR54.

2 Teach

Scaffolding Questions

Write the following on the board:
1 pound = 16 ounces. 1 ton = 2,000 pounds.

- **How would you convert 2 pounds to ounces? Explain.** There are 16 oz in 1 lb, so $2 \times 16 = 32$ oz.
- **How would you change 2 tons into pounds?** There are 2,000 lb in a ton, so $2 \times 2{,}000 = 4{,}000$ lbs.
- **How would you change 64 ounces into pounds?** Since there are 16 oz per pound, divide 64 by 16 = 4 lb.
- **When you convert from smaller units to larger units do you divide or multiply?** divide
- **When you convert from larger units to smaller units do you divide or multiply?** multiply

GET READY to Learn

Have students open their books and read the information in **Get Ready to Learn.** Introduce **weight, pound, ounce,** and **ton**. As a class, work through **Examples 1–4**.

11-3 Units of Weight

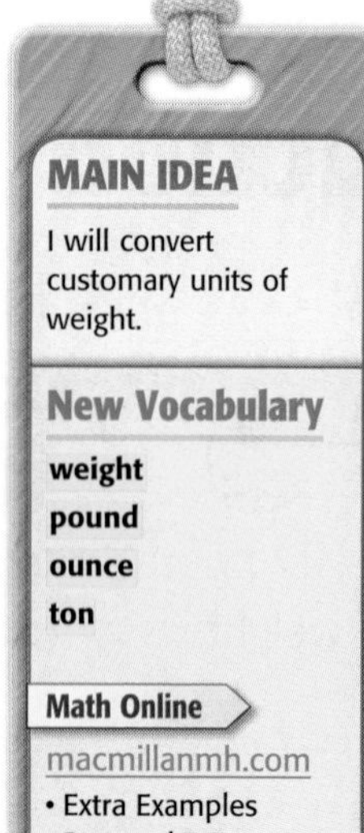

MAIN IDEA

I will convert customary units of weight.

New Vocabulary

weight
pound
ounce
ton

Math Online

macmillanmh.com

- Extra Examples
- Personal Tutor
- Self-Check Quiz

GET READY to Learn

A newborn lion cub weighs about 5 pounds. How many ounces is this?

Weight is a measure of how heavy an object is. Customary units of weight are ounce, pound, and ton.

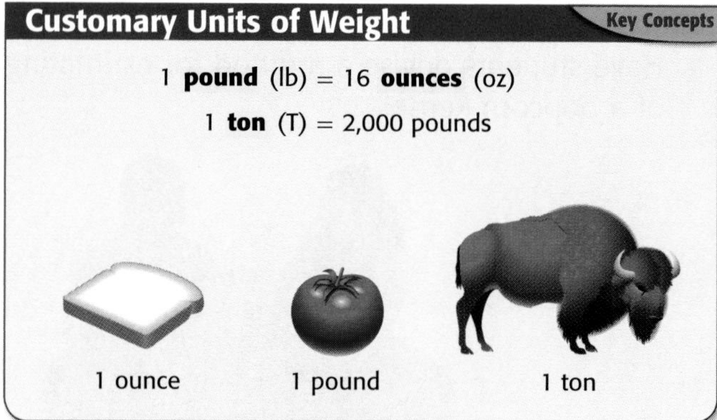

Customary Units of Weight — Key Concepts

1 **pound** (lb) = 16 **ounces** (oz)

1 **ton** (T) = 2,000 pounds

1 ounce 1 pound 1 ton

To convert a larger unit of weight to a smaller unit, *multiply*.

Real-World EXAMPLE Convert Larger Units to Smaller Units

1 ANIMALS Refer to the information above. How many ounces does a newborn lion cub weigh?

5 lb = ■ oz Larger units (pounds) are being converted to smaller units (ounces).

Since 1 pound = 16 ounces, multiply 5 by 16.

A newborn lion weighs about 5×16 or 80 ounces.

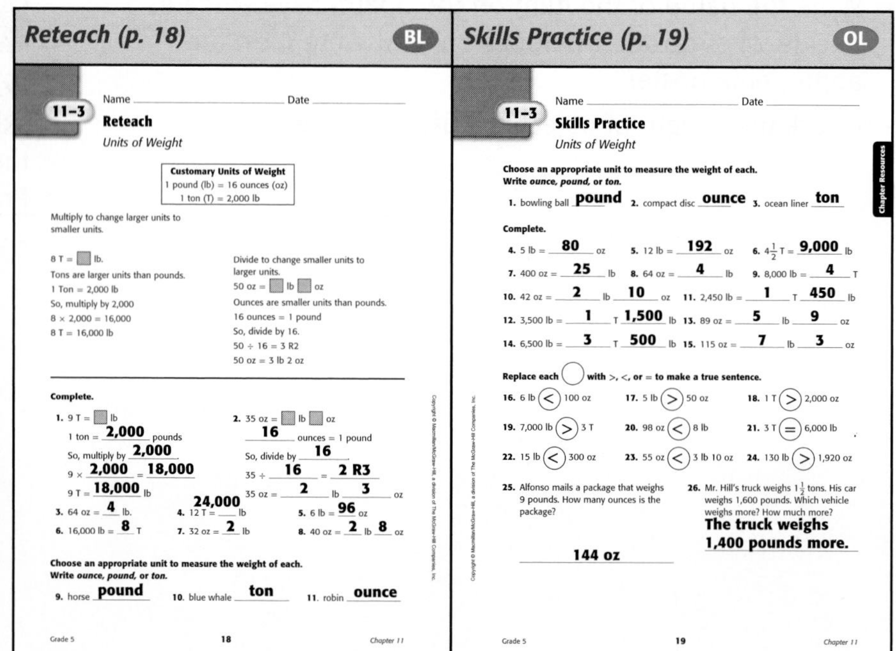

Reteach (p. 18) BL

11-3 Name ______ Date ______

Reteach

Units of Weight

Customary Units of Weight
1 pound (lb) = 16 ounces (oz)
1 ton (T) = 2,000 lb

Multiply to change larger units to smaller units.

8 T = ■ lb.
Tons are larger units than pounds.
1 Ton = 2,000 lb
So, multiply by 2,000
$8 \times 2{,}000 = 16{,}000$
8 T = 16,000 lb

Divide to change smaller units to larger units.
50 oz = ■ lb ■ oz
Ounces are smaller units than pounds.
16 ounces = 1 pound
So, divide by 16.
$50 \div 16 = 3$ R2
50 oz = 3 lb 2 oz

Complete.

1. 9 T = ■ lb
   1 ton = **2,000** pounds
   So, multiply by **2,000**.
   9 × **2,000** = **18,000**
   9 T = **18,000** lb
2. 35 oz = ■ lb ■ oz
   16 ounces = 1 pound
   So, divide by **16**.
   35 ÷ **16** = **2 R3**
   35 oz = **2** lb **3** oz
3. 64 oz = **4** lb.
4. 12 T = **24,000** lb
5. 6 lb = **96** oz
6. 16,000 lb = **8** T
7. 32 oz = **2** lb
8. 40 oz = **2** lb **8** oz

Choose an appropriate unit to measure the weight of each. Write *ounce, pound,* or *ton*.

9. horse **pound**
10. blue whale **ton**
11. robin **ounce**

Grade 5 18 *Chapter 11*

Skills Practice (p. 19) OL

11-3 Name ______ Date ______

Skills Practice

Units of Weight

Choose an appropriate unit to measure the weight of each. Write *ounce, pound,* or *ton*.

1. bowling ball **pound**
2. compact disc **ounce**
3. ocean liner **ton**

Complete.

4. 5 lb = **80** oz
5. 12 lb = **192** oz
6. $4\frac{1}{2}$ T = **9,000** lb
7. 400 oz = **25** lb
8. 64 oz = **4** lb
9. 8,000 lb = **4** T
10. 42 oz = **2** lb **10** oz
11. 2,450 lb = **1** T **450** lb
12. 3,500 lb = **1** T **1,500** lb
13. 89 oz = **5** lb **9** oz
14. 6,500 lb = **3** T **500** lb
15. 115 oz = **7** lb **3** oz

Replace each ○ with >, <, or = to make a true sentence.

16. 6 lb (<) 100 oz
17. 5 lb (>) 50 oz
18. 1 T (>) 2,000 oz
19. 7,000 lb (>) 3 T
20. 98 oz (<) 8 lb
21. 3 T (=) 6,000 lb
22. 15 lb (<) 300 oz
23. 55 oz (<) 3 lb 10 oz
24. 130 lb (>) 1,920 oz
25. Alfonso mails a package that weighs 9 pounds. How many ounces is the package? **144 oz**
26. Mr. Hill's truck weighs $1\frac{1}{2}$ tons. His car weighs 1,600 pounds. Which vehicle weighs more? How much more? **The truck weighs 1,400 pounds more.**

Grade 5 19 *Chapter 11*

Chapter Resources

Real-World EXAMPLE Parts of Units

2 FOOD Lindsay's mother bought $1\frac{1}{2}$ pounds of hamburger. How many ounces of hamburger did she buy?

Since $1\frac{1}{2}$ pounds means 1 pound + $\frac{1}{2}$ pound, convert each to ounces. Then add.

1 lb = 16 oz, $\frac{1}{2}$ lb = 8 oz

So, $1\frac{1}{2}$ pound = 16 + 8 or 24 ounces.

16 oz | 8 oz } $1\frac{1}{2}$ lb

Lindsay's mother bought 24 ounces of hamburger.

To convert a smaller unit to a larger unit, *divide*.

EXAMPLE Convert Smaller Units to Larger Units

3 Convert 6,000 pounds to tons.

6,000 lb = ■ T   Smaller units (pounds) are being converted to larger units (tons).

Since 2,000 pounds = 1 ton, divide 6,000 by 2,000.

6,000 ÷ 2,000 = 3

So, 6,000 pounds = 3 tons.

2,000 lb | 2,000 lb | 2,000 lb } 3 T

As with units of length, units of weight in the customary system can also be expressed using different units or as fractions.

EXAMPLE Parts of Units

4 Complete: 56 oz = ■ lb

Since you are converting a smaller unit to a larger unit, divide.

56 ÷ 16 = 3 R8

The remainder 8 means there are 8 ounces out of a pound left over. The fraction of a pound is $\frac{8}{16}$ or $\frac{1}{2}$.

So, 56 oz = 3 lb 8 oz or $3\frac{1}{2}$ lb.

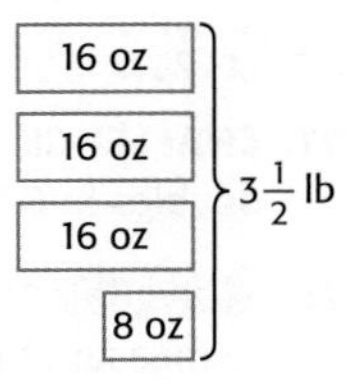

Remember

When converting measures, there will be more smaller units than larger units.

smaller units		larger units
6,000 lb	=	3 T
56 oz	=	$3\frac{1}{2}$ lb

Enrich (p. 22) AL

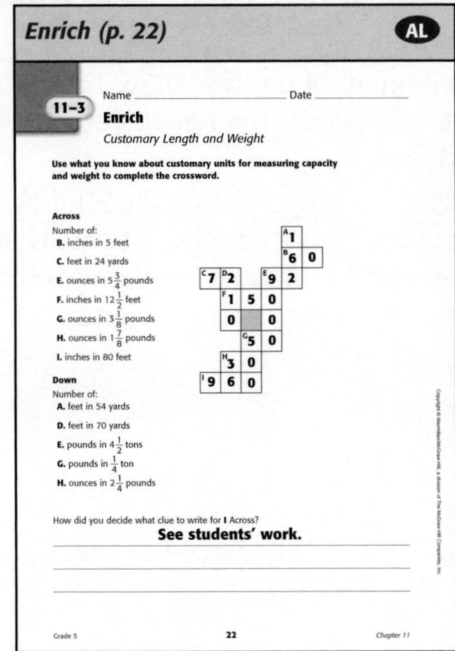

11-3 Name ______ Date ______

Enrich

Customary Length and Weight

Use what you know about customary units for measuring capacity and weight to complete the crossword.

Across

Number of:

B. inches in 5 feet

C. feet in 24 yards

E. ounces in $5\frac{3}{4}$ pounds

F. inches in $12\frac{1}{2}$ feet

G. ounces in $3\frac{1}{8}$ pounds

H. ounces in $1\frac{7}{8}$ pounds

I. inches in 80 feet

Down

Number of:

A. feet in 54 yards

D. feet in 70 yards

E. pounds in $4\frac{1}{2}$ tons

G. pounds in $\frac{1}{4}$ ton

H. ounces in $2\frac{1}{4}$ pounds

How did you decide what clue to write for **I** Across?

See students' work.

Parts of Units

Example 4 When changing a smaller unit to a larger unit, make sure students understand that after dividing, the remainder becomes the numerator and the divisor becomes the denominator to show the fractional amount of the larger unit. The fraction then needs to be written in simplest form.

ADDITIONAL EXAMPLES

1. A truck weighs about 2 tons. How many pounds does the truck weigh? 4,000 lb
2. Pravit needs $4\frac{3}{4}$ pounds of carrots to feed his rabbits. How many ounces of carrots does he need? 76 ounces
3. Convert 128 ounces to pounds. 8 lb
4. Complete: 6,500 lb = ■ T $3\frac{1}{4}$ T

CHECK What You Know

As a class, have students complete Exercises 1–8 in **Check What You Know** as you observe their work.

Exercise 8 Assess student comprehension before assigning practice exercises.

BL Alternate Teaching Strategy

If students have trouble converting customary units of weight…

Then use one of these reteach options:

1. CRM **Daily Reteach Worksheet** (p. 18)
2. Have them label one side of an index card "From Larger to Smaller" and write "Pounds × 16 = Ounces" and "Tons × 2,000 = Pounds".
   - Have them label the reverse side of the card as "From Smaller to Larger" and write "Ounces ÷ 16 = pounds (remainder = ounces or $\frac{R}{16}$)," and "Pounds ÷ 2,000 = tons (remainder = pounds or $\frac{R}{2,000}$)"

   Encourage students to use their cards as they convert units of weight.

3 Practice

Differentiate practice using these leveled assignments for Exercises 9–28.

Level	Assignment
BL Below/ Approaching Level	9–11, 14–16, 19–23
OL On Level	11–22, 24–25
AL Above/Beyond Level	10–26 even, 27–28

Have students discuss and complete the Higher Order Thinking problems. As students complete Exercise 28, encourage them to think of benchmarks they may know to help them decide which unit of weight they would use to measure the objects.

WRITING IN ▶MATH Have students complete Exercise 28 in their Math Journals. You may choose to use this as an optional formative assessment.

★ indicates multi-step problem

CHECK What You Know

Complete. See Examples 1–4 (pp. 484–485)

1. 3 lb = ■ oz 48
2. 32 oz = ■ lb 2
3. 8,000 lb = ■ T 4
4. $2\frac{1}{2}$ lb = ■ oz 40
5. 45 oz = ■ lb ■ oz 2; 13
6. 52 oz = ■ lb $3\frac{1}{4}$
7. A restaurant serves a 20-ounce steak. How much does the steak weigh in pounds and ounces? 1 lb 4 oz
8.  Explain how to convert from ounces to pounds. See margin.

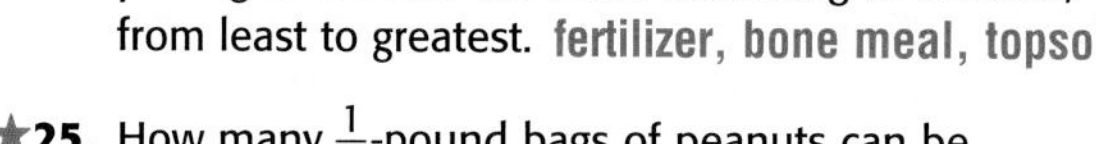

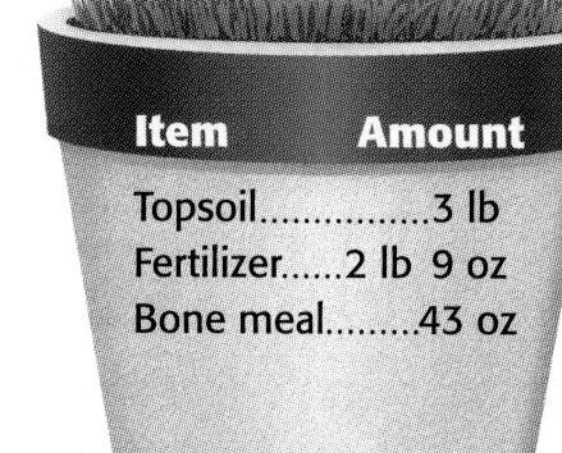

Complete. See Examples 1–4 (pp. 484–485)

9. 96 oz = ■ lb 6
10. 7 T = ■ lb 14,000
11. 10,000 lb = ■ T 5
12. $2\frac{1}{2}$ T = ■ lb 5,000
13. 50 oz = ■ lb ■ oz 3; 2
14. $1\frac{1}{4}$ lb = ■ oz 20
15. 7,000 lb = ■ T ■ lb 3; 1,000
16. 104 oz = ■ lb $6\frac{1}{2}$
17. 1,500 lb = ■ T $\frac{3}{4}$

Replace ● with <, >, or = to make a true statement. See Examples 1–4 (pp. 484–485)

18. 16 lb ● 246 oz >
19. 7,500 lb ● 4 T <
20. $\frac{1}{2}$ T ● 1,000 lb =
21. 1,200 oz ● 72 lb >
22. 7 T 500 lb ● 7,300 oz >
23. 6 lb 11 oz ● 117 oz <

★24. Mia combines the items in the table to make potting soil. Order the items according to amount, from least to greatest. fertilizer, bone meal, topsoil

Item	Amount
Topsoil	3 lb
Fertilizer	2 lb 9 oz
Bone meal	43 oz

★25. How many $\frac{1}{4}$-pound bags of peanuts can be filled from a 5-pound bag of peanuts? 20 bags

26. A puppy weighs 12 ounces. What fractional part of a pound is this? $\frac{3}{4}$

H.O.T. Problems

27. **CHALLENGE** A baby weighs 8 pounds 10 ounces. If her weight doubles in 6 months, how much will she weigh? 17 lb 4 oz

28. **WRITING IN ▶MATH** Tell which units of weight you would use to measure the following: a bag of oranges, a fork, and a submarine. Explain your reasoning. See margin.

Additional Answers

8. Divide the number of ounces by 16. The whole number is the number of pounds. The remainder is the number of ounces left over.
28. Sample answer: a bag of oranges: pounds; a fork: ounces; submarine: tons. Ounces are used to measure small objects, pounds are used to measure medium-sized objects, and tons are used to measure large objects.

COMMON ERROR!

Exercises 18–23 Students may struggle with comparing two different units of measure. Make sure they understand that in order to compare weights, the units of measure must be the same. In order to compare, students may choose to convert either one of the weights given.

29. Ladonna is placing blocks side-by-side on a shelf, as shown below. Measure the width in inches of one block.

If the shelf is 1 foot long, what is the greatest number of blocks that Ladonna can stack on the shelf? (Lesson 11-1) **C**

A 6 **C** 24

B 12 **D** 30

30. A rabbit weighs 4 pounds and 6 ounces. How many ounces does the rabbit weigh? (Lesson 11-3) **F**

1 pound = 16 ounces

F 70 oz

G 64 oz

H 16 oz

J 6 oz

31. SHORT RESPONSE A cabin is 450 yards away from the lake. What is this distance in feet? (Lesson 11-1) **1350**

Spiral Review

32. A tennis ball is dropped from a height of 12 feet. It hits the ground and bounces up half as high as it fell. This is true for each additional bounce. What height does the ball reach on the fourth bounce? Use the *draw a diagram* strategy. (Lesson 11-2) **1.5 ft**

33. Measurement Vultures have been known to fly 37,000 feet above sea level. About how many miles high is this? (Lesson 11-1) **7 mi**

Estimate. (Lesson 10-6)

34. $3\frac{12}{16} + 8\frac{5}{8}$ **13** **35.** $7\frac{5}{12} + 2\frac{7}{12}$ **10** **36.** $8\frac{7}{10} - 6\frac{3}{10}$ **3** **37.** $12\frac{2}{4} - 5\frac{6}{8}$ **7**

Replace each ● with $<$, $>$, or $=$ to make a true statement. (Lesson 9-9)

38. $\frac{5}{8} \bullet \frac{1}{2}$ $>$ **39.** $\frac{1}{3} \bullet \frac{3}{12}$ $>$ **40.** $\frac{3}{18} \bullet \frac{1}{6}$ $=$ **41.** $\frac{7}{10} \bullet \frac{4}{5}$ $<$

42. Is $\frac{3}{10}$ closest to 0, $\frac{1}{2}$, or 1? Explain. (Lesson 8-6) **$\frac{1}{2}$; On the number line $\frac{3}{10}$ is closer to $\frac{1}{2}$ than 0.**

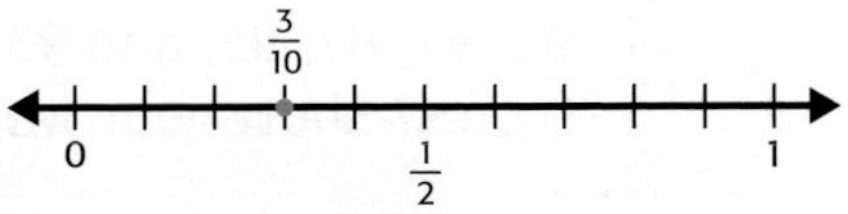

(Number line from 0 to 1 marked $\frac{3}{10}$, $\frac{1}{2}$)

43. A CD display has 128 boxes on the bottom row. Each row has half the number of boxes as the row below. If there is one box on top, how many rows are there? (Lesson 6-7) **8 rows**

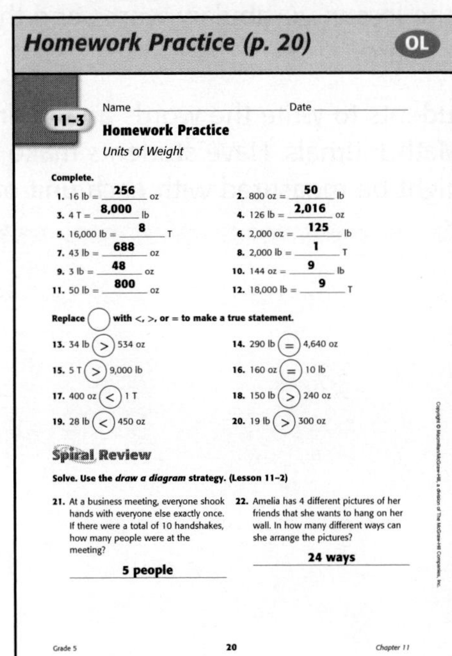

Homework Practice (p. 20) OL

11-3 Name ______ Date ______

Homework Practice

Units of Weight

Complete.

1. 16 lb = **256** oz
2. 800 oz = **50** lb
3. 4 T = **8,000** lb
4. 126 lb = **2,016** oz
5. 16,000 lb = **8** T
6. 2,000 oz = **125** lb
7. 43 lb = **688** oz
8. 2,000 lb = **1** T
9. 3 lb = **48** oz
10. 144 oz = **9** lb
11. 50 lb = **800** oz
12. 18,000 lb = **9** T

Replace ◯ with $<$, $>$, or $=$ to make a true statement.

13. 34 lb $>$ 534 oz
14. 290 lb $=$ 4,640 oz
15. 5 T $>$ 9,000 lb
16. 160 oz $=$ 10 lb
17. 400 oz $<$ 1 T
18. 150 lb $>$ 240 oz
19. 28 lb $<$ 450 oz
20. 19 lb $>$ 300 oz

Spiral Review

Solve. Use the *draw a diagram* strategy. (Lesson 11-2)

21. At a business meeting, everyone shook hands with everyone else exactly once. If there were a total of 10 handshakes, how many people were at the meeting? **5 people**

22. Amelia has 4 different pictures of her friends that she wants to hang on her wall. In how many different ways can she arrange the pictures? **24 ways**

Grade 5 20 Chapter 11

4 Assess

Formative Assessment

Write the following weight on the board: 352 oz.

- **How would you convert this weight to pounds? Explain.** Divide 352 oz by 16. There are 16 oz in a pound so dividing 352 by 16 would show how many pounds in 352 oz.
- **Convert 352 ounces to pounds.** 22 lb

Quick Check **Are students continuing to struggle with converting customary units of weight?**

If Yes → CRM Reteach Worksheet (p. 18)

If No → Independent Work Options (p. 484B)
CRM Skills Practice Worksheet (p. 19)
CRM Enrich Worksheet (p. 22)

Ticket Out the Door Write the following on the board: 13 tons. Give students small cards and have them show how to convert 13 tons to pounds.

Reviews Lessons 11-1 and 11-3

Assign the Test Practice problems to provide daily reinforcement of test-taking skills.

Spiral Review

Reviews Lessons 6-7, 8-6, 9-9, 10-6, 11-1, and 11-2

Review and assess mastery of skills and concepts from previous chapters.

Units of Capacity

Lesson Planner

Objective

Convert customary units of capacity.

Vocabulary

capacity, cup, fluid ounce, pint, quart, gallon

Resources

Materials: water
Manipulatives: capacity containers
Literature Connection: *Millions to Measure* by David M. Schwartz
Teacher Technology
TeacherWorks • Interactive Classroom

Focus on Math Background

Capacity is the amount of fluid that can be held in a container. Both weight and capacity are expressed by a numerical value and a unit of measure. An object can have both weight and capacity. For example, a jug of milk holds about a gallon and weighs about 8 pounds. The one unit both capacity and weight have in common is the ounce. For capacity, the unit is *fluid ounce* (fl oz). For weight, the unit is just *ounce* (oz). Be sure students use the units accurately.

Smaller to larger unit: divide.

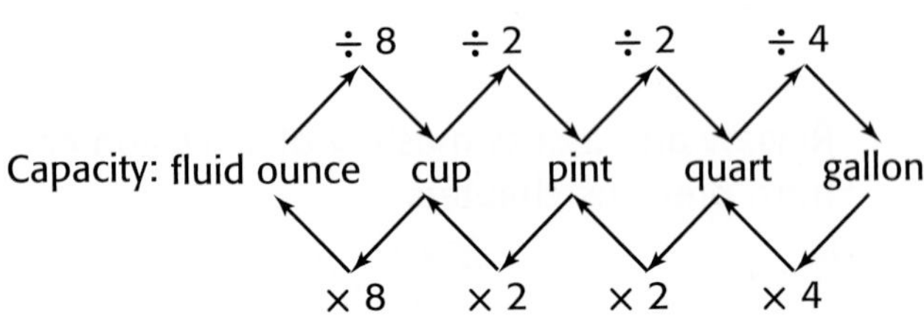

Larger unit to smaller unit: multiply.

Daily Routine

Use these suggestions before beginning the lesson on p. 488.

5-Minute Check

(Reviews Lesson 11-3)

Complete.

1. 48 oz = ■ lb 3
2. 3 T = ■ lb 6,000
3. ■ lb ■ oz = 46 oz 2; 14
4. ■ lb = 8 T 16,000
5. 8 oz = ■ lb $\frac{1}{2}$
6. 17 lb 4 oz = ■ oz 276

Problem of the Day

Selena received the following quiz scores: 83, 79, 95, 91, 87, 95, and 93. What is the median of her scores? Show your work. is 91

Building Math Vocabulary

Write the lesson vocabulary words and their definitions on the board.

Ask students to write the words and their definitions in their Math Journals. Have students make a list of items that might be measured with each unit of capacity.

Differentiated Instruction

Small Group Options

Option 1 Below Level BL

SPATIAL

Materials: scales

- Draw the following on the board and have students copy it in their notebook:

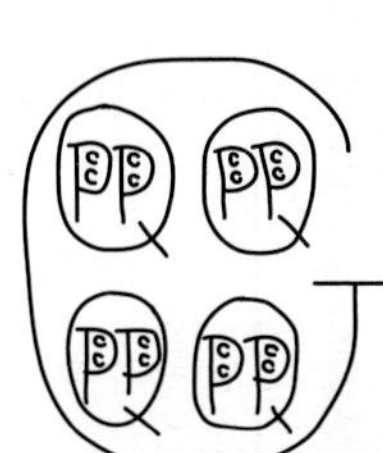

- Explain that the drawing shows units of capacity.
- **How many Cs are inside the G?** 16 This means that there are 16 cups in 1 gallon.
- Continue with Qs and Ps.

Option 2 English Language Learners ELL

TACTILE

Materials: cup, pint, quart, and gallon containers, water, funnel

Core Vocabulary: pour, fill up, containers

Common Use Verb: holds

See Math This strategy teaches students how to compare units of capacity by measuring and comparing cups, pints, quarts, and gallons.

- Label containers as cups, pints, quarts, and gallons.
- Fill a cup with water and have a student pour it into a pint container.
- Fill the cup again and have the student pour water into the container until the pint is full.
- Ask students how many cups filled a pint.
- On the board write two cups *fill* (or *equal*) a *pint* and ask students to repeat it 2-3 times.
- Repeat the procedure with other units of capacity.

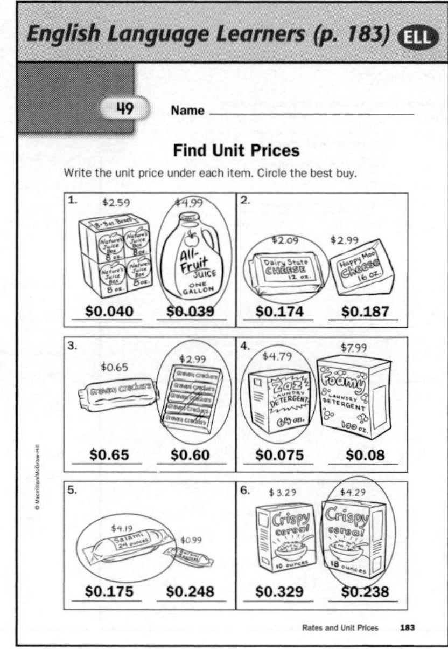

English Language Learners (p. 183) ELL

49 Name ____________

Find Unit Prices

Write the unit price under each item. Circle the best buy.

1. $2.59 / $4.99 — $0.040 / $0.039
2. $2.09 / $2.99 — $0.174 / $0.187
3. $0.65 / $2.99 — $0.65 / $0.60
4. $4.79 / $7.99 — $0.075 / $0.08
5. $4.19 / $0.99 — $0.175 / $0.248
6. $3.29 / $4.29 — $0.329 / $0.238

Rates and Unit Prices 183

Use this worksheet to provide additional support for English Language Learners.

Independent Work Options

Option 1 Early Finishers AL

INTRAPERSONAL

Materials: number cube, pencil, paper

- Have students draw a table labeling the columns: "Fluid Ounces," "Cups," "Pints," "Quarts," and "Gallons".
- Students roll the number cube twice and multiply the two numbers generated. They will then write the product in the "Pints" column.
- Have students complete the table by converting the pints into fluid ounces, cups, quarts and gallons. Roll as often as time allows.

Fl Ounces	Cups	Pints	Quarts	Gallons
192	24	12	6	$1\frac{1}{2}$
160	20	10	5	$1\frac{1}{4}$

Option 2 Student Technology

Math Online macmillanmh.com

Personal Tutor • Extra Examples

Math Adventures

Option 3 Learning Station: Science (p. 472H)

Direct students to the Science Learning Station for opportunities to explore and extend the lesson concept.

Option 4 Problem-Solving Practice

Reinforce problem-solving skills and strategies with the Problem-Solving Practice worksheet.

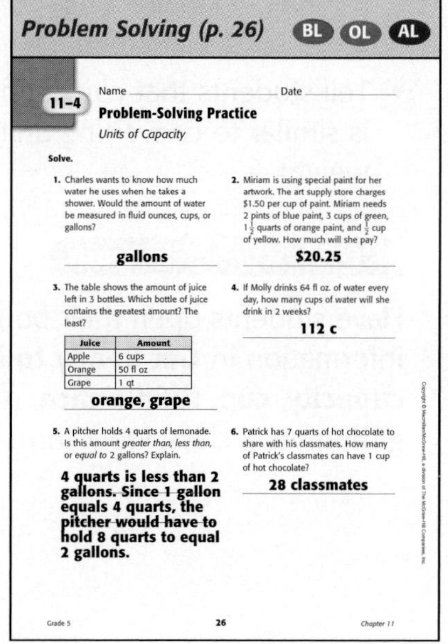

Problem Solving (p. 26) BL OL AL

11–4 Name ____________ Date ____________

Problem-Solving Practice

Units of Capacity

Solve.

1. Charles wants to know how much water he uses when he takes a shower. Would the amount of water be measured in fluid ounces, cups, or gallons?
   gallons
2. Miriam is using special paint for her artwork. The art supply store charges $1.50 per cup of paint. Miriam needs 2 pints of blue paint, 3 cups of green, $1\frac{1}{2}$ quarts of orange paint, and $\frac{1}{2}$ cup of yellow. How much will she pay?
   $20.25
3. The table shows the amount of juice left in 3 bottles. Which bottle of juice contains the greatest amount? The least?

Juice	Amount
Apple	6 cups
Orange	50 fl oz
Grape	1 qt

   orange, grape
4. If Molly drinks 64 fl oz. of water every day, how many cups of water will she drink in 2 weeks?
   112 c
5. A pitcher holds 4 quarts of lemonade. Is this amount *greater than, less than,* or *equal to* 2 gallons? Explain.
   4 quarts is less than 2 gallons. Since 1 gallon equals 4 quarts, the pitcher would have to hold 8 quarts to equal 2 gallons.
6. Patrick has 7 quarts of hot chocolate to share with his classmates. How many of Patrick's classmates can have 1 cup of hot chocolate?
   28 classmates

Grade 5 26 Chapter 11

Units of Capacity

1 Introduce

Activity Choice 1 • Hands-On 

- Display containers showing a cup, pint, quart, and gallon. Have student volunteers demonstrate, by pouring water from one container to another; 2 cups in a pint, 2 pints in a quart and 4 quarts in a gallon.
- Tell students that fluid ounces are often used to measure liquids. Demonstrate that there are 8 fluid ounces in 1 cup by pouring water from the fluid ounce container.
- Write the equivalencies for unit of capacity on the board. Use the equations from See the Key Concept section of the lesson.

Activity Choice 2 • Literature

Introduce the lesson with *Millions to Measure* by David M. Schwartz. For a related math activity, see p. TR54.

2 Teach

Scaffolding Questions

Use the capacity conversions for cup, pint, quart, and gallon that were written on the board in Activity Choice 1.

- **How do you convert 8 cups to pints?** Divide 8 ÷ 2 to get 4 pt.
- **How do you convert 2 gallons to quarts?** Multiply 2 × 4 to get 8 qt.
- **What is the rule for converting a smaller unit of measure to a larger unit?** Divide the number of smaller units by the number of those units that are equal to the larger unit.
- Tell students that converting units of capacity is similar to converting units of length and weight.

GET READY to Learn

Have students open their books and read the information in **Get Ready to Learn.** Introduce **capacity, cup, fluid ounce, pint, quart,** and **gallon**. As a class, work through **Examples 1–3**.

11-4 Units of Capacity

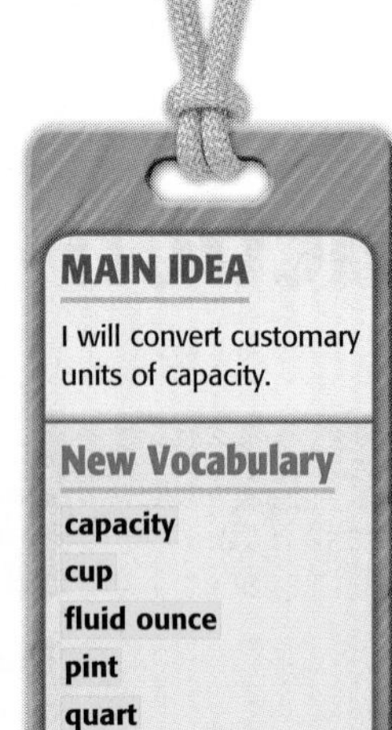

MAIN IDEA
I will convert customary units of capacity.
New Vocabulary
capacity
cup
fluid ounce
pint
quart
gallon
Math Online
macmillanmh.com
• Extra Examples
• Personal Tutor
• Self-Check Quiz

GET READY to Learn

Sondra tries to drink 9 cups of water each day. How many fluid ounces of water is 9 cups?

Capacity is the measure of how much a container can hold.

Customary Units of Capacity — Key Concepts

1 **cup** (c) = 8 **fluid ounces** (fl oz)

1 **pint** (pt) = 2 c = 16 fl oz

1 **quart** (qt) = 2 pt = 32 fl oz

1 **gallon** (gal) = 4 qt = 128 fl oz

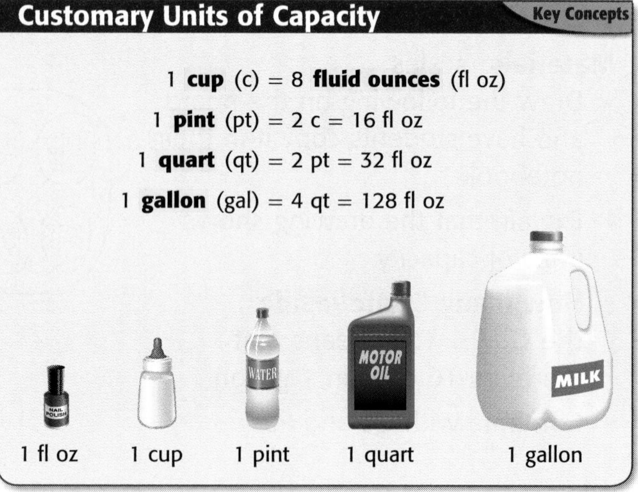

Real-World EXAMPLE Convert Units of Capacity

1. **Refer to the information at the beginning of the lesson. How many fluid ounces of water is in 9 cups?**

9 c = ■ fl oz Larger units (cups) are being converted to smaller units (fluid ounces).

Since 1 cup = 8 fluid ounces, multiply 9 by 8.

So, 9 cups of water is equal to 9 × 8 or 72 fluid ounces.

488 Chapter 11 Use Measures in the Customary System

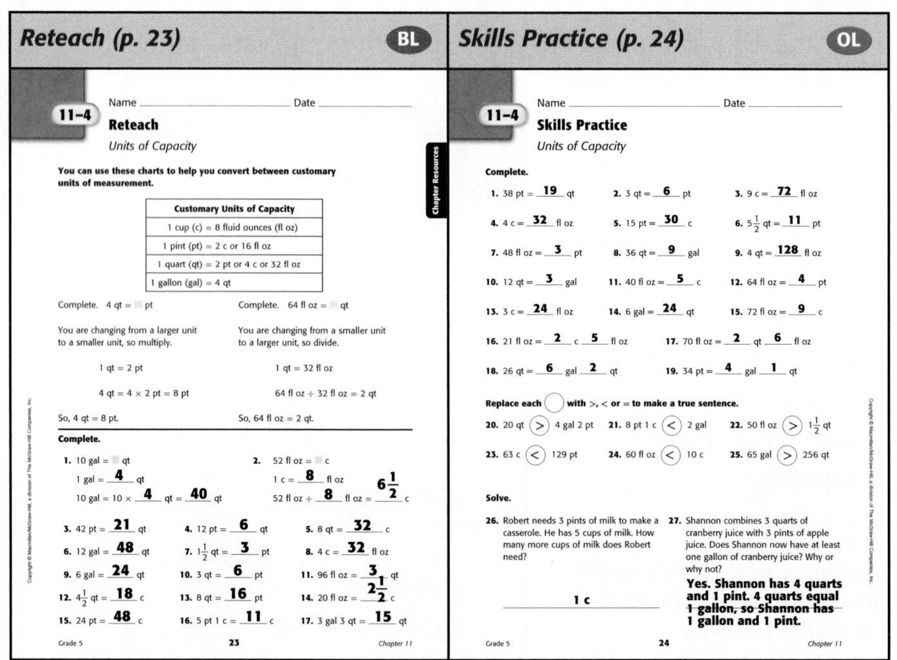

Reteach (p. 23) BL

11-4 Name ______ Date ______

Reteach

Units of Capacity

You can use these charts to help you convert between customary units of measurement.

Customary Units of Capacity
1 cup (c) = 8 fluid ounces (fl oz)
1 pint (pt) = 2 c or 16 fl oz
1 quart (qt) = 2 pt or 4 c or 32 fl oz
1 gallon (gal) = 4 qt

Complete. 4 qt = ■ pt

You are changing from a larger unit to a smaller unit, so multiply.

1 qt = 2 pt

4 qt = 4 × 2 pt = 8 pt

So, 4 qt = 8 pt.

Complete. 64 fl oz = ■ qt

You are changing from a smaller unit to a larger unit, so divide.

1 qt = 32 fl oz

64 fl oz ÷ 32 fl oz = 2 qt

So, 64 fl oz = 2 qt.

Complete.

1. 10 gal = ■ qt
   1 gal = **4** qt
   10 gal = 10 × **4** qt = **40** qt
2. 52 fl oz = ■ c
   1 c = **8** fl oz
   52 fl oz ÷ **8** fl oz = $6\frac{1}{2}$ c
3. 42 pt = **21** qt
4. 12 pt = **6** qt
5. 8 qt = **32** c
6. 12 gal = **48** qt
7. $1\frac{1}{2}$ qt = **3** pt
8. 4 c = **32** fl oz
9. 6 gal = **24** qt
10. 3 qt = **6** pt
11. 96 fl oz = **3** qt
12. $4\frac{1}{2}$ qt = **18** c
13. 8 qt = **16** pt
14. 20 fl oz = $2\frac{1}{2}$ c
15. 24 pt = **48** c
16. 5 pt 1 c = **11** c
17. 3 gal 3 qt = **15** qt

Grade 5 23 Chapter 11

Chapter Resources

Skills Practice (p. 24) OL

11-4 Name ______ Date ______

Skills Practice

Units of Capacity

Complete.

1. 38 pt = **19** qt
2. 3 qt = **6** pt
3. 9 c = **72** fl oz
4. 4 c = **32** fl oz
5. 15 pt = **30** c
6. $5\frac{1}{2}$ qt = **11** pt
7. 48 fl oz = **3** pt
8. 36 qt = **9** gal
9. 4 qt = **128** fl oz
10. 12 qt = **3** gal
11. 40 fl oz = **5** c
12. 64 fl oz = **4** pt
13. 3 c = **24** fl oz
14. 6 gal = **24** qt
15. 72 fl oz = **9** c
16. 21 fl oz = **2** c **5** fl oz
17. 70 fl oz = **2** qt **6** fl oz
18. 26 qt = **6** gal **2** qt
19. 34 pt = **4** gal **1** qt

Replace each ◯ with >, < or = to make a true sentence.

20. 20 qt (>) 4 gal 2 pt
21. 8 pt 1 c (<) 2 gal
22. 50 fl oz (>) $1\frac{1}{2}$ qt
23. 63 c (<) 129 pt
24. 60 fl oz (<) 10 c
25. 65 gal (>) 256 qt

Solve.

26. Robert needs 3 pints of milk to make a casserole. He has 5 cups of milk. How many more cups of milk does Robert need?
    1 c
27. Shannon combines 3 quarts of cranberry juice with 3 pints of apple juice. Does Shannon now have at least one gallon of cranberry juice? Why or why not?
    Yes. Shannon has 4 quarts and 1 pint. 4 quarts equal 1 gallon, so Shannon has 1 gallon and 1 pint.

Grade 5 24 Chapter 11

EXAMPLE Convert Units of Capacity

Remember

Any substance that takes on the shape of its container, such as liquids, some solids, and air can be measured in units of capacity.

2 Paco has 3 pints of juice plus 1 cup of juice. How many cups of juice does he have in all?

First, convert 3 pints 1 cup to cups.

Since 1 pint = 2 cups, multiply 3 by 2.

$3 \times 2 = 6$

Then add the remaining 1 cup.

So, Paco has 6 + 1 or 7 cups of juice.

As with units of length and units of weight, units of capacity in the customary system can also be expressed as fractions.

EXAMPLE Parts of Units

3 How many quarts are in 7 pints?

7 pt = ■ qt

To convert a smaller unit to a larger unit, divide. Since 2 pints = 1 quart, divide 7 by 2.

2 pt
2 pt
2 pt
1 pt

$3\frac{1}{2}$ qt

$7 \div 2 = 3$ R1, or $3\frac{1}{2}$

So, there are 3 quarts 1 pint or $3\frac{1}{2}$ quarts in 7 pints.

★ indicates multi-step problem

CHECK What You Know

Complete. See Examples 1–3 (pp. 488–489)

1. 3 c = ■ fl oz 24
2. 4 qt = ■ c 16
3. 18 pt = ■ qt 9
4. 50 gal = ■ qt 200
5. 16 pt 1 c = ■ c 33
6. 68 fl oz = ■ c $8\frac{1}{2}$
7. 5 qt = ■ gal ■ qt 1; 1
8. 75 fl oz = ■ c ■ fl oz 9; 3

★9. The cafeteria sells lemonade in glasses that hold 12 fluid ounces. How many glasses can be filled with 3 gallons of lemonade? 32 glasses

10. Talk About It Explain how to convert from fluid ounces to pints. Sample answer: Divide the number of fluid ounces by 16.

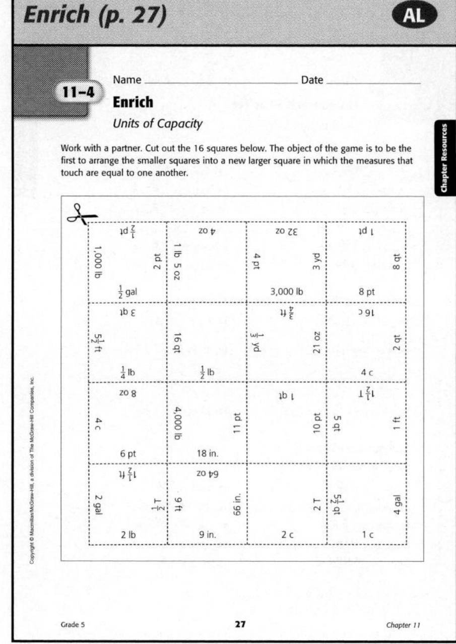

Enrich (p. 27) AL

11-4 Name Date

Enrich

Units of Capacity

Work with a partner. Cut out the 16 squares below. The object of the game is to be the first to arrange the smaller squares into a new larger square in which the measures that touch are equal to one another.

Grade 5 27 Chapter 11

Parts of Units

Example 3 Tell students that when they convert from smaller units to larger units, any remainder should be labeled as the smaller units.

ADDITIONAL EXAMPLES

1. Three gallons of juice were served at a class picnic. How many quarts of juice is 3 gallons? 12 qt
2. Mrs. Diego needs 5 pints plus 1 cup of blueberries to make muffins. How many cups of blueberries does she need? 11 cups
3. How many gallons are in 15 quarts? $3\frac{3}{4}$ gal

CHECK What You Know

As a class, have students complete Exercises 1–10 in **Check What You Know** as you observe their work.

Exercise 10 Assess student comprehension before assigning practice exercises.

BL Alternate Teaching Strategy

If students have trouble converting customary units of capacity…

Then use one of these reteach options:

1 CRM **Daily Reteach Worksheet** (p. 23)

2 Have them use cup, pint, quart, and gallon containers to see the relationships between the measures. Fill a cup measure and pour it into the pint container.

- **About how full is the pint container? How many cups will fit?** $\frac{1}{2}$ full; 2 cups Repeat for the other containers. Have students record their findings.

COMMON ERROR!

Exercises 17 and 18 Students may have trouble converting two different units of measure to the smaller of the two units. Encourage them to draw a picture showing how many of the smaller units are in each of the larger units. Then have them add the smaller units that are in the original problem to find the total number of smaller units.

3 Practice

Differentiate practice using these leveled assignments for Exercises 11–30.

Level	Assignment
BL Below/ Approaching Level	11–16, 20–23, 24–26
OL On Level	14–22, 25–27, 28
AL Above/Beyond Level	11–27 odd, 28–30

Have students discuss and complete the Higher Order Thinking problems. For Exercise 28 have students make the conversion before they try to find the error made by one of the students.

WRITING IN ▸MATH Have students complete Exercise 30 in their Math Journals. You may choose to use this exercise as an optional formative assessment.

Assess

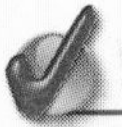

Formative Assessment

Write the following on the board: 13 quarts.

- **How would you convert this amount to gallons? How many gallons is this?** divide 13 by 4; $3\frac{1}{4}$ gal
- **How would you convert this amount to pints?** multiply $13 \times 2 = 26$ pt

Quick Check **Are students continuing to struggle with converting customary units of capacity?**

If Yes → Small Group Options (p. 488B)

If No → Independent Work Options (p. 488B)
CRM Skills Practice Worksheet (p. 24)
CRM Enrich Worksheet (p. 27)

Name the Math Write 256 fl oz on the board. Ask students to tell the steps in converting 256 fl oz to gallons.

Practice and Problem Solving

See page R30.

Complete. See Examples 1–3 (pp. 488–489)

11. 5 c = ■ fl oz 40 **12.** 2 gal = ■ fl oz 256 **13.** 16 fl oz = ■ c 2

14. 25 gal = ■ qt 100 **15.** 19 c = ■ fl oz 152 **16.** 50 c = ■ pt 25

17. 2 gal 3 qt = ■ qt 11 **18.** 2 qt 3 c = ■ c 11 **19.** 5 c = ■ pt ■ c 2; 1

20. 17 fl oz = ■ c ■ fl oz 2; 1 **21.** 19 qt = ■ gal ■ qt 4; 3

22. 18 qt = ■ gal $4\frac{1}{2}$ **23.** 7 c = ■ pt $3\frac{1}{2}$

24. Zach had 1 quart of milk. He used 1 pint to make pancakes and 1 cup to make scrambled eggs. How many cups of milk were left? 1 c

★25. The average person drinks 1 pint of milk a day. At this rate, how many gallons will a person drink in a leap year (366 days)? $45\frac{3}{4}$ gal

★26. The table shows the amount of paint left in each jar. Which jar contains the greatest amount of paint? the least? purple; blue

Jar	Amount
blue	2 pt 4 oz
purple	5 cups
green	39 fl oz

★27. Measurement A bucket has $1\frac{1}{2}$ gallons of water. Is this amount *greater, than less than,* or *equal to* 6 quarts? Explain. equal to; 4 quarts = 1 gallon and 2 quarts = $\frac{1}{2}$ gallon

H.O.T. Problems

28. FIND THE ERROR Jasmine and Pablo are converting 32 cups to quarts. Who is correct? Explain. Pablo; since 4 c = 1 qt, 32 should be divided by 4.

Jasmine
32 c = ■ qt
32 ÷ 2 = 16
32 c = 16 qt

Pablo
32 c = ■ qt
32 ÷ 4 = 8
32 c = 8 qt

29. CHALLENGE Convert the following to the greatest whole number units of capacity. 1; 2; 0; 1; 0

200 fl oz = ■ gal ■ qt ■ pt ■ c ■ fl oz

30. WRITING IN ▸MATH Write about a real-world situation that can be solved by converting between customary units of capacity. Then solve. See Ch. 11 Answer Appendix.

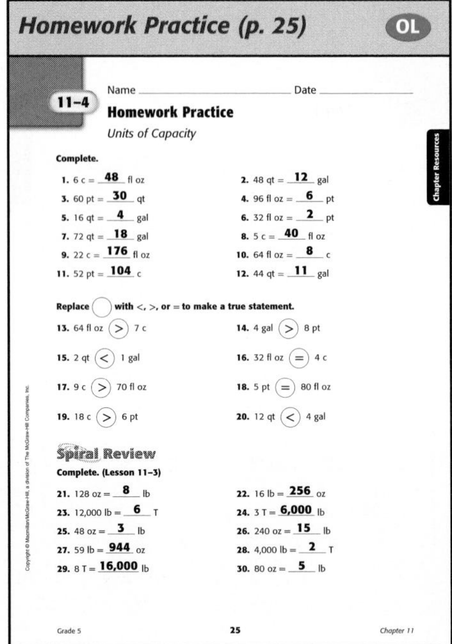

Homework Practice (p. 25) OL

11-4 Name ________ Date ________

Homework Practice

Units of Capacity

Complete.

1. 6 c = 48 fl oz **2.** 48 qt = 12 gal
3. 60 pt = 30 qt **4.** 96 fl oz = 6 pt
5. 16 qt = 4 gal **6.** 32 fl oz = 2 pt
7. 72 qt = 18 gal **8.** 5 c = 40 fl oz
9. 22 c = 176 fl oz **10.** 64 fl oz = 8 c
11. 52 pt = 104 c **12.** 44 qt = 11 gal

Replace ◯ with <, >, or = to make a true statement.

13. 64 fl oz (>) 7 c **14.** 4 gal (>) 8 pt
15. 2 qt (<) 1 gal **16.** 32 fl oz (=) 4 c
17. 9 c (>) 70 fl oz **18.** 5 pt (=) 80 fl oz
19. 18 c (>) 6 pt **20.** 12 qt (<) 4 gal

Spiral Review

Complete. (Lesson 11-3)

21. 128 oz = 8 lb **22.** 16 lb = 256 oz
23. 12,000 lb = 6 T **24.** 3 T = 6,000 lb
25. 48 oz = 3 lb **26.** 240 oz = 15 lb
27. 59 lb = 944 oz **28.** 4,000 lb = 2 T
29. 8 T = 16,000 lb **30.** 80 oz = 5 lb

Chapter Resources

Grade 5 25 Chapter 11

Mid-Chapter Check

Lessons 11-1 through 11-4

Complete. (Lesson 11-1)

1. 84 in. = ■ ft 7 **2.** 2 mi = ■ ft 10,560

3. 41 in. = ■ ft ■ in. 3; 5 **4.** 25 ft = ■ yd $8\frac{1}{3}$

Choose an appropriate unit to measure the length of each. (Lesson 11-1)

5. height of giraffe ft

6. length of soccer field yd

7. MULTIPLE CHOICE Alexander is 32 inches tall. His brother Josh is 4 feet tall. What fractional part of Josh's height is Alexander's height? (Lesson 11-1) D

A $\frac{1}{8}$ **C** $\frac{1}{2}$

B $\frac{1}{4}$ **D** $\frac{2}{3}$

8. Five toy remote cars are in a race. Car 2 is just ahead of Car 3. Car 3 is two places behind Car 4. Car 4 is a few seconds behind the leader, Car 1. Car 5 is in last place. Order the cars from first to last place. Use the *draw a diagram* strategy. Car 1, Car 4, Car 2, Car 3, Car 5

Complete. (Lesson 11-3)

9. $2\frac{1}{2}$ lb = ■ oz 40 **10.** 80 oz = ■ lb 5

11. 35 oz = ■ lb ■ oz 2; 3 **12.** 7,500 lb = ■ T $3\frac{3}{4}$

13. Refer to the sign at the right. What is the weight limit in pounds? (Lesson 11-3) 20,000 lb

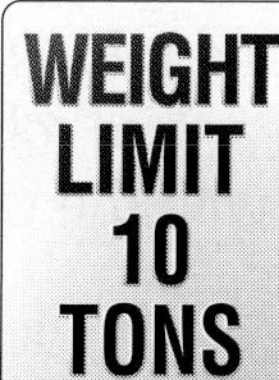

14. A motorcycle weighs 500 pounds. What fractional part of a ton is this? (Lesson 11-3) $\frac{1}{4}$ T

Complete. (Lesson 11-4)

15. 10 gal = ■ pt 80

16. 7 qt = ■ gal ■ qt 1; 3

17. 28 fl oz = ■ c $3\frac{1}{2}$

18. The table below shows the bottles of cleaning products that Lucas bought. Which cleaner contains the greatest amount? the least? (Lesson 11-4) window; bathroom

Cleaner	Amount
Rug	62 fl oz
Bathroom	3 pt 12 fl oz
Window	2 qt

19. MULTIPLE CHOICE What is the total number of cups in 7 quarts? (Lesson 11-4) J

1 pint = 2 cups
1 quart = 4 cups

F 6 cups

G 8 cups

H 14 cups

J 28 cups

20. WRITING IN MATH What is the difference between weight and capacity? Use objects to explain your answer. (Lessons 11-3 and 11-4) See Ch. 11 Answer Appendix.

Chapter 11 Mid-Chapter Check

Lessons 11-1 through 11-4

Formative Assessment

Use the Mid-Chapter Check to assess students' progress in the first half of the chapter.

ExamView® Assessment Suite Customize and create multiple versions of your Mid-Chapter Check and the test answer keys.

FOLDABLES® Dinah Zike's Foldables

Use these lesson suggestions to incorporate the Foldables during the chapter.

Lesson 11-1 Under the top left tab of the Foldable, have students record data as they measure and convert customary units of length. Students might glue a graphic of a ruler beneath the Foldable.

Lesson 11-3 Under the top right tab of the Foldable, have students record data as they measure and convert customary units of weight.

Lesson 11-4 Under the bottom left tab of the Foldable, have students record data as they measure and convert customary units of capacity. Students might draw or glue graphics showing the equivalencies of gallons, quarts, and pints beneath the Foldable tab.

Data-Driven Decision Making

Based on the results of the Mid-Chapter Check, use the following resources to review concepts that continue to present students with problems.

Exercises	State/Local Standards	What's the Math?	Error Analysis	Resources for Review
1–7 Lesson 11-1		Choose an appropriate customary unit for measurement.	Does not have concept of lengths of units of measurement. Does not know correct numbers to use to convert measurement.	Strategic Intervention Guide (pp. 122, 130) CRM Chapter 11 Resource Masters (Reteach) Math Adventures My Math Zone Chapter 11 Math Online Extra Examples • Concepts in Motion
8 Lesson 11-2		Write an equation to solve a problem.	Does not understand "many times greater." Does not compute accurately.	
9–14 Lesson 11-3		Convert customary units of weight.	Does not know abbreviations or units for conversion for "ounces," "pounds," "tons." Computes incorrectly.	
15–20 Lesson 11-4		Convert customary units of capacity.	Does not know units of conversion for ounces, pints, quarts, gallons. Computes incorrectly. Does not understand "capacity."	

LESSON 11-5

Units of Time

Lesson Planner

Objective

Convert units of time.

Review Vocabulary

units of time

Resources

Materials: chart paper
Literature Connection: *Measuring Penny* by Loreen Leedy
Alternate Lesson: Use *IMPACT Mathematics:* Unit H to provide practice with time.
Teacher Technology
TeacherWorks • Interactive Classroom

Focus on Math Background

Whereas units for measuring length, weight, and capacity are different in the customary and metric systems, units for time are the same in both systems. The use of multiples of 60 in our measurement of time probably dates back to the Babylonians, who used a *sexagesimal* number system based on 60.

Smaller to larger unit: divide

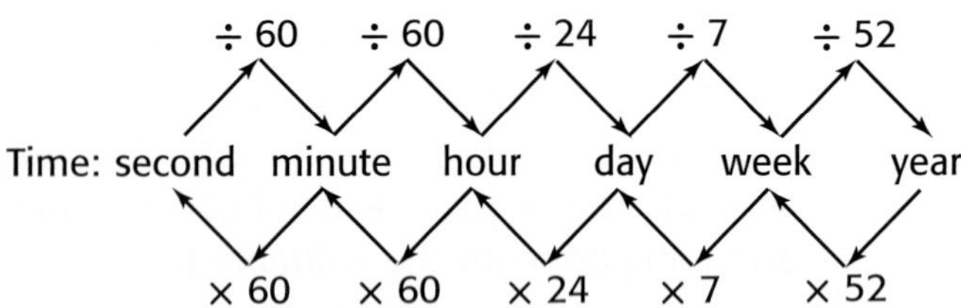

Larger unit to smaller unit: multiply.

Daily Routine

Use these suggestions before beginning the lesson on p. 492.

5-Minute Check

(Reviews Lesson 11-4)

Complete.

1. 8 c = ▪ fl oz 64 fl oz
2. 16 pt = ▪ qt 8 qt
3. 9 c = ▪ pt ▪ c 4 pt 1 c
4. 3 gal 3 qt = ▪ qt 15 qt
5. 9 qt = ▪ c 36 c
6. 56 fl oz = ▪ pt $3\frac{1}{2}$ pt

Problem of the Day

Kayla uses 3 yards of yarn to make one key chain. She has 36 feet of yarn in one roll, 216 inches in a second roll and 24 yards in a third roll. How many key chains can Kayla make with the yarn she has? 14 key chains

Review Math Vocabulary

Write the review vocabulary word and its definition on the board.

Have students write the vocabulary word and its meaning in their Math Journals. Have students create a list of all the units of time that they are familiar with.

Differentiated Instruction

Small Group Options

Option 1 Gifted and Talented AL

SPATIAL

Materials: pencil and paper

- Have students make a schedule of their daily activities and compute the elapsed time for each.

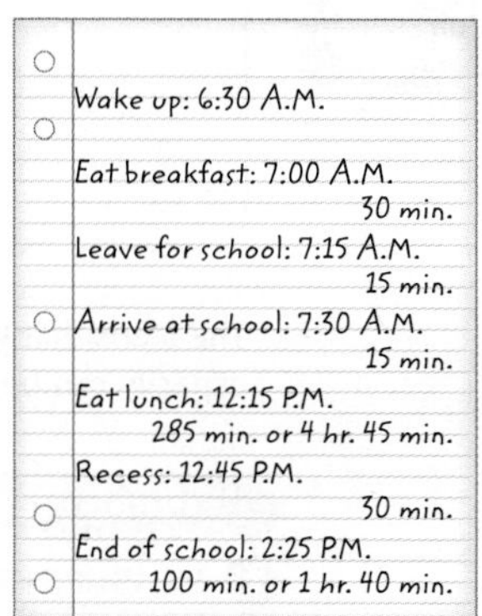

Wake up: 6:30 A.M.
Eat breakfast: 7:00 A.M.
30 min.
Leave for school: 7:15 A.M.
15 min.
Arrive at school: 7:30 A.M.
15 min.
Eat lunch: 12:15 P.M.
285 min. or 4 hr. 45 min.
Recess: 12:45 P.M.
30 min.
End of school: 2:25 P.M.
100 min. or 1 hr. 40 min.

Option 2 English Language Learners ELL

TACTILE

Materials: index cards

Core Vocabulary: quarter hour, half hour, three-quarters/ three-fourths of an hour

Common Use Verb: took

Hear Math This strategy teaches students to associate the spoken and written fractions with the minutes in an hour.

- Create sets of cards with one of each on a card: 15 min.; 30 min.; 45 min.; $\frac{1}{4}$ hour; $\frac{1}{2}$ hour; $\frac{3}{4}$ hour; one quarter hour; one half hour; three-fourths hour
- Give each pair of students a scrambled set of cards.
- Call out a sentence such as *Jill ran for one quarter hour. How long did she run?* Have students show the fraction that represents one quarter hour (e.g., $\frac{1}{4}$, 15 min., one quarter hour).
- Continue until the cards are used up; start over with new sentences.

Use this worksheet to provide additional support for English Language Learners.

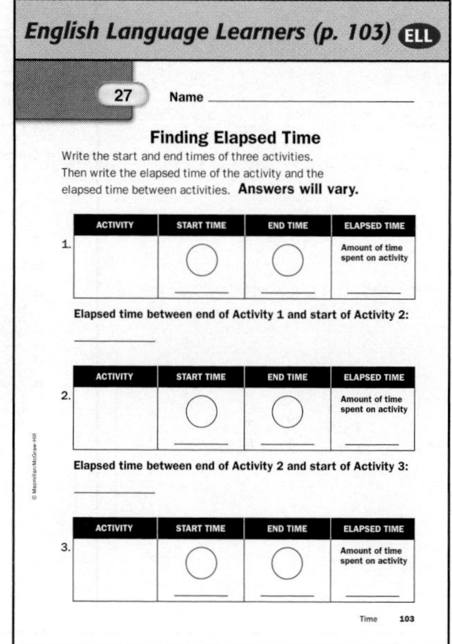

English Language Learners (p. 103) ELL

27 Name ____________

Finding Elapsed Time

Write the start and end times of three activities. Then write the elapsed time of the activity and the elapsed time between activities. **Answers will vary.**

1.

ACTIVITY	START TIME	END TIME	ELAPSED TIME
			Amount of time spent on activity

Elapsed time between end of Activity 1 and start of Activity 2: ________

2.

ACTIVITY	START TIME	END TIME	ELAPSED TIME
			Amount of time spent on activity

Elapsed time between end of Activity 2 and start of Activity 3: ________

3.

ACTIVITY	START TIME	END TIME	ELAPSED TIME
			Amount of time spent on activity

Time 103

Independent Work Options

Option 1 Early Finishers AL

SOCIAL

Materials: 4 index cards cut in half, number cube

- Students work in pairs. Have students write the following on index cards, one label per card: year to week, week to day, day to hour, hour to minute, minute to second, year to day, week to hour, hour to second.
- Each student draws a card and rolls the number cube. They will use the number rolled as the number of the first unit of time as shown on their card.
- Each student will write the conversion they must perform on his or her paper and complete the problem. Have partners check each other's work for accuracy. Continue with activity as time allows.

Option 2 Student Technology

Tech Link

Math Online macmillanmh.com

Personal Tutor • Extra Examples

Math Adventures

Option 3 Learning Station: Writing (p. 472G)

Direct students to the Writing Learning Station for opportunities to explore and extend the lesson concept.

Option 4 Problem-Solving Practice

Reinforce problem-solving skills and strategies with the Problem-Solving Practice worksheet.

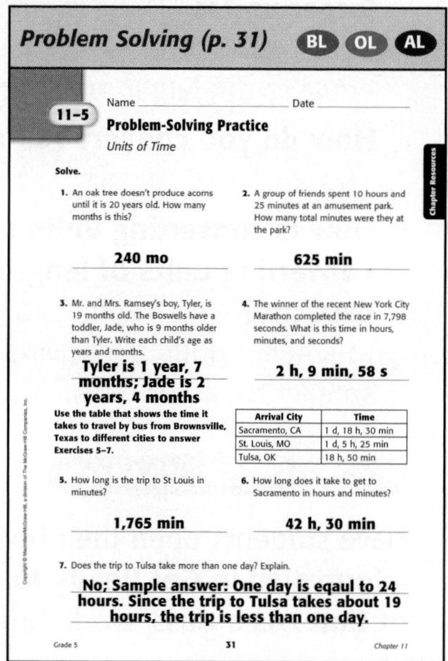
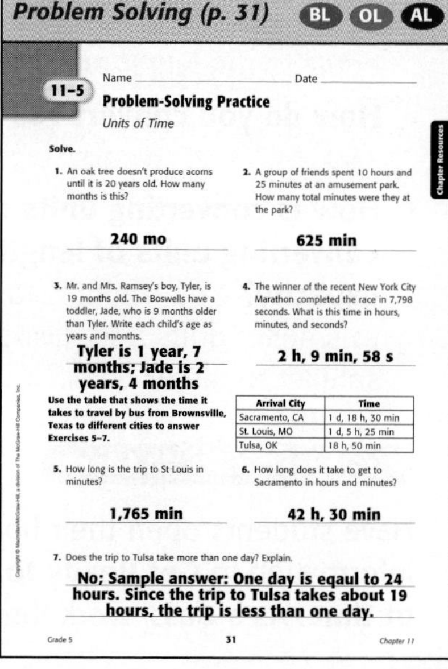

Problem Solving (p. 31) BL OL AL

11–5 Name ____________ Date ____________

Problem-Solving Practice

Units of Time

Solve.

1. An oak tree doesn't produce acorns until it is 20 years old. How many months is this?
   240 mo

2. A group of friends spent 10 hours and 25 minutes at an amusement park. How many total minutes were they at the park?
   625 min

3. Mr. and Mrs. Ramsey's boy, Tyler, is 19 months old. The Boswells have a toddler, Jade, who is 9 months older than Tyler. Write each child's age as years and months.
   Tyler is 1 year, 7 months; Jade is 2 years, 4 months

4. The winner of the recent New York City Marathon completed the race in 7,798 seconds. What is this time in hours, minutes, and seconds?
   2 h, 9 min, 58 s

Use the table that shows the time it takes to travel by bus from Brownsville, Texas to different cities to answer Exercises 5–7.

Arrival City	Time
Sacramento, CA	1 d, 18 h, 30 min
St. Louis, MO	1 d, 5 h, 25 min
Tulsa, OK	18 h, 50 min

5. How long is the trip to St Louis in minutes?
   1,765 min

6. How long does it take to get to Sacramento in hours and minutes?
   42 h, 30 min

7. Does the trip to Tulsa take more than one day? Explain.
   No; Sample answer: One day is eqaul to 24 hours. Since the trip to Tulsa takes about 19 hours, the trip is less than one day.

Chapter Resources

Grade 5 31 Chapter 11

11-5 Units of Time

1 Introduce

Activity Choice 1 • Hands-On 

- As a class, complete the list below.

  1 min = __ s 1 wk = __ d
  1 h = __ min 1 y = __ wk = __ mo
  1 d = __ h

- Tell students that some units of time can vary, such as length of years and months. **How many days are in a year? a month?** 365 or 366 days; 28, 29, 30 or 31 days
- Discuss the idea that time, as a measurement, can be converted like other measurements.

Activity Choice 2 • Literature

Introduce the lesson with *Measuring Penny* by Loreen Leedy. For a related math activity, see p. TR55.

2 Teach

Scaffolding Questions

Use the list created in Activity Choice 1 to answer the questions below.

- **How do you convert larger units of time to smaller units of time?** Multiply the number of larger units times how many smaller units one larger unit is equal to.
- **How do you convert 7 days into hours?** $7 \times 24 = 168$ h
- **How do you convert smaller units of time to larger units?** Divide the number of smaller units by the number of those units that are equal to the larger unit.
- **How do you convert 189 days into weeks?** $189 \div 7 = 27$ weeks
- **How is converting units of time similar to converting units of length and units of capacity?** You multiply to convert from larger to smaller units and divide to convert from smaller to larger units.

GET READY to Learn

Have students open their books and read the information in **Get Ready to Learn.** Review **units of time**. As a class, work through **Examples 1–3**.

11-5 Units of Time

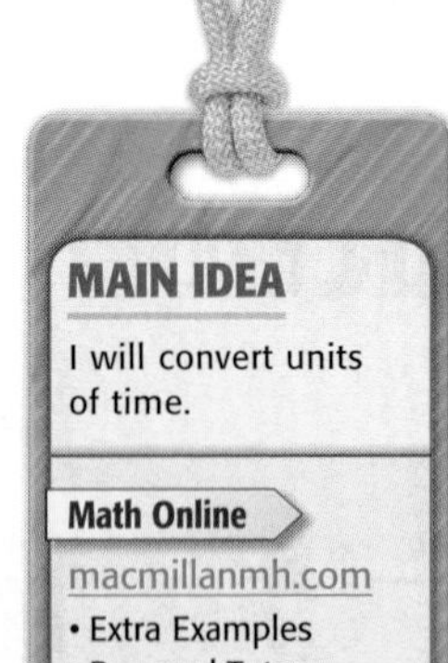

GET READY to Learn

Joe spends 1 hour a day doing his chores. He washes dishes, takes out the trash, and walks the dog.

Units of Time — Key Concepts

1 minute (min) = 60 seconds (s)
1 hour (h) = 60 min
1 day (d) = 24 h
1 week (wk) = 7 d
1 year (y) = 52 wk = 12 months (mo)

The steps that you use to convert units of length, weight, and capacity can be used to convert units of time.

Convert Units of Time

1 MEASUREMENT Joe walked his dog for 15 minutes before he went to school. How many seconds did he walk his dog?

15 min = ■ s

To convert larger units of time to smaller units, multiply. Since 1 minute = 60 seconds, multiply 15 by 60.

$15 \times 60 = 900$

So, Joe walked his dog for 900 seconds.

Use mental math to check the answer.
10 min = 10×60 or 600 s 20 min = 20×60 or 1,200 s

Since 900 seconds is between 600 and 1,200 seconds, the answer is reasonable.

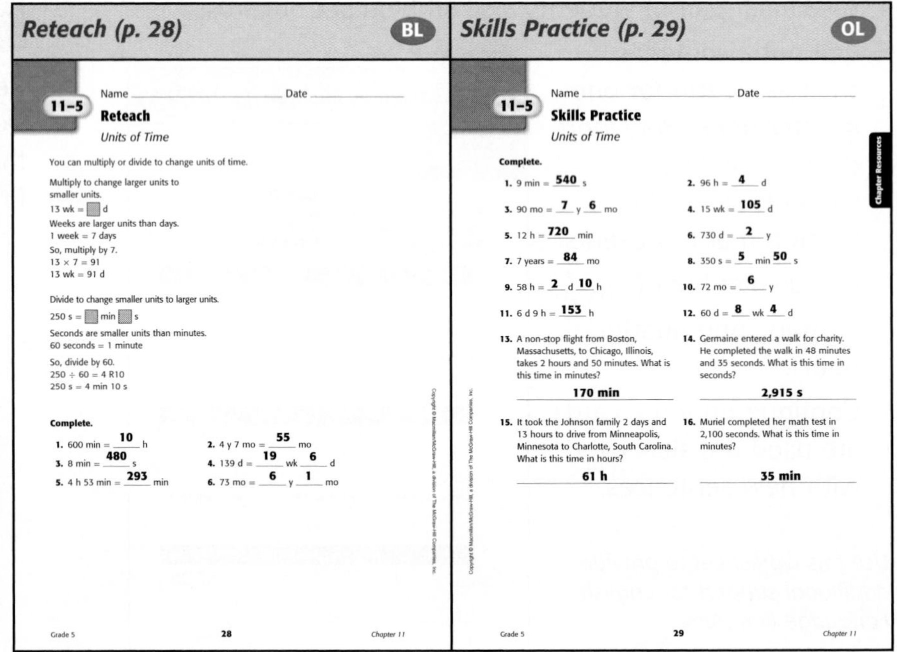

Reteach (p. 28) BL

11-5 Name ______ Date ______
Reteach
Units of Time

You can multiply or divide to change units of time.

Multiply to change larger units to smaller units.
13 wk = ■ d
Weeks are larger units than days.
1 week = 7 days
So, multiply by 7.
$13 \times 7 = 91$
13 wk = 91 d

Divide to change smaller units to larger units.
250 s = ■ min ■ s
Seconds are smaller units than minutes.
60 seconds = 1 minute
So, divide by 60.
$250 \div 60 = 4$ R10
250 s = 4 min 10 s

Complete.

1. 600 min = **10** h
2. 4 y 7 mo = **55** mo
3. 8 min = **480** s
4. 139 d = **19** wk **6** d
5. 4 h 53 min = **293** min
6. 73 mo = **6** y **1** mo

Grade 5 28 *Chapter 11*

Skills Practice (p. 29) OL

11-5 Name ______ Date ______
Skills Practice
Units of Time

Chapter Resources

Complete.

1. 9 min = **540** s
2. 96 h = **4** d
3. 90 mo = **7** y **6** mo
4. 15 wk = **105** d
5. 12 h = **720** min
6. 730 d = **2** y
7. 7 years = **84** mo
8. 350 s = **5** min **50** s
9. 58 h = **2** d **10** h
10. 72 mo = **6** y
11. 6 d 9 h = **153** h
12. 60 d = **8** wk **4** d
13. A non-stop flight from Boston, Massachusetts, to Chicago, Illinois, takes 2 hours and 50 minutes. What is this time in minutes? **170 min**
14. Germaine entered a walk for charity. He completed the walk in 48 minutes and 35 seconds. What is this time in seconds? **2,915 s**
15. It took the Johnson family 2 days and 13 hours to drive from Minneapolis, Minnesota to Charlotte, South Carolina. What is this time in hours? **61 h**
16. Muriel completed her math test in 2,100 seconds. What is this time in minutes? **35 min**

Grade 5 29 *Chapter 11*

To convert smaller units of time to larger units, divide.

EXAMPLE Use Different Units of Measure

2 **Complete: 56 hours = ■ days ■ hours.**

Since 24 hours = 1 day, divide 56 by 24 to find the number of days.

56 ÷ 24 = 2 R8

2 R8 means 2 whole days and 8 hours of another day. So, 56 hours = 2 days 8 hours.

As with other units of measure, units of time can also be expressed using fractions.

EXAMPLE Use Fractions in Measures

3 **How many hours are 150 minutes?**

150 min = ■ h

To convert a smaller unit to a larger unit, divide. Since 60 minutes = 1 hour, divide 150 by 60 to find the number of hours.

150 ÷ 60 = 2 R30

2 R30 means 2 whole hours and 30 minutes of another hour. So, 150 minutes = 2 hours 30 minutes or $2\frac{1}{2}$ hours.

CHECK What You Know

Complete. See Examples 1–3 (pp. 492–493)

1. 3 h = ■ min 180

2. 7 d = ■ h 168

3. 420 s = ■ min 7

4. 5 h = ■ s 18,000

5. 30 mo = ■ y $2\frac{1}{2}$

6. 84 h = ■ d $3\frac{1}{2}$

7. 500 s = ■ min ■ s 8; 20

8. 42 mo = ■ y ■ mo 3; 6

9. Some lungfish can live up to 4 years without water by forming a cocoon around their bodies. How many months can they live without water? up to 48 months

10. Talk About It Would you multiply or divide to find the number of seconds in 3 minutes? Explain. Multiply by 60 because minutes are larger units than seconds and 60 seconds = 1 minute.

Enrich (p. 32) AL

11-5 Name ______________ Date ______________

Enrich

Time

Choose the best answer for each problem. Write the letter of your answer above the Exercise number at the bottom of the page to find out about a unit of time.

1. How many seconds are in 3 hours 5 minutes 30 seconds?
N. 11,130 seconds
O. 11,100 seconds
P. 510 seconds

2. One million days is about ■.
K. 3,000 months
L. 19,000 months
M. 2,700 years

3. One million seconds is about ■.
R. 12 hours
S. 12 days
T. 12 months

4. One million hours is about ■.
Q. 1,114 months
R. 114 years
S. 1,114 years

5. Suppose you sleep an average of 9 hours each night. How long would you have slept by the age of 12 years?
C. 470 weeks
D. 108 months
E. $4\frac{1}{2}$ years

6. 4 hours 22 minutes afer 6:48 A.M. is ■.
I. 11:10 A.M.
J. 11:00 A.M.
K. 10:10 A.M.

7. 2 hours 47 minutes after 9:58 P.M. is ■.
X. 12:05 A.M.
Y. 12:45 A.M.
Z. 12:45 P.M.

8. Which time span is longest?
A. from 11:05 P.M. to 12:43 A.M.
B. from 10:37 P.M. to 12:12 A.M.
C. from 1:48 A.M. to 3:14 A.M.

9. The movie ended at 5:10 in the afternoon. If it lasted 1 hour 47 minutes, at what time did it start?
S. 4:57 P.M.
T. 4:23 P.M.
U. 3:23 P.M.

10. You are 3 years 8 months older than your friend. If your friend is 8 years 6 months old, how old are you?
J. 11 years 2 months
K. 11 years 11 months
L. 12 years 2 months

1,000	Y	E	A	R	S	= 1	M	I	L	L	E	N	N	I	U	M
	7	5	8	4	3		2	6	10	10	5	1	1	6	9	2

Use Different Units of Measure

Example 2 When students convert from a larger unit to a smaller unit, be sure they understand that the remainder will always be smaller units and must be labeled as such.

ADDITIONAL EXAMPLES

1 Students spend about 360 minutes a day in school. How many hours a day do they spend in school? 6 hours

2 Complete: 72 weeks = ■ years ■ weeks
1 year 20 weeks

3 How many days is 100 hours? $4\frac{1}{6}$ days

CHECK What You Know

As a class, have students complete Exercises 1–10 in **Check What You Know** as you observe their work.

Exercise 10 Assess student comprehension before assigning practice exercises.

BL Alternate Teaching Strategy

If students have trouble converting units of time…

Then use one of these reteach options:

1 CRM **Daily Reteach Worksheet** (p. 28)

2 Make a chart showing students how to convert from one unit of time to another. Hang the chart in the room.

- Make one list of conversions from smaller to larger units and a second list from larger to smaller units.
- Students can then narrow their choices and choose the equivalency that fits the problem they are solving.

3 Practice

Differentiate practice using these leveled assignments for Exercises 11–37.

Level	Assignment
BL Below/ Approaching Level	11–19, 27–28, 31
OL On Level	15–34, 37
AL Above/Beyond Level	12–34 even, 35–37

Have students discuss and complete the Higher Order Thinking problems. As students solve Exercise 36, encourage them to convert all four times to either hours and minutes or just minutes before writing their explanations.

WRITING IN ▸MATH Have students complete Exercise 37 in their Math Journals. You may choose to use this as an optional formative assessment.

COMMON ERROR!

Exercises 18 and 21 Students may struggle with converting a unit of time to another that is not the next increment larger or smaller. Have students write the units of time in order from smaller to larger and help them to understand that they will need to convert units more than one time to solve such problems.

★ indicates multi-step problem

Practice and Problem Solving

EXTRA PRACTICE See page R30.

Complete. See Examples 1–3 (pp. 492–493)

11. 840 s = ■ min 14
12. 3 mo = ■ y $\frac{1}{4}$
13. 8 wk = ■ d 56
14. 12 min = ■ s 720
15. 72 h = ■ d 3
16. 252 d = ■ wk 36
17. 24 h = ■ min 1,440
18. 1,095 d = ■ y 3
19. 270 min = ■ h $4\frac{1}{2}$
20. 156 h = ■ d $6\frac{1}{2}$
21. 36,000 s = ■ h 10
22. 28 mo = ■ y $2\frac{1}{3}$
23. 135 min = ■ h ■ min 2; 15
24. 200 s = ■ min ■ s 3; 20
25. 423 d = ■ y ■ d 1; 58
26. 50 d = ■ wk ■ d 7; 1
★**27.** 1 d 2 h = ■ min 1,560
28. 8 wk 2 d = ■ d 58

29. **Measurement** Katija spent 40 minutes raking leaves. What fraction of an hour did she spend raking leaves? $\frac{2}{3}$

★**30.** Jasper recorded 1 hour and 14 minutes on a CD. The CD can hold 80 minutes of music. How many seconds of recording time are left? 360 s

★**31.** Lamar and Jesse are running in a race. Lamar's time was 90 seconds. Jesse finished 15 seconds later. What were their times in minutes? Lamar: $1\frac{1}{2}$ min; Jesse: $1\frac{3}{4}$ min

32. Kari and her friend were comparing their number of days off for summer break. Kari has 85 days off and her friend has 7 weeks and 2 days off. Is there a difference between the number of days off? Explain. Yes; Kari's break is longer.

Data File

All United States human space flight missions are launched from the John F. Kennedy Space Center in eastern Florida. The longest space shuttle mission in United States history was the Columbia STS-80. It was launched on November 19, 1996. This mission lasted 423 hours.

33. How many days and hours did this mission last? 17 d 15 h

34. Write the number of days that this mission lasted as a mixed number in simplest form. $17\frac{5}{8}$ d

H.O.T. Problems

35. OPEN ENDED Write a word problem that includes a length of time that is between 4 hours and 5 hours. Then convert the time to minutes. **Sample answer: A lifeguard was on duty for 4 hours and 15 minutes. How many total minutes was the lifeguard on duty? 255 min.**

36. WHICH ONE DOESN'T BELONG? Identify the time that does not belong with the other three. Explain your reasoning. **See margin.**

2 h 104 min	2 h 114 min	3 h 54 min	234 min

37. WRITING IN ▶MATH Explain the steps you take to convert hours to seconds. **Sample answer: Multiply the number of hours by 3,600 since there are 3,600 seconds in 1 hour.**

TEST Practice

38. Mrs. Westin bought 3 gallons of apple cider for her class. What is the total number of pints in 3 gallons? (Lesson 11-4) **D**

1 quart = 2 pints
1 gallon = 8 pints

A 8 pints **C** 16 pints

B 10 pints **D** 24 pints

39. Which relationship between the units of time is correct? (Lesson 11-5) **G**

F One day is $\frac{1}{24}$ of one hour.

G One hour is $\frac{1}{24}$ of one day.

H One second is $\frac{1}{60}$ of one hour.

J One hour is $\frac{1}{60}$ of one second.

Spiral Review

40. Thomas is making a cake. The liquids that he uses are shown at the right. One cup is equal to 8 fluid ounces. What is the total number of cups of liquids? (Lesson 11-4) **2 c**

Liquid	Amount (fl oz)
Milk	12
Vegetable Oil	4

Complete. (Lessons 11-3 and 11-4)

41. 28 c = ■ pt **14**

42. 9 qt = ■ c **36**

43. 6 lb = ■ oz **96**

44. 7 T = ■ lb **14,000**

45. Tell whether the number represented by the model is prime or composite. Explain. (Lesson 9-2) **prime**

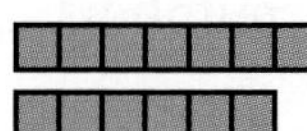

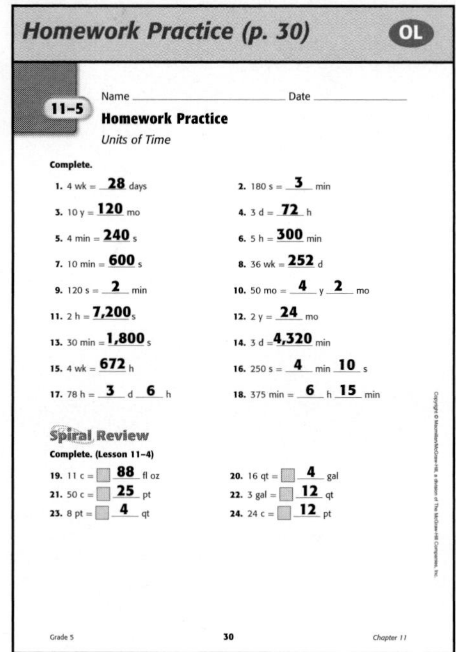

Homework Practice (p. 30) OL

11-5 Name ______ Date ______

Homework Practice

Units of Time

Complete.

1. 4 wk = **28** days
2. 180 s = **3** min
3. 10 y = **120** mo
4. 3 d = **72** h
5. 4 min = **240** s
6. 5 h = **300** min
7. 10 min = **600** s
8. 36 wk = **252** d
9. 120 s = **2** min
10. 50 mo = **4** y **2** mo
11. 2 h = **7,200** s
12. 2 y = **24** mo
13. 30 min = **1,800** s
14. 3 d = **4,320** min
15. 4 wk = **672** h
16. 250 s = **4** min **10** s
17. 78 h = **3** d **6** h
18. 375 min = **6** h **15** min

Spiral Review

Complete. (Lesson 11-4)

19. 11 c = **88** fl oz
20. 16 qt = **4** gal
21. 50 c = **25** pt
22. 3 gal = **12** qt
23. 8 pt = **4** qt
24. 24 c = **12** pt

Grade 5 30 Chapter 11

4 Assess

Formative Assessment

Write the following on the board: 15 minutes, 750 seconds.

- **How could you find out which time was longer?** Either convert 15 minutes to seconds, or convert 750 seconds to minutes and then compare.
- **How would you convert 15 minutes to seconds?** multiply 15 × 60 = 900 s
- **Which time is longer?** 15 minutes is longer

Quick Check **Are students continuing to struggle with converting units of time?**

If Yes → CRM Reteach Worksheet (p. 28)

If No → Independent Work Options (p. 492B)
CRM Skills Practice Worksheet (p. 29)
CRM Enrich Worksheet (p. 32)

Yesterday's News Have students write a paragraph about how the previous lessons in this chapter have helped them to convert units of time in this lesson. They may want to write about what is alike and what is different when converting units of time compared to converting units of length, weight and capacity.

TEST Practice

Reviews Lessons 11-4 and 11-5

Assign the Test Practice problems to provide daily reinforcement of test-taking skills.

Spiral Review

Reviews Lessons 9-2, 11-3, and 11-4

Review and assess mastery of skills and concepts from previous chapters.

Additional Answer

36. 2 h 104 min; The other three times equal 3 h 54 min.

11-6 Problem-Solving Investigation
Choose the Best Strategy

Lesson Planner

Objective

Choose the best strategy to solve a problem.

Resources

Teacher Technology

TeacherWorks • Interactive Classroom

Real-World Problem Solving Library
Math and Social Studies: *City Planning*

Use these leveled books to reinforce and extend problem-solving skills and strategies

Leveled for:

- OL On Level
- ELL Sheltered English
- SP Spanish

For additional support, see the Real-World Problem Solving Teacher Guide.

Daily Routine

Use these suggestions before beginning the lesson on p. 496.

5-Minute Check 

(Reviews Lesson 11-5)

Complete.

1. 9 mo = ■ y $\frac{3}{4}$ y
2. 250 s = ■ min ■ s 4 min 10 s
3. 15 h = ■ min 900 min
4. 330 s = ■ min $5\frac{1}{2}$ min
5. 13 wk = ■ d 91 d
6. 4 y = ■ wk 208 wk

Problem of the Day 

A four-digit number is between 3,000 and 4,000. The sum of its digits is 21. The product of the thousands and ones digits is 24. The hundreds digit is 2 less than the tens digit. What is the number? 3,468; explanations will vary.

Differentiated Instruction

Small Group Options

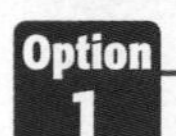

VISUAL, PAIR

Option 1 Below Level BL

Materials: paper and pencil

- Provide this problem to students:
- **How many pounds did the family harvest last year?** 150 pounds
- **If the family receives $.25 per pound, how much money did they receive last year?** $37.50

> Each year the Anderson family gathers the walnuts from the trees in their backyard to sell. This year's nut crop was 64 pounds. Last year's nut crop was 22 pounds more than 2 times this year's nut harvest.

LINGUISTIC, LOGICAL

Option 2 English Language Learners ELL

Materials: per group: envelopes with paper dolls or four pictures of individual children cut from magazines, index card

Core Vocabulary: in front of/behind, clues, arrange

Common Use Verb: line up

Write Math This strategy helps students use position vocabulary.

- Show 4 pictures labeled John, Mary, Tom, Penny. Say: "I have **clues** to help me **arrange** them. John is **behind** Mary. Tom is **in front of** Penny. Mary is **behind** Penny. Help me ***line*** them ***up*** in correct order." Students give suggestions.
- Say: "Label each picture. ***Line*** them ***up*** from left to right. Write 3 **clues** on the card about their order. On the back of the card, write the order."
- Challenge groups to line up the pictures.

Independent Work Options

LOGICAL

Option 1 Early Finishers OL AL

Materials: index cards, pencils

- Ask students to choose any of the problem-solving strategies and write a solve step including an answer with a label on the front of an index card. For example, if a student chooses the *make a table* strategy, that student will draw a table and write an answer.
- Have students exchange cards. On the back of the cards received, students will write a word problem that can be solved using the solution as written.
- Students pass back cards to the original writers to see how their strategies were used.

Option 2 Student Technology

Math Online macmillanmh.com

Personal Tutor • Extra Examples

Option 3 Learning Station: Social Studies (p. 472H)

Direct students to the Social Studies Learning Station for opportunities to explore and extend the lesson concept.

1 Introduce

Activity • Review

- Pose the following problem:

  Julietta builds flower boxes to sell. Each box is made with three pieces of wood that are 3 feet long each and two pieces that are $1\frac{1}{2}$ feet each. If wood comes in 15-foot lengths, how many 15-foot lengths will Julietta need to build the boxes without having any wood leftover? How many boxes can she build?
  4 pieces of wood; 5 boxes
- **What strategy could you use to solve this problem?** *draw a picture*
- **What would your picture show?** 15-ft lengths of wood with lines drawn to show three 3 ft and two $1\frac{1}{2}$-ft lengths per box. There would be extra wood until the end of the fourth length.

2 Teach

Have students read the problem on the CD Music Shop. Guide them through the steps.

Understand Using the questions, review what students know and need to find.

Plan Have them discuss their strategy.

Solve Guide students to use the *make a table* strategy to solve the problem.

- **How will a table help to keep track of the information?** A table can keep track of the time until 8:00, the number of people who come, and the total number of people.
- **What pattern does the table show?** The number of people doubles every 15 minutes. **How many people were in line at 8:00?** 32

Check Have students look back at the problem to make sure that the answer fits the facts given.

COMMON ERROR!

Exercise 5 Students may have trouble keeping track of all of the information in the problem. Have students label each section of their drawing with the correct measurements and write the total length each step of the way. Their running total will alert them when they have found their solution.

11-6 Problem-Solving Investigation

MAIN IDEA I will choose the best strategy to solve a problem.

P.S.I. TEAM +

BETHANY: They are giving away prizes at the grand opening of the CD Music Shop. At 7:00, there were two people in the line. At 7:15 when two more people arrived, there were 4 people in line. At 7:30, 4 more people arrived so there were 8 people in line. Every 15 minutes as many people as were already in line arrived.

YOUR MISSION: Find how many people were in line when the store opened at 8:00.

Understand You know how many people arrived every 15 minutes. You need to know how many people were in line when the store opened at 8:00.

Plan Make a table to show how many people are in line.

Solve

Time (A.M.)	Number Who Arrive	Number in Line
7:00	2	2
7:15	2	4
7:30	4	8
7:45	8	16
8:00	16	32

There were 32 people in line at 8:00.

Check Look back. Add the number of people who arrive.
$2 + 2 + 4 + 8 + 16 = 32$
So, the answer is correct.

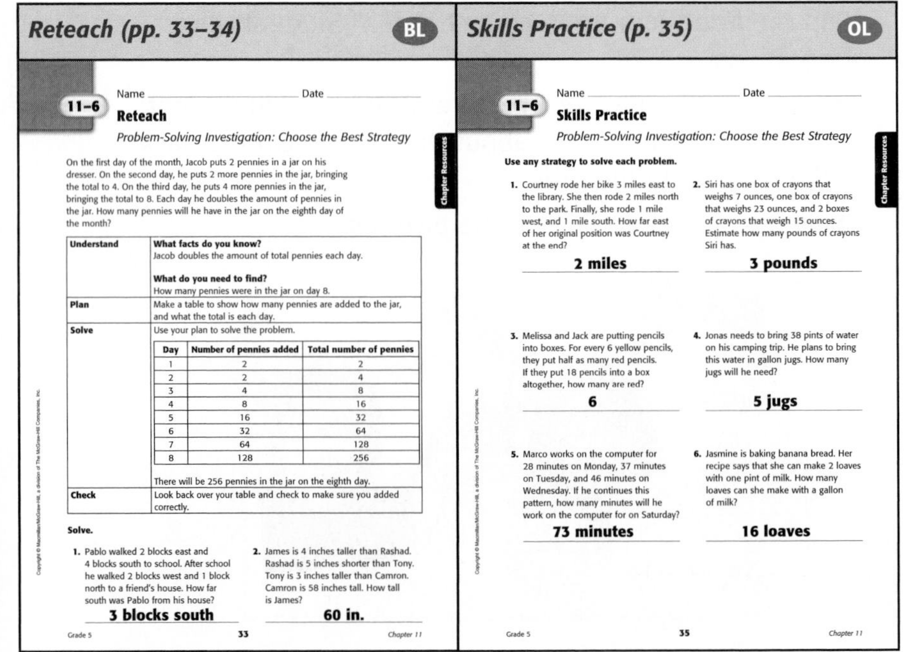

Reteach (pp. 33–34) BL

11-6 Name ____________ Date ____________

Reteach

Problem-Solving Investigation: Choose the Best Strategy

On the first day of the month, Jacob puts 2 pennies in a jar on his dresser. On the second day, he puts 2 more pennies in the jar, bringing the total to 4. On the third day, he puts 4 more pennies in the jar, bringing the total to 8. Each day he doubles the amount of pennies in the jar. How many pennies will he have in the jar on the eighth day of the month?

Understand — **What facts do you know?** Jacob doubles the amount of total pennies each day. **What do you need to find?** How many pennies were in the jar on day 8.

Plan — Make a table to show how many pennies are added to the jar, and what the total is each day.

Solve — Use your plan to solve the problem.

Day	Number of pennies added	Total number of pennies
1	2	2
2	2	4
3	4	8
4	8	16
5	16	32
6	32	64
7	64	128
8	128	256

There will be 256 pennies in the jar on the eighth day.

Check — Look back over your table and check to make sure you added correctly.

Solve.

1. Pablo walked 2 blocks east and 4 blocks south to school. After school he walked 2 blocks west and 1 block north to a friend's house. How far south was Pablo from his house? **3 blocks south**
2. James is 4 inches taller than Rashad. Rashad is 5 inches shorter than Tony. Tony is 3 inches taller than Camron. Camron is 58 inches tall. How tall is James? **60 in.**

Grade 5 33 Chapter 11

Skills Practice (p. 35) OL

11-6 Name ____________ Date ____________

Skills Practice

Problem-Solving Investigation: Choose the Best Strategy

Use any strategy to solve each problem.

1. Courtney rode her bike 3 miles east to the library. She then rode 2 miles north to the park. Finally, she rode 1 mile west, and 1 mile south. How far east of her original position was Courtney at the end? **2 miles**
2. Siri has one box of crayons that weighs 7 ounces, one box of crayons that weighs 23 ounces, and 2 boxes of crayons that weigh 15 ounces. Estimate how many pounds of crayons Siri has. **3 pounds**
3. Melissa and Jack are putting pencils into boxes. For every 6 yellow pencils, they put half as many red pencils. If they put 18 pencils into a box altogether, how many are red? **6**
4. Jonas needs to bring 38 pints of water on his camping trip. He plans to bring this water in gallon jugs. How many jugs will he need? **5 jugs**
5. Marco works on the computer for 28 minutes on Monday, 37 minutes on Tuesday, and 46 minutes on Wednesday. If he continues this pattern, how many minutes will he work on the computer for on Saturday? **73 minutes**
6. Jasmine is baking banana bread. Her recipe says that she can make 2 loaves with one pint of milk. How many loaves can she make with a gallon of milk? **16 loaves**

Grade 5 35 Chapter 11

Mixed Problem Solving

See page R31.

Use any strategy shown below to solve each problem.

PROBLEM-SOLVING STRATEGIES
- Look for a pattern.
- Draw a picture.
- Work backward.
- Draw a diagram.

1. The table shows the choices for ordering a sundae at the Ice Cream Shop. How many different sundaes could be made using one choice from ice cream and one choice from sauce? **9**

Ice Cream Shop	
Ice cream	vanilla, chocolate, strawberry
Sauce	chocolate, caramel, strawberry
Toppings	sprinkles, nuts, cherries
Cones	sugar, waffle

2. Tamika left her house and rode 3 miles east and then 2 miles south to the library. From there she rode 1 mile west and 4 miles north to Jodi's house. Jodi and Tamika rode 1 mile south and 2 miles west to the park. How far north was Tamika from her house? **1 mile**
3. A number is divided by 6. Next the quotient is multiplied by 2. Then 4 is added to the product. If the result is 12, what is the number? **24**
4. Alana is 4 years older than her brother Ernie. Ernie is 2 years older than their sister Amelia. Amelia is 10 years younger than their brother Mazo. If Mazo is 17 years old, how old is Alana? **13 years old**
5. Deidre is making a necklace by alternating long and short beads. The long beads are 0.5 inch long, and the short beads are 0.25 inch long. She starts and ends with a long bead, and the necklace is 14 inches long. How many of each size bead does she use? **See Ch. 11 Answer Appendix.**
6. Lake Superior is 531 feet deeper than Lake Ontario. Lake Ontario is 592 feet deeper than Lake Erie. Lake Erie is 210 feet deep. How deep is Lake Superior? **1,333 ft**
7. Annie and Max are putting roses into vases. For every 4 red roses, they put half as many white roses. If they put 18 roses in the vase altogether, how many are white? **6 white roses**
8. **Algebra** Austin took the same amount of time each day to walk his dog last week. The table shows the time he left his house and the time he arrived home on four days. If the pattern continues, what time will he arrive home on Friday? **6:40 P.M.**

Day	Time Left Home	Time Arrived Back Home
Monday	4:32 P.M.	5:00 P.M.
Tuesday	6:05 P.M.	6:33 P.M.
Wednesday	7:15 P.M.	7:43 P.M.
Thursday	5:20 P.M.	5:48 P.M.
Friday	6:12 P.M.	■

9. **WRITING IN MATH** Gino has $3.75 after spending $4.75 on lunch and $1.50 on bus fare. How much money did Gino have originally? Which strategy would you use to solve this problem? Explain your reasoning. Then solve. **See Ch. 11 Answer Appendix.**

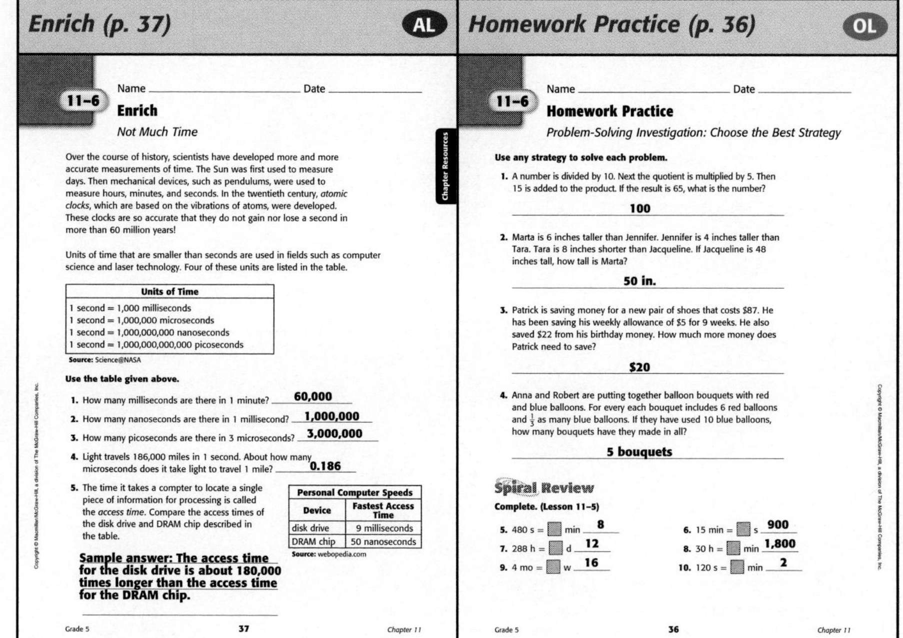

Enrich (p. 37) AL

11-6 Name ______ Date ______

Enrich

Not Much Time

Over the course of history, scientists have developed more and more accurate measurements of time. The Sun was first used to measure days. Then mechanical devices, such as pendulums, were used to measure hours, minutes, and seconds. In the twentieth century, *atomic clocks*, which are based on the vibrations of atoms, were developed. These clocks are so accurate that they do not gain nor lose a second in more than 60 million years!

Units of time that are smaller than seconds are used in fields such as computer science and laser technology. Four of these units are listed in the table.

Units of Time
1 second = 1,000 milliseconds
1 second = 1,000,000 microseconds
1 second = 1,000,000,000 nanoseconds
1 second = 1,000,000,000,000 picoseconds

Source: Science@NASA

Use the table given above.

1. How many milliseconds are there in 1 minute? **60,000**
2. How many nanoseconds are there in 1 millisecond? **1,000,000**
3. How many picoseconds are there in 3 microseconds? **3,000,000**
4. Light travels 186,000 miles in 1 second. About how many microseconds does it take light to travel 1 mile? **0.186**
5. The time it takes a compter to locate a single piece of information for processing is called the *access time*. Compare the access times of the disk drive and DRAM chip described in the table.

Personal Computer Speeds	
Device	Fastest Access Time
disk drive	9 milliseconds
DRAM chip	50 nanoseconds

Source: webopedia.com

Sample answer: The access time for the disk drive is about 180,000 times longer than the access time for the DRAM chip.

Chapter Resources

Grade 5 37 Chapter 11

Homework Practice (p. 36) OL

11-6 Name ______ Date ______

Homework Practice

Problem-Solving Investigation: Choose the Best Strategy

Use any strategy to solve each problem.

1. A number is divided by 10. Next the quotient is multiplied by 5. Then 15 is added to the product. If the result is 65, what is the number? **100**
2. Marta is 6 inches taller than Jennifer. Jennifer is 4 inches taller than Tara. Tara is 8 inches shorter than Jacqueline. If Jacqueline is 48 inches tall, how tall is Marta? **50 in.**
3. Patrick is saving money for a new pair of shoes that costs $87. He has been saving his weekly allowance of $5 for 9 weeks. He also saved $22 from his birthday money. How much more money does Patrick need to save? **$20**
4. Anna and Robert are putting together balloon bouquets with red and blue balloons. For every each bouquet includes 6 red balloons and $\frac{1}{3}$ as many blue balloons. If they have used 10 blue balloons, how many bouquets have they made in all? **5 bouquets**

Spiral Review

Complete. (Lesson 11–5)

5. 480 s = ■ min **8**
6. 15 min = ■ s **900**
7. 288 h = ■ d **12**
8. 30 h = ■ min **1,800**
9. 4 mo = ■ w **16**
10. 120 s = ■ min **2**

Grade 5 36 Chapter 11

BL Alternate Teaching Strategy

If students have trouble choosing the best strategy to solve a problem…

Then use one of these reteach options:

1. CRM **Daily Reteach Worksheet** (pp. 33–34)
2. Review each of the strategies listed and have students list clues for using each. For draw a diagram, clues might include that the problem describes measurements of an object or moving from place to place. For make a table, clues might include that the information changes over time.

3 Practice

Using the Exercises

Exercises 1–8 give students the opportunity to choose the best strategy.

Exercises 3 and 9 Students can use the *work backward* strategy to solve.

4 Assess

Formative Assessment

Pose the following problem:

A 200-ft fence borders one side of a field. Posts are placed every 8 feet to support the fence. How many posts are there? 26 posts

- **What strategy can you choose to solve the problem?** Sample answer: *draw a diagram; solve a simpler problem*

Quick Check **Are students continuing to struggle with choosing the best strategy to solve a problem?**

If Yes → Small Group Options (p. 496B)

If No → Independent Work Options (p. 496B)
CRM Skills Practice Worksheet (p. 35)
CRM Enrich Worksheet (p. 37)

Lesson Planner

Objective

Interpret information and data from health to solve problems.

National Standard

Students will demonstrate strategies to improve or maintain personal and family health.

Resources

Materials: paper, pencils

Activate Prior Knowledge

Before you turn students' attention to the pages, ask them to discuss soccer.

- **What is good about playing soccer?** It is fun; it is good exercise.
- **What is soccer called outside of the United States?** football

Use the Student Page

Ask students to read the information on p. 499 and answer these questions:

- **How many feet longer is the field used by 14 year olds than the field used by 6 year olds?** 210 feet
- **If the coach of a team of six year olds brought a bag of five balls to the field, how many ounces in total would they weigh?** 55 ounces

Soccer Rules!

Soccer is the most popular sport in the world, although it's called football in every country except the United States. The men's World Cup has been played every four years since 1930. The women's World Cup has been played every four years since 1991. Teams from all over the world compete to win the most exciting sports tournament on Earth.

If you're serious about playing soccer, who knows—maybe you'll be on a World Cup team!

Did You Know?

In 2006, about 5 billion people watched the World Cup.

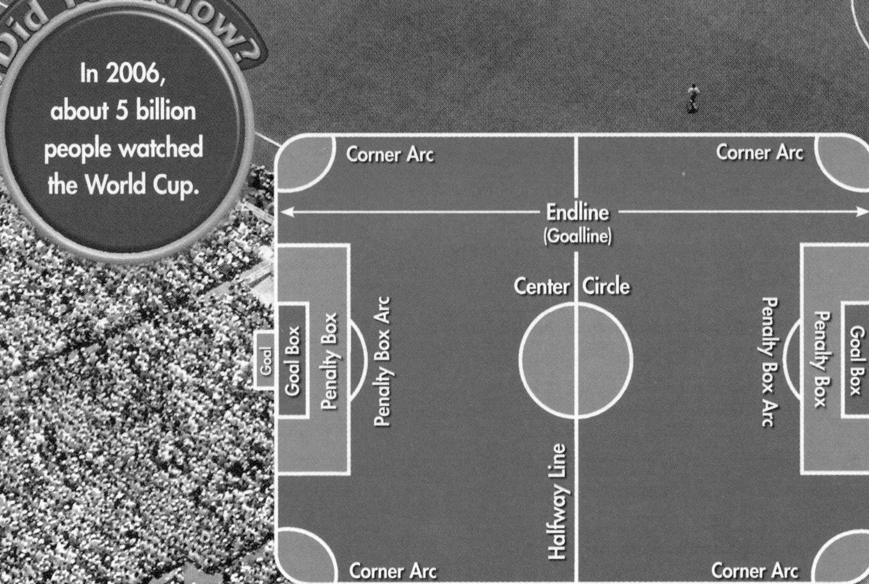

Youth Soccer Guidelines

Age (years)	Field Size (yards)	Weight of Ball (ounces)	Length of Game
14	60 x 100	15	two 45-minute halves
12	50 x 80	12	two 30-minute halves
10	40 x 70	12	two 25-minute halves
8	25 x 50	11	four 12-minute quarters
6	15 x 30	11	four 8-minute quarters

Source: U.S. Youth Soccer

Real-World Math

Use the information in the above table to solve each problem.

1. How many feet longer is the field used by 14-year-olds than the field used by 10-year-olds? 90 ft
2. Suppose on one Sunday, a referee officiated three 8-year-old soccer games. How much time did the official spend refereeing, not including breaks? 144 min or 2 h 24 min
3. A soccer game with 14-year-old players began at 9:30 ?,K, on a Saturday. If the players rested at half-time for 15 minutes, how long was the game? 1 hour 45 minutes
4. There are 16 players on a youth soccer team. Each player had a water bottle with $1\frac{1}{2}$ quarts of water for the game. How many gallons of water did the players have altogether? 6 gallons
5. A coach of a team of 10-year-olds has a bag of 6 soccer balls. What is the weight in pounds of the 6 soccer balls? $4\frac{1}{2}$ lb

Real-World Math

Assign the exercises on p. 499. Encourage students to choose a problem-solving strategy before beginning each exercise. If necessary, review the strategies suggested in Lesson 11-6, p. 497.

Exercise 1 Remind students that there are three feet in a yard.

WRITING IN ▶MATH Have students create a word problem that uses the information found in the text and in the chart on p. 489.

Extend the Activity

Have students calculate how many pounds of balls there would be on the field if each age group had one game on the same day at the same field and each group had a bag of six balls to play with.

LESSON

11-7 Elapsed Time

Lesson Planner

Objective

Add and subtract measures of time.

Vocabulary

elapsed time

Resources

Manipulatives: demonstration clock
Literature Connection: *Telling Time With Big Mama Cat* by Dan Harper
Alternate Lesson: Use *IMPACT Mathematics:* Unit H to provide practice with elapsed time.
Teacher Technology
TeacherWorks • Interactive Classroom

Focus on Math Background

Elapsed time is a difference in time measures:
elapsed time = (ending time) − (starting time).

Finding elapsed time is similar in some respects to subtracting mixed numbers, which students have studied in Lessons 10-7 and 10-8.

As with mixed numbers, regrouping (or renaming) may be needed. For example, to subtract 3 hours 47 minutes from 5 hours 12 minutes, the 5 hours must be renamed as 4 hours 60 minutes:

$$\begin{array}{rcr} 5 \text{ hours } 12 \text{ minutes} & \Rightarrow & \overset{4}{\cancel{5}} \text{ hours } 72 \text{ minutes} \\ -\ 3 \text{ hours } 47 \text{ minutes} & \Rightarrow & -\ 3 \text{ hours } 47 \text{ minutes} \\ \hline & & 1 \text{ hour } 25 \text{ minutes} \end{array}$$

Daily Routine

Use these suggestions before beginning the lesson on p. 498.

5-Minute Check

(Reviews Lesson 11-6)

Use any strategy to solve.
During a recycling drive, Noemi collected 6 more than twice as many cans as Jamal. Jamal collected 4 more than Maria and Maria collected three times as many as Steve. If Steve collected 36 cans, how many cans did Noemi collect? 230; *write an equation* or *work backward*

Problem of the Day

Two cars left from the same point and drove in opposite directions. One car left at 9:00 A.M. and drove east going 45 mph. The second car left at 11:00 A.M. and drove west going 55 mph. How far apart were the cars at 3:00 P.M.? 490 miles

Building Math Vocabulary

Write the lesson vocabulary word and its definition on the board.

Have students write the word and its definition in their Math Journals. Ask students to use the word "elapsed" in a sentence of their own.

Differentiated Instruction

Small Group Options

Option 1 SPATIAL

Below Level BL

Materials: paper and pencil

- Hand students this problem written on paper:

  When Jack left the house for baseball practice, the clock showed 10:30 A.M. When he arrived back home after practice, the clock showed 1:30 P.M. How long was he gone for practice? Show your work. 3 hours

Option 2 SPATIAL, LOGICAL

English Language Learners ELL

Materials: clock
Core Vocabulary: past, until, after
Common Use Verb: pass

Do Math This strategy helps students hear measurements of time intervals.

- Say: "This clock represents one hour. There are 60 minutes in an hour."
- Draw a "line of time" labeled as illustrated.

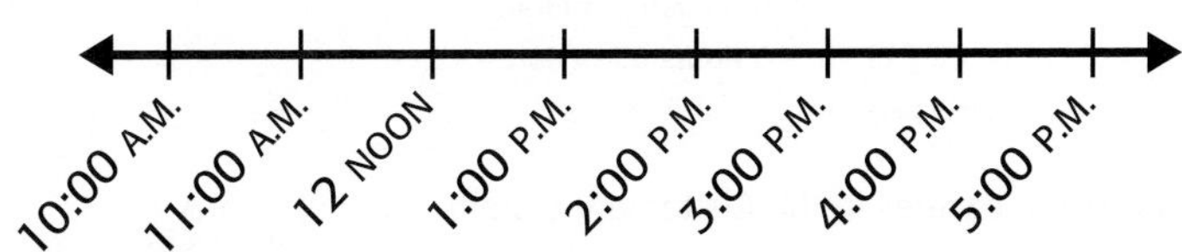

- Ask: "How many minutes are there between 2:00 P.M. and 3:00 P.M.? 60
- Put a dot at 10:30 A.M. Ask: "How many minutes **past** 10:00?" 30
- Put a dot at 3:15. Say: "This is 3:15. How many minutes **past** 3:00?" 15 "How many minutes **until** 4:00?" 45
- Repeat for other times, emphasizing pass, past, and until.

Independent Work Options

Option 1 INTRAPERSONAL

Early Finishers AL

Materials: four number cubes

- Have students write their own elapsed time problems. Students roll their number cubes twice and use the numbers generated to write two times that make sense. They may eliminate one of the numbers rolled as necessary to write a correct time. For example, if students roll a 2, 4, 5, and 8, they may choose to write 4:58 or 2:45
- Students use the times they wrote as beginning and ending times, labeling one of the numbers A.M. and one P.M.
- Ask students to figure the elapsed time for each of their own problems.

Option 2

Student Technology

Math Online macmillanmh.com

Personal Tutor • Extra Examples

Option 3

Learning Station: Art (p. 472G)

Direct students to the Art Learning Station for opportunities to explore and extend the lesson concept.

Option 4

Problem-Solving Practice

Reinforce problem-solving skills and strategies with the Problem-Solving Practice worksheet.

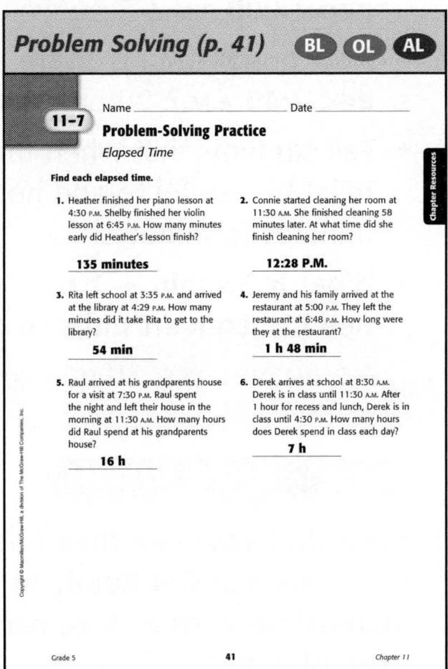

Problem Solving (p. 41) BL OL AL

11-7 Name ______ Date ______

Problem-Solving Practice

Elapsed Time

Chapter Resources

Find each elapsed time.

1. Heather finished her piano lesson at 4:30 P.M. Shelby finished her violin lesson at 6:45 P.M. How many minutes early did Heather's lesson finish? **135 minutes**
2. Connie started cleaning her room at 11:30 A.M. She finished cleaning 58 minutes later. At what time did she finish cleaning her room? **12:28 P.M.**
3. Rita left school at 3:35 P.M. and arrived at the library at 4:29 P.M. How many minutes did it take Rita to get to the library? **54 min**
4. Jeremy and his family arrived at the restaurant at 5:00 P.M. They left the restaurant at 6:48 P.M. How long were they at the restaurant? **1 h 48 min**
5. Raul arrived at his grandparents house for a visit at 7:30 P.M. Raul spent the night and left their house in the morning at 11:30 A.M. How many hours did Raul spend at his grandparents house? **16 h**
6. Derek arrives at school at 8:30 A.M. Derek is in class until 11:30 A.M. After 1 hour for recess and lunch, Derek is in class until 4:30 P.M. How many hours does Derek spend in class each day? **7 h**

Grade 5 41 Chapter 11

11-7 Elapsed Time

1 Introduce

Activity Choice 1 • Hands-On

- Use the demonstration clock and set the hands to show 10:35. **What time does the clock show? What time will it be one hour later?** 10:35; 11:35
- Show 11:35 on the clock. Discuss with students that when the clock reads 12:00, A.M. becomes P.M. or P.M. becomes A.M. **If the clock is referring to 11:35 A.M., in how many minutes will it be noon? How do you know?** 25 min.; count minutes by fives from 11:35 to 12:00.
- Show 2:15. **What time will it be in 3 hours and 25 minutes? Explain.** 5:40; 2:15 plus 3 hours is 5:15 and 25 min more will be 5:40.

Activity Choice 2 • Literature

Introduce the lesson with *Telling Time With Big Mama Cat* by Dan Harper. For a related math activity, see p. TR55.

2 Teach

Scaffolding Questions

Pose the following problem: How much time will have gone by between 9:25 A.M. and 2:45 P.M.? Write student responses on the board as each of the questions is answered.

- **How many minutes are there from 9:25 A.M. until 10:00 A.M.?** 35 minutes
- **How many hours are there from 10:00 A.M. and 12:00 P.M.?** 2 hours
- **How much time is there between 12:00 P.M. and 2:45 A.M.?** 2 hours and 45 minutes
- Tell students that when they add time, they must be careful to add hours to hours and minutes to minutes.
- **What is 35 min + 2 h + 2 h 45 min? Do you need to convert units to show your answer?** 4 h 80 min; yes, 80 min converts to 1 h 20 min so the final elapsed time is 5 h 20 min.

GET READY to Learn

Have students open their books and read the information in **Get Ready to Learn.** Introduce **elapsed time**. As a class, work through **Examples 1–3**.

11-7 Elapsed Time

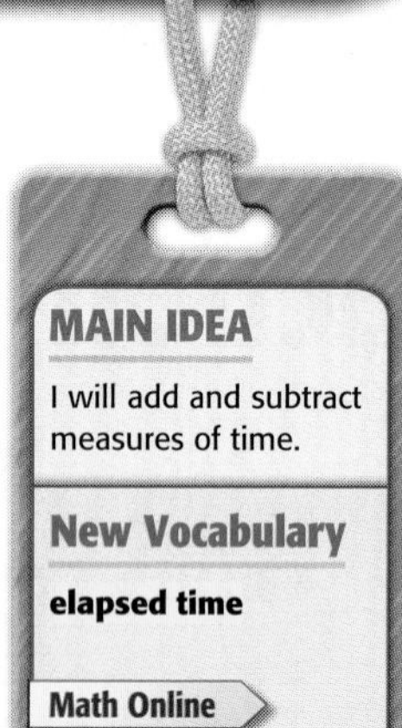

MAIN IDEA

I will add and subtract measures of time.

New Vocabulary

elapsed time

Math Online

macmillanmh.com

- Extra Examples
- Personal Tutor
- Self-Check Quiz

GET READY to Learn

Belinda started babysitting at 6:45 P.M. She finished at 10:55 P.M. How long did Belinda babysit?

6:45

10:55

Elapsed time is the difference in time between the start and the end of an event.

Real-World EXAMPLE — Elapsed Time

1 **MEASUREMENT Refer to the information above. How long did Belinda babysit?**

Step 1 Write the times in units of hours and minutes.

Ending time: 10:55 P.M. → 10 hours 55 minutes
Starting time: 6:45 P.M. → 6 hours 45 minutes

Step 2 Subtract the starting time from the ending time. Make sure you subtract hours from hours and minutes from minutes.

10 hours 55 minutes
− 6 hours 45 minutes
Elapsed time: 4 hours 10 minutes

So, Belinda babysat 4 hours and 10 minutes.

Check 4 hours 10 minutes
+ 6 hours 45 minutes
10 hours 55 minutes

500 Chapter 11 Use Measures in the Customary System

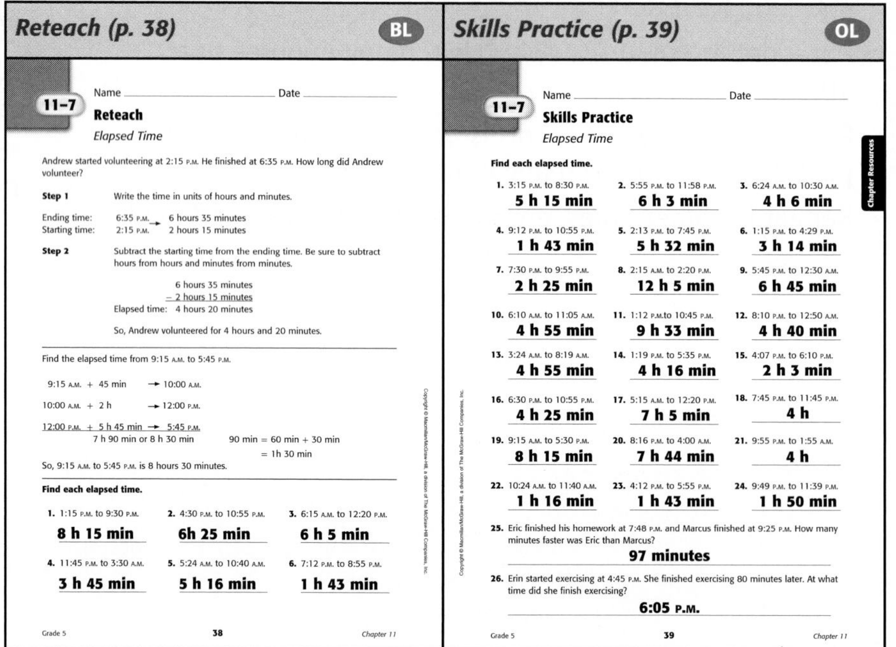

Reteach (p. 38) BL

11-7 Name ______ Date ______

Reteach

Elapsed Time

Andrew started volunteering at 2:15 P.M. He finished at 6:35 P.M. How long did Andrew volunteer?

Step 1 Write the time in units of hours and minutes.

Ending time: 6:35 P.M. → 6 hours 35 minutes
Starting time: 2:15 P.M. → 2 hours 15 minutes

Step 2 Subtract the starting time from the ending time. Be sure to subtract hours from hours and minutes from minutes.

6 hours 35 minutes
− 2 hours 15 minutes
Elapsed time: 4 hours 20 minutes

So, Andrew volunteered for 4 hours and 20 minutes.

Find the elapsed time from 9:15 A.M. to 5:45 P.M.

9:15 A.M. + 45 min → 10:00 A.M.
10:00 A.M. + 2 h → 12:00 P.M.
12:00 P.M. + 5 h 45 min → 5:45 P.M.
7 h 90 min or 8 h 30 min

90 min = 60 min + 30 min
= 1h 30 min

So, 9:15 A.M. to 5:45 P.M. is 8 hours 30 minutes.

Find each elapsed time.

1. 1:15 P.M. to 9:30 P.M. **8 h 15 min**
2. 4:30 P.M. to 10:55 P.M. **6h 25 min**
3. 6:15 A.M. to 12:20 P.M. **6 h 5 min**
4. 11:45 P.M. to 3:30 A.M. **3 h 45 min**
5. 5:24 A.M. to 10:40 A.M. **5 h 16 min**
6. 7:12 P.M. to 8:55 P.M. **1 h 43 min**

Grade 5 38 Chapter 11

Skills Practice (p. 39) OL

11-7 Name ______ Date ______

Skills Practice

Elapsed Time

Chapter Resources

Find each elapsed time.

1. 3:15 P.M. to 8:30 P.M. **5 h 15 min**
2. 5:55 P.M. to 11:58 P.M. **6 h 3 min**
3. 6:24 A.M. to 10:30 A.M. **4 h 6 min**
4. 9:12 P.M. to 10:55 P.M. **1 h 43 min**
5. 2:13 P.M. to 7:45 P.M. **5 h 32 min**
6. 1:15 P.M. to 4:29 P.M. **3 h 14 min**
7. 7:30 P.M. to 9:55 P.M. **2 h 25 min**
8. 2:15 A.M. to 2:20 P.M. **12 h 5 min**
9. 5:45 P.M. to 12:30 A.M. **6 h 45 min**
10. 6:10 A.M. to 11:05 A.M. **4 h 55 min**
11. 1:12 P.M.to 10:45 P.M. **9 h 33 min**
12. 8:10 P.M. to 12:50 A.M. **4 h 40 min**
13. 3:24 A.M. to 8:19 A.M. **4 h 55 min**
14. 1:19 P.M. to 5:35 P.M. **4 h 16 min**
15. 4:07 P.M. to 6:10 P.M. **2 h 3 min**
16. 6:30 P.M. to 10:55 P.M. **4 h 25 min**
17. 5:15 A.M. to 12:20 P.M. **7 h 5 min**
18. 7:45 P.M. to 11:45 P.M. **4 h**
19. 9:15 A.M. to 5:30 P.M. **8 h 15 min**
20. 8:16 P.M. to 4:00 A.M. **7 h 44 min**
21. 9:55 P.M. to 1:55 A.M. **4 h**
22. 10:24 A.M. to 11:40 A.M. **1 h 16 min**
23. 4:12 P.M. to 5:55 P.M. **1 h 43 min**
24. 9:49 P.M. to 11:39 P.M. **1 h 50 min**
25. Eric finished his homework at 7:48 P.M. and Marcus finished at 9:25 P.M. How many minutes faster was Eric than Marcus? **97 minutes**
26. Erin started exercising at 4:45 P.M. She finished exercising 80 minutes later. At what time did she finish exercising? **6:05 P.M.**

Grade 5 39 Chapter 11

Sometimes it is necessary to rename the units before subtracting.

Real-World EXAMPLE Rename Units of Time

2 **Ben started to do his homework at 7:30 P.M. He finished at 9:05 P.M. How long did Ben study?**

~~9~~ 8 hours ~~5~~ 60 minutes	→	8 hours 65 minutes
− 7 hours 30 minutes		− 7 hours 30 minutes
		1 hour 35 minutes

Ben studied for 1 hour 35 minutes.

Real-World EXAMPLE From P.M. to A.M.

Remember

To find elapsed time from P.M. to A.M., remember to count through midnight.

3 **Dr. Sedaca arrived at work at 10:03 P.M. and went home at 7:27 A.M. How long was her shift?**

10:03 P.M. +	57 min	→ 11:00 P.M.	Count 1 hour and 57 minutes until 12 A.M.
11:00 P.M. +	1 h	→ 12:00 A.M.	
12:00 A.M. +	7 h 27 min	→ 7:27 A.M.	Count 7 hours and 27 minutes until 7:27 A.M.
	8 h 84 min		

8 h + 84 min = 9 h 24 min   84 min = 60 min + 24 min = 1 h 24 min

So, Dr. Sedaca's shift was 9 hours 24 minutes long.

CHECK What You Know

Find the elapsed time. See Examples 1–3 (pp. 500–501)

1. 6:14 A.M. to 10:30 A.M. **4 h 16 min**

2. 8:18 P.M. to 9:22 P.M. **1 h 4 min**

3. 11:50 A.M. to 2:04 P.M. **2 h 14 min**

4. 7:22 A.M. to 9:20 A.M. **1 h 58 min**

5. 11:30 P.M. to 2:14 A.M. **2 h 44 min**

6. 3:40 P.M. to 6:09 P.M. **2 h 29 min**

7. Kevin finished walking a trail at 11:44 A.M., and Rogelio finished at 12:16 P.M. How many minutes faster was Kevin than Rogelio? **32 minutes**

8. Quan leaves for school at 7:15 A.M. He gets back home from school at 3:45 P.M. How long is he away from his house on a school day? **8 h 30 min**

9. **Measurement** An all night movie marathon begins at 9:30 P.M. The last movie ends at 5:27 A.M. How long is the movie marathon? **7 h 57 min**

10. **Talk About It** Compare how to find the elapsed time from 8:30 A.M. to 11:30 A.M. and from 10:30 P.M. to 1:30 A.M. **See margin.**

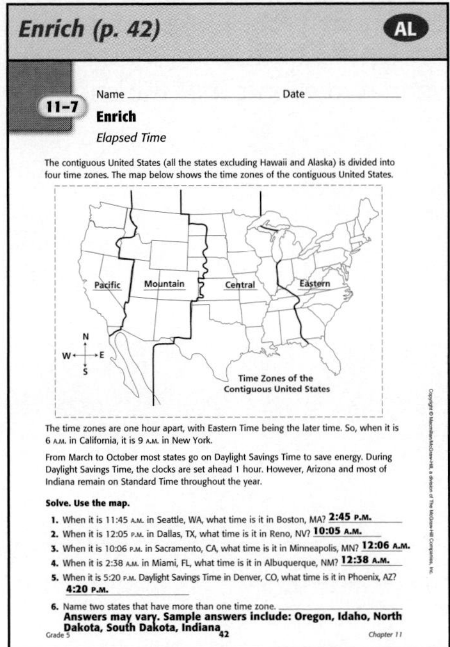

Enrich (p. 42) **AL**

11-7 Name ______ Date ______

Enrich

Elapsed Time

The contiguous United States (all the states excluding Hawaii and Alaska) is divided into four time zones. The map below shows the time zones of the contiguous United States.

The time zones are one hour apart, with Eastern Time being the later time. So, when it is 6 A.M. in California, it is 9 A.M. in New York.

From March to October most states go on Daylight Savings Time to save energy. During Daylight Savings Time, the clocks are set ahead 1 hour. However, Arizona and most of Indiana remain on Standard Time throughout the year.

Solve. Use the map.

1. When it is 11:45 A.M. in Seattle, WA, what time is it in Boston, MA? **2:45 P.M.**
2. When it is 12:05 P.M. in Dallas, TX, what time is it in Reno, NV? **10:05 A.M.**
3. When it is 10:06 P.M. in Sacramento, CA, what time is it in Minneapolis, MN? **12:06 A.M.**
4. When it is 2:38 A.M. in Miami, FL, what time is it in Albuquerque, NM? **12:38 A.M.**
5. When it is 5:20 P.M. Daylight Savings Time in Denver, CO, what time is it in Phoenix, AZ? **4:20 P.M.**
6. Name two states that have more than one time zone. **Answers may vary. Sample answers include: Oregon, Idaho, North Dakota, South Dakota, Indiana**

Grade 5 42 Chapter 11

From P.M. to A.M.

Example 3 Be sure students understand that they must keep track of each of the time increments as they count up to the nearest hour, then to 12 noon or midnight and finally to the end time given. Adding of the minutes may require converting from minutes to hours and minutes for the final answer.

ADDITIONAL EXAMPLES

1 Saul studied for his science test from 4:15 P.M. until 7:25 P.M. How long did Saul study for the test? 3 h 10 min

2 Jairo began riding his bike at 6:30 P.M. and stopped at 8:10 P.M. How long did he ride? 1 h 40 min

3 Clarita arrived at a slumber party at 7:21 P.M. and left at 9:06 A.M. How long did she stay at the party? 13 h 45 min

CHECK What You Know

As a class, have students complete Exercises 1–10 in **Check What You Know** as you observe their work.

Exercise 10 Assess student comprehension before assigning practice exercises.

BL Alternate Teaching Strategy

If students have trouble solving problems involving elapsed time…

Then use one of these reteach options:

1 CRM **Daily Reteach Worksheet** (p. 38)

2 Have students use a demonstration clock to show the beginning time. Have them move the minute hand to count and record the number of minutes to the next whole hour.

- Students can then move the hour hand and count the hours to 12:00. Then they count the hours and minutes to the end time, recording each number. Then have students find the total hours and the total minutes.

Additional Answer

10. Sample answer: In the first elapsed time, subtract 8 h 30 min from 11 h 30 min. In the second elapsed time, find the time from 10:30 P.M. to 12:00 A.M. and from 12:00 A.M. to 1:30 A.M.

3 Practice

Differentiate practice using these leveled assignments for Exercises 11–26.

Level	Assignment
BL Below/ Approaching Level	11–14, 19–20, 23, 24
OL On Level	13–20, 24, 26
AL Above/Beyond Level	10–22 even, 24–26

Have students discuss and complete the Higher Order Thinking problems. Encourage students to use a demonstration clock as they complete these problems.

WRITING IN MATH Have students complete Exercise 26 in their Math Journals. You may choose to use this as an optional formative assessment.

★ indicates multi-step problem

Practice and Problem Solving

See page R31.

Find the elapsed time. See Examples 1–3 (pp. 500–501)

11. 4:00 A.M. to 10:23 A.M. 6 h 23 min

12. 9:20 A.M. to 11:58 A.M. 2 h 38 min

13. 1:27 P.M. to 5:30 P.M. 4 h 3 min

14. 8:15 P.M. to 1:11 A.M. 4 h 56 min

15. 3:15 A.M. to 11:00 A.M. 7 h 45 min

16. 10:58 A.M. to 5:29 P.M. 6 h 31 min

17. 9:15 A.M. to 3:20 P.M. 6 h 5 min

18. 10:30 P.M. to 7:15 A.M. 8 h 45 min

19. Tyson starts talking on the phone at 6:29 P.M. He finishes 55 minutes later. At what time did he finish talking on the phone? 7:24 P.M.

20. Sed left his house at 4:58 P.M. to be at band practice at 5:45 P.M. How much time does he have to get to practice? 47 min

21. Alejandra was selling cookies at a bake sale. She started at 8:13 A.M. and finished at 5:47 P.M. How long did Alejandra sell cookies? 9 h 34 min

★**22.** Baltimore, Maryland, is two hours ahead of Cheyenne, Wyoming. Griselda left at 3:42 P.M. She arrived in Cheyenne at 9:58 P.M. How long was her flight? 4 h 16 min

23. Part of a bus schedule is shown below. Which trip from Springdale to Cheswick takes the most time? 8:43 A.M.

Bus Schedule				
Leave Springdale	6:52 A.M.	7:45 A.M.	8:43 A.M.	9:58 A.M.
Arrive in Cheswick	7:16 A.M.	8:20 A.M.	9:13 A.M.	10:23 A.M.

H.O.T. Problems

24. OPEN ENDED Write a beginning time and an ending time so that the elapsed time is 2 hours 16 minutes. Sample answer: 3:00 P.M. to 5:16 P.M.

25. FIND THE ERROR Megan and Anita are finding the elapsed time from 2:30 P.M. to 5:46 P.M. Who is correct? Explain. See margin.

Megan
5 h 46 min
+ 2 h 30 min
8 h 16 min

Anita
5 h 46 min
− 2 h 30 min
3 h 16 min

26. **WRITING IN MATH** Write a story that takes place all in one day, using the times 6:45 A.M., 1:07 P.M., and 8:39 P.M. Include the elapsed times in your story. See students' stories; elapsed times are 6 h 22 min and 7 h 32 min.

Additional Answer

25. Anita; elapsed time is the amount of time that passes between two events, not the sum of two times.

! COMMON ERROR!

Students may struggle with subtracting times. Have students set up the problem to subtract the earlier from the later time. When there are more minutes represented in the earlier time than the later, they must regroup one hour of the later time, change it to 60 minutes and add those minutes to the minutes in the earlier time.

TEST Practice

27. The Williams family spent 4 hours at a theme park. What fractional part of a day is 4 hours? (Lesson 11-5) **B**

A $\frac{1}{12}$

B $\frac{1}{6}$

C $\frac{1}{4}$

D $\frac{1}{3}$

28. Jordan went to the pool from 11:20 A.M. to 3:45 P.M., as shown on the clocks below.

Arrive

Leave

How many hours and minutes was Jordan at the pool? (Lesson 11-7) **J**

F 4 h 5 min H 4 h 20 min

G 4 h 15 min J 4 h 25 min

Spiral Review

29. Mrs. Spring needs to buy 2 dozen muffins for a family brunch. According to the sign, how much will she save by buying the muffins by the dozen instead of individually? (Lesson 11-6) **$8**

Complete. (Lesson 11-5)

30. 360 s = ■ min **6**

31. 7 wk = ■ d **49**

32. 12 h = ■ min **720**

33. 135 min = ■ h ■ min **2; 15**

34. Emily has a 4-foot long board to make some shelves for her desk. Her father cuts two shelves, each 19 inches long, from the board. How long is the piece of the board that is left? (Lesson 11-1) **10 in.**

Add. Write each sum in simplest form. Check your answer by drawing a picture. (Lesson 10-1) **35–38. See students' drawings.**

35. $\frac{1}{3} + \frac{1}{3}$ **$\frac{2}{3}$**

36. $\frac{2}{5} + \frac{1}{5}$ **$\frac{3}{5}$**

37. $\frac{5}{16} + \frac{7}{16}$ **$\frac{3}{4}$**

38. $\frac{9}{10} + \frac{3}{10}$ **$1\frac{1}{5}$**

Write each improper fraction as a mixed number. (Lesson 8-2)

39. $\frac{9}{2}$ **$4\frac{1}{2}$**

40. $\frac{13}{4}$ **$3\frac{1}{4}$**

41. $\frac{20}{3}$ **$6\frac{2}{3}$**

42. $\frac{27}{5}$ **$5\frac{2}{5}$**

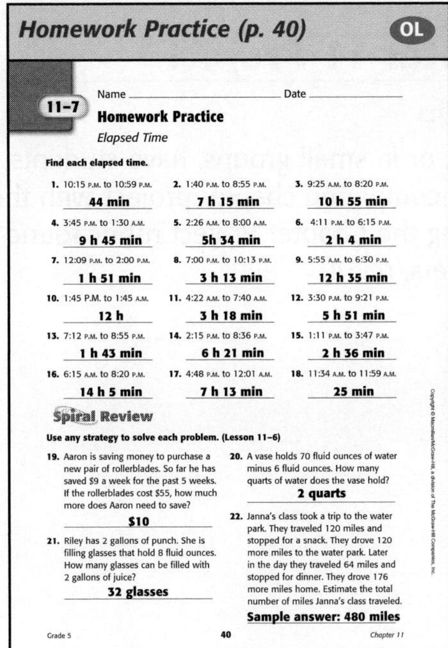

Homework Practice (p. 40) OL

11-7 Name ______ Date ______

Homework Practice

Elapsed Time

Find each elapsed time.

1. 10:15 P.M. to 10:59 P.M. **44 min**
2. 1:40 P.M. to 8:55 P.M. **7 h 15 min**
3. 9:25 A.M. to 8:20 P.M. **10 h 55 min**
4. 3:45 P.M. to 1:30 A.M. **9 h 45 min**
5. 2:26 A.M. to 8:00 A.M. **5h 34 min**
6. 4:11 P.M. to 6:15 P.M. **2 h 4 min**
7. 12:09 P.M. to 2:00 P.M. **1 h 51 min**
8. 7:00 P.M. to 10:13 P.M. **3 h 13 min**
9. 5:55 A.M. to 6:30 P.M. **12 h 35 min**
10. 1:45 P.M. to 1:45 A.M. **12 h**
11. 4:22 A.M. to 7:40 A.M. **3 h 18 min**
12. 3:30 P.M. to 9:21 P.M. **5 h 51 min**
13. 7:12 P.M. to 8:55 P.M. **1 h 43 min**
14. 2:15 P.M. to 8:36 P.M. **6 h 21 min**
15. 1:11 P.M. to 3:47 P.M. **2 h 36 min**
16. 6:15 A.M. to 8:20 P.M. **14 h 5 min**
17. 4:48 P.M. to 12:01 A.M. **7 h 13 min**
18. 11:34 A.M. to 11:59 A.M. **25 min**

Spiral Review

Use any strategy to solve each problem. (Lesson 11-6)

19. Aaron is saving money to purchase a new pair of rollerblades. So far he has saved $9 a week for the past 5 weeks. If the rollerblades cost $55, how much more does Aaron need to save? **$10**

20. A vase holds 70 fluid ounces of water minus 6 fluid ounces. How many quarts of water does the vase hold? **2 quarts**

21. Riley has 2 gallons of punch. She is filling glasses that hold 8 fluid ounces. How many glasses can be filled with 2 gallons of juice? **32 glasses**

22. Janna's class took a trip to the water park. They traveled 120 miles and stopped for a snack. They drove 120 more miles to the water park. Later in the day they traveled 64 miles and stopped for dinner. They drove 176 more miles home. Estimate the total number of miles Janna's class traveled. **Sample answer: 480 miles**

Grade 5 40 Chapter 11

4 Assess

Formative Assessment

Write the following on the board: Beginning Time: 3:25 A.M. Ending Time: 1:15 P.M.

- **How would you find the elapsed time?** 3:25 + 35 minutes is 4:00. 4:00 + 8 hours is 12:00 noon. 12:00 + 1 h 15 min is 1:15. So 35 min + 8 h + 1 h 15 min is 9 h 50 min.

Quick Check **Are students continuing to struggle with solving problems involving elapsed time?**

If Yes → Small Group Options (p. 498B)

If No → Independent Work Options (p. 498B)
CRM Skills Practice Worksheet (p. 39)
CRM Enrich Worksheet (p. 42)

Name the Math Have students write about how they would solve problems involving elapsed time if the times given were as follows: Beginning Time: Monday at 10:15 P.M. Ending Time Thursday at 8:10 A.M.

TEST Practice

Reviews Lessons 11-5 and 11-7

Assign the Test Practice problems to provide daily reinforcement of test-taking skills.

Spiral Review

Reviews Lessons 8-2, 10-1, 11-1, 11-5, and 11-6

Review and assess mastery of skills and concepts from previous chapters.

Lesson 11-7 Elapsed Time 503

Study Guide and Review

FOLDABLES® Dinah Zike's Foldables

Use these lesson suggestions to incorporate the Foldable during the chapter. Students can then use their Foldables to review for the test.

Lesson 11-5 Under the bottom right tab of the Foldable, have students record data as they measure and convert customary units of time. Students might glue a graphic of a clock beneath the Foldable tab.

Key Vocabulary

The page references after each word denote where that term was first introduced. If students have difficulty answering Exercises 1–9, remind them they can use the page references to review the vocabulary terms.

Vocabulary Review

Review chapter vocabulary using the following option.

- **eGlossary** at macmillanmh.com

Study Guide and Review

FOLDABLES Study Organizer GET READY to Study

Be sure the following Big Ideas are written in your Foldable.

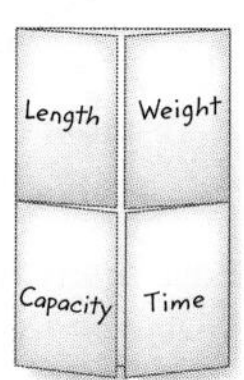

Key Concepts

Customary Units of Length (p. 477)

1 foot (ft) = 12 inches (in.)

1 yard (yd) = 3 ft or 36 in.

1 mile (mi) = 5,280 ft or 1,760 yd

Customary Units of Weight (p. 484)

1 pound (lb) = 16 ounces (oz)

1 ton (T) = 2,000 pounds

Customary Units of Capacity (p. 488)

1 cup (c) = 8 fluid ounces (fl oz)

1 pint (pt) = 2 c = 16 fl oz

1 quart (qt) = 2 pt = 32 fl oz

1 gallon (gal) = 4 qt = 128 fl oz

Units of Time (p. 492)

1 minute (min) = 60 seconds (s)

1 hour (h) = 60 min

1 day (d) = 24 h

1 week (wk) = 7 d

1 year (y) = 52 wk = 12 months (mo)

Key Vocabulary

capacity (p. 488)
customary units (p. 477)
elapsed time (p. 500)
length (p. 475)
weight (p. 484)

Vocabulary Check

State whether each sentence is *true* or *false*. If *false*, replace the underlined word or number to make a true sentence.

1. Capacity is the amount that a container can hold. true
2. The inch, foot, yard, and mile are called metric units. false; customary
3. Three feet equals 1 yard. true
4. One gallon equals 4 pints. false; quart
5. Fluid ounce is a customary measure of weight. false; capacity
6. To convert from feet to inches, divide by 12. false; multiply
7. A reasonable estimate for the height of an oak tree is 30 feet. true
8. Elapsed time is the amount of time that passes between two events. true
9. To change 3 days to hours, multiply 3 by 60. false; 24

Chapter 11 Project

Stepping It Up

Alone, in pairs, or in small groups, have students discuss the results of their completed chapter project with the class. Assess their work using the Chapter Project rubric found in Chapter 11 Resource Masters, p. 54.

Lesson-by-Lesson Review

11-1 Units of Length (pp. 477–480)

Example 1
Convert 54 inches to feet.

To change a smaller unit to a larger unit, divide.

Since 12 in. = 1 ft, divide 54 by 12.

$54 \div 12 = 4$ R6

4 R6 means 4 feet and 6 inches of another foot.

So, 54 inches = 4 feet 6 inches or $4\frac{1}{2}$ feet.

Complete.

10. 8 ft = ■ in. 96

11. 7 yd = ■ ft 21

12. 32 in. = ■ ft ■ in. 2; 8

13. 7,920 ft = ■ mi $1\frac{1}{2}$

14. Which unit of length would you use to measure the distance between two fire stations? mi

15. The bill of an Australian pelican can be as long as 18 inches. Write this measure in feet and inches. 1 ft 6 in.

11-2 Problem-Solving Strategy: Draw a Diagram (pp. 482–483)

Example 2
Mrs. Juarez left her house and drove 5 miles north to the bank, 6 miles west to the post office, 3 miles south to the store, 2 miles east to the cleaners, and 2 miles south to the school. How many miles is she from her house?

Solve by drawing a diagram.

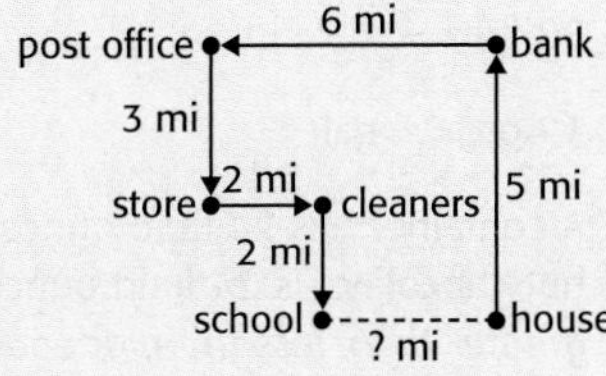

Mrs. Juarez is 4 miles from her house.

16. Mr. Muhammad rented a 5-gallon smoothie machine for a carnival. The smoothies will be sold in two sizes: 12 fluid ounces and 20 fluid ounces. Find two different combinations of both drink sizes that equal 5 gallons. See margin.

17. At a bakery, a tray of cookies is taken out of the oven every 10 minutes, and a pan of brownies is taken out every 25 minutes. At 1:00 P.M., both are taken out of the oven. How many trays of cookies will be taken out before both are taken out of the oven at the same time? What time will it be?
4 trays; 1:50

Lesson-by-Lesson Review

Have students complete the Lesson-by-Lesson Review on pp. 505–508. Then you can use ExamView® Assessment Suite to customize another review worksheet that practices all the objectives of this chapter or only the objectives on which your students need more help.

Intervention If the given examples are not sufficient to review the topics covered by the questions, use the page references next to the exercises to review that topic in the Student Edition.

Additional Answer

16. Sample answers: 40 12-fl. oz. cups and 8 20-fl. oz. cups; 30 12-fl. oz. cups and 14 20-fl. oz. cups

CHAPTER 11 Study Guide and Review

11-3 Units of Weight (pp. 484–487)

Example 3
In two weeks, Teresa feeds her cat 56 ounces of cat food. How many pounds of cat food does she feed her cat?

To change a smaller unit to a larger unit, divide. Since 16 oz = 1 lb, divide 56 by 16.

$56 \div 16 = 3$ R8

3 R8 means 3 pounds and 8 ounces of another pound.

So, 56 ounces = 3 pounds 8 ounces or $3\frac{1}{2}$ pounds.
Teresa feeds her cat $3\frac{1}{2}$ pounds of cat food.

Complete.

18. 112 oz = ■ lb 7

19. 12,000 lb = ■ T 6

20. 36 oz = ■ lb ■ oz 2; 4

21. 7,000 lb = ■ T $3\frac{1}{2}$

22. A 1-pound package of butter has four sticks. How many ounces does each stick weigh? 4 oz

11-4 Units of Capacity (pp. 488–490)

Example 4
How many pints are in 3 gallons?

3 gal = ■ pt

To convert a larger unit to a smaller unit, multiply. Since 1 gal = 8 pt, multiply 3 by 8.

$3 \times 8 = 24$

So, there are 24 pints in 3 gallons.

27. equal to; 1 pint = 16 oz and $\frac{1}{2}$ pint = 8 ounces

Complete.

23. 14 qt = ■ pt 28

24. 5 c = ■ fl oz 40

25. 90 fl oz = ■ c ■ fl oz 11; 2

26. 19 qt = ■ gal $4\frac{3}{4}$

27. A container has 24 fluid ounces of hot chocolate. Is 24 fluid ounces *greater than*, *less than*, or *equal to* $1\frac{1}{2}$ pints? Explain.

11-5 Units of Time (pp. 492–495)

Example 5
Complete: 200 minutes = ■ hours.

To change from a smaller unit to a larger unit, divide. Since 1 min = 60 s, divide 200 by 60.

200 ÷ 60 = 3 R20

3 R20 means 3 whole hours and 20 minutes of another hour. So,

200 minutes = 3 hours 20 minutes or $3\frac{1}{3}$ hours.

Complete.

28. 5 h = ■ min 300

29. 420 s = ■ min 7

30. 2 wk = ■ d 14

31. 580 min = ■ h ■ min 9; 40

32. Laura practices the piano 30 minutes every day. How many hours a week is this? $3\frac{1}{2}$ h

11-6 Problem-Solving Investigation: Choose a Strategy (pp. 496–497)

Example 6
An electronics store is having a grand opening in which every 15th customer receives a free CD and every 25th customer receives a free DVD. Which customer will be first one to receive a CD and a DVD?

Make a table to solve.

Multiples of 15	15	30	45	60	75
Multiples of 25	25	50	75	100	125

So, the 75th customer receives a CD and a DVD.

33. A forest fire covered 51 square miles by Friday. This is 3 less than 3 times the number of square miles it covered on Wednesday. How many square miles did it cover on Wednesday? 18 mi

34. A new train glides along a magnetic field. The train takes 5 hours to travel 1,200 miles. How far can it travel in 2 hours? 480 mi

35. The Eagles won 13 games and lost 5 games. The Gators won 12 games and lost 4 games. Which team won a greater fraction of their games? Gators

Chapter 11 Study Guide and Review **507**

CHAPTER 11 Study Guide and Review

11-7 Elapsed Time (pp. 500–503)

Example 7
Delmar started washing his bike at 4:16 P.M. He finished at 4:57 P.M. How long did it take Delmar to wash his bike?

Step 1 Write the times in units of hours and minutes.

End: 4:57 P.M. → 4 h 57 min

Start: 4:16 P.M. → 4 h 16 min

Step 2 Subtract the time starting from the ending time.

4 hours 57 minutes
− 4 hours 16 minutes
Elapsed time: 0 hours 41 minutes

So, Delmar spent 41 minutes washing his bike.

Example 8
Find the elapsed time from 2:20 P.M. to 9:15 P.M.

Step 1 Write the times in units of hours and minutes.

End: 9:15 P.M. → 9 h 15 min

Start: 2:20 P.M. → 2 h 20 min

Step 2 Subtract the starting time from the ending time.

9 h 15 min → 8 h 75 min
− 2 h 20 min → − 2 h 20 min
6 h 55 min

The elapsed time is 6 hours 55 minutes.

Find each elapsed time.

36. 4:15 P.M. to 5:40 P.M. **1 h 25 min**

37. 4:45 A.M. to 8:05 A.M. **3 h 20 min**

38. 12:17 A.M. to 1:57 A.M. **1 h 40 min**

39. 8:34 P.M. to 3:08 A.M. **6 h 34 min**

40. 3:16 P.M. to 9:26 A.M. **18 h 10 min**

41. A turkey is put into the oven at 11:25 A.M. The turkey was done at 4:10 P.M. How long did it take the turkey to cook? **4 h 45 min**

42. Erica arrived at school at 8:15 A.M. She left the house at 7:48 A.M. How long did it take Erica to get to school? **27 min**

43. Mr. Torre makes some bread for dinner using his bread machine. If he starts his bread at 2:45 P.M. and it is done at 5:30 P.M., how long did it take to make the bread? **2 h 45 min**

Chapter Test

Complete. 4. 166; 2

1. 132 in. = ■ ft 11
2. 4 mi = ■ yd 7,040
3. 64 in. = ■ ft $5\frac{1}{3}$
4. 500 ft = ■ yd ■ ft
5. Mariah is filling a wading pool with water. Every two minutes, the water level increases by $1\frac{1}{2}$ inches. If the pool is 9 inches deep, how long will it take to fill the pool to its capacity? 12 minutes

Complete.

6. 96 oz = ■ lb 6
7. 60 oz = ■ lb ■ oz 3; 12
8. 1,500 lb = ■ T $\frac{3}{4}$
9. 22 qt = ■ gal ■ qt 5; 2
10. **MULTIPLE CHOICE** A recipe for punch is shown below.

Ingredient	Amount
fruit juice	1 gal
lemon-lime soda	3 qt

Suppose you want to double the recipe. How many gallons of punch will the recipe make? C

A $1\frac{3}{4}$ gal **C** $3\frac{1}{2}$ gal
B 3 gal **D** 14 qt

11. Mr. Roland fences in a 20-foot by 25-foot section of his yard for his dog. He puts fence posts every 5 feet and at the corners. How many posts are there? 18
12. Manny bought $2\frac{1}{2}$ pounds of coleslaw and 42 ounces of potato salad. Which food item weighed more? potato salad

Complete.

13. 12 wk = ■ d 84
14. 585 min = ■ h $9\frac{3}{4}$
15. 84 h = ■ d ■ h 3; 12
16. Michelle leaves for school at 7:50 A.M. She gets home at 4:10 P.M. How long is Michelle gone from home? 8 h 20 min

Find each elapsed time.

17. 7:39 A.M. to 11:50 A.M. 4 h 11 min
18. 10:30 P.M. to 5:08 A.M. 6 h 38 min
19. **MULTIPLE CHOICE** Elijah leaves his house in the morning at the time shown on the clock.

He walks for 15 minutes to his friend's house. They play two video games for 25 minutes each game. Then they go outside. At what time do they go outside? J

F 10:10 A.M. **H** 10:30 A.M.
G 10:25 A.M. **J** 10:35 A.M.

20. **WRITING IN MATH** When you are finding the elapsed time between two events, why is it important to note whether the times are A.M. or P.M.? See Ch. 11 Answer Appendix.

Chapter 11 Chapter Test

Summative Assessment

Use these alternate leveled chapter tests to differentiate assessment for the specific needs of your students.

Leveled Chapter 11 Tests

Form	Type	Level	CRM Pages
1	Multiple Choice	BL	55–56
2A	Multiple Choice	OL	57–58
2B	Multiple Choice	OL	59–60
2C	Free Response	AL	61–62
2D	Free Response	AL	63–64
3	Free Response	AL	65–66

BL = below/approaching grade level
OL = on grade level
AL = above/beyond grade level

Vocabulary Test

CRM **Chapter 11 Resource Masters** (p. 50)

ExamView Assessment Suite Customize and create multiple versions of your Chapter Test and the test answer keys.

Data-Driven Decision Making

Based on the results of the Chapter Test, use the following to review concepts that continue to present students with problems.

Exercises	State/Local Standards	What's the Math?	Error Analysis	Resources for Review
1–5, 11		Measure length and convert units of length.	Does not know units to convert measurements. Does not read "2 times the width." Does not know "ft," "yd," "mi," "in" abbreviations	Strategic Intervention Guide (pp. 122, 130) CRM Chapter 11 Resource Masters (Reteach) Math Adventures My Math Zone Chapter 11 Math Online Extra Examples • Concepts in Motion
6–8, 12		Convert customary units of weight.	Does not know units for converting ounces, pounds, and tons. Computes incorrectly. Does not know "oz," "lb," "T" abbreviations.	
9–10		Convert customary units of capacity.	Does not know abbreviations or units of conversion for ounces, pints, quarts, gallons. Computes inaccurately.	
13–20		Convert units of time.	Does not know abbreviations or conversion units for seconds, hours, minutes, or difference between A.M. and P.M. Computes incorrectly.	

Chapter 11 Test Practice

Formative Assessment

- Use Student Edition pp. 510–511 as practice and cumulative review. The questions are written in the same style as many state tests.
- You can also use these two pages to benchmark student progress, or as an alternate homework assignment.

Additional practice pages can be found in the Chapter 11 Resource Masters.

Chapter 11 Resource Masters
Cumulative Test Practice
- Multiple Choice format (pp. 55–60)
- Free Response format (pp. 61–66)

Create practice worksheets or tests that align to your state standards.

Math Online Have students visit macmillanmh.com for additional practice to reinforce your state standards.

Math Online macmillanmh.com
- Test Practice

Chapter 11 Test Practice
Cumulative, Chapters 1–11

PART 1 Multiple Choice

Read each question. Then fill in the correct answer on the answer sheet provided by your teacher or on a sheet of paper.

1. Use a ruler to measure the line segment along the route from the lake to the archery field to the nearest inch. What is the actual distance in yards? C

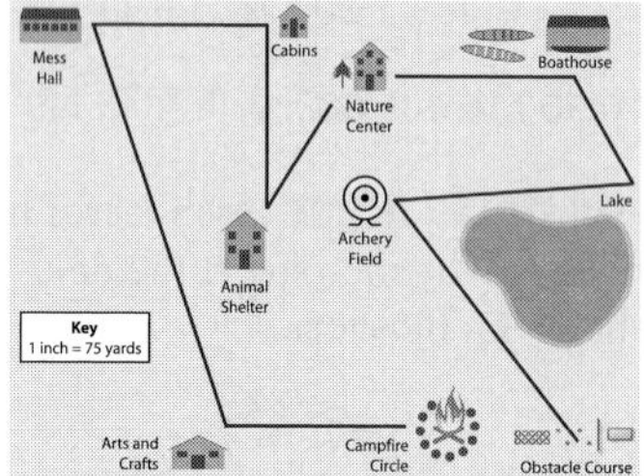

A 2 yd
B 6 yd
C 75 yd
D 150 yd

2. Refer to the map in Exercise 1. Use a ruler to measure the line segments along the route from the campfire circle to the cabins to the nearest $\frac{1}{4}$ inch. What is the total distance in yards? G

F 100 yd
G 225 yd
H 300 yd
J 400 yd

3. The fractions $\frac{2}{6}$, $\frac{3}{9}$, $\frac{4}{12}$, $\frac{5}{15}$, and $\frac{6}{18}$ are each equivalent to $\frac{1}{3}$. What is the relationship between the numerator and denominator in each fraction that is equivalent to $\frac{1}{3}$? C

A The denominator is three more than the numerator.
B The numerator is three more than the denominator.
C The denominator is three times the numerator.
D The numerator is three times the denominator.

4. Which group shows all the numbers that are common factors of 24 and 36? G

F 1, 2, 4, 6, 12
G 1, 2, 3, 4, 6, 12
H 1, 2, 3, 4, 6, 8, 12
J 1, 2, 3, 4, 6, 8, 9, 12

5. Harada wants to watch a television special. The program starts at 8:00 P.M. and is 105 minutes long. What time will the television special end? D

A 9:00 P.M.
B 9:15 P.M.
C 9:30 P.M.
D 9:45 P.M.

Test-Taking Tip

Tell students to always make sure they are answering the question they are being asked.

Preparing for Standardized Tests
For test-taking strategies and practice, see pages R42–R55.

6. Tori needs a string that is 2 inches long for a bracelet. Use the ruler on the Mathematics Chart to measure the line segment under each string. Which string is 2 inches long? **G**

   F ———

   G ——————

   H ————————

   J ————————

7. A new action movie is 134 minutes long. What is this time in hours and minutes? **C**

   A 1 hour 14 minutes

   B 1 hour 34 minutes

   C 2 hours 14 minutes

   D 2 hours 34 minutes

8. Five friends share three sandwiches equally. How much does each friend get? **F**

   F $\frac{3}{5}$ sandwich

   G $1\frac{1}{3}$ sandwich

   H $1\frac{3}{5}$ sandwich

   J $1\frac{2}{3}$ sandwich

PART 2 Short Response

Record your answers on the sheet provided by your teacher or on a sheet of paper.

9. Mykia weighed 7 pounds 5 ounces when she was born. How many ounces did she weigh when she was born? **117**

10. Name two unlike fractions that have a sum of $3\frac{5}{6}$. **Sample answer: $2\frac{1}{2}$ and $1\frac{1}{3}$**

11. Write any four digit number that has a 3 in the hundreds place and a 7 in the tens place. **Sample answer: 5,371**

PART 3 Extended Response

Record your answers on the answer sheet provided by your teacher or on a sheet of paper. Show your work.

12. For each item below, choose an appropriate unit. Choose from inches, feet, yards, or miles. Explain your choice.
    See margin for explanations.
    - the length of a football field **yards**
    - the distance around Earth **miles**
    - the length of a toothbrush **inches**
    - the height of a rollercoaster **feet**

NEED EXTRA HELP?												
If You Missed Question...	1	2	3	4	5	6	7	8	9	10	11	12
Go to Lesson...	11-1	11-1	9-3	9-1	11-5	11-1	11-5	8-1	11-3	10-3	1-1	11-1

Answer Sheet Practice

Have students simulate taking a state test by recording their answers on a practice recording sheet.

CRM Chapter 11 Resource Masters
Student Recording Sheet (p. 71)

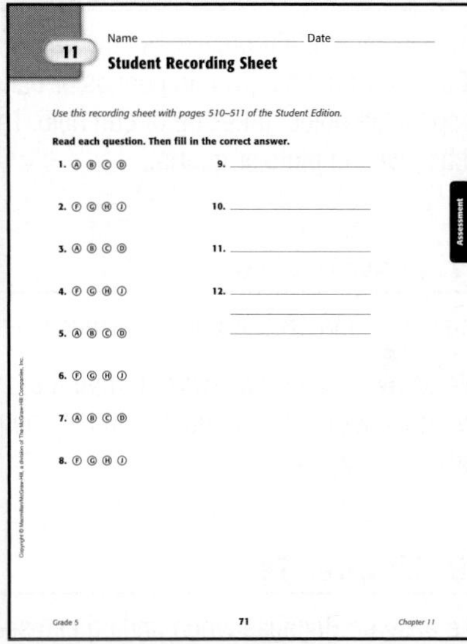

11 Name ________ Date ________

Student Recording Sheet

Use this recording sheet with pages 510–511 of the Student Edition.

Read each question. Then fill in the correct answer.

1. Ⓐ Ⓑ Ⓒ Ⓓ
2. Ⓕ Ⓖ Ⓗ Ⓙ
3. Ⓐ Ⓑ Ⓒ Ⓓ
4. Ⓕ Ⓖ Ⓗ Ⓙ
5. Ⓐ Ⓑ Ⓒ Ⓓ
6. Ⓕ Ⓖ Ⓗ Ⓙ
7. Ⓐ Ⓑ Ⓒ Ⓓ
8. Ⓕ Ⓖ Ⓗ Ⓙ
9. ________
10. ________
11. ________
12. ________

Grade 5 71 Chapter 11

Additional Answer

12a. Sample answer: A football field is too large to be measured in inches and too small to be measured in miles; yards are appropriate.

12b. Sample answer: The distance around Earth is too large to be measured in any other unit except miles.

12c. Sample answer: The length of a toothbrush is smaller than a foot, so inches are appropriate.

12d. Sample answer: The height of a rollercoaster is too large to be measured in inches and too small to be measured in miles, so feet are appropriate.

Page 483, Lesson 11-2

2. Sample answer: A diagram visually helps to figure out the information in the problem which helps to find the right answer.

7. dunk tank, face painting, ring toss, cupcake walk

11. Sample answer: I drew the dunk tank on the left. Since the ring toss is in between the face painting booth and the cupcake walk and the cupcake walk has only one neighbor, I drew the cupcake walk on the right, the ring toss to the left of the cupcake walk, and the face painting between the dunk tank and the ring toss.

Page 490, Lesson 11-4

30. Sample answer: A cook needs to use a measuring cup to get $1\frac{1}{2}$ pints of milk. $1\frac{1}{2}$ pt $= 3$ c.

Page 491, Mid-Chapter Check

20. Sample answer: Weight measures how heavy an object is. The weight of a box of cereal would be given in pounds or ounces. Capacity measures how much space an object takes up or can hold. The capacity of a box of cereal would be given in pints or quarts.

Page 497, Lesson 11-6

5. 19 long beads and 18 short beads; *draw a picture*

9. Sample answer: *work backward*; To find the original amount of money, work backward by adding the amount of money he has spent to the amount he has left over; $10

Page 509, Chapter Test

20. Sample answer: Because when finding elapsed time, a change from A.M. to P.M. could mean that you have to add another 12 hours to the total elapsed time. For example, the elapsed time between 5:45 A.M. and 6:15 P.M. is 12 hours and 30 minutes, not 30 minutes.

Chapter Overview

Chapter-at-a-Glance

In Chapter 12, the emphasis is on using Metric units of length, mass, and capacity and measuring temperature in degrees Fahrenheit and Celsius.

Lesson	Math Objective	State/Local Standards
EXPLORE 12-1 **Metric Rulers** (pp. 515–516)	Measure length to the nearest millimeter.	
12-1 Units of Length (pp. 517–521)	Choose an appropriate metric unit for measuring length and convert metric units of length.	
12-2 Problem-Solving Skill: Determine Reasonable Answers (pp. 522–523)	Solve problems by determining reasonable answers.	
12-3 Units of Mass (pp. 524–526)	Convert metric units of mass.	
12-4 Units of Capacity (pp. 527–530)	Convert metric units of capacity.	
12-5 Integers and Graphing on Number Lines (pp. 533–535)	Use integers to represent real-life situations and graph them on a number line.	
EXPLORE 12-6 **Units of Temperature** (p. 536)	Use technology to make and explain line graphs.	
12-6 Units of Temperature (pp. 537–541)	Choose appropriate temperatures in degrees Fahrenheit and Celsius.	
12-7 Problem-Solving Investigation: Choose a Strategy (pp. 544–545)	Choose the best strategy to solve a problem.	

Use Measures in the Metric System

BIG Idea In this chapter, students will measure using more precise units and focus on the number sense associated with multiplication and division of base ten. Provide students with many opportunities to use mental mathematics throughout this chapter. Students should be able to verbalize the processes they use for mental computation and explain why a solution is reasonable or unreasonable. In the end, the best way to improve students' skills in measurement is to let them measure.

Algebra Students convert among units of length, mass, and capacity. This concept will help prepare them for algebra concepts, such as using formulas to solve problems.
(Lessons 12-1, 12-3, 12-4)

G5-FP5C Measurement: Students' experiences connect their work with solids and volume to their earlier work with capacity and weight or mass. They solve problems that require attention to both approximation and precision of measurement.

Skills Trace

Vertical Alignment

Fourth Grade

In fourth grade, students learned to:

- Estimate, measure, and convert customary units of length, capacity, weight, and volume.
- Measure temperature and calculate changes in temperature.

Fifth Grade

During this chapter, students learn to:

- Convert metric units of length, mass, and capacity.
- Choose an appropriate metric unit for measuring length.
- Choose appropriate temperatures in degrees Fahrenheit and Celsius for real-life situations.

After this chapter, students learn to:

- Select and use appropriate units and formulas to measure length, perimeter, area, and volume.

Sixth Grade

In sixth grade, students learn to:

- Change units of length and measure length, capacity, weight, and time in the customary system.

Backmapping and Vertical Alignment McGraw-Hill's ***Math Connects*** program was conceived and developed with the final results in mind: student success in Algebra 1 and beyond. The authors, using the **NCTM Focal Points and Focal Connections** as their guide, developed this brand new series by backmapping from Algebra 1 concepts and vertically aligning the topics so that they build upon prior skills and concepts and serve as a foundation for future topics.

Math Vocabulary

The following math vocabulary words for Chapter 12 are listed in the glossary of the ***Student Edition***. You can find interactive definitions in 13 languages in the ***eGlossary*** at macmillanmh.com.

centimeter A metric unit for measuring length and height. 100 centimeters = 1 meter. (p. 517A)

degrees A unit of measure for temperature. (p. 537A)

gram A metric unit for measuring mass. (p. 524A)

integer Whole numbers and their opposites, including zero. (p. 533A)
Example: ...−3, −2, −1, 0, 1, 2, 3...

kilogram A metric unit for measuring mass. (p. 524A)

kilometer A metric unit for measuring length. (p. 517A)

liter A metric unit for measuring volume or capacity. 1 liter = 1000 milliliters. (p. 527A)

mass The amount of matter in an object. (p. 524A)

meter A metric unit for measuring length or height. 1 meter = 100 centimeters. (p. 517A)

metric system The measurement system based on powers of 10 that includes units such as meter, gram, liter, and degrees Celsius. (p. 517A)

Celsius (°C) A metric unit for measuring temperature. Water freezes at 0°C and boils at 100°C. (p. 537A)

Fahrenheit (°F) A customary unit for measuring temperature. (p. 537A)

Visual Vocabulary Cards

Use Visual Vocabulary Card 18 to reinforce the vocabulary in this lesson. (The Define/Example/Ask routine is printed on the back of each card.)

integer

Chapter Planner

Suggested Pacing		
Instruction	Review & Assessment	TOTAL
8 days	1 day	**9 days**

Diagnostic Assessment
Quick Check (p. 514)

	Explore 12-1 (Pacing: 1 day)	Lesson 12-1 (Pacing: 1 day)	Lesson 12-2 (Pacing: 1 day)
Lesson/ Objective	**Metric Rulers** (pp. 515–516) **Objective:** Measure length to the nearest millimeter.	**Units of Length** (pp. 517–521) **Objective:** Choose an appropriate metric unit for measuring length and convert metric units of length.	**Problem-Solving Skill Determine Reasonable Answers** (pp. 522–523) **Objective:** Solve problems by determining reasonable answers.
State/Local Standards			
Math Vocabulary		**metric system, centimeter, millimeter, meter, kilometer**	
Lesson Resources	**Manipulatives** ruler	**Materials** meter sticks **Manipulatives** rulers **Other Resources** CRM Leveled Worksheets (pp. 8–12) Daily Reteach • 5-Minute Check • Problem of the Day	**Manipulatives** measurement tools, such as, rulers and scales **Other Resources** CRM Leveled Worksheets (pp. 13–17) Daily Reteach • 5-Minute Check • Problem of the Day *How Big is the Solar System*
Technology		Math Adventures	
Math Online	Concepts in Motion	Personal Tutor	
Reaching All Learners		English Learners, p. 517B ELL Below Level, p. 517B BL Early Finishers, p. 517B AL	English Learners, p. 522B ELL Below Level, p. 522B BL Early Finishers, p. 522B OL AL
Alternate Lesson		*IMPACT Mathematics*: Unit H	

KEY

BL Below/Approaching Level　OL On Level　AL Above/Beyond Level　ELL English Learners
SE Student Edition　TE Teacher Edition　CRM Chapter 1 Resource Masters　CD-Rom
Transparency　Real-World Problem Solving Library

Use Measures in the Metric System

	Lesson 12-3 (Pacing: 1 day)	Lesson 12-4 (Pacing: 1 day)	Lesson 12-5 (Pacing: 1 day)
Lesson/ Objective	**Units of Mass** (pp. 524–526) **Objective:** Convert metric units of mass.	**Units of Capacity** (pp. 527–530) **Objective:** Convert metric units of capacity.	**Integers and Graphing on Number Lines** (pp. 533–535) **Objective:** Use integers to represent real-life situations and graph them on a number line.
State/Local Standards			
Math Vocabulary	**mass, gram, milligram, kilogram**	**liter, milliliter**	**positive number, negative number, integer, opposite integer, negative integers, positive integers**
Lesson Resources	**Materials** kilogram scale **Manipulatives** pan balance **Other Resources** CRM Leveled Worksheets (pp. 18–22) Daily Reteach • 5-Minute Check • Problem of the Day	**Materials** bottles of varying sizes with labels showing liters and milliliters **Other Resources** CRM Leveled Worksheets (pp. 23–27) Daily Reteach • 5-Minute Check • Problem of the Day	**Materials** meter stick **Manipulatives** ruler **Other Resources** CRM Leveled Worksheets (pp. 28–32) Daily Reteach • 5-Minute Check • Problem of the Day
Technology **Math Online**	Personal Tutor	Math Adventures Personal Tutor	Math Adventures Personal Tutor
Reaching All Learners	English Learners, p. 524B ELL Below Level, p. 524B BL Early Finishers, p. 524B AL	English Learners, p. 527B ELL Below Level, p. 527B BL Early Finishers, p. 527B AL	English Learners, p. 533B ELL Below Level, p. 533B BL Early Finishers, p. 533B AL
Alternate Lesson			

Game Time
Metric Pairs! (p. 531)

Formative Assessment
Mid-Chapter Check (p. 532)

Chapter Planner

	Explore 12-6 (Pacing: $\frac{1}{2}$ day)	Lesson 12-6 (Pacing: $\frac{1}{2}$ day)	Lesson 12-7 (Pacing: 1 day)
Lesson/ Objective	**Units of Temperature** (p. 536) Tech Link **Objective:** Use technology to make and explain line graphs.	**Units of Temperature** (pp. 537–541) **Objective:** Choose appropriate temperatures in degrees Fahrenheit and Celsius.	**Problem-Solving Investigation Choose a Strategy** (pp. 544–545) **Objective:** Choose the best strategy to solve a problem.
State/Local Standards			
Math Vocabulary		**degrees, Celsius (°C), Fahrenheit (°F)**	
Lesson Resources		**Manipulatives** thermometers **Other Resources** CRM Leveled Worksheets (pp. 33–37) Daily Reteach • 5-Minute Check • Problem of the Day	**Other Resources** CRM Leveled Worksheets (pp. 38–42) Daily Reteach • 5-Minute Check • Problem of the Day *How Big is the Solar System*
Technology	Math Tool Chest		
Math Online		Personal Tutor	
Reaching All Learners		English Learners, p. 537B ELL Below Level, p. 537B BL Early Finishers, p. 537B AL	English Learners, p. 544B ELL Gifted and Talented, p. 544B AL Early Finishers, p. 544B OL AL
Alternate Lesson		*IMPACT Mathematics*: Unit H	

Problem Solving in Social Studies (p. 542)

Summative Assessment
- Study Guide and Review (p. 546)
- Chapter Test (p. 551)
- Test Practice (p. 552)

Assessment Options

Diagnostic Assessment

- SE *Option 1:* Quick Check (p. 514)
- *Option 2:* Online Quiz macmillanmh.com
- CRM *Option 3:* Diagnostic Test (p. 44)
- CRM *Option 4:* Chapter Pretest (p. 45)

Formative Assessment

- TE Alternate Teaching Strategies (every lesson)
- SE Talk About It (every lesson)
- SE Writing in Math (every lesson)
- SE Check What You Know (every lesson)
- TE Ticket Out the Door (p. 535)
- TE Name the Math (pp. 526, 530)
- SE Mid-Chapter Check (p. 532)
- CRM Lesson Quizzes (pp. 46–48)
- CRM Mid-Chapter Test (p. 49)

Summative Assessment

- SE Chapter Test (p. 551)
- SE Test Practice (p. 552)
- CRM Vocabulary Test (p. 50)
- CRM Leveled Chapter Tests (pp. 55–66)
- CRM Cumulative Test Practice (pp. 69–71)
- CRM Oral Assessment (pp. 51–52)
- ExamView® Assessment Suite
- Advance Tracker

Mc Graw Hill Professional Development

Targeted professional development has been articulated throughout **McGraw-Hill's *Math Connects*** program. The **McGraw-Hill Professional Development Video Library** provides short videos that support the **NCTM Focal Points and Focal Connections.** For more information visit macmillanmh.com.

Model Lessons

Instructional Strategies

Teacher Notes

Learning Stations

Cross-Curricular Links

Science

Mass Guessing

- Take turns picking an object from the pile of objects at the learning station. One partner picks an object and the other partner gets to guess the metric mass of that object. The partner who picked the object gets to weigh it to see what its actual mass is.
- Use the balance scale and metric mass measures to find out the actual mass of each object you choose. How close are your guesses? Are you getting better at guessing as you continue to play this game?

Materials:

- small objects, such as pebbles, pencils, erasers, paper clips, notebooks, etc.
- balance scale with metric mass counters
- paper
- pencils

Art

pair | SPATIAL

Decimeter Puzzle

- Measure and cut a 10-centimeter by 10-centimeter piece of paper. Draw a grid on top of the paper so that there will be 100 squares.
- Draw a colorful picture over the grid and then cut the picture into a puzzle.
- Have your partner measure objects within your picture to the nearest $\frac{1}{2}$ centimeter and write them down. For example, in this picture, your partner may measure the horse's tail to be $4\frac{1}{2}$ centimeters.

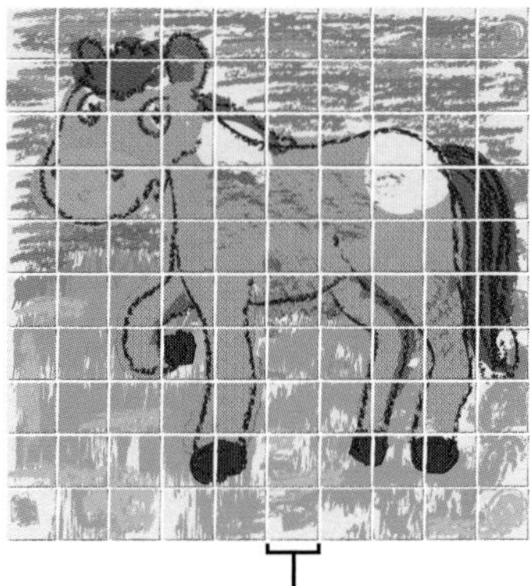

Materials:

- paper
- metric ruler
- scissors
- colored markers

Writing

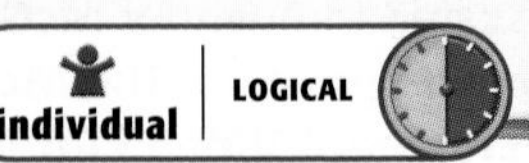

Pen Pals

- Every country in the world, except the United States, uses the metric system to measure height, mass, and capacity. Now that you're learning to measure using this system, write a letter to an imaginary pen pal in another country describing your experience.
- Do you find the system easy or difficult to use? Tell your pen pal how the metric system compares with the customary system, and give some examples of things you have learned to measure using the metric system.

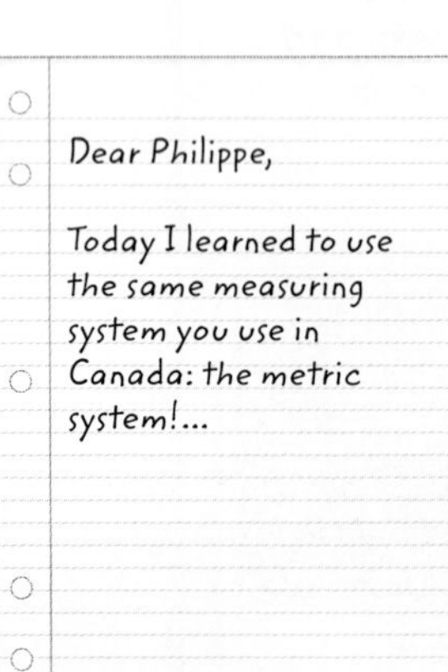

Dear Philippe,

Today I learned to use the same measuring system you use in Canada: the metric system!...

Materials:

- paper
- pencils

Use Measures in the Metric System

Reading

LOGICAL

Measuring Up

- Read *Measure Up!* by Sandra Markle by yourself or with a partner.
- One thing you have probably measured is your height and know how tall you are using the customary system. See if you can guess how tall you are using the metric system, to the nearest centimeter, and write your guess down on an index card.
- Have your partner measure your height using a meter stick. Write the measurement, down to the nearest millimeter, on your index card next to your guess. Then round it to the nearest centimeter to see how close you got to your guess.

Guess: 125 centimeters

Actual measurement: 129.54 centimeters

Materials:

- *Measure Up!* by Sandra Markle
- metric measuring stick
- index cards
- pencils

Health

SPATIAL

Sugar and Salt

- For fifth graders, the daily intake for sodium should be about 2,000 milligrams. Too much sugar can boost calories way beyond what you need.
- Check the measurements for salt and sugar on snack food packages. Then add how much sugar and salt you would take in if you ate one of these snack foods each day for a week.
- Now, using your totals, measure your intake of sugar and salt, using the balance scale and metric mass measures to weigh each ingredient. The size of each pile might surprise you.

Materials:

- can of soda, box of juice, box of crackers, bag of popcorn, other snack food packages
- sugar and salt
- balance scale
- metric mass counters

Social Studies

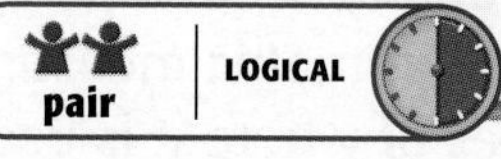

Gas Conservation

- Imagine that each of you is driving a car that uses one liter of fuel for every 15 kilometers you drive. Take turns rolling the number cubes. Multiply the numbers you roll to get your travel distance in kilometers. Then figure out how much fuel you use to travel that distance. Write your travel distance and fuel usage for each turn.
- After ten rounds, the player who used the least fuel wins. How far in total did you each travel? Add up your total fuel usage, too. Then check your fuel totals, using your total travel distances.

15 km/liter

Traveled 45 km so the car used 3 liters of fuel.

Materials:

- two number cubes
- paper
- pencils

CHAPTER 12

Introduce the Chapter

Real World: Metrics and Place Value

Share with students that they are going to learn about metric measurement. Explain that the units in metric measurement are based on base-ten place value.

Have students make the following metric place-value chart.

1,000	100	10	Units 1	0.1	0.01	0.001
kilo-	hecto-	deca-	meter liter gram	deci-	centi-	milli-

- **How much larger is 1,000 than 1?** 1,000 times larger **How much larger is a kilometer than a meter?** 1,000 times larger
- **How many 0.01's are in 1?** 100 **How many centimeters are in a meter?** 100

Direct students to Student Edition p. 512. Have students read the paragraph at the top of the page.

- **How are the metric system and the decimal system alike?** The decimal system is based on the number ten and the metric system is based on multiples of ten.
- **What are some units in the metric system?** kilograms, centimeters, liters

WRITING IN MATH

Starting the Chapter
Have students write a paragraph about what they know about metric measurement and real world examples of where it is used. Prompt students to give specific examples of items they may have seen marked with metric measures.

Key Vocabulary Introduce the key vocabulary in the chapter using the routine below.

Define: Mass is the amount of matter in an object.
Example: A piece of bread has a mass of about 1 gram.
Ask: When is finding mass important?

Read-Aloud Anthology For an optional reading activity to introduce this chapter's math concepts, see the Read-Aloud Anthology on p. TR30.

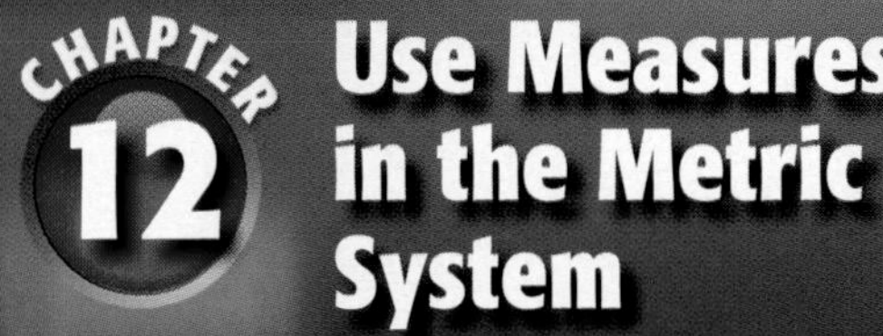

CHAPTER 12 Use Measures in the Metric System

BIG Idea What is the metric system?

The **metric system** is a decimal system of measurement.

Example Speed skating at the Olympic Games consists of the events listed in the table.

Speed Skating Events	
• 500 meter	• 1,500 meter
• 1,000 meter	• 5,000 meter

In the metric system, a meter is a unit of length.

What will I learn in this chapter?

- Choose appropriate metric units for measuring length.
- Convert metric units of length, mass, and capacity.
- Use integers to represent real-world situations.
- Solve problems involving changes in temperature.
- Solve problems by determining reasonable answers.

Key Vocabulary

metric system
mass
negative number
positive number
integer

Math Online Student Study Tools at macmillanmh.com

Chapter 12 Project

Morning, Noon, and Night

Students chart temperatures in degrees Fahrenheit for a week, and then estimate them in degrees Celsius.

- Students create a chart to record the outside temperature in the morning, at noon, and in the evening for a week (set a time for morning and evening measuring and stick to it).
- Students calculate and compare the differences between the morning, noon, and evening temperatures. Then they estimate the temperatures on the chart in degrees Celsius and create a new chart for these estimates.
- Challenge students to calculate and compare the differences in morning, noon, and evening temperatures for each day in degrees Celsius.

CRM *Refer to Chapter 12 Resource Masters, p. 53, for a rubric to assess students' progress on this project.*

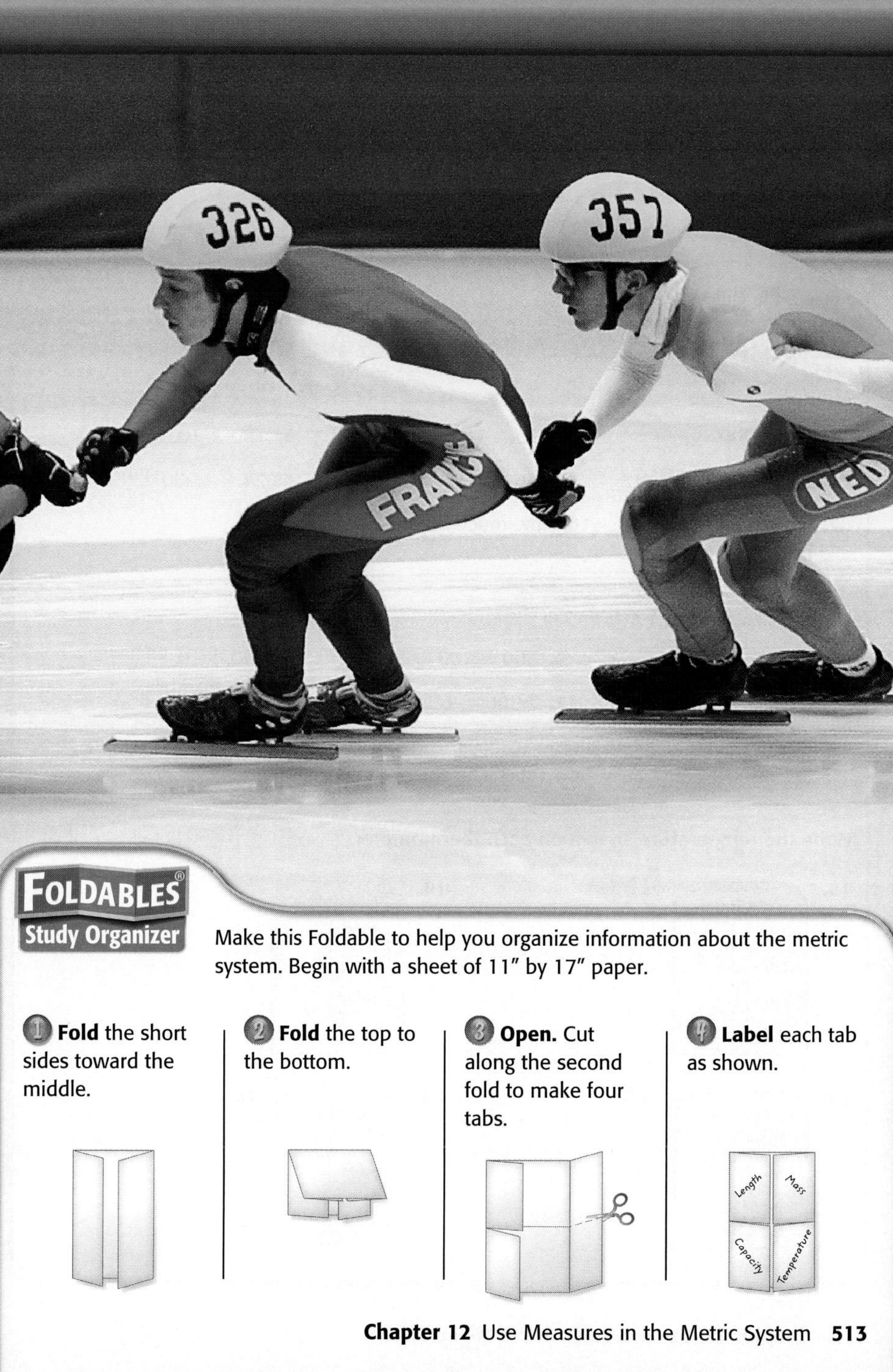

FOLDABLES Study Organizer

Make this Foldable to help you organize information about the metric system. Begin with a sheet of 11″ by 17″ paper.

1. **Fold** the short sides toward the middle.
2. **Fold** the top to the bottom.
3. **Open.** Cut along the second fold to make four tabs.
4. **Label** each tab as shown.

FOLDABLES Dinah Zike's Foldables

Guide students through the directions on p. 513 to create their own Foldable graphic organizers for the metric system. Students may also use their Foldables to study and review for chapter assessments.

When to Use It Lessons 12-1, 12-3, 12-4, and 12-6. (Additional instructions for using the Foldables with these lessons are found on pp. 532 and 546.)

Chapter 12 Literature List

Lesson	Book Title
12-1	**How Tall, How Short, How Far Away?** David A. Adler
12-2	**Minnie's Diner** Dayle Ann Dodds
12-3	**Measure with Metric** Franklyn Mansfield Branley
12-4	**Millions to Measure** David M. Schwartz
12-5	**Mathematics** Irving Adler
12-6	**Measuring Up!** Sandra Markle
Any	**Math Mini-Mysteries** Sandra Markle

ELL **National ESL Standards Alignment for Chapter 12**			
Lesson, Page	ESL Standards	Modality	Level
12-1, p. 517B	Goal 2, Standard 2, b	Spatial, Social	Intermediate
12-2, p. 522B	Goal 2, Standard 2, f	Logical	Advanced
12-3, p. 524B	Goal 1, Standard 3, c	Auditory, Linguistic	Advanced
12-4, p. 527B	Goal 2, Standard 1, h	Visual, Spatial	Intermediate
12-5, p. 533B	Goal 2, Standard 2, i	Kinesthetic	Beginning
12-6, p. 537B	Goal 2, Standard 2, g	Linguistic, Logical	Intermediate
12-7, p. 544B	Goal 2, Standard 3, g	Interpersonal	Advanced

The National ESL Standards can be found in the Teacher Reference Handbook.

- Read the Math at Home letter found in Chapter 12 Resource Masters, p. 4, with the class and have each student sign it. (A Spanish version is found on p. 5.)
- Send home copies of the Math at Home letter with each student.

Diagnostic Assessment

Check for students' prerequisite skills before beginning the chapter.

- **Option 1:** ***Quick Check***

  SE Student Edition, p. 514

- **Option 2:** ***Online Assessment***

  Math Online macmillanmh.com

- **Option 3:** ***Diagnostic Test***

  CRM Chapter 12 Resource Masters, p. 44–45

RTI (Response to Intervention)

Apply the Results Based on the results of the diagnostics assessment on Student Edition p. 514, use the chart below to address individual needs before beginning the chapter.

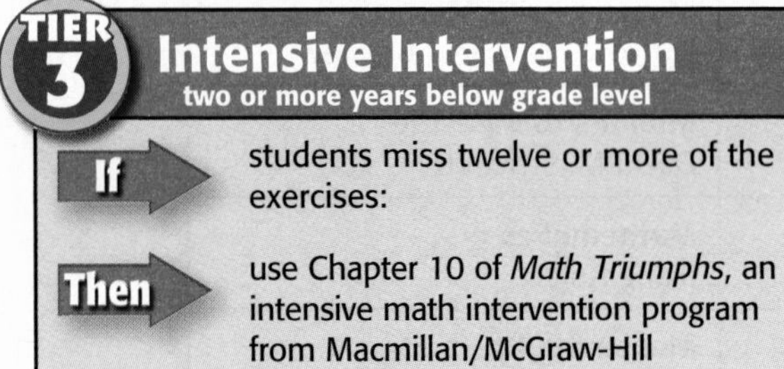

TIER 3 Intensive Intervention
two or more years below grade level

If students miss twelve or more of the exercises:

Then use Chapter 10 of *Math Triumphs*, an intensive math intervention program from Macmillan/McGraw-Hill

ARE YOU READY for Chapter 12?

You have two ways to check prerequisite skills for this chapter.

Option 2

Math Online Take the Chapter Readiness Quiz at macmillanmh.com.

Option 1

Complete the Quick Check below.

QUICK Check

Multiply. (Lessons 3-1 and 3-8) (Used in Lessons 12-1, 12-3, and 12-4)

1. 6 × 1,000 6,000 **2.** 15 × 100 1,500 **3.** 180 × 10 1,800

4. 947 × 100 94,700 **5.** 36 × 10 360 **6.** 24 × 1,000 24,000

7. A bean bag chair costs $16. How much do one hundred bean bag chairs cost? $1,600

Divide. (Lessons 4-1 and 4-7) (Used in Lessons 12-1, 12-3, and 12-4)

8. 150 ÷ 10 15 **9.** 500 ÷ 100 5 **10.** 140 ÷ 10 14

11. 64,000 ÷ 1,000 64 **12.** 7,900 ÷ 100 79 **13.** 3,120 ÷ 10 312

14. Roz has $480 to spend on her 10-day trip. If she wants to spend the same amount daily, how much can she spend each day? $48

Write the temperature shown on each thermometer. (Prior Grade) (Used in Lesson 12-6)

15. 220°F

°Fahrenheit
230°
220°
210°
200°

16. 19°F

°Fahrenheit
30°
20°
10°
0°

17. 15°C

°Celsius
30°
20°
10°
0°

18. 78°C

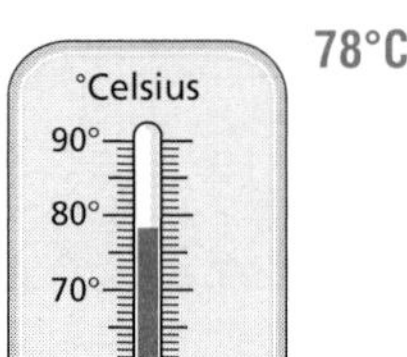

TIER 2 Strategic Intervention below/approaching grade level	TIER 1 On-Level	Above/Beyond-Level
If students miss six to eleven in: **Exercises 1–17**	**If** students miss three to five in: **Exercises 1–17**	**If** students miss two or less in: **Exercises 1–17**
Then choose a resource	**Then** choose a resource	**Then** choose a resource
CRM Chapter 11 Resource Masters (Reteach Worksheets) **Math Online** Extra Examples • Personal Tutor Concepts in Motion	TE Learning Stations (pp. 512G–512H) TE Chapter Project (p. 512) CRM Game Flash Card Mania! Math Adventures My Math Zone Chapter 11 **Math Online** Fact Dash	TE Learning Stations (pp. 512G–512H) TE Chapter Project (p. 512) Real-World Problem Solving Reader: *How Big is the Solar System?* My Math Zone Chapter 11, 12 **Math Online** Games

Explore Measurement Activity for 12-1 Metric Rulers

MAIN IDEA

I will measure length to the nearest millimeter.

You Will Need
a ruler

Math Online
macmillanmh.com
• Concepts in Motion

In the customary system, you measure length using inches, feet, or yards. In the metric system, you use meters, centimeters, or millimeters.

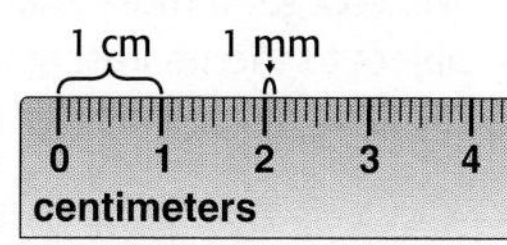

Use a ruler like the one above to measure objects to the nearest centimeter or to the nearest millimeter.

ACTIVITY

1. **Find the length of the piece of chalk to the nearest centimeter.**

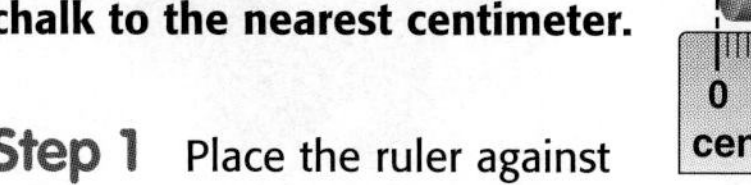

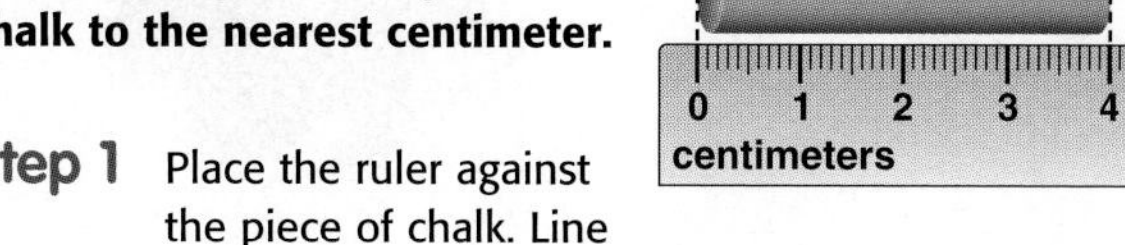

Step 1 Place the ruler against the piece of chalk. Line up the zero on the ruler with the end of the piece of chalk.

Step 2 Find the centimeter mark that is closest to the other end.

To the nearest centimeter, the length of the piece of chalk is 4 centimeters long.

ACTIVITY

2. **Find the length of the toy car to the nearest millimeter.**

To the nearest millimeter, the toy car is 82 millimeters long.

Measurement Activity for 12-1 Metric Rulers

Lesson Planner

Objective

Measure length to the nearest millimeter.

Resources

Materials: pencils and paper
Manipulatives: ruler

1 Introduce

- Before beginning the lesson, assess students' knowledge of the units of linear measure in the metric system. **What unit of length would be used to measure the distance between two cities? the length of a soccer field? the length of a paper? the length of an insect wing?** kilometers; meters; centimeters; millimeters
- Explain to students that metric measurement and customary measurement are two different systems of measurement. When using the metric system, only metric units can be used.

2 Teach

Activity 1 Make sure students understand that they must begin measuring at 0, which may not be on the very edge of their ruler. To measure to the nearest centimeter, students may need to round up if an object measures greater than halfway between the two whole centimeters, or down if the object measures less than halfway between the two whole centimeters.

Activity 2 As students measure to the nearest millimeter, encourage them to count by tens for each centimeter mark and then to count on the remaining millimeters. Tell students that in the metric system, only one unit is used to describe each measurement.

Think About It

Assign Exercises 1–2 to assess student comprehension of the concept presented in the activity.

3 Assess

Formative Assessment

Use **Check What You Know** Exercises 3–5 to assess whether students understand measuring to the nearest centimeter and to the nearest millimeter.

From Concrete to Abstract Use Exercise 15 to bridge the gap between measuring in centimeters and millimeters and choosing the most appropriate unit to measure an object.

Extending the Concept

- **How would you convert centimeters to millimeters?** Because centimeters are 10 times larger than millimeters, multiply the number of centimeters by 10.

Think About It

1. Is it easier to measure objects to the nearest centimeter or to the nearest millimeter? Explain. Sample answer: It is easier to measure to the nearest centimeter because the units are larger.
2. Will you get a more exact measurement if you measure an object to the nearest centimeter or to the nearest millimeter? Explain your reasoning. Sample answer: Millimeter because it is a smaller unit so you can get a more precise measurement.

CHECK What You Know

Use a metric ruler to find the length of each object to the nearest centimeter and to the nearest millimeter.

3. 

2 cm; 19 mm

4. 
4 cm; 39 mm

5. 
5 cm; 47 mm

***Millimeters* and *centimeters* are used to measure small objects. You can measure the length of larger objects using *meters*. One meter is a little longer than one yard. Select an appropriate unit to measure the length of each object.**

6. width of your textbook cm
7. height of a classmate cm or m
8. length of classroom m
9. length of an ant mm
10. Copy the table below. Then complete the table using ten objects found in your classroom. The first one is done for you. See students' work.

Object	Unit of Measure	Estimate	Actual Length
Pencil	centimeter	15 centimeters	17 centimeters

Name an object that you would measure using each unit. 11–13. Sample answers are given.

11. millimeter thickness of a dime
12. centimeter width of calculator
13. meter length of hallway
14. **OPEN ENDED** Draw a line that is between 5 and 6 centimeters long. Then measure the length of the line to the nearest millimeter. See students' work.
15. **WRITING IN MATH** Would you measure the length of a bicycle in centimeters or millimeters? Explain your reasoning. Sample answer: centimeters; A millimeter is too small to measure such a large object.

LESSON 12-1

Units of Length

Lesson Planner

Objective

Choose an appropriate metric unit for measuring length and convert metric units of length.

Vocabulary

metric system, centimeter, millimeter, meter, kilometer

Resources

Materials: meter sticks
Manipulatives: rulers
Literature Connection: *How Tall, How Short, How Far Away?* by David A. Adler
Alternate Lesson: Use *IMPACT Mathematics*: Unit H to provide practice with length.
Teacher Technology
TeacherWorks • Interactive Classroom • Concepts in Motion

Focus on Math Background

Students were introduced to the metric system in Grade 4. The units in this system are referred to as SI units (abbreviated from the French *Systeme Internationale*). This system of measurement is used internationally as well as in the scientific world. The prefix (*milli-, centi-, kilo-*) of a metric unit tells you how that unit is related to the basic unit. Since the metric system is based on powers of 10, a background in decimals is essential.

In this lesson, the meter takes a starring role—it is the basic unit of length. A meter stick can be used to measure length in centimeters and millimeters. It is important to the understanding of the metric system for students to be able to make a comparison of SI units to everyday objects as well as to U.S. customary units; *e.g.*, 1 kilometer is a little more than half a mile or about 6 city blocks long.

Daily Routine

Use these suggestions before beginning the lesson on p. 517.

5-Minute Check

(Reviews Lesson 11-7)

Find each elapsed time.

1. 6:40 A.M. to 11:17 A.M. 4 h 37 min
2. 1:25 P.M. to 8:10 P.M. 6 h 45 min
3. 10:36 A.M. to 4:26 P.M. 5 h 50 min
4. 10:13 P.M. to 7:06 A.M. 8 h 53 min
5. 9:40 A.M. to 1:55 P.M. 4 h 15 min
6. 6:22 P.M. to 2:34 A.M. 8 h 12 min

Problem of the Day

A kitten weighed 6 ounces when it was born. Its weight doubled in one week. In two months, it weighed three times what it weighed at two weeks old. How much did the kitten weigh when it was two months old? 36 oz or 2 lb 4 oz

Building Math Vocabulary

Write the lesson vocabulary words and their definitions on the board.

Have students write the words and their definitions in their Math Journals. Then ask students to write a sentence for each unit of measure to tell what they would measure using each.

Differentiated Instruction

Small Group Options

SPATIAL

Option 1 Below Level BL

Materials: centimeter rulers

- Have students determine how tall they are in centimeters.
- Next, have them measure the length of their arms, index fingers, and feet in centimeters.
- Have them explain in a paragraph which measurements would have been easier to make in meters. Students will probably mention their height and maybe the length of their arms.

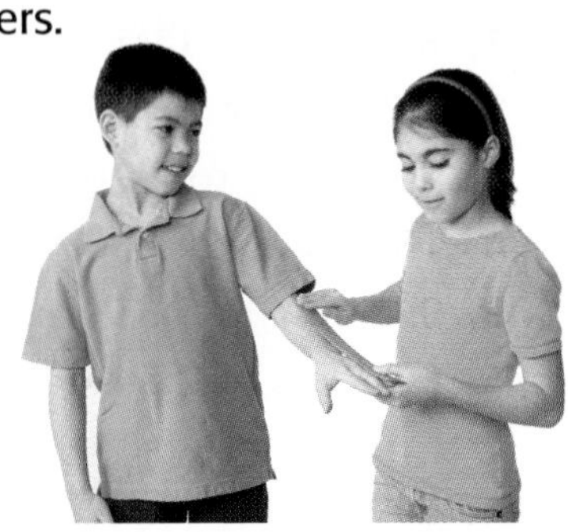

SPATIAL, SOCIAL

Option 2 English Language Learners ELL

Materials: index cards
Core Vocabulary: shorter, longer, compared to
Common Use Verb: looks

See Math This strategy activates background knowledge and comparison vocabulary.

- Make cards for each student labeling each card with the abbreviation and the term:

cm	dm
centimeter	decimeter
m	km
meter	kilometer

- Give each student a card with various lengths, e.g., 3 cm, 10 cm.
- Have students compare and order them. For example: *a centimeter is less than a meter* or *10 centimeters equal 1 decimeter*.

Use this worksheet to provide additional support for English Language Learners.

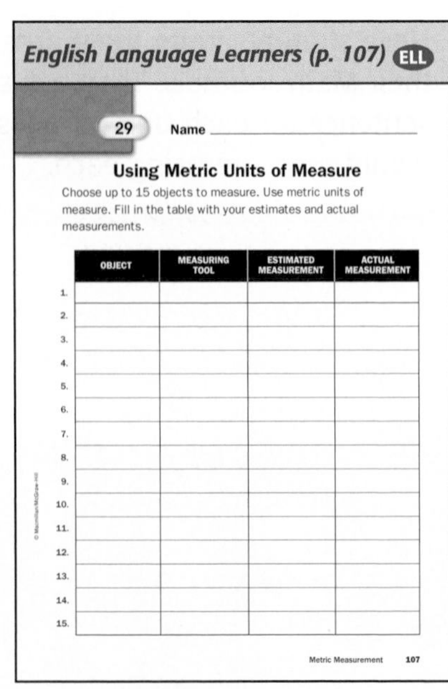

English Language Learners (p. 107) ELL

29 Name ______

Using Metric Units of Measure

Choose up to 15 objects to measure. Use metric units of measure. Fill in the table with your estimates and actual measurements.

	OBJECT	MEASURING TOOL	ESTIMATED MEASUREMENT	ACTUAL MEASUREMENT
1.				
2.				
3.				
4.				
5.				
6.				
7.				
8.				
9.				
10.				
11.				
12.				
13.				
14.				
15.				

Metric Measurement 107

Independent Work Options

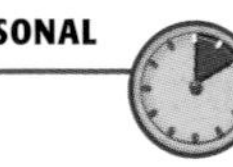

INTRAPERSONAL

Option 1 Early Finishers AL

Materials: pencil, paper, dictionary

- Have students brainstorm a list of words related to the prefix *centi-*, such as century, centipide, and centurion.
- Students may use a dictionary for help.

Option 2 Student Technology

Math Online macmillanmh.com

Personal Tutor • Extra Examples

Math Adventures

Option 3 Learning Station: Art (p. 512G)

Direct students to the Art Learning Station for opportunities to explore and extend the lesson concept.

Option 4 Problem-Solving Practice

Reinforce problem-solving skills and strategies with the Problem-Solving Practice worksheet.

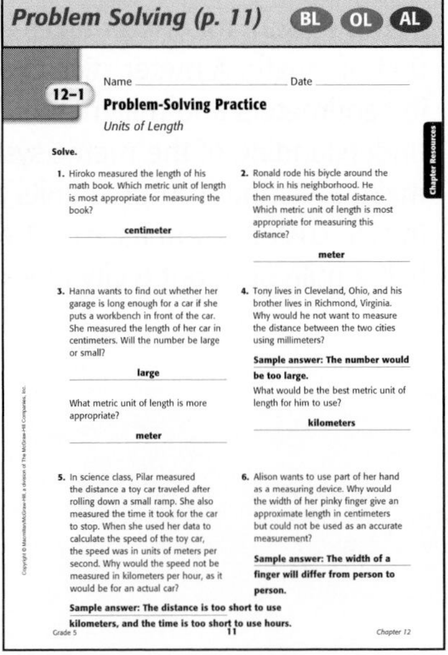

Problem Solving (p. 11) BL OL AL

12-1 Name ______ Date ______

Problem-Solving Practice

Units of Length

Solve.

1. Hiroko measured the length of his math book. Which metric unit of length is most appropriate for measuring the book?
   centimeter
2. Ronald rode his biycle around the block in his neighborhood. He then measured the total distance. Which metric unit of length is most appropriate for measuring this distance?
   meter
3. Hanna wants to find out whether her garage is long enough for a car if she puts a workbench in front of the car. She measured the length of her car in centimeters. Will the number be large or small?
   large
   What metric unit of length is more appropriate?
   meter
4. Tony lives in Cleveland, Ohio, and his brother lives in Richmond, Virginia. Why would he not want to measure the distance between the two cities using millimeters?
   Sample answer: The number would be too large.
   What would be the best metric unit of length for him to use?
   kilometers
5. In science class, Pilar measured the distance a toy car traveled after rolling down a small ramp. She also measured the time it took for the car to stop. When she used her data to calculate the speed of the toy car, the speed was in units of meters per second. Why would the speed not be measured in kilometers per hour, as it would be for an actual car?
   Sample answer: The distance is too short to use kilometers, and the time is too short to use hours.
6. Alison wants to use part of her hand as a measuring device. Why would the width of her pinky finger give an approximate length in centimeters but could not be used as an accurate measurement?
   Sample answer: The width of a finger will differ from person to person.

Chapter Resources

Grade 5 11 Chapter 12

Units of Length

MAIN IDEA

I will choose an appropriate metric unit for measuring length and convert metric units of length.

New Vocabulary

- metric system
- centimeter
- millimeter
- meter
- kilometer

Math Online

macmillanmh.com
- Extra Examples
- Personal Tutor
- Self-Check Quiz

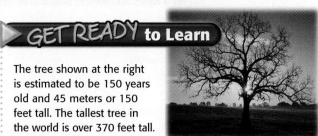

GET READY to Learn

The tree shown at the right is estimated to be 150 years old and 45 meters or 150 feet tall. The tallest tree in the world is over 370 feet tall.

The **metric system** is a decimal system of measurement. The common units of length in the metric system are millimeter, centimeter, meter, and kilometer.

Metric Units of Length — Key Concepts

1 **centimeter** (cm) = 10 **millimeters** (mm)

1 **meter** (m) = 100 cm or 1,000 mm

1 **kilometer** (km) = 1,000 m

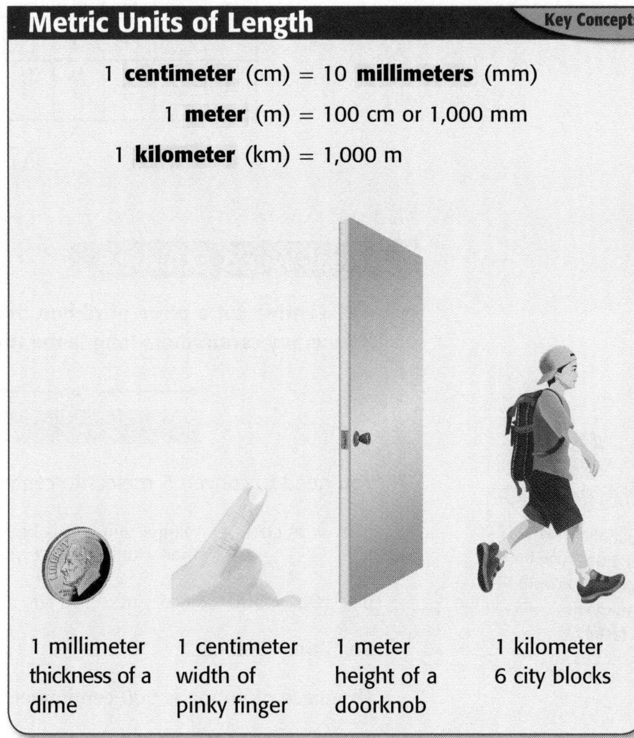

1 millimeter thickness of a dime	1 centimeter width of pinky finger	1 meter height of a doorknob	1 kilometer 6 city blocks

12-1 Units of Length

1 Introduce

Activity Choice 1 • Hands-On

- Ask students to use a ruler to draw a line 30 centimeters long. Have them draw and label centimeters 1–10 and draw millimeters 0–10. **How many millimeters are there between each centimeter mark?** 10
- Tell students that all units of length in the metric system are based on the meter. The prefixes before "-meter" have specific meanings.
- **Since a centimeter is one-hundredth of a meter, what does "centi-" mean?** 0.01
- Tell students that *milli-* means "thousandths", *deci-* means "tenths" and *kilo-* means "thousand." **What do "millimeter," "decimeter," and "kilometer" mean?** 0.001 of a meter, 0.1 of a meter and 1,000 meters

Activity Choice 2 • Literature

Introduce the lesson with *How Tall, How Short, How Far Away?* by David A. Adler. For a related math activity, see p. TR55.

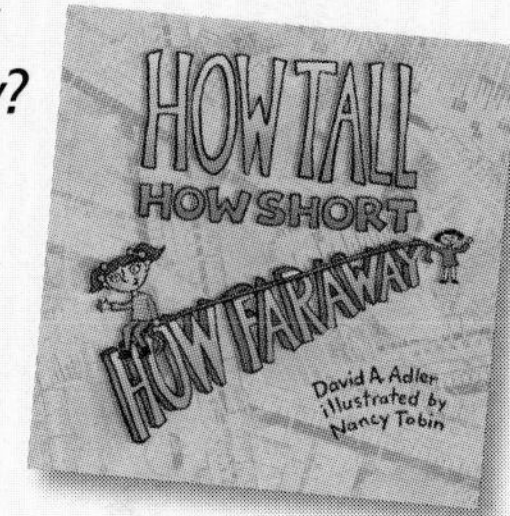

2 Teach

Scaffolding Questions

Write on the board: 3-story building, plant growth, distance between cities, person's height.

- **Which item would be measured using the smallest unit? Which metric unit would you use?** plant growth; millimeter
- **Which metric unit is used to measure distances between cities?** kilometer
- **Which metric unit is used to measure a building's height? About how tall is a 3-story building?** meters; about 10 meters
- Tell students that only one unit is used to express metric measures, rarely a combination.
- **Which unit is used to measure the height of a person?** centimeters

GET READY to Learn

Have students open their books and read the information in **Get Ready to Learn**. Introduce **metric system**, **centimeter**, **millimeter**, **meter**, and **kilometer**. As a class, work through **Examples 1–3**.

Convert Larger Units to Smaller Units

Example 2 Make sure students understand that whenever they convert larger units to smaller units they will multiply the number of larger units by the number of smaller units that equal one larger unit.

ADDITIONAL EXAMPLES

1. Which unit would you use to measure the height of a street light pole: *millimeter, centimeter, meter,* or *kilometer?* meter
2. An art project required strips of paper 8 centimeters long. How many millimeters long is each strip? 80 mm

Select an Appropriate Unit

1 SCIENCE Which unit would you use to measure the length of a river: *millimeter, centimeter, meter,* or *kilometer?*

The length of a river is much greater than the height of a doorknob. So, *kilometer* is an appropriate unit of measure.

Remember

To convert a larger unit to a smaller unit, *multiply*.

To convert a smaller unit to a larger unit, *divide*.

In the chart below, each place value is 10 times the place value to its right. To convert metric units, multiply or divide by a multiple of 10, such as 10, 100, or 1,000.

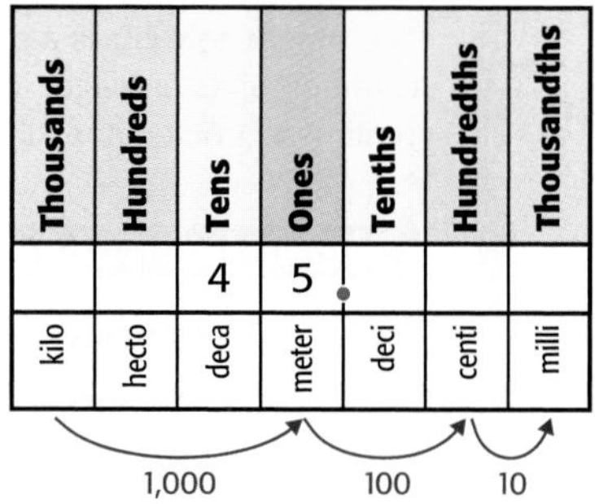

Thousands
Hundreds
Tens
Ones
Tenths
Hundredths
Thousandths
4
5
kilo
hecto
deca
meter
deci
centi
milli
1,000
100
10

Real-World EXAMPLE

Convert Larger Units to Smaller Units

2 ART Cynthia cut a piece of ribbon that is 5 meters long. How many centimeters long is the ribbon?

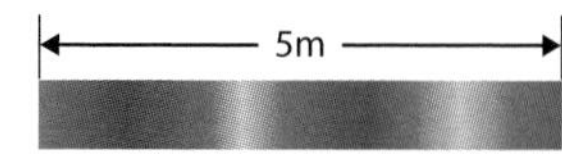

Remember

To multiply by 10, 100, or 1,000, use basic facts and count the number of zeros in the factors.

You need to convert 5 meters to centimeters.

5 m = ■ cm — A larger unit (m) is being converted to a smaller unit (cm), so you will multiply.

$5 \times 100 = 500$ — Since 1 m = 100 cm, multiply 5 by 100.

So, 5 m = 500 cm.

The piece of ribbon is 500 centimeters long.

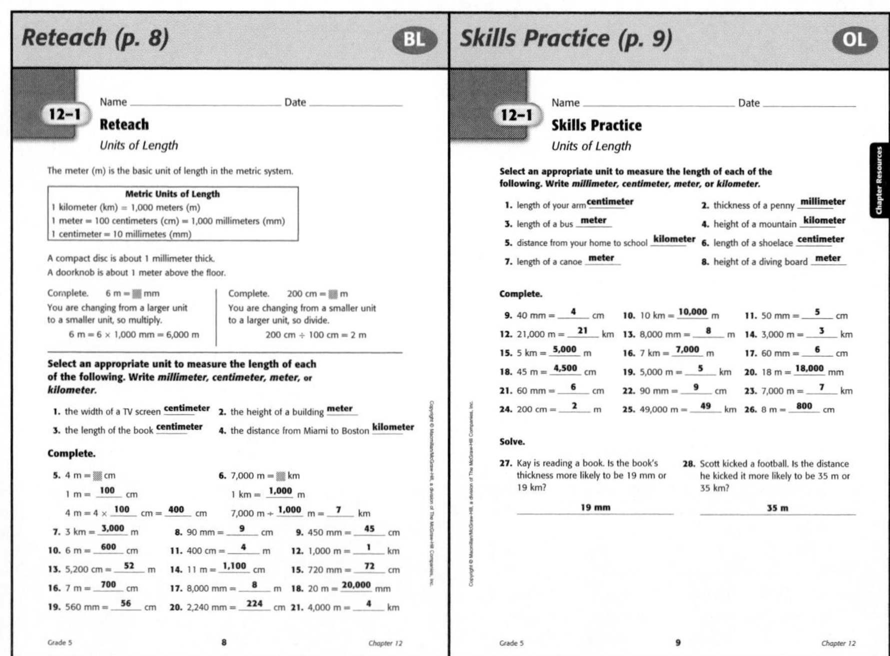

Reteach (p. 8) BL

12-1 Name ______ Date ______

Reteach

Units of Length

The meter (m) is the basic unit of length in the metric system.

Metric Units of Length
1 kilometer (km) = 1,000 meters (m)
1 meter = 100 centimeters (cm) = 1,000 millimeters (mm)
1 centimeter = 10 millimetes (mm)

A compact disc is about 1 millimeter thick.
A doorknob is about 1 meter above the floor.

Complete. 6 m = ■ mm
You are changing from a larger unit to a smaller unit, so multiply.
6 m = 6 × 1,000 mm = 6,000 m

Complete. 200 cm = ■ m
You are changing from a smaller unit to a larger unit, so divide.
200 cm ÷ 100 cm = 2 m

Select an appropriate unit to measure the length of each of the following. Write *millimeter, centimeter, meter,* or *kilometer.*

1. the width of a TV screen **centimeter**
2. the height of a building **meter**
3. the length of the book **centimeter**
4. the distance from Miami to Boston **kilometer**

Complete.

5. 4 m = ■ cm
   1 m = **100** cm
   4 m = 4 × **100** cm = **400** cm
6. 7,000 m = ■ km
   1 km = **1,000** m
   7,000 m ÷ **1,000** m = **7** km
7. 3 km = **3,000** m
8. 90 mm = **9** cm
9. 450 mm = **45** cm
10. 6 m = **600** cm
11. 400 cm = **4** m
12. 1,000 m = **1** km
13. 5,200 cm = **52** m
14. 11 m = **1,100** cm
15. 720 mm = **72** cm
16. 7 m = **700** cm
17. 8,000 mm = **8** m
18. 20 m = **20,000** mm
19. 560 mm = **56** cm
20. 2,240 mm = **224** cm
21. 4,000 m = **4** km

Grade 5 8 Chapter 12

Skills Practice (p. 9) OL

12-1 Name ______ Date ______

Skills Practice

Units of Length

Chapter Resources

Select an appropriate unit to measure the length of each of the following. Write *millimeter, centimeter, meter,* or *kilometer.*

1. length of your arm **centimeter**
2. thickness of a penny **millimeter**
3. length of a bus **meter**
4. height of a mountain **kilometer**
5. distance from your home to school **kilometer**
6. length of a shoelace **centimeter**
7. length of a canoe **meter**
8. height of a diving board **meter**

Complete.

9. 40 mm = **4** cm
10. 10 km = **10,000** m
11. 50 mm = **5** cm
12. 21,000 m = **21** km
13. 8,000 mm = **8** m
14. 3,000 m = **3** km
15. 5 km = **5,000** m
16. 7 km = **7,000** m
17. 60 mm = **6** cm
18. 45 m = **4,500** cm
19. 5,000 m = **5** km
20. 18 m = **18,000** mm
21. 60 mm = **6** cm
22. 90 mm = **9** cm
23. 7,000 m = **7** km
24. 200 cm = **2** m
25. 49,000 m = **49** km
26. 8 m = **800** cm

Solve.

27. Kay is reading a book. Is the book's thickness more likely to be 19 mm or 19 km? **19 mm**
28. Scott kicked a football. Is the distance he kicked it more likely to be 35 m or 35 km? **35 m**

Grade 5 9 Chapter 12

Convert Smaller Units to Larger Units

3 GAMES Roshonda has 50 dominoes. Each domino is 4 centimeters long. She lines them up end to end as shown. How many meters long is the line of dominoes?

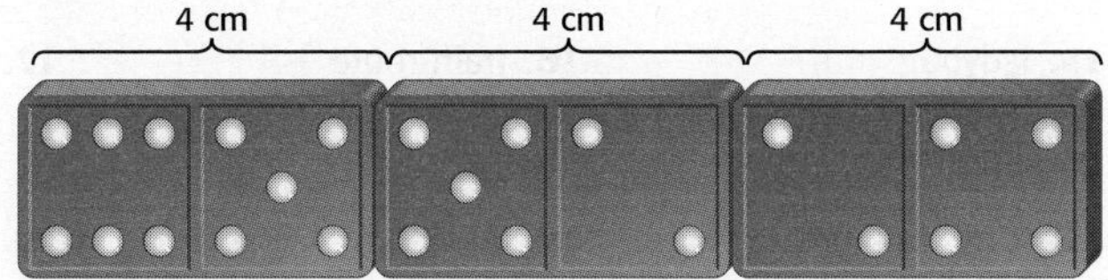

Step 1 Find the length in centimeters.

number of dominoes		length of each domino		total length
50	×	4 cm	=	200 cm

Step 2 Convert 200 centimeters to meters.

200 cm = ■ m — A smaller unit (cm) is being converted to a larger unit (m), so divide.

200 ÷ 100 = 2 — Since 100 cm = 1 m, divide 200 by 100.

So, 200 cm = 2 m.

The line of 50 dominoes is 2 meters long.

Remember

To divide by 10, 100, or 1,000, cross out the same number of zeros in both the dividend and divisor.

CHECK What You Know

Select an appropriate unit to measure each length. Write *millimeter, centimeter, meter,* or *kilometer.* See Example 1 (p. 518)

1. soccer field m
2. necklace cm
3. distance between two cities km

Complete. See Examples 2, 3 (pp. 518–519)

4. 5 m = ■ cm 500
5. 9 km = ■ m 9,000
6. 700 cm = ■ m 7
7. 20 mm = ■ cm 2
8. 6,000 m = ■ km 6
9. 45 cm = ■ mm 450
10. Which is the most reasonable estimate for the depth of a pond: 6 millimeters, 6 centimeters, or 6 meters? Explain. 6 m; both 6 mm and 6 cm are too small.
11. **Talk About It** Find three items in your classroom: one that is about 3 meters long, one that is about 3 centimeters long, and one that is about 3 millimeters long. Check by measuring each item. Sample answer: bulletin board, chalk, thickness of a dime

ADDITIONAL EXAMPLE

A high school track measures 250 meters. Luis ran 12 times around the track. How many kilometers did he run? 3 km

CHECK What You Know

As a class, have students complete Exercises 1–11 in **Check What You Know** as you observe their work.

Exercise 11 Assess student comprehension before assigning practice exercises.

BL Alternate Teaching Strategy

If students have trouble choosing an appropriate metric unit for measuring length…

Then use one of these reteach options:

1. CRM **Daily Reteach Worksheet** (p. 8)
2. Have students write lists of items that would be measured with each unit. Head the lists with the units: millimeters, centimeters, meters, and kilometers. Encourage students to add to and use their lists to identify size similarities with items requiring the identification of an appropriate metric unit for measuring.

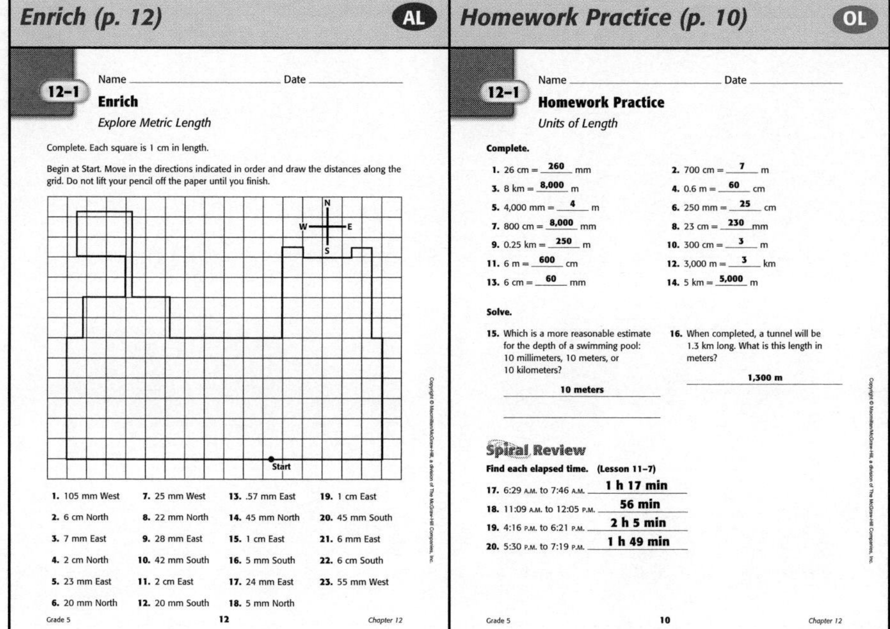

Enrich (p. 12) AL

12-1 Name ______ Date ______

Enrich

Explore Metric Length

Complete. Each square is 1 cm in length.

Begin at Start. Move in the directions indicated in order and draw the distances along the grid. Do not lift your pencil off the paper until you finish.

N W E S Start

1. 105 mm West
2. 6 cm North
3. 7 mm East
4. 2 cm North
5. 23 mm East
6. 20 mm North
7. 25 mm West
8. 22 mm North
9. 28 mm East
10. 42 mm South
11. 2 cm East
12. 20 mm South
13. .57 mm East
14. 45 mm North
15. 1 cm East
16. 5 mm South
17. 24 mm East
18. 5 mm North
19. 1 cm East
20. 45 mm South
21. 6 mm East
22. 6 cm South
23. 55 mm West

Grade 5 12 Chapter 12

Homework Practice (p. 10) OL

12-1 Name ______ Date ______

Homework Practice

Units of Length

Complete.

1. 26 cm = 260 mm
2. 700 cm = 7 m
3. 8 km = 8,000 m
4. 0.6 m = 60 cm
5. 4,000 mm = 4 m
6. 250 mm = 25 cm
7. 800 cm = 8,000 mm
8. 23 cm = 230 mm
9. 0.25 km = 250 m
10. 300 cm = 3 m
11. 6 m = 600 cm
12. 3,000 m = 3 km
13. 6 cm = 60 mm
14. 5 km = 5,000 m

Solve.

15. Which is a more reasonable estimate for the depth of a swimming pool: 10 millimeters, 10 meters, or 10 kilometers? **10 meters**
16. When completed, a tunnel will be 1.3 km long. What is this length in meters? **1,300 m**

Spiral Review

Find each elapsed time. (Lesson 11–7)

17. 6:29 A.M. to 7:46 A.M. **1 h 17 min**
18. 11:09 A.M. to 12:05 P.M. **56 min**
19. 4:16 P.M. to 6:21 P.M. **2 h 5 min**
20. 5:30 P.M. to 7:19 P.M. **1 h 49 min**

Grade 5 10 Chapter 12

COMMON ERROR!

Exercise 11 Some students will not think of length and depth as related. Develop a list of terms that represent measuring distance between two points (length, depth, height).

3 Practice

Differentiate practice using these leveled assignments for Exercises 13–40.

Level	Assignment
BL Below/ Approaching Level	12–15, 19–24, 30–31, 34
OL On Level	15–25, 31–35, 38
AL Above/Beyond Level	12–36 even, 37–40

Have students discuss and complete the Higher Order Thinking problems. As students work on Exercise 40, encourage them to convert the lengths to a common unit as a first step towards a solution.

WRITING IN ▸MATH Have students complete Exercise 41 in their Math Journals. You may choose to use this as an optional formative assessment.

COMMON ERROR!

Exercises 19–27 Students may have trouble remembering what factors to use when converting centimeters to millimeters (× 10), meters to centimeters (× 100), and kilometers to meters (× 1,000). Posting a chart with the number of millimeters in a centimeter, the number of centimeters in a meter and the number of meters in a kilometer will help students to identify and learn the conversion factors for each unit.

★ indicates multi-step problem

Practice and Problem Solving

See page R31.

Select an appropriate unit to measure each length. Write *millimeter*, *centimeter*, *meter*, or *kilometer*. See Example 1 (p. 518)

12. height of oak tree m
13. cell phone cm
14. water slide m
15. ladybug mm
16. train route km
17. book cm

Complete. See Examples 2, 3 (pp. 518–519)

18. 2 m = ■ mm 2,000
19. 73,000 m = ■ km 73
20. 3 cm = ■ mm 30
21. 170 mm = ■ cm 17
22. 15 km = ■ m 15,000
23. 8,000 mm = ■ m 8
24. 9 m = ■ cm 900
25. 300 cm = ■ m 3
26. 6 cm = ■ mm 60

★**27.** A spider is 6 millimeters long. What fractional part of 1 centimeter is 6 millimeters? $\frac{3}{5}$

28. Which is the most reasonable estimate for the length of a piano: 170 millimeters, 170 centimeters, or 170 meters? Explain.
170 cm; 170 mm is too small and 170 m is too large.

29. Two lizards are shown below. How many millimeters longer is the larger lizard than the smaller lizard? 140 mm

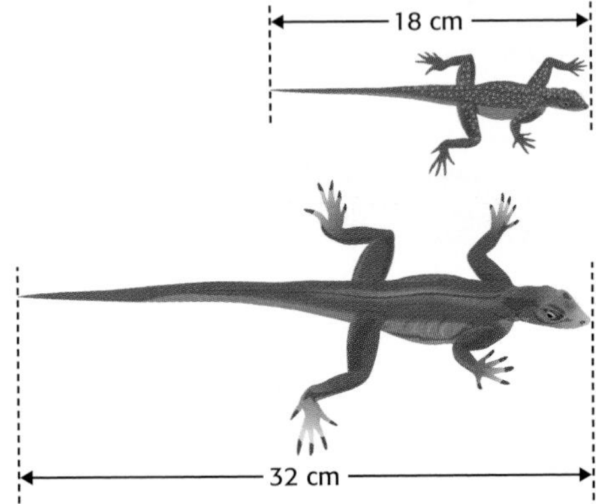

★**30.** Measure the distance across the sunflower shown. What is this measurement to the nearest centimeter? How many centimeters smaller than 1 meter is the width of the sunflower?
4 cm; 96 cm

★**31.** A hiking trail is 1 kilometer long. Ronan just passed the 250-meter marker. What fractional part of the trail does he still have to hike? $\frac{3}{4}$

★**32.** The table shows the lengths of Julian's backpack and notebook binder. How much longer is the backpack than the binder? **170 mm**

Object	Length
Backpack	60 cm
Notebook binder	430 mm

Real-World PROBLEM SOLVING

Science The largest active volcano in the world is Mauna Loa in Hawaii.

- Its crater is 180 meters deep.
- Its dome is 120 kilometers long and 50 kilometers wide.
- Its summit is 17 kilometers above its base.

33. What is the depth of the crater in centimeters? **18,000 cm**

★**34.** How many centimeters above the base is the summit? **1,700,000 cm**

★**35.** How many meters greater is the length of the dome than the width? **70,000 m**

H.O.T. Problems

36. OPEN ENDED Estimate the length of three objects in your classroom. Then measure and compare the measurements to your estimates. Tell what metric units you used. **See students' work.**

37. REASONING Explain how you decide which metric unit to use when measuring the length of an object. Provide examples to explain your reasoning. **See margin.**

38. WHICH ONE DOESN'T BELONG? Identify the measure that does not belong with the other three. Explain your reasoning. **3,500 km; The other measures are equal.**

3,500 km	35 m	350 cm	3,500 mm

39. CHALLENGE Explain how to find 30 cm + 1 m + 4,000 mm. Then solve. **Sample answer: First convert all of the same unit. 5,300 mm, 530 cm, or 53 m.**

40. WRITING IN MATH Compare and contrast converting customary units of length and converting metric units of length. Which type of conversion is easier? Explain. **See margin.**

4 Assess

Formative Assessment

Write the following on the board: 500 cm.

- **How would you convert 500 cm to meters? How many meters is 500 cm?** Divide 500 by 100; 5 meters
- **How would you convert 500 cm to millimeters?** Multiply 500 × 10.
- **How many millimeters is 500 cm?** 5,000 mm

Quick Check **Are students continuing to struggle with converting metric units of length?**

If Yes → Small Group Options (p. 517B)

If No → Independent Work Options (p. 517B)
CRM Skills Practice Worksheet (p. 9)
CRM Enrich Worksheet (p. 12)

Into the Future Tell students that mass in the metric system is measured in grams. Based on what they learned about the metric system in this lesson, have them write about how they know how many grams are in a kilogram.

Additional Answers

37. Sample answer: The size of the object determines which unit should be used. For example, to measure a small object like a pen, you would use a small unit like a centimeter. To measure a large object like a house, you would use meters. To measure great distances, you would use the largest metric unit, kilometers.

40. Sample answer: To convert customary units, you multiply or divide by different numbers. To convert metric units, you multiply or divide by powers of 10. It is often easier to convert metric units because it simply involves moving the decimal point. Also, customary units often involve fractions, so multiplying and dividing becomes more difficult.

12-2 Problem-Solving Skill
Determine Reasonable Answers

Lesson Planner

Objective

Solve problems by determining reasonable answers.

Resources

Manipulatives: measurement tools, such as, rulers and scales

Literature Connection: *Minnie's Diner* by Dayle Ann Dodds

Teacher Technology

TeacherWorks • Interactive Classroom

Real-World Problem Solving Library
Math and Science: ***How Big is the Solar System?***

Use these leveled books to reinforce and extend problem-solving skills and strategies.

Leveled for:

- OL On Level
- ELL Sheltered English
- SP Spanish

For additional support, see the Real-World Problem Solving Teacher Guide.

Daily Routine

Use these suggestions before beginning the lesson on p. 522.

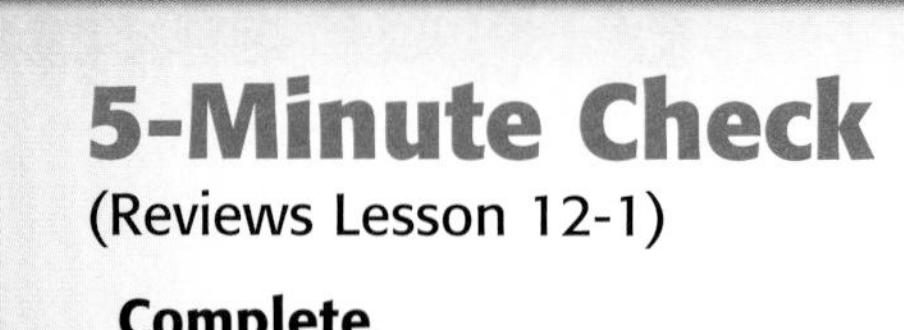

5-Minute Check

(Reviews Lesson 12-1)

Complete.

1. 5 m = ■ cm 500 cm
2. 2 km = ■ m 2,000 m
3. 30 mm = ■ cm 3 cm
4. 6,000 m = ■ km 6 km
5. 4 m = ■ mm 4,000 mm
6. 1 km = ■ cm 100,000 cm

Problem of the Day

Mrs. Keller bought $\frac{3}{4}$ pound of pecans and $\frac{5}{6}$ pound of almonds. Mrs. Perez bought twice as many almonds and the same amount of pecans. How many pounds of nuts did each woman buy? Mrs. Keller bought $1\frac{7}{12}$ lb; Mrs. Perez bought $2\frac{5}{12}$ lb.

Differentiated Instruction

Small Group Options

LOGICAL

Option 1 Below Level BL

Materials: money manipulatives

- Pass out a $10-, $5-, and $1-bill to each student.
- Pair students and ask each student to make up three word problems where a reasonable answer for each of them is either $10, $5, or $1.
- Partners exchange papers and solve. They should tape the appropriate bill next to each problem.
- Switch back to check.

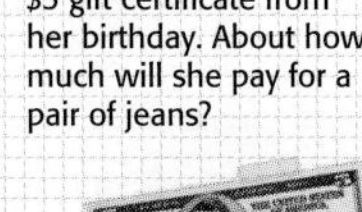

Kayla goes to a clothing sale. Normally socks are $10.95 a pair. She has a $5 gift certificate from her birthday. About how much will she pay for a pair of jeans?

LOGICAL

Option 2 English Language Learners ELL

Materials: different size containers (i.e., soda can, water bottle, gallon jug, large bucket, eye dropper)
Core Vocabulary: size, good/better/best, useful/more/most
Common Use Verb: make sense

See Math This strategy helps students understand superlatives and "reasonableness" by relating real world applications.

- Display containers. Allow students to hold and observe them.
- Ask which container they would use if they had to:
  Fill up a bathtub, feed a baby bird, water an indoor plant, get a drink of water, give a dog a bath, use with watercolors
- Discuss how you may choose more than one container for some jobs, while others are limited to one choice.

Independent Work Options

LINGUISTIC

Option 1 Early Finishers OL AL

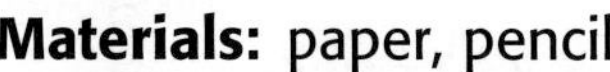

Materials: paper, pencil

- Have students write a real-world problem with an unreasonable answer on their paper. Then have them rewrite the problem with a reasonable answer.
- Have students exchange papers.
- Ask students to circle the problem they think has the reasonable answer. Have them write a solution to the problem to prove the reasonableness of the answer. Papers can then be returned to the original writers.

Option 2 Student Technology

Math Online macmillanmh.com

Personal Tutor • Extra Examples

Option 3 Learning Station: Science (p. 512H)

Direct students to the Science Learning Station for opportunities to explore and extend the lesson concept.

1 Introduce

Activity Choice 1 • Review

- Pose the following problem:

  Nakeisha has 6 more than three times as many shells in her collection than Josh has. If Nakeisha has 150 shells, how many shells does Josh have?
- **What strategy could be used to solve this problem?** *write an equation*
- **What will be represented by a variable?** the number of shells Josh has
- **What equation will solve this problem? What is the answer?** $3n + 6 = 150$; 48 shells

Activity Choice 2 • Literature

Introduce the lesson with *Minnie's Diner* by Dayle Ann Dodds. For a related math activity, see p. TR55.

2 Teach

Have students read the problem about a cord. Guide them through the problem-solving steps.

Understand Using the questions, review what students know and need to find.

Plan Have them discuss their skill.

Solve Guide students to use *determining reasonable answers* to solve the problem.

- **How does knowing 100 centimeters are in a meter help you to determine for reasonableness?** Since each cord is 3,500 cm, convert centimeters to meters to show that each cord is 35 meters long.
- **How many meters of cord are needed to reach the hedge?** 37 m
- **How many more meters are needed?** 2 m

Check Have students look back at the problem to make sure that the answer fits the facts given.

COMMON ERROR!

Exercises 5–11 Students may have trouble remembering all of the conversion factors. Encourage them to refer to the tables in earlier lessons showing the conversion factors for each type of measurement before solving.

12-2 Problem-Solving Skill

MAIN IDEA I will solve problems by determining reasonable answers.

Juanita is trimming hedges. They are 37 meters from an electrical outlet. Her extension cord is 3,500 centimeters long. Juanita estimates that the extension cord is long enough to reach the hedges. Is she correct? If not, how much longer does an extension cord need to be to reach the hedges?

Understand	**What facts do you know?** • The distance from the hedges to the electrical outlet. • The length of the extension cord in centimeters. **What do you need to find?** • Does Juanita have a long enough extension cord?
Plan	Convert 3,500 centimeters to meters. Then compare.
Solve	First, convert 3,500 centimeters to meters. 3,500 centimeters = ■ meters $3,500 \div 100 = 35$ So, 3,500 centimeters = 35 meters. Since $35 < 37$ meters, Juanita's extension cord will not be long enough to reach the hedges. To find how much longer the extension cord needs to be, subtract. $37 - 35 = 2$ So, Juanita will need an extension cord that is 2 meters or 200 centimeters longer to reach the hedges.
Check	Look back. Since $3,700 > 3,500$ and $3,700 - 3,500 = 200$. The answer is reasonable. ✓

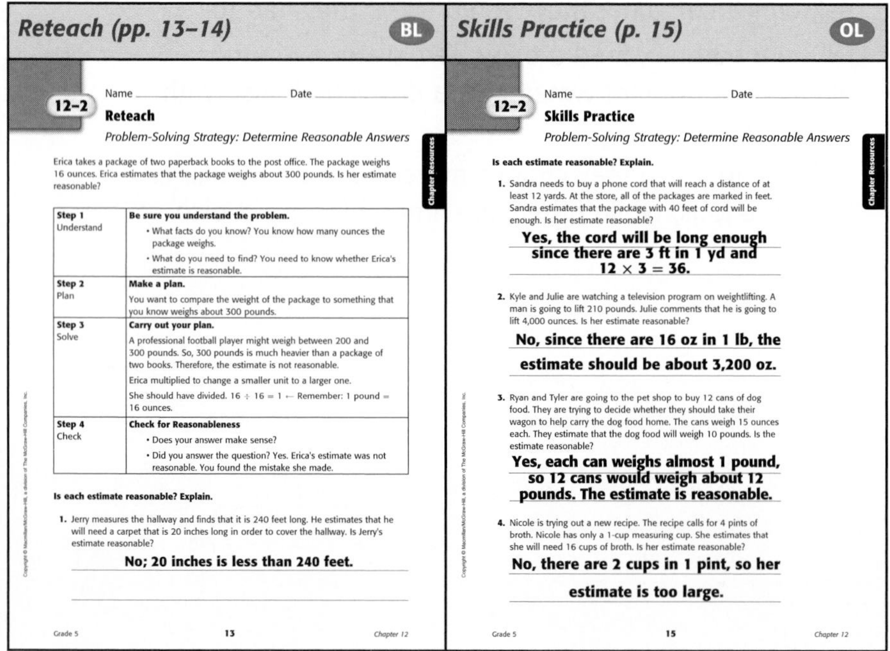

Reteach (pp. 13–14) BL

12–2 Name ______ Date ______

Reteach

Problem-Solving Strategy: Determine Reasonable Answers

Erica takes a package of two paperback books to the post office. The package weighs 16 ounces. Erica estimates that the package weighs about 300 pounds. Is her estimate reasonable?

Step 1 Understand	**Be sure you understand the problem.** • What facts do you know? You know how many ounces the package weighs. • What do you need to find? You need to know whether Erica's estimate is reasonable.
Step 2 Plan	**Make a plan.** You want to compare the weight of the package to something that you know weighs about 300 pounds.
Step 3 Solve	**Carry out your plan.** A professional football player might weigh between 200 and 300 pounds. So, 300 pounds is much heavier than a package of two books. Therefore, the estimate is not reasonable. Erica multiplied to change a smaller unit to a larger one. She should have divided. $16 \div 16 = 1$ ← Remember: 1 pound = 16 ounces.
Step 4 Check	**Check for Reasonableness** • Does your answer make sense? • Did you answer the question? Yes. Erica's estimate was not reasonable. You found the mistake she made.

Is each estimate reasonable? Explain.

1. Jerry measures the hallway and finds that it is 240 feet long. He estimates that he will need a carpet that is 20 inches long in order to cover the hallway. Is Jerry's estimate reasonable?

   No; 20 inches is less than 240 feet.

Chapter Resources

Grade 5 13 Chapter 12

Skills Practice (p. 15) OL

12–2 Name ______ Date ______

Skills Practice

Problem-Solving Strategy: Determine Reasonable Answers

Is each estimate reasonable? Explain.

1. Sandra needs to buy a phone cord that will reach a distance of at least 12 yards. At the store, all of the packages are marked in feet. Sandra estimates that the package with 40 feet of cord will be enough. Is her estimate reasonable?

   Yes, the cord will be long enough since there are 3 ft in 1 yd and $12 \times 3 = 36$.

2. Kyle and Julie are watching a television program on weightlifting. A man is going to lift 210 pounds. Julie comments that he is going to lift 4,000 ounces. Is her estimate reasonable?

   No, since there are 16 oz in 1 lb, the estimate should be about 3,200 oz.

3. Ryan and Tyler are going to the pet shop to buy 12 cans of dog food. They are trying to decide whether they should take their wagon to help carry the dog food home. The cans weigh 15 ounces each. They estimate that the dog food will weigh 10 pounds. Is the estimate reasonable?

   Yes, each can weighs almost 1 pound, so 12 cans would weigh about 12 pounds. The estimate is reasonable.

4. Nicole is trying out a new recipe. The recipe calls for 4 pints of broth. Nicole has only a 1-cup measuring cup. She estimates that she will need 16 cups of broth. Is her estimate reasonable?

   No, there are 2 cups in 1 pint, so her estimate is too large.

Chapter Resources

Grade 5 15 Chapter 12

ANALYZE the Skill

Refer to the problem on the previous page. 1, 4. See Ch. 12 Answer Appendix.

1. Would Juanita be able to reach the hedges using one extension cord that is 4,000 centimeters long? Explain.
2. Juanita wants to trim a tree that is 75 meters from the outlet. How many 3,500-centimeter extension cords will she need? 3
3. Describe another method you could use to check if an estimate is reasonable. draw a diagram
4. Explain why it is always a good idea to check if your answers are reasonable.

PRACTICE the Skill

See page R32.

Solve. Determine reasonable answers.

5. Estella needs 4 pints of vegetable broth to make soup. She has only a 1-cup measuring cup. Will Estella need 4 cups, 8 cups, or 16 cups of broth? Explain. See Ch. 12 Answer Appendix.
6. Dylan is making bookmarks. It takes him 15 minutes to make one bookmark. Dylan estimates that he can make 14 bookmarks in 3 hours. Is he correct? If not, how many bookmarks can he make in 3 hours? no; 12
7. For a small art project, Mr. Adams estimates that each student will need the amount of clay shown below. Does this seem reasonable? Explain.

No; it would more likely be 1 or 2 pounds.

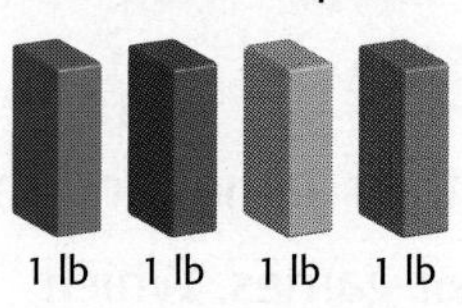

8. To make one cup of hot chocolate you need 8 ounces of water. Elsu's mother is making 12 cups of hot chocolate. Will she need 2 quarts, 3 quarts, or 4 quarts of water? Explain. See Ch. 12 Answer Appendix.
9. Ahmik buys a carpet that is 7,300 centimeters long in order to cover the hallway shown below. Is the carpet long enough to cover the hallway? If not, how much of the hallway will not be covered by the carpet? yes

10. Tonya needs to buy a cable that is at least 12 yards long. At the store, all of the cables are marked in feet. Tonya estimates that a 40-foot cable will be long enough. Is her estimate reasonable? Explain. Yes; there are 3 feet in 1 yard and $12 \times 3 = 36$. The cable is long enough.
11. Tommy estimates that his skateboard is about 90 millimeters long. Is this a reasonable estimate? Explain. See Ch. 12 Answer Appendix.
12. **WRITING IN MATH** Write a real-world problem that has an unreasonable answer. Explain why the answer is unreasonable. See Ch. 12 Answer Appendix.

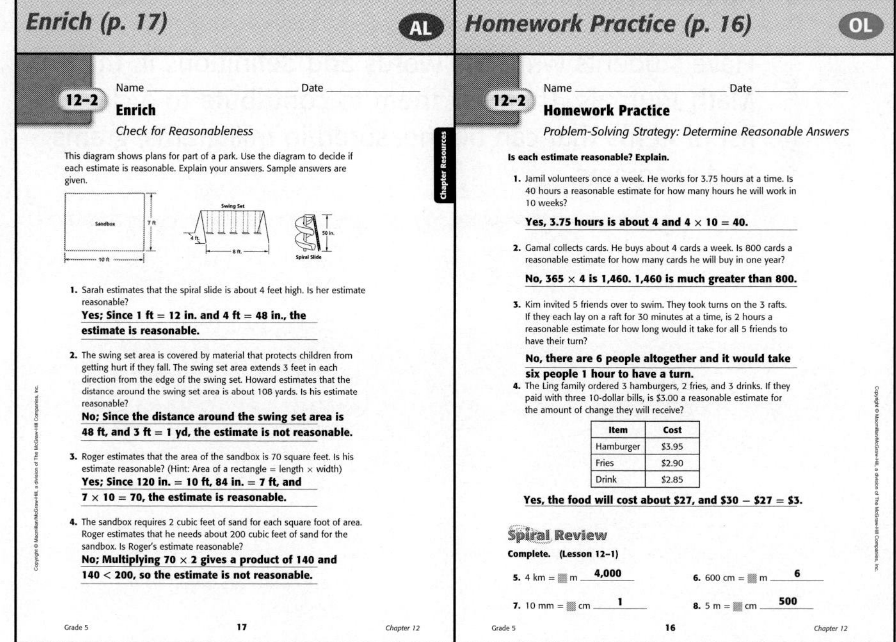

Enrich (p. 17) AL

12–2 Name ________ Date ________

Enrich

Check for Reasonableness

This diagram shows plans for part of a park. Use the diagram to decide if each estimate is reasonable. Explain your answers. Sample answers are given.

1. Sarah estimates that the spiral slide is about 4 feet high. Is her estimate reasonable?
Yes; Since 1 ft = 12 in. and 4 ft = 48 in., the estimate is reasonable.
2. The swing set area is covered by material that protects children from getting hurt if they fall. The swing set area extends 3 feet in each direction from the edge of the swing set. Howard estimates that the distance around the swing set area is about 108 yards. Is his estimate reasonable?
No; Since the distance around the swing set area is 48 ft, and 3 ft = 1 yd, the estimate is not reasonable.
3. Roger estimates that the area of the sandbox is 70 square feet. Is his estimate reasonable? (Hint: Area of a rectangle = length × width)
Yes; Since 120 in. = 10 ft, 84 in. = 7 ft, and $7 \times 10 = 70$, the estimate is reasonable.
4. The sandbox requires 2 cubic feet of sand for each square foot of area. Roger estimates that he needs about 200 cubic feet of sand for the sandbox. Is Roger's estimate reasonable?
No; Multiplying 70×2 gives a product of 140 and $140 < 200$, so the estimate is not reasonable.

Grade 5 17 Chapter 12

Chapter Resources

Homework Practice (p. 16) OL

12–2 Name ________ Date ________

Homework Practice

Problem-Solving Strategy: Determine Reasonable Answers

Is each estimate reasonable? Explain.

1. Jamil volunteers once a week. He works for 3.75 hours at a time. Is 40 hours a reasonable estimate for how many hours he will work in 10 weeks?
Yes, 3.75 hours is about 4 and $4 \times 10 = 40$.
2. Gamal collects cards. He buys about 4 cards a week. Is 800 cards a reasonable estimate for how many cards he will buy in one year?
No, 365×4 is 1,460. 1,460 is much greater than 800.
3. Kim invited 5 friends over to swim. They took turns on the 3 rafts. If they each lay on a raft for 30 minutes at a time, is 2 hours a reasonable estimate for how long would it take for all 5 friends to have their turn?
No, there are 6 people altogether and it would take six people 1 hour to have a turn.
4. The Ling family ordered 3 hamburgers, 2 fries, and 3 drinks. If they paid with three 10-dollar bills, is $3.00 a reasonable estimate for the amount of change they will receive?

Item	Cost
Hamburger	$3.95
Fries	$2.90
Drink	$2.85

Yes, the food will cost about $27, and $30 − $27 = $3.

Spiral Review

Complete. (Lesson 12–1)

5. 4 km = ▒ m **4,000**
6. 600 cm = ▒ m **6**
7. 10 mm = ▒ cm **1**
8. 5 m = ▒ cm **500**

Grade 5 16 Chapter 12

Analyze the Strategy Use Exercises 1–4 to analyze and discuss the problem-solving strategy.

BL Alternate Teaching Strategy

If students have trouble solving problems by determining reasonableness…

Then use one of these reteach options:

1 CRM **Daily Reteach Worksheet** (pp. 13–14)

2 Have students refer to and use measurement tools such as rulers, scales and containers to demonstrate volume as they check for reasonableness. Encourage students to identify the conversion factors as they use the physical tools.

3 Practice

Using the Exercises

Exercise 7 requires students to know that 4 lb of clay is a fairly large amount for a small project.

4 Assess

Formative Assessment

Pose the following problem:

Mr. Johnson will rope off an area for the annual school fair. The distance around the fair is 500 meters. Mr. Johnson has 2 km of rope. He estimates that he has enough rope to go around the area 3 times. Is his estimate reasonable?

- **How could you find out how many meters of rope is needed to surround the area three times?** Multiply 500 m × 3 = 1,500 m.
- **How much rope does he have?** 2 km or 2,000 m
- **Is his estimate reasonable? Explain.** Yes; 2,000 m > 1,500 m

Quick Check **Are students continuing to struggle with determining reasonableness?**

If Yes → Small Group Options (p. 522B)
Strategic Intervention Guide (p. 130)

If No → Independent Work Options (p. 522B)
CRM Skills Practice Worksheet (p. 15)
CRM Enrich Worksheet (p. 17)

LESSON

12-3 Units of Mass

Lesson Planner

Objective

Convert metric units of mass.

Vocabulary

mass, gram, milligram, kilogram

Resources

Materials: kilogram scale
Manipulatives: pan balance
Literature Connection: *Measure with Metric* by Franklyn Mansfield Branley
Teacher Technology
TeacherWorks • Interactive Classroom • Concepts in Motion

Focus on Math Background

Units of mass in the metric system are based on the gram. One gram is approximately the mass of a paper clip. As with all measured quantities, mass is always expressed by a numerical value and a unit of measure. People are often confused between the mass and weight of an object. The mass of an object refers to the quantity of matter contained in the object, while the weight of an object is equal to the force that the Earth's gravity exerts on it. Hence, an object's mass is constant everywhere, while its weight can vary depending on its location in relation to the center of the Earth. The standard SI unit *kilogram* is a measure of mass while the U.S. unit *pound* is a measure of weight. For situations that are restricted to the Earth's surface, a mass of 1 kilogram has a weight of about 2.2 pounds.

Daily Routine

Use these suggestions before beginning the lesson on p. 524.

5-Minute Check

(Reviews Lesson 12-2)

Solve. Determine if the answer is reasonable.
Consuela can swim 100 yards in 3 minutes. At that rate, she estimated that she could swim 1 mile in 20 minutes. Is her estimate reasonable? Why or why not? No; 1 mile equals 1,760 yards. 1,760 $\div$ 100 yds $=$ 17.60 one hundred yard lengths. Since each length takes 3 minutes to swim, the total time would be 17.60 $\times$ 3 min $=$ about 53 minutes.

Problem of the Day

The girls' soccer team won $\frac{2}{3}$ of their games and the boys' soccer team won $\frac{3}{4}$ of their games. Which team won more of their games? boys' team

Building Math Vocabulary

Write the lesson vocabulary words and their definitions on the board.

Have students write the words and definitions in their Math Journals. Then ask them to contribute to a class list of items that can be measured in milligrams, grams, and kilograms.

Differentiated Instruction

Small Group Options

Option 1 SPATIAL, LOGICAL

Below Level BL

Materials: balance, scale, paper clips, quarters, dimes

Have students work in pairs to extend the Activity Choice 1 with several other items.

- **How many paper clips are needed to balance a quarter?**
- **What is the mass of a quarter?**
- **How many paper clips are needed to balance a dime?**
- **What is the mass of a dime?**
- Use the information you discovered about the mass of a quarter and a dime.
- **About how many dimes would balance a quarter?**
- **How could you check your estimate?**
- Have pairs compare their findings and discuss any differences they discover.

Option 2 AUDITORY, LINGUISTIC

English Language Learners ELL

Core Vocabulary: matter (scientific meaning), between, do/don't care

Common Use Verb: does/doesn't matter

Hear Math This strategy helps students distinguish between the everyday and scientific/mathematic meanings of matter.

- Say: "In math and science, matter is something that you can see or touch," (books, people, water, clouds).
- Give examples of things that aren't matter (sounds, feelings, smells).
- Write on the board and say *"I **don't care** what I eat for lunch. It **doesn't matter** what I eat for lunch."*
- Say: "These sentences mean the same thing. What does ***matter*** mean now?"
- Have students use "matter" in sentences that show they understand the two meanings.

Independent Work Options

Option 1 INTRAPERSONAL

Early Finishers AL

Materials: a variety of food packages, pencils, paper

- Ask students to make a table with the following headings: Food Product, Mass in Kilograms, Mass in Grams, Mass in Milligrams.
- Have students write the food product and the metric mass as labeled on the product in the correct column.
- Students can then convert the units given to the two units in their table that are not used on the label.

Food Product	Mass in Kilograms	Mass in Grams	Mass in Milligrams
almonds	0.311 kg	311 g	311,000 mg

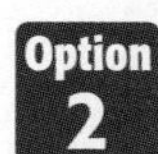

Option 2

Student Technology

Math Online macmillanmh.com

Personal Tutor • Extra Examples

Option 3

Learning Station: Reading (p. 512G)

Direct students to the Reading Learning Station for opportunities to explore and extend the lesson concept.

Option 4

Problem-Solving Practice

Reinforce problem-solving skills and strategies with the Problem-Solving Practice worksheet.

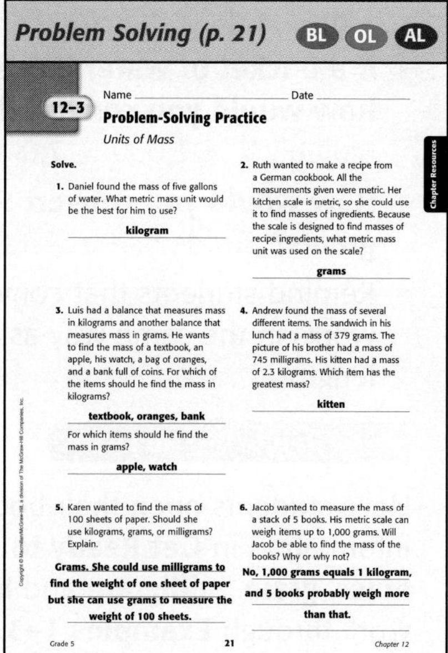

Problem Solving (p. 21) BL OL AL

12–3 Name ________ Date ________

Problem-Solving Practice

Units of Mass

Chapter Resources

Solve.

1. Daniel found the mass of five gallons of water. What metric mass unit would be the best for him to use?

   kilogram

2. Ruth wanted to make a recipe from a German cookbook. All the measurements given were metric. Her kitchen scale is metric, so she could use it to find masses of ingredients. Because the scale is designed to find masses of recipe ingredients, what metric mass unit was used on the scale?

   grams

3. Luis had a balance that measures mass in kilograms and another balance that measures mass in grams. He wants to find the mass of a textbook, an apple, his watch, a bag of oranges, and a bank full of coins. For which of the items should he find the mass in kilograms?

   textbook, oranges, bank

   For which items should he find the mass in grams?

   apple, watch

4. Andrew found the mass of several different items. The sandwich in his lunch had a mass of 379 grams. The picture of his brother had a mass of 745 milligrams. His kitten had a mass of 2.3 kilograms. Which item has the greatest mass?

   kitten

5. Karen wanted to find the mass of 100 sheets of paper. Should she use kilograms, grams, or milligrams? Explain.

   Grams. She could use milligrams to find the weight of one sheet of paper but she can use grams to measure the weight of 100 sheets.

6. Jacob wanted to measure the mass of a stack of 5 books. His metric scale can weigh items up to 1,000 grams. Will Jacob be able to find the mass of the books? Why or why not?

   No, 1,000 grams equals 1 kilogram, and 5 books probably weigh more than that.

Grade 5 21 Chapter 12

12-3 Units of Mass

1 Introduce

Activity Choice 1 • Hands-On 

- Have students choose items from around the classroom to be weighed on the pan balance or the kilogram scale. **Which items weigh about 1 gram? 10 grams? 1 kilogram? 10 kilograms?** Answers will vary.
- Review the words meter, millimeter and kilometer. **Based on what you know about measurement of length in the metric system, how many grams are in a kilogram? Explain.** 1,000 grams; kilo means 1,000 and the base unit is grams.
- **Based on what you know about the metric system, what is the mass of milligram in comparison to a gram?** 0.001 of a gram
- Explain that the metric system is used extensively in science and that finding the mass in milligrams allows for very accurate measurement of very small things.

Activity Choice 2 • Literature

Introduce the lesson with *Measure with Metric* by Franklyn Mansfield Branley. For a related math activity, see p. TR56.

2 Teach

Scaffolding Questions

Write the following on the board: a person, 1 piece of candy, a grain of sand.

- **Which item could have a mass of 5 g?** candy
- **Which item could have a mass of 45 kg? 1 mg?** a person; a grain of sand
- **If a bucket of water has a mass of 7 kg, how would you convert that to grams?** Multiply $7 \times 1{,}000 = 7{,}000$.
- **How would you convert 5,000 milligrams to grams?** Divide $5{,}000 \div 1{,}000 = 5$.
- Remind students that converting units of mass works in the same way as converting units of length.

GET READY to Learn

Have students open their books and read the information in **Get Ready to Learn**. Introduce **mass, gram, milligram** and **kilogram**. As a class, work through **Examples 1–3**.

12-3 Units of Mass

MAIN IDEA

I will convert metric units of mass.

New Vocabulary

mass
gram
milligram
kilogram

Math Online

macmillanmh.com

- Extra Examples
- Personal Tutor
- Self-Check Quiz

GET READY to Learn

The goliath beetle is the heaviest insect in the world. At 100 grams, it has about the same *mass* as a can of sardines.

Mass is a measure of the amount of matter in an object. Metric units of mass are milligram, gram, and kilogram.

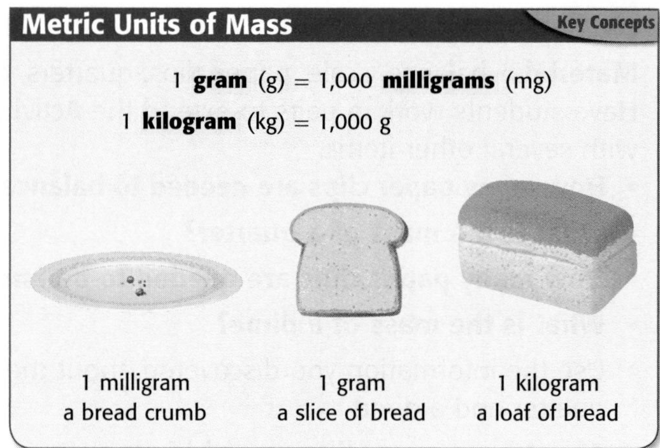

Metric Units of Mass — Key Concepts

1 **gram** (g) = 1,000 **milligrams** (mg)

1 **kilogram** (kg) = 1,000 g

1 milligram
a bread crumb

1 gram
a slice of bread

1 kilogram
a loaf of bread

Convert Larger Units to Smaller Units

1 **SCIENCE In 1876, pieces of a meteorite were found in Tennessee. The largest single piece of meteorite had a mass of 136 kilograms. What was the mass of this piece in grams?**

136 kg = ■ g — A kilogram is a larger unit than a gram.

$136 \times 1{,}000 = 136{,}000$ — 1 kg = 1,000 g, so multiply 136 by 1,000.

So, 136 kg = 136,000 g.

The mass of the meteorite was 136,000 grams.

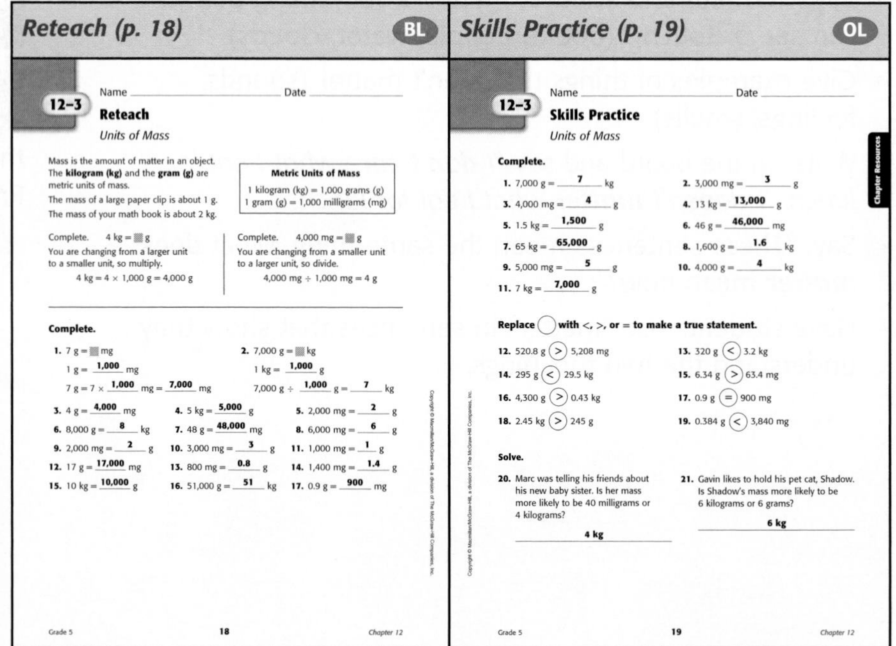

Reteach (p. 18) BL

12-3 Name ______ Date ______

Reteach

Units of Mass

Mass is the amount of matter in an object. The **kilogram (kg)** and the **gram (g)** are metric units of mass.

The mass of a large paper clip is about 1 g.

The mass of your math book is about 2 kg.

Metric Units of Mass

1 kilogram (kg) = 1,000 grams (g)
1 gram (g) = 1,000 milligrams (mg)

Complete. 4 kg = ■ g
You are changing from a larger unit to a smaller unit, so multiply.
$4\text{ kg} = 4 \times 1{,}000\text{ g} = 4{,}000\text{ g}$

Complete. 4,000 mg = ■ g
You are changing from a smaller unit to a larger unit, so divide.
$4{,}000\text{ mg} \div 1{,}000\text{ mg} = 4\text{ g}$

Complete.

1. 7 g = ■ mg
   1 g = **1,000** mg
   7 g = 7 × **1,000** mg = **7,000** mg
2. 7,000 g = ■ kg
   1 kg = **1,000** g
   7,000 g ÷ **1,000** g = **7** kg
3. 4 g = **4,000** mg
4. 5 kg = **5,000** g
5. 2,000 mg = **2** g
6. 8,000 g = **8** kg
7. 48 g = **48,000** mg
8. 6,000 mg = **6** g
9. 2,000 mg = **2** g
10. 3,000 mg = **3** g
11. 1,000 mg = **1** g
12. 17 g = **17,000** mg
13. 800 mg = **0.8** g
14. 1,400 mg = **1.4** g
15. 10 kg = **10,000** g
16. 51,000 g = **51** kg
17. 0.9 g = **900** mg

Grade 5 18 Chapter 12

Skills Practice (p. 19) OL

12-3 Name ______ Date ______

Skills Practice

Units of Mass

Chapter Resources

Complete.

1. 7,000 g = **7** kg
2. 3,000 mg = **3** g
3. 4,000 mg = **4** g
4. 13 kg = **13,000** g
5. 1.5 kg = **1,500** g
6. 46 g = **46,000** mg
7. 65 kg = **65,000** g
8. 1,600 g = **1.6** kg
9. 5,000 mg = **5** g
10. 4,000 g = **4** kg
11. 7 kg = **7,000** g

Replace ◯ with $<$, $>$, or $=$ to make a true statement.

12. 520.8 g $(>)$ 5,208 mg
13. 320 g $(<)$ 3.2 kg
14. 295 g $(<)$ 29.5 kg
15. 6.34 g $(>)$ 63.4 mg
16. 4,300 g $(>)$ 0.43 kg
17. 0.9 g $(=)$ 900 mg
18. 2.45 kg $(>)$ 245 g
19. 0.384 g $(<)$ 3,840 mg

Solve.

20. Marc was telling his friends about his new baby sister. Is her mass more likely to be 40 milligrams or 4 kilograms? **4 kg**
21. Gavin likes to hold his pet cat, Shadow. Is Shadow's mass more likely to be 6 kilograms or 6 grams? **6 kg**

Grade 5 19 Chapter 12

Real-World EXAMPLE — Convert Smaller Units to Larger Units

Remember

Mass and weight are different measures. If you were flying in the space shuttle, you would have the same mass as on Earth, but a different weight.

2 FOOD Mr. Benavides bakes muffins that have a mass of about 2,000 milligrams. What is the mass in grams?

2,000 mg = ■ g — A milligram is smaller than a gram.

2,000 ÷ 1,000 = 2 — 1,000 mg = 1 g, so divide 2,000 by 1,000.

So, 2,000 mg = 2 g.

Each muffin has a mass of 2 grams.

Real-World EXAMPLE — Compare Mass

3 MAIL Luke is shipping a box that has a mass of 4,300 grams. If the mass of the box is greater than 5 kilograms, shipping will cost extra. Will shipping cost extra? Explain.

5 kg = ■ g — Convert a larger unit to a smaller unit.

5 × 1,000 = 5,000 — 1 kg = 1,000 g, so multiply 5 by 1,000.

So, 5 kg = 5,000 g.

The mass of the box is 4.3 kilograms. Since 4,300 grams $<$ 5,000 grams, shipping will not cost extra.

CHECK What You Know

Complete. See Examples 1, 2 (pp. 524–525)

1. 5,000 mg = ■ g 5
2. 9 g = ■ mg 9,000
3. 230 mg = ■ g 0.23
4. 8,000 g = ■ mg 8000
5. 4 kg = ■ g 4,000
6. 5,000 g = ■ kg 5

Replace ● with $<$, $>$, or = to make a true statement. See Example 3 (p. 525)

7. 2,300 mg ● 2 g $>$
8. 3 kg ● 3,000 g =
9. 75 g ● 800 mg $>$
10. One highlighter has a mass of 11 grams. Another highlighter has a mass of 108 milligrams. Which highlighter has the greater mass? 11 g

11. Talk About It — Which is a more reasonable estimate for the mass of a baseball: 140 milligrams, 140 grams, or 140 kilograms? Explain. See margin.

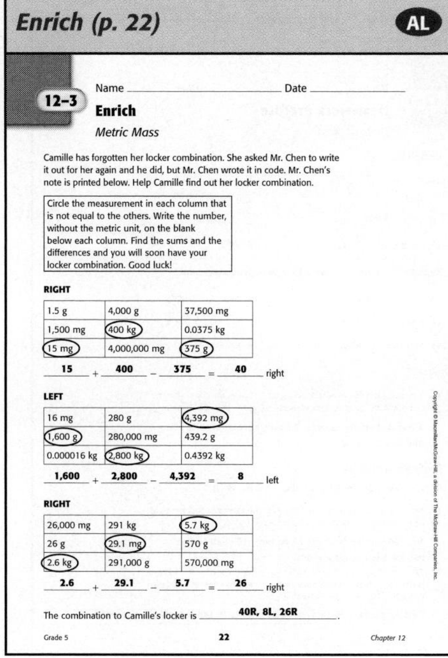

Enrich (p. 22) AL

12–3 Name ______ Date ______

Enrich

Metric Mass

Camille has forgotten her locker combination. She asked Mr. Chen to write it out for her again and he did, but Mr. Chen wrote it in code. Mr. Chen's note is printed below. Help Camille find out her locker combination.

Circle the measurement in each column that is not equal to the others. Write the number, without the metric unit, on the blank below each column. Find the sums and the differences and you will soon have your locker combination. Good luck!

RIGHT

1.5 g	4,000 g	37,500 mg
1,500 mg	(400 kg)	0.0375 kg
(15 mg)	4,000,000 mg	(375 g)

15 + 400 − 375 = 40 right

LEFT

16 mg	280 g	(4,392 mg)
(1,600 g)	280,000 mg	439.2 g
0.000016 kg	(2,800 kg)	0.4392 kg

1,600 + 2,800 − 4,392 = 8 left

RIGHT

26,000 mg	291 kg	(5.7 kg)
26 g	(29.1 mg)	570 g
(2.6 kg)	291,000 g	570,000 mg

2.6 + 29.1 − 5.7 = 26 right

The combination to Camille's locker is 40R, 8L, 26R.

Grade 5 22 Chapter 12

11. To convert kilograms to grams, multiply by 1,000 because a larger unit is being converted to a smaller unit. To convert milligrams to grams, divide by 1,000 because a smaller unit is being converted to a larger unit.

Compare Masses

Example 3 Be sure students understand that only one unit can be used to express mass. Decimals are used to show mass that is between two whole units.

ADDITIONAL EXAMPLES

1. Hamsters have a mass of about 45 grams. What is the mass in milligrams? 45,000 mg
2. Jill's dog has a mass of 9,500 grams. What is its mass in kilograms? 9.5 kg
3. Raina put birdseed in two feeders. At the end of three days, Feeder A had 56 grams of seeds in it and Feeder B had 46,350 milligrams of seed in it. Which feeder had more seed in it? Explain. Feeder A; 56 g = 56,000 mg and 56,000 mg $>$ 46,350 mg.

CHECK What You Know

As a class, have students complete Exercises 1–11 in **Check What You Know** as you observe their work.

Exercise 11 Assess student comprehension before assigning practice exercises.

BL Alternate Teaching Strategy

If students have trouble converting metric units of mass…

Then use one of these reteach options:

1. CRM **Daily Reteach Worksheet** (p. 18)
2. Have students make a table with the headings "Kilograms: g ÷ 1,000", "Grams", and "Milligrams: g × 1,000". Students can then weigh several objects using the pan balance and record the mass of each in the "Grams" column. Ask students to complete their table by dividing the number of grams by 1,000 to find kilograms and multiplying the number of grams by 1,000 to find milligrams.

COMMON ERROR!

Exercises 7–9 Students may have trouble comparing the two amounts because they will compare only the numbers. Remind them to convert the amounts to the same unit in order to find the greater or lesser quantity.

3 Practice

Differentiate practice using these leveled assignments for Exercises 12–30.

Level	Assignment
BL Below/ Approaching Level	12–14, 18–20, 27–28
OL On Level	13–17, 19–28, 29
AL Above/Beyond Level	13–27 odd, 28–30

Have students discuss and complete the Higher Order Thinking problems. As students estimate in Exercise 28, encourage them to refer to the mass in grams of items they have weighed to use as a benchmark for their estimate.

WRITING IN ▶MATH Have students complete Exercise 30 in their Math Journals. You may choose to use this as an optional formative assessment.

4 Assess

Formative Assessment

Write the following on the board: 4 kilograms.

- **What would be an example of an item that has a mass of about 4 kilograms?** Answers will vary. Possible answer: a cat, a small puppy
- **How would you convert 4 kilograms to grams?** Multiply $4 \times 1{,}000 = 4{,}000$.
  How would you convert 4,000 milligrams to grams? $4{,}000 \div 1{,}000 = 4$

Quick Check **Are students continuing to struggle with converting metric units of mass?**

If Yes → Small Group Options (p. 524B)

If No → Independent Work Options (p. 524B)
CRM Skills Practice Worksheet (p. 19)
CRM Enrich Worksheet (p. 22)

Yesterday's News Have students write a paragraph about how the concepts in Lesson 12-1 about measuring length using the metric system helped them with the concepts in this lesson.

★ indicates multi-step problem

Practice and Problem Solving

See page R32.

Complete. See Examples 1, 2 (pp. 524–525)

12. 2 g = ■ mg 2,000 **13.** 6 kg = ■ g 6,000 **14.** 3,000 g = ■ kg 3

15. 1,000 mg = ■ g 1 **16.** 4,000 g = ■ kg 4 **17.** 7 g = ■ mg 7,000

Replace ● with $<$, $>$, or $=$ to make a true statement. See Example 3 (p. 525)

18. 1.9 kg ● 1,900 g $=$ **19.** 3,500 mg ● 0.35 g $>$ **20.** 814 g ● 8.14 kg $<$

21. 0.7 g ● 700 mg $=$ **22.** 690 g ● 6,900 mg $>$ **23.** 2.2 g ● 22,000 mg $<$

For Exercises 24–26, use the table at the right.

Macaws	
Species	**Mass (grams)**
Blue and Gold	800
Green-winged	900
Red-footed	525
Yellow-collared	250

24. Which macaw has a mass closest to 1 kilogram? Green-winged

25. How many yellow-colored macaws would have a combined mass of 1 kilogram? 4

★**26.** Is the combined mass of two red-footed macaws and three blue and gold macaws closer to 3 kilograms or 4 kilograms? Explain. See Ch. 12 Answer Appendix.

★**27.** One computer has a mass of 0.8 kilogram and another has a mass of 800 grams. Compare the masses of the computers. The computers have the same mass.

H.O.T. Problems

28. OPEN ENDED Estimate how many paper clips have a mass of 10 grams. Then use a balance to check your estimate. See students' work.

29. FIND THE ERROR Terrez and Ella are converting 3,000 grams to kilograms. Who is correct? Explain. See Ch. 12 Answer Appendix.

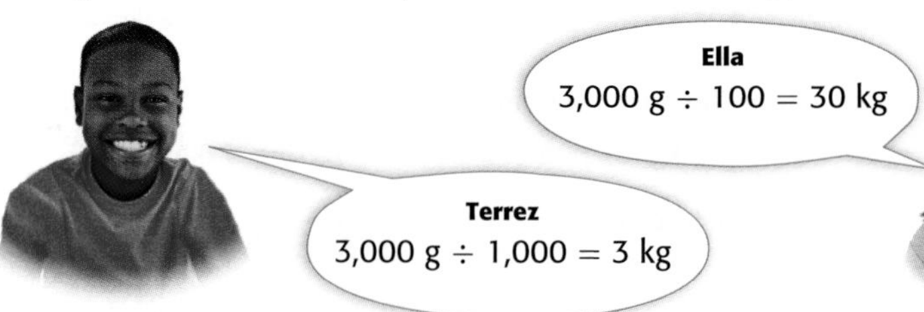

30. **WRITING IN ▶MATH** Explain which units of mass you would use to measure the following: a grain of salt, a bowl of cereal, a football player, and a tube of toothpaste. See Ch. 12 Answer Appendix.

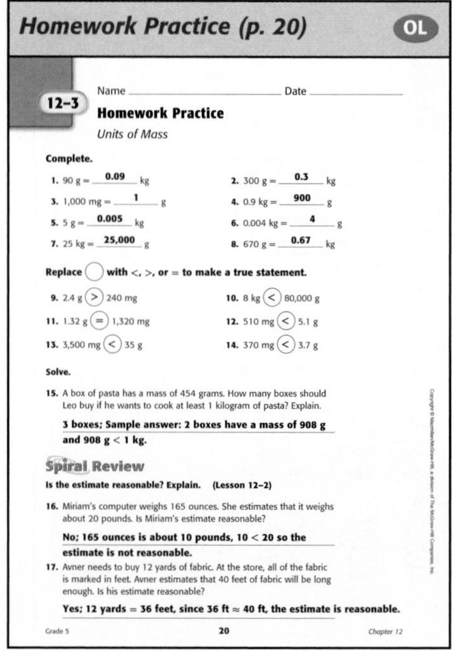

Homework Practice (p. 20) OL

12-3 Name ______ Date ______

Homework Practice

Units of Mass

Complete.

1. 90 g = **0.09** kg
2. 300 g = **0.3** kg
3. 1,000 mg = **1** g
4. 0.9 kg = **900** g
5. 5 g = **0.005** kg
6. 0.004 kg = **4** g
7. 25 kg = **25,000** g
8. 670 g = **0.67** kg

Replace ◯ with $<$, $>$, or $=$ to make a true statement.

9. 2.4 g $>$ 240 mg
10. 8 kg $<$ 80,000 g
11. 1.32 g $=$ 1,320 mg
12. 510 mg $<$ 5.1 g
13. 3,500 mg $<$ 35 g
14. 370 mg $<$ 3.7 g

Solve.

15. A box of pasta has a mass of 454 grams. How many boxes should Leo buy if he wants to cook at least 1 kilogram of pasta? Explain.
3 boxes; Sample answer: 2 boxes have a mass of 908 g and 908 g $<$ 1 kg.

Spiral Review

Is the estimate reasonable? Explain. (Lesson 12–2)

16. Miriam's computer weighs 165 ounces. She estimates that it weighs about 20 pounds. Is Miriam's estimate reasonable?
No; 165 ounces is about 10 pounds, 10 $<$ 20 so the estimate is not reasonable.

17. Avner needs to buy 12 yards of fabric. At the store, all of the fabric is marked in feet. Avner estimates that 40 feet of fabric will be long enough. Is his estimate reasonable?
Yes; 12 yards = 36 feet, since 36 ft $\approx$ 40 ft, the estimate is reasonable.

Grade 5 20 Chapter 12

LESSON 12-4

Units of Capacity

Lesson Planner

Objective

Convert metric units of capacity

Vocabulary

liter, milliliter

Resources

Materials: bottles of varying sizes with labels showing liters and milliliters

Literature Connection: *Millions to Measure* by David M. Schwartz

Teacher Technology

TeacherWorks • Interactive Classroom

Focus on Math Background

The liter takes a starring role in this lesson—it is the basic unit of volume (capacity). One liter is slightly larger than a quart. The two most commonly used units of capacity are the liter and the milliliter. It takes 1,000 milliliters to equal a liter. Capacity is always expressed by a numerical value **and** a unit of measure.

Metric units for length and volume (capacity) are connected by the fact that one cubic centimeter is exactly equal in size to one milliliter. Furthermore, one gram of water occupies exactly one cubic centimeter (or one milliliter) of volume under normal conditions. This fact is based on the original definition of the kilogram as the mass of a liter of water, as established when the metric system was invented in 1793. The metric system became the core of the *Systeme Internationale* when it was agreed upon by most of the world's nations in 1960.

Daily Routine

Use these suggestions before beginning the lesson on p. 527.

5-Minute Check

(Reviews Lesson 12-3)

Replace ● with <, >, or = to make a true statement.

1. 450 mg ● 45 g <
2. 3 kg ● 3,000 g =
3. 750,000 g ● 75 kg >
4. 32 g ● 3,200 mg =
5. 36.5 g ● 30,605 mg >
6. 290 mg ● 2.9 g <

Problem of the Day

Iman Blue, Amy Black, and Federico Green are wearing sweaters that are blue, black, and green. The sweaters do not match the wearers' names. Federico is not wearing a blue sweater. Who is wearing which sweater? Iman: green, Amy: blue, Federico: black

Building Math Vocabulary

Write the lesson vocabulary words and their definitions on the board.

Have students write the words and their definitions in their Math Journals. Ask students to share sentences that compare liters with milliliters, grams with milligrams, and meters with millimeters. Then have them write that the meaning of the word beginning *milli-* means 0.001.

Differentiated Instruction

Small Group Options

SPATIAL, VISUAL

Option 1 Below Level BL

Materials: various sized bottles with liter or mL, labels including an exact 1 liter or 2 liter bottle, eyedropper

- Remind students that an eyedropper contains about one mL and that it takes 1,000 mLs to make one liter.
- Read the capacity labels and discuss the size in relation to each. Find one that is half of a liter.
- **How many mL are in a half L?** 500 mL
- **How many of these bottles hold less than 500 mL? more than 500 mL? more than 1 liter?**
- **Why do these bottle hold so many different amounts of liquid that are not a half liter or 1 whole liter?** Accept any reasonable answer.

VISUAL, SPATIAL

Option 2 English Language Learners ELL

Materials: sandwich-size plastic bag with popcorn kernels, same size bag full of popped popcorn, small box (like a juice box)
Core Vocabulary: smaller, popped, kernels
Common Use Verb: fill up

See Math

- Show students materials. Say: "Both of these are popcorn. How are they different?" (One has been popped, the other hasn't.)
- Ask: "Which bag has more?" kernels "Why?" smaller
- Say: "So if something is **smaller**, I need more of them to **fill** something **up**."
- Show box. Say: "Make a prediction of how many **kernels** I will need to **fill up** this box. How many popped popcorns?" Write predictions on board. Fill up with popped popcorn first. Write answer. Then take turns counting the kernels discussing how many more or less you will need.

Independent Work Options

LOGICAL

Option 1 Early Finishers AL

Materials: bottles of products with liter or mL labels

- Have students make a table with the following headings: Product, Milliliters, Liters.
- Have students list the product name and metric capacity in the appropriate columns.
- Ask students to complete by converting the units from liters to milliliters or milliliters to liters.

Option 2 Student Technology

Math Online macmillanmh.com

Personal Tutor • Extra Examples

Math Adventures

Option 3 Learning Station: Health (p. 512H)

Direct students to the Health Learning Station for opportunities to explore and extend the lesson concept.

Option 4 Problem-Solving Practice

Reinforce problem-solving skills and strategies with the Problem-Solving Practice worksheet.

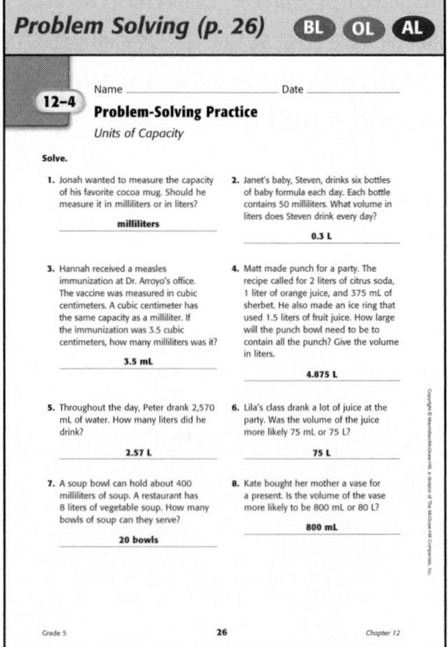

Problem Solving (p. 26) BL OL AL

12–4 Name ______ Date ______

Problem-Solving Practice

Units of Capacity

Solve.

1. Jonah wanted to measure the capacity of his favorite cocoa mug. Should he measure it in milliliters or in liters? **milliliters**
2. Janet's baby, Steven, drinks six bottles of baby formula each day. Each bottle contains 50 milliliters. What volume in liters does Steven drink every day? **0.3 L**
3. Hannah received a measles immunization at Dr. Arroyo's office. The vaccine was measured in cubic centimeters. A cubic centimeter has the same capacity as a milliliter. If the immunization was 3.5 cubic centimeters, how many milliliters was it? **3.5 mL**
4. Matt made punch for a party. The recipe called for 2 liters of citrus soda, 1 liter of orange juice, and 375 mL of sherbet. He also made an ice ring that used 1.5 liters of fruit juice. How large will the punch bowl need to be to contain all the punch? Give the volume in liters. **4.875 L**
5. Throughout the day, Peter drank 2,570 mL of water. How many liters did he drink? **2.57 L**
6. Lila's class drank a lot of juice at the party. Was the volume of the juice more likely 75 mL or 75 L? **75 L**
7. A soup bowl can hold about 400 milliliters of soup. A restaurant has 8 liters of vegetable soup. How many bowls of soup can they serve? **20 bowls**
8. Kate bought her mother a vase for a present. Is the volume of the vase more likely to be 800 mL or 80 L? **800 mL**

Grade 5 26 Chapter 12

12-4 Units of Capacity

MAIN IDEA

I will convert metric units of capacity.

New Vocabulary

liter

milliliter

Math Online

macmillanmh.com

- Extra Examples
- Personal Tutor
- Self-Check Quiz

GET READY to Learn

The pitcher of orange juice at the right holds 1 liter. This is a little more than a quart.

In the metric system, the common units of capacity are liter and milliliter.

Metric Units of Capacity

Key Concept

1 **liter** (L) = 1,000 **milliliters** (mL)

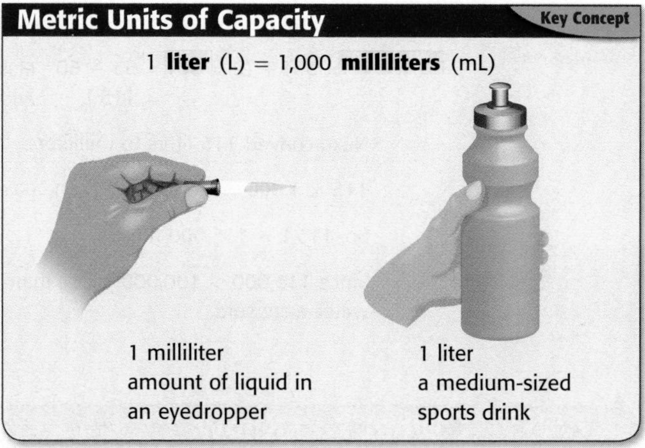

1 milliliter
amount of liquid in
an eyedropper

1 liter
a medium-sized
sports drink

Convert units of capacity just as you convert units of length.

Real-World EXAMPLE **Convert Larger Units to Smaller Units**

1 **WATER A faucet that is constantly dripping wastes about 90 liters of water every week. How many milliliters of water is this?**

90 L = ■ mL	A liter is larger than a milliliter, so multiply.
90 × 1,000 = 90,000	1 L = 1,000 mL, so multiply 90 by 1,000.
90 L = 90,000 mL	So, 90,000 milliliters of water are wasted.

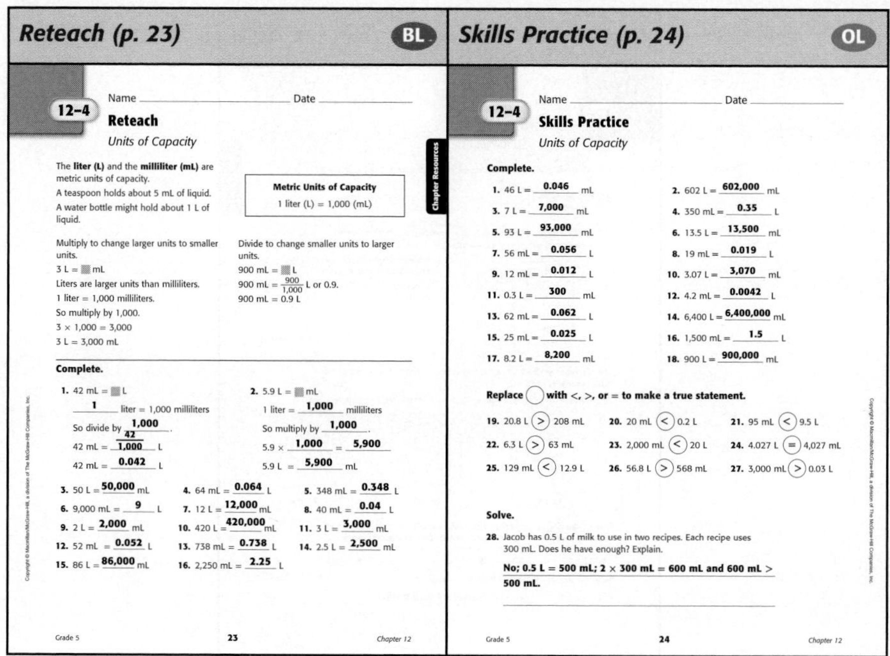

Reteach (p. 23) BL

12-4 Name ______ Date ______

Reteach

Units of Capacity

The **liter (L)** and the **milliliter (mL)** are metric units of capacity.
A teaspoon holds about 5 mL of liquid.
A water bottle might hold about 1 L of liquid.

Metric Units of Capacity
1 liter (L) = 1,000 (mL)

Multiply to change larger units to smaller units.
3 L = ■ mL
Liters are larger units than milliliters.
1 liter = 1,000 milliliters.
So multiply by 1,000.
3 × 1,000 = 3,000
3 L = 3,000 mL

Divide to change smaller units to larger units.
900 mL = ■ L
900 mL = $\frac{900}{1,000}$ L or 0.9.
900 mL = 0.9 L

Complete.

1. 42 mL = ■ L
 1 liter = 1,000 milliliters
 So divide by **1,000**.
 42 mL = $\frac{\textbf{42}}{\textbf{1,000}}$ L
 42 mL = **0.042** L

2. 5.9 L = ■ mL
 1 liter = **1,000** milliliters
 So multiply by **1,000**.
 5.9 × **1,000** = **5,900**
 5.9 L = **5,900** mL

3. 50 L = **50,000** mL
4. 64 mL = **0.064** L
5. 348 mL = **0.348** L
6. 9,000 mL = **9** L
7. 12 L = **12,000** mL
8. 40 mL = **0.04** L
9. 2 L = **2,000** mL
10. 420 L = **420,000** mL
11. 3 L = **3,000** mL
12. 52 mL = **0.052** L
13. 738 mL = **0.738** L
14. 2.5 L = **2,500** mL
15. 86 L = **86,000** mL
16. 2,250 mL = **2.25** L

Chapter Resources

Grade 5 23 Chapter 12

Skills Practice (p. 24) OL

12-4 Name ______ Date ______

Skills Practice

Units of Capacity

Complete.

1. 46 L = **0.046** mL
2. 602 L = **602,000** mL
3. 7 L = **7,000** mL
4. 350 mL = **0.35** L
5. 93 L = **93,000** mL
6. 13.5 L = **13,500** mL
7. 56 mL = **0.056** L
8. 19 mL = **0.019** L
9. 12 mL = **0.012** L
10. 3.07 L = **3,070** mL
11. 0.3 L = **300** mL
12. 4.2 mL = **0.0042** L
13. 62 mL = **0.062** L
14. 6,400 L = **6,400,000** mL
15. 25 mL = **0.025** L
16. 1,500 mL = **1.5** L
17. 8.2 L = **8,200** mL
18. 900 L = **900,000** mL

Replace ◯ with <, >, or = to make a true statement.

19. 20.8 L (>) 208 mL
20. 20 mL (<) 0.2 L
21. 95 mL (<) 9.5 L
22. 6.3 L (>) 63 mL
23. 2,000 mL (<) 20 L
24. 4.027 L (=) 4,027 mL
25. 129 mL (<) 12.9 L
26. 56.8 L (>) 568 mL
27. 3,000 mL (>) 0.03 L

Solve.

28. Jacob has 0.5 L of milk to use in two recipes. Each recipe uses 300 mL. Does he have enough? Explain.
 No; 0.5 L = 500 mL; 2 × 300 mL = 600 mL and 600 mL > 500 mL.

Grade 5 24 Chapter 12

12-4 Units of Capacity

1 Introduce

Activity Choice 1 • Hands-On

- Show students several bottles that are marked in liters or milliliters. **Based on what you know about the metric system, how many milliliters are in a liter?** 1,000
- Tell students that there are units of capacity called centiliters and kiloliters, but the most common units are liters and milliliters. **What do you notice about the labels on the bottles that contain less than 1,000 mL?** They are labeled as milliliters.
- Show students bottles which contain more than one liter. **How are amounts that are greater than one liter written?** as a decimal showing liters and parts of a liter
- Discuss with students that liters are somewhat similar in size to a quart in the customary system and that 250 mL compares to about one cup in the customary system.

Activity Choice 2 • Literature

Introduce the lesson with *Millions to Measure* by David M. Schwartz. For a related math activity, see p. TR56.

2 Teach

Scaffolding Questions

Write 1.5 L and 450 mL on the board

- **How many milliliters are in one liter? How do you know?** 1,000 milliliters; *milli-* means 0.001
- **How would you convert 1.5 L to milliliters?** Multiply 1.5 by 1,000 to equal 1,500.
- **How would you convert 450 mL to liters?** Divide 450 by 1,000 to get 0.45.
- Tell students that sometimes capacities larger than liters are measured in milliliters; for example, in science investigations or in medical settings.

GET READY to Learn

Have students open their books and read the information in **Get Ready to Learn**. Introduce **liter** and **milliliter**. As a class, work through **Examples 1–3**.

Solve Problems Involving Capacity

Example 3 Encourage students to use the *four-step plan* as they solve problems involving capacity. If they find the total number of liters sold first, they will have to convert liters to milliliters only one time to solve the problem.

ADDITIONAL EXAMPLES

1. As part of a science experiment, a plant was given three liters of water each week for twelve weeks. How many milliliters of water were given to the plant in all? 36,000 mL
2. How many liters is 850 milliliters? 0.85 L
3. The Jackson family bought two cases of bottled water. Each case has 28 bottles with 250 mL of water in each bottle. Find the total number of liters in the two cases. 14 L

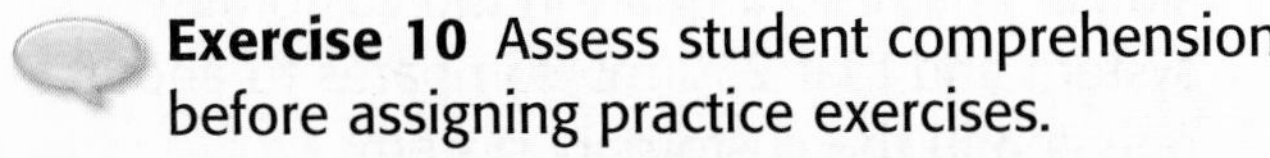

As a class, have students complete Exercises 1–10 in **Check What You Know** as you observe their work.

Exercise 10 Assess student comprehension before assigning practice exercises.

BL Alternate Teaching Strategy

If students have trouble converting metric units of capacity…

Then use one of these reteach options:

1 CRM **Daily Reteach Worksheet** (p. 23)

2 Have students observe and draw pictures of 1 mL and 1 L of a liquid. Have them label their picture with the equation, 1 mL × 1,000 = 1 L. Ask students to draw a second picture below showing 1 L and 1 mL, in that order, with the equation 1 L ÷ 1,000 = 1 mL.

- **Which unit is larger, milliliter or liter? How much bigger?** liter; 1,000 times bigger
- Have students use their pictures as they convert units of capacity from milliliters to liters and from liters to milliliters.

Remember

In everyday life, customary units of capacity such as gallons and pints are often compared to the metric units liters and milliliters.

Real-World EXAMPLES Convert Units of Capacity

2 JUICE A container of orange juice holds 580 milliliters. How many liters is 580 milliliters?

Estimate 580 mL < 1,000 mL, so the number of liters is less than 1.

580 mL = ■ L	580 mL is what part of 1,000 mL?
580 mL = $\frac{580}{1,000}$ L or 0.58 L	Write $\frac{580}{1,000}$ as a decimal.
So, 580 mL = 0.58 L.	0.58 liter is less than a whole liter. So, the answer is reasonable.

3 ALGEBRA The table shows the number of water bottles sold on a recent day. Were more than 100,000 milliliters sold?

Bottle	Number Sold
1-liter	55
2-liter	30

First, find the total number of liters sold.

(1 × 55) + (2 × 30) = 55 + 60 Multiply.
= 115 L Add.

Next, convert 115 liters to milliliters.

115 × 1,000 = 115,000 1 L = 1,000 mL, so multiply 115 by 1,000.

So, 115 L = 115,000 mL.

Since 115,000 > 100,000, more than 100,000 milliliters of water were sold.

CHECK What You Know

Complete. See Examples 1, 2 (pp. 527–528)

1. 6 L = ■ mL 6,000
2. 7,000 mL = ■ L 7
3. 4 L = ■ mL 4,000
4. 325 mL = ■ L 0.325
5. 42 mL = ■ L 0.042
6. 1.5 L = ■ mL 1,500

Replace each ● with <, >, or = to make a true statement. See Example 3 (p. 528)

7. 1.7 L ● 1,000 mL >
8. 390 mL ● 0.39 L =
9. A detergent bottle holds 700 milliliters. Find the capacity in liters. 0.7 L
10. Talk About It Which unit would you use to measure the capacity of a glass of milk? Explain. milliliter; A liter is too large.

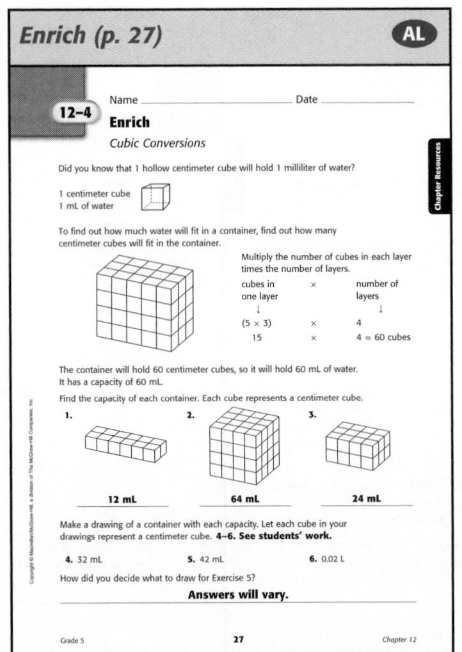
Enrich (p. 27) AL

12-4 Name ______ Date ______

Enrich

Cubic Conversions

Did you know that 1 hollow centimeter cube will hold 1 milliliter of water?

1 centimeter cube
1 mL of water

To find out how much water will fit in a container, find out how many centimeter cubes will fit in the container.

Multiply the number of cubes in each layer times the number of layers.

cubes in one layer × number of layers
(5 × 3) × 4
15 × 4 = 60 cubes

The container will hold 60 centimeter cubes, so it will hold 60 mL of water. It has a capacity of 60 mL.

Find the capacity of each container. Each cube represents a centimeter cube.

1. **12 mL**
2. **64 mL**
3. **24 mL**

Make a drawing of a container with each capacity. Let each cube in your drawings represent a centimeter cube. **4–6. See students' work.**

4. 32 mL
5. 42 mL
6. 0.02 L

How did you decide what to draw for Exercise 5?

Answers will vary.

Chapter Resources

Grade 5 27 *Chapter 12*

★ indicates multi-step problem

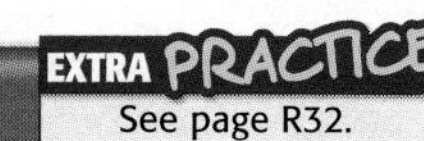

Practice and Problem Solving

EXTRA PRACTICE See page R32.

Complete. See Examples 1, 2 (pp. 527–528)

11. 70 L = ■ mL **70,000** **12.** 4 L = ■ mL **4,000** **13.** 3,000 mL = ■ L **3**

14. 230 mL = ■ L **0.23** **15.** 6 L = ■ mL **6,000** **16.** 10 mL = ■ L **0.01**

17. 5,000 mL = ■ L **5** **18.** 0.5 L = ■ mL **500** **19.** 1.5 L = ■ mL **1,500**

Replace each ● with <, >, or = to make a true statement. See Example 3 (p. 528)

20. 82.5 L ● 825 mL **>** **21.** 0.07 L ● 70 mL **=** **22.** 834 mL ● 8.34 L **<**

23. To prepare for his camping trip, Emanuel filled his canteen with water. Is 15,000 milliliters or 1,500 milliliters a more reasonable estimate for the amount of water in the canteen? Explain. **See margin.**

★**24.** One serving of punch is 250 milliliters. Will ten servings fit in a 2-liter bowl? Explain.
No; 10 servings equals 2,500 mL, or 2.5 L. This is greater than 2 liters.

★**25.** Yesterday, Audrey drank the liquids shown. How many liters of liquids did she drink in all? **1.89 L**

Liquid	Amount
Juice	210 mL
Milk	480 mL
Water	1.2 L

★**26.** The Nail Shop purchases nail polish in 13-milliliter bottles. Find the total capacity of 1,000 bottles in liters. **13 L**

H.O.T. Problems

27. OPEN ENDED Name three things that have a capacity greater than 10 liters. **Sample answers: fish tank, swimming pool, bath tub**

28. FIND THE ERROR Joseph and Kendra are converting 14 milliliters to liters. Who is correct? Explain. **Kendra; Joseph incorrectly multiplied 14 by 1,000 instead of dividing 14 by 1,000.**

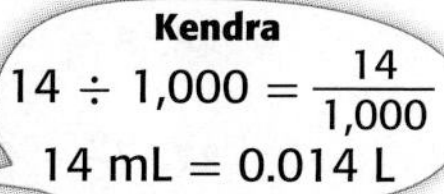

Kendra
$14 \div 1{,}000 = \frac{14}{1{,}000}$
14 mL = 0.014 L

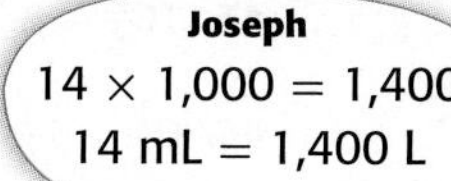

29. WRITING IN ►MATH Write a real-world problem that can be solved by converting milliliters to liters. Then solve. **See margin.**

Additional Answers

23. 1,500 mL, which is equal to 1.5 L; 15,000 mL is equal to 15 L, which is too much water for a single canteen.

29. Sample answer: I bought a 2-liter bottle of fruit punch. How many 220-milliliter cups can I fill? Answer: 9 cups

3 Practice

Differentiate practice using these leveled assignments for Exercises 11–29.

Level	Assignment
BL Below/ Approaching Level	11–16, 20–24,
OL On Level	14–27, 28
AL Above/Beyond Level	11–25 odd, 27–29

Have students discuss and complete the Higher Order Thinking problems. For Exercise 28, encourage students to write the rule for converting smaller units to larger units and to convert 14 milliliters to liters before they write their explanation.

WRITING IN ►MATH Have student complete Exercise 29 in their Math Journals. You may choose to use this exercise as an optional formative assessment.

Tips for New Teachers Help students to differentiate volume and capacity by explaining that volume refers to the space taken up by an object itself, while capacity refers to the amount of a liquid a container can hold.

COMMON ERROR!

Exercises 11–19 Students may have trouble multiplying and dividing by 1,000 accurately. Demonstrate that multiplying by 1,000 causes the decimal point to move three places to the right in a number while dividing by 1,000 causes the decimal point to move three places to the left.

Assess

Formative Assessment

Write the following on the board:
56 L > 5,600 mL

- **How would you prove that this is a true number sentence?** by either converting 56 L to milliliters or converting 5,600 mL to liters and comparing
- **How would you convert 56 L to milliliters?** Multiply 56 × 1,000 = 56,000
- **Is the number sentence true?** yes

Quick Check **Are students continuing to struggle with converting metric units of capacity?**

If Yes → Small Group Options (p. 527B)

If No → Independent Work Options (p. 527B)
CRM Skills Practice Worksheet (p. 24)
CRM Enrich Worksheet (p. 27)

Name the Math Write the following on the board: Is 34.5 mL equal to 3.45 L, 0.345 L, or 0.0345 L? On a small card or paper, have students choose the correct answer and explain all the steps they used to find the correct answer.

Reviews Lessons 12-3 and 12-4

Assign the Test Practice problems to provide daily reinforcement of test-taking skills.

Spiral Review

Reviews Lessons 2-2, 9-5, 10-8, 10-10, 11-7, 12-1, 12-2, and 12-3

Objective: Review and assess mastery of skills and concepts from previous chapters.

Additional Answer

38. Yes; 0.92 meter equals 92 centimeters. The total width of 90 CDs is 90 centimeters, so the CDs will fit.

30. How many milligrams are equivalent to 900 grams? (Lesson 12-3) D

A 0.9 mg
B 9 mg
C 90 mg
D Not here

31. Claudio's fish tank has 3 liters of water in it. How many milliliters of water are in the fish tank? (Lesson 12-4) H

F 30 mL
G 300 mL
H 3,000 mL
J 30,000 mL

Spiral Review

Complete. (Lessons 12-1 and 12-3)

32. 12 km = ■ m 12,000
33. 400 cm = ■ m 4
34. 8,000 cm = ■ mm 80,000
35. 34 g = ■ mg 34,000
36. 9 kg = ■ g 9,000
37. 2,000 mg = ■ g 2

38. Mara wants to put 90 CDs on the shelf shown below. Each CD is 1 centimeter wide. Is it reasonable for her to expect to fit all the CDs on the shelf? Explain. (Lesson 12-2) See margin.

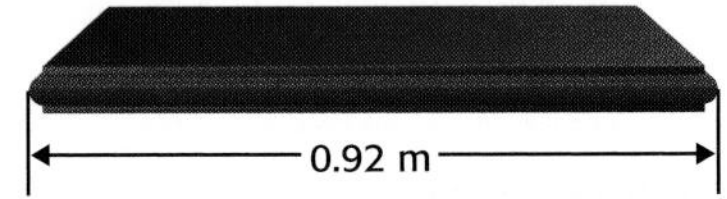

Find each elapsed time. (Lesson 11-7)

39. 3:10 A.M. to 5:20 A.M. 2 h 10 min
40. 1:08 P.M. to 7:39 P.M. 6 h 31 min
41. 10:30 A.M. to 2:14 P.M. 3 h 44 min

Subtract. (Lessons 10-8 and 10-10)

42. $8\frac{5}{6} - 6\frac{2}{6}$ $2\frac{1}{2}$
43. $10\frac{2}{5} - 3\frac{1}{5}$ $7\frac{1}{5}$
44. $8\frac{3}{12} - 5\frac{1}{12}$ $3\frac{1}{6}$
45. $3\frac{1}{4} - 1\frac{3}{4}$ $1\frac{1}{2}$
46. $6\frac{1}{5} - 1\frac{3}{5}$ $4\frac{3}{5}$
47. $7\frac{4}{8} - 4\frac{5}{8}$ $2\frac{7}{8}$

48. The model represents 0.014. Write 0.014 as a fraction in simplest form. (Lesson 9-5) $\frac{7}{500}$

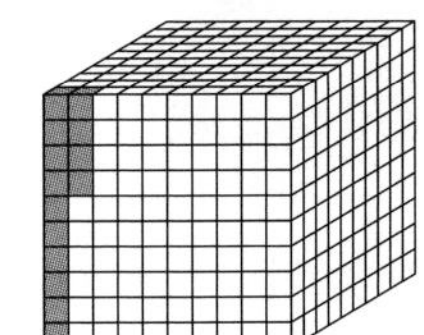

49. Mrs. Rexroad's cell phone bill for one month was $48.70. The next month it was $56.04. Estimate the total cost of the two bills using compatible numbers. (Lesson 2-2) $100

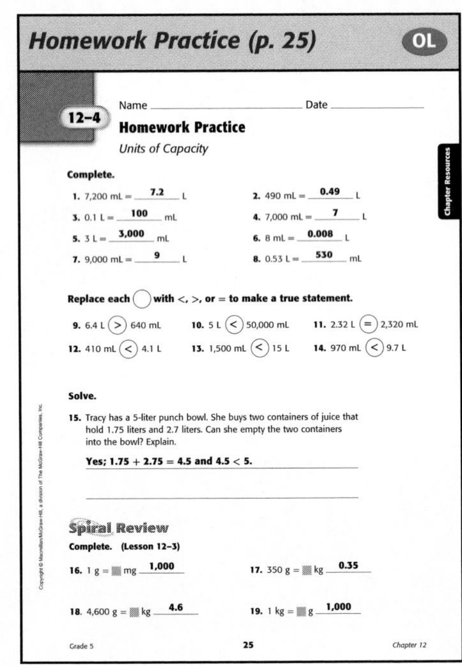

Homework Practice (p. 25) OL

12–4
Name ________ Date ________

Homework Practice
Units of Capacity

Complete.

1. 7,200 mL = **7.2** L
2. 490 mL = **0.49** L
3. 0.1 L = **100** mL
4. 7,000 mL = **7** L
5. 3 L = **3,000** mL
6. 8 mL = **0.008** L
7. 9,000 mL = **9** L
8. 0.53 L = **530** mL

Replace each ◯ with <, >, or = to make a true statement.

9. 6.4 L (>) 640 mL
10. 5 L (<) 50,000 mL
11. 2.32 L (=) 2,320 mL
12. 410 mL (<) 4.1 L
13. 1,500 mL (<) 15 L
14. 970 mL (<) 9.7 L

Solve.

15. Tracy has a 5-liter punch bowl. She buys two containers of juice that hold 1.75 liters and 2.7 liters. Can she empty the two containers into the bowl? Explain.

Yes; 1.75 + 2.75 = 4.5 and 4.5 < 5.

Spiral Review

Complete. (Lesson 12–3)

16. 1 g = ■ mg **1,000**
17. 350 g = ■ kg **0.35**
18. 4,600 g = ■ kg **4.6**
19. 1 kg = ■ g **1,000**

Chapter Resources

Grade 5 25 Chapter 12

530 Chapter 12 Use Measures in the Metric System

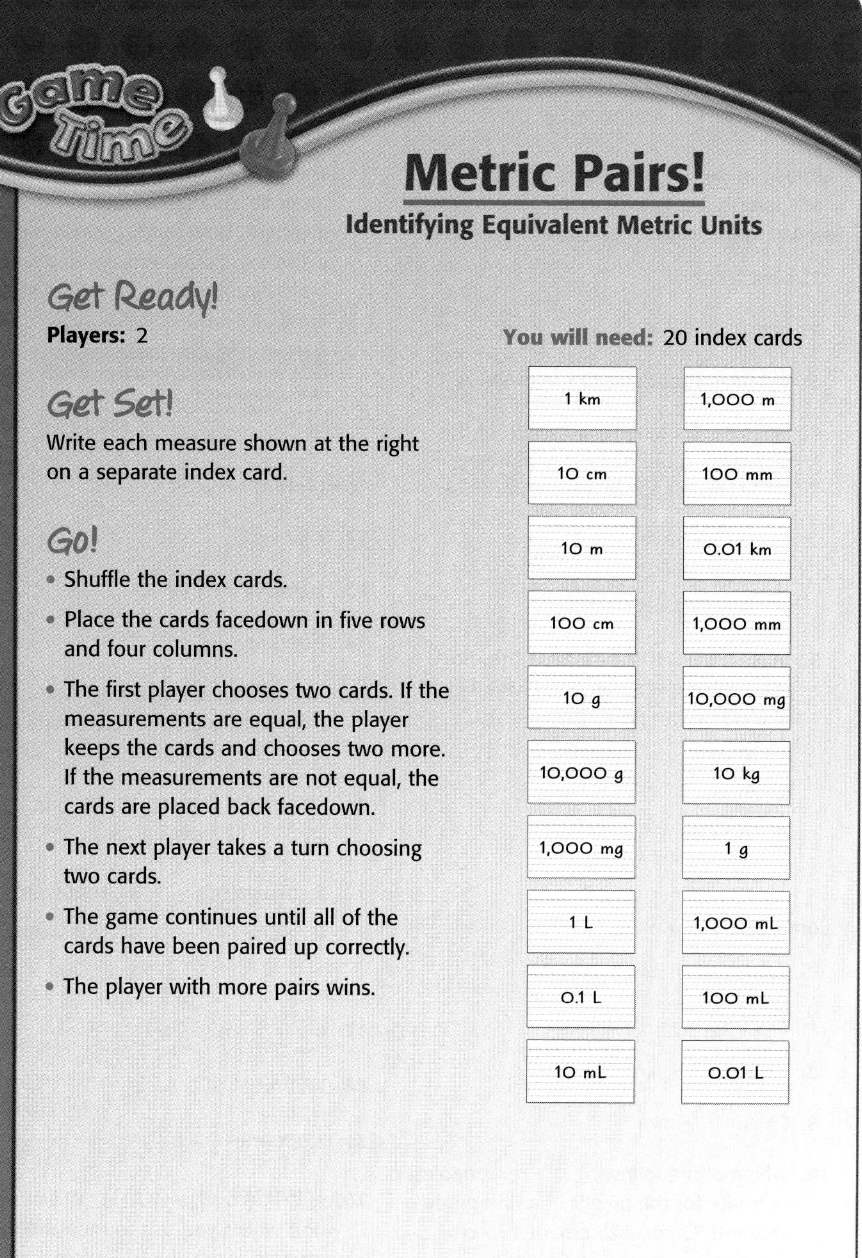

Metric Pairs!

Identifying Equivalent Metric Units

Get Ready!

Players: 2

You will need: 20 index cards

Get Set!

Write each measure shown at the right on a separate index card.

Go!

- Shuffle the index cards.
- Place the cards facedown in five rows and four columns.
- The first player chooses two cards. If the measurements are equal, the player keeps the cards and chooses two more. If the measurements are not equal, the cards are placed back facedown.
- The next player takes a turn choosing two cards.
- The game continues until all of the cards have been paired up correctly.
- The player with more pairs wins.

1 km	1,000 m
10 cm	100 mm
10 m	0.01 km
100 cm	1,000 mm
10 g	10,000 mg
10,000 g	10 kg
1,000 mg	1 g
1 L	1,000 mL
0.1 L	100 mL
10 mL	0.01 L

Game Time Metric Pairs! **531**

Differentiated Practice

Use these leveled suggestions to differentiate the game for all learners.

Level	Assignment
BL Below/Approaching Level	Students work in teams of two and help each other pair up the cards.
OL On Level	Have students play the game with the rules as written.
AL Above/Beyond Level	Students create their own card pairs using equivalent measurements of their choosing.

Metric Pairs!

Math Concept:
Identifying Equivalent Metric Units

Materials: 20 index cards, pencils

Introduce the game on p. 531 to your students to play as a class, in small groups, or at a learning workstation to review concepts introduced in this chapter.

Instructions

- Students play in pairs. They write each measurement shown on p. 531 on a separate index card.
- One player shuffles the index cards and places them face down, one by one, in five rows and four columns.
- Player 1 chooses two cards. If the measurements are equal, Player 1 keeps the cards and chooses two more. If the measurements are not equal, the cards are placed back in their positions, face down, and Player 2 takes a turn choosing two cards.
- Play continues until all of the cards have been paired up correctly.
- The player with more pairs of cards wins the game.

Extend the Game

Have students measure objects around the classroom and use those measurements to create card pairs to play the game.

CHAPTER 12 Mid-Chapter Check

Lessons 12-1 through 12-4

Formative Assessment

Use the Mid-Chapter Check to assess students' progress in the first half of the chapter.

Customize and create multiple versions of your Mid-Chapter Check and the test answer keys.

FOLDABLES Dinah Zike's Foldables

Use these lesson suggestions to incorporate the Foldables during the chapter.

Lesson 12-1 Under the top left tab of the Foldable, have students record data as they measure and convert metric units of length. Students might glue a graphic of a ruler beneath the Foldable.

Lesson 12-3 Under the top right tab of the Foldable, have students record data as they measure and convert metric units of mass.

Lesson 12-4 Under the bottom left tab of the Foldable, have students record data as they measure and convert metric units of capacity.

Additional Answer

10. 125 cm; Sample answer 75 cm is too small and 175 cm is too large for a fifth grader.

CHAPTER 12 Mid-Chapter Check

Lessons 12-1 through 12-4

Choose an appropriate unit to measure each length. Write *millimeter, centimeter, meter,* or *kilometer.* (Lesson 12-1)

1. pencil cm
2. house m
3. distance from Earth to the moon km
4. Measure the length and width of the rectangle to the nearest millimeter. (Lesson 12-1) length: 30 mm; width: 13 mm

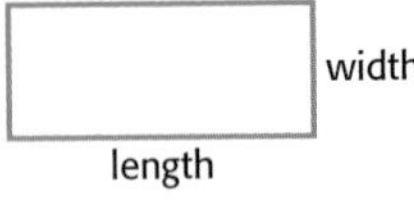

5. **MULTIPLE CHOICE** Choose the most reasonable measurement for the height of a classroom door. (Lesson 12-1) D
   - **A** 20 cm
   - **B** 20 m
   - **C** 200 mm
   - **D** 200 cm

Complete. (Lesson 12-1)

6. 4 m = ■ cm 400
7. 750 mm = ■ cm 75
8. 1,000 m = ■ km 1
9. 63 cm = ■ mm 630
10. Which of the following is a reasonable estimate for the height of a fifth grade student: 75 cm, 125 cm, or 175 cm? Explain. (Lesson 12-2) See margin.
11. The table shows the average brain mass of a human and of an African elephant. How many grams greater is the mass of an African elephant brain than the mass of a human brain? (Lesson 12-3) 4,000 g

Brain	Average Mass (kg)
African elephant	5.4
Human	1.4

Complete. (Lesson 12-3)

12. 7 kg = ■ g 7,000
13. 10,000 g = ■ kg 10
14. 2,000 mg = ■ g 2
15. Tamara has a bag of dog food that weighs 4 kilograms. How many grams are in the bag? (Lesson 12-3) 4,000
16. **MULTIPLE CHOICE** Which unit is $\frac{1}{1,000}$ of a kilogram? (Lesson 12-3) G
    - **F** milligram
    - **G** gram
    - **H** centigram
    - **J** Not Here

Complete. (Lesson 12-4)

17. 6 L = ■ mL 6,000
18. 280 mL = ■ L 0.28
19. 3,000 mL = ■ L 3
20. **WRITING IN MATH** Which metric unit would you use to measure the capacity of a bathtub? Explain. (Lesson 12-4)
Sample answer: liters; milliliters is too small.

Data-Driven Decision Making

Based on the results of the Mid-Chapter Check, use the following to review concepts that continue to present students with problems.

Exercises	State/Local Standards	What's the Math?	Error Analysis	Resources for Review
1–9 Lesson 12-1		Choose an appropriate metric unit for measuring length and convert metric units of length.	Does not know methods of unit conversion. Does not have sense of reasonableness of measurement. Does not know "milli-, centi-, kilo-, meter."	Strategic Intervention Guide (p. 130) CRM Chapter 12 Resource Masters (Reteach) Math Adventures My Math Zone Chapter 12 Math Online Extra Examples • Concepts in Motion
11–16 Lesson 12-3		Convert metric units of mass.	Does not accurately compute when converting units of measurement. Does not know relationships among metric units.	
17–20 Lesson 12-4		Convert metric units of capacity.	Does not know relationships among metric units, or "capacity." Does not multiply or divide accurately when converting in metric units.	

Integers and Graphing on Number Lines

Lesson Planner

Objective

Use integers to represent real-life situations and graph them on a number line.

Vocabulary

positive number, negative number, integer, negative integers, positive integers, opposite integers

Resources

Materials: meterstick
Manipulatives: ruler
Literature Connection: *Mathematics* by Irving Adler
Teacher Technology
TeacherWorks • Interactive Classroom • Concepts in Motion

Focus on Math Background

Students are gradually introduced to more inclusive sets of numbers. They first learned of the *natural* or *counting numbers*, later including 0 to form the *whole numbers*. The set of *integers* includes the whole numbers (positive integers and 0) and negative integers. Later, they will incorporate integers, fractions, and decimals into the *rational numbers; real numbers* ultimately include *irrational numbers* as well.

For negative integers, the minus sign is always written, but for positive integers, the plus sign is often omitted. A number line can be used to compare the sizes of numbers. For any pair of numbers, the number to the right on the number line is larger.

Daily Routine

Use these suggestions before beginning the lesson on p. 533.

5-Minute Check

(Reviews Lesson 12-4)

Complete.

1. 4,500 mL = ■ L 4.5
2. 3 L = ■ mL 3,000
3. 344 mL = ■ L 0.344
4. 0.6 L = ■ mL 600
5. 44,000 mL = ■ L 44
6. 2.5 L = ■ mL 2,500

Problem of the Day

Alex has 72 inches of twine. Habika has $2\frac{2}{3}$ yards of twine. How many more feet of twine does Habika have? Explain how you found your answer. 2 ft; convert inches to feet. Then convert yards to feet and subtract.

Building Math Vocabulary

Write the lesson vocabulary words and their definitions on the board.

Have students write the words and their definitions in their Math Journals. Ask them to write and share aloud five examples of each term using the words positive and negative correctly.

Visual Vocabulary Cards

Use Visual Vocabulary Card 18 to reinforce the vocabulary introduced in this lesson. (The Define/Example/Ask routine is printed on the back of each card.)

Differentiated Instruction

Small Group Options

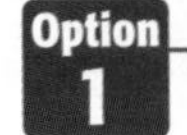

Option 1 SPATIAL, KINESTHETIC

Below Level (BL)

Materials: chart paper, markers, counters

- Work with students to make long, oversized posters of number lines, from −10 to 10, along which they can move counters.
- Encourage students to use their number lines and counters to solve the Check What You Know exercises.

Option 2 KINESTHETIC

English Language Learners (ELL)

Materials: per pair: ruler, 10 feet masking tape, pen
Core Vocabulary: right/left, start on, where are you?
Common Use Verb: jump back and forth

Do Math This strategy kinesthetically connects right and left movement with addition and subtraction on a number line.

- Draw a number line 1–10. Write 3 + 4. Explain how to start on 3 and jump 4 spaces to the right. Write 7 − 2. Start on 7 and jump 2 spaces to the left.
- Pairs put 10 feet of masking tape on floor and make 1 foot intervals with the pen. They label the tape:

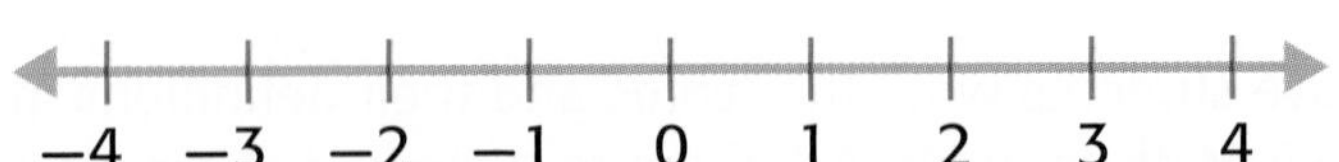

- Write 0 + 3. "Stand on 0, move 3 feet to the **right**." Ask: **"Where are you?"** on 3
- Repeat for 4 − 2, −3 + 5, and 3 − 5.

Independent Work Options

Option 1 LINGUISTIC

Early Finishers (AL)

Materials: number cube, pencil, paper

- Have students draw a number line showing −6 to +6.
- Students will roll the number cube and graph each number and its opposite integer on the number line.
- For each number and its opposite, have students write phrases to describe a situation where the numbers make sense.

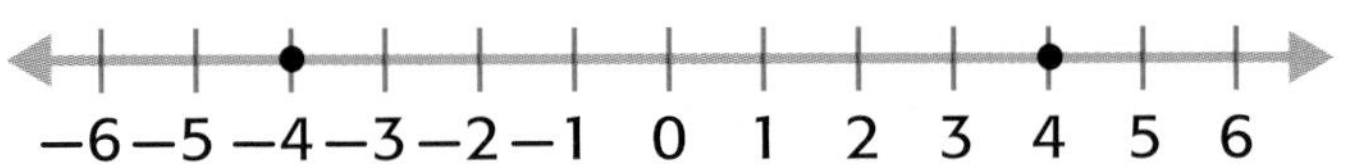

I walked four blocks to school and four blocks back home.

Option 2

Student Technology

Math Online macmillanmh.com

Personal Tutor • Extra Examples

 Math Adventures

Option 3

Learning Station: Social Studies (p. 512H)

Direct students to the Social Studies Learning Station for opportunities to explore and extend the lesson concept.

Option 4

Problem-Solving Practice

Reinforce problem-solving skills and strategies with the Problem-Solving Practice worksheet.

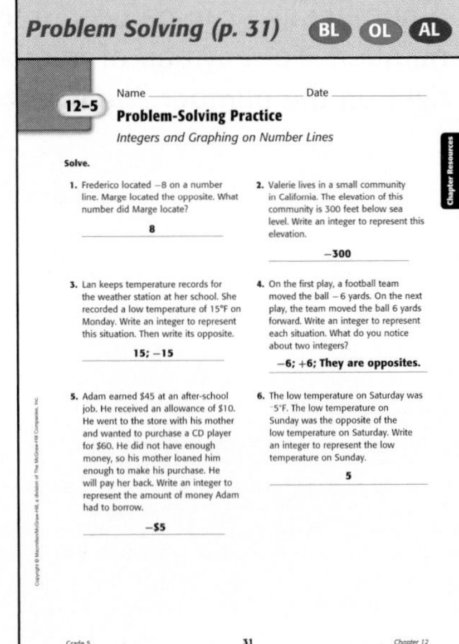

Problem Solving (p. 31) BL OL AL

12–5 Name ______ Date ______

Problem-Solving Practice

Integers and Graphing on Number Lines

Chapter Resources

Solve.

1. Frederico located −8 on a number line. Marge located the opposite. What number did Marge locate?
   8
2. Valerie lives in a small community in California. The elevation of this community is 300 feet below sea level. Write an integer to represent this elevation.
   −300
3. Lan keeps temperature records for the weather station at her school. She recorded a low temperature of 15°F on Monday. Write an integer to represent this situation. Then write its opposite.
   15; −15
4. On the first play, a football team moved the ball − 6 yards. On the next play, the team moved the ball 6 yards forward. Write an integer to represent each situation. What do you notice about two integers?
   −6; +6; They are opposites.
5. Adam earned $45 at an after-school job. He received an allowance of $10. He went to the store with his mother and wanted to purchase a CD player for $60. He did not have enough money, so his mother loaned him enough to make his purchase. He will pay her back. Write an integer to represent the amount of money Adam had to borrow.
   −$5
6. The low temperature on Saturday was −5°F. The low temperature on Sunday was the opposite of the low temperature on Saturday. Write an integer to represent the low temperature on Sunday.
   5

Grade 5 31 Chapter 12

12-5 Integers and Graphing on Number Lines

GET READY to Learn

The top of an underwater mountain is about 2 kilometers above sea level. The base of the mountain is 6 kilometers below sea level. You can represent the distance *2 km above sea level* as +2 or 2, and the distance *6 km below sea level* as −6.

2 km above sea level
sea level
6 km below sea level

MAIN IDEA

I will use integers to represent real-life situations and graph them on a number line.

New Vocabulary

- positive number
- negative number
- integer
- negative integers
- positive integers
- opposite integers

Math Online

macmillanmh.com
- Extra Examples
- Personal Tutor
- Self-Check Quiz

The number 2 is a **positive number**, or a number greater than 0. The number −6 is a **negative number**, or a number less than 0. Numbers like 2 and −6 are called **integers**.

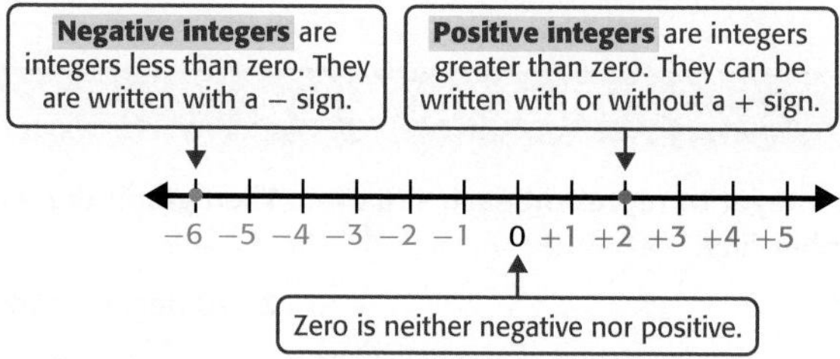

Negative integers are integers less than zero. They are written with a − sign.
Positive integers are integers greater than zero. They can be written with or without a + sign.
−6 −5 −4 −3 −2 −1 0 +1 +2 +3 +4 +5
Zero is neither negative nor positive.

Real-World EXAMPLE — Number Line

1 TEMPERATURE Yesterday, the temperature was 4 degrees below zero. Today, it is 4 degrees above zero. Use integers to represent these situations. Then graph the integers on a number line.

4° below: −4 4° above: +4 or 4

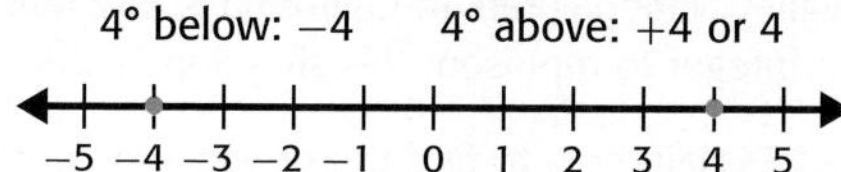

−5 −4 −3 −2 −1 0 1 2 3 4 5

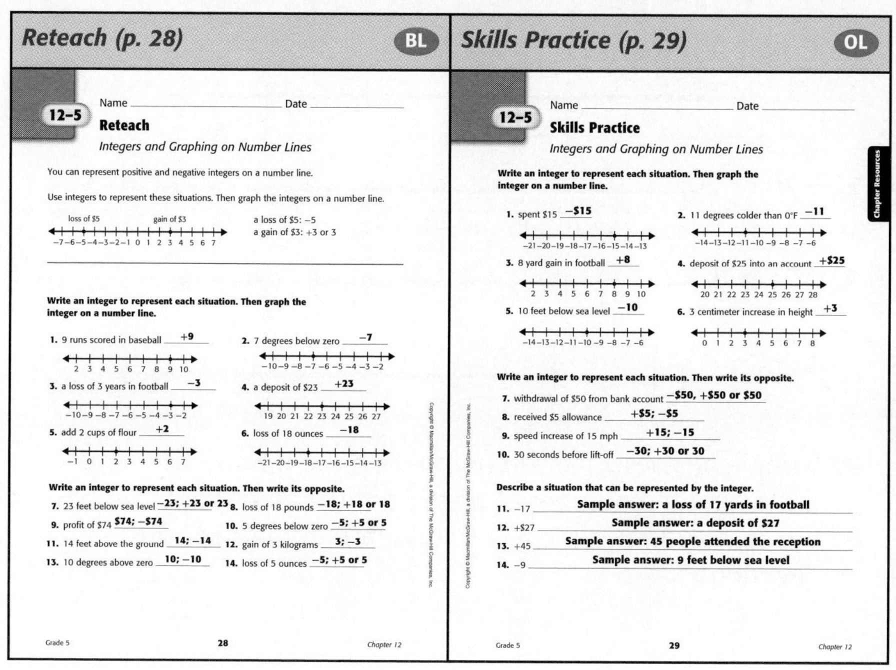

Reteach (p. 28) BL

12-5 Name ______ Date ______

Reteach

Integers and Graphing on Number Lines

You can represent positive and negative integers on a number line.

Use integers to represent these situations. Then graph the integers on a number line.

loss of $5 gain of $3

−7 −6 −5 −4 −3 −2 −1 0 1 2 3 4 5 6 7

a loss of $5: −5
a gain of $3: +3 or 3

Write an integer to represent each situation. Then graph the integer on a number line.

1. 9 runs scored in baseball **+9** (2 3 4 5 6 7 8 9 10)
2. 7 degrees below zero **−7** (−10 −9 −8 −7 −6 −5 −4 −3 −2)
3. a loss of 3 years in football **−3** (−10 −9 −8 −7 −6 −5 −4 −3 −2)
4. a deposit of $23 **+23** (19 20 21 22 23 24 25 26 27)
5. add 2 cups of flour **+2** (−1 0 1 2 3 4 5 6 7)
6. loss of 18 ounces **−18** (−21 −20 −19 −18 −17 −16 −15 −14 −13)

Write an integer to represent each situation. Then write its opposite.

7. 23 feet below sea level **−23; +23 or 23**
8. loss of 18 pounds **−18; +18 or 18**
9. profit of $74 **$74; −$74**
10. 5 degrees below zero **−5; +5 or 5**
11. 14 feet above the ground **14; −14**
12. gain of 3 kilograms **3; −3**
13. 10 degrees above zero **10; −10**
14. loss of 5 ounces **−5; +5 or 5**

Grade 5 28 Chapter 12

Skills Practice (p. 29) OL

12-5 Name ______ Date ______

Skills Practice

Integers and Graphing on Number Lines

Chapter Resources

Write an integer to represent each situation. Then graph the integer on a number line.

1. spent $15 **−$15** (−21 −20 −19 −18 −17 −16 −15 −14 −13)
2. 11 degrees colder than 0°F **−11** (−14 −13 −12 −11 −10 −9 −8 −7 −6)
3. 8 yard gain in football **+8** (2 3 4 5 6 7 8 9 10)
4. deposit of $25 into an account **+$25** (20 21 22 23 24 25 26 27 28)
5. 10 feet below sea level **−10** (−14 −13 −12 −11 −10 −9 −8 −7 −6)
6. 3 centimeter increase in height **+3** (0 1 2 3 4 5 6 7 8)

Write an integer to represent each situation. Then write its opposite.

7. withdrawal of $50 from bank account **−$50, +$50 or $50**
8. received $5 allowance **+$5; −$5**
9. speed increase of 15 mph **+15; −15**
10. 30 seconds before lift-off **−30; +30 or 30**

Describe a situation that can be represented by the integer.

11. −17 **Sample answer: a loss of 17 yards in football**
12. +$27 **Sample answer: a deposit of $27**
13. +45 **Sample answer: 45 people attended the reception**
14. −9 **Sample answer: 9 feet below sea level**

Grade 5 29 Chapter 12

12-5 Integers and Graphing on Number Lines

1 Introduce

Activity Choice 1 • Hands-On

- Hold a meterstick vertically so that 0 rests on a desktop. Point to 20 cm. **How many centimeters above the desk is this?** 20 cm
- Tell students that 20 cm above the desktop will be called positive 20. Hold a meter stick vertically so that 0 rests on the bottom of the desktop. Point to 20 cm on the ruler. **How far below the desktop is this number?** 20 cm
- Tell students that 20 cm below the desktop will be called negative 20. **In our model of positive 20 and negative 20, what does the desktop represent?** 0
- Discuss with students places or situations where they have seen positive and negative numbers.

Activity Choice 2 • Literature

Introduce the lesson with *Mathematics* by Irving Adler. For a related math activity, see p. TR56.

2 Teach

Scaffolding Questions

Draw a horizontal line on the board. Mark the halfway point on the line with 0.

- **What kind of numbers are greater than 0?** positive numbers
- **What kind of numbers are less than 0?** negative numbers
- **How should the line be numbered to the right of 0?** +1, +2, +3 and so on
- Explain that negative numbers work in the same way.
- **How should the line to the left of 0 be labeled?** −1, −2, −3 and so on

GET READY to Learn

Have students open their books and read the information in **Get Ready to Learn.** Introduce **positive number**, **negative number**, **integer**, **negative integers**, **positive integers**, and **opposite integers**. As a class, work through **Examples 1–3.**

Temperature

Example 1 Ask students to make two columns with headings *positive* and *negative*. In the *positive* column, write *gain* and in the negative column, write *below zero*. Have students add helpful words to the list as they work through the lesson.

ADDITIONAL EXAMPLES

1. Mark earned $6 by cutting a lawn. He spent $6 downloading some music. Use integers to represent these situations. Then graph the integers on a number line. earned $6: +6, spent $6: −6

2. The Grand Canyon is about 1,600 meters deep. Write an integer to represent this situation. Then write its opposite. −1,600; opposite is +1,600, or 1,600

3. Kavita wrote a check for $48 to pay for some new sneakers. Write an integer to represent this situation. Then write its opposite. −48; 48

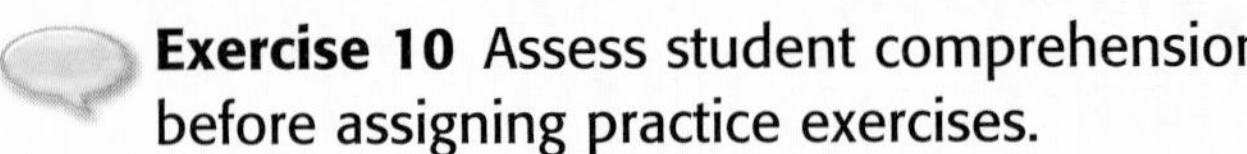

As a class, have students complete Exercises 1–10 in **Check What You Know** as you observe their work.

Exercise 10 Assess student comprehension before assigning practice exercises.

BL Alternate Teaching Strategy

If students have trouble graphing integers on a number line…

Then use one of these reteach options:

1. CRM **Daily Reteach Worksheet** (p. 28)

2. Have them use a vertical number line to demonstrate order of integers. Have students use positional terms in relation to 0 such as "above" and "below" to describe positive and negative integers.
   - **Where on the number line is positive 4?** 4 marks above 0
   - **Where on the number line is negative 5?** 5 marks below 0

   After they are comfortable with identifying integers on the vertical number line, place it horizontally so that positive integers are on the right and negative integers are on the left.

Opposite integers are integers that are the same distance from 0 on the number line, but on opposite sides of 0. The integers −4 and 4 are opposite integers.

- The opposite of 4 is −4.
- The opposite of −4 is 4.

Real-World EXAMPLES Opposites

2. **TEMPERATURE One winter day, the temperature in Rapid City, South Dakota, was 5° below zero. Write an integer to represent this situation. Then write its opposite.**

   5° below zero: −5
   The opposite of −5 is +5 or 5.

   So, −5 represents this situation. The integer +5 or 5 is its opposite.

3. **MONEY Demont deposited $75 into his bank account. Write an integer to represent this situation. Then write its opposite.**

   deposited $75: +75 or 75

   The opposite of 75 is −75. It represents withdrawing $75 from the account.

CHECK What You Know

Write an integer to represent each situation. Then graph the integer on a number line. See Example 1 (p. 533) 1–4. See margin.

1. lost $2
2. 20 degrees above 0
3. 5 points deducted from a grade
4. 6 yards gained in football

Write an integer to represent each situation. Then write its opposite. See Examples 2, 3 (p. 534)

5. Meagan spent $35. −35; +35 or 35
6. Geraldo gained 9 yards on the play. +9 or 9; −9
7. The temperature is 14° below zero. −14; +14 or 14
8. Mai earned $28 babysitting. +28 or 28; −28
9. Death Valley National Park in California is 282 feet below sea level. Write an integer to represent this situation. −282
10. Talk About It Explain how to find the opposite of an integer using a number line. See margin.

Additional Answers

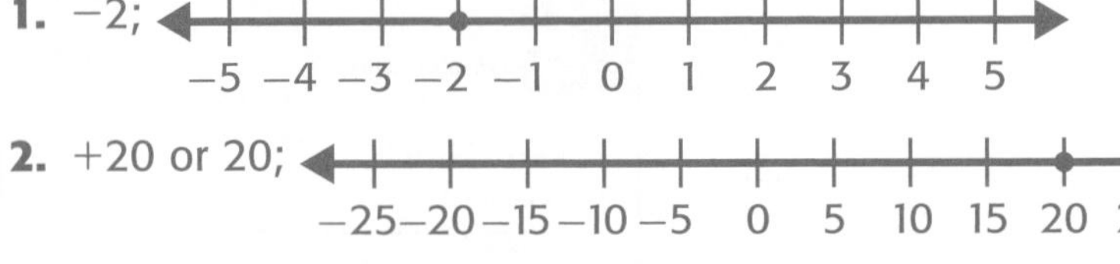

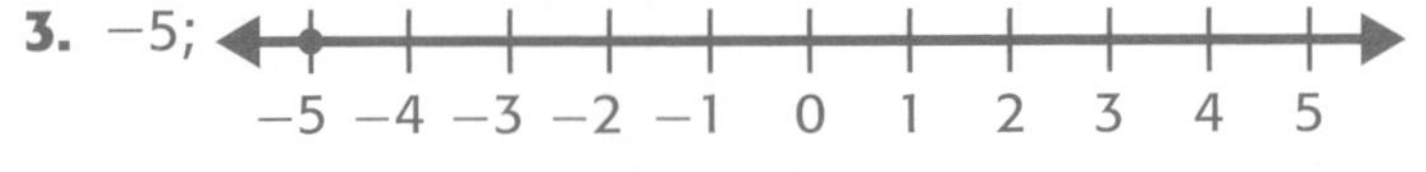

10. Sample answer: Find the number on the number line and determine the number of units from 0. The opposite number is the same number of units from 0, but in the opposite direction.

Practice and Problem Solving

See page R33.

Write an integer to represent each situation. Then graph the integer on a number line. See Example 1 (pp. 533–534) 11–16. See Ch. 12 Answer Appendix.

11. spent $3

12. profit of $8

13. 40° above zero

14. loss of 15 yards in football

15. 25 feet below sea level

16. 200 feet above ground

For Exercises 17–22, write an integer to represent each situation. Then write its opposite. See Examples 2, 3 (p. 534)

17. Sandi had to backtrack 32 meters. −32; +32 or 32

18. The lake was 42 feet deep. −42; +42 or 42

19. The temperature was 11° below zero. −11; +11 or 11

20. The cliff was 140 feet above sea level. +140 or 140; −140

21. A Ferris wheel goes up 212 feet. +212 or 212; −212

22. The elevation of Daytona Beach is 7 feet above sea level. 7; −7

Real-World PROBLEM SOLVING

Science The table shows the deepest dives of birds.

Bird	Deepest Dive (m)
Flying: thick-billed murre	210
Non-flying: Emperor penguin	534

23. Represent the dive of each bird using an integer. −210; −534

24. Which bird is able to dive deeper? Explain how you know. See Ch. 12 Answer Appendix.

H.O.T. Problems

25. OPEN ENDED Write an integer to represent an outside temperature today. Then write the opposite. Sample answer: +70 or 70; −70

26. WHICH ONE DOESN'T BELONG? Identify the situation that does not belong with the other three. Explain your reasoning. See Ch. 12 Answer Appendix.

17 feet below sea level	17 degrees	spending $17.00	17 points subtracted from a perfect score

27. WRITING IN MATH Write about a real-world situation that can be described using the integers −18 and 10. Sample answer: A diver descends 18 feet, then goes up 10 feet.

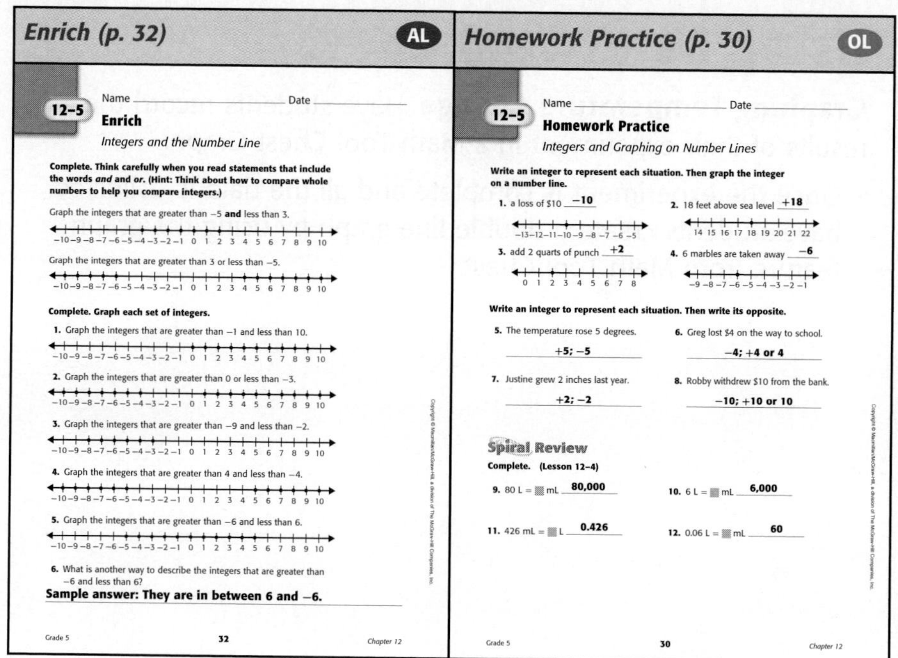

Enrich (p. 32) AL

12-5 Name ______ Date ______

Enrich

Integers and the Number Line

Complete. Think carefully when you read statements that include the words *and* and *or*. (Hint: Think about how to compare whole numbers to help you compare integers.)

Graph the integers that are greater than −5 **and** less than 3.

−10 −9 −8 −7 −6 −5 −4 −3 −2 −1 0 1 2 3 4 5 6 7 8 9 10

Graph the integers that are greater than 3 or less than −5.

−10 −9 −8 −7 −6 −5 −4 −3 −2 −1 0 1 2 3 4 5 6 7 8 9 10

Complete. Graph each set of integers.

1. Graph the integers that are greater than −1 and less than 10.

−10 −9 −8 −7 −6 −5 −4 −3 −2 −1 0 1 2 3 4 5 6 7 8 9 10

2. Graph the integers that are greater than 0 or less than −3.

−10 −9 −8 −7 −6 −5 −4 −3 −2 −1 0 1 2 3 4 5 6 7 8 9 10

3. Graph the integers that are greater than −9 and less than −2.

−10 −9 −8 −7 −6 −5 −4 −3 −2 −1 0 1 2 3 4 5 6 7 8 9 10

4. Graph the integers that are greater than 4 and less than −4.

−10 −9 −8 −7 −6 −5 −4 −3 −2 −1 0 1 2 3 4 5 6 7 8 9 10

5. Graph the integers that are greater than −6 and less than 6.

−10 −9 −8 −7 −6 −5 −4 −3 −2 −1 0 1 2 3 4 5 6 7 8 9 10

6. What is another way to describe the integers that are greater than −6 and less than 6?

Sample answer: They are in between 6 and −6.

Grade 5 32 Chapter 12

Homework Practice (p. 30) OL

12-5 Name ______ Date ______

Homework Practice

Integers and Graphing on Number Lines

Write an integer to represent each situation. Then graph the integer on a number line.

1. a loss of $10 **−10**

−13 −12 −11 −10 −9 −8 −7 −6 −5

2. 18 feet above sea level **+18**

14 15 16 17 18 19 20 21 22

3. add 2 quarts of punch **+2**

0 1 2 3 4 5 6 7 8

4. 6 marbles are taken away **−6**

−9 −8 −7 −6 −5 −4 −3 −2 −1

Write an integer to represent each situation. Then write its opposite.

5. The temperature rose 5 degrees. **+5; −5**

6. Greg lost $4 on the way to school. **−4; +4 or 4**

7. Justine grew 2 inches last year. **+2; −2**

8. Robby withdrew $10 from the bank. **−10; +10 or 10**

Spiral Review

Complete. (Lesson 12–4)

9. 80 L = ▒ mL **80,000**

10. 6 L = ▒ mL **6,000**

11. 426 mL = ▒ L **0.426**

12. 0.06 L = ▒ mL **60**

Grade 5 30 Chapter 12

3 Practice

Differentiate practice using these leveled assignments for Exercises 11–27.

Level	Assignment
BL Below/Approaching Level	11–14, 17–18, 21–24, 27
OL On Level	13–24, 26–27
AL Above/Beyond Level	12–24 even, 25–27

Have students discuss and complete the Higher Order Thinking problems. Encourage students to draw and use a number line as they work to solve Exercise 26.

WRITING IN MATH Have students complete Exercise 27 in their Math Journals. You may choose to use this exercise as an optional formative assessment.

4 Assess

Formative Assessment

Tell students that Rafael spent $5 from his savings.

- **What integer does the situation show?** −5
- **What is the opposite integer?** +5 or 5

Quick Check

Are students continuing to struggle with using integers to represent real-life situations?

If Yes → Small Group Options (p. 533B)

If No → Independent Work Options (p. 533B)

CRM Skills Practice Worksheet (p. 29)

CRM Enrich Worksheet (p. 32)

Ticket Out the Door Write the following on the board: 6° below zero. Ask students to graph this situation and its opposite.

COMMON ERROR!

Exercises 11–24 Students may have difficulty understanding which problems describe a positive or negative integer. Encourage them to make a list of key words that indicate positive and another that indicate negative integers.

Technology Activity for 12-6

Lesson Planner

Objective

Use technology to make and explain line graphs.

Resources

Math Online macmillanmh.com

Math Tool Chest

Getting Started

- The activities and exercises on p. 536 use the Graphs Tool in Math Tool Chest. They may be completed as a class, in pairs, or individually.
- Have students read each example on p. 536.
- As a class, work through the activity in each example following the instructions on the page.

Think About It

Alone or in pairs, have students complete Exercises 1–4 in **Think About It** as you observe their work.

Extending the Link

- Students can chart the temperature throughout the day and create a graph showing temperature change over time.

Additional Answer

1. Both graphs show a gradual change in temperature. In the first graph, the line is decreasing, and in the second graph, the line is increasing.

Technology Activity for 12-6

Units of Temperature

MAIN IDEA
I will use technology to make and explain line graphs.

Mrs. Rodriguez did a science experiment for her class that measured how fast a cup of hot water cooled. She measured its temperature every two minutes. The line graph shows her data.

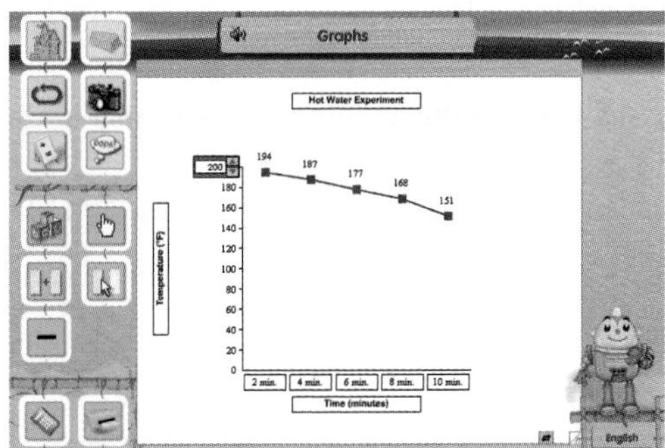

In the following Activity, you will make a similar line graph.

ACTIVITY Graphing Temperature Change

Step 1 Pour 1 cup of cold water into a glass.

Step 2 Measure the temperature of the water every two minutes for ten minutes.

Step 3 Use the Graph feature from the Math Tool Chest™ to make a line graph of the data.

Think About It 2–4. See students' work.

1. Compare and contrast your graph with the graph above. See margin.
2. After 10 minutes, what was the change in temperature of your water?
3. Predict what the temperature will be if 5 more minutes pass.
4. Room temperature is about 65°F. Predict how long it will be until the temperature of the water reaches room temperature. Check your prediction by continuing to measure the temperature of the water every five minutes.

Using Math Tool Chest

Graphing Temperature Change Have students record the results of their experiment in a Math Tool Chest Graph.

- Once the experiment is complete and all the data is collected, have students create a double line graph by using the graph feature from Math Tool Chest.

LESSON

12-6 Units of Temperature

Lesson Planner

Objective

Choose appropriate temperatures in degrees Fahrenheit and Celsius.

Vocabulary

degrees, Celsius (°C), Fahrenheit (°F)

Resources

Materials: self-sticking notes
Manipulatives: thermometers
Literature Connection: *Measuring Up!* by Sandra Markle
Alternate Lesson: Use *IMPACT Mathematics*: Unit H to provide practice with temperature.
Teacher Technology
TeacherWorks • Interactive Classroom

Focus on Math Background

The Celsius temperature scale was formerly known as the *Centigrade* scale, and some people still refer to it by that name. Similar to other metric units, there are 100 Celsius degrees between the freezing point of water (0°C) and the boiling point of water (100°C). The corresponding Fahrenheit temperatures are 32°F and 212°F. The Celsius and Fahrenheit scales are numerically equal at one point only, as −40°C measures the same temperature as −40°F. Calculating temperature change is similar to calculating elapsed time (Lesson 11-7). In this lesson, change in temperature is only found for situations in which both the initial and final temperatures are positive. This is done in order to avoid operations with negative integers.

There is no theoretical upper limit to temperature. But no object can ever be cooled below *absolute zero*, the temperature at which all molecular motion would stop. Absolute zero, also the zero point of the SI *kelvin* scale, is approximately −273°C or −459°F.

Daily Routine

Use these suggestions before beginning the lesson on p. 537.

5-Minute Check

(Reviews Lesson 12-5)

Write an integer to represent each situation. Then write its opposite.

1. 400 feet above sea level +400; −400
2. 5 degrees below 0 −5; +5
3. Spent $7 −7; +7
4. Dove 20 feet below the surface −20; +20
5. Flew at 15,000 feet altitude +15,000; −15,000

Problem of the Day

Forty out of fifty people surveyed said that they preferred chocolate ice cream over vanilla ice cream. What fraction of the people surveyed preferred vanilla ice cream? $\frac{1}{5}$ of the people; check students' explanations.

Building Math Vocabulary

Write the lesson vocabulary words and their definitions on the board.

Have students write the words and their definitions in their notes. Ask them to look up and report on interesting facts about the two scientists for whom the two temperature scales are named.

Differentiated Instruction

Small Group Options

SPATIAL, KINESTHETIC 

Option 1 Below Level BL

Materials: chart paper, markers, counters

- Pair students. Have each student draw three pictures of activities they do outdoors.
- Partners switch papers and write down an appropriate temperature in °F and °C to match the picture.
- Switch back to check.

LINGUISTIC, LOGICAL 

Option 2 English Language Learners ELL

Materials: magazine pictures
Core Vocabulary: hot, warm/cool, freezing
Common Use Verb: feel
See Math This strategy uses background knowledge and visuals to introduce temperature vocabulary.

- Show students a model of a thermometer.
- Label 100°C as hot (boiling water)
- Label 25°C as warm (sunny with flowers)
- Label 10°C as cool (person in jacket, hands in pockets)
- Label 0°C as freezing (ice)
- Have groups sort through the pictures and put them in order of hottest to coolest. Encourage them to use target vocabulary.
- Students then discuss what the corresponding temperatures in degrees Fahrenheit would be.

Use this worksheet to provide additional support for English Language Learners.

English Language Learners (p. 109) ELL

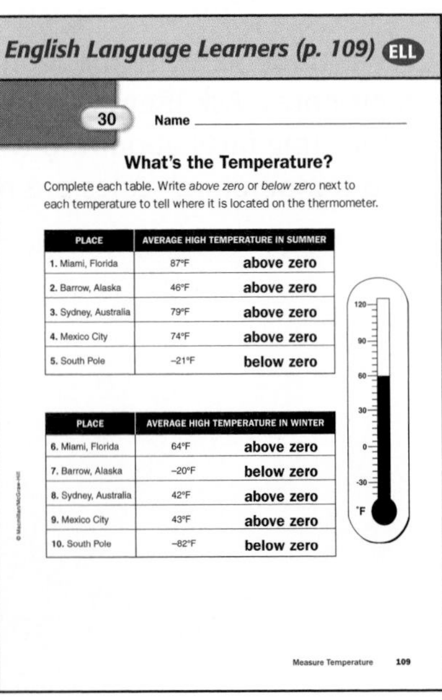

30 Name ____________

What's the Temperature?

Complete each table. Write *above zero* or *below zero* next to each temperature to tell where it is located on the thermometer.

PLACE	AVERAGE HIGH TEMPERATURE IN SUMMER	
1. Miami, Florida	87°F	above zero
2. Barrow, Alaska	46°F	above zero
3. Sydney, Australia	79°F	above zero
4. Mexico City	74°F	above zero
5. South Pole	−21°F	below zero

PLACE	AVERAGE HIGH TEMPERATURE IN WINTER	
6. Miami, Florida	64°F	above zero
7. Barrow, Alaska	−20°F	below zero
8. Sydney, Australia	42°F	above zero
9. Mexico City	43°F	above zero
10. South Pole	−82°F	below zero

Measure Temperature 109

Independent Work Options

SOCIAL 

Option 1 Early Finishers AL

Materials: thermometer, two number cubes

- Have students work in pairs. One student rolls the number cubes and uses the digits to write a temperature.
- The second student rolls one number cube. If an odd number is rolled, both students write the temperature in degrees Celsius. If an even number is rolled, they write the temperature in degrees Fahrenheit.
- Each student writes a situation for which they think the temperature is appropriate. After they finish writing, have the students compare their ideas to the thermometers to check for reasonableness. Continue the activity as time allows.

Option 2 Student Technology

Math Online macmillanmh.com

Personal Tutor • Extra Examples

Option 3 Learning Station: Reading (p. 512G)

Direct students to the Reading Learning Station for opportunities to explore and extend the lesson concept.

Option 4 Problem-Solving Practice

Reinforce problem-solving skills and strategies with the Problem-Solving Practice worksheet.

Problem Solving (p. 36) BL OL AL

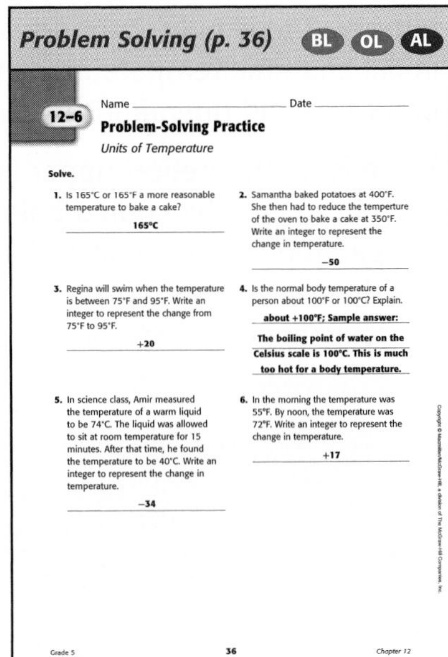

Name ____________ Date ____________

12–6 **Problem-Solving Practice**

Units of Temperature

Solve.

1. Is 165°C or 165°F a more reasonable temperature to bake a cake?
   165°C
2. Samantha baked potatoes at 400°F. She then had to reduce the temperture of the oven to bake a cake at 350°F. Write an integer to represent the change in temperature.
   −50
3. Regina will swim when the temperature is between 75°F and 95°F. Write an integer to represent the change from 75°F to 95°F.
   +20
4. Is the normal body temperature of a person about 100°F or 100°C? Explain.
   about +100°F; Sample answer: The boiling point of water on the Celsius scale is 100°C. This is much too hot for a body temperature.
5. In science class, Amir measured the temperature of a warm liquid to be 74°C. The liquid was allowed to sit at room temperature for 15 minutes. After that time, he found the temperature to be 40°C. Write an integer to represent the change in temperature.
   −34
6. In the morning the temperature was 55°F. By noon, the temperature was 72°F. Write an integer to represent the change in temperature.
   +17

Grade 5 36 Chapter 12

12-6 Units of Temperature

GET READY to Learn

Animals that are cold-blooded take on the temperature of their surroundings. So, if the outside temperature is 70°F, the body temperature of a snake will also be 70°F.

MAIN IDEA

I will choose appropriate temperatures in degrees Fahrenheit and Celsius.

New Vocabulary

degrees
Celsius (°C)
Fahrenheit (°F)

Math Online

macmillanmh.com

- Extra Examples
- Personal Tutor
- Self-Check Quiz

Degrees are the units of measurement used to describe temperature. Temperature can be measured in degrees **Celsius (°C)** and in degrees **Fahrenheit (°F)**.

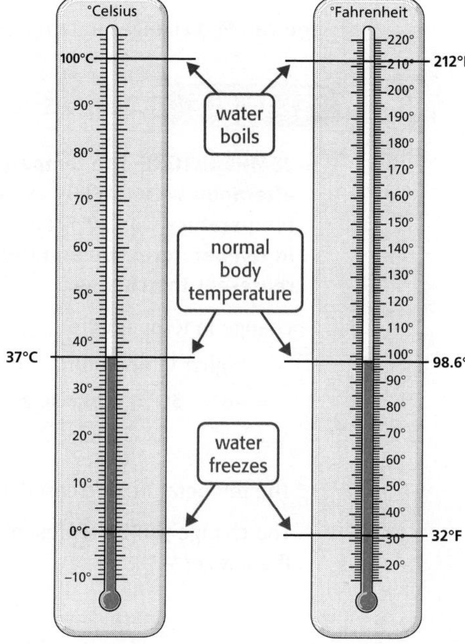

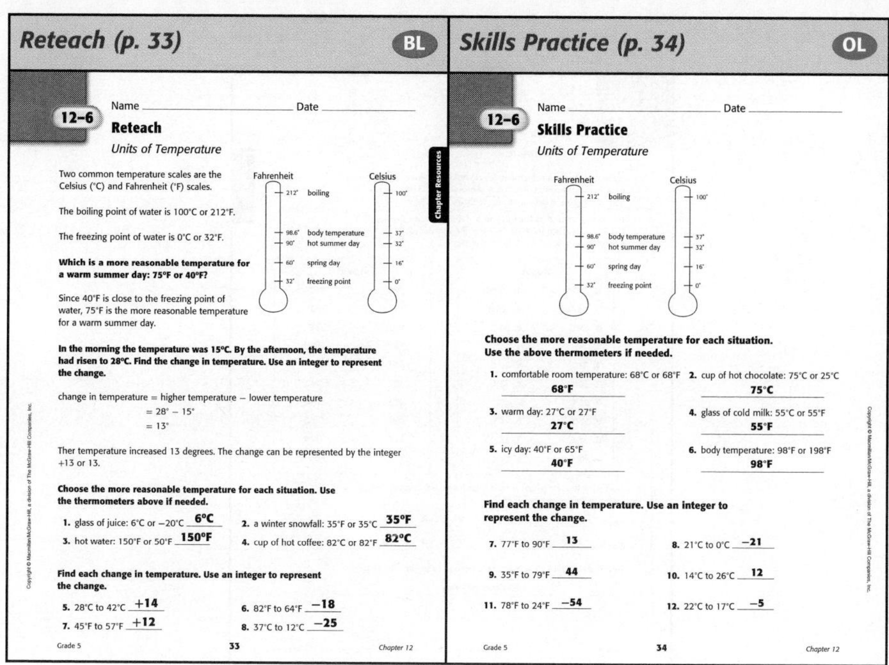

Reteach (p. 33) BL

12-6 Name ______ Date ______

Reteach

Units of Temperature

Two common temperature scales are the Celsius (°C) and Fahrenheit (°F) scales.

The boiling point of water is 100°C or 212°F.

The freezing point of water is 0°C or 32°F.

Fahrenheit: 212° boiling; 98.6° body temperature; 90° hot summer day; 60° spring day; 32° freezing point
Celsius: 100°; 37°; 32°; 16°; 0°

Which is a more reasonable temperature for a warm summer day: 75°F or 40°F?

Since 40°F is close to the freezing point of water, 75°F is the more reasonable temperature for a warm summer day.

In the morning the temperature was 15°C. By the afternoon, the temperature had risen to 28°C. Find the change in temperature. Use an integer to represent the change.

change in temperature = higher temperature – lower temperature
= 28° – 15°
= 13°

Ther temperature increased 13 degrees. The change can be represented by the integer +13 or 13.

Choose the more reasonable temperature for each situation. Use the thermometers above if needed.

1. glass of juice: 6°C or –20°C **6°C**
2. a winter snowfall: 35°F or 35°C **35°F**
3. hot water: 150°F or 50°F **150°F**
4. cup of hot coffee: 82°C or 82°F **82°C**

Find each change in temperature. Use an integer to represent the change.

5. 28°C to 42°C **+14**
6. 82°F to 64°F **–18**
7. 45°F to 57°F **+12**
8. 37°C to 12°C **–25**

Grade 5 33 *Chapter 12*

Chapter Resources

Skills Practice (p. 34) OL

12-6 Name ______ Date ______

Skills Practice

Units of Temperature

Fahrenheit: 212° boiling; 98.6° body temperature; 90° hot summer day; 60° spring day; 32° freezing point
Celsius: 100°; 37°; 32°; 16°; 0°

Choose the more reasonable temperature for each situation. Use the above thermometers if needed.

1. comfortable room temperature: 68°C or 68°F **68°F**
2. cup of hot chocolate: 75°C or 25°C **75°C**
3. warm day: 27°C or 27°F **27°C**
4. glass of cold milk: 55°C or 55°F **55°F**
5. icy day: 40°F or 65°F **40°F**
6. body temperature: 98°F or 198°F **98°F**

Find each change in temperature. Use an integer to represent the change.

7. 77°F to 90°F **13**
8. 21°C to 0°C **–21**
9. 35°F to 79°F **44**
10. 14°C to 26°C **12**
11. 78°F to 24°F **–54**
12. 22°C to 17°C **–5**

Grade 5 34 *Chapter 12*

12-6 Units of Temperature

1 Introduce

Activity Choice 1 • Hands-On

- Ask students to meet in small groups to create a list of situations where measurement of temperature is used.
- On the board, write general categories, such as cooking or weather, from students' ideas.
- **What are ways that temperature is reported in weather reports?** high temperature, low temperature, record high and low temperatures
- Have students meet in their groups again to discuss reasonable temperatures in the situations they previously listed. **What is a reasonable temperature for baking a cake?** 350°–400°F
- Ask students to report on their reasonable temperatures for each situation.

Activity Choice 2 • Literature

Introduce the lesson with *Measuring Up!* by Sandra Markle. For a related math activity, see p. TR56.

2 Teach

Scaffolding Questions

Have students examine a thermometer that is marked with both Fahrenheit and Celsius.

- **Water boils at 212°F. What temperature is that in °C?** 100°C
- **A nice summer day is about 85°F. About what temperature is that in °C?** about 30°C
- Have students read the current temperature on their thermometers.
- **What is the current temperature of our classroom in Celsius and Fahrenheit?** Answers will vary; 68°F is about 20°C.

GET READY to Learn

Have students open their books and read the information in **Get Ready to Learn**. Introduce **degrees**, **Celsius °C** and **Fahrenheit °F**. As a class, work through **Examples 1–3**.

Choose Reasonable Temperatures

Example 2 Be sure students understand how to use the information about freezing point, boiling point, and normal body temperature on the Celsius thermometer and the Fahrenheit thermometer to help them to make judgments about the questions in the problems.

ADDITIONAL EXAMPLES

1. Which thermometer shows a more reasonable temperature for a swimming pool that is comfortable to swim in? 80°F

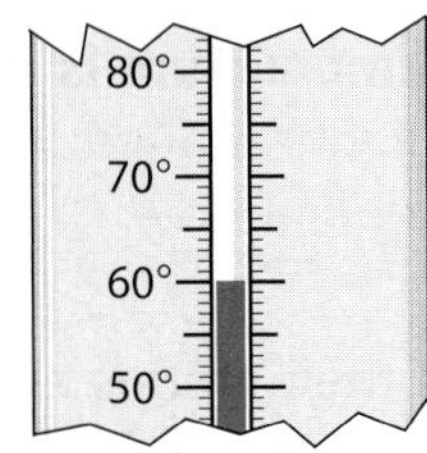

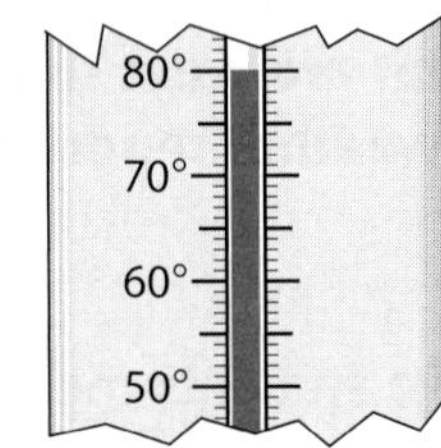

2. Which is a more reasonable temperature for a spring day: 20°C or 40°C? 20°C
3. In early summer, a swimming pool had a temperature of 24°C. By the end of summer the temperature was 39°C. Find the change in temperature. Use an integer to represent the change. 15°C; +15

CHECK What You Know

As a class, have students complete Exercises 1–9 in **Check What You Know** as you observe their work.

Exercise 9 Assess student comprehension before assigning practice exercises.

BL Alternate Teaching Strategy

If students have trouble choosing appropriate temperatures...

Then use one of these reteach options:

1. CRM **Daily Reteach Worksheet** (p. 33)
2. Display a poster of Celsius and Fahrenheit thermometers. Have students write a situation and its temperature in °F on a self-sticking note. Ask them to place the note near that temperature.
   - Then have students determine and write the same situation and the temperature in °C on a second self-sticking note to be placed on the Celsius thermometer.
   - Have students use the poster for reference.

Real-World EXAMPLES — Choose Reasonable Temperatures

Remember
Some thermometers have both °F and °C. If you know the temperature in one scale, you can read across to tell the temperature in the other scale.

1. **WEATHER Which shows a more reasonable temperature for a snowy day?**

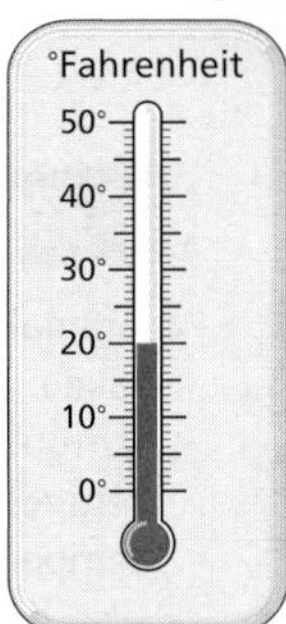

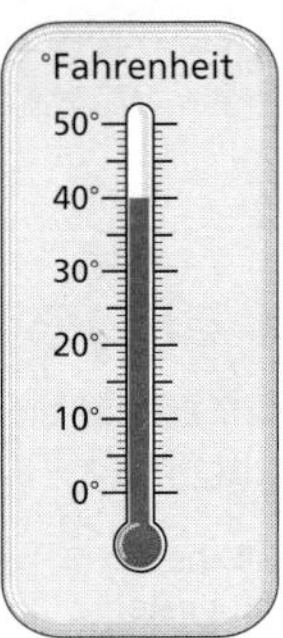

The freezing point of water is 32°F. 20°F is below the freezing point of water. 40°F is too warm for snow. So, the more reasonable temperature is 20°F.

2. **Which is a more reasonable temperature for warm water: 23°C or 43°C? Use the thermometers on page 537 to help you decide.**

23°C is cooler than body temperature. Water that is 23°C would feel cool to the touch. So, the more reasonable estimate is 43°C.

You can find changes in temperature by using subtraction.

EXAMPLE — Subtract Temperature

3. **TEMPERATURE The temperature this afternoon was 48°F. By evening, the temperature was 30°F. Find the change in temperature. Use an integer to represent the change.**

change in temperature
= higher temperature − lower temperature
= 48° − 30° Substitute the temperatures.
= 18° Subtract.

The temperature decreased 18 degrees.

The change can be represented by the integer −18.

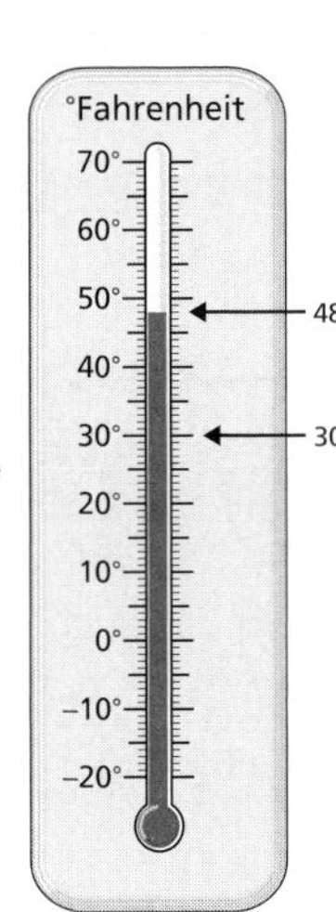

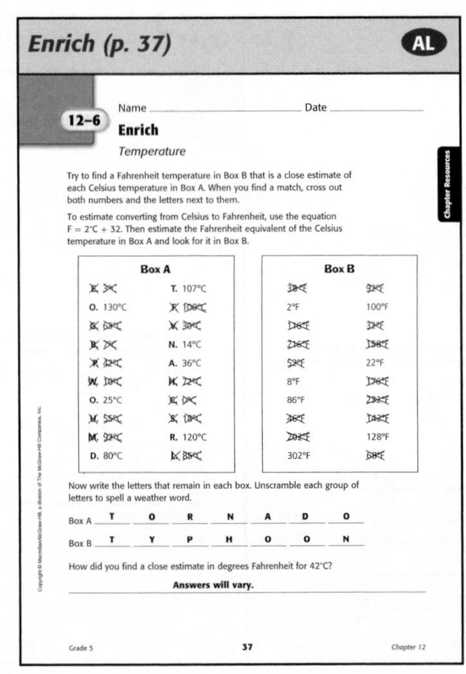

Enrich (p. 37) AL

12–6
Name ______ Date ______
Enrich
Temperature

Try to find a Fahrenheit temperature in Box B that is a close estimate of each Celsius temperature in Box A. When you find a match, cross out both numbers and the letters next to them.

To estimate converting from Celsius to Fahrenheit, use the equation F = 2°C + 32. Then estimate the Fahrenheit equivalent of the Celsius temperature in Box A and look for it in Box B.

Box A		Box B	
E. 3°C	T. 107°C	38°F	92°F
O. 130°C	K. 100°C	2°F	100°F
G. 63°C	V. 30°C	136°F	32°F
B. 7°C	N. 14°C	216°F	158°F
R. 42°C	A. 36°C	52°F	22°F
W. 18°C	H. 72°C	8°F	176°F
O. 25°C	C. 0°C	86°F	232°F
U. 55°C	S. 13°C	46°F	142°F
M. 92°C	R. 120°C	202°F	128°F
D. 80°C	L. 85°C	302°F	68°F

Now write the letters that remain in each box. Unscramble each group of letters to spell a weather word.

Box A T O R N A D O

Box B T Y P H O O N

How did you find a close estimate in degrees Fahrenheit for 42°C?

Answers will vary.

Chapter Resources

Grade 5 37 Chapter 12

CHECK What You Know

Choose the more reasonable temperature for each situation. Use the thermometers on page 537. See Examples 1, 2 (p. 538)

1. a cold day: 5°C or 32°C **5°C**
2. hot water: 65°F or 190°F **190°F**
3. a snow cone: 30°C or 30°F **30°F**
4. warm bowl of soup: 82°C or 82°F **82°F**
5. The thermometer at the right shows the temperature outside. Could it snow today? Explain. **No; 10°C is about 50°F, which is above the freezing point and too warm for snow.**

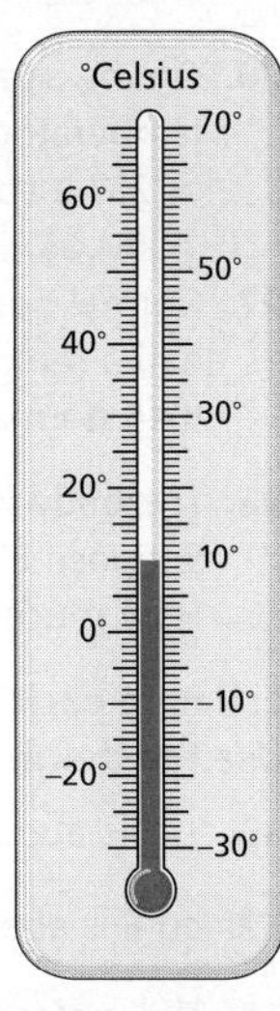

Find each change in temperature. Use an integer to represent the change. See Example 3 (p. 538)

6. 0°C to 12°C **+12**
7. 65°F to 59°F **−6**
8. Yesterday, the temperature of the water in a swimming pool was 82°F. Today, the temperature of the water is 78°F. Describe the change in temperature with an integer. **−4°**
9. Talk About It Describe how you can estimate the temperature in degrees Celsius when you know the temperature in degrees Fahrenheit. Give an example. **Sample answer: Use a thermometer that has both Celsius and Fahrenheit scales. Find the temperature in degrees Fahrenheit on the scale and read across to find the temperature in degrees Celsius. For example, 65°F is about 18°C.**

Practice and Problem Solving

See page R33.

Choose the more reasonable temperature for each situation. Use the thermometers on page 537. See Examples 1, 2 (p. 538)

10. person with a fever: 38°C or 98°C **38°C**
11. glass of lemonade: 46°F or 10°F **46°F**
12. bicycling: 130°F or 75°F **75°F**
13. swimming: 30°C or 10°C **30°C**
14. a summer day: 82°C or 82°F **82°F**
15. boiling water: 100°F or 100°C **100°C**
16. frozen yogurt: 20°F or 20°C **20°F**
17. melting ice: 1°C or 1°F **1°C**

Find each change in temperature. Use an integer to represent the change. See Example 3 (p. 538)

18. 55°F to 65°F **+10**
19. 16°C to 0°C **−16**
20. 36°C to 12°C **−24**
21. 8°C to 11°C **+3**
22. 94°F to 61°F **−33**
23. 49°F to 77°F **+28**

3 Practice

Differentiate practice using these leveled assignments for Exercises 10–43.

Level	Assignment
BL Below/ Approaching Level	10–13, 18–20, 24–26, 29–31, 37–40
OL On Level	12–17, 24–40, 43
AL Above/Beyond Level	13–39 odd, 41–43

Have students discuss and complete the Higher Order Thinking problems. Encourage students to use a thermometer to compare temperatures in degrees Celsius with those in degrees Fahrenheit as they solve each problem.

WRITING IN ▶MATH Have students complete Exercise 43 in their Math Journals. You may choose to use this as an optional formative assessment.

! COMMON ERROR!

Exercises 18–23 Students may have trouble using an integer to express the change in temperature when the beginning temperature is not 0°. Help students to see that if they must add (+) degrees to the beginning temperature to arrive at the second temperature, the change is a positive integer. If they must subtract (−) degrees from the beginning temperature to arrive at the second temperature, the change is a negative integer.

Assess

Formative Assessment

Write the following on the board: Morning temperature: 66°F, Evening temperature: 25°C.

- **Which temperature is warmer? Explain.** 25°C is warmer; 25°C is about 77°F
- **How would you find the change in temperature between the two measurements?** Sample answer: Change degrees Celsius to degrees Fahrenheit and compare. **What integer would be used to describe the change in degrees Fahrenheit?** +11

Quick Check **Are students continuing to struggle with choosing appropriate temperatures in degrees Fahrenheit and Celsius for real life situations?**

If Yes → Small Group Options (p. 537B)
Strategic Intervention Guide (p. 124)

If No → Independent Work Options (p. 537B)
CRM Skills Practice Worksheet (p. 34)
CRM Enrich Worksheet (p. 37)

Yesterday's News Have students write a short paragraph about how the concepts learned in Lesson 12-5 about integers helped them to work successfully with the new material today.

For Exercises 24–26, use the table at the right. It shows the high and low temperatures for several cities for a certain day in January.

City	High Temperature (°F)	Low Temperature (°F)
Boston	37	22
Detroit	31	18
Omaha	32	12
Pittsburgh	35	20
Seattle	43	36

24. Which city had the greatest temperature change? What was the temperature change? Omaha, 20°F

25. Which city had the least temperature change? What was the temperature change? Seattle, 10°F

26. On the same day, Denver's high temperature was 43°F and low temperature was 15°F. Does this change your answer to Exercise 24 or 25? If so, how? Yes, it had a temperature change of 28°F, which changes the answer to Exercise 24.

27. Normal body temperature for a human is 98.6°F. Lilly's little brother had a temperature of 101.3°F. How much greater is his temperature than normal body temperature? 2.7°F

28. The body temperature of a snake is the same as its environment. Suppose it was 25°C outside, and the temperature is now 21.5°C. How much did the snake's body temperature decrease? 3.5°C

Estimate each temperature in degrees Celsius or degrees Fahrenheit. Use the thermometers on page 537. 29–34. Sample answers given.

29. 1°C is about ■ °F 34
30. 212°F is about ■ °C 100
31. 68°F is about ■ °C 20
32. 30°F is about ■ °C −1
33. 15°C is about ■ °F 59
34. 44°F is about ■ °C 7

35. The preferred temperature for the inside of a refrigerator is about 35°F. Estimate this temperature in degrees Celsius. 3°C

36. If you wanted to go to a water park, describe a good outside temperature in degrees Celsius. Sample answer: 28°C

Data File

In New Orleans, Louisiana, it is not uncommon for summer days to reach 100°F. The average temperature in August is 83°F. The temperature at night may drop to 74°F.

Estimate each temperature in degrees Celsius.

37. 83°F Sample answer: 30°C
38. 74°F Sample answer: 25°C

Use an integer to represent each change in temperature.

39. 83°F to 100°F +17°F
40. 83°F to 74°F −9°F

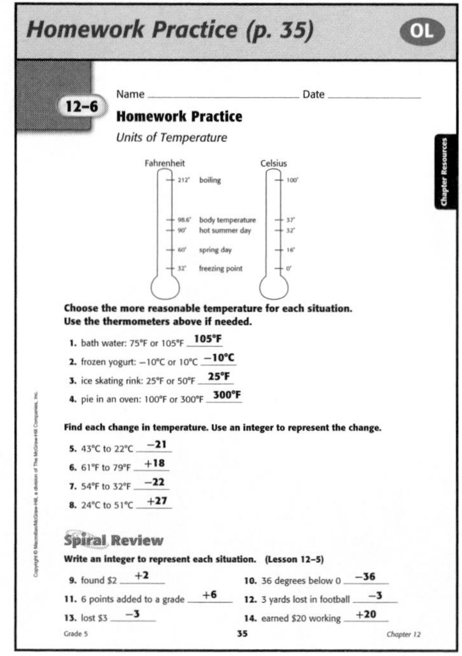

Homework Practice (p. 35) OL

12–6 Name ______ Date ______

Homework Practice

Units of Temperature

Choose the more reasonable temperature for each situation. Use the thermometers above if needed.

1. bath water: 75°F or 105°F **105°F**
2. frozen yogurt: −10°C or 10°C **−10°C**
3. ice skating rink: 25°F or 50°F **25°F**
4. pie in an oven: 100°F or 300°F **300°F**

Find each change in temperature. Use an integer to represent the change.

5. 43°C to 22°C **−21**
6. 61°F to 79°F **+18**
7. 54°F to 32°F **−22**
8. 24°C to 51°C **+27**

Spiral Review

Write an integer to represent each situation. (Lesson 12–5)

9. found $2 **+2**
10. 36 degrees below 0 **−36**
11. 6 points added to a grade **+6**
12. 3 yards lost in football **−3**
13. lost $3 **−3**
14. earned $20 working **+20**

Chapter Resources

H.O.T. Problems

41. **OPEN ENDED** Describe two real-world situations in which the temperatures 21°C and 210°F would be appropriate. Sample answers: 21°C, a warm day; 210°F: cooking food on the stove

42. **CHALLENGE** Cora was in a place where the temperature was about 10°C. When she walked to a different place, the temperature was about 26°C. Describe a situation in which these temperatures are reasonable. Sample answer: She is outside during winter, and then walks inside a house.

43. **WRITING IN MATH** Write a problem that requires you to find the change in temperature. Then exchange problems with a classmate and solve. See margin.

TEST Practice

44. Which situation is best represented by the integer graphed below? (Lesson 12-5) C

−20 −15 −10 −5 0 5 10 15 20

A 15° below zero

B giving away $15

C 15 feet above sea level

D 15 meters deep

45. The temperature at 10:15 A.M. in Chicago was 57°F. By 3:45 P.M., the temperature was 78°F. How many degrees Fahrenheit did the temperature rise? (Lesson 12-6) G

F 5°F

G 21°F

H 23°F

J 30°F

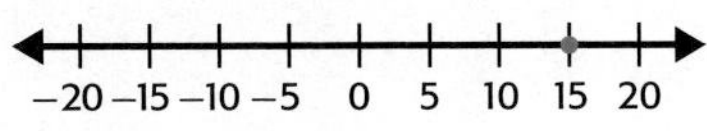

Spiral Review

Write an integer to represent each situation. Then write its opposite. (Lesson 12-5)

46. An altitude is 139 feet below sea level. −139; +139 or 139

47. A baby gained 12 ounces. +12 or 12; −12

48. The temperature is 58° above zero. +58 or 58; −58

49. Hai spent $4. −4; +4 or 4

Complete. (Lesson 12-4)

50. 2 L = ■ mL 2,000

51. 5,000 mL = ■ L 5

52. 750 mL = ■ L 0.75

53. One can of soup is 12 fluid ounces and makes two servings. If 8 fluid ounces of water are added, what is the capacity of one serving? (Lesson 11-4) 10 fl oz

TEST Practice

Reviews Lessons 12-5 and 12-6

Assign the Test Practice problems to provide daily reinforcement of test-taking skills.

Spiral Review

Reviews Lessons 11-4, 12-4, and 12-5

Review and assess mastery of skills and concepts from previous chapters.

Additional Answers

43. Sample answer: The temperature of a room is 82°F. After the air conditioner is turned on, the temperature is 66°F. What is the change in temperature? Sample answer: a decrease of 16°

Lesson Planner

Objective

Interpret information and data from social studies to solve problems.

National Standard 

Students will understand the history of science.

Activate Prior Knowledge

Before you turn students' attention to the pages, ask them to discuss the Wright Brothers.

- **For what accomplishment were the Wright Brothers famous?** They were the first people to fly.
- **What was the name of their flyer?** The Kitty Hawk

Use the Student Page

Ask students to read the information on p. 542 and answer these questions:

- **Was the temperature on the day of the Wright Brothers' first flight greater or less than 0 degrees Celsius?** greater
- **What was the difference between the length and the height of the flyer?** 3.6 meters

The Wright Measurements

The Wright brothers were self-trained engineers from Ohio who designed, built, and piloted the first engine-powered airplane. On December 17, 1903, the Wright brothers completed the world's first successful controlled flight. They later named the flyer the *Kitty Hawk*, after the location in North Carolina near where they made this historic flight.

The temperature at Kitty Hawk on this day was 34°F, but because of the wind chill factor, the temperature felt like 8°F. These might not have been the most comfortable weather conditions, but the winds definitely helped the Wright Brothers' flyer to stay in the air!

On that cold December day, the Wright brothers made four flights in their flyer. On the first flight, which was piloted by Orville Wright, the flyer traveled 39 meters in 12 seconds. On the fourth flight, Wilbur flew 279 meters in 59 seconds.

Wright Brothers' 1903 Flyer Data	
Wingspan	12.3 m
Length	6.4 m
Height	2.8 m
Wing Droop	25.4 cm
Mass	229 kg
Speed	17 km/h

Did You Know?
Before their experiments with airplanes, the Wright brothers were successful bicycle manufacturers.

Orville and Wilbur Wright

Real-World Math

Use the information and the table on page 542 to solve each problem.

1. What was the wingspan of the *Kitty Hawk* flyer in centimeters? 1,230 cm
2. What was the mass of the flyer in grams? 229,000 g
3. What was the wing droop of the flyer in millimeters? 254 mm
4. What was the air speed of the flyer in meters per hour? 17,000 m/h
5. How many more meters did Wilbur fly on the fourth flight than Orville flew on the first flight? 240 m
6. What was the difference between the wingspan and the length of the flyer? 5.9 m
7. If Orville Wright's mass was 81 kilograms at the time of the flight, what was the combined mass of the flyer and Orville Wright? 310 kg

Real-World Math

Assign the exercises on p. 543. Encourage students to choose a problem-solving strategy before beginning each exercise. If necessary, review the strategies suggested in Lesson 12-7, p. 545.

Exercise 1 Remind students to multiply meters by 100 to get centimeters.

Exercise 2 Remind students that there are 1,000 grams in a kilogram.

Exercise 4 Remind students that there are 1,000 meters in a kilometer.

WRITING IN ▶MATH Have students create a word problem that uses the information found in the text and in the chart on pp. 542–543.

Extend the Activity

Have students estimate the actual temperature and the temperature with wind chill in degrees Celsius, and plot the two temperatures on a number line to show the difference between the two.

Problem-Solving Investigation
Choose a Strategy

Lesson Planner

Objective

Choose the best strategy to solve a problem.

Resources

Teacher Technology

TeacherWorks • Interactive Classroom

Real-World Problem Solving Library
Math and Science: *How Big is the Solar System?*

Use these leveled books to reinforce and extend problem-solving skills and strategies.

Leveled for:

- OL On Level
- ELL Sheltered English
- SP Spanish

For additional support, see the Real-World Problem Solving Teacher Guide.

Daily Routine

Use these suggestions before beginning the lesson on p. 544.

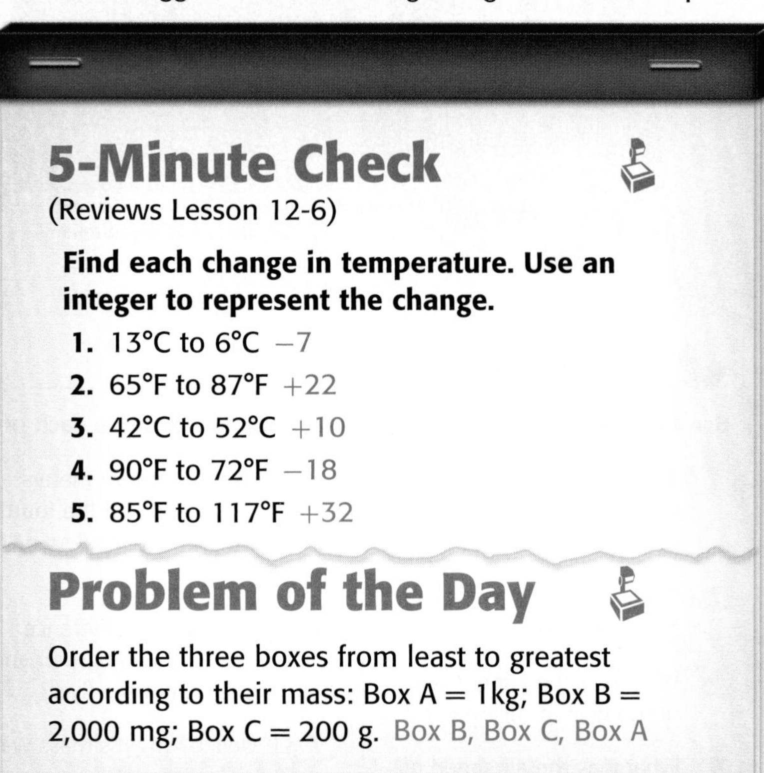

5-Minute Check

(Reviews Lesson 12-6)

Find each change in temperature. Use an integer to represent the change.

1. 13°C to 6°C −7
2. 65°F to 87°F +22
3. 42°C to 52°C +10
4. 90°F to 72°F −18
5. 85°F to 117°F +32

Problem of the Day

Order the three boxes from least to greatest according to their mass: Box A = 1kg; Box B = 2,000 mg; Box C = 200 g. Box B, Box C, Box A

Differentiated Instruction

Small Group Options

LOGICAL

Option 1 Gifted and Talented AL

Materials: chart paper, markers, pencils, paper

- Copy the following problem on chart paper:

Use only one digit from 1–9. Make numbers with that digit that have a sum of 1000. You may use the digit you choose only eight times.

$888 + 88 + 8 + 8 + 8 = 1{,}000$

- If students have difficulty beginning, use the example $222 + 222 + 22 = 466$.
- Students should identify the strategy of *guess and check* to solve this problem.

INTERPERSONAL

Option 2 English Language Learners ELL

Core Vocabulary: broke, eat, lunch
Common Use Verb: break apart
Do Math This strategy uses solving simpler problems to help students integrate strategies when dividing.

- Read and post: "There are 300 5th grade students in the school. $\frac{1}{4}$ of them eat school lunch. How many lunches does the school make each day?"
- Write: "$\frac{1}{4}$ of 300 is ___ lunches."
- Say: "What ways can we break apart the problem to make it simpler to solve?"
- Allow students to attempt solving in groups. Allow groups to show their solutions. If groups are struggling, prompt them to break 300 into 3 groups of 100.
- Discuss results and methods.

Independent Work Options

LINGUISTIC

Option 1 Early Finishers OL AL

Materials: index cards, pencils

- On the front of an index card, students write a real-world problem that can be solved using a number line. Encourage students to write a problem about situations in which negative integers are used.
- Ask students to exchange cards.
- Have students solve the problem by using the *four-step plan* and drawing a number line on the back of the card. Students can then return the card to the writer for evaluation. Repeat activity as time allows.

Option 2 Student Technology

Math Online macmillanmh.com

Personal Tutor • Extra Examples

Option 3 Learning Station: Health (p. 512H)

Direct students to the Health Learning Station for opportunities to explore and extend the lesson concept.

12-7 Problem-Solving Investigation

1 Introduce

Activity Choice • Review

- Pose the following problem:

  Emilio wants to plant flowers along both sides of a walkway that is 64 feet long. The plants come in flats of twelve. If he places a plant every 6 inches and one at the beginning and end of each side of the walkway, how many flats of plants will he need? 22 flats
- **What strategies can be used to solve the problem?** *draw a picture* or *write an equation*
- **What equation could be used to solve the problem?** $[(64 \times 2) + 1] \div 12 = 10.75$ flats for each side of the walk, $10.75 \times 2 = 21.5$ flats.

2 Teach

Have students read the problem. Guide them through the problem-solving steps.

Understand Using the questions, review what students know and need to find.

Plan Have them discuss their strategy.

Solve Guide students to use *make a model* strategy to solve the problem.

- **How can using a number line help you to answer the question in the problem?** You can see where −3°F is and count the number of degrees to +7.
- **Does the change in temperature show a positive or negative change? Explain.** Positive; it is warmer in the afternoon so add to the morning temperature.

  What is the change in temperature? +10°F

Check Have students look back at the problem to make sure that the answer fits the facts given.

- **How do you know there are +3°F between −3°F and 0°F?** Start at −3 on the number line; count 3 spaces to the right to arrive at 0. Counting from left to right means it is +3°F degrees.

! COMMON ERROR!

Exercise 1 Students may have trouble remembering to convert units. Have them list the information needed to solve each problem. Then have them write the unit as requested in the question to identify necessary conversions.

12-7 Problem-Solving Investigation

MAIN IDEA I will choose the best strategy to solve a problem.

P.S.I. TEAM +

ARIANA: I checked the temperature this morning, and according to the thermometer, it was −3°F. This afternoon, the temperature was 7°F. I know it got warmer outside, but by how much?

YOUR MISSION: Find the change in temperature.

Understand	The morning temperature was −3°F. The afternoon temperature was 7°F. You need to find how many degrees the temperature increased.
Plan	You can use a model such as a number line to find the change in temperature. Graph the morning and afternoon temperatures on the number line and find the distance between them.
Solve	Draw a number line that includes −3 and 7. morning afternoon −4 −3 −2 −1 0 1 2 3 4 5 6 7 8 10 Since the distance between −3 and 7 is 10, the temperature rose 10° from the morning to the afternoon.
Check	The increase in temperature from −3°F to 0°F is 3 degrees. The increase in temperature from 0°F to 7°F is 7 degrees. Since 3 + 7 = 10, the answer is reasonable.

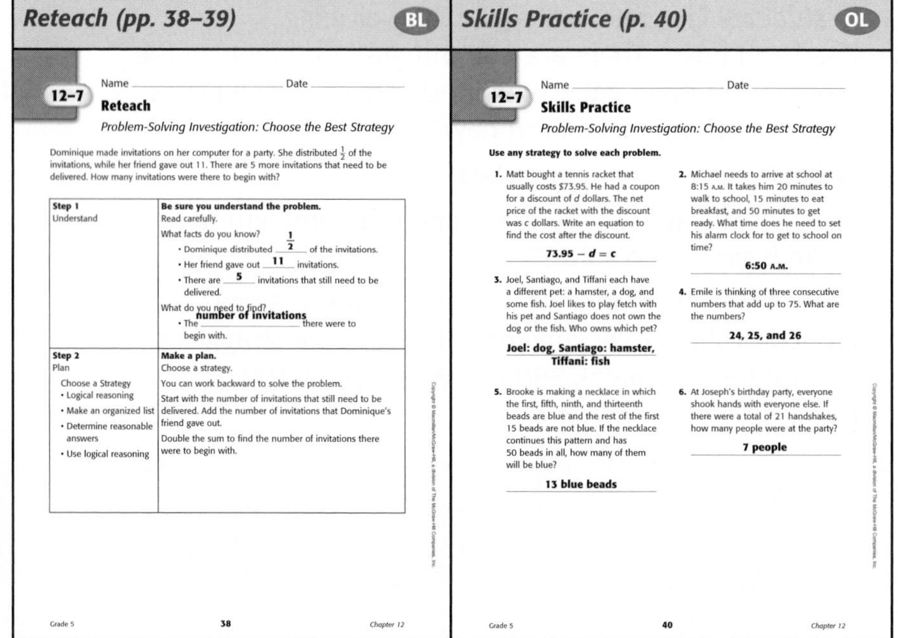

Reteach (pp. 38–39) BL

12-7 Name ______ Date ______

Reteach

Problem-Solving Investigation: Choose the Best Strategy

Dominique made invitations on her computer for a party. She distributed $\frac{1}{2}$ of the invitations, while her friend gave out 11. There are 5 more invitations that need to be delivered. How many invitations were there to begin with?

Step 1 Understand	**Be sure you understand the problem.** Read carefully. What facts do you know? • Dominique distributed **$\frac{1}{2}$** of the invitations. • Her friend gave out **11** invitations. • There are **5** invitations that still need to be delivered. What do you need to find? • The **number of invitations** there were to begin with.
Step 2 Plan Choose a Strategy • Logical reasoning • Make an organized list • Determine reasonable answers • Use logical reasoning	**Make a plan.** Choose a strategy. You can work backward to solve the problem. Start with the number of invitations that still need to be delivered. Add the number of invitations that Dominique's friend gave out. Double the sum to find the number of invitations there were to begin with.

Grade 5 38 *Chapter 12*

Skills Practice (p. 40) OL

12-7 Name ______ Date ______

Skills Practice

Problem-Solving Investigation: Choose the Best Strategy

Use any strategy to solve each problem.

1. Matt bought a tennis racket that usually costs $73.95. He had a coupon for a discount of *d* dollars. The net price of the racket with the discount was c dollars. Write an equation to find the cost after the discount.

   $73.95 - d = c$
2. Michael needs to arrive at school at 8:15 A.M. It takes him 20 minutes to walk to school, 15 minutes to eat breakfast, and 50 minutes to get ready. What time does he need to set his alarm clock for to get to school on time?

   6:50 A.M.
3. Joel, Santiago, and Tiffani each have a different pet: a hamster, a dog, and some fish. Joel likes to play fetch with his pet and Santiago does not own the dog or the fish. Who owns which pet?

   Joel: dog, Santiago: hamster, Tiffani: fish
4. Emile is thinking of three consecutive numbers that add up to 75. What are the numbers?

   24, 25, and 26
5. Brooke is making a necklace in which the first, fifth, ninth, and thirteenth beads are blue and the rest of the first 15 beads are not blue. If the necklace continues this pattern and has 50 beads in all, how many of them will be blue?

   13 blue beads
6. At Joseph's birthday party, everyone shook hands with everyone else. If there were a total of 21 handshakes, how many people were at the party?

   7 people

Grade 5 40 *Chapter 12*

Mixed Problem Solving

See page R34.

Use any strategy shown below to solve each problem.

PROBLEM-SOLVING STRATEGIES
- Work backward.
- Look for a pattern.
- Use a model.
- Solve a simpler problem.

1. See Ch. 12 Answer Appendix.

1. **Measurement** Charlene is putting up a border along both sides of a path. Between each stake, she will use 0.61 meter of rope. She will need 48 stakes for each side of the path. There is a stake at the beginning and at the end of the path. Which is the best estimate for the number of centimeters of rope she will need; 280 cm, 2,800 cm, or 28,000 cm? Explain.

2. Gabriella is cutting out stars. First she cuts a 5-centimeter star. Then she cuts a 4.5-centimeter star, followed by a 4-centimeter star. The last star she cuts is a 2-centimeter star. If she followed the pattern, how many stars did she make? 7 stars
3. Two students make 14 party bags in 20 minutes. How many party bags can 4 students make at the same rate in 40 minutes? 56 party bags
4. **Measurement** It takes Jasmine 40 minutes to paint a bookshelf with one coat of paint. After each coat, she waits 50 minutes for the paint to dry. How long will it take Jasmine to apply three coats of paint to the bookshelf? 270 min or $4\frac{1}{2}$ h
5. The greatest temperature change on Earth in a 24-hour period was in Loma, Montana, on January 15, 1972. The temperature rose from –54°F to 49°F. How much did the temperature increase? 103°F
6. Brady planted vegetables in his garden. The table shows the height of a plant during a 2-week period. If the plant grows at the same rate, estimate its height on June 15th. 74.1 cm

Vegetable Heights

Date	Height (cm)
May 18	48.5
May 25	54.9
June 1	61.3

7. **Algebra** Describe the pattern below. Then find the next three numbers in the pattern. See Ch. 12 Answer Appendix.

   2, 4, 7, 11, 16, 22, ■, ■, ■ . . .

8. **Algebra** A number is divided by 3. Next, the quotient is multiplied by 5. Then 5 is added to the product. If the result is 25, what is the number? 12
9. **WRITING IN MATH** The temperature in Calgary rose from –17°C to 13°C in four hours on January 11, 1983. Explain how to use a number line to find the change in temperature. See Ch. 12 Answer Appendix.

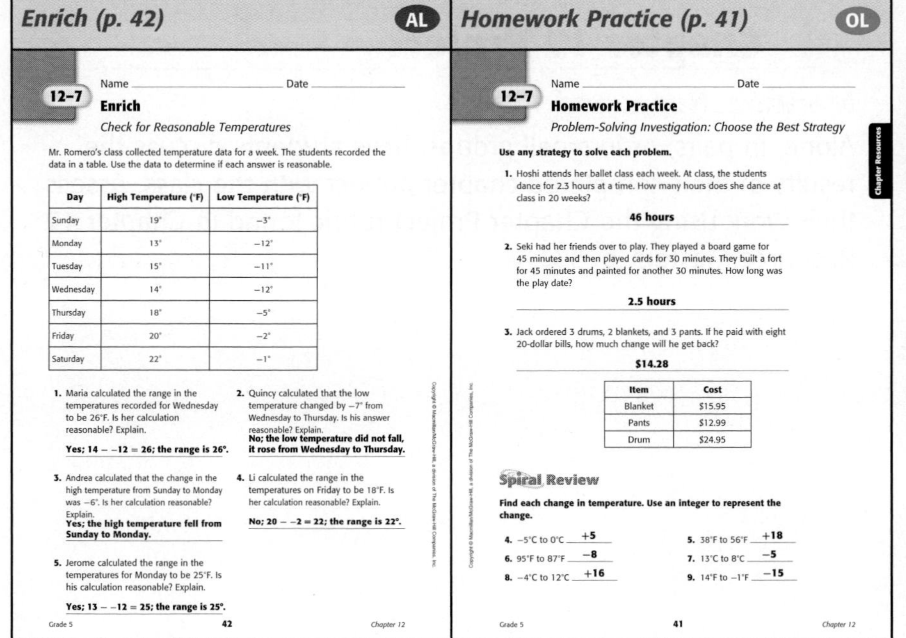

Enrich (p. 42) AL

12-7 Name ______ Date ______

Enrich

Check for Reasonable Temperatures

Mr. Romero's class collected temperature data for a week. The students recorded the data in a table. Use the data to determine if each answer is reasonable.

Day	High Temperature (°F)	Low Temperature (°F)
Sunday	19°	–3°
Monday	13°	–12°
Tuesday	15°	–11°
Wednesday	14°	–12°
Thursday	18°	–5°
Friday	20°	–2°
Saturday	22°	–1°

1. Maria calculated the range in the temperatures recorded for Wednesday to be 26°F. Is her calculation reasonable? Explain. **Yes; 14 – –12 = 26; the range is 26°.**
2. Quincy calculated that the low temperature changed by –7° from Wednesday to Thursday. Is his answer reasonable? Explain. **No; the low temperature did not fall, it rose from Wednesday to Thursday.**
3. Andrea calculated that the change in the high temperature from Sunday to Monday was –6°. Is her calculation reasonable? Explain. **Yes; the high temperature fell from Sunday to Monday.**
4. Li calculated the range in the temperatures on Friday to be 18°F. Is her calculation reasonable? Explain. **No; 20 – –2 = 22; the range is 22°.**
5. Jerome calculated the range in the temperatures for Monday to be 25°F. Is his calculation reasonable? Explain. **Yes; 13 – –12 = 25; the range is 25°.**

Grade 5 42 Chapter 12

Homework Practice (p. 41) OL

12-7 Name ______ Date ______

Homework Practice

Problem-Solving Investigation: Choose the Best Strategy

Chapter Resources

Use any strategy to solve each problem.

1. Hoshi attends her ballet class each week. At class, the students dance for 2.3 hours at a time. How many hours does she dance at class in 20 weeks? **46 hours**
2. Seki had her friends over to play. They played a board game for 45 minutes and then played cards for 30 minutes. They built a fort for 45 minutes and painted for another 30 minutes. How long was the play date? **2.5 hours**
3. Jack ordered 3 drums, 2 blankets, and 3 pants. If he paid with eight 20-dollar bills, how much change will he get back? **$14.28**

Item	Cost
Blanket	$15.95
Pants	$12.99
Drum	$24.95

Spiral Review

Find each change in temperature. Use an integer to represent the change.

4. –5°C to 0°C **+5**
5. 38°F to 56°F **+18**
6. 95°F to 87°F **–8**
7. 13°C to 8°C **–5**
8. –4°C to 12°C **+16**
9. 14°F to –1°F **–15**

Grade 5 41 Chapter 12

BL Alternate Teaching Strategy

If students have trouble choosing the best strategy to solve a problem…

Then use one of these reteach options:

1. CRM **Daily Reteach Worksheet** (pp. 38–39)
2. Have students discuss the Understand and Plan steps of the *four-step plan* for several of the problems. Ask students questions such as "What information does the problem tell us?" and "What do we need to find out?" on their way towards discovering an appropriate strategy to use.
   - Guide them to retell the problem in their own words and to explain their choice of a strategy before they solve the problems.

3 Practice

Using the Exercises

Exercise 1 requires that students determine there are 47 lengths of rope between 48 stakes on each of two sides of the path. They will also need to convert meters to centimeters for their answer.

4 Assess

Formative Assessment

Pose the following problem:

Satushi babysat 3 hours one day, 4 hours the next and 3.5 hours on a third day. He earned $47.25 in all. How much did he earn per hour?

- **What strategy would you use to solve the problem? Why?** *Work backward*; you know the total earned and have to work backward to find how much he earned each hour.
- **How many hours did he work?** 10.5 hr
- **How much did he earn per hour?** $4.50

Quick Check **Are students continuing to struggle with choosing the best strategy to solve a problem?**

If Yes → CRM Reteach Worksheet (pp. 38–39)

If No → Independent Work Options (p. 544B)
CRM Skills Practice Worksheet (p. 40)
CRM Enrich Worksheet (p. 42)

Chapter 12 Study Guide and Review

FOLDABLES® Dinah Zike's Foldables

Use these lesson suggestions to incorporate the Foldable during the chapter. Students can then use their Foldables to review for the test.

Lesson 12-6 Under the bottom right tab of the Foldable, have students record data as they measure and convert metric units of temperature. Students might glue a graphic of a thermometer beneath the Foldable tab.

Key Vocabulary

The page references after each word denote where that term was first introduced. If students have difficulty answer Exercises 1–8, remind them they can use the page references to review the vocabulary terms.

Vocabulary Review

Review chapter vocabulary using one of the following options.

- **Visual Vocabulary Card** (18)
- **eGlossary** at macmillanmh.com

Chapter 12 Study Guide and Review

Math Online macmillanmh.com
- STUDY TO GO
- Vocabulary Review

FOLDABLES Study Organizer GET READY to Study

Be sure the following Big Ideas are written in your Foldable.

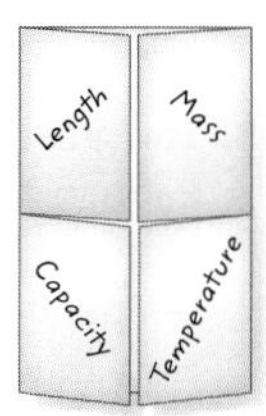

Key Concepts

Metric Units of Length (p. 517)

- 1 centimeter (cm) = 10 millimeters (mm)
- 1 meter (m) = 100 cm or 1,000 mm
- 1 kilometer (km) = 1,000 m

Metric Units of Mass (p. 524)

- 1 gram (g) = 1,000 milligrams (mg)
- 1 kilogram (kg) = 1,000 g

Metric Units of Capacity (p. 527)

- 1 liter (L) = 1,000 mL

Integers (p. 533)

- **Negative numbers** are less than 0.
- **Positive numbers** are greater than 0.
- **Integers** are negative and positive whole numbers and zero.

Units of Temperature (p. 537)

- Temperature can be measured in degrees **Fahrenheit** (°F) or degrees **Celsius** (°C).

Key Vocabulary

integer (p. 533)
mass (p. 524)
metric system (p. 517)
negative number (p. 533)
positive number (p. 533)

Vocabulary Check

Choose the correct word or number that completes each sentence.

1. One (liter, kiloliter) equals 1,000 milliliters.
2. A (centimeter, kilometer) is one hundredth of a meter.
3. One thousand grams equals 1 (milligram, kilogram).
4. Gram is a metric measure of (mass, length).
5. Temperature is measured in (grams, degrees).
6. A good outside temperature for water sports is 30 degrees (Celsius, Fahrenheit).
7. A reasonable estimate for the capacity of a soup can is (360, 36) milliliters.
8. To change meters to millimeters, multiply by (1,000, 100).

Chapter 12 Project

Morning, Noon, and Night

Alone, in pairs, or in small groups, have students discuss the results of their completed chapter project with the class. Assess their work using the Chapter Project rubric found in Chapter 12 Resource Masters, p. 53.

Lesson-by-Lesson Review

12-1 Units of Length (pp. 517–521)

Example 1
Complete: 7 m = ■ cm.

7 × 100 = 700   1 m = 100 cm

So, 7 meters = 700 centimeters.

Example 2
Complete: 6,000 m = ■ km.

6,000 ÷ 1,000 = 6   1,000 m = 1 km

So, 6,000 meters = 6 kilometers.

Complete.

9. 4,000 m = ■ km 4
10. 5 m = ■ mm 5,000
11. 30 mm = ■ cm 3
12. 12 cm = ■ mm 120
13. A giant squid that was found in the 1800s had a body 6 meters long and a tentacle 11 meters long. How many centimeters longer was the tentacle than the body? 500 cm

12-2 Problem-Solving Skill: Determine Reasonable Answers
(pp. 522–523)

Example 3
A marathon race is about 42 kilometers long. The length of the average person's stride is 1 meter. Is it reasonable to say that a person takes about 4,200 strides in a marathon race?

42 × 1,000 = 42,000   1 km = 1,000 m

A marathon is about 42,000 meters long.

Since a person runs about 1 meter for each stride, the average person takes about 42,000 strides in a marathon race. So, 4,200 strides is not a reasonable estimate.

Solve. Determine reasonable answers.

14. A cube of small self-stick notes is 5.2 centimeters long. Will it fit in a square container that is 50 millimeters long? Explain. 14–16. See margin.
15. A doorway is 0.95 meter wide, and a desk is 120 centimeters wide. Will the desk fit through the doorway without having to tilt it? Explain.
16. Leroy estimates that his kite flew 2,000 centimeters high. Does this seem reasonable? Explain.

Lesson-by-Lesson Review

Have students complete the Lesson-by-Lesson Review on pp. 547–550. Then you can use ExamView® Assessment Suite to customize another review worksheet that practices all the objectives of this chapter or only the objectives on which your students need more help.

Intervention If the given examples are not sufficient to review the topics covered by the questions, use the page references next to the exercises to review that topic in the Student Edition.

Additional Answers

14. No; 50 mm = 5.0 cm. Since 5.0 cm < 5.2 cm, the sticky notes will not fit in the square container.
15. No; 0.95 m = 95 cm. Since 95 cm < 120 cm, the desk will not fit through the doorway without tilting the desk.
16. Yes; 2,000 cm = 20 m and 20 m is a reasonable estimate for the height of a kite.

CHAPTER 12 Study Guide and Review

12-3 Units of Mass (pp. 524–526)

Example 4
A bag of flour has a mass of 2,000 grams. What is the mass of the bag of flour in kilograms?

To convert a smaller unit to a larger unit, divide.

2,000 ÷ 1,000 = 2   1,000 g = 1 kg

So, 2,000 grams equals 2 kilograms.

The mass of the bag of flour is 2 kg.

Complete.

17. 8 kg = ■ g **8,000**

18. 24,000 g = ■ kg **24**

19. 9 g = ■ mg **9,000**

20. 165 mg = ■ g **0.165**

21. 75 kg = ■ g **75,000**

22. Mrs. Mathews bought the cheese shown in the table. How many grams of cheese did she buy altogether? **15 g**

Cheese	Amount
American	8,000 mg
Swiss	7,000 mg

12-4 Units of Capacity (pp. 527–530)

Example 5
Mr. Rueben bought 15 liters of orange juice for a class party. How many milliliters of orange juice did he buy?

To convert a larger unit to a smaller unit, multiply.

15 × 1,000 = 15,000   1 L = 1,000 mL

15 liters = 15,000 milliliters

So, Mr. Rueben bought 15,000 milliliters of orange juice.

Complete.

23. 3 L = ■ mL **3,000**

24. 6,000 mL = ■ L **6**

25. 4,000 mL = ■ L **4**

26. 250 mL = ■ L **0.25**

27. 1 L = ■ mL **1,000**

28. A 2-liter bottle of fruit juice is used to fill 3 glasses. Each glass holds 300 milliliters. How many milliliters are left in the bottle? **1,100 mL**

12-5 Integers and Graphing on Number Lines (pp. 533–535)

Example 6
A swimmer dove 6 feet below the surface of the water. Write an integer to represent this situation. Then graph the integer on a number line.

6 feet below: –6

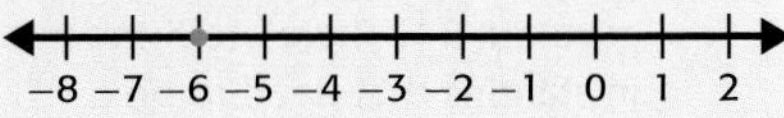

Example 7
A plant grew to a height of 8 inches. Write an integer to represent this situation. Then write its opposite.

grew 8 inches: +8 or 8

The opposite of 8 is –8.

Write an integer to represent each situation. Then graph the integer on a number line. 29–30. See margin.

29. a golf score of 3 under par

30. stock value up $1

Write an integer to represent each situation. Then write its opposite.

31. gaining 12 points +12 or 12; –12

32. 10 miles below the surface –10; +10 or 10

33. An airport control tower is 18 meters above the ground. The subway is 6 meters below the ground. Write two integers to represent these situations. +18 or 18; –6

12-6 Units of Temperature (pp. 537–541)

Example 8
Which is the more reasonable temperature for a chilly room: 60°C or 60°F?

- 60°C is warmer than body temperature.
- 60°F is cooler than body temperature.

The more reasonable temperature is 60°F.

Example 9
The temperature changed from 77°F to 70°F in one day. Use an integer to represent the change in temperature.

77° – 70° = 7° decrease in temperature

The change in temperature is –7.

Choose the more reasonable temperature for each situation.

34. hot sandwich: 40°F or 160°F 160°F

35. inside a refrigerator: 5°C or 50°C 5°C

Find each change in temperature. Use an integer to represent the change.

36. 29°C to 31°C +2

37. 14°F to 0°F –14

38. The temperature at 6:30 P.M. was 43°F. By 10:00 P.M. it was 28°F. Find the change in temperature. Use an integer to represent the change. –15

Additional Answers

29. –3

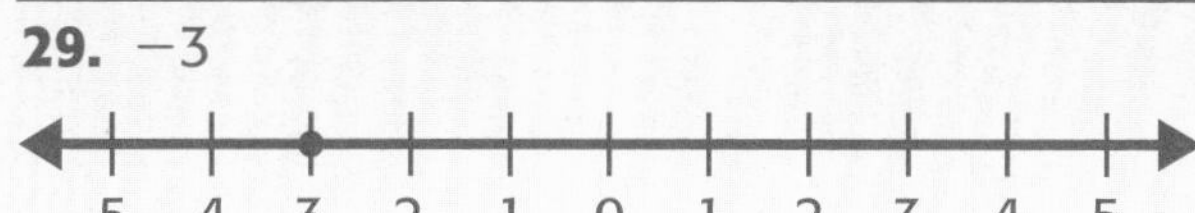

30. +1 or 1

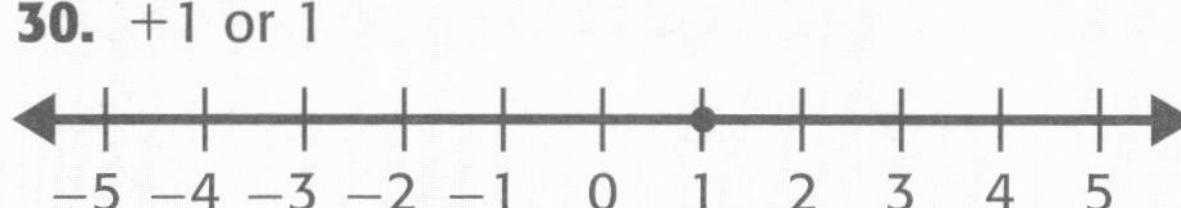

CHAPTER 12 Study Guide and Review

12-7 Problem-Solving Investigation: Choose a Strategy (pp. 544–545)

Example 10

Selena has $80. She wants to buy 2 shirts, a pair of jeans, and a belt. The belt costs $8. Each shirt costs twice this amount. Together, both shirts cost $10 less than the jeans. Does Selena have enough money to buy all the items?

To solve the problem, you can use the *work backward* strategy.

One shirt costs twice what the belt costs. So, multiply the cost of the belt by 2.

$8 × 2 = $16

Since she bought 2 shirts, multiply the cost of one shirt by 2.

2 × $16 or $32

The cost of the jeans is $10 more than the cost of both shirts. So, add 10 to the cost of the 2 shirts.

$32 + $10 = $42

Next, find the total cost of all the items.

belt + 2 shirts + jeans = total cost

$8 + $32 + $42 = $82

Since $82 > $80, Selena does not have enough money to buy all the items.

Use any strategy to solve each problem.

39. Dominique made party invitations on her computer. She gave out half of the invitations, while her friend gave out 11. There are 5 more invitations that need to be delivered. How many invitations did Dominique make? **32**

40. An antique desk is 1.5 meters wide. Will it fit in a space that is 2,000 centimeters wide? Explain. **Yes; 1.5 m = 1,500 and 1,500 cm < 2,000 cm.**

41. **Algebra** Describe the change in temperature from 1:00 to 3:00.

Time	Temperature (°F)
1:00 P.M.	59
3:00 P.M.	65

increase of 6°F

42. On Day 1, Troy swam 350 meters. On Day 2, he swam 500 meters, and on Day 3 he swam 650 meters. If he continues this pattern, how many meters will he have swum in 5 days? **3,250 m**

43. Andrew and 2 friends can blow up 15 balloons in 10 minutes. How many balloons can Andrew and 5 friends blow up at the same rate in 20 minutes? **60 balloons**

Chapter Test

Math Online macmillanmh.com
• Chapter Test

Complete. 1. 15 2. 4,000 3. 3

1. 150 mm = ■ cm **2.** 4 km = ■ m

3. 3,000 m = ■ km **4.** 8 m = ■ cm 800

5. MULTIPLE CHOICE Lance needs to draw line segment *PL* to complete the figure. Use a metric ruler to measure the distance from point *P* to point *L*.

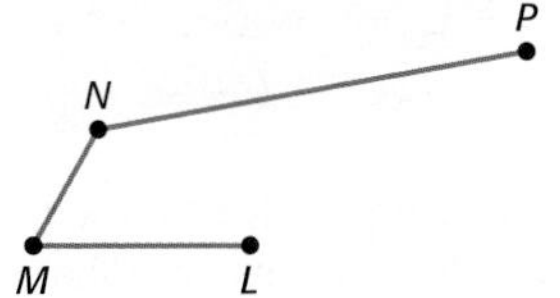

To the nearest centimeter, what is the length of line segment *PL*? C

A 2 cm **C** 4 cm

B 3 cm **D** 5 cm

6. Is 20 kilometers a reasonable estimate for the length of an Olympic-sized swimming pool? Explain. See Ch. 12 Answer Appendix.

Complete. 7. 21 8. 0.39 10. 74,000

7. 21,000 g = ■ kg **8.** 390 mg = ■ g

9. 4,000 mL = ■ L 4 **10.** 74 L = ■ mL

11. A loaf of bread has 20 slices. Each slice has a mass of 24 grams. Find the mass of the loaf in kilograms. 0.48 kg

12. A nickel has a mass of 5 grams. Find the total mass of the roll of nickels shown in grams. 200 g

$2.00

Find each change in temperature. Use an integer to represent the change.

13. 20°C to 11°C −9° **14.** 43°F to 58°F +15°

15. 35°C to 48°C +13° **16.** 92°F to 74°F −18°

17. MULTIPLE CHOICE Which is the best estimate for the capacity of a trash can? J

F 2 mL **H** 2 L

G 20 mL **J** 20 L

Write an integer to represent each situation. Then write its opposite.

18. 11° below zero −11; +11 or 11

19. a hole 3 feet deep −3; +3 or 3

20. 5 points added to a grade +5 or 5; −5

21. Algebra Write a real-world situation that can be represented by the integer graphed. See Ch. 12 Answer Appendix.

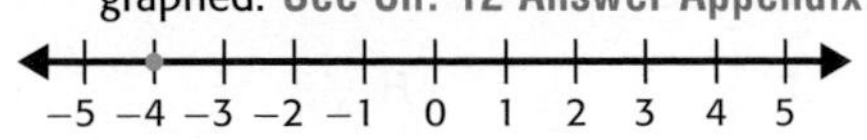

Choose the more reasonable temperature for each situation.

22. hot tea: 300°F or 200°F 200°F

23. cold water: 5°C or 25°C 5°C

24. Jayden has a tropical fish tank. Is 40° Fahrenheit or 75° Fahrenheit a more reasonable temperature for the water in the tank? Explain. See Ch. 12 Answer Appendix.

25. WRITING IN MATH Explain how you can use integers to represent changes in temperature. See Ch. 12 Answer Appendix.

CHAPTER 12

Chapter Test

Summative Assessment

Use these alternate leveled chapter tests to differentiate assessment for the specific needs of your students.

Leveled Chapter 12 Tests			
Form	**Type**	**Level**	**CRM Pages**
1	Multiple Choice	BL	55–56
2A	Multiple Choice	OL	57–58
2B	Multiple Choice	OL	59–60
2C	Free Response	AL	61–62
2D	Free Response	AL	63–64
3	Free Response	AL	65–66

BL = below/approaching grade level
OL = on grade level
AL = above/beyond grade level

Vocabulary Test

CRM **Chapter 12 Resource Masters** (p. 50)

ExamView Assessment Suite Customize and create multiple versions of your Chapter Test and the test answer keys.

Data-Driven Decision Making

Based on the results of the Chapter Test, use the following to review concepts that continue to present students with problems.

Exercises	State/Local Standards	What's the Math?	Error Analysis	Resources for Review
1-6		Choose an appropriate metric unit for measuring length and convert metric units of length.	Does not know methods of unit conversion. Does not have sense of length of centimeters, kilometers, or meters. Does not know "segment."	Strategic Intervention Guide (pp. 124, 130) CRM Chapter 12 Resource Master (Reteach) Math Adventures My Math Zone Chapter 12 Math Online Extra Examples • Concepts in Motion
7-12 17		Convert metric units of mass or capacity.	Does not convert units of metric measurement accurately. Does not use units of ten to convert metrics. Does not know "estimate."	
13-16 22-24		Choose appropriate temperatures in degrees Fahrenheit or Celsius.	Adds degrees. Does not put negative sign for decreasing temperatures. Does not have concept of Celsius measurement.	
18-21, 25		Use integers to represent real-life situations.	Does not put negative sign to indicate decreasing situations. Does not understand "integer." Does not understand "opposite."	

Chapter 12 Test Practice

Formative Assessment

- Use Student Edition pp. 552–553 as practice and cumulative review. The questions are written in the same style as many state tests.
- You can also use these two pages to benchmark student progress, or as an alternate homework assignment.

Additional practice pages can be found in the Chapter 12 Resource Masters.

CRM **Chapter 12 Resource Masters**
Cumulative Test Practice
- Multiple Choice format (pp. 55–60)
- Free Response format (pp. 61–66)

Create practice worksheets or tests that align to your state standards.

Math Online Have students visit macmillanmh.com for additional practice to reinforce your state standards.

Chapter 12 Test Practice

Cumulative, Chapters 1–12

PART 1 Multiple Choice

Read each question. Then fill in the correct answer on the answer sheet provided by your teacher or on a sheet of paper.

1. A bag of dog food has a mass of 96 kilograms. The food is divided equally into 2 containers. How many grams of dog food are in each container? A

   A 48,000 grams
   B 4,800 grams
   C 480 grams
   D Not Here

2. Xavier used the lemon juice shown to make lemonade. What fraction of a liter did he use? G

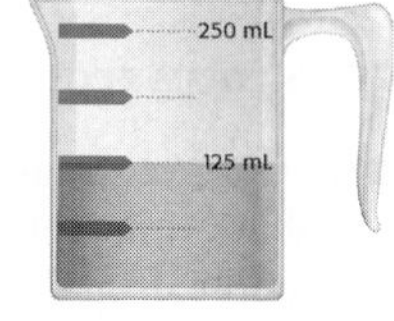

   F $\frac{1}{4}$
   G $\frac{1}{8}$
   H $\frac{1}{12}$
   J $\frac{1}{16}$

3. Eduardo says that the next term in the sequence below is 35. Which shows that his solution is not reasonable? B

   55, 47, 39, 31, …

   A The terms are increasing.
   B The terms are decreasing.
   C The terms are multiples of 5.
   D The terms are odd numbers.

4. An advertisement is shown below. Which word problem matches this advertisement? G

   F The regular price is $25. The television is on sale for 24.5% off. What is the sale price?
   G The regular price is $245. The television is on sale for 25% off. What is the sale price?
   H The sale price is $245 at 25% off. What is the regular price of a television?
   J The regular price is $245. If you buy two televisions, the second one is priced at 25% off the regular price. What is the total cost of two televisions?

5. Dion and his brother bought a bag of roasted nuts at the fair. If they ate $\frac{5}{6}$ of the roasted nuts, what fraction of the nuts remained? D

   A $\frac{1}{2}$
   B $\frac{1}{4}$
   C $\frac{1}{5}$
   D $\frac{1}{6}$

Test-Taking Tip

Tell students to examine each question carefully. They can break it into smaller parts to make it easier to solve.

Preparing for Standardized Tests
For test-taking strategies and practice, see pages R42–R55.

6. Hunter has four old stamps. Stamp A is worth $3. Stamp B is worth 4 times the value of stamp A. Stamp C is worth 5 times the value of Stamp A. The stamps are worth $45 altogether. What is the value of stamp D? **G**

F $12 **H** $18

G $15 **J** $27

7. What fraction of their games did the soccer team win? **C**

Soccer Team's Games	
Played	**Won**
20	15

A $\frac{1}{5}$ **C** $\frac{3}{4}$

B $\frac{1}{4}$ **D** $\frac{4}{5}$

8. Larry ran a 5-kilometer race. When he was halfway to the finish line, how many meters did he have left to run? **G**

F 5,000 meters

G 2,500 meters

H 500 meters

J 250 meters

PART 2 Short Response

Record your answers on the answer sheet provided by your teacher or on a sheet of paper.

9. The table shows the number of cars washed during the 3 days of a fundraiser car wash. Estimate how many cars were washed in all. Is your estimate greater or less than the exact number? **See margin.**

Day	Cars Washed
Friday	62
Saturday	83
Sunday	78

PART 3 Extended Response

Record your answers on the answer sheet provided by your teacher or on a sheet of paper.

10. Write an example where the temperature drops 10°F and an example where the temperature rises 10°F. **See margin.**

11. A fence is placed around a playground in the shape of a rectangle. The length of the fence is 32 meters. The width of the fence is 1,200 centimeters. How much fence is needed for the playground? Explain. **See margin.**

NEED EXTRA HELP?											
If You Missed Question...	1	2	3	4	5	6	7	8	9	10	11
Go to Lesson...	12-3	12-4	6-6	5-3	10-4	6-2	9-3	12-1	2-4	12-6	12-1

Answer Sheet Practice

Have students simulate taking a state test by recording their answers on a practice recording sheet.

CRM **Chapter 12 Resource Masters**
Student Recording Sheet (p. 71)

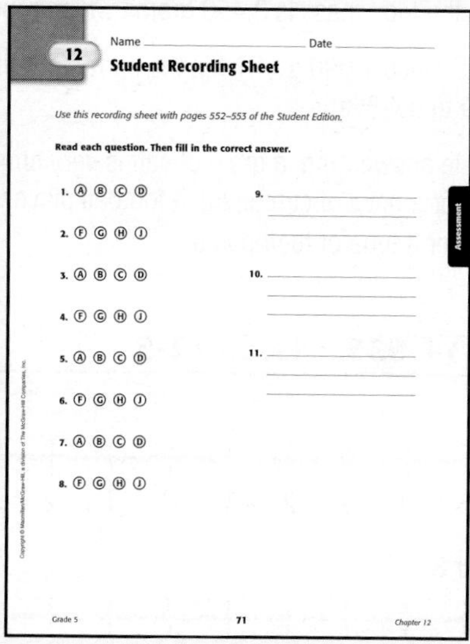

Additional Answers

9. 60 + 80 + 80 = 220; The estimate is lower than the exact.

10. Sample answers: The temperature may drop 10°F when the sun goes down. It may rise 10°F if you stepped out of the shade and into the sunlight.

11. Sample answer: convert all centimeters to meters and then find the perimeter. 88m

Page 523, Lesson 12-2

1. Yes; 37 m = 3,700. So, 4,000 cm > 3.700 cm
4. You can identify a mistake without making a calculation. You can use what you know to check if your answer makes sense.
5. 8 cups; Since 1 pint = 2 cups, multiply the number of pints by 2. So, $4 \times 2 = 8$.
8. 3 quarts; 8 oz × 12 c = 96 oz; 96 oz ÷ 32 oz = 3 qt
11. 100; The skateboard's length is 90 ÷ 10 or 9 cm long. A skateboard is is much longer than 9 cm.
12. Sample answer: Paulo estimates that he will need a 3 foot ladder to reach the top of his house. His estimate is unreasonable because most houses are taller than 3 feet.

Pages 525–526, Lesson 12-3

26. 3 kg; the total mass is 3,450 grams which rounds to 3,000 g or 3 kg
29. Terrez; since 1,000 g = 1 kg, the correct method is to divide 3,000 by 1,000 to get 3 kg.
30. Sample answer: mg, a grain of salt is very small; g, kilograms would be too large for a bowl of cereal; kg, a football player is large; g, milligrams is too small for a tube of toothpaste.

Pages 534–535, Lesson 12-5

11. −3

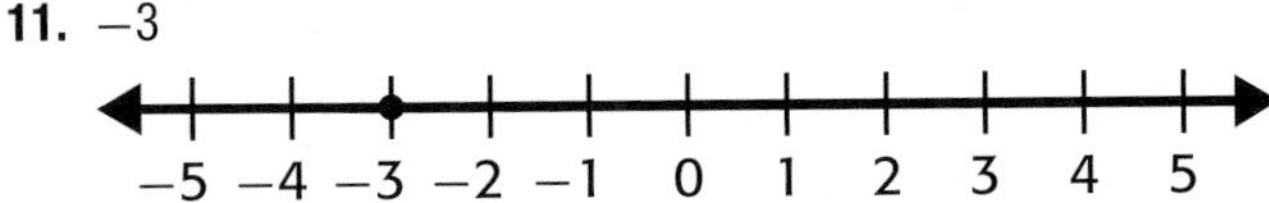

12. +8 or 8

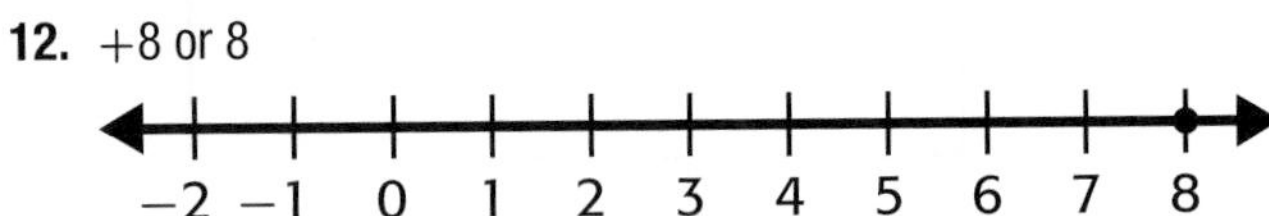

13. +40 or 40

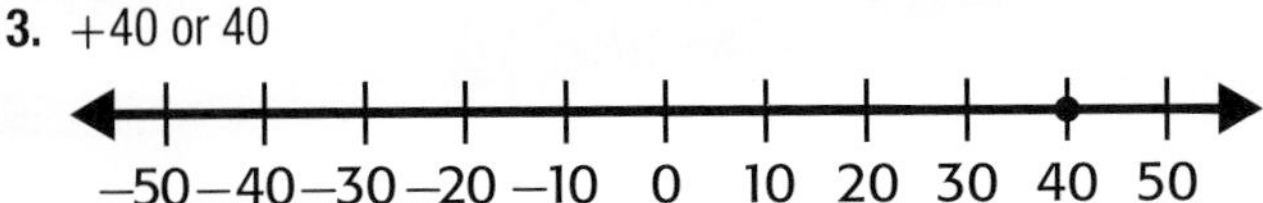

14. −15

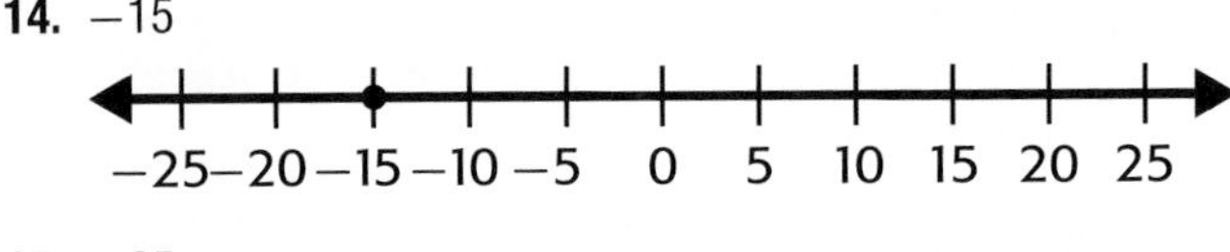

15. −25

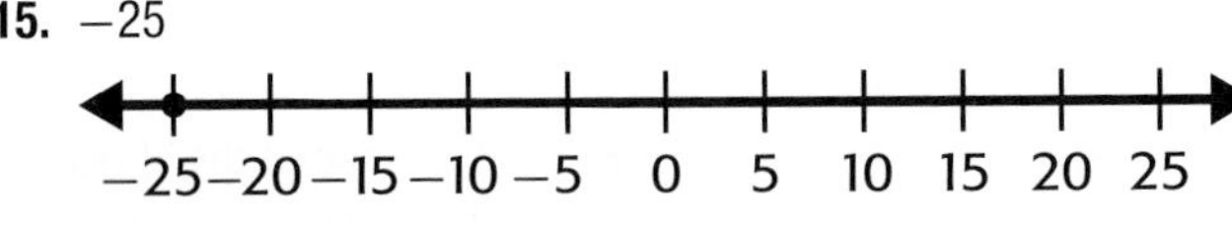

16. +200 or 200

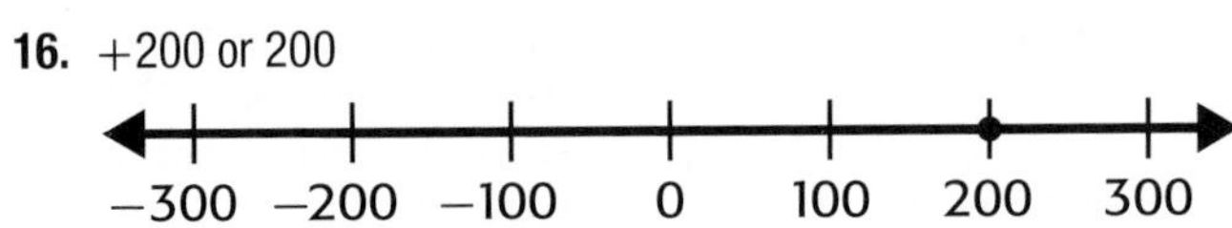

24. Emperor penguin; Sample answer: −534 is to the left of −210 on a number line. −534 is farther from 0, which represents the water's surface.
26. 17 degrees, because it can be represented by the integer 17. The other situations can be represented by −17.

Page 545, Lesson 12-7

1. 2,800 cm; Sample answer: 0.61 m = 61 cm; 61 cm × 48 = 2,928 cm.
7. Add 2, then increase the number added by 1 for each number; 29, 37, 46
9. Sample answer: Graph the two temperatures on a number line. Then count the number of digits from −17 to 13 to find the temperature change.

Page 551, Chapter Test

6. No; 1 km = 1,000 m, so 20 km = 20,000 m, which is too long.
21. Sample answer: 4 degrees below zero
24. Sample answer: 75°F; Water that is 45°F is far too cold for tropical fish to survive.
25. If the change is an increase in temperature, you can use a positive integer. If the change is a decrease in temperature, you can use a negative integer.

NOTES

Chapter Overview

Chapter-at-a-Glance

In Chapter 13, the emphasis is on identifying, comparing, and classifying geometric figures.

Lesson	Math Objective	State/Local Standards
13-1 Geometry Vocabulary (pp. 557–560)	Identify and label basic geometric terms.	
13-2 Problem-Solving Strategy: Use Logical Reasoning (pp. 562–563)	Solve problems by using logical reasoning.	
EXPLORE **13-3 Identify Angles** (pp. 564–565)	Use turns on circles to identify angles.	
13-3 Triangles (pp. 566–569)	Identify characteristics of triangles.	
13-4 Quadrilaterals (pp. 570–574)	Identify characteristics of quadrilaterals.	
13-5 Problem-Solving Investigation: Choose a Strategy (pp. 576–577)	Choose the best strategy to solve a problem.	
13-6 Translations and Graphs (pp. 578–581)	Sketch translations on a coordinate grid.	
13-7 Reflections and Graphs (pp. 582–585)	Sketch reflections on a coordinate grid.	
13-8 Rotations and Graphs (pp. 586–590)	Sketch rotations on a coordinate grid.	
13-9 Identify Transformations (pp. 591–593)	Identify transformations.	

Identify, Compare, and Classify Geometric Figures

BIG Idea In this chapter, students work on the mastery of three important skills in geometry:

- **Identify** different types of angles, triangles, and quadrilaterals.
- **Compare** polygons using different types of angles.
- **Classify** polygons using these terms: translation, reflection, rotation, and transformation.

Geometry Students learn about the characteristics of right triangles. This concept will help prepare them for geometry concepts, such as using the Pythagorean theorem. (Lesson 13-3)

G5-FP3 Geometry and Measurement and Algebra: **Describing three-dimensional shapes and analyzing their properties, including volume and surface area** Students relate two-dimensional shapes to three-dimensional shapes and analyze properties of polyhedral solids, describing them by the number of edges, faces, or vertices as well as the types of faces. Students recognize volume as an attribute of three-dimensional space. They understand that they can quantify volume by finding the total number of same-sized units of volume that they need to fill the space without gaps or overlaps. They understand that a cube that is 1 unit on an edge is the standard unit for measuring volume. They select appropriate units, strategies, and tools for solving problems that involve estimating or measuring volume. They decompose three-dimensional shapes and find surface areas and volumes of prisms. As they work with surface area, they find and justify relationships among the formulas for the areas of different polygons. They measure necessary attributes of shapes to use area formulas to solve problems.

Identify, Compare, and Classify Geometric Figures

Skills Trace

Vertical Alignment

Fourth Grade

In fourth grade, students learned to:

- Identify, and describe, two and three-dimensional figures, angles, triangles, quadrilaterals.

Fifth Grade

During this chapter, students learn to:

- Identify characteristics of triangles, quadrilaterals, and use turns on circles to identify angles.
- Sketch translations, reflections, and rotations on a coordinate grid.
- Identify transformations.

After this chapter, students learn to:

- Identify characteristics of three-dimensional figures.
- Find the areas and perimeters of polygons.

Sixth Grade

In sixth grade, students learn to:

- Measure, draw, and classify angles, and estimate measures of angles.
- Classify and find missing angle measures in quadrilaterals and triangles.

Backmapping and Vertical Alignment **McGraw-Hill's *Math Connects*** program was conceived and developed with the final results in mind: student success in Algebra 1 and beyond. The authors, using the **NCTM Focal Points and Focal Connections** as their guide, developed this brand new series by backmapping from Algebra 1 concepts, and vertically aligning the topics so that they build upon prior skills and concepts and serve as a foundation for future topics.

Math Vocabulary

The following math vocabulary words for Chapter 13 are listed in the glossary of the ***Student Edition***. You can find interactive definitions in 13 languages in the ***eGlossary*** at macmillanmh.com.

angle Two rays with a common endpoint. (p. 564)

line A set of points that form a straight path that goes in opposite directions without ending. (p. 557A)

line segment A part of a line between two endpoints. The length of the line segment can be measured. (p. 557A)

point An exact location in space. (p. 557A)

quadrilateral A polygon that has four sides and four angles. (p. 570A)
Examples: square, rectangle, and parallelogram.

reflection A transformation that flips a figure across a line to make a mirror image of that figure. (p. 582A)

rotation A transformation that turns a figure around a point. (p. 586A)

transformation A movement of a geometric figure. (p. 578A)
Examples: translation (slide), reflection (flip), rotation (turn)

translation A transformation in which the figure is slid without truning it. (p. 578A)

triangle A polygon with three sides and three angles. (p. 566A)

vertex a. The point where two rays meet in an angle. b. A point where two or more edges of a 3-dimensional or 2-dimensional figure meet. (plural: vertices) (p. 564)

Visual Vocabulary Cards
Use Visual Vocabulary Card 37 to reinforce the vocabulary in this lesson. (The Define/Example/Ask routine is printed on the back of each card.)

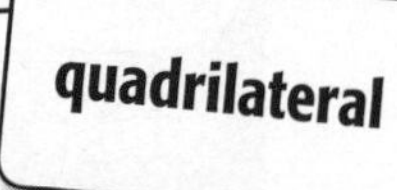

Chapter Planner

Suggested Pacing		
Instruction	Review & Assessment	TOTAL
10 days	1 day	**11 days**

Diagnostic Assessment
Quick Check (p. 556)

	Lesson 13-1 (Pacing: 1 day)	Lesson 13-2 (Pacing: 1 day)	Explore 13-3 (Pacing: 1 day)
Lesson/Objective	**Geometry Vocabulary** (pp. 557–560) **Objective:** Identify and label basic geometric terms.	**Problem-Solving Strategy** **Use Logical Reasoning** (pp. 562–563) **Objective:** Solve problems by using logical reasoning.	**Identify Angles** (pp. 564–565) **Objective:** Use turns on circles to identify angles.
State/Local Standards			
Math Vocabulary	**point, line, ray, line segment, plane, intersecting lines, perpendicular lines, parallel lines, congruent line segments**		**angle, vertex, degree, right angle, acute angle, obtuse angle**
Lesson Resources	**Materials** index cards **Manipulatives** rulers **Other Resources** CRM Leveled Worksheets (pp. 8–12) Daily Reteach • 5-Minute Check • Problem of the Day	**Other Resources** CRM Leveled Worksheets (pp. 13–17) Daily Reteach • 5-Minute Check • Problem of the Day *Flags: Shaping History*	**Materials** paper circles, scissors, glue, drawing paper **Manipulatives** protractor
Technology	Math Adventures		
Math Online	Personal Tutor		Concepts in Motion
Reaching All Learners	English Learners, p. 557B ELL Below Level, p. 557B BL Early Finishers, p. 557B AL	English Learners, p. 562B ELL Gifted and Talented, p. 562B AL Early Finishers, p. 562B OL AL	
Alternate Lesson			

Game Time
Geometry Concentration (p. 561)

	Lesson 13-3 Pacing: 1 day	Lesson 13-4 Pacing: 1 day	Lesson 13-5 Pacing: 1 day
Lesson/ Objective	**Triangles** (pp. 566–569) **Objective:** Identify characteristics of triangles.	**Quadrilaterals** (pp. 570–574) **Objective:** Identify characteristics of quadrilaterals.	**Problem-Solving Investigation Choose a Strategy** (pp. 576–577) **Objective:** Choose the best strategy to solve a problem.
State/Local Standards			
Math Vocabulary	**isosceles triangle, equilateral triangle, scalene triangle, right triangle, acute triangle, obtuse triangle**	**quadrilateral, parallelogram, rhombus, rectangle, square, trapezoid**	
Lesson Resources	**Materials** 4 in. × 7 in. paper rectangles, scissors, rulers, toothpicks, glue **Other Resources** CRM Leveled Worksheets (pp. 18–22) Daily Reteach • 5-Minute Check • Problem of the Day	**Manipulatives** pattern blocks **Other Resources** CRM Leveled Worksheets (pp. 23–27) Daily Reteach • 5-Minute Check • Problem of the Day	**Materials** index cards **Other Resources** CRM Leveled Worksheets (pp. 28–32) Daily Reteach • 5-Minute Check • Problem of the Day *Flags: Shaping History*
Technology	Math Adventures	Math Adventures Math Song Track 14	
Math Online	Personal Tutor	Personal Tutor	
Reaching All Learners	English Learners, p. 566B ELL Gifted and Talented, p. 566B AL Early Finishers, p. 566B AL	English Learners, p. 570B ELL Gifted and Talented, p. 570B AL Early Finishers, p. 570B AL	English Learners, p. 576B ELL Below Level, p. 576B BL Early Finishers, p. 576B OL AL
Alternate Lesson			

Formative Assessment
Mid-Chapter Check (p. 575)

Chapter Planner

	Lesson 13-6 (Pacing: 1 day)	Lesson 13-7 (Pacing: 1 day)	Lesson 13-8 (Pacing: 1 day)
Lesson/ Objective	**Translations and Graphs** (pp. 578–581) **Objective:** Sketch translations on a coordinate grid.	**Reflections and Graphs** (pp. 582–585) **Objective:** Sketch reflections on a coordinate grid.	**Rotations and Graphs** (pp. 586–590) **Objective:** Sketch rotations on a coordinate grid.
State/Local Standards			
Math Vocabulary	**transformation, image, translation**	**reflection, line of reflection**	**rotation**
Lesson Resources	**Materials** grid paper, colored pencils **Other Resources** CRM Leveled Worksheets (pp. 33–37) Daily Reteach • 5-Minute Check • Problem of the Day	**Materials** grid paper, mirrors **Manipulatives** pattern blocks **Other Resources** CRM Leveled Worksheets (pp. 38–42) Daily Reteach • 5-Minute Check • Problem of the Day	**Materials** paper circles, scissors **Manipulatives** pattern blocks **Other Resources** CRM Leveled Worksheets (pp. 43–47) Daily Reteach • 5-Minute Check • Problem of the Day
Technology **Math Online**	Personal Tutor	Personal Tutor	Personal Tutor
Reaching All Learners	English Learners, p. 578B ELL Below Level, p. 578B BL Early Finishers, p. 578B AL	English Learners, p. 582B ELL Below Level, p. 582B BL Early Finishers, p. 582B AL	English Learners, p. 586B ELL Below Level, p. 586B BL Early Finishers, p. 586B AL
Alternate Lesson			

KEY

BL Below /Approaching Level · OL On Level · AL Above /Beyond Level · ELL English Learners

SE Student Edition · TE Teacher Edition · CRM Chapter 13 Resource Masters · CD-Rom

Transparency · Real-World Problem Solving Library

Lesson 13-9

Pacing: 1 day

Identify Transformations

(pp. 591–593)

Objective: Identify transformations.

Materials
grid paper, tracing paper

Other Resources
CRM Leveled Worksheets (pp. 48–52)
Daily Reteach • 5-Minute Check • Problem of the Day

Personal Tutor

English Learners, p. 591B ELL
Gifted and Talented, p. 591B AL
Early Finishers, p. 591B AL

Problem Solving in Art
(p. 594)

Summative Assessment
- Study Guide and Review (p. 596)
- Chapter Test (p. 601)
- Test Practice (p. 602)

Assessment Options

Diagnostic Assessment

SE *Option 1:* Quick Check (p. 556)
Option 2: Online Quiz macmillanmh.com
CRM *Option 3:* Diagnostic Test (p. 54)
CRM *Option 4:* Chapter Pretest (p. 55)

Formative Assessment

TE Alternate Teaching Strategies (every lesson)
SE Talk About It (every lesson)
SE Writing in Math (every lesson)
SE Check What You Know (every lesson)
TE Ticket Out the Door (pp. 560, 581, 593)
TE Into the Future (pp. 569, 589)
SE Mid-Chapter Check (p. 575)
CRM Lesson Quizzes (pp. 56–58)
CRM Mid-Chapter Test (p. 59)

Summative Assessment

SE Chapter Test (p. 601)
SE Test Practice (p. 602)
CRM Vocabulary Test (p. 60)
CRM Leveled Chapter Tests (pp. 65–76)
CRM Cumulative Test Practice (pp. 79–81)
CRM Oral Assessment (pp. 61–62)
ExamView® Assessment Suite
Advance Tracker

Professional Development

Mc Graw Hill

Targeted professional development has been articulated throughout **McGraw-Hill's *Math Connects*** program. The **McGraw-Hill Professional Development Video Library** provides short videos that support the **NCTM Focal Points and Focal Connections.** For more information, visit macmillanmh.com.

Model Lessons

Instructional Strategies

Learning Stations

Cross-Curricular Links

Science

VISUAL

Animal Rotations

- With a partner, cut out pictures of animals from animal magazines and glue them on index cards to make animal cards. Each person makes a deck of ten cards. Make sure to rotate some of the animals, and use a protractor to help you figure out the rotations. Write the rotation angle on the back of each card, even if it is zero (don't show that part to your partner). Switch decks.
- Place the decks of animal faces up on the table. Take turns picking a card from the top of your new deck and guessing the animal's rotation. Check your answer on the back of the card. You get a point if you are right. The person with the most points at the end of the deck wins.

Materials:

- animal magazines for clipping
- scissors
- index cards
- glue
- protractor
- pencils

Art

SPATIAL

Perspective

- Find a landscape painting you like. Pick an image in the forefront of the painting, that is, whatever object that looks like it is closest to you. Mark a point on either side of the image or object.
- Now, pick a point on the horizon in the landscape that is directly behind the image you chose.
- Draw lines from your two points on either side of the object to the point on the landscape. Using a protractor, measure the angle you just drew. What angle did the artist use to show perspective?

Materials:

- art magazines with landscape paintings
- protractors
- pencils

Writing

individual

LOGICAL

A Line Here And There

- Write a journal entry describing the places you went on a given day.
- In your journal entry, describe each place using the types of lines you notice.
- Roads might have parallel lines, crossroads might have intersecting lines, and lines on buildings might form particular angles. Signs might have rays on them, and if you are using a map to get where you want to go in your journal entry, you might have points on that map.
- Be creative, using as many geometric terms as you can to describe your journey.

November 2, 2008

Yesterday on the way home, I noticed that the first streets we crossed were perpendicular.

Materials:

- paper
- pencils

Identify, Compare, and Classify Geometric Figures

Reading

pair | LOGICAL

What's Your Angle?

- Read *Museum Shapes* by the Metropolitan Museum of Art by yourself or with a partner.
- Pick a shape with angles from the book and challenge your partner to find out what angles are in the shape. Your partner will do the same with you.
- Measure the angles using a protractor, and decide what kind of angles they are based on your measurement. Have your partner check your measurements and talk about why you named the angles as you did.

Materials:

- *Museum Shapes* by the Metropolitan Museum of Art
- protractors

Health

pair | LOGICAL

Turn Your Health Around

- Draw different types of triangles and quadrilaterals on index cards. Put the cards in a basket.
- Take turns pulling a card out of the basket. Each time you pull a card, your partner draws the shape on a grid, and then sketches a transformation on the grid. You have to guess if the transformation is a reflection, a rotation, or a translation. The first person to guess correctly gets a positive apple point. If the guess is incorrect, that person gets a negative donut point.
- Play ten rounds and add up the points to see whose energy is the highest. Remember, donuts cancel out apples.

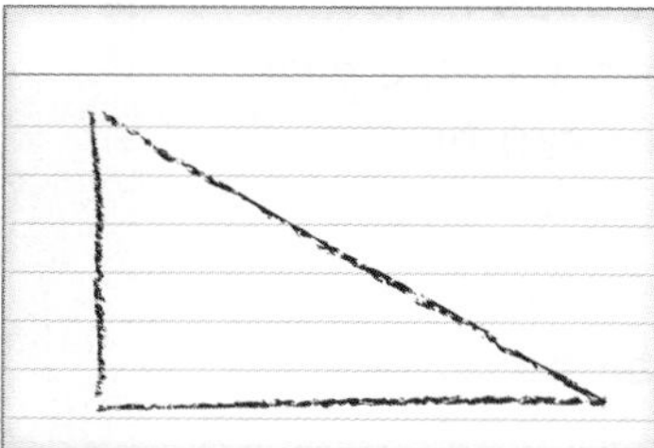
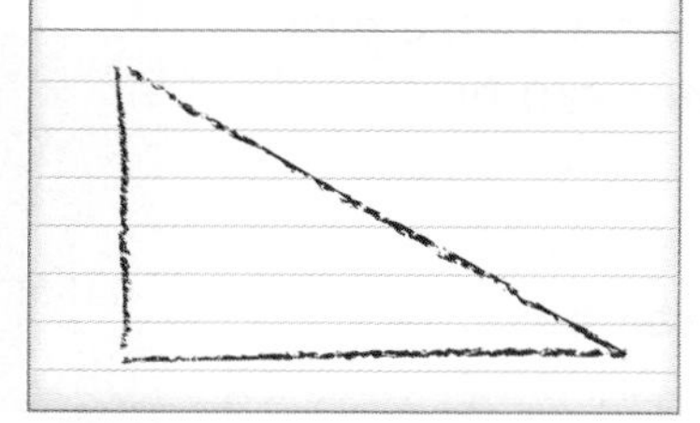

Materials:

- index cards
- basket
- grid paper
- pencils

Social Studies

pair | SPATIAL

Is There An Architect In The House?

- Pick a picture of a famous building in the United States from the pile, and place it so that you and your partner can see it well. Set the timer for one minute.
- As quickly as you can, list how many triangles and quadrilaterals you can see in the picture. Your partner will do the same. Be sure to specify which type of triangles or quadrilaterals you see.
- When the time is up, compare your list with that of your partner. The person who accurately listed the most shapes wins. Then play another round or two using the other pictures at this station.

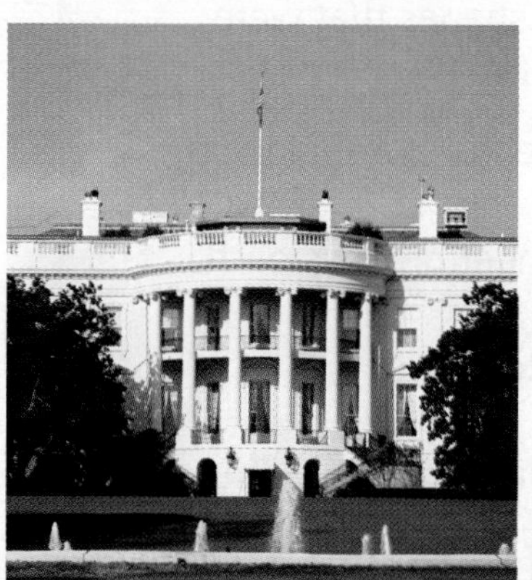

Materials:

- pictures of famous buildings throughout the United States
- timer
- paper
- pencils

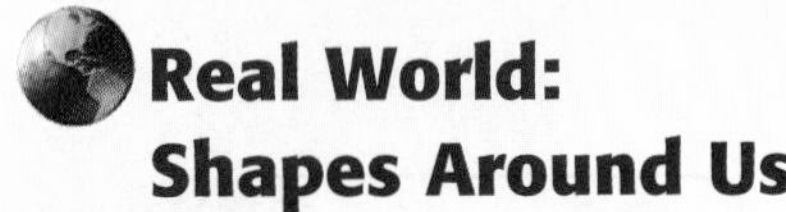

Introduce the Chapter

Real World: Shapes Around Us

Materials: magazines, scissors, glue, drawing paper, pencils

Share with students that they are going to learn about geometry in this chapter. Explain that as they describe lines and shapes, they will use many new terms related to geometry.

Have students work in small groups to look through magazines for pictures showing geometric shapes. Have them cut out examples of shapes they recognize, glue them onto a large paper, and label them with the correct geometric name. Students can present their findings to the class.

Review some common shapes and their properties, such as triangles with three sides and three angles and squares with four equal sides and four right angles. Make a list on the board of words and ideas that students have about geometry in general.

Direct students to Student Edition p. 554. Have students read the paragraph at the top of the page.

- **What are some ways that lines can be described?** by their length and how they join or cross other lines
- **What are ways that shapes can be described?** by the number of sides they have and what their angles look like

WRITING IN MATH

Starting the Chapter
Have students write a paragraph about their experiences in studying geometry in school or in using geometry in the real world. Encourage students to describe geometric shapes that were a part of the activity they describe.

Key Vocabulary Introduce the key vocabulary in the chapter using the routine below.

Define: Perpendicular lines meet or cross each other to form right angles.
Example: The lines in the letter T are perpendicular.
Ask: What are some perpendicular lines in the classroom?

Read-Aloud Anthology For an optional reading activity to introduce this chapter's math concepts, see the Read-Aloud Anthology on p. TR32.

CHAPTER 13 Identify, Compare, and Classify Geometric Figures

BIG Idea What is geometry?

Geometry is the study of lines and shapes.

Example Every year, a sandcastle building competition is held along the Outer Banks of North Carolina. Sandcastles are composed of many geometric figures. Geometric figures include triangles, squares, and rectangles.

What will I learn in this chapter?

- Identify and label basic geometric terms.
- Identify characteristics of triangles and quadrilaterals.
- Sketch translations, rotations, and reflections on a coordinate grid.
- Identify transformations.
- Solve problems by using *logical reasoning*.

Key Vocabulary

parallel lines
perpendicular lines
translation
reflection
rotation

Math Online Student Study Tools at macmillanmh.com

554 **Chapter 13** Identify, Compare, and Classify Geometric Figures

Chapter 13 Project

Identify It!

Students play a game to identify geometry terms and shapes.

- Students divide into three teams. Each team creates numbered picture cards to place in one of three baskets. The baskets should contain the following cards: 1. ray, line segment, point, right angle, acute angle, obtuse angle, plane; 2. isosceles, equilateral, scalene, and right triangles; 3. parallelogram, rhombus, rectangle, square, trapezoid.
- Teams start at a different basket station than the one they created. One member writes the number of each card and its name. Teams have five minutes to identify all the cards in the basket, then switch stations. The team with the most correct answers wins the game.

CRM *Refer to Chapter 13 Resource Masters, p. 63, for a rubric to assess students' progress on this project.*

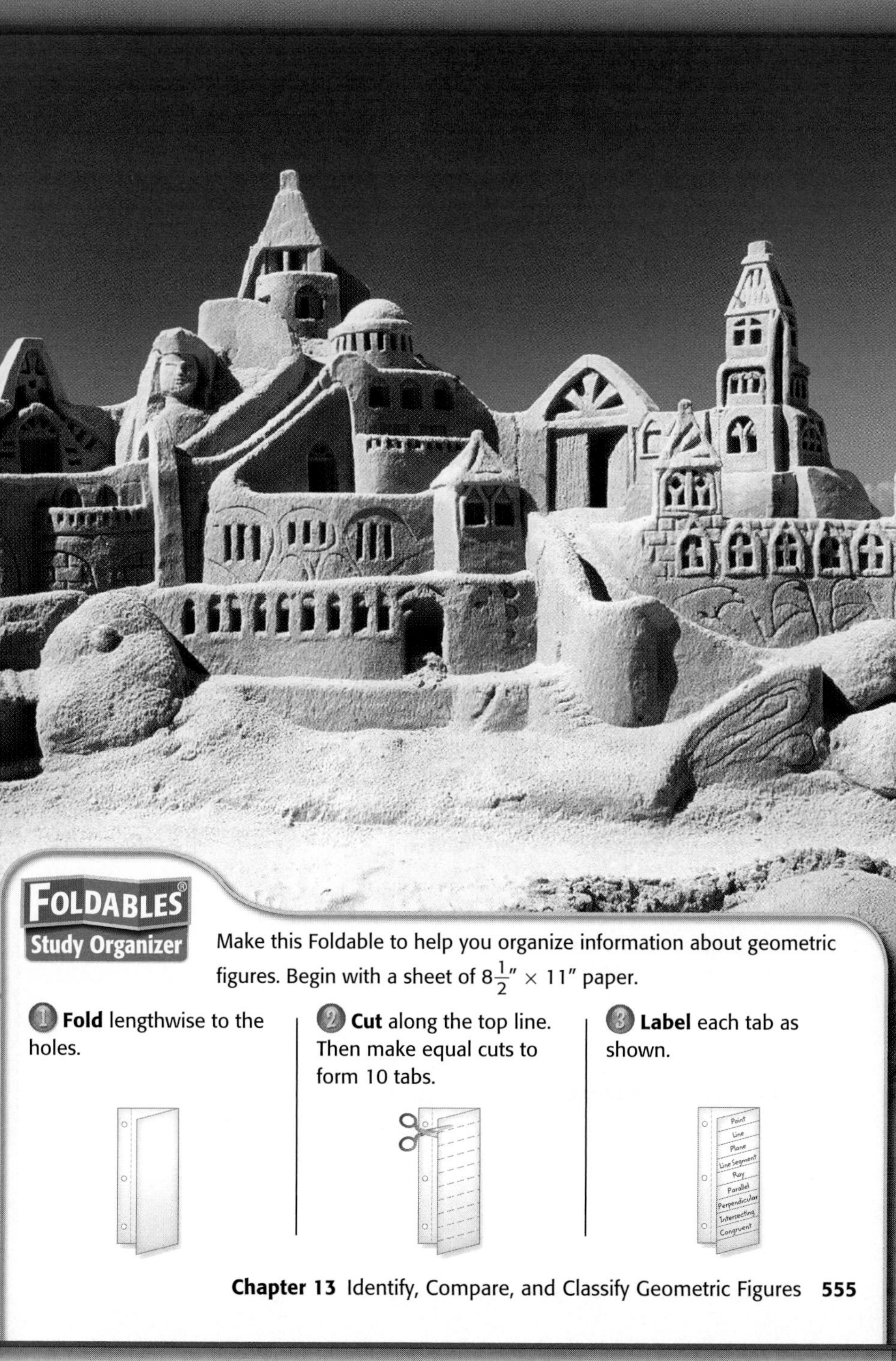

FOLDABLES
Study Organizer
Make this Foldable to help you organize information about geometric figures. Begin with a sheet of $8\frac{1}{2}$" × 11" paper.
1 Fold lengthwise to the holes.
2 Cut along the top line. Then make equal cuts to form 10 tabs.
3 Label each tab as shown.
Point
Line
Plane
Line Segment
Ray
Parallel
Perpendicular
Intersecting
Congruent
Chapter 13 Identify, Compare, and Classify Geometric Figures 555

ELL National ESL Standards Alignment for Chapter 15

Lesson, Page	ESL Standards	Modality	Level
13-1, p. 557B	Goal 2, Standard 3, l	Kinesthetic, Auditory	Beginning
13-2, p. 562B	Goal 2, Standard 3, l	Logical, Interpersonal	Intermediate
13-3, p. 566B	Goal 2, Standard 3, c	Kinesthetic	Beginning
13-4, p. 570B	Goal 2, Standard 2, g	Visual/Spatial,	Intermediate
13-5, p. 576B	Goal 1, Standard 3, l	Logical, Kinesthetic	Advanced
13-6, p. 578B	Goal 1, Standard 3, f	Spatial	Beginning
13-7, p. 582B	Goal 2, Standard 1, c	Kinesthetic	Beginning
13-8, p. 586B	Goal 1, Standard 3, d	Intrapersonal, Visual	Beginning
13-9, p. 591B	Goal 2, Standard 1, f	Kinesthetic	Advanced

The National ESL Standards can be found in the Teacher Reference Handbook.

FOLDABLES® Dinah Zike's Foldables

Guide students through the directions on p. 555 to create their own Foldable graphic organizers for geometric figures. Students may also use their Foldables to study and review for chapter assessments.

When to Use It Additional instructions for using the Foldables with these lessons are found on pp. 575 and 596.

Chapter 13 Literature List

Lesson	Book Title
13-1	**Shape Up!** David A. Adler
13-2	**Circus Caps for Sale** Esphyr Siobodkina
13-3	**Square, Triangle, Round, Skinny** Vladimir Radunsky
13-4	**Zachery Zormer Shape Transformer** Joanne Reisberg
13-6	**Geometry** Lucille Caron and Philip M. St. Jacques
13-7	**Round Trip** Ann Jonas
13-8	**Geometry** Lucille Caron and Philip M. St. Jacques
13-9	**Geometry** Lucille Caron and Philip M. St. Jacques
Any	**Sir Cumference and the Knight of Angleland** Cindy Neuschwander
Any	**Sweet Clara and the Freedom Quilt** Deborah Hopkinson

- Read the Math at Home letter found in Chapter 3 Resource Masters, p. 4, with the class and have each student sign it. (A Spanish version is found on p. 5.)
- Send home copies of the Math at Home letter with each student.

Diagnostic Assessment

Check for students' prerequisite skills before beginning the chapter.

- **Option 1:** ***Quick Check***

  SE Student Edition, p. 556

- **Option 2:** ***Online Assessment***

  Math Online macmillanmh.com

- **Option 3:** ***Diagnostic Test***

  CRM Chapter 13 Resource Masters, p. 54

RTI (Response to Intervention)

Apply the Results Based on the results of the diagnostics assessment on Student Edition p. 556, use the chart below to address individual needs before beginning the chapter.

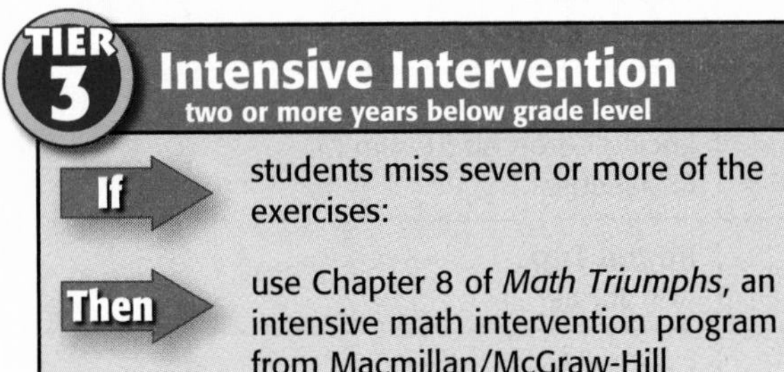

TIER 3
Intensive Intervention
two or more years below grade level
If
students miss seven or more of the exercises:
Then
use Chapter 8 of Math Triumphs, an intensive math intervention program from Macmillan/McGraw-Hill

ARE YOU READY for Chapter 13?

You have two ways to check prerequisite skills for this chapter.

Option 2

Math Online Take the Chapter Readiness Quiz at macmillanmh.com.

Option 1

Complete the Quick Check below.

QUICK Check

Describe the number of sides and the number of angles in each figure. (Prior Grade) (Used in Lessons 13-3 and 13-4)

1. 4; 4 **2.** 3; 3 **3.** 4; 4

Use the figure below for Exercises 4 and 5. (Prior Grade) (Used in Lessons 13-3 and 13-4)

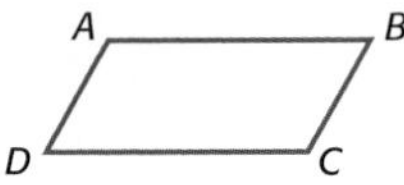

4. Which side appears to have the same length as side *AB*? side *DC*

5. At which point do sides *BC* and *DC* meet? *C*

6. Anthony is drawing a triangle that has two sides that are equal. Draw a sketch of this triangle. See Ch.13 Answer Appendix.

Graph each point on a coordinate grid. (Lesson 6-5) 7-10. See Ch.13 Answer Appendix.

7. *J*(1, 7) **8.** *K*(6, 0)

9. *L*(5, 6) **10.** *M*(3, 3)

TIER 2 Strategic Intervention below /approaching grade level	TIER 1 On-Level	Above/Beyond Level
If students miss four to six in: **Exercises 1–10**	**If** students miss two or three in: **Exercises 1–10**	**If** students miss one or less in: **Exercises 1–10**
Then choose a resource	**Then** choose a resource	**Then** choose a resource
Strategic Intervention Guide (pp. 126, 128) TE Start Smart 4: Geometry and Spatial Reasoning (p. 8) **Math Online** Extra Examples • Personal Tutor • Concepts in Motion	TE Learning Stations (pp. 554G–554H) TE Chapter Project (p. 554) CRM Game: Transform It! Math Adventures My Math Zone Chapter 12 **Math Online** Fact Dash	TE Learning Stations (pp. 554G–554H) TE Chapter Project (pp. 554) Real-World Problem Solving Reader: *Flags: Shaping History* My Math Zone Chapter 12, 13 **Math Online** Games

LESSON 13-1

Geometry Vocabulary

Lesson Planner

Objective

Identify and label basic geometric terms.

Vocabulary

point, line, ray, line segment, plane, intersecting lines, perpendicular lines, parallel lines, congruent line segments

Resources

Materials: index cards
Manipulatives: rulers
Literature Connection: *Shape Up!* by David A. Adler
Teacher Technology
TeacherWorks • Interactive Classroom

Focus on Math Background

In previous grades, points, lines, and planes were treated intuitively. In this lesson, descriptions of these terms are introduced. (Note that in Euclidean geometry, lines, points, and planes are often undefined terms, and only informal descriptions are given.) Proper use of these terms and symbols along with the ones listed below should be practiced and encouraged:

- *ray* and *line segment*: A ray has one endpoint, and goes on forever in one direction; a line segment has two endpoints, and contains all the points between them.
- *intersecting lines*: If $\overleftrightarrow{AB}$ and $\overleftrightarrow{CD}$ meet or cross at a common point, then $\overleftrightarrow{AB}$ and $\overleftrightarrow{CD}$ are said to intersect.
- *parallel lines*: If $\overleftrightarrow{AB} \parallel \overleftrightarrow{CD}$, then $\overleftrightarrow{AB}$ never intersects $\overleftrightarrow{CD}$. No angles are formed by this pair of lines.
- *perpendicular lines*: If $\overleftrightarrow{AB} \perp \overleftrightarrow{CD}$, they meet to form right angles.

Daily Routine

Use these suggestions before beginning the lesson on p. 557

5-Minute Check

(Reviews Lesson 12-7)

Use any of the following strategies to solve: *use the four-step plan, work backward, check for reasonableness, choose a method of computation*. Tell what strategy you used.

Salvador and his family will visit a theme park. Adult tickets cost $21. The total cost of tickets for the two adults and four children in Salvador's family is $106. How much are children's tickets? $16; *work backward*

Problem of the Day

Josie and her sister each bought a bag of dried cherries. Josie's bag weighed 12.4 ounces and her sister's bag weighed 19.6 ounces. If dried cherries cost $5.40 per pound, how much did the sisters spend altogether? $10.80

Building Math Vocabulary

Write the lesson vocabulary words and their definitions on the board.

Have students write the words, definitions and a drawing of each in their notes. Encourage them to discuss related words and phrases, such as "ray of sunshine" and "intersection."

Visual Vocabulary Cards

Use Visual Vocabulary Cards 19, 29, and 33 to reinforce the vocabulary introduced in this lesson. (The Define/Example/Ask routine is printed on the back of each card.)

Differentiated Instruction

Small Group Options

Option 1 Below Level BL

LOGICAL, KINESTHETIC

- To help students remember all of the terms in this lesson, make up a game of Simon Says.
- The motions can be as follows:

  Intersecting lines–make an X with your arms

  Perpendicular lines–make a right angle with your arms

  Parallel lines–hold your arms out parallel

  Point–make a fist

  Line segment–spread your arms and make two fists

  Line–spread your arms and point in both directions

Option 2 English Language Learners ELL

KINESTHETIC, AUDITORY

Materials: shapes, bag, pipe cleaners
Core Vocabulary: reshape, see, holds its shape
Common Use Verb: bend

See Math This strategy allows students to use their native language to recognize shapes.

- Call out the number of sides to a shape hidden in a bag.
- Ask students to make a shape with that number of sides with pipe cleaners and hold it up.
- Count the number of correct shapes and say something like: "I see 12 triangles."
- Allow students to reshape or keep their shape.
- Hold up your shape and say: "A triangle has 3 sides."
- Repeat with other shapes.

Independent Work Options

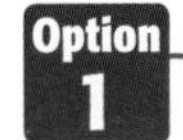

Option 1 Early Finishers AL

SOCIAL

Materials: index cards, pencils and paper

- Students work in pairs. Have each student write the symbol representation for eight of the vocabulary terms in this lesson, each on its own card.
- Shuffle all of the cards and place them in one deck on the table.
- Students take a card from the deck, draw the figure represented by the symbol, and label it with its correct term. Have partners check for accuracy in naming and drawing.

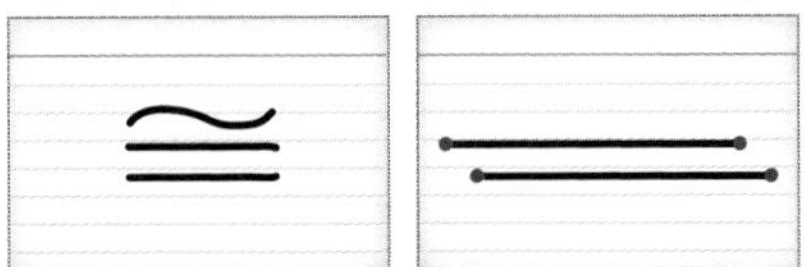

Option 2 Student Technology

Tech Link

Math Online macmillanmh.com

Personal Tutor • Extra Examples

Math Adventures

Option 3 Learning Station: Social Studies (p. 554G)

Direct students to the Social Studies Learning Station for opportunities to explore and extend the lesson concept.

Option 4 Problem-Solving Practice

Reinforce problem-solving skills and strategies with the Problem-Solving Practice worksheet.

Problem Solving (p. 11) BL OL AL

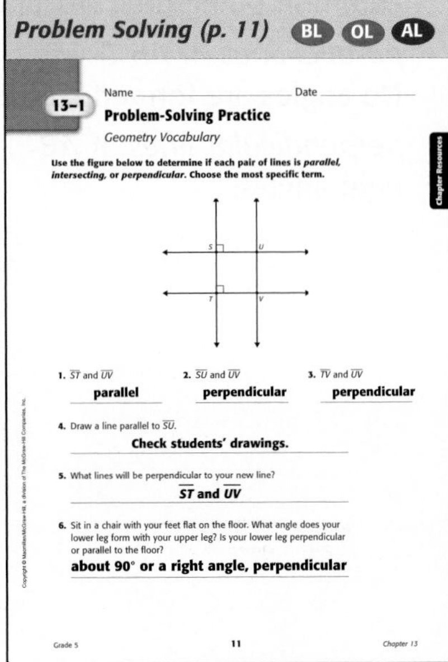

Name ______ Date ______

13-1 **Problem-Solving Practice**

Geometry Vocabulary

Use the figure below to determine if each pair of lines is *parallel, intersecting,* or *perpendicular*. Choose the most specific term.

1. $\overline{ST}$ and $\overline{UV}$ **parallel**
2. $\overline{SU}$ and $\overline{UV}$ **perpendicular**
3. $\overline{TV}$ and $\overline{UV}$ **perpendicular**
4. Draw a line parallel to $\overline{SU}$. **Check students' drawings.**
5. What lines will be perpendicular to your new line? **$\overline{ST}$ and $\overline{UV}$**
6. Sit in a chair with your feet flat on the floor. What angle does your lower leg form with your upper leg? Is your lower leg perpendicular or parallel to the floor? **about 90° or a right angle, perpendicular**

Chapter Resources

Grade 5 11 Chapter 13

13-1 Geometry Vocabulary

MAIN IDEA

I will identify and label basic geometric terms.

New Vocabulary

- point
- line
- ray
- line segment
- plane
- intersecting lines
- perpendicular lines
- parallel lines
- congruent line segments

Math Online

macmillanmh.com

- Extra Examples
- Personal Tutor
- Self-Check Quiz

GET READY to Learn

The butterfly kite at the right is made up of different geometric figures. Can you identify a point and a line segment on the kite?

The table shows basic geometric figures.

Geometric Figures — Key Concepts

Definition	Model
A **point** is an exact location in space, represented by a dot.	• A **Words** point *A*
A **line** is a set of points that form a straight path that goes in opposite directions without ending.	C D **Words** line *CD* or line *DC* **Symbols** $\overleftrightarrow{CD}$ or $\overleftrightarrow{DC}$
A **ray** is a line that has an endpoint and goes on forever in one direction.	S T **Words** ray *ST* **Symbols** $\overrightarrow{ST}$
A **line segment** is part of a line between two endpoints.	G H **Words** line segment *GH* or line segment *HG* **Symbols** $\overline{GH}$ or $\overline{HG}$
A **plane** is a flat surface that goes on forever in all directions.	M O N **Words** plane *MNO*

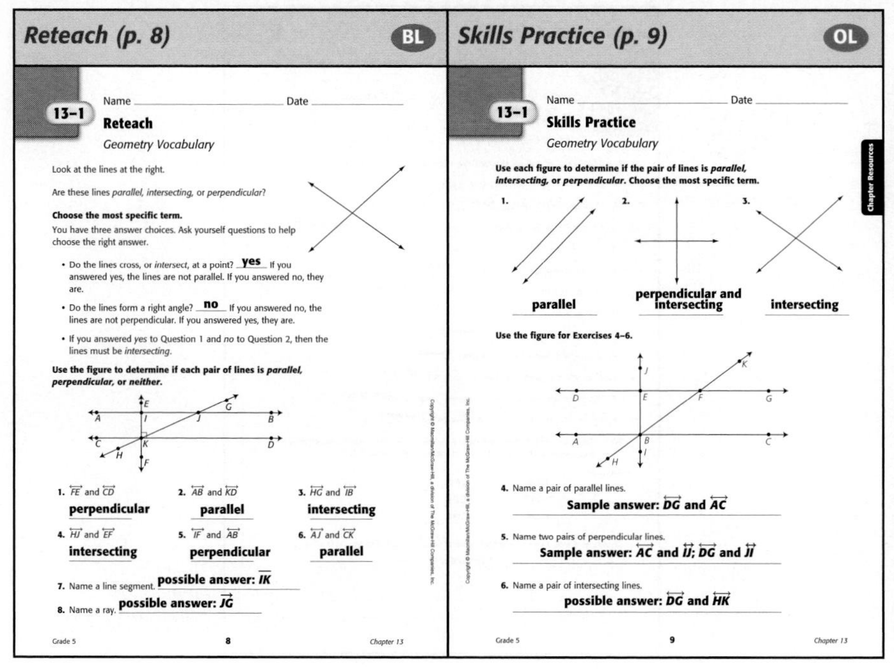

Reteach (p. 8) BL

13-1 Name ______ Date ______

Reteach

Geometry Vocabulary

Look at the lines at the right.

Are these lines *parallel, intersecting,* or *perpendicular*?

Choose the most specific term.

You have three answer choices. Ask yourself questions to help choose the right answer.

- Do the lines cross, or *intersect*, at a point? **yes** If you answered yes, the lines are not parallel. If you answered no, they are.
- Do the lines form a right angle? **no** If you answered no, the lines are not perpendicular. If you answered yes, they are.
- If you answered *yes* to Question 1 and *no* to Question 2, then the lines must be *intersecting*.

Use the figure to determine if each pair of lines is *parallel, perpendicular,* or *neither*.

1. $\overleftrightarrow{FE}$ and $\overleftrightarrow{CD}$ **perpendicular**
2. $\overleftrightarrow{AB}$ and $\overleftrightarrow{KD}$ **parallel**
3. $\overleftrightarrow{HG}$ and $\overleftrightarrow{IB}$ **intersecting**
4. $\overleftrightarrow{HJ}$ and $\overleftrightarrow{EF}$ **intersecting**
5. $\overleftrightarrow{IF}$ and $\overleftrightarrow{AB}$ **perpendicular**
6. $\overleftrightarrow{AJ}$ and $\overleftrightarrow{CK}$ **parallel**
7. Name a line segment. **possible answer: $\overline{IK}$**
8. Name a ray. **possible answer: $\overrightarrow{JG}$**

Grade 5 8 Chapter 13

Copyright © Macmillan/McGraw-Hill, a division of The McGraw-Hill Companies, Inc.

Skills Practice (p. 9) OL

13-1 Name ______ Date ______

Skills Practice

Geometry Vocabulary

Use each figure to determine if the pair of lines is *parallel, intersecting,* or *perpendicular*. Choose the most specific term.

1. **parallel**
2. **perpendicular and intersecting**
3. **intersecting**

Use the figure for Exercises 4–6.

4. Name a pair of parallel lines.
   Sample answer: $\overleftrightarrow{DG}$ and $\overleftrightarrow{AC}$
5. Name two pairs of perpendicular lines.
   Sample answer: $\overleftrightarrow{AC}$ and $\overleftrightarrow{IJ}$; $\overleftrightarrow{DG}$ and $\overleftrightarrow{JI}$
6. Name a pair of intersecting lines.
   possible answer: $\overleftrightarrow{DG}$ and $\overleftrightarrow{HK}$

Grade 5 9 Chapter 13

Chapter Resources

Copyright © Macmillan/McGraw-Hill, a division of The McGraw-Hill Companies, Inc.

13-1 Geometry Vocabulary

1 Introduce

Activity Choice 1 • Hands-On

- **Use a ruler to draw a design using straight lines. What shapes did you draw in your design?** Answers will vary.
- Have students discuss their designs using words related to dimensions such as length, width, and height. **What are the two dimensions in a 2-dimensional shape?** length and width or width and height
- Discuss the idea that students actually drew line segments, not lines. **What is the difference between a line and a line segment?** A line goes on forever, and a line segment has a beginning point and an end point.
- **On one of your line segments, label three points *A*, *B*, and *C*.** Explain that points labeled with letters are used to name geometric figures.

Activity Choice 2 • Literature

Shape Up! by David A. Adler. For a related math activity, see p. TR57.

2 Teach

Scaffolding Questions

Have students refer to their line segment drawing from Activity Choice 1.

- **Name the points in your drawing.** point *A*, point *B*, and point *C*
- **What is the name of the line segment between point *B* and point *C*?** line segment *BC* or line segment *CB*
- **Lines that cross at one point are intersecting. Are there intersecting lines in your drawing?** Answers will vary.
- **Congruent line segments are segments that have the same length. Are there congruent line segments in your drawing?** Answers will vary.

GET READY to Learn

Have students open their books and read the information in **Get Ready to Learn**. Introduce the new vocabulary words. As a class, work through **Examples 1–3**.

Describe a Pair of Lines

Example 2 Be sure students understand that more than one description may be needed to describe intersecting lines. Lines may be intersecting as well as perpendicular.

ADDITIONAL EXAMPLES

1. Identify the figure. Then name it using symbols. line segment; $\overline{PQ}$ or $\overline{QP}$

2. Describe the lines as *intersecting, perpendicular,* or *parallel.* intersecting and perpendicular

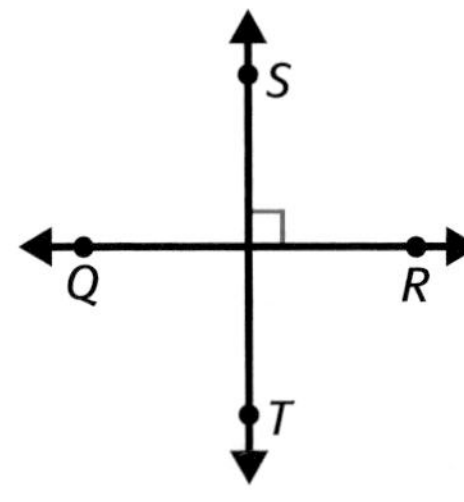

3. Determine whether the line segments are congruent. Write *yes* or *no*. yes

CHECK What You Know

As a class, have students complete Exercises 1–9 in **Check What You Know** as you observe their work.

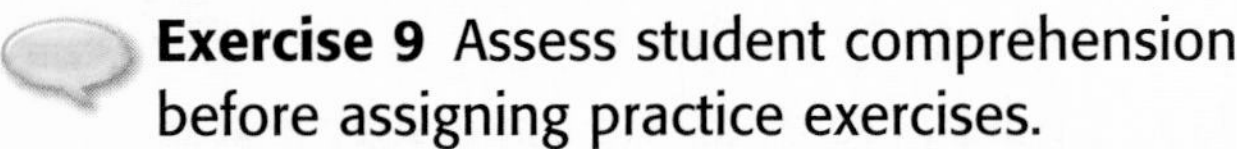

Exercise 9 Assess student comprehension before assigning practice exercises.

BL Alternate Teaching Strategy

If students have trouble identifying geometric terms...

Then use one of these reteach options:

1 CRM **Daily Reteach Worksheet** (p. 8)

2 Have students draw and label an example of each term on a set of index cards. Encourage them to write the word that the figure illustrates as well as the symbols used to name the figure.

Encourage students to use their cards as they work with geometric terms.

EXAMPLE Identify a Figure

Remember
The endpoint is named first in a ray. The ray in Example 1 cannot be named $\overrightarrow{KJ}$.

1. **Identify the figure at the right. Then name it using symbols.**

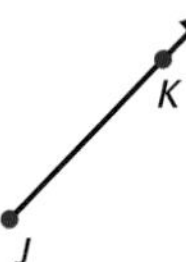

The figure has one endpoint. The arrow indicates that it goes on forever in one direction. So, it is a ray.

symbol: $\overrightarrow{JK}$

Two lines in a plane can be related in three ways. They can be intersecting, perpendicular, or parallel.

Vocabulary Link
Perpendicular
Everyday Use vertical or meeting at a corner

Pairs of Lines — Key Concepts

Definition	Model
Intersecting lines are lines that meet or cross at a point.	
Perpendicular lines are lines that meet or cross each other to make a square corner.	
Parallel lines are lines that are the same distance apart and do not intersect.	

EXAMPLE Describe a Pair of Lines

2. **Describe the lines at the right as *intersecting, perpendicular,* or *parallel.* Choose the most specific term.**

The lines cross at one point, so they are intersecting. Since they do not form a square corner, they are not perpendicular lines.

Enrich (p. 12) AL

Name ____________ Date ____________

13-1 Enrich
Basic Geometric Ideas

Tell whether each statement is *always, sometimes,* or *never* true.

A. To draw a polygon, you must draw at least three line segments. **always**
E. Lines are part of a ray. **never**
I. A line segment that connects two vertices of a polygon is a side. **sometimes**
I. A polygon has more vertices than sides. **never**
L. A line segment is longer than a ray. **never**
N. Vertical line segments have the same length. **sometimes**
N. You can measure the length of a line. **never**
O. A closed figure is a polygon. **sometimes**
P. An octagon is larger than a pentagon. **sometimes**
R. A hexagon has fewer sides than an octagon. **always**
T. Congruent line segments have a common endpoint. **sometimes**
Y. A point on a line is the endpoint of two rays. **always**

Write the letters of the problems whose answer is *always, sometimes,* or *never*. Then unscramble each group of letter to form a math word.

Answers

always	**ARY**	**RAY**
sometimes	**INOPT**	**POINT**
never	**EILN**	**LINE**

Choose one statement above that is never true. Rewrite it so that it is always true.

See students' work.

Grade 5 **12** *Chapter 13*

Congruent Segments

Key Concept

Line segments that have the same length are called **congruent line segments**.

Words $\overline{EF}$ is congruent to $\overline{HG}$.

Symbols $\overline{EF} \cong \overline{HG}$

EXAMPLE Identify Congruent Line Segments

3 MEASUREMENT Determine whether the line segments at the right are congruent.

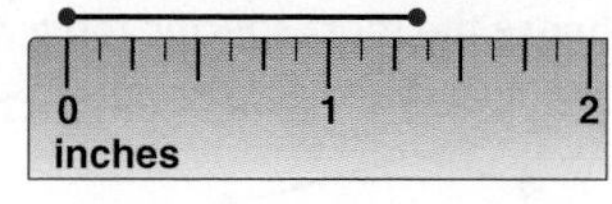

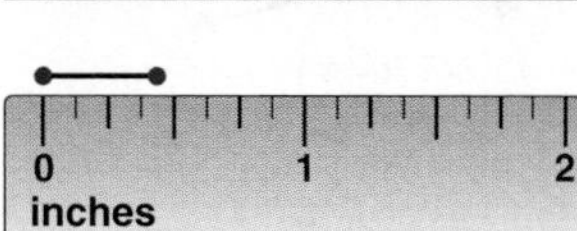

The segments do not have the same length. So, they are not congruent.

CHECK What You Know

Identify each figure. Then name it using symbols. See Example 1 (p. 558)

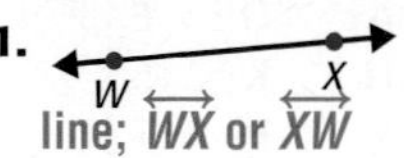

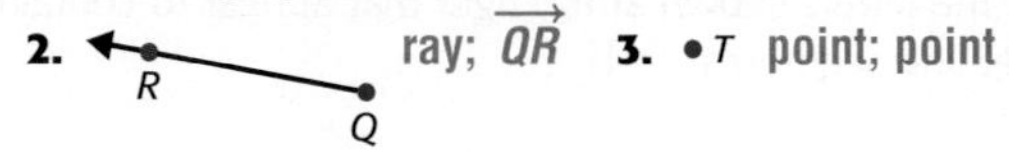

1. line; $\overleftrightarrow{WX}$ or $\overleftrightarrow{XW}$
2. ray; $\overrightarrow{QR}$
3. • T point; point T

Describe each pair of lines as *intersecting, perpendicular*, or *parallel*. Choose the most specific term. See Example 2 (p. 558)

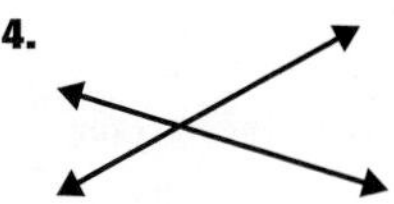

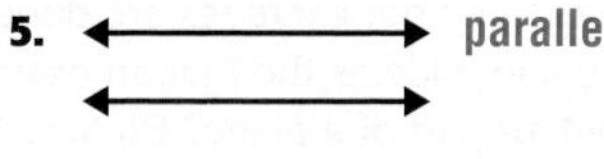

4. intersecting
5. parallel

Measure each segment. Then determine whether each pair of line segments are congruent. Write *yes* or *no*. See Example 3 (p. 559)

6. yes
7. no

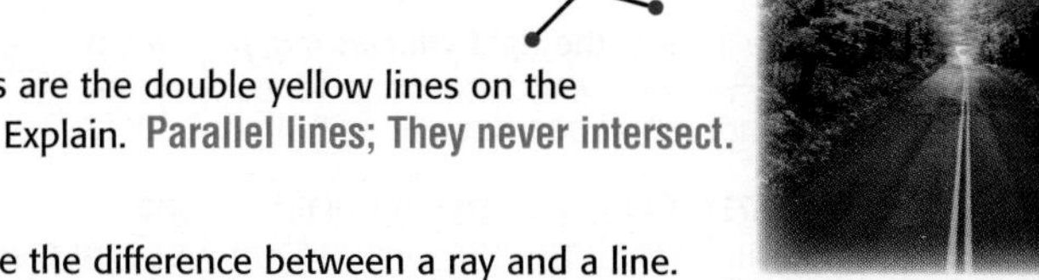

8. What type of lines are the double yellow lines on the road at the right? Explain. Parallel lines; They never intersect.

9. Talk About It Describe the difference between a ray and a line. Sample answer: A ray has an endpoint and goes on forever in one direction. A line goes on forever in both directions.

3 Practice

Differentiate practice using these leveled assignments for Exercises 10–27.

Level	Assignment
BL Below/ Approaching Level	10–13, 17–18, 19–20, 22, 27
OL On Level	10–14, 16–18, 19–25, 27
AL Above/Beyond Level	10–24 even, 26–27

Have students discuss and complete the Higher Order Thinking problems. Encourage students to refer back to the definition of line before explaining their reasoning for Exercise 26.

WRITING IN MATH Have student complete Exercise 27 in their Math Journals. You may choose to use this exercise as an optional formative assessment.

COMMON ERROR!

Exercises 19–21 Students may have trouble determining if line segments are congruent using a ruler. Encourage students to place the edge of a paper along one line segment and mark its length. They can then use the marked paper to compare the length of the second line segment.

Assess

Formative Assessment

Pose the following questions:

- **How are lines, line segments and rays different from each other?** A line goes on forever in both directions; a line segment is part of a line with two end points; and a ray has one endpoint and continues on forever in one direction.
- **What would a figure look like if it was made of two congruent line segments that were intersecting and perpendicular?** Two line segments of equal length crossing each other at right angles.

Quick Check **Are students continuing to struggle with identifying and labeling basic geometric terms?**

If Yes → Small Group Options (p. 557B)
Strategic Intervention Guide (p. 126)

If No → Independent Work Options (p. 557B)
CRM Skills Practice Worksheet (p. 9)
CRM Enrich Worksheet (p. 12)

Ticket Out the Door Write the following on the board: Line segment $\overline{BC}$, ray $\overrightarrow{MN}$, point A, line $\overline{QR}$, perpendicular lines $\overleftrightarrow{ST}$ and $\overleftrightarrow{QR}$, parallel lines $\overleftrightarrow{EF}$ and $\overleftrightarrow{GH}$. Have students draw each figure on an index card and write the symbols for each.

Additional Answer

23. Sample answer: On a window, opposite sides are parallel. A side and the top of a chalkboard are perpendicular.

10. line segment; $\overline{EF}$ or $\overline{FE}$ 12. line; $\overleftrightarrow{AB}$ or $\overleftrightarrow{BA}$

Practice and Problem Solving

EXTRA PRACTICE See page R34.

Identify each figure. Then name it using symbols. See Example 1 (p. 558)

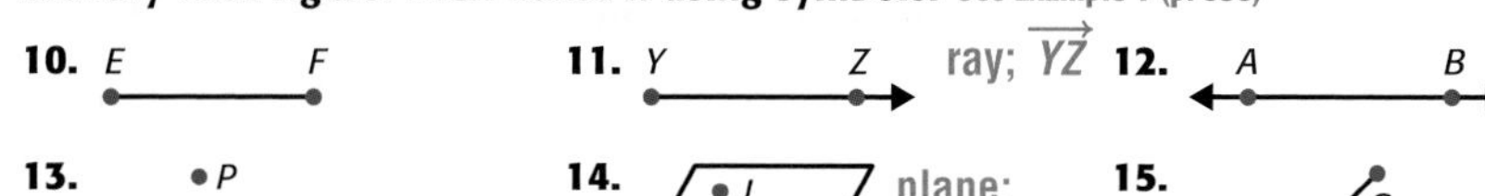

10. E F
11. Y Z ray; $\overrightarrow{YZ}$
12. A B
13. P point; point P
14. 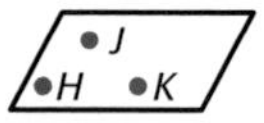 J H K plane; plane HJK
15. 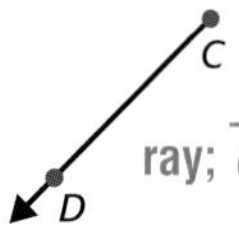 C D ray; $\overrightarrow{CD}$

Describe each pair of lines as *intersecting, perpendicular,* or *parallel*. Choose the most specific term. See Example 2 (p. 558)

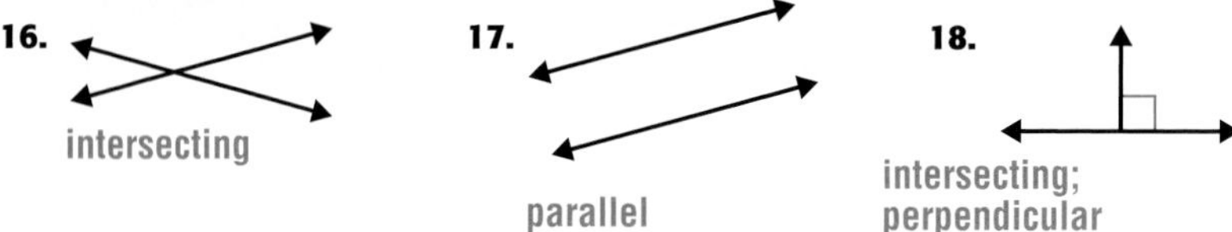

16. intersecting
17. parallel
18. intersecting; perpendicular

Measure each line segment. Then determine whether each pair of line segments are congruent. Write *yes* or *no*. See Example 3 (p. 559)

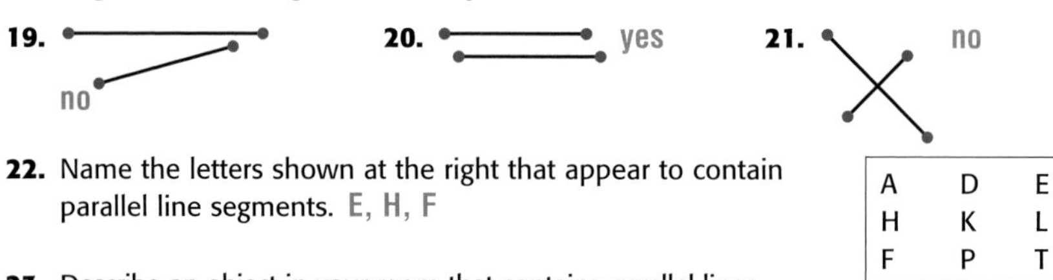

19. no
20. yes
21. no

22. Name the letters shown at the right that appear to contain parallel line segments. E, H, F

A	D	E
H	K	L
F	P	T

23. Describe an object in your room that contains parallel lines. Then describe an object that contains lines that are perpendicular. See margin.

24. In gymnastics, the floor exercises are done on a mat that is 40 feet long and 40 feet wide. Is the mat an example of a point, a line, a line segment, or part of a plane? Explain. Part of a plane; A plane is a flat surface that extends in all directions.

H.O.T. Problems

25. **OPEN ENDED** Name three objects in your classroom that are a part of a plane. Sample answer: floor, ceiling, wall

26. **CHALLENGE** Are the lines at the right *intersecting, parallel,* or *neither*? Explain your reasoning. Intersecting; Since they are lines, they extend forever. These lines eventually intersect.

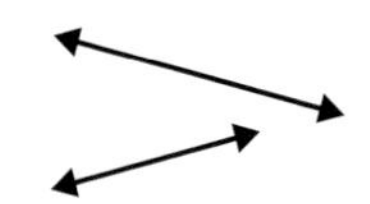

27. **WRITING IN MATH** Compare perpendicular lines and parallel lines. Perpendicular lines intersect to form a square corner. Parallel lines do not intersect.

Homework Practice (p. 10) OL

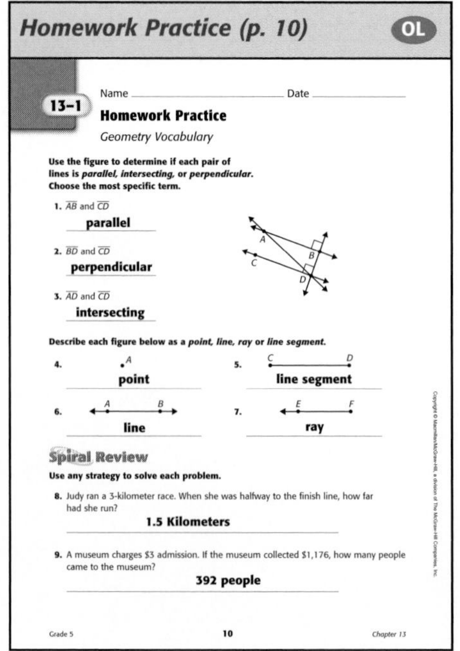

Name ______ Date ______

13–1 **Homework Practice**
Geometry Vocabulary

Use the figure to determine if each pair of lines is *parallel, intersecting,* or *perpendicular.* Choose the most specific term.

1. $\overline{AB}$ and $\overline{CD}$ **parallel**
2. $\overline{BD}$ and $\overline{CD}$ **perpendicular**
3. $\overline{AD}$ and $\overline{CD}$ **intersecting**

Describe each figure below as a *point, line, ray* or *line segment.*

4. A **point**
5. C D **line segment**
6. A B **line**
7. E F **ray**

Spiral Review

Use any strategy to solve each problem.

8. Judy ran a 3-kilometer race. When she was halfway to the finish line, how far had she run? **1.5 Kilometers**

9. A museum charges $3 admission. If the museum collected $1,176, how many people came to the museum? **392 people**

Grade 5 10 Chapter 13

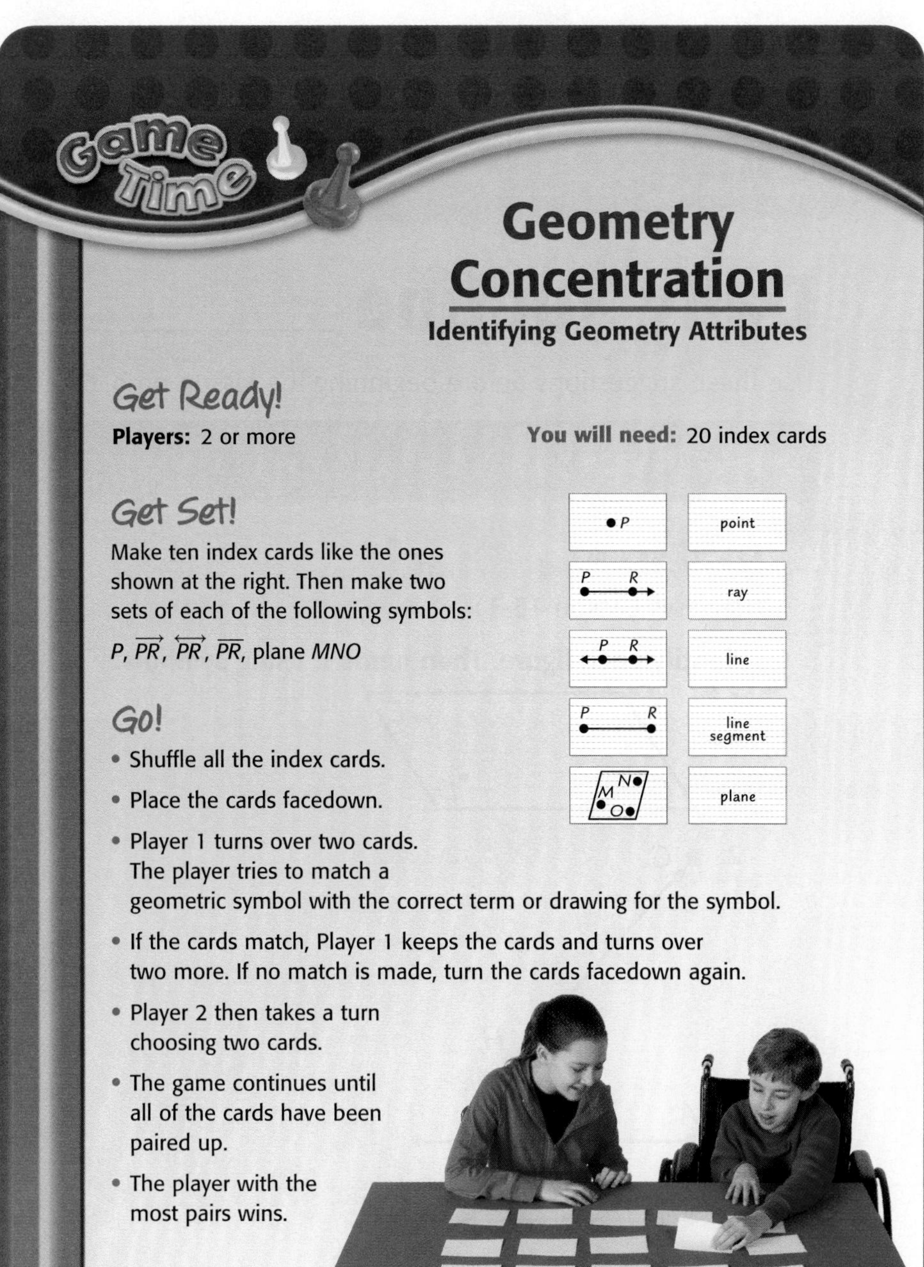

Geometry Concentration

Identifying Geometry Attributes

Get Ready!

Players: 2 or more

You will need: 20 index cards

Get Set!

Make ten index cards like the ones shown at the right. Then make two sets of each of the following symbols:

P, $\overrightarrow{PR}$, $\overleftrightarrow{PR}$, $\overline{PR}$, plane MNO

Go!

- Shuffle all the index cards.
- Place the cards facedown.
- Player 1 turns over two cards. The player tries to match a geometric symbol with the correct term or drawing for the symbol.
- If the cards match, Player 1 keeps the cards and turns over two more. If no match is made, turn the cards facedown again.
- Player 2 then takes a turn choosing two cards.
- The game continues until all of the cards have been paired up.
- The player with the most pairs wins.

Game Time Geometry Concentration **561**

Geometry Concentration

Math Concept:
Identifying Geometry Vocabulary

Materials: 20 index cards

Introduce the game on p. 561 to your students to play as a class, in small groups, or at a learning station to review concepts introduced in this chapter.

Instructions

- Students play in teams of two or more. They write geometry vocabulary terms on ten cards, as shown on page 561. They write the corresponding symbols on the other ten cards, as shown on page 561.
- One player shuffles the cards and places them face down on the table, one at a time.
- Player 1 turns over two cards and tries to match a geometric symbol with the corresponding geometry term or drawing. If a correct match is made, Player 1 keeps the cards and turns over two more. If a correct match is not made, Player 1 returns the cards, face down, to their positions on the table, and Player 2 takes a turn.
- Play continues, with each player taking turns trying to make matches until all of the cards have been correctly matched. The player who has the most correct matches wins the game.

Extend the Game

Have students play the game using angles and shapes from the chapter.

Differentiated Practice

Use these leveled suggestions to differentiate the game for all learners.

Level	Assignment
BL Below/ Approaching Level	Students work in teams of two and help each other pair up the cards.
OL On Level	Have students play the game with the rules as written.
AL Above/Beyond Level	Students give the definitions of the geometric terms before they get to keep their matched pairs.

Use Logical Reasoning

Lesson Planner

Objective

Solve problems by using logical reasoning.

Resources

Materials: pencil and paper
Literature Connection: *Circus Caps for Sale* by Esphyr Siobodkina
Teacher Technology
TeacherWorks • Interactive Classroom

Real-World Problem Solving Library
Math and Social Studies: *Flags: Shaping History*
Use these leveled books to reinforce and extend problem-solving skills and strategies.

Leveled for:

- OL On Level
- ELL Sheltered English
- SP Spanish

For additional support, see the Real-World Problem Solving Teacher Guide.

Daily Routine

Use these suggestions before beginning the lesson on p. 562.

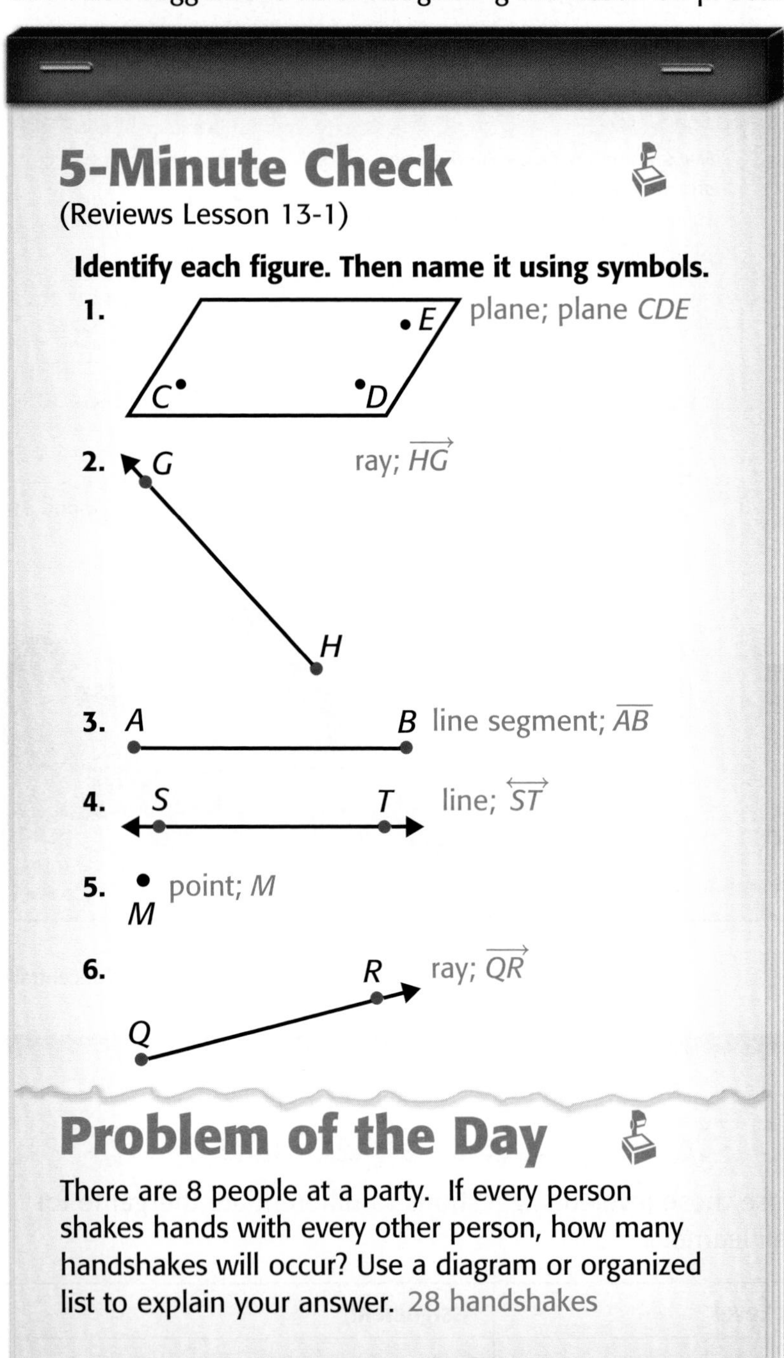

5-Minute Check

(Reviews Lesson 13-1)

Identify each figure. Then name it using symbols.

1. plane; plane *CDE*
2. ray; $\overrightarrow{HG}$
3. line segment; $\overline{AB}$
4. line; $\overleftrightarrow{ST}$
5. point; *M*
6. ray; $\overrightarrow{QR}$

Problem of the Day

There are 8 people at a party. If every person shakes hands with every other person, how many handshakes will occur? Use a diagram or organized list to explain your answer. 28 handshakes

Differentiated Instruction

Small Group Options

LOGICAL

Option 1 Gifted and Talented AL

Materials: pencil and paper

Hand students this problem written on paper:

Kia, Tom, Fernando, and Uma call in orders for lunch. All the food comes in one big bag and must be separated quickly while hot. There is a grilled chicken wrap, a garden salad, baked potato with broccoli, and a black bean burger plus fruit for all. One of the girls ordered a garden salad. Tom is a vegetarian, but Fernando always orders a dish with meat in it. Uma prefers cold food she can eat with a fork. Who gets which food?

Kia got the baked potato with broccoli, Fernando ordered the grilled chicken wrap, Uma got the garden salad, and Tom ordered the black bean burger.

LOGICAL, INTERPERSONAL

Option 2 English Language Learners ELL

Materials: currency chart from students' native countries

Core Vocabulary: exchange rate, tool, reasonable

Common Use Verb: went

Do Math This strategy helps students understand the idea of *reasonable*.

- Locate a chart dealing with the currency in the students' native country.
- Ask student to look at the currency exchange between money in his or her native country and America.
- "I ***went*** to Guatemala, I took $100. Was this **reasonable**?"
- Present problems to the student dealing with this information. Ask the student to locate reasonable answers.

Independent Work Options

LINGUISTIC

Option 1 Early Finishers OL AL

Materials: index cards, pencil and paper

- Have students list the names of four people in an order of their choice on their paper.
- Students write a series of three to four sentences on an index card that give clues to the order of the names on their list. Encourage them to make a table and mark off the boxes that cannot be true based on their clues.
- After students determine that their clues will yield the correct order of their list, have them exchange cards, read the clues, and solve. Return the solutions to the original writers.

Option 2 Student Technology

Math Online macmillanmh.com

Personal Tutor • Extra Examples

Option 3 Learning Station: Health (p. 554H)

Direct students to the Health Learning Station for opportunities to explore and extend the lesson concept.

1 Introduce

Activity Choice 1 • Review

- Pose the following problem:

  Jasmine is training for a hundred mile bicycle ride. On the first day of training, she rode 4 miles. On the second day, she rode 6 miles, and on the third day she rode 10 miles. On the fourth day she rode 12 miles. **If the pattern continues, how many miles will Jasmine ride on her 9th day of training?** 28 miles
- **What are some strategies that you might use to help you solve this problem?** *use the four-step plan, look for a pattern*, and *make a table*
- **What is the pattern you see in the problem?** +2, +4, +2 for each day of training

Activity Choice 2 • Literature

Introduce the lesson with *Circus Caps for Sale* by Esphyr Siobodkina. For a related math activity, see p. TR57.

2 Teach

Have students read the problem about colors of notebooks. Guide them through the problem-solving steps.

Understand Using the questions, review what students know and need to find.

Plan Have them discuss their strategy.

Solve Guide students to use *logical reasoning* to solve the problem.

- **What clues tell you that the boys own the blue and red notebooks?** The girls own the purple and green notebooks.
- **What does clue 3 really tell you?** Nicolas does not own the red notebook.

  How can the clues telling what one person owns help you to discover what other people own? If one person owns an object, no one else can own it so it can be crossed off for the others in the table.

Check Have students look back at the problem to make sure that the answer fits the facts given.

- **Does the order of the clues matter? Explain.** No; all of the clues work together to give the answer, so order does not matter.

Problem-Solving Strategy

MAIN IDEA I will solve problems by using logical reasoning.

Maggie, Sam, Aisha, and Nicolás each have a different colored notebook: blue, red, purple, and green. Use the clues to determine which person has each notebook.

1. Sam and the girl with the green notebook are in the same class.
2. A girl has the purple notebook.
3. Nicolás and the person with the red notebook eat lunch together.
4. Maggie is not in the same class as Sam.

Understand

What facts do you know?
- The four clues that are listed above.

What do you need to find?
- Which person has each notebook.

Plan

You can use logical reasoning to find which person has each notebook. Make a table to help organize the information.

Solve

Place an "X" in each box that cannot be true.

	Blue	Red	Purple	Green
Maggie	X	X	yes	X
Sam	X	yes	X	X
Aisha	X	X	X	yes
Nicolás	yes	X	X	X

- Clue 3 shows that Nicolás does not have the red notebook.
- Clues 1 and 2 show that girls have the green and purple notebooks and the boys have the blue and red notebooks.
- Clue 4 shows that Maggie is not in the same class as Sam, so she does not have the green notebook.

So, Maggie has a purple notebook, Sam has a red notebook, Aisha has a green notebook, and Nicolás has a blue notebook.

Check

Look back. Since all of the answers match the clues, the solution is reasonable.

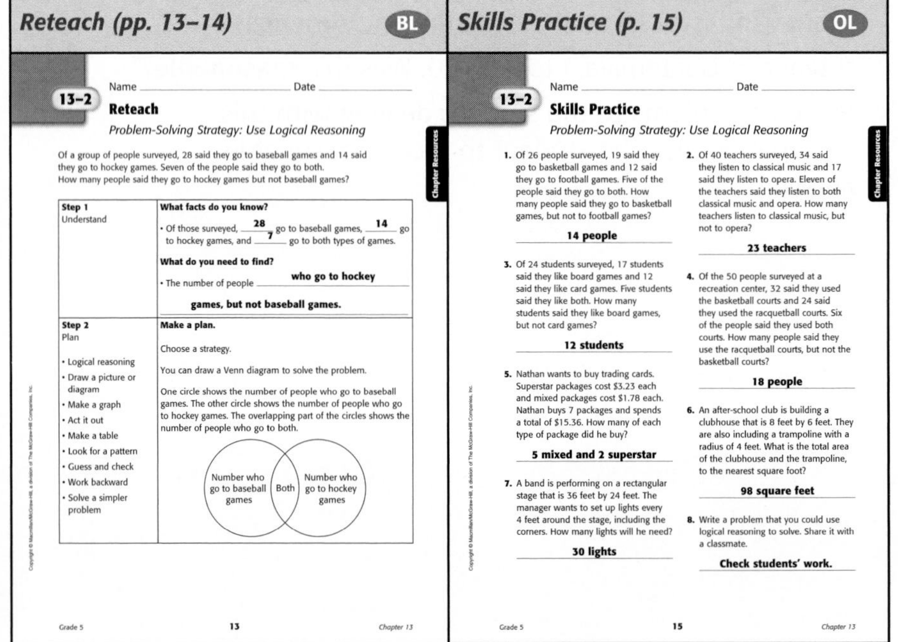

Reteach (pp. 13–14) BL

13-2 Name ______ Date ______

Reteach

Problem-Solving Strategy: Use Logical Reasoning

Of a group of people surveyed, 28 said they go to baseball games and 14 said they go to hockey games. Seven of the people said they go to both. How many people said they go to hockey games but not baseball games?

Step 1 Understand	**What facts do you know?** • Of those surveyed, **28** go to baseball games, **14** go to hockey games, and **7** go to both types of games. **What do you need to find?** • The number of people **who go to hockey games, but not baseball games.**
Step 2 Plan • Logical reasoning • Draw a picture or diagram • Make a graph • Act it out • Make a table • Look for a pattern • Guess and check • Work backward • Solve a simpler problem	**Make a plan.** Choose a strategy. You can draw a Venn diagram to solve the problem. One circle shows the number of people who go to baseball games. The other circle shows the number of people who go to hockey games. The overlapping part of the circles shows the number of people who go to both. (Number who go to baseball games / Both / Number who go to hockey games)

Chapter Resources

Grade 5 13 Chapter 13

Skills Practice (p. 15) OL

13-2 Name ______ Date ______

Skills Practice

Problem-Solving Strategy: Use Logical Reasoning

1. Of 26 people surveyed, 19 said they go to basketball games and 12 said they go to football games. Five of the people said they go to both. How many people said they go to basketball games, but not to football games? **14 people**
2. Of 40 teachers surveyed, 34 said they listen to classical music and 17 said they listen to opera. Eleven of the teachers said they listen to both classical music and opera. How many teachers listen to classical music, but not to opera? **23 teachers**
3. Of 24 students surveyed, 17 students said they like board games and 12 said they like card games. Five students said they like both. How many students said they like board games, but not card games? **12 students**
4. Of the 50 people surveyed at a recreation center, 32 said they used the basketball courts and 24 said they used the racquetball courts. Six of the people said they used both courts. How many people said they use the racquetball courts, but not the basketball courts? **18 people**
5. Nathan wants to buy trading cards. Superstar packages cost $3.23 each and mixed packages cost $1.78 each. Nathan buys 7 packages and spends a total of $15.36. How many of each type of package did he buy? **5 mixed and 2 superstar**
6. An after-school club is building a clubhouse that is 8 feet by 6 feet. They are also including a trampoline with a radius of 4 feet. What is the total area of the clubhouse and the trampoline, to the nearest square foot? **98 square feet**
7. A band is performing on a rectangular stage that is 36 feet by 24 feet. The manager wants to set up lights every 4 feet around the stage, including the corners. How many lights will he need? **30 lights**
8. Write a problem that you could use logical reasoning to solve. Share it with a classmate. **Check students' work.**

Chapter Resources

Grade 5 15 Chapter 13

1–4, 5, 11–12. See Ch. 13 Answer Appendix.

ANALYZE the Strategy

Refer to the problem on the previous page.

1. If you did not know that a girl had the purple notebook, would it be possible to determine who had each notebook? Explain your reasoning.
2. Suppose Aisha is not in the same class as Sam. Who has which notebook?
3. The area of a garden is 16 square feet. If the length and width are whole numbers, is the garden definitely a square? Explain.
4. Explain when to use the *logical reasoning* strategy to solve a problem.

PRACTICE the Strategy

See page R34.

Solve the problem. Use *logical reasoning*.

5. Main Street and Park Street do not meet. They are always the same distance apart. Central Avenue crosses both streets to form square corners. Central Avenue and Fletcher Avenue also do not meet. Which streets are perpendicular?
6. **Algebra** If the pattern below continues, how many pennies will be in the fifth figure? **15 pennies**

Figure 1

Figure 2

Figure 3

7. Charlotte, Ramon, and Nora have different professions: scientist, athlete, and teacher. Charlotte does not like sports. Ramon is not a teacher nor an athlete. Nora likes to run. Who is the teacher? **Charlotte**
8. Three dogs are sitting in a line. Rocky is not last. Coco is in front of the tallest dog. Marley is sitting behind Rocky. List the dogs in order from first to last. **Coco, Rocky, Marley**
9. Ethan has $1.25 in change. He has twice as many dimes as pennies, and the number of nickels is one less than the number of pennies. How many dimes, nickels, and pennies does he have? **10 dimes, 4 nickels, and 5 pennies**
10. There are 4 more girls in Mrs. Pitt's class than Mr. Brown's class. Five girls moved from Mrs. Pitt's class to Mr. Brown's class. Now there are twice as many girls in Mr. Brown's class as there are in Mrs. Pitt's. How many girls were in Mr. Brown's class to begin with? **7 girls**
11. **Geometry** Set up 12 toothpicks as shown below. Move three toothpicks so that you form four squares.

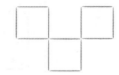

12. **WRITING IN MATH** How did you use logical reasoning to determine that Nora is not the teacher in Exercise 7?

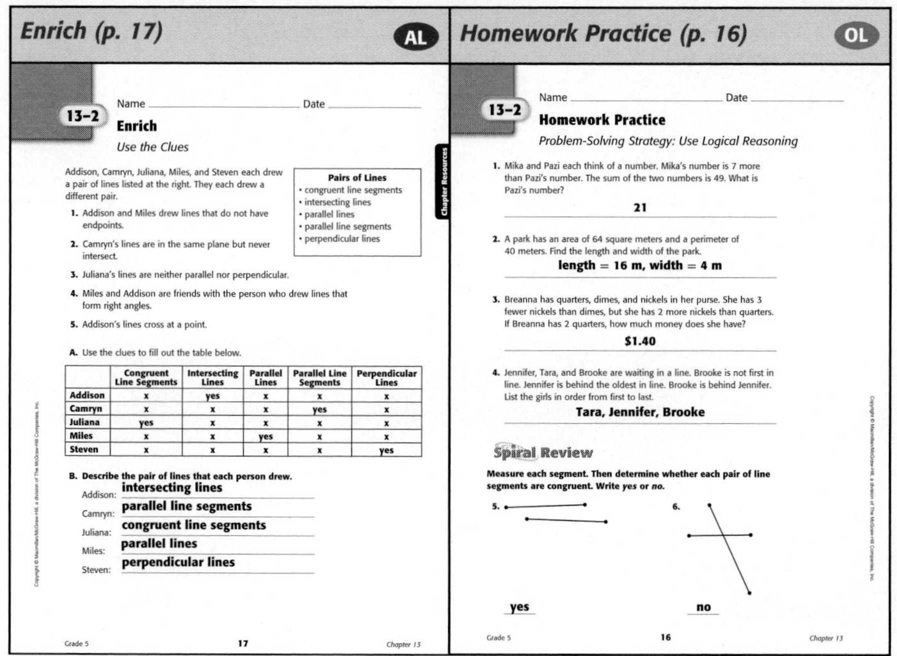

Enrich (p. 17) AL

13–2 Name ______ Date ______

Enrich

Use the Clues

Addison, Camryn, Juliana, Miles, and Steven each drew a pair of lines listed at the right. They each drew a different pair.

Pairs of Lines
- congruent line segments
- intersecting lines
- parallel lines
- parallel line segments
- perpendicular lines

1. Addison and Miles drew lines that do not have endpoints.
2. Camryn's lines are in the same plane but never intersect.
3. Juliana's lines are neither parallel nor perpendicular.
4. Miles and Addison are friends with the person who drew lines that form right angles.
5. Addison's lines cross at a point.

A. Use the clues to fill out the table below.

	Congruent Line Segments	Intersecting Lines	Parallel Lines	Parallel Line Segments	Perpendicular Lines
Addison	x	yes	x	x	x
Camryn	x	x	x	yes	x
Juliana	yes	x	x	x	x
Miles	x	x	yes	x	x
Steven	x	x	x	x	yes

B. Describe the pair of lines that each person drew.

Addison: **intersecting lines**
Camryn: **parallel line segments**
Juliana: **congruent line segments**
Miles: **parallel lines**
Steven: **perpendicular lines**

Grade 5 17 Chapter 13

Homework Practice (p. 16) OL

13–2 Name ______ Date ______

Homework Practice

Problem-Solving Strategy: Use Logical Reasoning

1. Mika and Pazi each think of a number. Mika's number is 7 more than Pazi's number. The sum of the two numbers is 49. What is Pazi's number? **21**
2. A park has an area of 64 square meters and a perimeter of 40 meters. Find the length and width of the park. **length = 16 m, width = 4 m**
3. Breanna has quarters, dimes, and nickels in her purse. She has 3 fewer nickels than dimes, but she has 2 more nickels than quarters. If Breanna has 2 quarters, how much money does she have? **$1.40**
4. Jennifer, Tara, and Brooke are waiting in a line. Brooke is not first in line. Jennifer is behind the oldest in line. Brooke is behind Jennifer. List the girls in order from first to last. **Tara, Jennifer, Brooke**

Spiral Review

Measure each segment. Then determine whether each pair of line segments are congruent. Write *yes* or *no*.

5. **yes**
6. **no**

Grade 5 16 Chapter 13

Analyze the Strategy Use Exercises 1–4 to analyze and discuss the problem-solving strategy.

BL Alternate Teaching Strategy

If students have trouble using logical reasoning to solve problems…

Then use one of these reteach options:

1. CRM **Daily Reteach Worksheet** (pp. 13–14)
2. Have students draw a table to organize the problem and use markers to designate cells in the table that are not true. After reading each clue, pose questions that will lead students to designate all possible "not true" cells. Use questions to help students understand how each clue affects the results.

3 Practice

Using the Exercises

Exercises 5–11 give students the opportunity to practice the *use logical reasoning* strategy.

Exercises 7 and 8 require students to draw a table and consider clues to solve the problems.

4 Assess

Formative Assessment

Pose the following problem:

Abby, Kwame, Celeste, and Don are in line. Don is not first or last in line. Kwame was ahead of Don and behind Celeste. What is their order?

- **How would you solve the problem?** Make a table and use logical reasoning to place Xs in the boxes that cannot be true.
- **From first to last, what is their order?** Celeste, Kwame, Donato, Abby

Quick Check **Are students continuing to struggle with solving problems by using logical reasoning?**

If Yes → Strategic Intervention Guide (p. 128)

If No → Independent Work Options (p. 562B)
CRM Skills Practice Worksheet (p. 15)
CRM Enrich Worksheet (p. 17)

Geometry Activity for 13-3

Lesson Planner

Objective

Use turns on circles to identify angles.

Vocabulary

angle, vertex, degree, right angle, acute angle, obtuse angle

Resources

Materials: paper circles, scissors, glue, drawing paper
Manipulatives: protractor

1 Introduce

- Have students cut out two circles each. Students glue one circle to the top half of a piece of drawing paper. Have them make a point in the center of the circle. **What would you create if you were to draw two line segments each with one point at the center of the circle and the other on the edge of the circle?** an angle
- Ask students to draw the two line segments and label the point in the center *B*. The points on the edge of the circle should be labeled *A* and *C*. **What is the name of the angle you drew?** $\angle ABC$
- Remind students that, in naming angles, the vertex is always in the middle of the three letters. Tell students that circles are measured in degrees and that there are 360° all the way around one whole circle. **If one whole circle measures 360°, what does $\frac{1}{2}$ of a circle measure?** How do you know? 180°; $\frac{1}{2}$ of 360° is 180°.
- Have students draw a line around their circle and label it 360°.

Explore

Geometry Activity for 13-3
Identify Angles

MAIN IDEA

I will use turns on circles to identify angles.

New Vocabulary

angle
vertex
degree
right angle
acute angle
obtuse angle

You Will Need
protractor

Math Online
macmillanmh.com
• Concepts in Motion

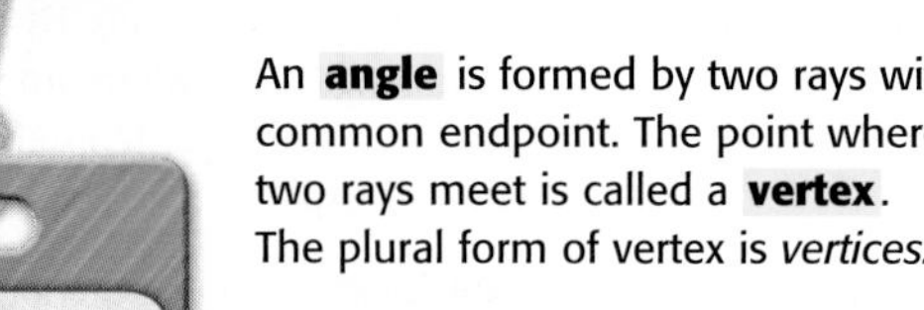

An **angle** is formed by two rays with a common endpoint. The point where the two rays meet is called a **vertex**. The plural form of vertex is *vertices*.

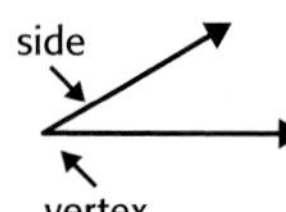

The unit used to measure an angle is called a **degree** (°). A circle contains 360°. So, a full turn on a circle is 360°.

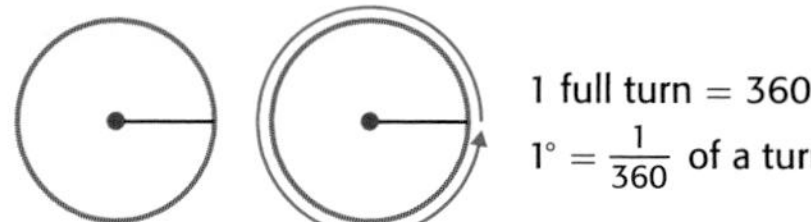

When a turn on a circle is less than full, the angle formed is less than 360°.

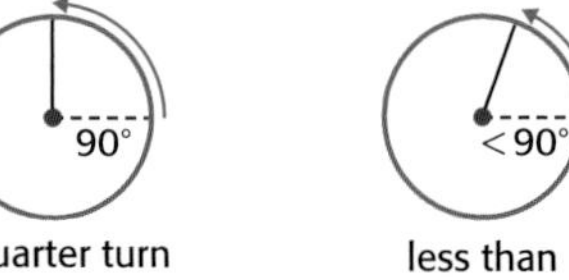

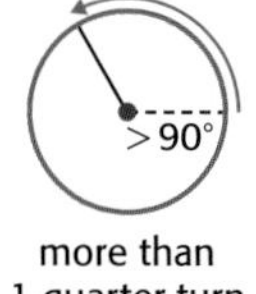

Angles can be identified according to whether they measure 90°, less than 90°, or greater than 90°.

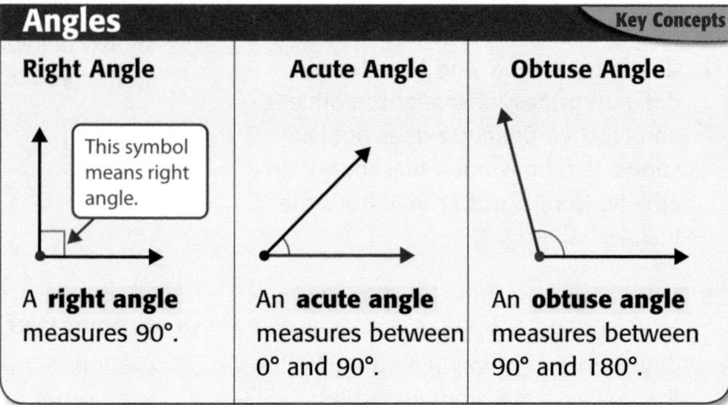

Angles — Key Concepts

Right Angle	Acute Angle	Obtuse Angle
This symbol means right angle.		
A **right angle** measures 90°.	An **acute angle** measures between 0° and 90°.	An **obtuse angle** measures between 90° and 180°.

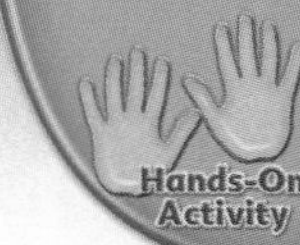

It is easy to identify acute and obtuse angles because they are less than or greater than 90°. You can use a protractor.

ACTIVITY

1 **Identify the angle as *acute, right,* or *obtuse.***

The angle appears to be a right angle. Use a protractor to measure the angle.

So, the measure of the angle is 90°. It is a right angle.

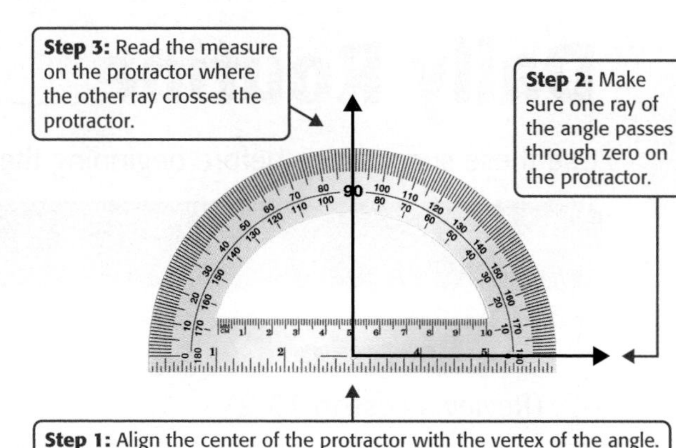

Step 3: Read the measure on the protractor where the other ray crosses the protractor.
Step 2: Make sure one ray of the angle passes through zero on the protractor.
Step 1: Align the center of the protractor with the vertex of the angle.

CHECK What You Know

Use a protractor to identify each angle as *acute, right,* or *obtuse.*

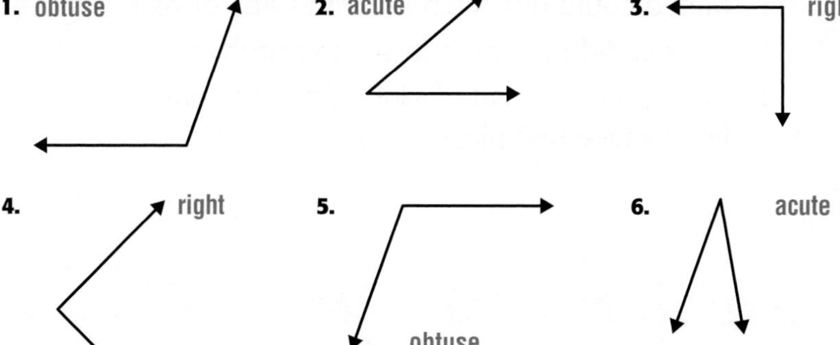

7. **OPEN ENDED** Draw an obtuse angle. See margin.

8. **WRITING IN MATH** Write a definition for perpendicular lines that includes the words *right angle.* Sample answer: Perpendicular lines meet at right angles.

Additional Answer

7. Sample answer:

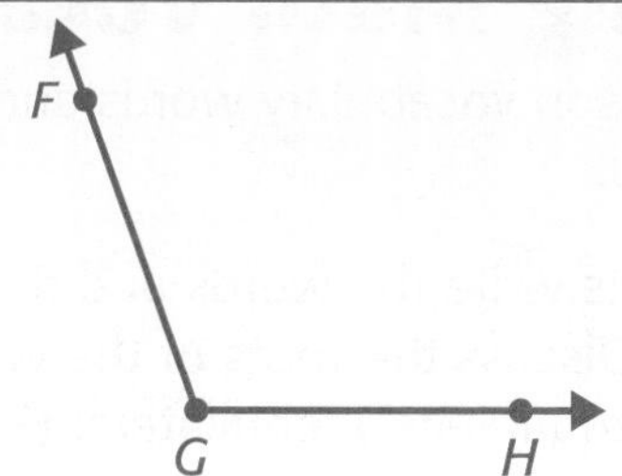

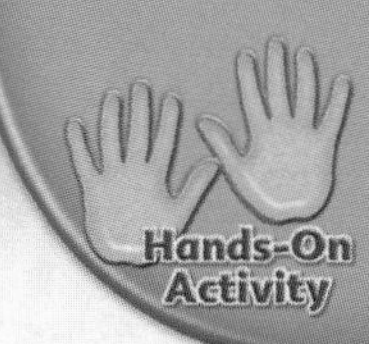

2 Teach

Activity Make sure students understand that it may be difficult to determine if an angle is acute, right, or obtuse simply by looking at it. Placing a known right angle, such as the corner of a piece of paper, on an unknown angle can help students to decide more easily.

3 Assess

Formative Assessment

Use the **Check What You Know** Exercises 1–8 to assess whether students comprehend how to identify angles.

From Concrete to Abstract Use Exercise 7 to bridge the gap between naming angles as acute, obtuse, and right and drawing angles given a specific description.

Extending the Concept
What kinds of geometric shapes might have acute, obtuse, or right angles?

LESSON 13-3

Triangles

Lesson Planner

Objective

Identify characteristics of triangles.

Vocabulary

isosceles triangle, equilateral triangle, scalene triangle, acute triangle, right triangle, obtuse triangle

Resources

Materials: 4 in. by 7 in. paper rectangles, scissors, rulers, toothpicks, glue

Literature Connection: *Square, Triangle, Round, Skinny* by Vladimir Radunsky

Teacher Technology

TeacherWorks • Interactive Classroom • Concepts in Motion

Focus on Math Background

It is likely that students at this level have used a corner of an index card to check to see if an angle is a right angle. They should also have a basic understanding that seeing a right angle symbol in a figure indicates that the angle is a right angle. In this lesson, students classify triangles by their sides (equilateral, isosceles, and scalene) and by their angles (acute, right, and obtuse). Equilateral and isosceles triangles are discussed in terms of the number of congruent sides contained in the triangle. Note that an equilateral triangle is also equiangular, that is, each of its angles measures 60°. Because it is both equilateral and equiangular, such a triangle is an example of a *regular polygon*.

Daily Routine

Use these suggestions before beginning the lesson on p. 566.

5-Minute Check

(Reviews Lesson 13-2)

Solve. Use the *logical reasoning* strategy.
Andrea, Gaby, Mateo, and Akil raced in the hundred meter dash. Use the following clues to determine the order of the runners at the finish line.

1. Mateo could not catch up with Gaby or Akil.
2. Andrea did not come in second or third.
3. Gaby pulled ahead of Akil right at the finish line to take first place.

Gaby-first, Akil-second, Mateo-third, Andrea-fourth

Problem of the Day

Cami used 5 ounces of raisins, $\frac{3}{8}$ pound blueberries, $\frac{3}{4}$ pound strawberries, 1 pound oranges and 4 ounces raspberries in a fruit salad. Find the total weight of the fruit in pounds and ounces. 2 pounds, 11 ounces

Building Math Vocabulary

Write the lesson vocabulary words and their definitions on the board.

Have students write the words and their definitions in their notes. Discuss the roots of the words isosceles (Greek for "equal legs"), equilateral (Latin for "equal sides") and scalene (Greek for "uneven"). Ask students to draw a small model of each of the triangles next to each definition.

Differentiated Instruction

Small Group Options

Option 1 Gifted and Talented AL

SPATIAL

Materials: paper and pencil

- Have students prove, with diagrams and measurements, whether or not an obtuse triangle can have 2 obtuse angles or if a right triangle can also be acute. no; no

Option 2 English Language Learners ELL

KINESTHETIC

Core Vocabulary: an example of, extend, straighten
Common Use Verb: bend
Do Math This strategy teaches the difference between types of triangles.

- Use your arms to demonstrate what a right angle looks like, as well as angles that are more or less than a right angle.
- Ask students to use their arms to demonstrate that they understand these terms.

- Draw, and label, a right, scalene, isosceles, and equilateral triangle on the board.
- Ask students to identify which of these triangles has right and more or less than right angles.

Independent Work Options

Option 1 Early Finishers AL

VISUAL/SPATIAL

Materials: narrow strips of colored paper, drawing paper, glue, pencil

- Have students fold a drawing paper into 6 sections and label the sections with the following: 1. Right Isosceles, 2. Right Scalene, 3. Equilateral, 4. Acute Isosceles, 5. Obtuse Isosceles, 6. Acute Scalene.
- Direct students to use strips of paper to make triangles that match each description. Have them glue the triangles in the proper place.
- When completed, the posters may be displayed in the classroom.

Option 2 Student Technology

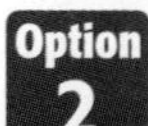

Math Online macmillanmh.com

Personal Tutor • Extra Examples

Math Adventures

Option 3 Learning Station: Science (p. 554H)

Direct students to the Science Learning Station for opportunities to explore and extend the lesson concept.

Option 4 Problem-Solving Practice

Reinforce problem-solving skills and strategies with the Problem-Solving Practice worksheet.

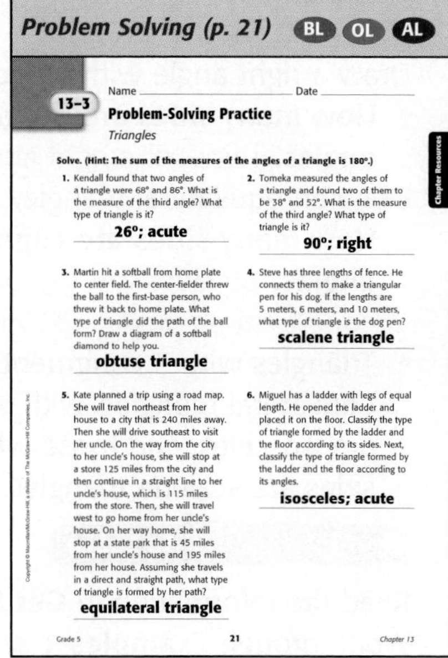

Problem Solving (p. 21) BL OL AL

13-3 Name ______ Date ______

Problem-Solving Practice

Triangles

Solve. (Hint: The sum of the measures of the angles of a triangle is 180°.)

1. Kendall found that two angles of a triangle were 68° and 86°. What is the measure of the third angle? What type of triangle is it?
   26°; acute
2. Tomeka measured the angles of a triangle and found two of them to be 38° and 52°. What is the measure of the third angle? What type of triangle is it?
   90°; right
3. Martin hit a softball from home plate to center field. The center-fielder threw the ball to the first-base person, who threw it back to home plate. What type of triangle did the path of the ball form? Draw a diagram of a softball diamond to help you.
   obtuse triangle
4. Steve has three lengths of fence. He connects them to make a triangular pen for his dog. If the lengths are 5 meters, 6 meters, and 10 meters, what type of triangle is the dog pen?
   scalene triangle
5. Kate planned a trip using a road map. She will travel northeast from her house to a city that is 240 miles away. Then she will drive southeast to visit her uncle. On the way from the city to her uncle's house, she will stop at a store 125 miles from the city and then continue in a straight line to her uncle's house, which is 115 miles from the store. Then, she will travel west to go home from her uncle's house. On her way home, she will stop at a state park that is 45 miles from her uncle's house and 195 miles from her house. Assuming she travels in a direct and straight path, what type of triangle is formed by her path?
   equilateral triangle
6. Miguel has a ladder with legs of equal length. He opened the ladder and placed it on the floor. Classify the type of triangle formed by the ladder and the floor according to its sides. Next, classify the type of triangle formed by the ladder and the floor according to its angles.
   isosceles; acute

Chapter Resources

Grade 5 21 Chapter 13

13-3 Triangles

1 Introduce

Activity Choice 1 • Hands-On

- **What do all triangles have in common?** three sides and three angles
- Distribute a 4 in. by 7 in. paper rectangle to each student. **Draw a diagonal. Cut along the diagonal. Describe one of the figures you made.** a triangle with 1 right angle and 2 acute angles, no sides are the same length
- **Label the angles as *right* or *acute*. On your other triangle, use your ruler to measure 4 inches along the longest side. Make a mark there. Draw a line from this mark to the vertex of the right angle. Cut along this line. Describe.** One triangle has all sides congruent and all acute angles. The other has 2 sides congruent, one obtuse angle, and 2 acute angles.
- **Label each angle *acute* or *obtuse* and tell the number of congruent sides each triangle has.**

Activity Choice 2 • Literature

Introduce the lesson with *Square, Triangle, Round, Skinny* by Vladimir Radunsky. For a related math activity, see p. TR57.

2 Teach

Scaffolding Questions

Draw a right triangle with two congruent sides.

- **How many sides are congruent? Describe the angles.** 2 sides are congruent; 2 acute angles, one right angle

Draw a right angle with no congruent sides.

- **How many sides are congruent? Describe the angles.** none; one right angle, 2 acute angles

Draw an equilateral triangle.

- **How many sides are cogruent? Describe the angles.** all sides are congruent; 3 acute, congruent angles
- Triangles with 3 congruent sides are equilateral triangles, with 2 congruent sides are isosceles, and those with no congruent sides are scalene triangles.

GET READY to Learn

Read the information in **Get Ready to Learn.** Work through **Examples 1 and 2.**

13-3 Triangles

MAIN IDEA

I will identify characteristics of triangles.

New Vocabulary

isosceles triangle
equilateral triangle
scalene triangle
acute triangle
right triangle
obtuse triangle

Math Online

macmillanmh.com

- Extra Examples
- Personal Tutor
- Self-Check Quiz

GET READY to Learn

There is a large pyramid standing in front of the Louvre (loo-vrah) museum in Paris, France. The sides of the pyramid are shaped like triangles.

You can classify triangles by the lengths of their sides.

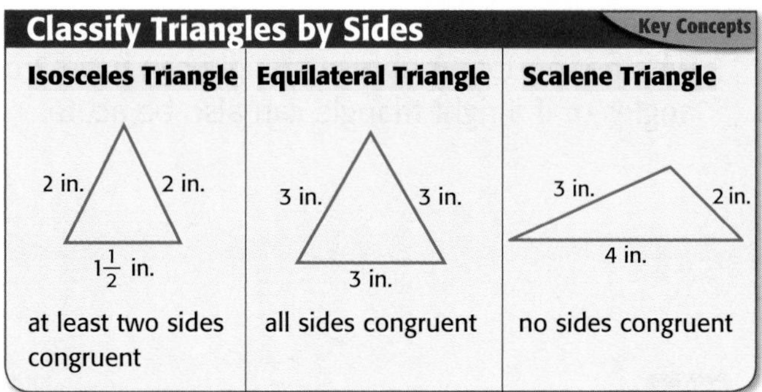

Classify Triangles by Sides — Key Concepts

Isosceles Triangle	Equilateral Triangle	Scalene Triangle
2 in., 2 in., $1\frac{1}{2}$ in.	3 in., 3 in., 3 in.	3 in., 2 in., 4 in.
at least two sides congruent	all sides congruent	no sides congruent

Real-World EXAMPLE Identify Sides

1. **MEASUREMENT Measure each side of the triangle. Then find the number of congruent sides. State whether any of the sides appear to be perpendicular. Write *yes* or *no*.**

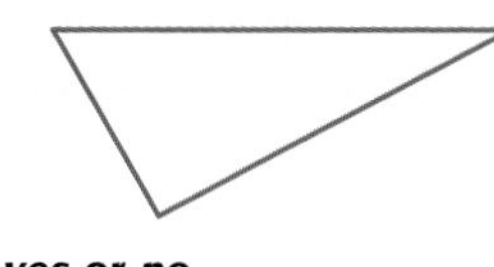

None of the sides of the triangle have the same length. So, no sides are congruent.

Yes; two sides of the triangle appear to be perpendicular.

566 Chapter 13 Identify, Compare, and Classify Geometric Figures

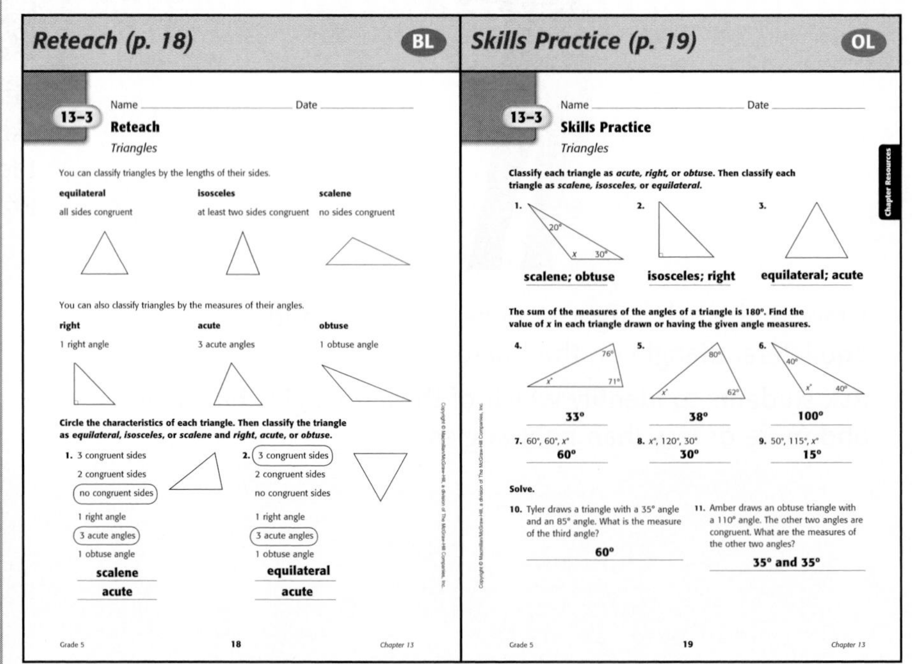

Reteach (p. 18) BL

13-3 Name ______ Date ______

Reteach

Triangles

You can classify triangles by the lengths of their sides.

equilateral	isosceles	scalene
all sides congruent	at least two sides congruent	no sides congruent

You can also classify triangles by the measures of their angles.

right	acute	obtuse
1 right angle	3 acute angles	1 obtuse angle

Circle the characteristics of each triangle. Then classify the triangle as *equilateral, isosceles,* or *scalene* and *right, acute,* or *obtuse*.

1. 3 congruent sides / 2 congruent sides / (no congruent sides) / 1 right angle / (3 acute angles) / 1 obtuse angle — **scalene**, **acute**
2. (3 congruent sides) / 2 congruent sides / no congruent sides / 1 right angle / (3 acute angles) / 1 obtuse angle — **equilateral**, **acute**

Grade 5 18 Chapter 13

Skills Practice (p. 19) OL

13-3 Name ______ Date ______

Skills Practice

Triangles

Classify each triangle as *acute, right,* or *obtuse*. Then classify each triangle as *scalene, isosceles,* or *equilateral*.

1. 20°, x, 30° — **scalene; obtuse**
2. **isosceles; right**
3. **equilateral; acute**

The sum of the measures of the angles of a triangle is 180°. Find the value of x in each triangle drawn or having the given angle measures.

4. 76°, 71°, x° — **33°**
5. 80°, 62°, x° — **38°**
6. 40°, 40°, x° — **100°**
7. 60°, 60°, x° — **60°**
8. x°, 120°, 30° — **30°**
9. 50°, 115°, x° — **15°**

Solve.

10. Tyler draws a triangle with a 35° angle and an 85° angle. What is the measure of the third angle? **60°**
11. Amber draws an obtuse triangle with a 110° angle. The other two angles are congruent. What are the measures of the other two angles? **35° and 35°**

Chapter Resources

Grade 5 19 Chapter 13

Remember

A right angle is formed by perpendicular lines.

Hands-On Mini Activity

Step 1 Draw and cut out three different triangles that each have one right angle. Draw and cut out three different triangles that do not have any right angles.

Right Triangles | **Not Right Triangles**

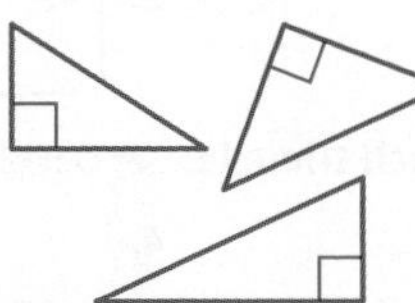

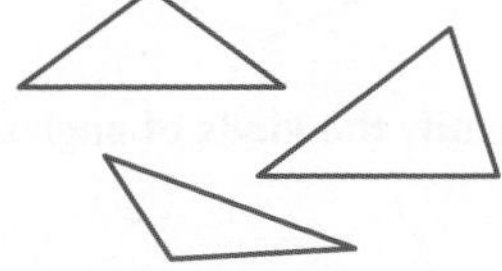

Step 2 Draw and cut out three different triangles that each have one obtuse angle.

Step 3 Draw and cut out three different triangles that do not have either a right angle or an obtuse angle.

Step 4 Separate your triangles into three different groups, based on the measures of the angles. **See students' work.**

In the Hands-On Mini Activity, you classified triangles by the measures of their angles.

Classify Triangles by Angles — Key Concepts

Acute Triangle	Right Triangle	Obtuse Triangle
3 acute angles	1 right angle, 2 acute angles	1 obtuse angle, 2 acute angles

Real-World EXAMPLE Identify Angles

2 **GEOMETRY Triangles form the sides of the Khafre Pyramid in Egypt. Identify the kinds of angles in the triangle.**

All three angles are acute.

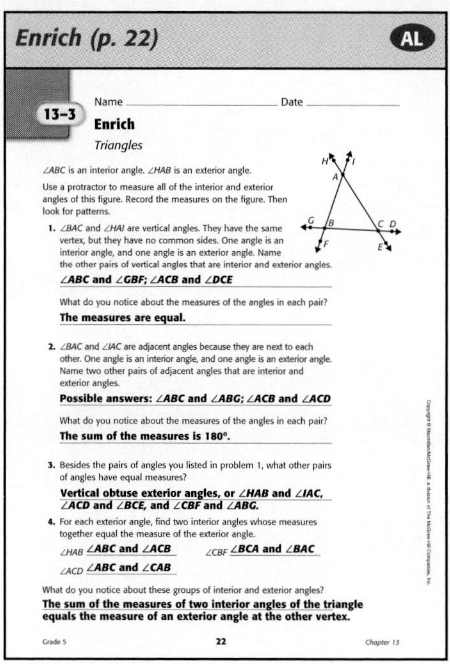

Enrich (p. 22) **AL**

13-3 Name ______ Date ______

Enrich

Triangles

∠ABC is an interior angle. ∠HAB is an exterior angle.

Use a protractor to measure all of the interior and exterior angles of this figure. Record the measures on the figure. Then look for patterns.

1. ∠BAC and ∠HAI are vertical angles. They have the same vertex, but they have no common sides. One angle is an interior angle, and one angle is an exterior angle. Name the other pairs of vertical angles that are interior and exterior angles.
∠ABC and ∠GBF; ∠ACB and ∠DCE
What do you notice about the measures of the angles in each pair?
The measures are equal.

2. ∠BAC and ∠IAC are adjacent angles because they are next to each other. One angle is an interior angle, and one angle is an exterior angle. Name two other pairs of adjacent angles that are interior and exterior angles.
Possible answers: ∠ABC and ∠ABG; ∠ACB and ∠ACD
What do you notice about the measures of the angles in each pair?
The sum of the measures is 180°.

3. Besides the pairs of angles you listed in problem 1, what other pairs of angles have equal measures?
Vertical obtuse exterior angles, or ∠HAB and ∠IAC, ∠ACD and ∠BCE, and ∠CBF and ∠ABG.

4. For each exterior angle, find two interior angles whose measures together equal the measure of the exterior angle.
∠HAB **∠ABC and ∠ACB** ∠CBF **∠BCA and ∠BAC**
∠ACD **∠ABC and ∠CAB**

What do you notice about these groups of interior and exterior angles?
The sum of the measures of two interior angles of the triangle equals the measure of an exterior angle at the other vertex.

Grade 5 22 Chapter 13

Identify Angles

Example 2 Be sure students understand that the number of congruent angles matches the number of congruent sides in a triangle and that there can be no more than one right angle or obtuse angle in any given triangle.

ADDITIONAL EXAMPLES

1 Measure to find the number of congruent sides. Then state whether any of the sides appear to be perpendicular. Write *yes* or *no*.

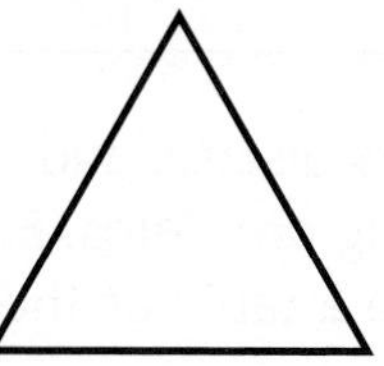

3 congruent sides; no

2 Triangles form the dome of Spaceship Earth at Epcot Center in Florida. Identify the kind of angles in the triangles. 2 acute angles; 1 obtuse angle

CHECK What You Know

As a class, have students complete Exercises 1–6 in **Check What You Know** as you observe their work.

Exercise 6 Assess student comprehension before assigning practice exercises.

BL Alternate Teaching Strategy

If students have trouble identifying characteristics of triangles…

Then use one of these reteach options:

1. CRM **Daily Reteach Worksheet** (p. 18)
2. Have them use toothpicks to create, label, and tape down models of isosceles, equilateral, scalene, acute, obtuse, and right triangles. Ask students to write clue words or phrases below each model to describe each triangle. For isosceles, equilateral, and scalene triangles, clues should be related to sides, while for right, acute, and obtuse triangles, clues should be related to angles.

3 Practice

Differentiate practice using these leveled assignments for Exercises 7–24.

Level	Assignment
BL Below/ Approaching Level	7–12, 15, 17, 19, 24
OL On Level	7–19, 24
AL Above/Beyond Level	7–19 odd, 21–24

Have students discuss and complete the Higher Order Thinking problems. Encourage students to draw and use a table as they solve Exercise 23.

WRITING IN MATH Have students complete Exercise 24 in their Math Journals. You may choose to use this as an optional formative assessment.

COMMON ERROR!

Exercise 18 Students may have trouble determining the sum of angle measures of triangles. Draw a rectangle on the board pointing out that each angle is a right angle or 90°. Have students determine that the sum of the angles in the rectangle is 360°. Draw a diagonal across the rectangle and guide students to determine that the angles in each of the two triangles created have a sum of $\frac{1}{2}$ of 360° or 180°.

★ indicates multi-step problem

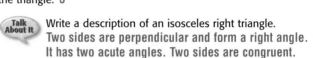

CHECK What You Know

Measure the sides of each triangle. Then find the number of congruent sides. State whether any of the sides appear to be perpendicular. Write *yes* or *no*. See Example 1 (p. 566)

1. 2; no
2. 0; yes

Identify the kinds of angles in each triangle. See Example 2 (p. 567)

3. 3 acute
4. 2 acute, 1 obtuse

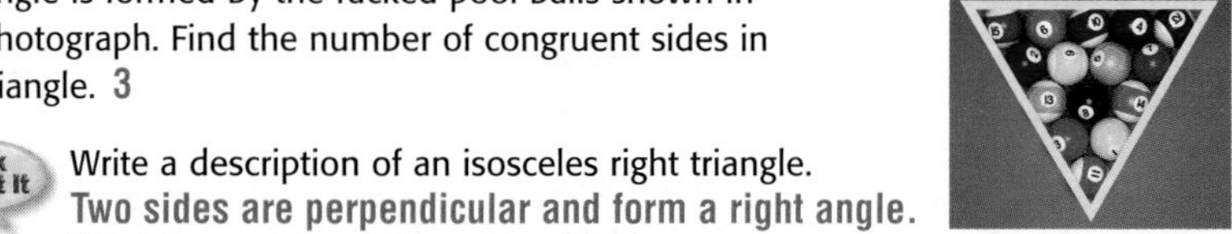

5. A triangle is formed by the racked pool balls shown in the photograph. Find the number of congruent sides in the triangle. 3
6. Talk About It Write a description of an isosceles right triangle. Two sides are perpendicular and form a right angle. It has two acute angles. Two sides are congruent.

Practice and Problem Solving

EXTRA PRACTICE See page R35.

Measure the sides of each triangle. Then find the number of congruent sides. State whether any of the sides appear to be perpendicular. Write *yes* or *no*. See Example 1 (p. 566) 8. 0; yes

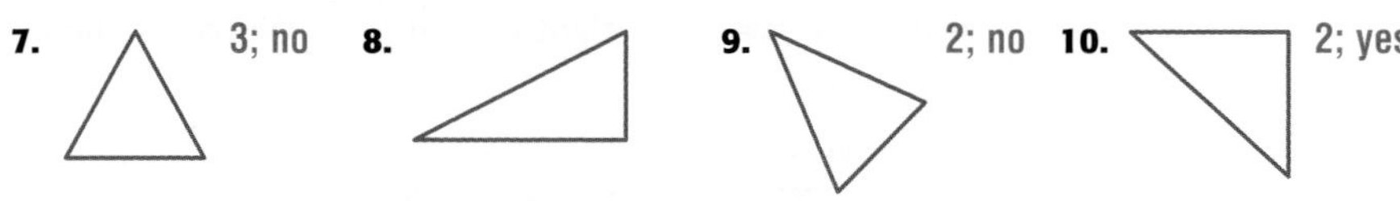

7. 3; no
8.
9. 2; no
10. 2; yes

Identify the kinds of angles in each triangle. See Example 2 (p. 567) 11. 2 acute, 1 obtuse

11.
12. 3 acute
13. 2 acute, 1 right
14. 3 acute

15. the triangles in the bridge 3 acute
16. half of a square sandwich 2 acute, 1 right

17. Look at the triangle on the top of the White House on a twenty dollar bill. Describe the sides and angles of the triangle. two congruent sides; one obtuse angle, two acute angles

★18. The sum of the measures of the angles of a triangle is 180°. In a right triangle, what is the sum of the measures of the two acute angles? 90°

Real-World PROBLEM SOLVING

Art The image shown at the right contains many triangles.

19. Describe the different types of triangles found in the image. Sample answer: isosceles, scalene, acute, right

20. Look at the purple triangle. State whether any sides appear to be perpendicular. Then identify the triangle. no; obtuse

H.O.T. Problems

21. **OPEN ENDED** Draw a triangle that has all acute angles and two congruent sides. Then classify the triangle by its side lengths and by its angle measures. 21–24. See margin.

22. **WHICH ONE DOESN'T BELONG?** Identify the triangle that does not belong with the other three. Explain your reasoning.

A  B 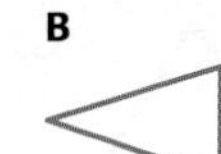 C 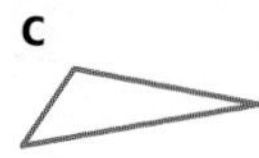 D 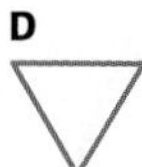

23. **CHALLENGE** Emma, Gabriel, Jorge, and Makayla each have a different triangle. Use the clues below to describe each person's triangle as isosceles, equilateral, or scalene and as acute, right, or obtuse. Explain your process.

- Gabriel and Jorge each have a 90° angle in their triangles.
- Gabriel's triangle does not have any congruent sides.
- One of Emma's angles measures greater than 90°.
- Each side of Makayla's triangle and two sides of Emma's and Jorge's triangles are four centimeters long.

24. **WRITING IN MATH** A triangle has two sides that are perpendicular. Could the triangle be isosceles, equilateral, or scalene? Explain.

Homework Practice (p. 20) OL

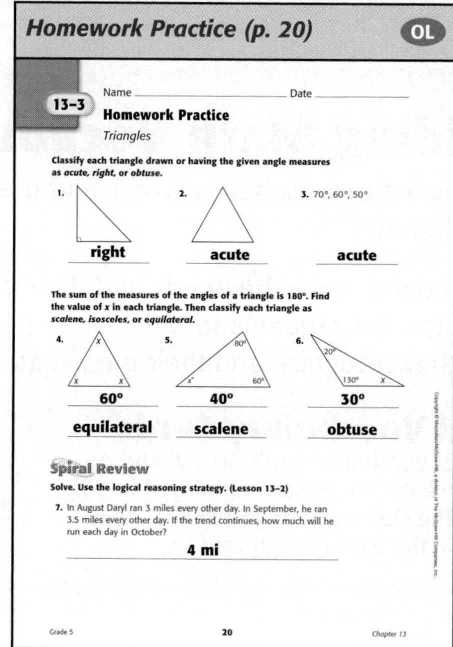

13-3 Name ______ Date ______

Homework Practice

Triangles

Classify each triangle drawn or having the given angle measures as *acute, right,* or *obtuse.*

1. right
2. acute
3. 70°, 60°, 50° acute

The sum of the measures of the angles of a triangle is 180°. Find the value of *x* in each triangle. Then classify each triangle as *scalene, isosceles,* or *equilateral.*

4. 60° equilateral
5. 80°, 60° 40° scalene
6. 20°, 130° 30° obtuse

Spiral Review

Solve. Use the logical reasoning strategy. (Lesson 13-2)

7. In August Daryl ran 3 miles every other day. In September, he ran 3.5 miles every other day. If the trend continues, how much will he run each day in October? 4 mi

Grade 5 20 Chapter 13

4 Assess

Formative Assessment

Draw a right scalene triangle on the board.

- **What are the two ways the triangle would be classified?** by its sides and by its angles
- **Based on its sides, what kind of triangle is this? Explain.** Scalene triangle; none of its sides are congruent. **Based on its angles, what kind of triangle is it? Explain.** A right triangle; it has one right angle.

Quick Check **Are students continuing to struggle with identifying characteristics of triangles?**

If Yes → Strategic Intervention Guide (p. 128)

If No → Independent Work Options (p. 566B)
CRM Skills Practice Worksheet (p. 19)
CRM Enrich Worksheet (p. 22)

Into the Future Have students write a short paragraph to tell how what they learned today about describing triangles will be useful as they describe other geometric figures in future lessons.

Additional Answers

21. Sample answer: isosceles, acute

22. C; It is the only triangle that does not have two congruent sides.

23. Emma: isosceles, obtuse; Gabriel: scalene, right; Jorge: isosceles, right; Makayla: equilateral, acute; Sample explanation: Gabriel and Jorge have right triangles since they each have a 90° angle. Gabriel's triangle is scalene since it does not have any congruent sides. Emma's triangle is obtuse since it has an angle that measures greater than 90°. Makayla's triangle is equilateral since all the sides have the same measure. Emma's triangle is isosceles since it has 2 congruent sides.

24. If two sides of a triangle are perpendicular, then the triangle is a right triangle. It can be isosceles or scalene. It cannot be equilateral because all the angles in an equilateral triangle are acute.

LESSON 13-4

Quadrilaterals

Lesson Planner

Objective

Identify characteristics of quadrilaterals.

Vocabulary

quadrilateral, parallelogram, rhombus, rectangle, square, trapezoid

Resources

Manipulatives: pattern blocks
Literature Connection: *Zachery Zormer Shape Transformer* by Joanne Reisberg
Teacher Technology
TeacherWorks • Interactive Classroom • Math Songs Track 14 Lesson Plan

Focus on Math Background

In the previous grade, students identified and described parallelograms, rectangles, squares, trapezoids, and rhombi. In this lesson, students use the following criteria as they explore the essential attributes of these figures:

- congruent sides
- parallel sides
- perpendicular sides
- congruent angles

Diagrams such as this one are helpful in showing the relationships among the different types of quadrilaterals:

Daily Routine

Use these suggestions before beginning the lesson on p. 570.

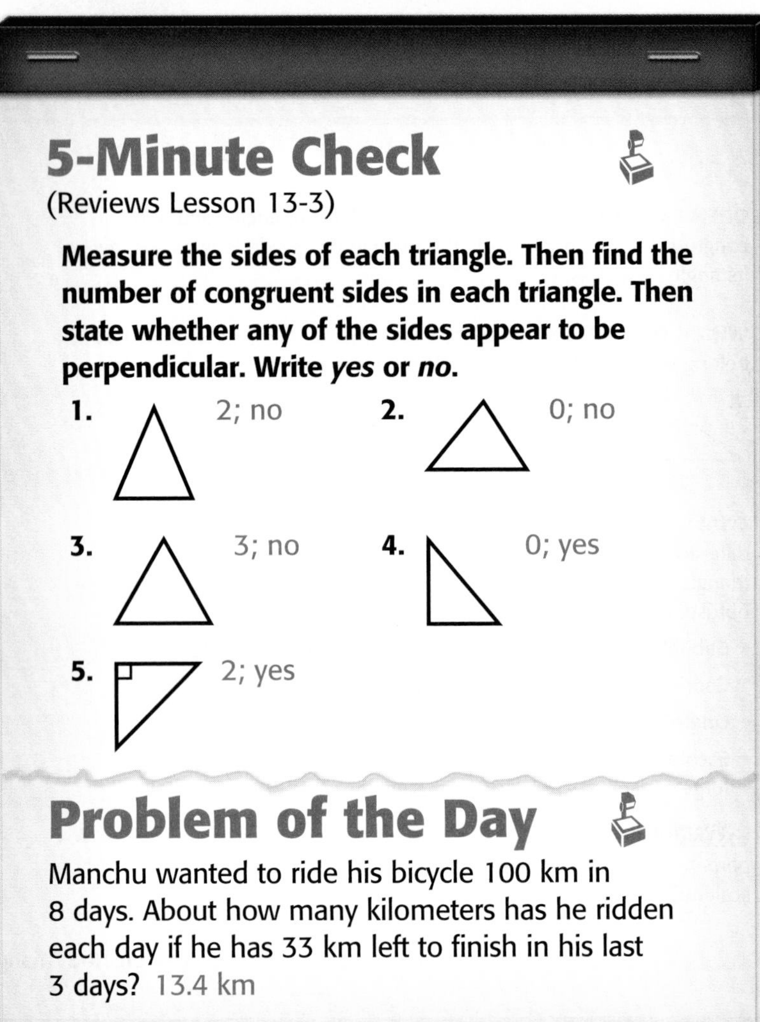

5-Minute Check

(Reviews Lesson 13-3)

Measure the sides of each triangle. Then find the number of congruent sides in each triangle. Then state whether any of the sides appear to be perpendicular. Write *yes* or *no*.

1. 2; no
2. 0; no
3. 3; no
4. 0; yes
5. 2; yes

Problem of the Day

Manchu wanted to ride his bicycle 100 km in 8 days. About how many kilometers has he ridden each day if he has 33 km left to finish in his last 3 days? 13.4 km

Building Math Vocabulary

Write the lesson vocabulary words and their definitions on the board.

Have students write the words and their definitions in their notes. Ask students to identify the parts of the words they recognize and their meanings.

Visual Vocabulary Cards

Use Visual Vocabulary Cards 30, 37, and 41 to reinforce the vocabulary introduced in this lesson. (The Define/Example/Ask routine is printed on the back of each card.)

Differentiated Instruction

Small Group Options

Option 1 SPATIAL 

Gifted and Talented AL

Materials: newspapers or magazines or your textbook, ruler, paper, and pencil

- Tell students that another measure that can be used to identify quadrilaterals is their diagonals, the length from corner to opposite corner.
- Have students use their textbook, newspaper, or magazine to locate some rectangles, squares, parallelograms, rhombi, and both kinds of trapezoids.
- Ask them to measure the pair of diagonals in a rectangle. **What did you discover?** They are the same size.
- Do the same for squares, parallelograms, rhombi, and trapezoids.

Option 2 VISUAL, SPATIAL 

English Language Learners ELL

Materials: piece of yarn per student tied into a loop
Core Vocabulary: loop, change, look like
Common Use Verb: to shape

See Math This strategy helps students visualize and connect shapes with their total degrees.

- Give each student a loop of yarn, calling it a loop.
- Tell students to shape the loop into a circle.
- Say: "All circles have 360°."
- Have students shape the loop into a quadrilateral. Ask students if the length of the yarn changed. no
- Say: "If the length of the yarn has not **changed**, are the degrees the same?" They still add up to 360°.
- Repeat for other quadrilaterals including squares.

Use this worksheet to provide additional support for English Language Learners.

***English Language Learners (p. 141)* ELL**

38 Name ______

Triangles and Quadrilaterals

Trace over the figures with a marker. Use one color for triangles and another color for quadrilaterals. Use the word box. Write the name of each figure.

acute triangle	isosceles triangle	scalene triangle
obtuse triangle	equilateral triangle	trapezoid
square	rhombus	
rectangle	parallelogram	

1. acute or scalene triangle
2. obtuse or scalene triangle
3. rhombus
4. square
5. parallelogram
6. rectangle
7. obtuse or scalene triangle
8. equilateral triangle
9. trapezoid

© Macmillan/McGraw-Hill

Triangles and Quadrilaterals 141

Independent Work Options

Option 1 VISUAL/SPATIAL 

Early Finishers AL

Materials: pattern blocks, drawing paper, pencils

- **Use pattern blocks to make a parallelogram, rectangle, rhombus, square, trapezoid, and a quadrilateral that is not any of those figures. Name and describe each figure.**

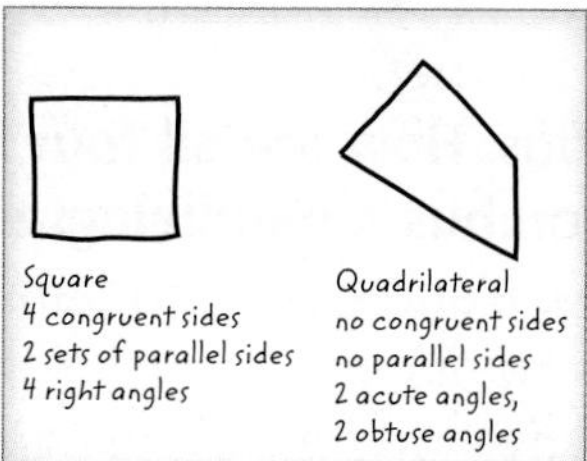

Option 2 

Student Technology

Math Online macmillanmh.com

Personal Tutor • Extra Examples

 Math Adventures

 Math Songs, Quadrilaterals Track 14

Option 3

Learning Station: Reading (p. 554H)

Direct students to the Reading Learning Station for opportunities to explore and extend the lesson concept.

Option 4

Problem-Solving Practice

Reinforce problem-solving skills and strategies with the Problem-Solving Practice worksheet.

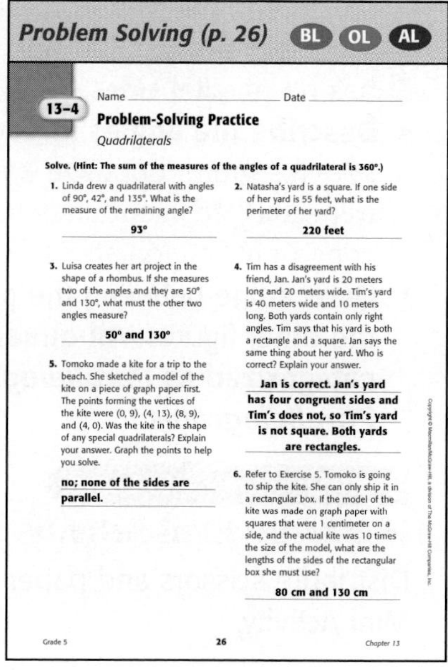

***Problem Solving (p. 26)* BL OL AL**

13–4 Name ______ Date ______

Problem-Solving Practice
Quadrilaterals

Solve. (Hint: The sum of the measures of the angles of a quadrilateral is 360°.)

1. Linda drew a quadrilateral with angles of 90°, 42°, and 135°. What is the measure of the remaining angle?
   93°
2. Natasha's yard is a square. If one side of her yard is 55 feet, what is the perimeter of her yard?
   220 feet
3. Luisa creates her art project in the shape of a rhombus. If she measures two of the angles and they are 50° and 130°, what must the other two angles measure?
   50° and 130°
4. Tim has a disagreement with his friend, Jan. Jan's yard is 20 meters long and 20 meters wide. Tim's yard is 40 meters wide and 10 meters long. Both yards contain only right angles. Tim says that his yard is both a rectangle and a square. Jan says the same thing about her yard. Who is correct? Explain your answer.
   Jan is correct. Jan's yard has four congruent sides and Tim's does not, so Tim's yard is not square. Both yards are rectangles.
5. Tomoko made a kite for a trip to the beach. She sketched a model of the kite on a piece of graph paper first. The points forming the vertices of the kite were (0, 9), (4, 13), (8, 9), and (4, 0). Was the kite in the shape of any special quadrilaterals? Explain your answer. Graph the points to help you solve.
   no; none of the sides are parallel.
6. Refer to Exercise 5. Tomoko is going to ship the kite. She can only ship it in a rectangular box. If the model of the kite was made on graph paper with squares that were 1 centimeter on a side, and the actual kite was 10 times the size of the model, what are the lengths of the sides of the rectangular box she must use?
   80 cm and 130 cm

Copyright © Macmillan/McGraw-Hill, a division of The McGraw-Hill Companies, Inc.

Grade 5 26 Chapter 13

13-4 Quadrilaterals

1 Introduce

Activity Choice 1 • Hands-On

- Draw a square and a rectangle on the board. **Use what you know about angles and sides to describe each figure.** List responses below each figure. square: 4 right angles, 4 congruent sides; rectangle: 4 right angles, opposite sides congruent
- Discuss that a square is a rectangle because its sides are opposite and congruent. Draw a parallelogram and 4 right angles. **Describe the parallelogram.** 4 sides, opposite sides are parallel and congruent
- Draw a rhombus. **How are all four figures alike? Is a rhombus a parallelogram?** They all have opposite sides that are parallel and congruent. A rhombus is a parallelogram with 4 congruent sides, and a parallelogram has opposite sides that are congruent.

Activity Choice 2 • Literature

Introduce the lesson with *Zachary Zormer Shape Transformer* by Joanne Reisberg. For a related math activity, see p. TR57.

2 Teach

Scaffolding Questions

On the board, draw a parallelogram, trapezoid, and a quadrilateral with no parallel sides.

- **How are these figures alike?** Each have alike sides.
- **How are they different?** The parallelogram has opposite sides that are parallel and congruent, the trapezoid has only one pair of sides that are parallel, and the quadrilateral has no parallel sides.
- **Describe the angles in each figure.** parallelogram: opposite angles congruent; trapezoid: adjacent angles may or may not be congruent; quadrilateral: no angles congruent
- Draw a line between the parallelogram and the other figures. **All quadrilaterals can be categorized as *Parallelograms* or *Not Parallelograms*.**

GET READY to Learn

Hands-On Mini Activity

Distribute scissors and paper for the Hands-On Mini Activity.

13-4 Quadrilaterals

MAIN IDEA

I will identify characteristics of quadrilaterals.

New Vocabulary

- quadrilateral
- rectangle
- square
- parallelogram
- rhombus
- trapezoid

Math Online

macmillanmh.com

- Extra Examples
- Personal Tutor
- Self-Check Quiz

GET READY to Learn

The image shown at the right includes squares and rectangles. These are two different types of *quadrilaterals*.

A **quadrilateral** is a polygon with four sides and four angles.

Hands-On Mini Activity

Draw and cut out three different parallelograms like the ones shown. Then draw and cut out three different quadrilaterals that are *not* parallelograms.

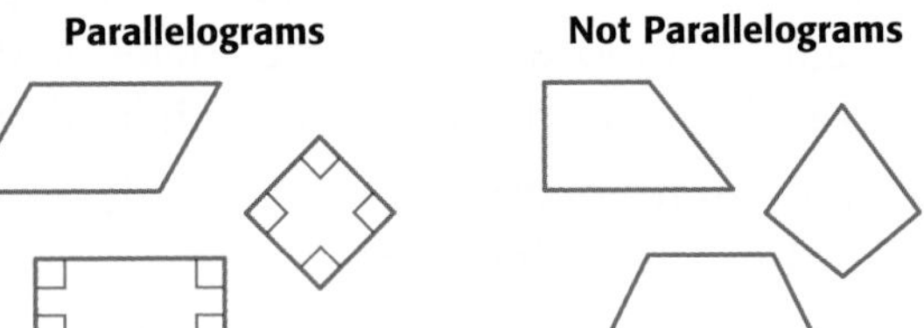

a. What attribute do all the parallelograms have that the other quadrilaterals do not? **They have opposite sides parallel and congruent.**

b. Use the figures above and your figures to write a definition for *parallelogram*. **Sample answer: A quadrilateral with both pairs of opposite sides parallel and congruent.**

You can classify quadrilaterals using one or more of the attributes listed below.

- congruent sides
- parallel sides
- perpendicular sides

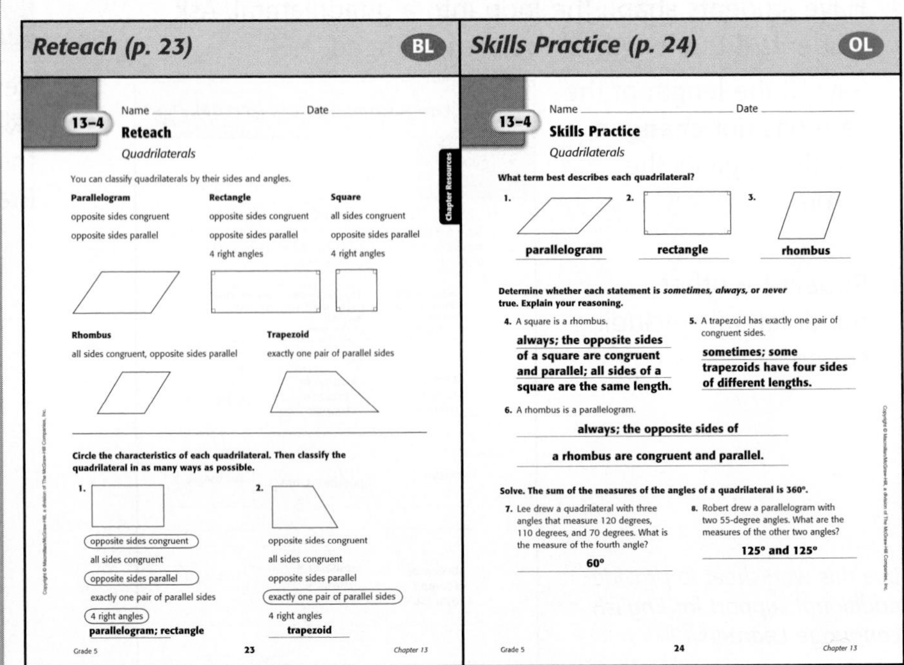

Reteach (p. 23) BL

13-4 Name ______ Date ______

Reteach

Quadrilaterals

You can classify quadrilaterals by their sides and angles.

Parallelogram: opposite sides congruent; opposite sides parallel

Rectangle: opposite sides congruent; opposite sides parallel; 4 right angles

Square: all sides congruent; opposite sides parallel; 4 right angles

Rhombus: all sides congruent, opposite sides parallel

Trapezoid: exactly one pair of parallel sides

Circle the characteristics of each quadrilateral. Then classify the quadrilateral in as many ways as possible.

1. (opposite sides congruent) / all sides congruent / (opposite sides parallel) / exactly one pair of parallel sides / (4 right angles) — **parallelogram; rectangle**
2. opposite sides congruent / all sides congruent / opposite sides parallel / (exactly one pair of parallel sides) / 4 right angles — **trapezoid**

Grade 5 23 Chapter 13

Chapter Resources

Skills Practice (p. 24) OL

13-4 Name ______ Date ______

Skills Practice

Quadrilaterals

What term best describes each quadrilateral?

1. **parallelogram**
2. **rectangle**
3. **rhombus**

Determine whether each statement is *sometimes, always,* or *never* true. Explain your reasoning.

4. A square is a rhombus. **always; the opposite sides of a square are congruent and parallel; all sides of a square are the same length.**
5. A trapezoid has exactly one pair of congruent sides. **sometimes; some trapezoids have four sides of different lengths.**
6. A rhombus is a parallelogram. **always; the opposite sides of a rhombus are congruent and parallel.**

Solve. The sum of the measures of the angles of a quadrilateral is 360°.

7. Lee drew a quadrilateral with three angles that measure 120 degrees, 110 degrees, and 70 degrees. What is the measure of the fourth angle? **60°**
8. Robert drew a parallelogram with two 55-degree angles. What are the measures of the other two angles? **125° and 125°**

Grade 5 24 Chapter 13

Classifying Quadrilaterals

Key Concepts

Quadrilateral	Example	Attributes
Rectangle		• Opposite sides congruent • All angles are right angles • Opposite sides parallel
Square		• All sides congruent • All angles are right angles • Opposite sides parallel
Parallelogram		• Opposite sides congruent • Opposite sides parallel
Rhombus		• All sides congruent • Opposite sides parallel
Trapezoid		• Exactly one pair of opposite sides parallel

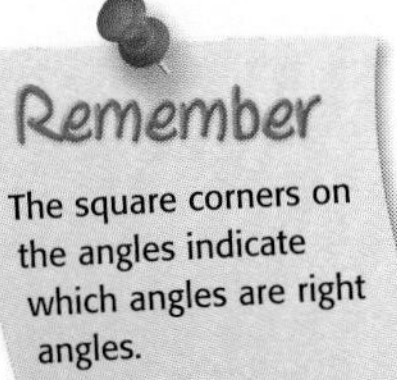

Vocabulary Link
Prefixes
The prefix *quad-* means four. A **quadruped** is an animal that has four feet.

EXAMPLES Describe Sides and Angles

1 **Describe the congruent sides in the quadrilateral shown at the right. Then state whether any sides appear to be parallel or perpendicular.**

Opposite sides are congruent and parallel. Adjacent sides are perpendicular.

2 **The design below is made up of repeating quadrilaterals. Find the number of acute and obtuse angles in each quadrilateral.**

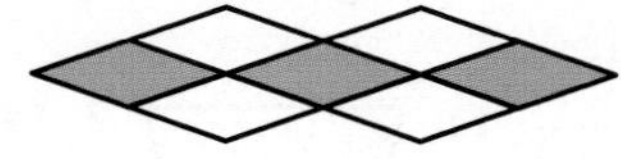

Each quadrilateral has two acute angles and two obtuse angles.

Describe Sides

Example 1 Be sure students understand that the word "adjacent" means "next to." Adjacent sides have an angle between them which may or may not be a right angle.

ADDITIONAL EXAMPLES

1 Describe the congruent sides in the quadrilateral. Then state whether any sides appear to be parallel or perpendicular. Opposite sides are congruent and parallel. No sides are perpendicular.

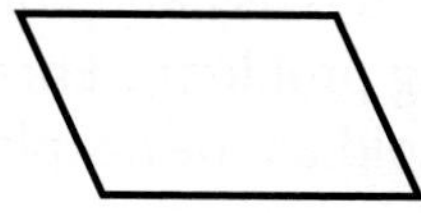

2 The design is made up of repeating quadrilaterals. Find the number of acute and obtuse angles. Each quadrilateral has two acute angles and two obtuse angles.

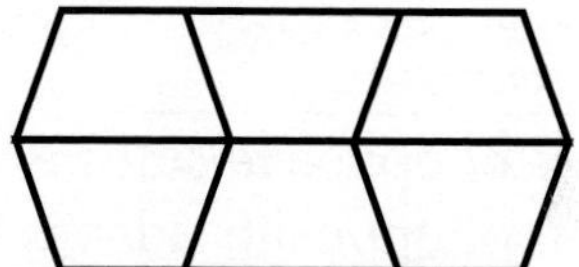

CHECK What You Know

As a class, have students complete Exercises 1–7 in **Check What You Know** as you observe their work.

Exercise 7 Assess student comprehension before assigning practice exercises.

BL Alternate Teaching Strategy

If students have trouble identifying characteristics of quadrilaterals…

Then use one of these reteach options:

1 CRM **Daily Reteach Worksheet** (p. 23)

2 Have students trace the square, rhombus, parallelogram, and trapezoid pattern blocks three times each in a row across their paper. For the first figure in each row, have students mark the congruent sides. For the second figure, have them mark the parallel sides, and for the third figure, have them mark the congruent angles and tell the number of acute and obtuse angles. Ask students to draw a trapezoid with no congruent angles and describe the sides as congruent, parallel, or both.

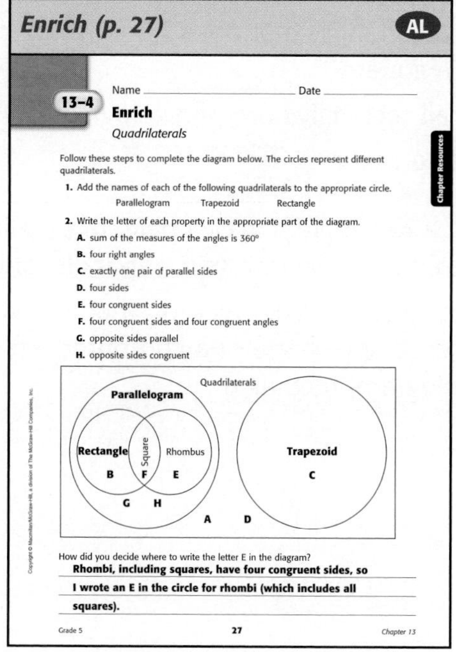

Enrich (p. 27) AL

13–4 Name ________ Date ________

Enrich

Quadrilaterals

Follow these steps to complete the diagram below. The circles represent different quadrilaterals.

1. Add the names of each of the following quadrilaterals to the appropriate circle.
   Parallelogram Trapezoid Rectangle
2. Write the letter of each property in the appropriate part of the diagram.
   A. sum of the measures of the angles is 360°
   B. four right angles
   C. exactly one pair of parallel sides
   D. four sides
   E. four congruent sides
   F. four congruent sides and four congruent angles
   G. opposite sides parallel
   H. opposite sides congruent

How did you decide where to write the letter E in the diagram?
Rhombi, including squares, have four congruent sides, so I wrote an E in the circle for rhombi (which includes all squares).

Grade 5 27 Chapter 13

Chapter Resources

3 Practice

Differentiate practice using these leveled assignments for Exercises 8–29.

Level	Assignment
BL Below/ Approaching Level	8–14, 16–17, 20, 23, 29
OL On Level	8–19, 20–21, 23–26, 29
AL Above/Beyond Level	8–26 even, 27–29

Have students discuss and complete the Higher Order Thinking problems. Encourage them to draw a trapezoid as they explain their reasoning in Exercise 28.

WRITING IN ►MATH Have students complete Exercise 29 in their Math Journals. You may choose to use this as an optional formative assessment.

Additional Answers

1. One pair of opposite sides is congruent. One pair of opposite sides is parallel.
2. Opposite sides are congruent and parallel. Adjacent sides are perpendicular.
7. Sample answer: A rhombus has two pairs of parallel sides and has all sides congruent. A trapezoid has only one pair of parallel sides. None of the sides has to be congruent.
8. Opposite sides are congruent and parallel.
9. All sides are congruent. Opposite sides are parallel.
10. No sides are congruent. One pair of opposite sides is parallel.
11. All sides are congruent. Opposite sides are parallel and adjacent sides are perpendicular.
16. True; all squares have two pair of parallel sides.
17. True; a rhombus that has all right angles is a square.

COMMON ERROR!

Exercises 23–26 Students may struggle with naming all possible figures with the given characteristics. As students read each description, have them draw several different figures that fit the description and then name the figures they drew.

★ indicates multi-step problem

CHECK What You Know

Describe the sides that appear to be congruent in each quadrilateral. Then state whether any sides appear to be parallel or perpendicular.
See Example 1 (p. 571) 1, 2. See margin.

1. 2.

Find the number of acute angles in each quadrilateral. See Example 2 (p. 571)

3. 2 4. 1 5. 0

6. Many aircraft display the shape of the American flag as shown below to indicate motion. Find the number of obtuse angles in each figure.

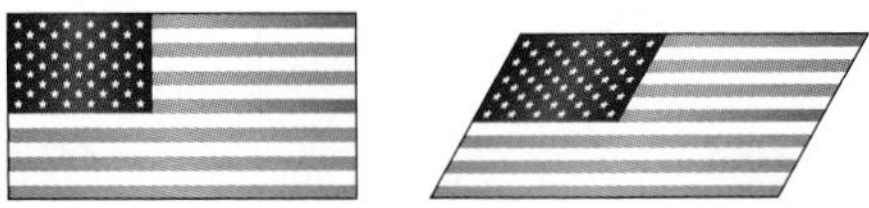

The rectangular flag has no obtuse angles. The flag that is shaped like a parallelogram has 3 obtuse angles.

7. Talk About It Tell the difference between a rhombus and a trapezoid. See margin.

Practice and Problem Solving

Describe the sides that appear to be congruent in each quadrilateral. Then state whether any sides appear to be parallel or perpendicular.
See Example 1 (p. 571) 8–11. See margin.

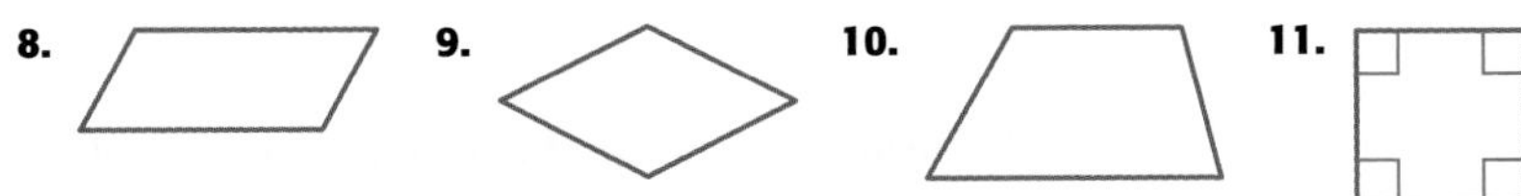

Find the number of acute angles in each quadrilateral.
See Example 2 (p. 571)

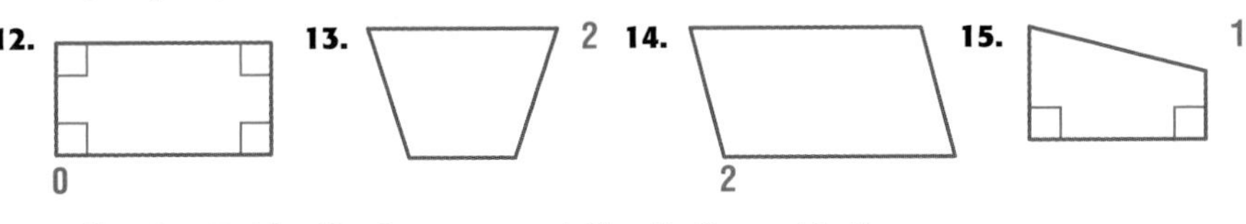

18. False; a rectangle that does not have all sides congruent is not a square.
19. False; all rectangles are parallelograms.
27. Sample answer:
28. Levon; a rectangle has two pairs of parallel sides and a trapezoid has only one pair of parallel sides.
29. Sample answer: What type of quadrilaterals can be used to describe the shape of a computer screen? Answer: parallelogram, rectangle

Determine whether each statement is *true* or *false*. Explain. 16–19. See margin.

16. All squares are parallelograms.

17. Some rhombi are squares.

18. All rectangles are squares.

19. Some rectangles are parallelograms.

Real-World PROBLEM SOLVING

Art For Exercises 20 and 21, use the photo of the New York Knicks basketball court.

20. What kind of quadrilateral does the basketball court resemble most? rectangle

21. Describe two more quadrilaterals that are shown in the photo. Sample answer: rectangles on the court and the backboard.

★**22.** Traci has a piece of wood that is 1 inch wide and 1 foot long. She cuts the wood into four 3-inch strips. What type of quadrilateral can the strips be classified as? parallelogram, rectangle

Name the quadrilaterals that have the given attributes.

23. two pairs of parallel sides parallelogram, rectangle, rhombus, square

24. all adjacent sides are perpendicular rectangle, square

25. exactly one pair of parallel sides trapezoid

26. four congruent sides square, rhombus

H.O.T. Problems

27. OPEN ENDED Draw a parallelogram that is not a square, rhombus, or rectangle. 27–29. See margin.

28. FIND THE ERROR Aliane and Levon are discussing the relationship between quadrilaterals. Who is correct? Explain your reasoning.

Aliane
Some trapezoids are rectangles.

Levon
No trapezoids are rectangles.

29. WRITING IN ▶MATH Write a real-world problem that involves quadrilaterals. Solve and explain your reasoning.

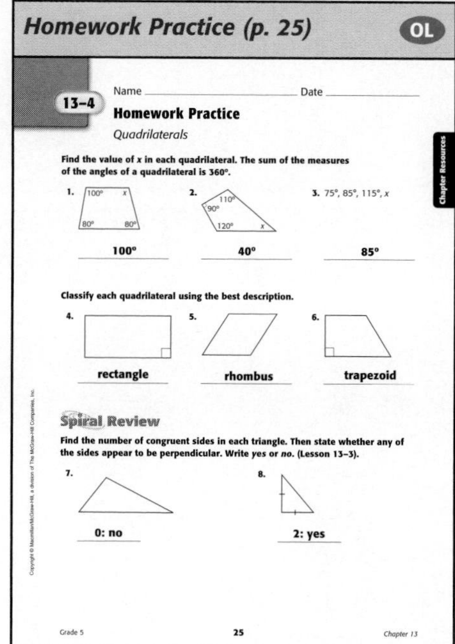

Homework Practice (p. 25) OL

13-4 Name ______ Date ______

Homework Practice

Quadrilaterals

Find the value of x in each quadrilateral. The sum of the measures of the angles of a quadrilateral is 360°.

1. 100°, x, 80°, 80° — 100°
2. 110°, 90°, 120°, x — 40°
3. 75°, 85°, 115°, x — 85°

Classify each quadrilateral using the best description.

4. rectangle
5. rhombus
6. trapezoid

Spiral Review

Find the number of congruent sides in each triangle. Then state whether any of the sides appear to be perpendicular. Write *yes* or *no*. (Lesson 13–3).

7. 0: no
8. 2: yes

Grade 5 25 Chapter 13

4 Assess

Formative Assessment

On the board, draw a trapezoid that has two right angles and exactly two adjacent sides that are congruent.

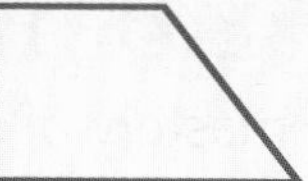

- **Describe the sides of this figure.** It has one pair of parallel sides and one pair of adjacent congruent sides. Two sides are perpendicular.
- **Describe the angles of this figure.** It has two congruent angles that are right angles, one acute angle, and one obtuse angle. **What is the name of the figure?** trapezoid

Quick Check **Are students continuing to struggle with identifying characteristics of quadrilaterals?**

If Yes → Strategic Intervention Guide (p. 126)

If No → Independent Work Options (p. 570B)
CRM Skills Practice Worksheet (p. 24)
CRM Enrich Worksheet (p. 27)

Name the Math Draw a rhombus on the board. Ask students to write the steps they would use to classify the quadrilateral. Encourage them to consider the sides and the angles of the figure and to tell more than one category in which the rhombus belongs.

Reviews Lessons 13-3 and 13-4

Assign the Test Practice problems to provide daily reinforcement of test-taking skills.

Reviews Lessons 5-3, 6-1, 12-4, 13-2, and 13-3

Review and assess mastery of skills and concepts from previous chapters.

TEST Practice

30. Which statement about the figures shown below is true? (Lessons 13-3 and 13-4) C

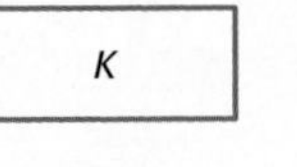

L

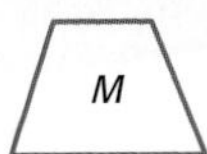

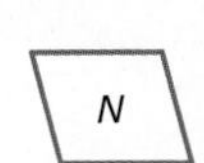

A Figures *K* and *L* are congruent.

B Figures *L* and *N* have all acute angles.

C Figures *M* and *N* each have at least two obtuse angles.

D Figures *M* and *N* are congruent.

31. Which is NOT a true statement? (Lesson 13-4) J

F All parallelograms have opposite sides parallel.

G Squares have four congruent angles and sides.

H All trapezoids have exactly one pair of parallel sides.

J Parallelograms have exactly one pair of parallel sides.

Spiral Review

Identify the kinds of angles in each triangle. (Lesson 13-3)

32.  3 acute

33. 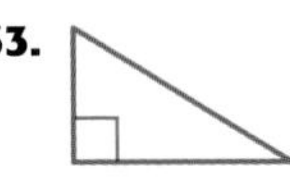 2 acute, 1 right

34. 2 acute, 1 obtuse

35. Can a triangle be both right and obtuse? Explain your reasoning. (Lesson 13-2) No; if a triangle has a right angle, then the other two angles are acute.

Complete. (Lesson 12-4)

36. 3 L = ■ mL 3,000 **37.** 900 mL = ■ L 0.9 **38.** 7,000 mL = ■ L 7

39. Algebra A bag contained 16 balloons. Rama's mom used 9 balloons to decorate her bedroom. Which of the following equations can be used to find the number of balloons left in the bag: $y = 16 + 9$, $y = 16 - 9$, or $y = 16 \times 9$? Then find the number of balloons. (Lesson 6-1) $y = 16 - 9$; 7 balloons

40. Algebra Some bamboo plants can grow 3 feet in one day. Write an expression to show the number of feet a bamboo plant can grow in *x* days. (Lesson 5-3) $3x$

574 Chapter 13 Identify, Compare, and Classify Geometric Figures

CHAPTER 13 Mid-Chapter Check

Lessons 13-1 through 13-4

Identify each figure. Then name it using symbols. (Lesson 13-1) 2. plane; plane *CDE*

1. 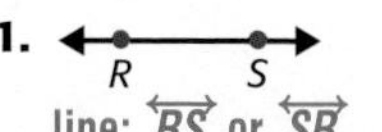
line; $\overleftrightarrow{RS}$ or $\overleftrightarrow{SR}$

2. 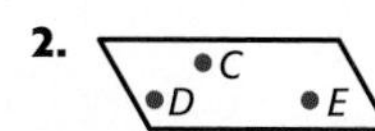

Describe each pair of lines as *intersecting, perpendicular,* or *parallel.* (Lesson 13-1)

3. 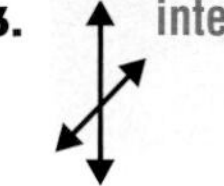 intersecting

4. 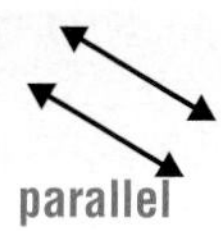 parallel

5. On Monday, Gavin bought some apples. He bought twice as many on Tuesday as he did on Monday. On Wednesday, he bought 5 more than he did on Monday. He bought a total of 21 apples. How many apples did he buy on Tuesday? (Lesson 13-2) 8 apples

6. The sum of the measures of the angles in the figure below is 540°.

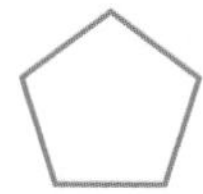

If all the angles have equal measure, what is the measure of each angle? (Lesson 13-2) 108°

Measure the sides of each triangle. Then find the number of congruent sides. State whether any of the sides appear to be perpendicular. Write *yes* or *no*. (Lesson 13-3)

7.  2; yes

8. 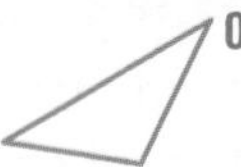 0; no

Identify the kinds of angles in each triangle. (Lesson 13-3)

9.  3 acute

10. 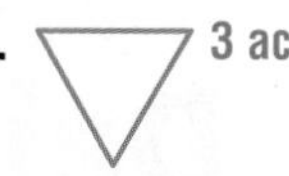 3 acute

11. **MULTIPLE CHOICE** Which shape could never have parallel sides? (Lessons 13-3 and 13-4) D

A rectangle
B rhombus
C trapezoid
D triangle

Find the number of acute angles in each quadrilateral. (Lesson 13-4)

12. 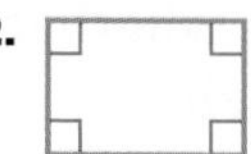 0

13. 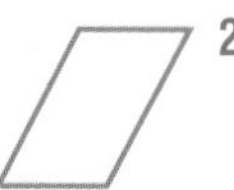 2

14. **MULTIPLE CHOICE** Which statement about the trapezoid shown at the right is true? (Lesson 13-4) G

F The trapezoid has two right angles.
G The trapezoid has two acute angles.
H The trapezoid has two pairs of parallel sides.
J The trapezoid has three obtuse angles.

15. **WRITING IN MATH** Is every parallelogram a quadrilateral? Explain. (Lesson 13-4) See Ch. 13 Answer Appendix.

CHAPTER 13 Mid-Chapter Check

Lessons 13-1 through 13-4

Formative Assessment

Use the Mid-Chapter Check to assess students' progress in the first half of the chapter.

Customize and create multiple versions of your Mid-Chapter Check and the test answer keys.

FOLDABLES Dinah Zike's Foldables

Use these lesson suggestions to incorporate the Foldables during the chapter.

Have students make a Ten-tab Vocabulary Foldable using one sheet of 8.5 × 11 notebook paper and label as shown. Students provide definitions of the terms beneath the tabs. Students can place related words in the same tab. Ask students to discover and supply a new vocabulary word related to geometry and record the definition on the last tab. The Foldable can be used as a self-checking study aid to improve vocabulary recall.

Data-Driven Decision Making

Based on the results of the Mid-Chapter Check, use the following to review concepts that continue to present students with problems.

Exercises	State/Local Standards	What's the Math?	Error Analysis	Resources for Review
1–4 Lesson 13-1		Use basic geometric terms to identify and label basic geometric shapes.	Does not know vocabulary and characteristics of basic geometric shapes. Does not know signs for triangle or line.	Strategic Intervention Guide (pp. 126, 128) CRM Chapter 13 Resource Masters (Reteach Worksheets) pp. 8, 13, 18, 23 Math Adventures My Math Zone Chapter 13 Math Online Extra Examples • Concepts in Motion
5–6 Lesson 13-2		Solve problems using logical reasoning.	Does not understand "congruent." Does not understand "twice as many." Does not divide accurately.	
7–11 Lesson 13-3		Identify characteristics of triangles.	Does not understand "congruent." Does not understand "parallel" or "perpendicular." Does not recognize an "acute" angle.	
12–15 Lesson 13-4		Identify characteristics of quadrilaterals.	Does not know definitions of quadrilaterals. Does not know "acute," "obtuse," or "right" angles. Does not know "parallelogram."	

13-5 Problem-Solving Investigation
Choose a Strategy

Lesson Planner

Objective

Choose the best strategy to solve a problem.

Resources

Materials: index cards

Teacher Technology

TeacherWorks • Interactive Classroom

Real-World Problem Solving Library
Math and Social Studies: *Flags: Shaping History*

Use these leveled books to reinforce and extend problem-solving skills and strategies.

Leveled for:

- OL On Level
- ELL Sheltered English
- SP Spanish

For additional support, see the Real-World Problem Solving Teacher Guide.

Daily Routine

Use these suggestions before beginning the lesson on p. 576.

5-Minute Check

(Reviews Lesson 13-4)

Determine whether each statement is *true* or *false*. Explain.

1. All squares are rhombi. True; opposite sides are parallel and all sides are congruent.
2. Some parallelograms are rectangles. True; parallelograms with 4 right angles are rectangles.
3. All parallelograms are rhombi. False; only parallelograms with 4 congruent sides are rhombi.
4. Some rectangles are squares. True; rectangles with 4 congruent sides are squares.

Problem of the Day

A sports drink bottle contains 8 fluid ounces. Mr. Garcia wants to take one gallon of sports drink to the soccer game. How many bottles does he need? Draw a picture to explain your answer. 16 bottles; see students' drawings.

Differentiated Instruction

Small Group Options

LOGICAL

Option 1 Below Level BL

Materials: chart paper, markers, pencils, paper

- Copy the problem on chart paper.
- Read the problem aloud to students.
- **What is the question you have to answer in this problem? What operation should you use to solve this problem?** how many teams were in the race; addition
- Ask students to solve the problem.
- Remind students that in problems like this, they must include your team in the count as well as the others.

> It's Field Day and your team came in fourth in the relay race. If there were 10 teams that finished after your team, how many teams were in the relay race? 14 teams

LOGICAL, KINESTHETIC

Option 2 English Language Learners ELL

Materials: paper and pencil
Core Vocabulary: exact, big step, little step
Common Use Verb: estimate

See Math This strategy uses kinesthetic action to integrate vocabulary with logical reasoning and problem solving.

- Say: "How many steps does it take to get to the cafeteria? How could we solve this?"
- Say: "Sometimes, we need to know **exact** numbers and other times ***estimating*** is fine." Prompt students to predict which will work best with this question.
- Guide and model counting steps to the cafeteria.
- Ask: "Would I have the same number of steps as you?"
- Prompt students to reason out longer legs means fewer steps.

Independent Work Options

LINGUISTIC

Option 1 Early Finishers OL AL

Materials: index cards, pencils

- Have students choose one of the following problem solving strategies: *draw a diagram, look for a pattern, use logical reasoning.*
- Ask students to write a word problem on an index card which can be solved using the strategy they chose. Have them begin writing by either drawing a diagram, drawing or writing a pattern, or drawing a table showing data for logical reasoning on a separate paper.
- Students can exchange cards, solve the problem showing their work, and return their work to the original writer for checking.

Option 2 Student Technology

Math Online macmillanmh.com

Personal Tutor • Extra Examples

Option 3 Learning Station: Art (p. 554G)

Direct students to the Art Learning Station for opportunities to explore and extend the lesson concept.

1 Introduce

Activity Choice 1 • Review

- Pose the following problem:

  In her running club, Sierra is able to run 27 miles during 18 days of practice. At this rate, how many miles will she run during 24 days of practice? 36 miles

- Use the four-step plan to discuss the problem with the students. **What are some possible strategies you could use to solve the problem?** *solve a simpler problem*
- What simpler problem would be a first step to solving the problem? Find out how many miles she runs in one day by dividing 27 ÷ 18, then multiply that number by 24 days.

2 Teach

Have students read the problem on quilt patterns. Guide them through the problem-solving steps.

Understand Using the questions, review what students know and need to find.

Plan Have them discuss their strategy.

Solve Guide students to use *look for a pattern* strategy to solve the problem.

- **What pattern do you see in the numbers 1, 4, and 9? Explain.** They are all square numbers: $1 \times 1 = 1$, $2 \times 2 = 4$, $3 \times 3 = 9$.
- **What number would you multiply by 2 to find the number of triangles in the fourth square? Explain.** 16; it is 4×4 and the next square number in the pattern.
- **How would you find the number of triangles in the fifth square?** $2 \times (5 \times 5) = 50$ triangles

Check Have students look back at the problem to make sure that the answer fits the facts given.

COMMON ERROR!

Students often solve the problem correctly but make mistakes in their calculations. Encourage students to double-check their calculations if they find something is wrong when they check the solution.

13-5 Problem-Solving Investigation

MAIN IDEA I will choose the best strategy to solve a problem.

P.S.I. TEAM +

EMILIO: To make a quilt pattern, I pieced together triangles to make squares of different sizes. The first square has 2 triangles, the second square has 8 triangles, and the third square has 18 triangles. The quilt will have squares of five different sizes.

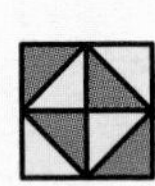

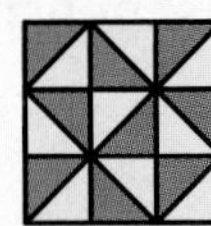

YOUR MISSION: Find how many triangles are in the fifth square.

Understand	You know how many triangles are in the first, second, and third squares. You need to find how many triangles are in the fifth square.
Plan	Look for a pattern to find the number of triangles.
Solve	Each square has twice as many triangles as small squares. First square 2×1 or 2 triangles Second square 2×4 or 8 triangles Third square 2×9 or 18 triangles Continuing the pattern, the fourth square has 2×16 or 32 triangles. The fifth square has 2×25 or 50 triangles.
Check	Draw the fifth square and count the number of triangles. Since there are 50 triangles in the fifth square, the answer is correct. ✓

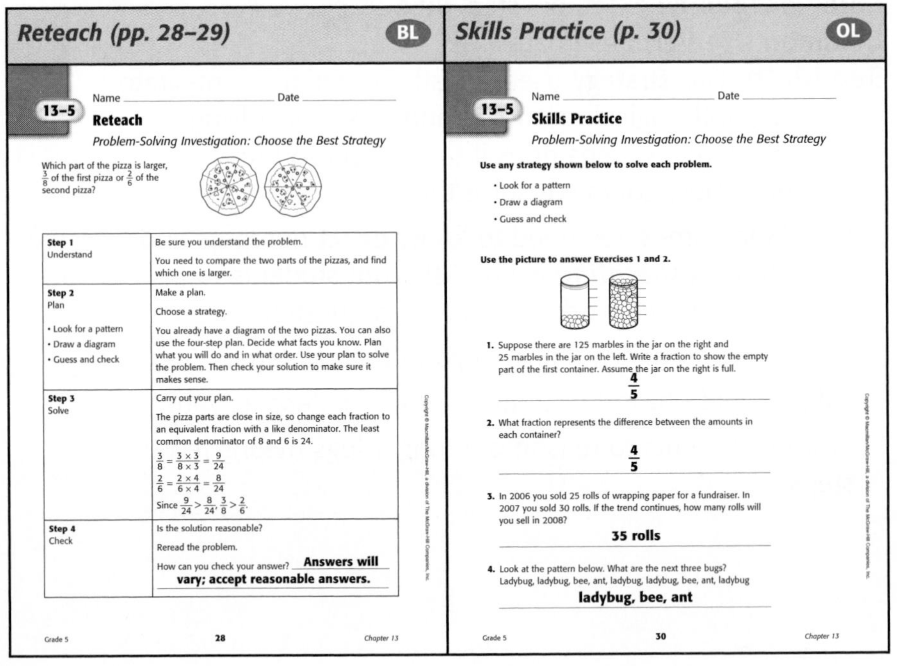

Reteach (pp. 28–29) BL

13-5 Name ________ Date ________

Reteach

Problem-Solving Investigation: Choose the Best Strategy

Which part of the pizza is larger, $\frac{3}{8}$ of the first pizza or $\frac{2}{6}$ of the second pizza?

Step 1 Understand	Be sure you understand the problem. You need to compare the two parts of the pizzas, and find which one is larger.
Step 2 Plan • Look for a pattern • Draw a diagram • Guess and check	Make a plan. Choose a strategy. You already have a diagram of the two pizzas. You can also use the four-step plan. Decide what facts you know. Plan what you will do and in what order. Use your plan to solve the problem. Then check your solution to make sure it makes sense.
Step 3 Solve	Carry out your plan. The pizza parts are close in size, so change each fraction to an equivalent fraction with a like denominator. The least common denominator of 8 and 6 is 24. $\frac{3}{8} = \frac{3 \times 3}{8 \times 3} = \frac{9}{24}$ $\frac{2}{6} = \frac{2 \times 4}{6 \times 4} = \frac{8}{24}$ Since $\frac{9}{24} > \frac{8}{24}$, $\frac{3}{8} > \frac{2}{6}$.
Step 4 Check	Is the solution reasonable? Reread the problem. How can you check your answer? **Answers will vary; accept reasonable answers.**

Grade 5 28 Chapter 13

Skills Practice (p. 30) OL

13-5 Name ________ Date ________

Skills Practice

Problem-Solving Investigation: Choose the Best Strategy

Use any strategy shown below to solve each problem.

- Look for a pattern
- Draw a diagram
- Guess and check

Use the picture to answer Exercises 1 and 2.

1. Suppose there are 125 marbles in the jar on the right and 25 marbles in the jar on the left. Write a fraction to show the empty part of the first container. Assume the jar on the right is full. **$\frac{4}{5}$**
2. What fraction represents the difference between the amounts in each container? **$\frac{4}{5}$**
3. In 2006 you sold 25 rolls of wrapping paper for a fundraiser. In 2007 you sold 30 rolls. If the trend continues, how many rolls will you sell in 2008? **35 rolls**
4. Look at the pattern below. What are the next three bugs? Ladybug, ladybug, bee, ant, ladybug, ladybug, bee, ant, ladybug **ladybug, bee, ant**

Grade 5 30 Chapter 13

Mixed Problem Solving

See page R35.

Use any strategy shown below to solve each problem.

PROBLEM-SOLVING STRATEGIES
- Draw a diagram.
- Look for a pattern.
- Use logical reasoning.

1. Mr. Toshi's fifth grade class sold containers of popcorn and peanuts. If each day they sold 25 less containers of peanuts than popcorn, how many containers of popcorn and peanuts did they sell in all? **1,645**

	Day 1	Day 2	Day 3	Day 4
Popcorn	225	200	150	300
Peanuts	■	■	■	■

2. **Algebra** Find the fifteenth term in the pattern shown below.

   5, 4, 7, 6, 9, 8, 11, ... **19**

3. Selma is taller than Motega and shorter than Cheye. If Cheye is shorter than Dominic, who is the shortest person? **Motega**

4. There are 8 girls for every 7 boys on a field trip. If there are 56 girls on the trip, how many students are on the trip? **105 students**

5. **Measurement** When Cheryl goes mountain climbing, she rests 5 minutes for every 15 minutes that she climbs. If Cheryl climbs for 2 hours, how many minutes does she rest? **30 min**

6. The fraction $\frac{a}{b}$ is equivalent to $\frac{5}{20}$, and $b - a = 3$. Find the values of a and b. **$a = 1$, $b = 4$**

7. A family has four cats. Fluffy is 8 years old and is 4 years younger than Tiger. Tiger is 2 years older than Max, and Max is 3 years older than Patches. List the cats from oldest to youngest. **Tiger, Max, Fluffy, Patches**

8. The number of fifth grade students who helped clean the park this year was 5 less than twice as many as last year. If 39 fifth graders helped clean up the park this year, how many cleaned the park last year? **22 fifth graders**

9. Five friends go to a batting cage. Andrea bats after Daniel and before Jessica. Juwan bats after Andrea and before Jessica and Filipe. Jessica always bats immediately after Juwan. Who bats last? **Filipe**

10. Madeline has 2 times the number of games as Paulo. Paulo has 4 more games than Tyler. If Tyler has 9 games, how many games are there between the 3 friends? **48 games**

11. **Algebra** The first three *triangular numbers* are shown below. How many dots will be in the sixth triangular number? **21 dots**

1

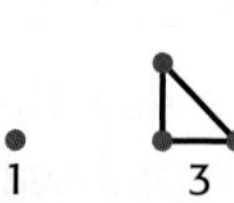
3

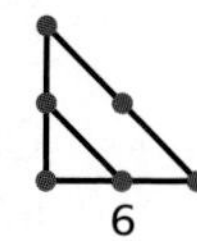
6

12. WRITING IN MATH In addition to logical reasoning, what is another strategy that you could use to solve Exercise 11? **Sample answer: draw a picture**

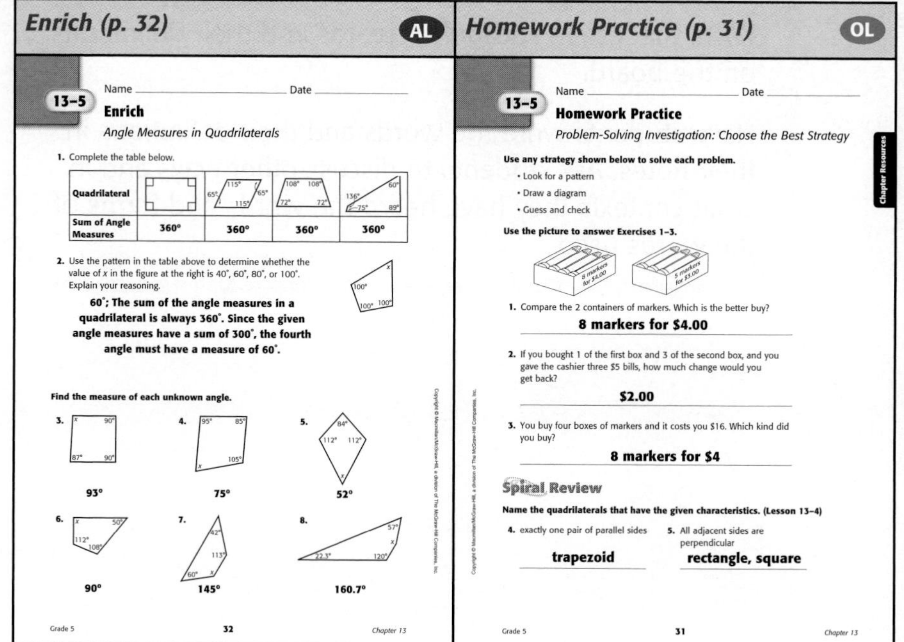

Enrich (p. 32) AL

13–5 Name ________ Date ________

Enrich

Angle Measures in Quadrilaterals

1. Complete the table below.

Quadrilateral	(rectangle)	(parallelogram: 115°, 65°, 115°, 65°)	(trapezoid: 108°, 108°, 72°, 72°)	(quadrilateral: 60°, 136°, 75°, 89°)
Sum of Angle Measures	360°	360°	360°	360°

2. Use the pattern in the table above to determine whether the value of x in the figure at the right is 40°, 60°, 80°, or 100°. Explain your reasoning.

   60°; The sum of the angle measures in a quadrilateral is always 360°. Since the given angle measures have a sum of 300°, the fourth angle must have a measure of 60°.

Find the measure of each unknown angle.

3. x, 90°, 87°, 90° — **93°**
4. 95°, 85°, 105°, x — **75°**
5. 84°, 112°, 112°, x — **52°**
6. x, 50°, 112°, 108° — **90°**
7. 42°, 113°, 60°, x — **145°**
8. 57°, x, 22.3°, 120° — **160.7°**

Grade 5 32 Chapter 13

Homework Practice (p. 31) OL

13–5 Name ________ Date ________

Homework Practice

Problem-Solving Investigation: Choose the Best Strategy

Use any strategy shown below to solve each problem.
- Look for a pattern
- Draw a diagram
- Guess and check

Use the picture to answer Exercises 1–3.

8 markers for $4.00 | 5 markers for $3.00

1. Compare the 2 containers of markers. Which is the better buy? **8 markers for $4.00**
2. If you bought 1 of the first box and 3 of the second box, and you gave the cashier three $5 bills, how much change would you get back? **$2.00**
3. You buy four boxes of markers and it costs you $16. Which kind did you buy? **8 markers for $4**

Spiral Review

Name the quadrilaterals that have the given characteristics. (Lesson 13–4)

4. exactly one pair of parallel sides **trapezoid**
5. All adjacent sides are perpendicular **rectangle, square**

Grade 5 31 Chapter 13

Chapter Resources

BL Alternate Teaching Strategy

If students have trouble choosing the best strategy to solve a problem…

Then use one of these reteach options:

1 CRM **Daily Reteach Worksheet** (pp. 28–29)

2 Have students fold a paper into 3 columns and label the colums, *draw a diagram*, *look for a pattern*, and *use logical reasoning*. Below each of the strategies, students write clue words or phrases that indicate using the strategy. Then read and discuss each problem with the clues in mind. Ask students to write their solutions in the column that contains the strategy they used.

3 Practice

Using the Exercises

Exercises 1–12 involve choosing a strategy from among the three listed to solve the problem. Encourage students to *use the four-step plan*.

Exercise 3 requires students to *make a table* and *use logical reasoning* to solve it.

4 Assess

Formative Assessment

Pose the following problem:

The number of people who visited a seaside resort in June was 143 more than twice as many who visited in April. If 3,620 people visited in April, how many people visited in June?

- **What strategy would be the best one to solve this problem? Explain.** *write an equation;* You are solving for a variable that stands for the number who visited in June.
- **What equation would you write?** $2 \times 3{,}620 + 143 = n$ **How many people visited in June?** 7,383

Quick Check **Are students continuing to struggle with choosing the best strategy to solve a problem?**

If Yes → Small Group Options (p. 576B)

If No → Independent Work Options (p. 576B)
CRM Skills Practice Worksheet (p. 30)
CRM Enrich Worksheet (p. 32)

LESSON

13-6 Translations and Graphs

Lesson Planner

Objective

Sketch translations on a coordinate grid.

Vocabulary

transformation, image, translation

Resources

Materials: grid paper, colored pencils, pencils and paper
Literature Connection: *Geometry* by Lucille Caron and Philip M. St. Jacques.
Teacher Technology
TeacherWorks • Interactive Classroom

Focus on Math Background

Students learned how to graph an ordered pair and identify the coordinates of points on a coordinate grid in Chapter 6. In this and the following lessons they study three different types of rigid transformations (also called isometries): translations, reflections, and rotations. These movements of all the points in a figure leave distances and angles unaltered. After a rigid transformation, the new figure (image) is congruent to the original figure (preimage).

A translation is the simplest type of transformation. It is often referred to as a slide or shift and involves no reflection or rotation. The *x*-coordinate of each point on a figure is increased or decreased by an identical amount. Similarly, the *y*-coordinate of each point on the figures is also changed by an identical amount (which is not necessarily the same as the change in the *x*-coordinate). Students should be able to recognize and perform translations of a figure.

Daily Routine

Use these suggestions before beginning the lesson on p. 578.

5-Minute Check

(Reviews Lesson 13-5)

Use any of the following strategies to solve: *draw a diagram, look for a pattern,* or *use logical reasoning.*

Jared runs laps at the track three times a week. On Mondays he runs $\frac{2}{3}$ as many laps as on Wednesdays and $\frac{1}{2}$ as many laps as he runs on Fridays. If he runs 24 laps on Fridays, how many laps does he run on Mondays and Wednesdays? 12 laps on Mondays, 18 laps on Wednesdays

Problem of the Day

On one day, there were 40 half-pint water bottles, 16 one-pint water bottles, 12 one-quart water bottles and 4 one-gallon water bottles. How many pints of water were there? 92 pints

Building Math Vocabulary

Write the lesson vocabulary words and their definitions on the board.

Have students write the words and their definitions in their notes. Ask students to discuss other ways and in what contexts they have heard the words and forms of the words used.

Differentiated Instruction

Small Group Options

SPATIAL

Option 1 Below Level BL

Materials: centimeter graph paper, identical shapes for each student to use (these should be cut from and fit on the graph paper so they can be moved about on it).

- Review the concept of translation as an object or shape moving through space on the same plane without changing size or shape.
- Ask the students to take one shape and trace it on the graph paper, making sure that the verticals match up with the intersecting grid lines.
- Ask the students to move the shape in one direction and trace around it again to form a translation.
- Encourage the students to try this again, moving in a different direction.
- Model this with some examples of your own.

SPATIAL

Option 2 English Language Learners ELL

Materials: ruler with 2 same length pencils taped securely at either end at an angle, large sheet of paper

Core Vocabulary: duplicate, distance, must be the same

Common Use Verb: copy

See Math This strategy allows students to visualize translations.

- Show students the ruler with 2 pencils. Ask: "What do you think will happen if I write my name with one of these pencils on a sheet of paper?" Students make predictions. The other pencil will copy the name.
- Ask: "Do you think the name will copy exactly the same? Smaller or larger? Why?" Pencils are at the same distance and will always be at the same distance.
- Write your name carefully and discuss how both names look the same.
- Students take turns writing their own names.

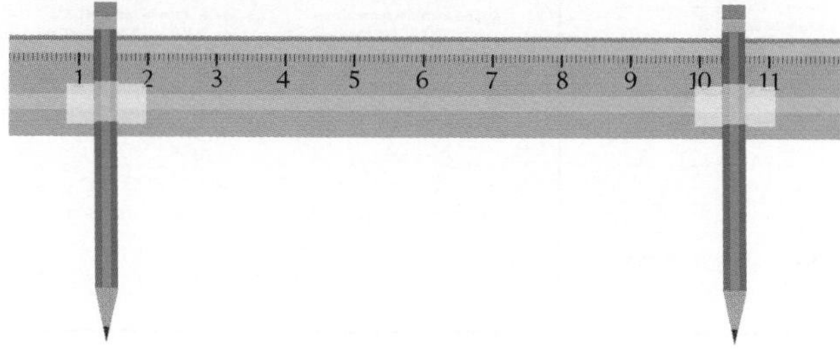

Independent Work Options

AUDITORY

Option 1 Early Finishers AL

Materials: grid paper, colored pencils

- Have students work with a partner. Partner 1 sketches a figure on a grid with the vertices at specific coordinates without showing it to their partner.
- Partner 1 states the coordinate pairs while Partner 2 graphs the points and sketches the figure.
- Partner 1 gives directions for two different translations of the figure. The translations may have one or two moves. Partner 2 sketches each translation and states the two new coordinate pairs. Partners can then trade roles and repeat the activity.

Option 2 Student Technology

Math Online macmillanmh.com

Personal Tutor • Extra Examples

Option 3 Learning Station: Writing (p. 554G)

Direct students to the Writing Learning Station for opportunities to explore and extend the lesson concept.

Option 4 Problem-Solving Practice

Reinforce problem-solving skills and strategies with the Problem-Solving Practice worksheet.

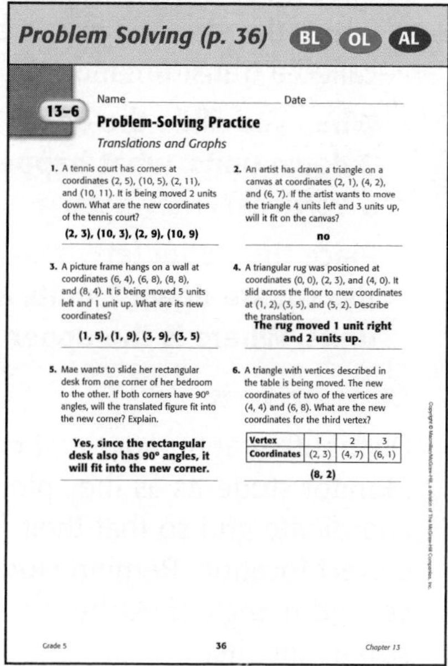

Problem Solving (p. 36) BL OL AL

13–6 Name ______ Date ______

Problem-Solving Practice

Translations and Graphs

1. A tennis court has corners at coordinates (2, 5), (10, 5), (2, 11), and (10, 11). It is being moved 2 units down. What are the new coordinates of the tennis court?

   (2, 3), (10, 3), (2, 9), (10, 9)

2. An artist has drawn a triangle on a canvas at coordinates (2, 1), (4, 2), and (6, 7). If the artist wants to move the triangle 4 units left and 3 units up, will it fit on the canvas?

   no

3. A picture frame hangs on a wall at coordinates (6, 4), (6, 8), (8, 8), and (8, 4). It is being moved 5 units left and 1 unit up. What are its new coordinates?

   (1, 5), (1, 9), (3, 9), (3, 5)

4. A triangular rug was positioned at coordinates (0, 0), (2, 3), and (4, 0). It slid across the floor to new coordinates at (1, 2), (3, 5), and (5, 2). Describe the translation.

   The rug moved 1 unit right and 2 units up.

5. Mae wants to slide her rectangular desk from one corner of her bedroom to the other. If both corners have 90° angles, will the translated figure fit into the new corner? Explain.

   Yes, since the rectangular desk also has 90° angles, it will fit into the new corner.

6. A triangle with vertices described in the table is being moved. The new coordinates of two of the vertices are (4, 4) and (6, 8). What are the new coordinates for the third vertex?

Vertex	1	2	3
Coordinates	(2, 3)	(4, 7)	(6, 1)

   (8, 2)

Copyright © Macmillan/McGraw-Hill, a division of The McGraw-Hill Companies, Inc.

Grade 5 36 Chapter 13

Translations and Graphs

Activity Choice 1 • Hands-On 

- Review coordinate grids and their usefulness in locating points on maps. **A coordinate grid is used to locate points on a plane; how many numbers are used to name a point?** 2
- Distribute grid paper and instruct students to draw a coordinate grid, labeling the *x* and *y* axes 0–9. **When locating a point, what direction will you move from zero first?** horizontally along the *x*-axis
- Have students locate and connect (2, 1) (2, 4) (4, 6) (6, 4) (6, 1) (2, 1). **What figure did you draw?** pentagon

Activity Choice 2 • Literature

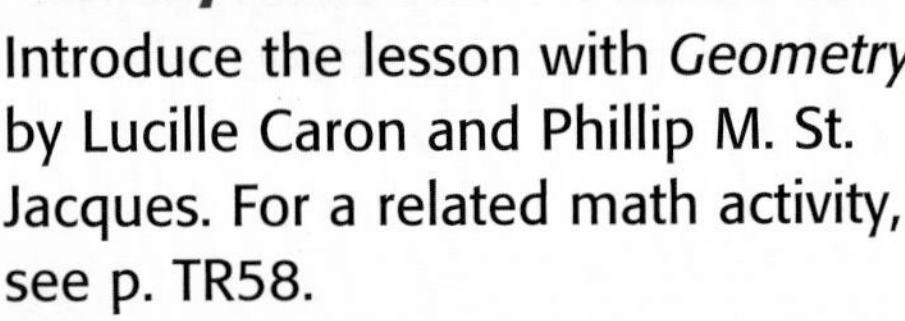

Introduce the lesson with *Geometry* by Lucille Caron and Phillip M. St. Jacques. For a related math activity, see p. TR58.

2 Teach

Scaffolding Questions

Have students place the upper left corner of a square pattern block on a coordinate grid at (1, 8).

- **When you slide the square to the right so that the upper left vertex is on (3, 8) what happens to the upper right vertex of the square?** It moves 2 units to the right.
- **Does the shape of the square change?** no
- Tell students that any movement of a figure in which the size and shape do not change is called a transformation.
- **When you slide the upper right vertex 2 down units, what happens to the other 3 vertices?** They each move down 2 units.
- **Place the upper left vertex on (3, 9). Move the square down 2 units and to the right 3 units. Where is the upper left vertex?** (6, 7)

Mini Activity

Distribute graph paper and colored pencils. Monitor students as they plot their points on the coordinate grid so that their first triangle is in the correct location. Remind students that the second triangle must be the same shape and size as the first.

13-6 Translations and Graphs

MAIN IDEA
I will sketch translations on a coordinate grid.
New Vocabulary
transformation
image
translation
Math Online
macmillanmh.com
• Extra Examples
• Personal Tutor
• Self-Check Quiz

GET READY to Learn

Helena slid her desk from one side of her room to the other. This movement is an example of a translation.

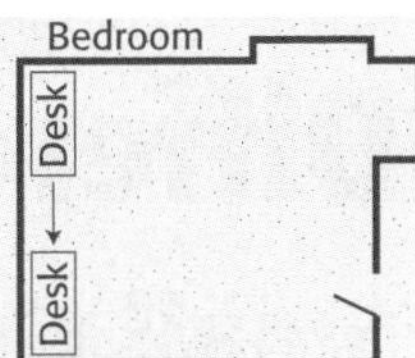

A **transformation** is a movement of a geometric figure. The resulting figure is called the **image**. One type of transformation is a translation.

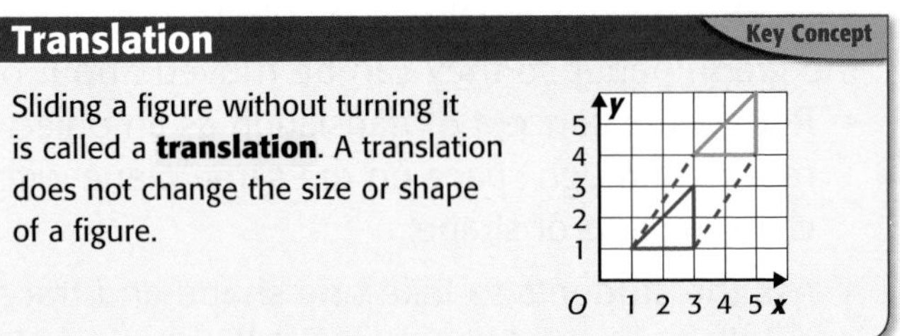

Translation
Key Concept
Sliding a figure without turning it is called a **translation**. A translation does not change the size or shape of a figure.
y
5
4
3
2
1
O 1 2 3 4 5 x

To translate a figure, move all of the vertices the same distance and in the same direction.

Hands-On Mini Activity

A triangle has vertices at *A*(3, 6), *B*(4, 9), and *C*(7, 6). Draw a coordinate grid on graph paper. Copy the triangle.

a. With a different colored pencil, graph points *A*, *B*, and *C* after they are moved down 4 units.

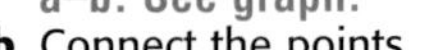

b. Connect the points.

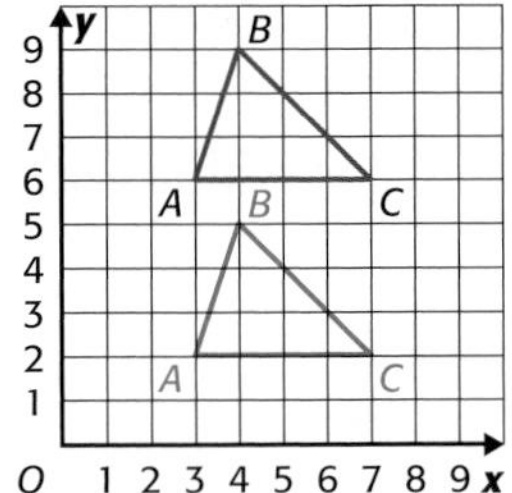

c. What are the vertices of the image?

c. *A*(3, 2), *B*(4, 5), *C*(7, 2)

578 Chapter 13 Identify, Compare, and Classify Geometric Figures

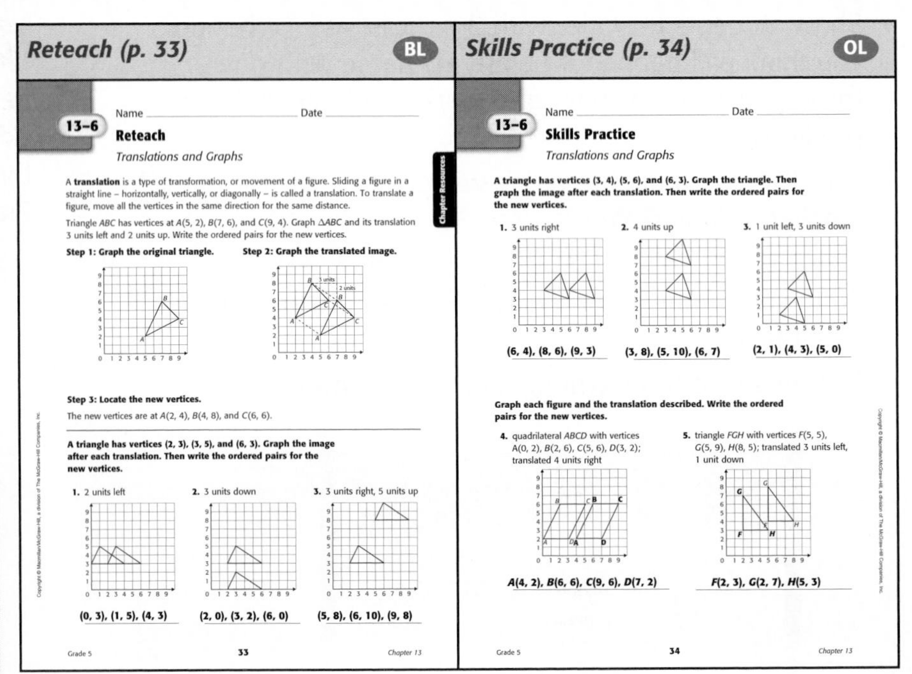

Reteach (p. 33) BL

Name ______ Date ______

13-6 **Reteach**

Translations and Graphs

A **translation** is a type of transformation, or movement of a figure. Sliding a figure in a straight line – horizontally, vertically, or diagonally – is called a translation. To translate a figure, move all the vertices in the same direction for the same distance.

Triangle *ABC* has vertices at *A*(5, 2), *B*(7, 6), and *C*(9, 4). Graph △*ABC* and its translation 3 units left and 2 units up. Write the ordered pairs for the new vertices.

Step 1: Graph the original triangle. **Step 2: Graph the translated image.**

Step 3: Locate the new vertices.

The new vertices are at *A*(2, 4), *B*(4, 8), and *C*(6, 6).

A triangle has vertices (2, 3), (3, 5), and (6, 3). Graph the image after each translation. Then write the ordered pairs for the new vertices.

1. 2 units left — **(0, 3), (1, 5), (4, 3)**
2. 3 units down — **(2, 0), (3, 2), (6, 0)**
3. 3 units right, 5 units up — **(5, 8), (6, 10), (9, 8)**

Grade 5 33 Chapter 13

Skills Practice (p. 34) OL

Name ______ Date ______

13-6 **Skills Practice**

Translations and Graphs

A triangle has vertices (3, 4), (5, 6), and (6, 3). Graph the triangle. Then graph the image after each translation. Then write the ordered pairs for the new vertices.

1. 3 units right — **(6, 4), (8, 6), (9, 3)**
2. 4 units up — **(3, 8), (5, 10), (6, 7)**
3. 1 unit left, 3 units down — **(2, 1), (4, 3), (5, 0)**

Graph each figure and the translation described. Write the ordered pairs for the new vertices.

4. quadrilateral *ABCD* with vertices A(0, 2), *B*(2, 6), *C*(5, 6), *D*(3, 2); translated 4 units right — ***A*(4, 2), *B*(6, 6), *C*(9, 6), *D*(7, 2)**
5. triangle *FGH* with vertices *F*(5, 5), *G*(5, 9), *H*(8, 5); translated 3 units left, 1 unit down — ***F*(2, 3), *G*(2, 7), *H*(5, 3)**

Grade 5 34 Chapter 13

EXAMPLE Sketch a Translation

1 A triangle has vertices $F(1, 5)$, $G(5, 7)$, and $H(3, 4)$. Graph the triangle. Then graph its translation image 2 units right and 3 units down. Graph and then write the ordered pairs for the new vertices.

Remember

In a translation, you slide a figure from one position to another without turning it.

Step 1 Graph the original triangle.

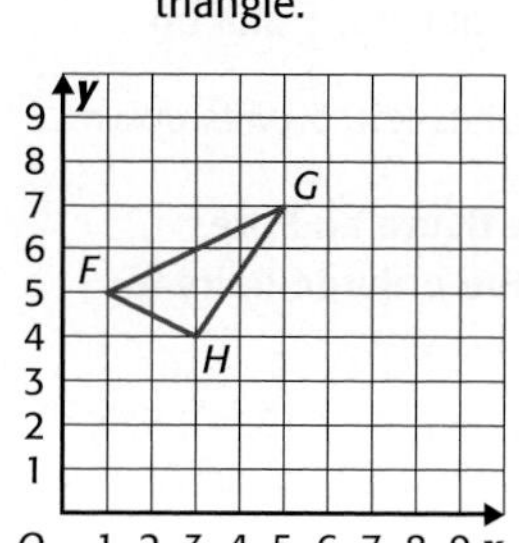

Step 2 Graph the translated image.

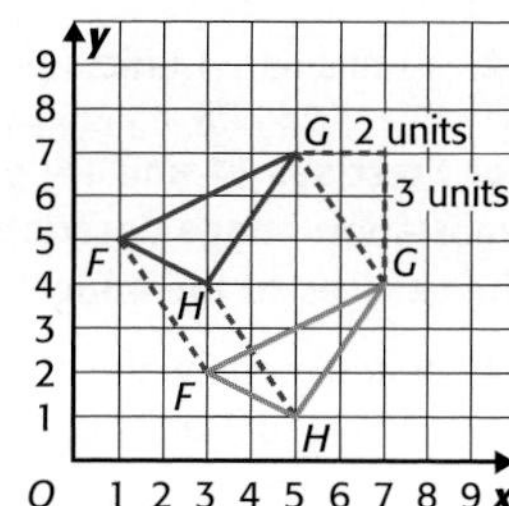

The new vertices are $F(3, 2)$, $G(7, 4)$, and $H(5, 1)$.

CHECK What You Know

Graph the triangle after each translation. Then write the ordered pairs for the vertices of the image. See Example 1 (p. 579)

1. 3 units left 1–3. See Ch. 13 Answer Appendix.
2. 4 units up
3. 5 units left, 2 units down

For Exercises 4 and 5, graph each figure and the translation image described. Write the ordered pairs for the vertices of the image. See Example 1 (p. 579) 4, 5. See Ch.13 Answer Appendix.

4. quadrilateral with vertices $J(1, 5)$, $K(2, 8)$, $L(4, 8)$, $M(3, 5)$; translated 5 units right
5. triangle with vertices $W(7, 2)$, $X(8, 6)$, $Y(9, 3)$; translated 6 units left, 1 unit up
6. Jerome walks 2 blocks west and then 4 blocks north. Describe this transformation. a translation 2 units left and 4 units up
7. 

Explain why a translation is sometimes called a slide.

7. Sample answer: When a figure is translated, it is slid from one position to another without being turned.

Enrich (p. 37) AL

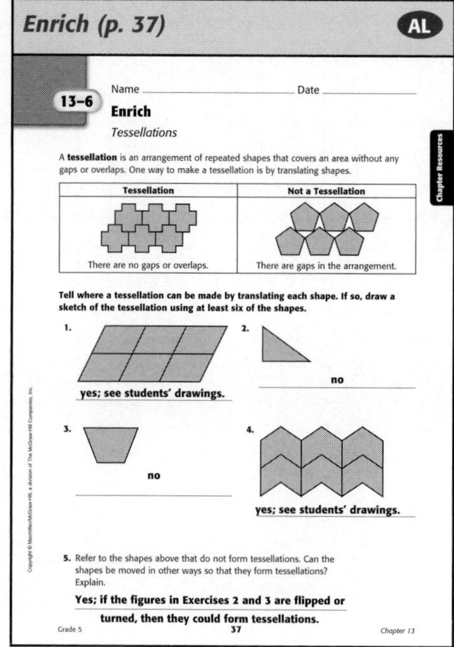

13-6

Name ____________ Date ____________

Enrich

Tessellations

A **tessellation** is an arrangement of repeated shapes that covers an area without any gaps or overlaps. One way to make a tessellation is by translating shapes.

Tessellation	Not a Tessellation
There are no gaps or overlaps.	There are gaps in the arrangement.

Tell where a tessellation can be made by translating each shape. If so, draw a sketch of the tessellation using at least six of the shapes.

1. yes; see students' drawings.
2. no
3. no
4. yes; see students' drawings.
5. Refer to the shapes above that do not form tessellations. Can the shapes be moved in other ways so that they form tessellations? Explain.
Yes; if the figures in Exercises 2 and 3 are flipped or turned, then they could form tessellations.

Grade 5 37 Chapter 13

Sketch a Translation

Example 1 Be sure students understand that each of the vertices move exactly the same number of units to the right and down. Encourage students to graph each vertex and then connect the vertices.

ADDITIONAL EXAMPLES

1 Parallelogram *ABCD* has vertices at $A(6, 4)$, $B(5, 2)$, $C(8, 2)$, and $D(9, 4)$. Graph parallelogram *ABCD* and its translation image 4 units to the left and 3 units up. Graph and then write the ordered pairs for the new vertices. The new vertices are at $A(2, 7)$, $B(1, 5)$, $C(4, 5)$ and $D(5, 7)$.

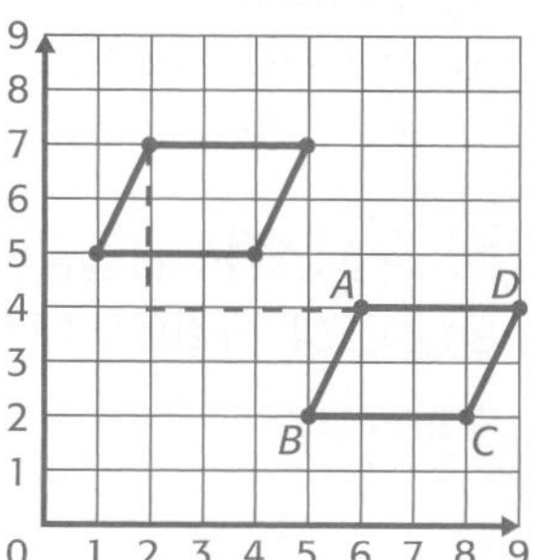

CHECK What You Know

As a class, have students complete Exercises 1–7 in **Check What You Know** as you observe their work.

Exercise 7 Assess student comprehension before assigning practice exercises.

BL Alternate Teaching Strategy

If students have trouble sketching translations on a coordinate grid…

Then use one of these reteach options:

1 CRM **Daily Reteach Worksheet** (p. 33)

2 Have students use triangle pattern blocks and centimeter grid paper to show translations. Trace a triangle so that the top left vertex is at (5, 5). Draw a straight line to (9, 5) and move the triangle to the right so that the top left vertex is at (9, 5). **How many units did the two bottom vertices move when the top vertex moved 4 units to (9, 5)?** 4 units

Have the students do several more translations using the triangles. Ask them to record beginning and ending coordinate pairs.

3 Practice

Differentiate practice using these leveled assignments for Exercises 8–21.

Level	Assignment
BL Below/Approaching Level	8–11, 14–15, 17, 21
OL On Level	10–18, 21
AL Above/Beyond Level	9–19 odd, 20–21

Have students discuss and complete the Higher Order Thinking problems. As students draw a triangle for Exercise 20, encourage them to place each vertex on the intersection of two grid lines.

WRITING IN ▶MATH Have students complete Exercise 21 in their Math Journals.

Additional Answers

8.

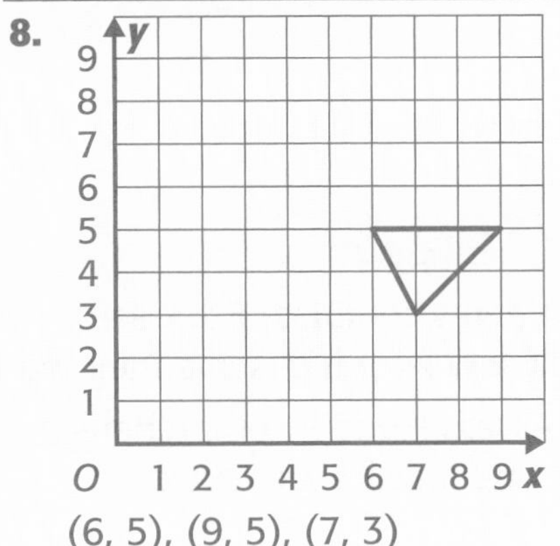

(6, 5), (9, 5), (7, 3)

9.

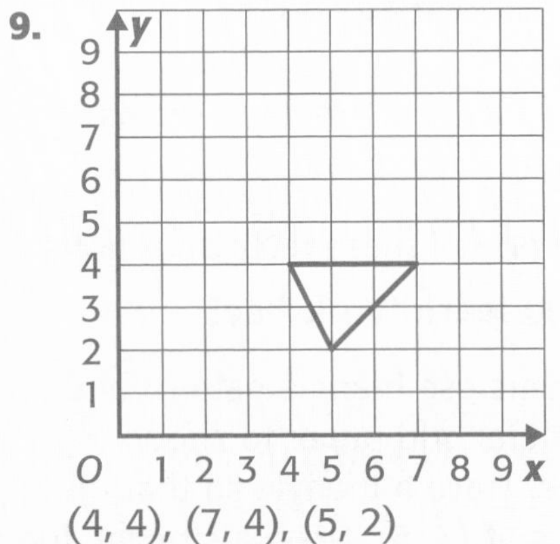

(4, 4), (7, 4), (5, 2)

COMMON ERROR!

Exercise 16 If students have difficulty determining the coordinates of translations when the vertices are not identified in the same order as the original figure. Have students sketch the figure, then find the two known vertices of the translated figure. Now, they can see where the third vertex will be.

★ indicates multi-step problem

Practice and Problem Solving

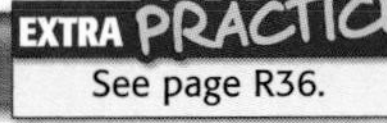

See page R36.

Graph the triangle after each translation image. Then write the ordered pairs for the vertices of the image. See Example 1 (p. 579) 8–11. See margin.

8. 2 units right

9. 1 unit down

10. 5 units up

11. 1 unit right, 1 unit up

12. 3 units left, 4 units up

13. 2 units left, 3 units down

12,13. See Ch. 13 Answer Appendix.

For Exercises 14 and 15, graph each figure and the translation image described. Write the ordered pairs for the vertices of the image. See Example 1 (p. 579)

14. quadrilateral with vertices $N(6, 1)$, $P(7, 4)$, $Q(9, 4)$, $R(9, 1)$; translated 5 units up 14–15. See Ch. 13 Answer Appendix.

15. triangle with vertices $D(1, 3)$, $E(4, 5)$, $F(3, 0)$; translated 3 units right, 4 units up

16. A triangular picture with vertices described in the table is being moved. The new coordinates for two of the vertices are (6, 5) and (6, 7). What are the new coordinates for the third vertex? (9, 7)

Vertex	1	2	3
Coordinates	(1, 2)	(1, 4)	(4, 4)

17. A swing set has posts at (10, 2), (6, 6), (14, 14), and (18, 10). It is being moved 4 units up. What are the new coordinates? Draw a sketch of the translation. See Ch. 13 Answer Appendix.

18. A table tennis table has coordinates (0, 0), (0, 5), (9, 5), and (9, 0). Each unit represents 1 foot. If the table is moved 6 feet to the right and 2 feet up, what are the new coordinates of the table? (6, 2), (6, 7), (15, 7), (15, 2)

★**19.** Anne wants to move a right-triangular table from one corner of a room to another. If both corners have 90° angles, will the translated figure fit in the new corner? Explain. No; the table must be turned to fit in a different corner.

H.O.T. Problems

20. OPEN ENDED Draw a triangle on a coordinate grid with one vertex at (5, 1). Then translate the triangle so the same vertex is at (6, 5). Describe the translation. See Ch. 13 Answer Appendix.

21. WRITING IN ▶MATH Explain how to translate a figure in a diagonal direction. Sample answer: First translate the figure left or right. Then translate the figure up or down.

580 Chapter 13 Identify, Compare, and Classify Geometric Figures

10.

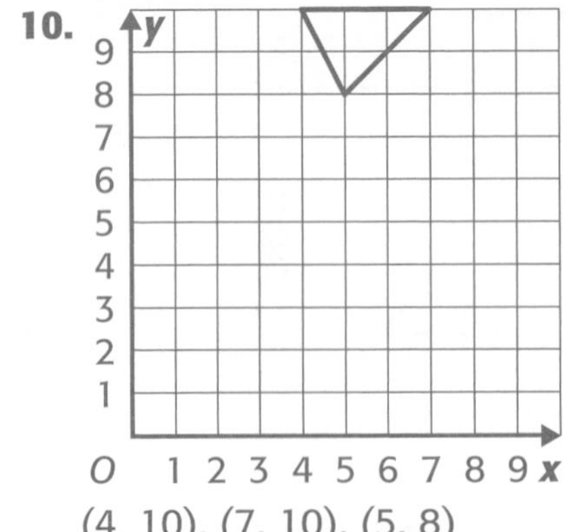

(4, 10), (7, 10), (5, 8)

11.

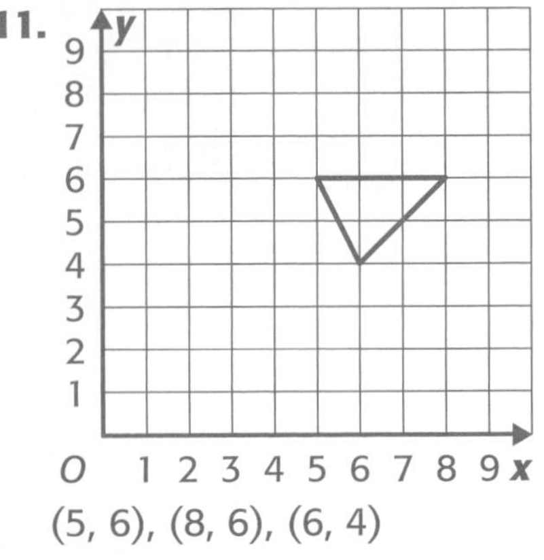

(5, 6), (8, 6), (6, 4)

TEST Practice

22. Which statement about trapezoid *ABCD* appears to be true? (Lesson 13-4) B

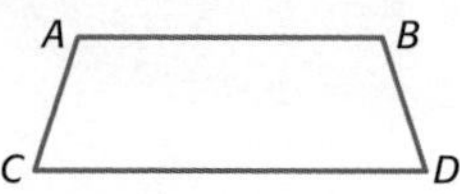

A $\overline{AC}$ and $\overline{CD}$ form a right angle.

B $\overline{AB}$ and $\overline{CD}$ are parallel.

C $\overline{AB}$ and $\overline{BD}$ are parallel.

D $\overline{AC}$ and $\overline{AB}$ form an acute angle.

23. Which diagram shows only a translation of the figure? (Lesson 13-6) F

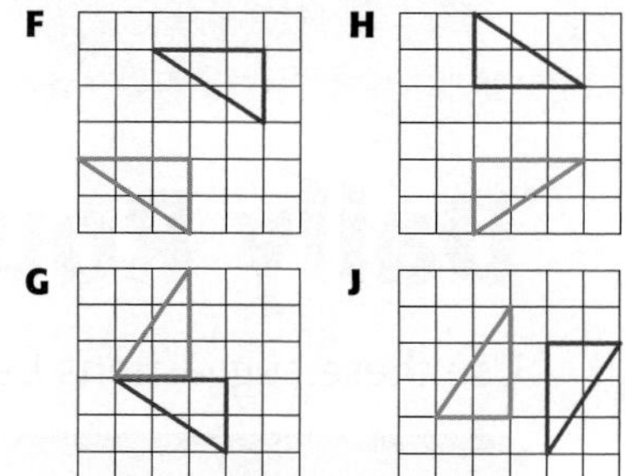

Spiral Review

24. The number of chairs in each row in an amphitheater is shown in the table. If this pattern continues, how many chairs will be in the tenth row? Explain. (Lesson 13-5) 104; Each row has 4 more chairs than the previous row.

Row	Number of Chairs
1	68
2	72
3	76
4	80

Describe the sides that appear to be congruent in each quadrilateral. Then state whether any sides appear to be parallel or perpendicular. (Lesson 13-4) 25–27. See Ch. 13 Answer Appendix.

25. 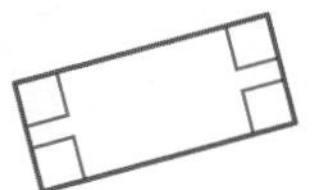

26. 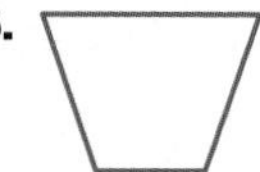

27. 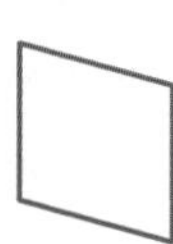

Find each change in temperature. Use an integer to represent the change. (Lesson 12-6)

28. 57°F to 60°F +3

29. 110°F to 102°F −8

30. 22°C to 0°C −22

31. Carlota walked her dog from 10:47 [illegible] to 11:23 [illegible] How long did she walk her dog? (Lesson 11-7) 36 min

32. Yesterday, Oscar drank 3 cups of water, 2 cups of milk, and 3 cups of juice. How many quarts of liquid did he drink? (Lesson 11-4) 2 qt

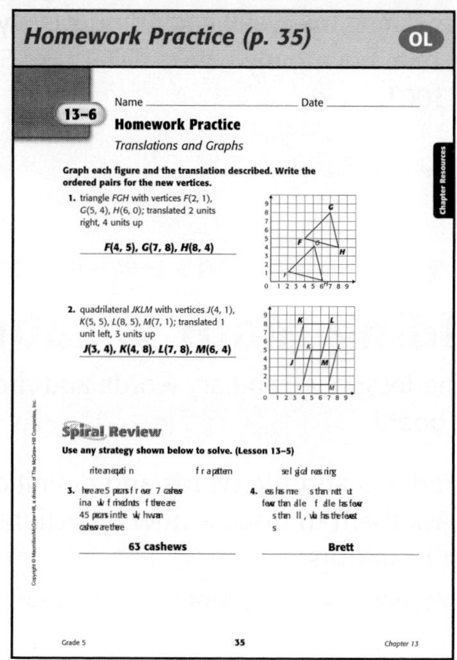

Homework Practice (p. 35) OL

13-6 Name ________ Date ________

Homework Practice

Translations and Graphs

Graph each figure and the translation described. Write the ordered pairs for the new vertices.

1. triangle *FGH* with vertices *F*(2, 1), *G*(5, 4), *H*(6, 0); translated 2 units right, 4 units up

   ***F*(4, 5), *G*(7, 8), *H*(8, 4)**

2. quadrilateral *JKLM* with vertices *J*(4, 1), *K*(5, 5), *L*(8, 5), *M*(7, 1); translated 1 unit left, 3 units up

   ***J*(3, 4), *K*(4, 8), *L*(7, 8), *M*(6, 4)**

Spiral Review

Use any strategy shown below to solve. (Lesson 13–5)

[illegible]

3. [illegible] **63 cashews**

4. [illegible] **Brett**

Grade 5 | 35 | Chapter 13

Chapter Resources

4 Assess

Formative Assessment

State the following coordinate pairs and have students graph and sketch the figure: $R(1, 3)$, $S(2, 6)$, $T(3, 3)$.

- **How would you translate the figure 4 units right and 3 units down?** Move each vertex 4 units to the right and 3 units down.
- **After doing the translation, what are the ordered pairs for the new vertices?** $R(5, 0)$, $S(6, 3)$, $T(7, 0)$

Quick Check **Are students continuing to struggle with sketching translations on a coordinate grid?**

If Yes → Small Group Options (p. 578B)

If No → Independent Work Options (p. 578B)
CRM Skills Practice Worksheet (p. 34)
CRM Enrich Worksheet (p. 37)

Ticket Out the Door Write the following coordinate pairs on the board: $A(4, 8)$, $B(3, 6)$, $C(5, 5)$, and $D(8, 7)$. On a small piece of grid paper, students do the following: graph the points and sketch the figure, translate the figure in two directions of their choice, describe the translation they performed, and name the ordered pairs for the new vertices.

TEST Practice

Reviews Lessons 13-4 and 13-6

Assign the Test Practice problems to provide daily reinforcement of test-taking skills.

Spiral Review

Reviews Lessons 11-4, 11-7, 12-6, 13-4, and 13-5

Review and assess mastery of skills and concepts from previous chapters.

LESSON 13-7

Reflections and Graphs

Lesson Planner

Objective

Sketch reflections on a coordinate grid.

Vocabulary

reflection, line of reflection

Resources

Materials: grid paper, pencil and paper, mirrors
Manipulatives: pattern blocks
Literature Connection: *Round Trip* by Ann Jonas
Teacher Technology
TeacherWorks • Interactive Classroom

Focus on Math Background

By drawing reflections of figures, students begin to grasp the underpinnings of the concept of *symmetry*. When a figure is reflected across a line, that line is called the *line of reflection*. If the figure can be reflected over a line so that the resulting image coincides with the original, then the reflection line is called the *line of symmetry* and the figure is said to have *reflectional symmetry*. When a figure is reflected across a line, the points on the image and the corresponding points on the preimage are the same distance from the line of reflection.

Daily Routine

Use these suggestions before beginning the lesson on p. 582.

5-Minute Check

(Reviews Lesson 13-6)

Graph the figure and the translation described. Write the ordered pairs for the vertices of the image.

triangle *CDE* with vertices *C*(5, 9), *D*(3, 7), *E*(4, 6); translated 2 units right, 2 units down

C(7, 7), *D*(5, 5), *E*(6, 4)

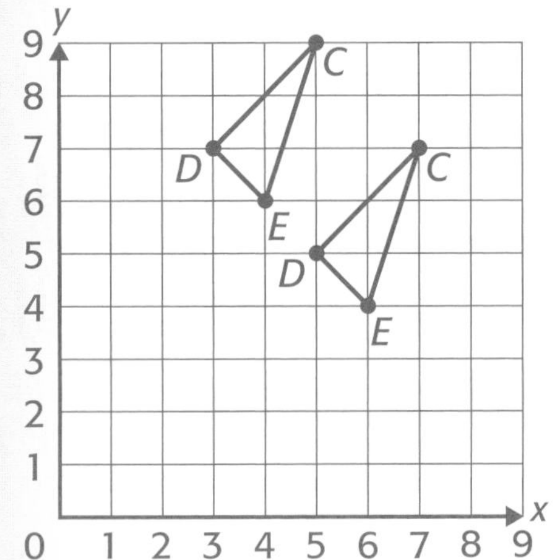

Problem of the Day

Solana earns $6 an hour for babysitting. She babysits 4 hours during the week and 5 hours every weekend. At this rate, how many weeks will it take Solana to earn $300? 6 weeks

Building Math Vocabulary

Write the lesson vocabulary words and their definitions on the board.

Have students add the words and definitions to their notes. Ask them to discuss how reflections work in relation to mirrors.

Differentiated Instruction

Small Group Options

Option 1 Below Level BL

SPATIAL

Materials: cardboard triangles, rulers

- Have students make cardboard triangles to investigate reflections and rotations. Instruct students to make scalene triangles.
- Draw outlines for the triangles on blank paper and then perform the transformation.
- Compare the transformed triangle with the outline left behind.

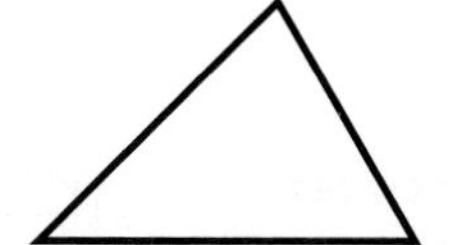

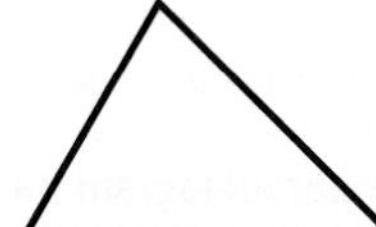

Option 2 English Language Learners ELL

KINESTHETIC

Core Vocabulary: move slowly, reflect, face each other
Common Use Verb: must mirror
Do Math This strategy helps students kinesthetically understand reflections.

- Count off 1, 2, etc. and pair accordingly. Students stand facing their partner.
- Say: "You ***must mirror*** each other and **reflect** what your partner does without talking. You must **move slowly**."
- Demonstrate as needed.
- Repeat the strategy, having 1s move first while 2s watch.
- After one minute, let 2s reflect the movements they remember.
- Monitor for accuracy.
- Discuss the difference between moving simultaneously and moving from memory. Connect recording movements with graphing as you discuss accuracy.
- Switch starting partners and repeat as time permits.

Independent Work Options

Option 1 Early Finishers AL

VISUAL, SPATIAL

Materials: pattern blocks, grid paper, pencils

- Ask students to choose one of the shapes of pattern block. Have them fold their grid paper in fourths and draw perpendicular lines in each section so that each has vertical and horizontal lines of reflection.
- Have students place and sketch a pattern block in one of the 4 sections. Then have students reflect the shape across the horizontal and vertical lines in that section. Tell students to repeat this procedure in the other 3 sections.
- Students may repeat the activity with another shape.

Option 2 Student Technology

Math Online macmillanmh.com

Personal Tutor • Extra Examples

Option 3 Learning Station: Science (p. 554H)

Direct students to the Science Learning Station for opportunities to explore and extend the lesson concept.

Option 4 Problem-Solving Practice

Reinforce problem-solving skills and strategies with the Problem-Solving Practice worksheet.

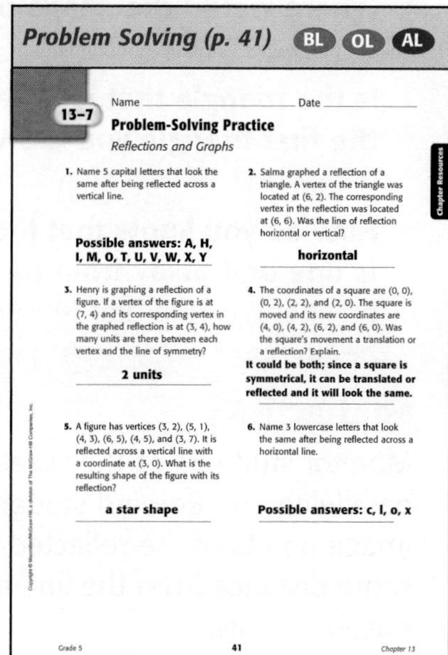

Problem Solving (p. 41) BL OL AL

13–7 Name ____________ Date ____________

Problem-Solving Practice

Reflections and Graphs

1. Name 5 capital letters that look the same after being reflected across a vertical line.
   Possible answers: A, H, I, M, O, T, U, V, W, X, Y
2. Salma graphed a reflection of a triangle. A vertex of the triangle was located at (6, 2). The corresponding vertex in the reflection was located at (6, 6). Was the line of reflection horizontal or vertical?
   horizontal
3. Henry is graphing a reflection of a figure. If a vertex of the figure is at (7, 4) and its corresponding vertex in the graphed reflection is at (3, 4), how many units are there between each vertex and the line of symmetry?
   2 units
4. The coordinates of a square are (0, 0), (0, 2), (2, 2), and (2, 0). The square is moved and its new coordinates are (4, 0), (4, 2), (6, 2), and (6, 0). Was the square's movement a translation or a reflection? Explain.
   It could be both; since a square is symmetrical, it can be translated or reflected and it will look the same.
5. A figure has vertices (3, 2), (5, 1), (4, 3), (6, 5), (4, 5), and (3, 7). It is reflected across a vertical line with a coordinate at (3, 0). What is the resulting shape of the figure with its reflection?
   a star shape
6. Name 3 lowercase letters that look the same after being reflected across a horizontal line.
   Possible answers: c, l, o, x

Chapter Resources

Copyright © Macmillan/McGraw-Hill, a division of The McGraw-Hill Companies, Inc.

Grade 5 41 Chapter 13

13-7 Reflections and Graphs

1 Introduce

Activity Choice 1 • Hands-On

- Have students draw a coordinate grid numbered 0–9 on each axis. Ask them to graph the following points and sketch the figure: $A(3, 4)$, $B(1, 2)$, $C(3, 1)$.
- Discuss what the reflection of the triangle would look like if a mirror were placed on line segment AC. Use a mirror to demonstrate.
- **How does the reflection of the triangle look different than a translation of the triangle would?** The reflection is flipped so that the vertex B is to the right of side $\overline{AC}$. In a translation the triangle would be the same as originally drawn but in a different place on the grid.

Activity Choice 2 • Literature

Introduce the lesson with *Round Trip* by Ann Jonas. For a related math activity, see p. TR58.

2 Teach

Scaffolding Questions

Ask students to draw another coordinate grid. Have them graph the following points and sketch the figure: $R(2, 8)$, $S(2, 5)$, $T(4, 5)$. Have them draw a vertical line at 5 on the x-axis.

- **Where would the image of vertex R be if a mirror was placed on the line to reflect triangle RST?** (8, 8)
- **Where would the image of vertex T be? Vertex S?** $T(6, 5)$; $S(8, 5)$
- **Is the triangle that is reflected congruent to the first triangle you drew? Explain.** Yes; it is the same size and shape but just flipped over.
- **How do you know that the image of vertex T is one unit away from the line?** Since the original T is one unit from the line, it has to be one unit away on the reflected side.

Mini Activity

Monitor students as they sketch the parallelogram. Remind students that each of the image points of the reflected figure must be the same distance from the line of reflection as the original points.

13-7 Reflections and Graphs

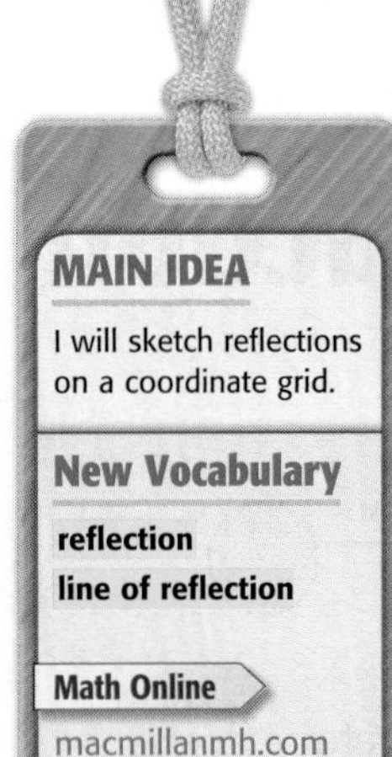

MAIN IDEA

I will sketch reflections on a coordinate grid.

New Vocabulary

reflection

line of reflection

Math Online

macmillanmh.com

- Extra Examples
- Personal Tutor
- Self-Check Quiz

GET READY to Learn

Cartoonists sometimes use transformations to change characters. The figures at the right are *reflections* of each other.

Another transformation that does not change the size or shape of a figure is a reflection.

Reflection — Key Concepts

Flipping a figure over a line to create a mirror image of the figure is called a **reflection**. The line is called a **line of reflection**.

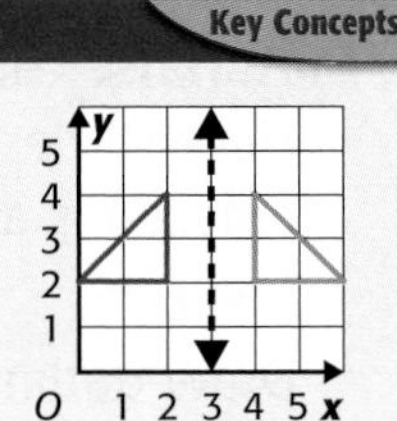

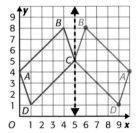

When a figure is reflected across a line, corresponding vertices are the same distance from the line of reflection.

Hands-On Mini Activity

A parallelogram has vertices $A(0, 4)$, $B(4, 8)$, $C(5, 5)$, and $D(1, 1)$. Draw a coordinate grid on graph paper. Copy the parallelogram.

a. With a different colored pencil, graph points A, B, C, and D after they are reflected across the line. a–b. See graph.

b. Connect the points.

c. What are the vertices of the image?

c. $A(10, 4)$, $B(6, 8)$, $C(5, 5)$, $D(9, 1)$

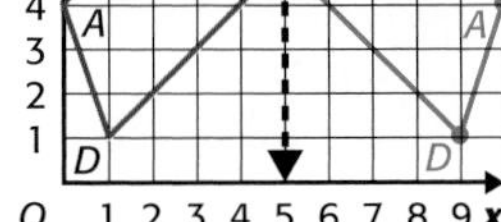

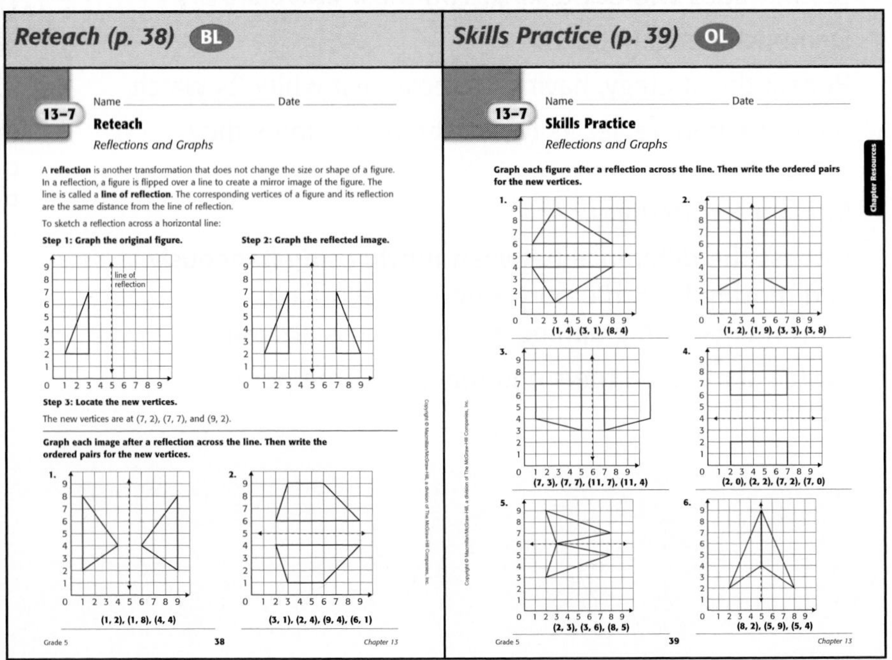

Reteach (p. 38) BL

13-7 Name ______ Date ______

Reteach

Reflections and Graphs

A **reflection** is another transformation that does not change the size or shape of a figure. In a reflection, a figure is flipped over a line to create a mirror image of the figure. The line is called a **line of reflection**. The corresponding vertices of a figure and its reflection are the same distance from the line of reflection.

To sketch a reflection across a horizontal line:

Step 1: Graph the original figure.

Step 2: Graph the reflected image.

Step 3: Locate the new vertices.

The new vertices are at (7, 2), (7, 7), and (9, 2).

Graph each image after a reflection across the line. Then write the ordered pairs for the new vertices.

1. **(1, 2), (1, 8), (4, 4)**
2. **(3, 1), (2, 4), (9, 4), (6, 1)**

Grade 5 38 Chapter 13

Skills Practice (p. 39) OL

13-7 Name ______ Date ______

Skills Practice

Reflections and Graphs

Graph each figure after a reflection across the line. Then write the ordered pairs for the new vertices.

1. **(1, 4), (3, 1), (8, 4)**
2. **(1, 2), (1, 9), (3, 3), (3, 8)**
3. **(7, 3), (7, 7), (11, 7), (11, 4)**
4. **(2, 0), (2, 2), (7, 2), (7, 0)**
5. **(2, 3), (3, 6), (8, 5)**
6. **(8, 2), (5, 9), (5, 4)**

Grade 5 39 Chapter 13

EXAMPLE Reflect Across a Horizontal Line

Remember

In a reflection, a figure is flipped from one position to another without being turned. Reflections are sometimes called *flips*.

1 Graph the triangle after it is reflected across the line. Then write the ordered pairs for the new vertices.

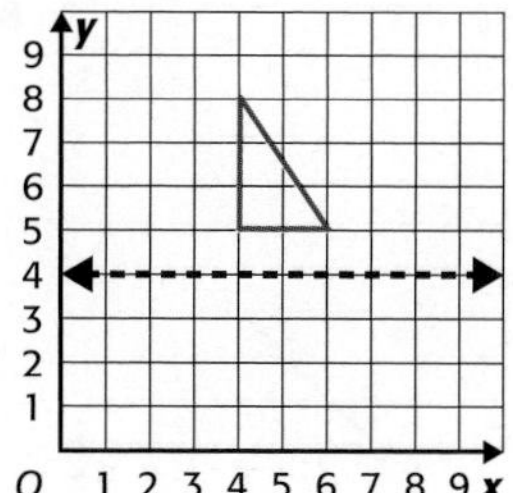

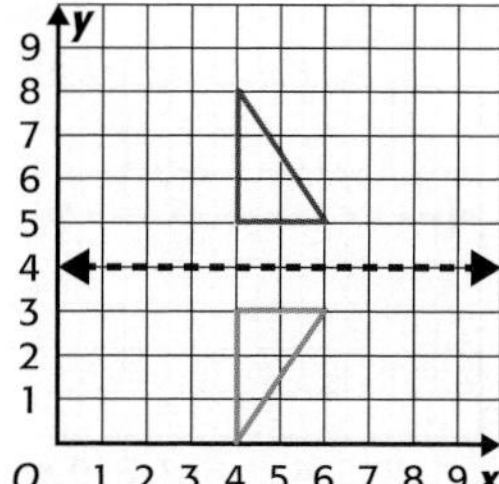

The ordered pairs for the new vertices are (4, 0), (4, 3), and (6, 3).

You can check the reasonableness of the vertices by drawing the triangles on grid paper. When the paper is folded, they should match exactly.

CHECK What You Know

Graph each figure after a reflection across the line. Then write the ordered pairs for the new vertices. See Example 1 (p. 583) 1–3. See Ch. 13 Answer Appendix.

1\.

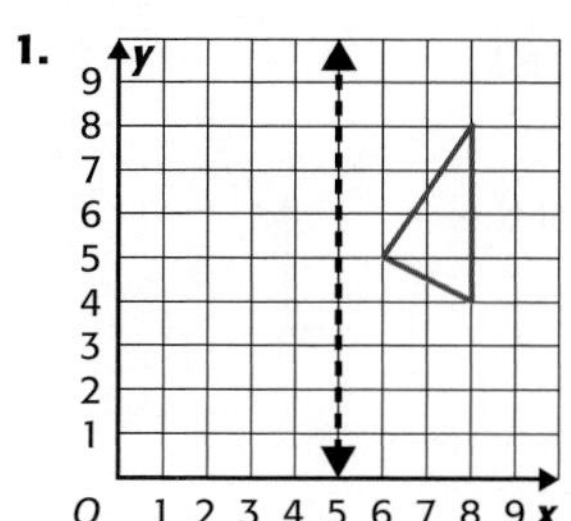

2\.

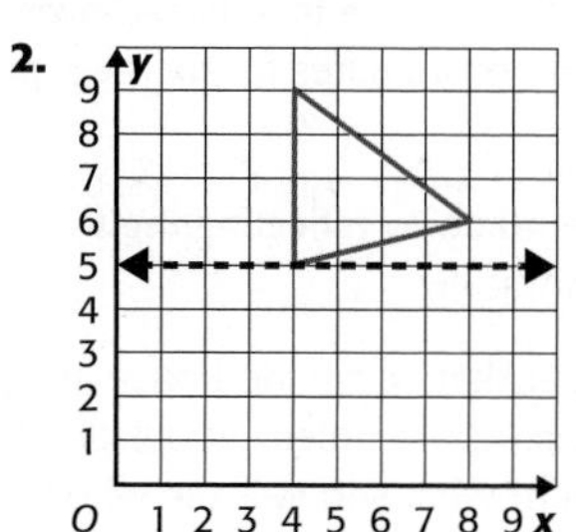

3\.

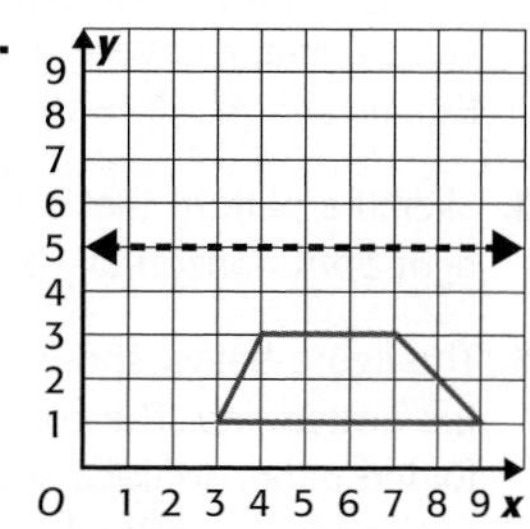

4. Which letters in GEOMETRY can be reflected over a vertical line and remain the same? OMTY

5. Talk About It Compare and contrast translations and reflections.
See Ch. 13 Answer Appendix.

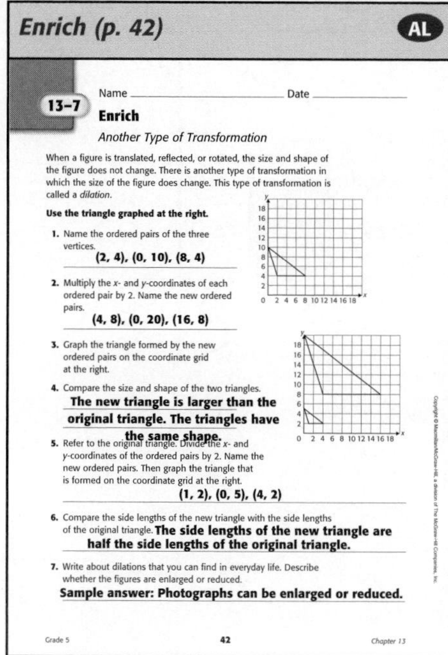

Enrich (p. 42) AL

13–7 Name ________ Date ________

Enrich

Another Type of Transformation

When a figure is translated, reflected, or rotated, the size and shape of the figure does not change. There is another type of transformation in which the size of the figure does change. This type of transformation is called a *dilation*.

Use the triangle graphed at the right.

1. Name the ordered pairs of the three vertices. **(2, 4), (0, 10), (8, 4)**
2. Multiply the *x*- and *y*-coordinates of each ordered pair by 2. Name the new ordered pairs. **(4, 8), (0, 20), (16, 8)**
3. Graph the triangle formed by the new ordered pairs on the coordinate grid at the right.
4. Compare the size and shape of the two triangles. **The new triangle is larger than the original triangle. The triangles have the same shape.**
5. Refer to the original triangle. Divide the *x*- and *y*-coordinates of the ordered pairs by 2. Name the new ordered pairs. Then graph the triangle that is formed on the coordinate grid at the right. **(1, 2), (0, 5), (4, 2)**
6. Compare the side lengths of the new triangle with the side lengths of the original triangle. **The side lengths of the new triangle are half the side lengths of the original triangle.**
7. Write about dilations that you can find in everyday life. Describe whether the figures are enlarged or reduced. **Sample answer: Photographs can be enlarged or reduced.**

Grade 5 42 Chapter 13

Reflect Across a Horizontal Line

Example 1 Be sure students understand that marking each vertex of the reflected figure the same distance from the line of reflection as they are in the original figure is an important first step in representing the reflection correctly.

ADDITIONAL EXAMPLE

1 Graph a reflection of the quadrilateral across the line. Then write the ordered pairs for the new vertices.

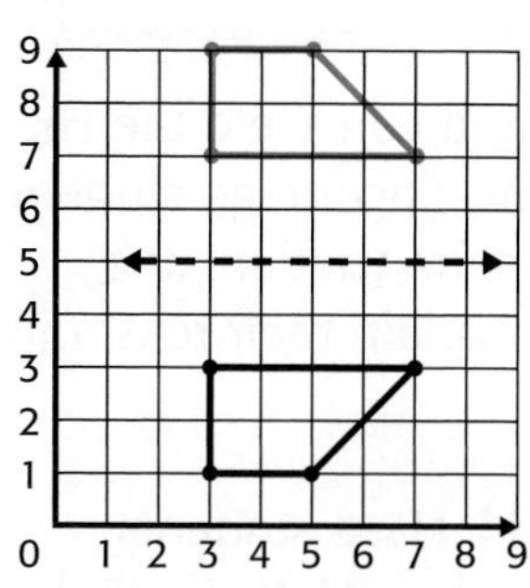

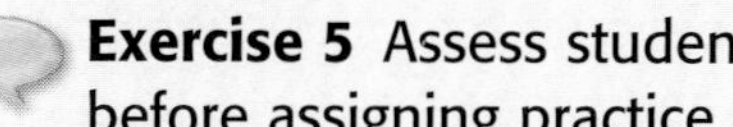

(3, 7), (3, 9), (5, 9), (7, 7)

CHECK What You Know

As a class, have students complete Exercises 1–5 in **Check What You Know** as you observe their work.

Exercise 5 Assess student comprehension before assigning practice exercises.

BL Alternate Teaching Strategy

If students have trouble sketching reflections on a coordinate grid…

Then use one of these reteach options:

1 CRM **Daily Reteach Worksheet** (p. 38)

2 Have students use pattern blocks and a mirror to see what a reflected figure will look like. Ask students to place a trapezoid with the longer base on the grid line at the 1 on the *x*-axis.

- Have them place a mirror along the shorter base. Describe where you see the vertices in the mirror.
- Draw a line along the edge of the mirror, remove the mirror, and flip the trapezoid over the line to match the reflection they saw. Ask them to describe the vertices in relation to the line of reflection.

3 Practice

Differentiate practice using these leveled assignments for Exercises 6–21.

Level	Assignment
BL Below/ Approaching Level	6–9, 13, 15, 17, 21
OL On Level	7–17, 21
AL Above/Beyond Level	7–17 odd, 18–21

Have students discuss and complete the Higher Order Thinking problems. Encourage students to use the words reflection, translation, and transformation as they explain their reasoning for Exercise 20.

WRITING IN ▸MATH Have students complete Exercise 21 in their Math Journals. You may choose to use this as an optional formative assessment.

Additional Answers

13. Sample answer: If the vertical line goes through (0, 5), then the points reflected across the line would have the coordinates (7, 8), (5, 1), and (8, 1).

14. Sample answer:

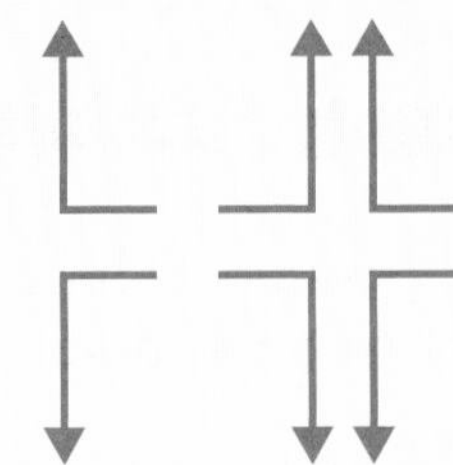

15. Sample answer:

COMMON ERROR!

Exercises 12–14 Students may struggle with remembering the meanings of the words horizontal and vertical. Remind students that the word horizontal comes from the word horizon and means parallel to the horizon while vertical means straight up and down. Have students draw a horizontal and a vertical line on their paper and label them correctly for reference as they complete the problems.

★ indicates multi-step problem

Practice and Problem Solving

See page R36.

Graph each figure after a reflection across the line. Then write the ordered pairs for the new vertices. See Example 1 (p. 583) 6–11. See Ch. 13 Answer Appendix.

6. 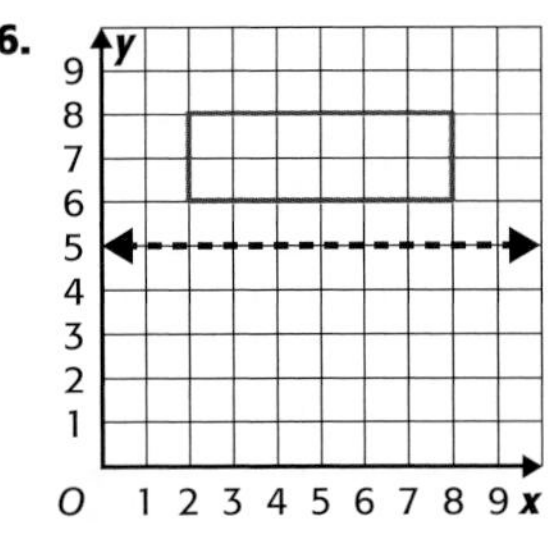

7. 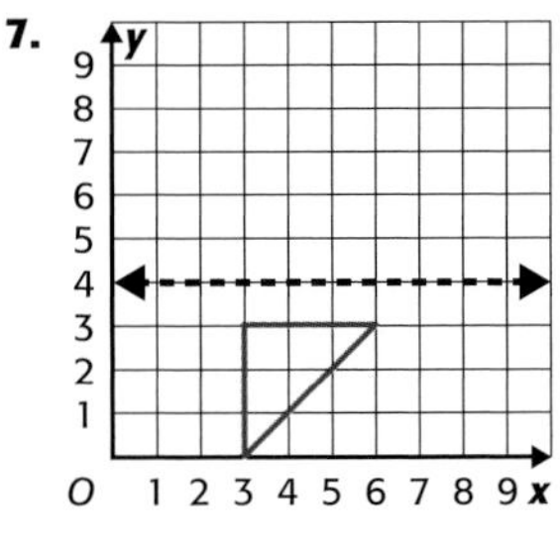

8. 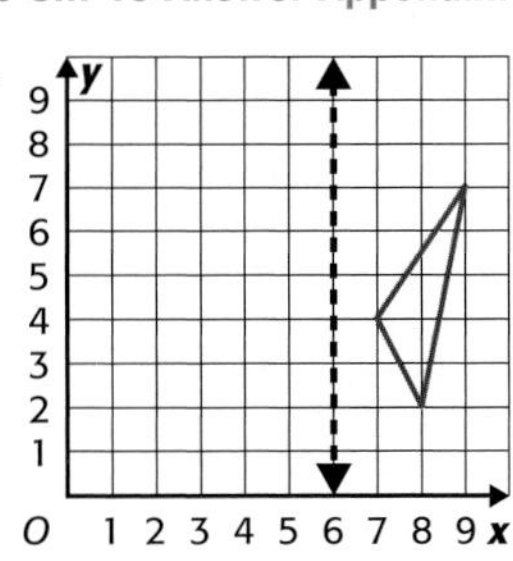

9. 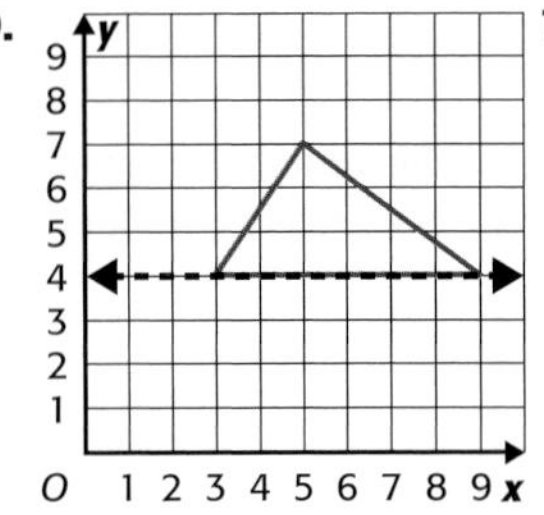

10. 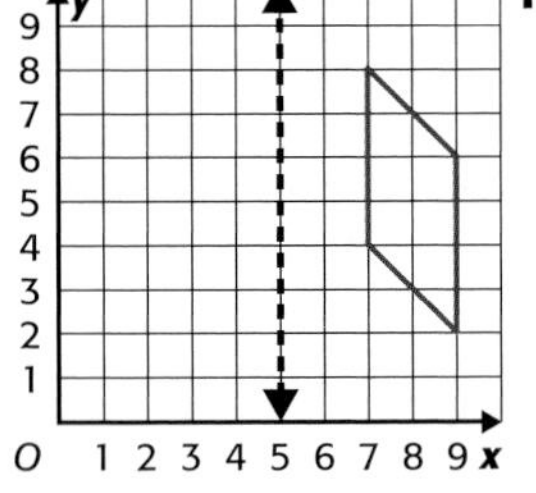

11. 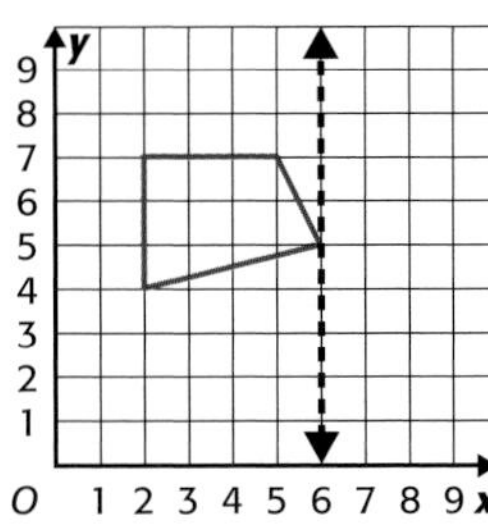

12. Name four capital letters that look the same after being reflected across a horizontal line. Sample answers: B, D, E, H

13. A cartoonist draws a figure whose head is at (3, 8) and whose feet are at (2, 1) and (5, 1). If the figure is reflected over a vertical line, what are possible coordinates for the new points? Explain. 13–15. See margin.

14. Sketch a pattern that can be made by reflecting the figure at the right both horizontally and vertically.

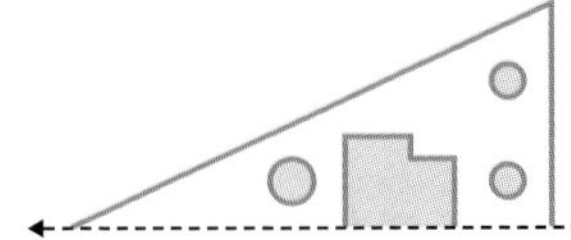

★**15.** The figure below shows paper that was folded once along the dotted line. The colored parts are holes cut out of the folded paper. Make a sketch of what you will see when the paper is unfolded.

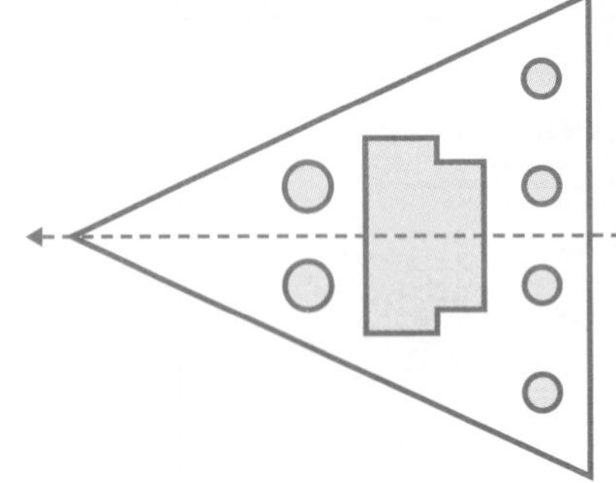

Real-World PROBLEM SOLVING

Music Some melodies have patterns of notes that are reflections. In the figure below, notice that the notes on each side of the dashed line are mirror images of each other.

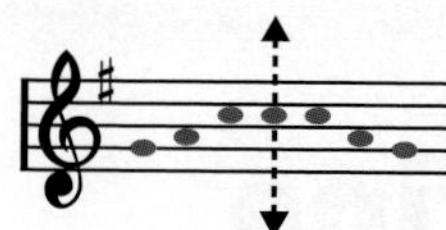

Copy and complete each set of notes so that the right and left sides are reflections of each other. 16–17. See margin.

16.

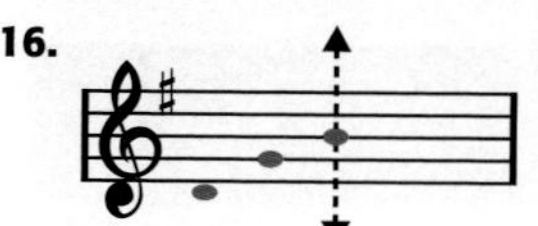

17.

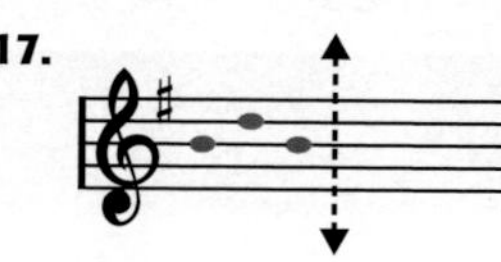

H.O.T. Problems 18–21. See Ch. 13 Answer Appendix.

18. OPEN ENDED Copy the figure at the right on graph paper. Draw two different lines of reflection and use them to draw the reflected images of the triangle.

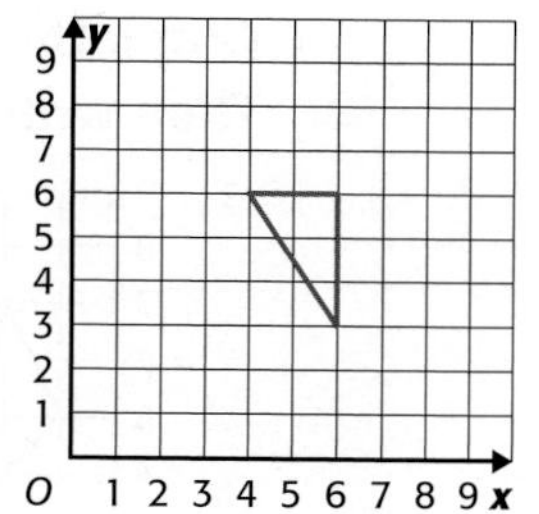

19. CHALLENGE Draw a figure on a coordinate grid and its reflection over the y-axis. Explain how the x- and y-coordinates of the image relate to the x- and y-coordinates of the original figure.

20. FIND THE ERROR Alexis and Devon are reflecting a triangle across a vertical line. Who is correct? Explain your reasoning.

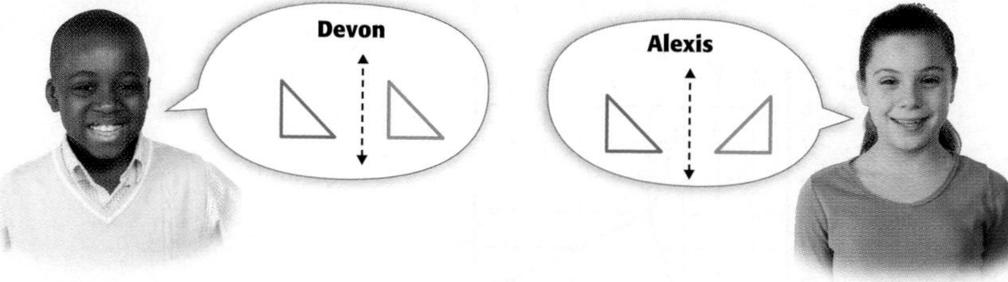

21. WRITING IN MATH Describe the steps for sketching the reflection of a quadrilateral over a line on a coordinate grid.

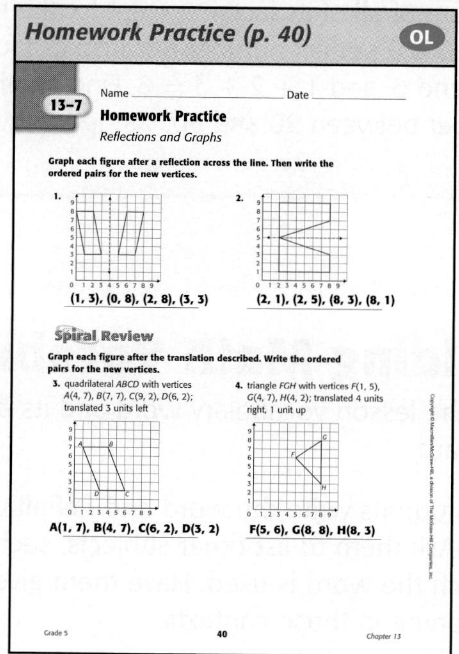

Homework Practice (p. 40) OL

13-7 Name ______ Date ______

Homework Practice

Reflections and Graphs

Graph each figure after a reflection across the line. Then write the ordered pairs for the new vertices.

1. (1, 3), (0, 8), (2, 8), (3, 3)

2. (2, 1), (2, 5), (8, 3), (8, 1)

Spiral Review

Graph each figure after the translation described. Write the ordered pairs for the new vertices.

3. quadrilateral ABCD with vertices A(4, 7), B(7, 7), C(9, 2), D(6, 2); translated 3 units left

A(1, 7), B(4, 7), C(6, 2), D(3, 2)

4. triangle FGH with vertices F(1, 5), G(4, 7), H(4, 2); translated 4 units right, 1 unit up

F(5, 6), G(8, 8), H(8, 3)

Grade 5 40 Chapter 13

4 Assess

Formative Assessment

List the following ordered pairs on the board: (2, 8), (2, 5), (4, 6), (4, 7).

- **How would you sketch the reflection of the figure, with the given vertices, located over a vertical line of reflection at 5 on the x-axis?** Draw a line vertically at 5 and then place each vertex the same number of units to the right of the line as they are to the left in the original figure. Then connect the points.
- **What are the ordered pairs for the reflected figure?** (6, 7), (6, 6), (8, 5), (8, 8)

Quick Check **Are students continuing to struggle with sketching reflections on a coordinate grid?**

If Yes → Small Group Options (p. 582B)

If No → Independent Work Options (p. 582B)
CRM Skills Practice Worksheet (p. 34)
CRM Enrich Worksheet (p. 37)

Yesterday's News Have students write a short paragraph about how what they learned in Lesson 13-6 about translations helped them to work successfully with the material about reflections today. Encourage students to compare and contrast the two kinds of transformations.

Additional Answers

16. Sample answer:

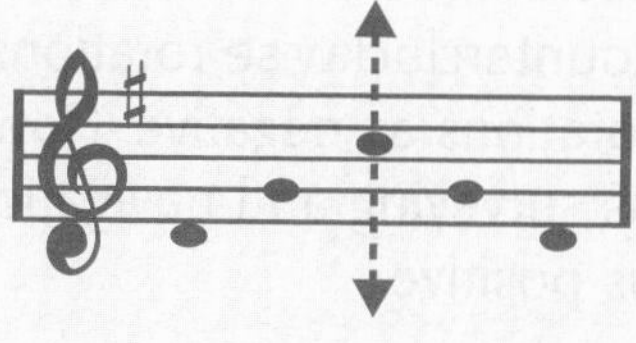

17. Sample answer:

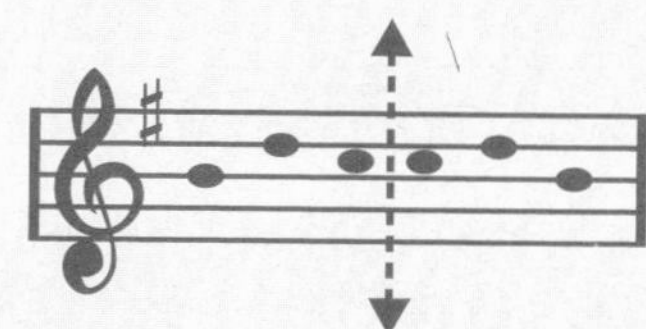

LESSON 13-8

Rotations and Graphs

Lesson Planner

Objective

Sketch rotations on a coordinate grid.

Vocabulary

rotation

Resources

Materials: paper circles, scissors
Manipulatives: pattern blocks
Literature Connection: *Geometry* by Lucille Caron and Philip M. St. Jacques
Teacher Technology
TeacherWorks • Interactive Classroom

Focus on Math Background

A rotation, or turn, also changes the coordinates of points on a figure by different amounts. But a rotation makes all the points on a figure turn through the same angle with respect to the center of rotation. Since the shape of a figure under rotation does not change, the name "rigid body rotation" is sometimes applied to such transformations. Students at this level should be able to rotate figures through 90° or 180° on graph paper without using a protractor.

It is standard mathematical practice to label counterclockwise rotations as positive and clockwise rotations as negative. However, there are exceptions such as surveying and navigation in which clockwise is regarded as positive.

Daily Routine

Use these suggestions before beginning the lesson on p. 586.

5-Minute Check

(Reviews Lesson 13-7)

Graph the figure after a reflection across the line. Then write the ordered pairs for the new vertices.

1. (8, 7), (7, 3), (9, 5)

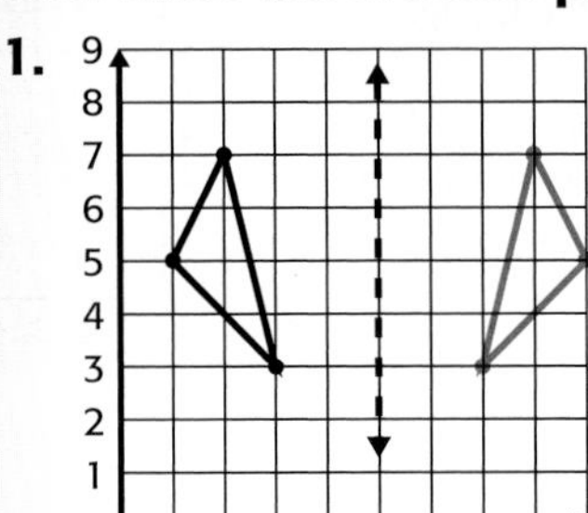

2. (4, 5), (3, 8), (6, 8), (8, 7)

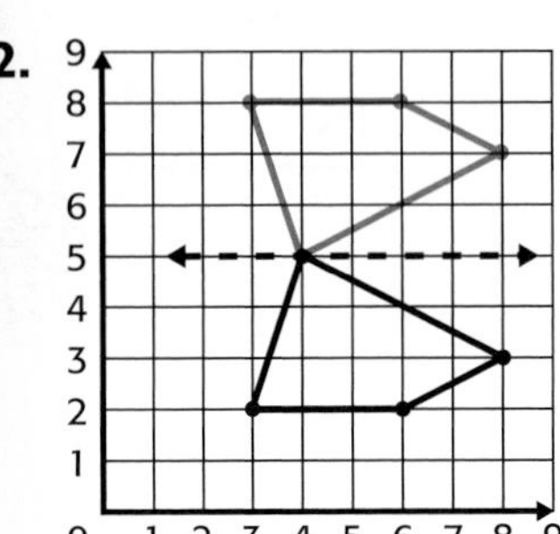

Problem of the Day

A perfect number is a whole number that is equal to the sum of all of its factors except for the number itself. 6 is a perfect number because its factors are 1, 2, 3, and 6, and $1 + 2 + 3 = 6$. Find another perfect number between 20 and 30. Sample answer: $1 + 2 + 4 + 7 + 14 = 28$

Building Math Vocabulary

Write the lesson vocabulary word and its definition on the board.

Have students write the word and definition in their notes. Ask them to list other subjects, such as science, in which the word is used. Have them give examples of its meaning in those contexts.

Differentiated Instruction

Small Group Options

Option 1 Below Level BL

SPATIAL

Materials: poster board, markers

- Review the concepts of translations, reflections, and rotations with students.
- Have small groups work together to create a poster that contains all three vocabulary words, their definitions, and a picture to describe each word.
- Display the poster to help students when beginning Lesson 13-9, Identify Transformations.

Option 2 English Language Learners ELL

INTRAPERSONAL, VISUAL

Materials: magazines, construction paper, scissors, glue, push pin, pencils with erasers
Core Vocabulary: turn, point, wheel
Common Use Verb: rotate

Do Math This strategy helps students understand rotations and rotational symmetry.

- Discuss the items rotating from one center point.
- Using construction paper, pencil, and push pin have students make a pinwheel.
- Start by making two 4″ × 4″ pieces of paper.
- Fold the squares in half twice to make 4 triangles in each; unfold. Decorate one side of each square. Put the undecorated sides of the paper together.
- Make four cuts along the fold lines through both squares—about halfway to the center.
- Using the push pin, put holes in the pinwheel, one in the upper left corner of each of the 4 sides of the squares.
- Gently gather each of the four points (with a hole) to the center. (Be careful not to crease the paper.)
- Push a push-pin through the four punched holes through the center of the pinwheel to attach the pinwheel to the side of a pencil's eraser.

Independent Work Options

Option 1 Early Finishers AL

LOGICAL

Materials: grid paper, pencils

- Have students fold their grid paper in fourths and draw a coordinate grid on each section.
- Ask students to sketch a triangle and list the vertices as ordered pairs in the first section. Have them choose a vertex around which to rotate and one of the following rotations: clockwise; 90°, 180° counterclockwise; 90°, 180°.
- Have students copy the triangle from their previous rotation on another grid and choose another rotation.

Option 2 Student Technology

Math Online macmillanmh.com

Personal Tutor • Extra Examples

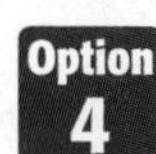

Option 3 Learning Station: Art (p. 554G)

Direct students to the Art Learning Station for opportunities to explore and extend the lesson concept.

Option 4 Problem-Solving Practice

Reinforce problem-solving skills and strategies with the Problem-Solving Practice worksheet.

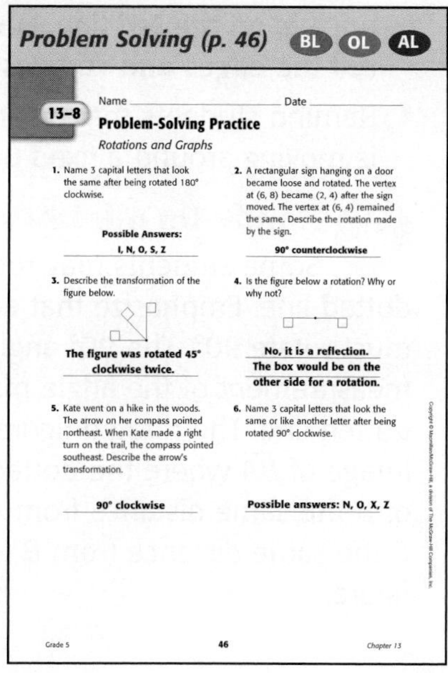

Problem Solving (p. 46) BL OL AL

13-8 Name ______ Date ______

Problem-Solving Practice

Rotations and Graphs

1. Name 3 capital letters that look the same after being rotated 180° clockwise.
   Possible Answers: I, N, O, S, Z
2. A rectangular sign hanging on a door became loose and rotated. The vertex at (6, 8) became (2, 4) after the sign moved. The vertex at (6, 4) remained the same. Describe the rotation made by the sign.
   90° counterclockwise
3. Describe the transformation of the figure below.
   The figure was rotated 45° clockwise twice.
4. Is the figure below a rotation? Why or why not?
   No, it is a reflection. The box would be on the other side for a rotation.
5. Kate went on a hike in the woods. The arrow on her compass pointed northeast. When Kate made a right turn on the trail, the compass pointed southeast. Describe the arrow's transformation.
   90° clockwise
6. Name 3 capital letters that look the same or like another letter after being rotated 90° clockwise.
   Possible answers: N, O, X, Z

Grade 5 46 Chapter 13

Rotations and Graphs

1 Introduce

Activity Choice 1 • Hands-On

- Have students cut out paper circles, fold them in fourths, and mark the folds to show 4 sections and the center. **How many degrees are there in a whole circle?** 360°
- Ask students to label 0° where one line touches the circle. Place the eraser end of a pencil on the center of the circle and lay the pencil on the line that points to 0°. Ask them to rotate their pencils clockwise, keeping the eraser on the center, until it arrives at the next line.
- **How many degrees is $\frac{1}{4}$ of the way around the circle? Explain.** 90°; $\frac{1}{4}$ of 360° equals 90°
- **Label circles at 0°, 90°, 180°, 270°, and 360°.**

Activity Choice 2 • Literature

Introduce the lesson with *Geometry* by Lucille Caron and Philip M. St. Jacques. For a related math activity, see p. TR58.

2 Teach

Scaffolding Questions

Have students use the marked circle from the previous activity and a rhombus pattern block.

- **Place the vertex of an acute angle on the center of the circle and the left edge on the 0° line. If you rotate the rhombus, what does the center of the circle do?** It does not move.
- **Rotate the rhombus clockwise so that the left edge is on the 90° line. How many degrees did the edges and vertices rotate?** 90°
- Remind students that when a figure rotates, it is moving around a fixed point.

Hands-On Mini Activity

Some students may rotate $\overline{CA}$ to meet the dotted line. Emphasize that each line segment must rotate 90°. The 90° angle shown is a measurement of the angle made by $\overline{BA}$ and the dotted line. The rotated figure will have the image of $\overline{BA}$ where the dotted line is, the image of *B* the same distance from *A*, and the image of *C* the same distance from *B* as in the original figure.

13-8 Rotations and Graphs

MAIN IDEA
I will sketch rotations on a coordinate grid.
New Vocabulary
rotation
Math Online
macmillanmh.com
• Extra Examples
• Personal Tutor
• Self-Check Quiz

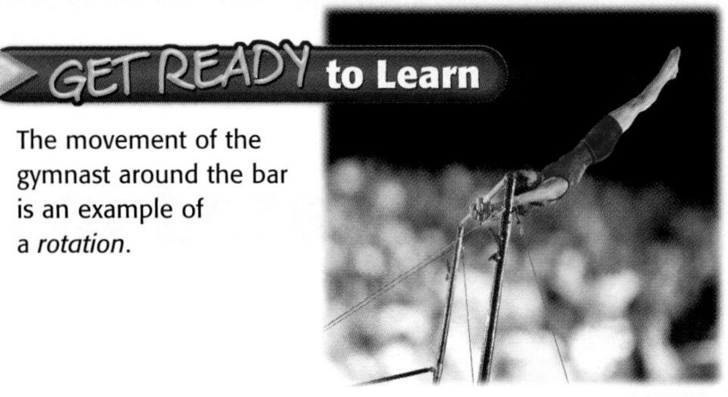

The movement of the gymnast around the bar is an example of a *rotation*.

A rotation is another type of transformation.

Rotation — Key Concept

Rotating a figure about a point is called a **rotation**. A rotation is also called a turn. It does not change the size or shape of a figure.

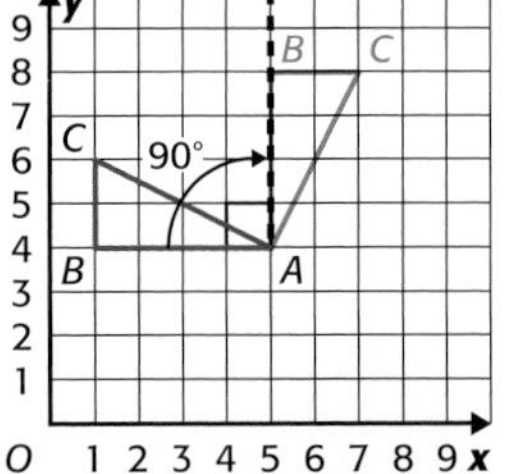

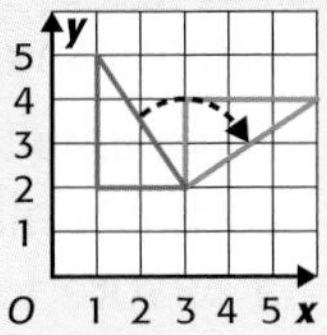

Hands-On Mini Activity c. $A(5, 4)$, $B(5, 8)$, $C(7, 8)$

A triangle has vertices $A(5, 4)$, $B(1, 4)$, and $C(1, 6)$. Draw a coordinate grid on graph paper. Copy the triangle.

a. With a different colored pencil, graph points *A*, *B*, and *C* after they are rotated 90° clockwise about point *A*. a–b. See graph.

b. Connect the points.

c. What are the vertices of the image?

(Graph: y-axis 1–9, x-axis 1–9, points B, C, A, 90°)

To check the new vertices, use tracing paper. Trace the original triangle. Then turn it to see if it is congruent to the new triangle.

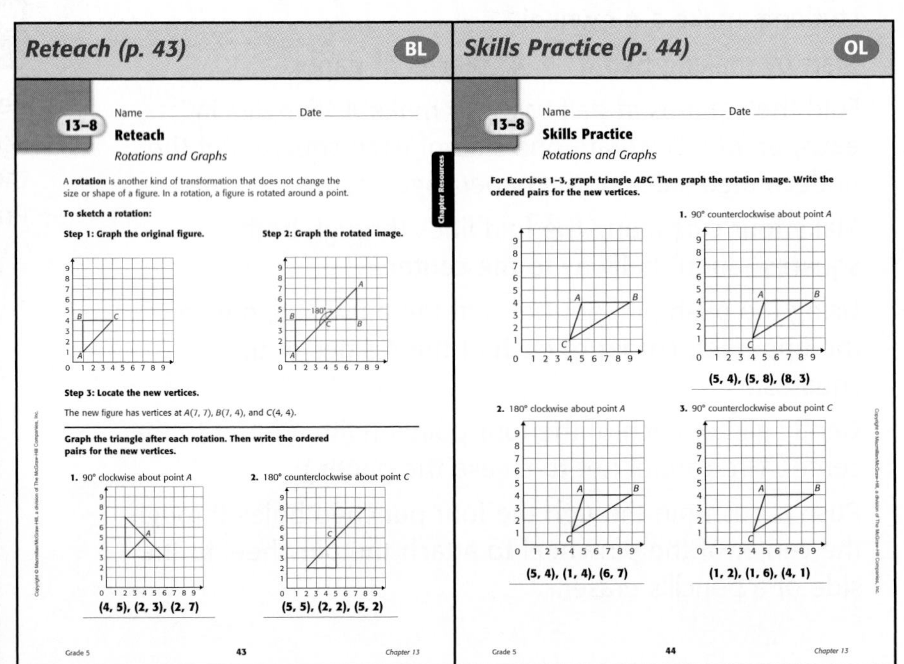

Reteach (p. 43) BL

13-8 Name ______ Date ______

Reteach

Rotations and Graphs

A **rotation** is another kind of transformation that does not change the size or shape of a figure. In a rotation, a figure is rotated around a point.

To sketch a rotation:

Step 1: Graph the original figure.

Step 2: Graph the rotated image.

Step 3: Locate the new vertices.

The new figure has vertices at *A*(7, 7), *B*(7, 4), and *C*(4, 4).

Graph the triangle after each rotation. Then write the ordered pairs for the new vertices.

1. 90° clockwise about point *A* — **(4, 5), (2, 3), (2, 7)**
2. 180° counterclockwise about point *C* — **(5, 5), (2, 2), (5, 2)**

Grade 5 — 43 — Chapter 13

Skills Practice (p. 44) OL

13-8 Name ______ Date ______

Skills Practice

Rotations and Graphs

For Exercises 1–3, graph triangle *ABC*. Then graph the rotation image. Write the ordered pairs for the new vertices.

1. 90° counterclockwise about point *A* — **(5, 4), (5, 8), (8, 3)**
2. 180° clockwise about point *A* — **(5, 4), (1, 4), (6, 7)**
3. 90° counterclockwise about point *C* — **(1, 2), (1, 6), (4, 1)**

Grade 5 — 44 — Chapter 13

EXAMPLE Sketch a Rotation

1 **A triangle has vertices *G*(1, 1), *H*(5, 4), and *J*(5, 1). Graph the triangle. Then graph its rotation 180° clockwise about point *H*. Write the ordered pairs for the new vertices.**

Step 1 Graph the original triangle.

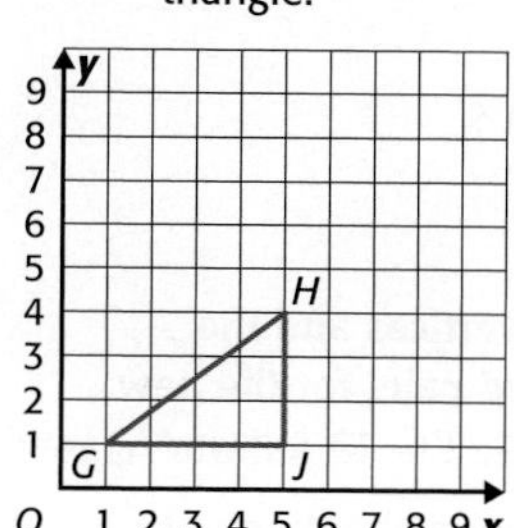

Step 2 Graph the rotated image.

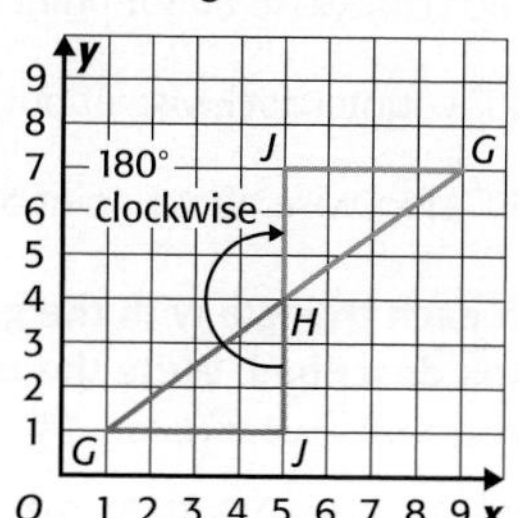

The ordered pairs for the new vertices are *G*(9, 7), *H*(5, 4), and *J*(5, 7).

CHECK What You Know

Graph the triangle after each rotation about point *P*. Then write the ordered pairs for the new vertices.

See Example 1 (p. 587) 1–2. See Ch. 13 Answer Appendix.

1. 90° clockwise

2. 180° counterclockwise

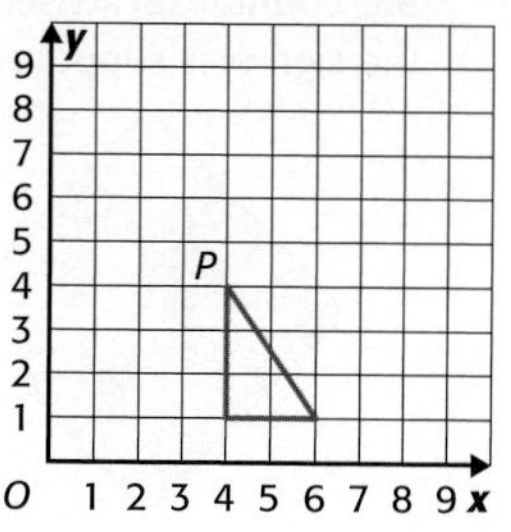

Graph each triangle with the given vertices and the rotation described. Write the ordered pairs for the new vertices.

See Example 1 (p. 587) 3–4. See Ch. 13 Answer Appendix.

3. *L*(5, 5), *M*(5, 2), *N*(1, 5); 90° counterclockwise about point *L*

4. *A*(6, 5), *B*(6, 9), *C*(9, 8); 180° clockwise about point *A*

5. Name two lowercase letters that are transformations of the letter b. Describe the transformation. d: reflection; p: rotation

6. Talk About It Explain the differences between a rotation and reflection. Sample answer: In a rotation, a figure is turned about a point. In a reflection, a figure is flipped over a line.

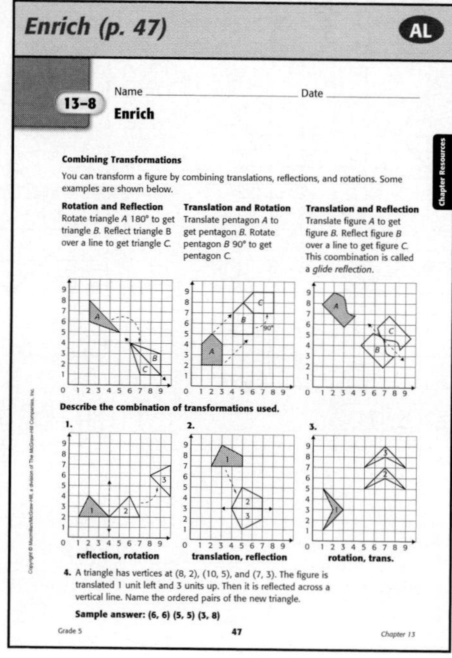

Enrich (p. 47) AL

13–8 Name ______ Date ______

Enrich

Chapter Resources

Combining Transformations

You can transform a figure by combining translations, reflections, and rotations. Some examples are shown below.

Rotation and Reflection Rotate triangle *A* 180° to get triangle *B*. Reflect triangle B over a line to get triangle *C*.

Translation and Rotation Translate pentagon *A* to get pentagon *B*. Rotate pentagon *B* 90° to get pentagon *C*.

Translation and Reflection Translate figure *A* to get figure *B*. Reflect figure *B* over a line to get figure *C*. This coombination is called a *glide reflection*.

Describe the combination of transformations used.

1. reflection, rotation

2. translation, reflection

3. rotation, trans.

4. A triangle has vertices at (8, 2), (10, 5), and (7, 3). The figure is translated 1 unit left and 3 units up. Then it is reflected across a vertical line. Name the ordered pairs of the new triangle.

Sample answer: (6, 6) (5, 5) (3, 8)

Grade 5 47 Chapter 13

Sketch a Rotation

Example 1 Be sure students understand that they must choose one of the sides of the figure and then sketch the rotation in relation to that side. They will identify the orientation of the image of the chosen side after the rotation. Each of the vertices of the image can be graphed based on their relationship to the vertices in the original figure.

ADDITIONAL EXAMPLES

1 Triangle *ABC* has vertices at *A*(3, 8), *B*(1, 5), and *C*(5, 5). Graph $\triangle ABC$ and its rotation 90° clockwise about point *C*. Write the ordered pair for the new vertices.

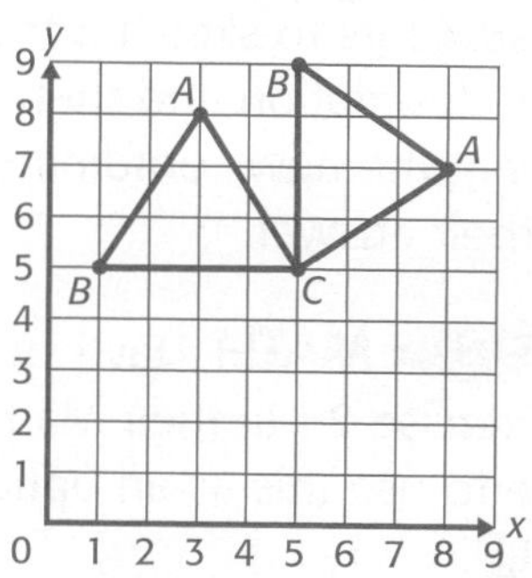

A(8, 7), *B*(5, 9), *C*(5, 5)

CHECK What You Know

As a class, have students complete Exercises 1–6 in **Check What You Know** as you observe their work.

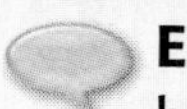

Exercise 6 Assess student comprehension before assigning practice exercises.

BL Alternate Teaching Strategy

If students have trouble sketching rotations on a coordinate grid...

Then use one of these reteach options:

1 CRM **Daily Reteach Worksheet** (p. 43)

2 Have students trace a triangle pattern block on grid paper with one side labeled $\overline{AB}$ on a horizontal line and the opposite vertex labeled *C* pointing up. Ask students to draw a line perpendicular to the horizontal side of the triangle through *C*.

- **How many degrees are in the angle you drew?** 90°
- Tell students that the line they drew is where $\overline{AB}$ will be after a 90° clockwise rotation.
- Have them rotate their triangle. Have students trace the triangle to see the rotation.

3 Practice

Differentiate practice using these leveled assignments for Exercises 7–24.

Level	Assignment
BL Below/ Approaching Level	7–9, 11–13, 16, 19–21, 24
OL On Level	7–13, 15, 17, 20–21, 24
AL Above/Beyond Level	8–20 even, 22–24

Have students discuss and complete the Higher Order Thinking problems. For Exercise 23, encourage students to sketch a triangle that matches the description and then rotate it until the vertex is at the new coordinates given before explaining their answer.

WRITING IN ▸MATH Have students complete Exercise 24 in their Math Journals. You may choose to use this as an optional formative assessment.

Additional Answers

7.

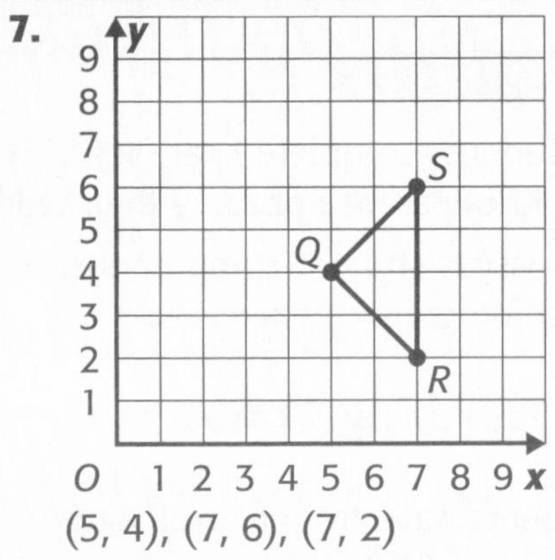

(5, 4), (7, 6), (7, 2)

8.

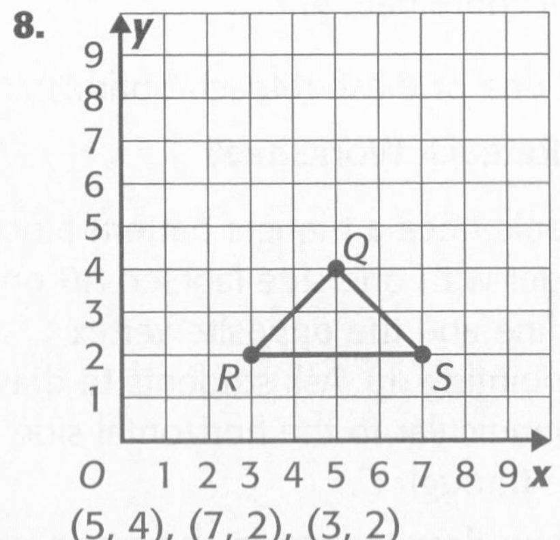

(5, 4), (7, 2), (3, 2)

! COMMON ERROR!

Exercises 7–14 Students may have trouble remembering which way is clockwise or counterclockwise. Suggest students look at the hands of a clock. Clockwise is the same direction the hands on a clock move.

Practice and Problem Solving

EXTRA PRACTICE See page R36.

Graph the triangle after each rotation. Then write the ordered pairs for the new vertices. See Example 1 (p. 587)

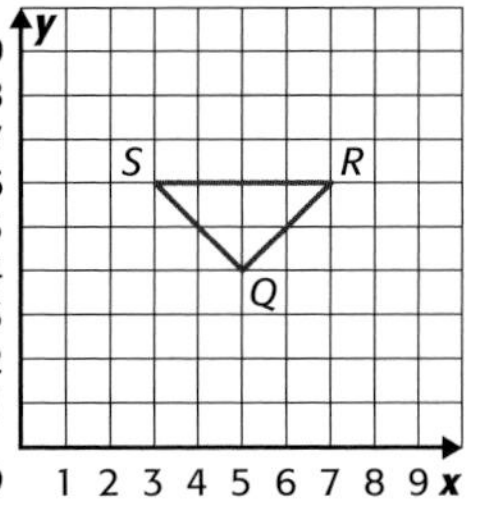

7. 90° clockwise about point Q 7–10. See margin.

8. 180° clockwise about point Q

9. 90° counterclockwise about point S

10. 90° clockwise about point S

Graph each triangle with the given vertices and the rotation described. Write the ordered pairs for the new vertices. See Example 1 (p. 587) 11–15. See Ch. 13 Answer Appendix.

11. $J(7, 2)$, $K(5, 2)$, $L(5, 5)$; 90° clockwise about point L

12. $T(5, 5)$, $U(4, 8)$, $V(9, 8)$; 180° counterclockwise about point T

13. $L(1, 4)$, $M(5, 1)$, $N(5, 3)$; 90° counterclockwise about point L

14. $W(2, 7)$, $X(2, 1)$, $Y(0, 8)$; 90° clockwise about point X

15. The sign was incorrectly rotated 90° counterclockwise. Sketch how the sign was supposed to look.

16. Geometry Describe the transformation of the letter F shown below. rotation 180°

17. Sample answer: The triangle is translated 1 unit left and 3 units down. It is then rotated 90° counterclockwise about the point at (3, 3).

★**17.** A triangle with vertices at (4, 6), (8, 6), and (7, 8) is transformed so that the new vertices are at (3, 3), (7, 3), and (6, 5). Then that figure is transformed so that the final figure has vertices at (3, 3), (3, 7), and (1, 6). Describe the transformations.

★**18.** A rectangular trampoline at (2, 4), (2, 9), (5, 9) and (5, 4) is being moved to a new location. The corner at (2, 4) becomes the corner at (2, 4). The corner at (2, 9) becomes the corner at (7, 4). Describe the type of move made for the trampoline. Name the new location of the other two corners. Include a drawing. See Ch. 13 Answer Appendix.

9.

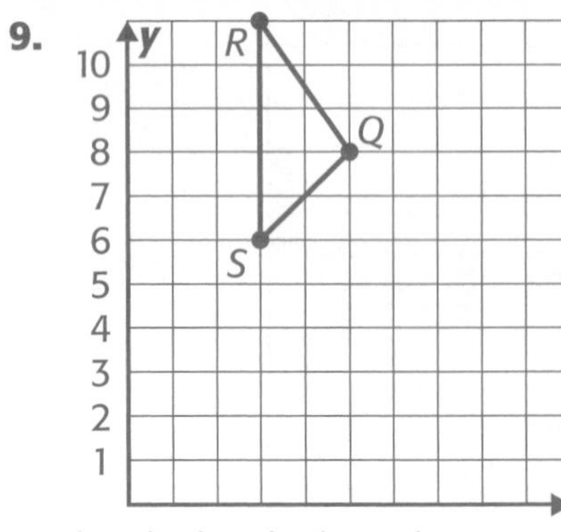

(3, 6), (5, 8), (3, 10)

10.

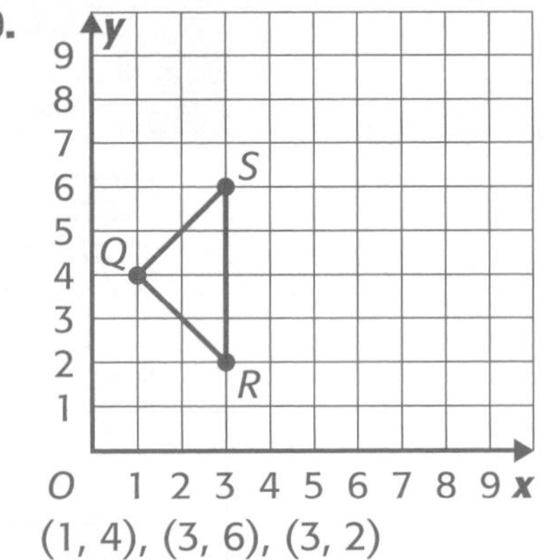

(1, 4), (3, 6), (3, 2)

Real-World PROBLEM SOLVING

Science Some objects in nature have *rotational symmetry*. This means that if they are rotated less than 360°, they look the same as in their original position. An example is the snowflake shown below.

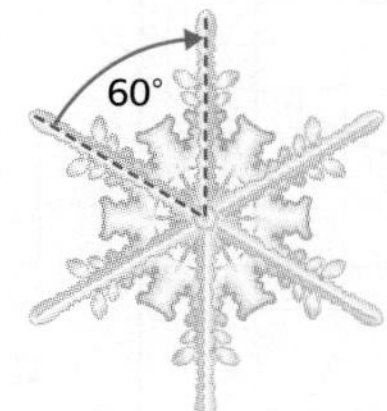

Determine whether each object has rotational symmetry. Write *yes* or *no*.

19. starfish yes 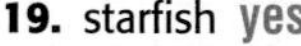

20. clover yes 

21. dragonfly no

H.O.T. Problems

22. OPEN ENDED Draw a figure on a coordinate plane. Then draw the figure after it is rotated 180° clockwise. Describe the coordinates of the point around which the figure was rotated. See margin.

23. NUMBER SENSE A triangle graphed on the coordinate plane has a vertex at (0, 9). What type of rotation would move the vertex to (9, 0)? Explain your reasoning. A rotation 90° clockwise about the point at (0, 0); the *y*-axis and *x*-axis are perpendicular.

24. WRITING IN ▸MATH Rotate the original figure that you drew in Exercise 22 180° counterclockwise. Describe the difference between rotating a figure 180° clockwise and 180° counterclockwise. Both rotations give the same result.

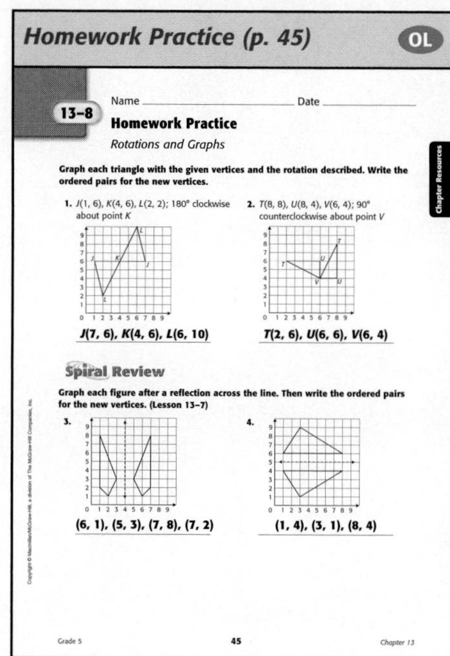

Homework Practice (p. 45) OL

13–8 Name ______ Date ______

Homework Practice

Rotations and Graphs

Graph each triangle with the given vertices and the rotation described. Write the ordered pairs for the new vertices.

1. *J*(1, 6), *K*(4, 6), *L*(2, 2); 180° clockwise about point *K*

***J*(7, 6), *K*(4, 6), *L*(6, 10)**

2. *T*(8, 8), *U*(8, 4), *V*(6, 4); 90° counterclockwise about point *V*

***T*(2, 6), *U*(6, 6), *V*(6, 4)**

Spiral Review

Graph each figure after a reflection across the line. Then write the ordered pairs for the new vertices. (Lesson 13–7)

3. **(6, 1), (5, 3), (7, 8), (7, 2)**

4. **(1, 4), (3, 1), (8, 4)**

Chapter Resources

Copyright © Macmillan/McGraw-Hill, a division of The McGraw-Hill Companies, Inc.

Grade 5 45 *Chapter 13*

Assess

Formative Assessment

Write the following ordered pairs on the board: *R*(1, 1), *S*(7, 3), *T*(3, 3).

- **How would you find the vertices of triangle *RST* if it were rotated 90° clockwise around point *S*?** Graph the ordered pairs and sketch the triangle. Then draw a line perpendicular to $\overline{TS}$ at point *S*. Place the image of vertex *T* four units above vertex *S* and place the image of vertex *R* two units left and two units up from vertex *T*.
- **What are the ordered pairs for the new vertices?** *R*(5, 9), *S*(7, 3), *T*(7, 7)

Quick Check **Are students continuing to struggle with sketching rotations on a coordinate grid?**

If Yes → Small Group Options (p. 586B)

If No → Independent Work Options (p. 586B)
CRM Skills Practice Worksheet (p. 44)
CRM Enrich Worksheet (p. 47)

Into the Future Based on what they have learned about transformations thus far, students write a short paragraph telling what they think they will learn tomorrow. Encourage them to pose a question that they might have to answer.

Additional Answer

22. Sample answer:

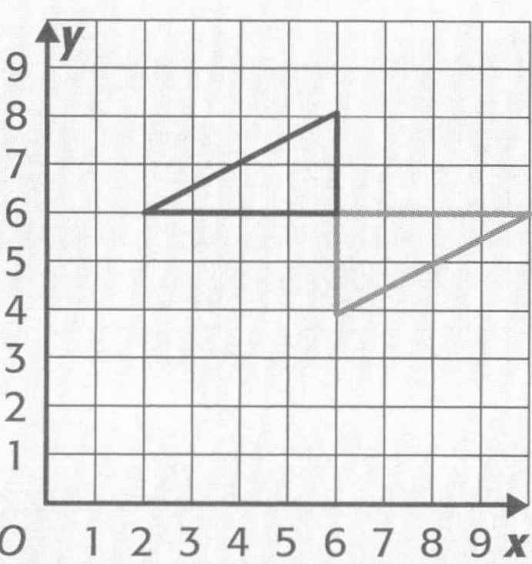

Reviews Lessons 13-7 and 13-8

Assign the Test Practice problems to provide daily reinforcement of test-taking skills.

Spiral Review

Reviews Lessons 11-1, 12-6, 13-6, and 13-7

Review and assess mastery of skills and concepts from previous chapters.

Additional Answers

27.

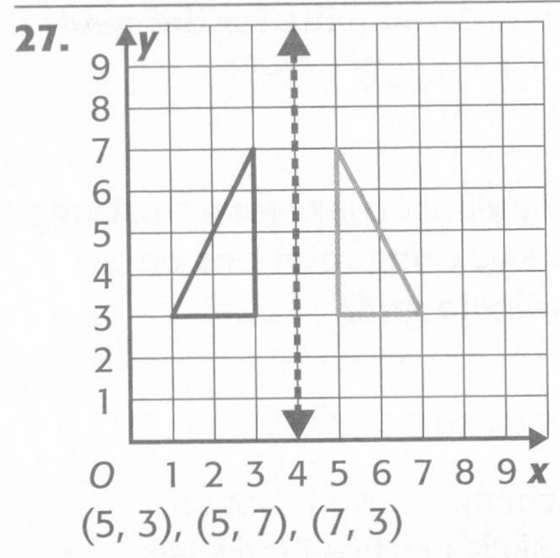

(5, 3), (5, 7), (7, 3)

28.

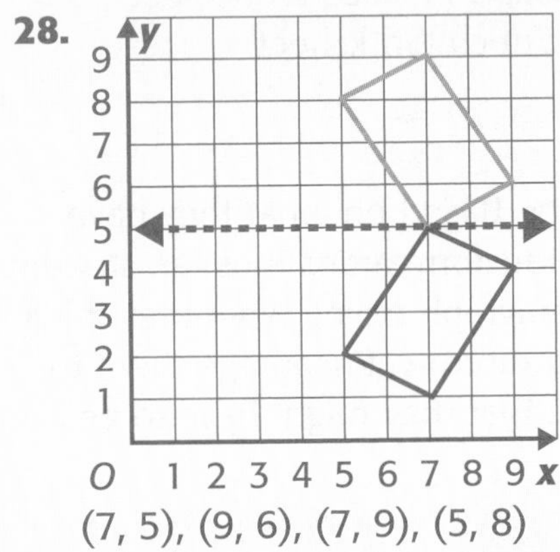

(7, 5), (9, 6), (7, 9), (5, 8)

29.

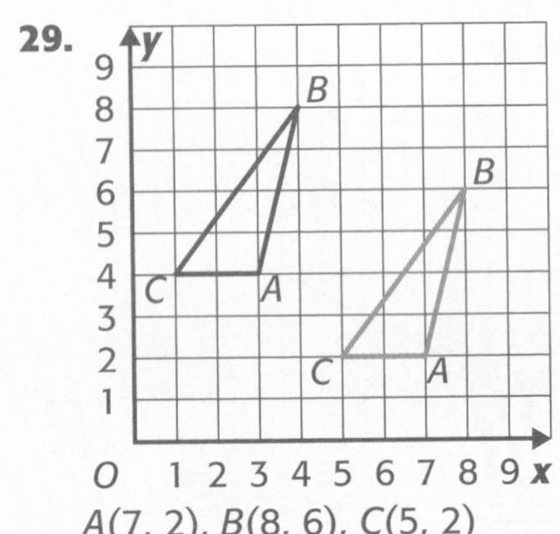

$A(7, 2)$, $B(8, 6)$, $C(5, 2)$

25. Which of these does NOT show a reflection? (Lesson 13-7) B

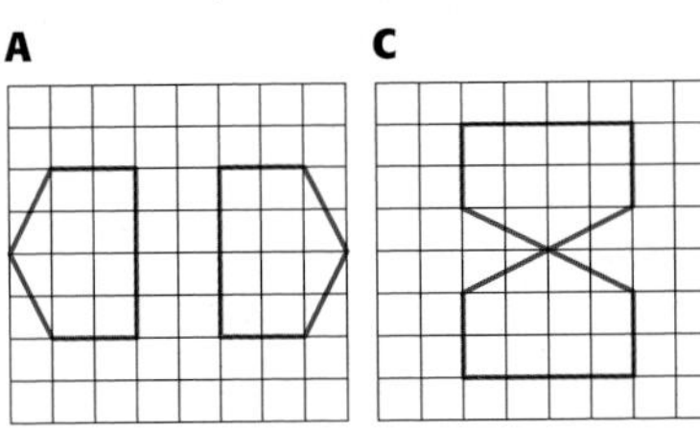

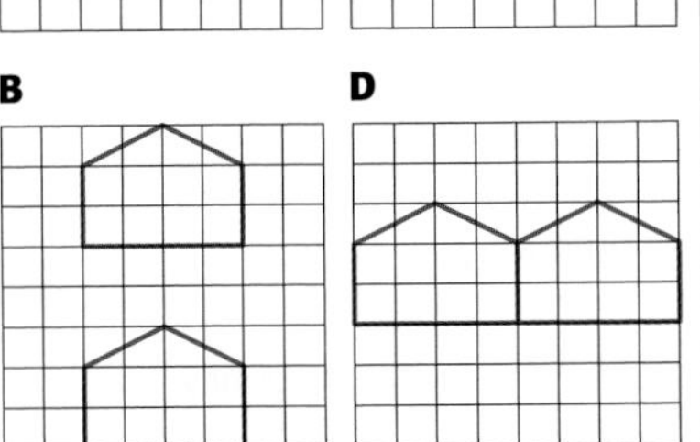

26. Which represents a rotation of the shaded figure? (Lesson 13-8) J

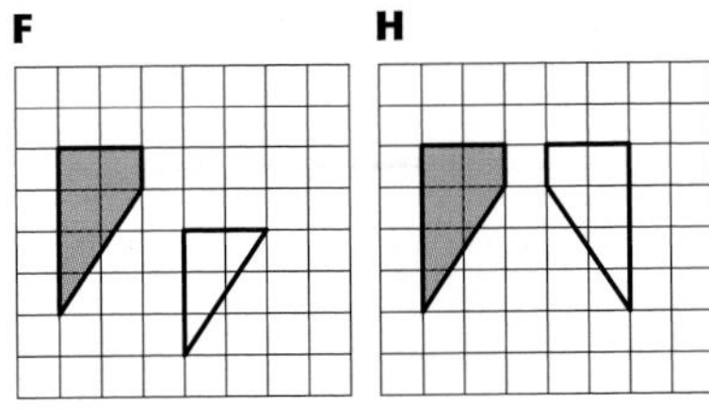

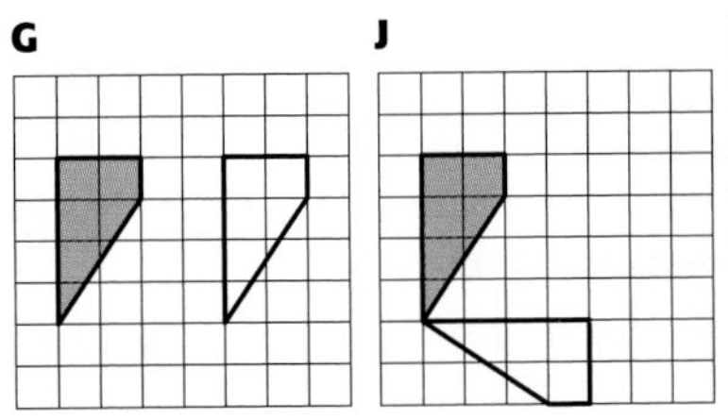

Spiral Review

Graph each figure after a reflection across the line. Then write the ordered pairs for the vertices of the image. (Lesson 13-7) 27–29. See margin.

27.

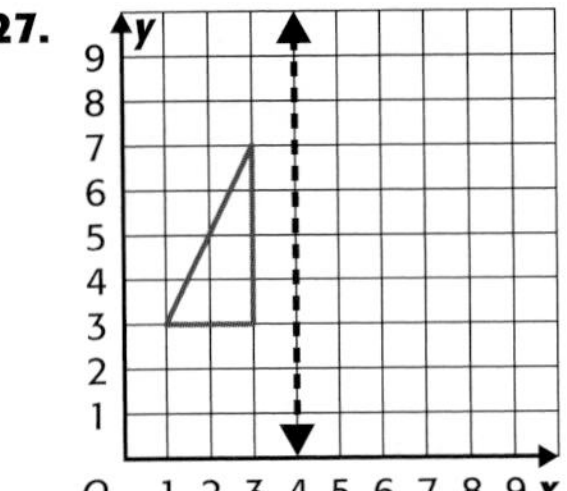

28.

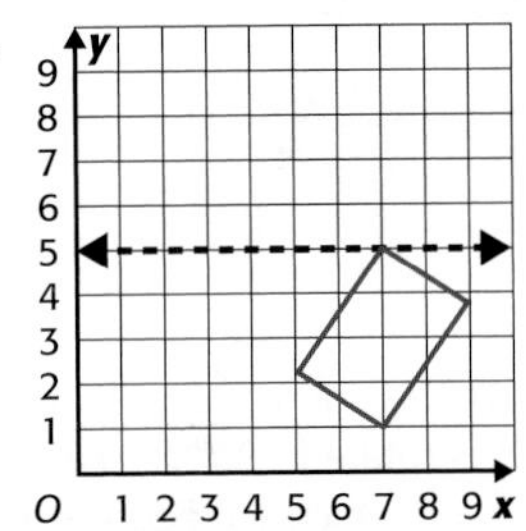

29. Graph triangle *ABC* with vertices $A(3, 4)$, $B(4, 8)$, and $C(1, 4)$. Then graph the triangle after it is translated 4 units right and 2 units down. Write the ordered pairs for the new vertices. (Lesson 13-6)

30. Suppose today's forecast says it will be 10°C. Could you go on a picnic? Explain your reasoning. (Lesson 12-6) No; 10°C is just a few degrees above the freezing point of water.

Complete. (Lesson 11-1)

31. 36 in. = ■ ft 3

32. 15 ft = ■ yd 5

33. 4 ft = ■ in. 48

LESSON 13-9

Identify Transformations

Lesson Planner

Objective

Identify transformations.

Review Vocabulary

transformations, translation, reflection, rotation

Resources

Materials: grid paper, tracing paper, pencils

Literature Connection: *Geometry* by Lucille Caron and Philip M. St. Jacques

Teacher Technology

TeacherWorks • Interactive Classroom

Focus on Math Background

Students should be able to state whether a given transformation of a figure is a translation, reflection, or rotation. In some cases, more than one type of transformation can result in the same change. This is especially true for figures that contain many lines of symmetry. For example, the rectangle with unlabeled vertices on the left below can be transformed into the rectangle on the right by a translation, by a reflection, or by a rotation.

In a more involved example, the triangle at the left below can be transformed into the triangle at the right either by a single rotation, or by a sequence of two reflections, or by a translation followed by a rotation, etc.

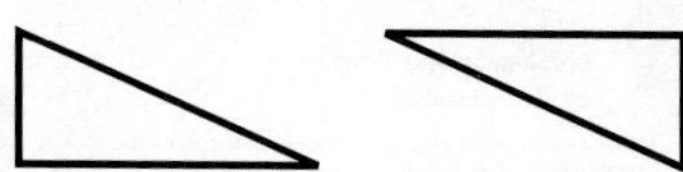

Transformations like those studied in this chapter are at the heart of all work involving computer graphics.

Daily Routine

Use these suggestions before beginning the lesson on p. 591.

5-Minute Check

(Reviews Lesson 13-8)

Graph the triangle after the rotation. Then write the ordered pairs for the new vertices.

1. 90° clockwise about point S

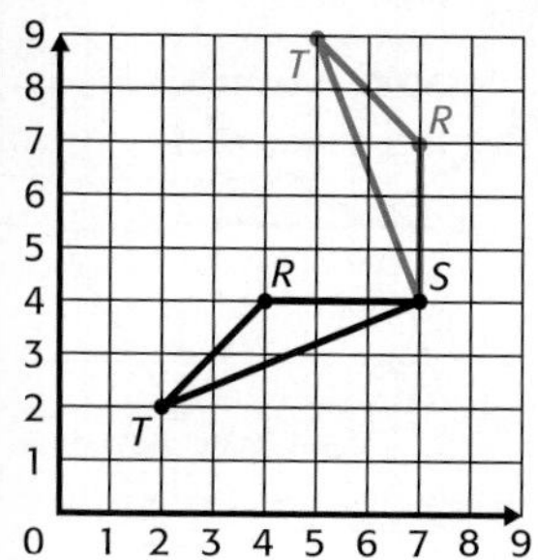

Problem of the Day

The sum of a number and the same number multiplied by itself is 72. What is the number? Show how you found your answer. 8; $8 + (8 \times 8) = 72$

Building Math Vocabulary

Write the review vocabulary words and their definitions on the board.

Have students work together to make a list of how a figure and its image are alike and different after each type of transformation has been performed. Include their correct ideas on a class chart as a reference.

Differentiated Instruction

Small Group Options

Option 1 Gifted and Talented AL

SPATIAL

Materials: graph paper

- Challenge students to design a triangle pattern on graph paper that uses different transformations.
- Label each transformation, rotation, or relfection.

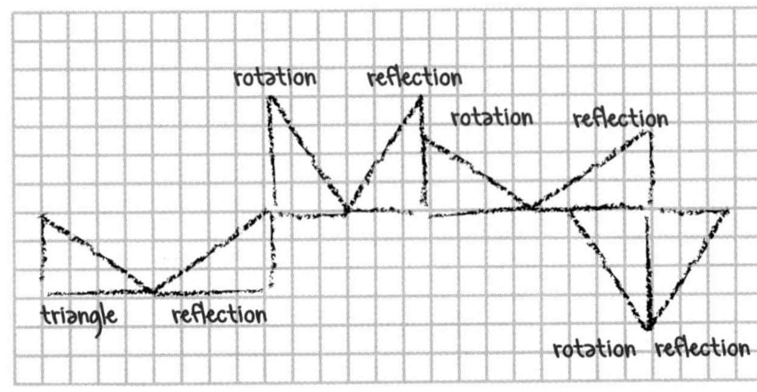

Option 2 English Language Learners ELL

KINESTHETIC

Materials: paper, pencils
Core Vocabulary: slide, turn, flip
Common Use Verb: move

Do Math This strategy uses kinesthetic movement to integrate understanding of transformation, rotation and reflection.

- In groups of three, have students construct a "machine" that will show how to turn, flip or slide items.
- Students can use their bodies or classroom objects to demonstrate their "machine" to the class.

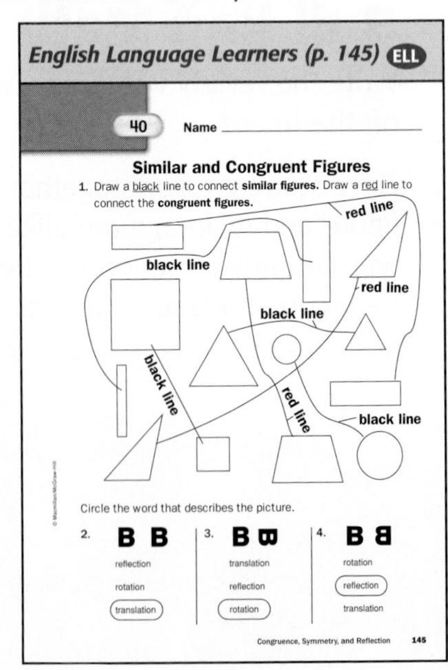

English Language Learners (p. 145) ELL

40 Name ______

Similar and Congruent Figures

1. Draw a black line to connect **similar figures.** Draw a red line to connect the **congruent figures.**

Circle the word that describes the picture.

2. B B — reflection / rotation / (translation)
3. B ꓭ — translation / reflection / (rotation)
4. B ꓤ — rotation / (reflection) / translation

Congruence, Symmetry, and Reflection 145

Use this worksheet to provide additional support for English Language Learners.

Independent Work Options

Option 1 Early Finishers AL

LINGUISTIC

Materials: grid paper, pencils, paper

- Ask students to draw a coordinate grid on each of 3 grid papers. Have them sketch figures showing translation on one paper and reflection and rotation on the other two. Student exchange papers.
- Students write one sentence for each sketch telling how they know that the sketch is either a translation, reflection or a rotation. Have students check for correct answers.

Option 2 Student Technology

Tech Link

Math Online macmillanmh.com

Personal Tutor • Extra Examples

Option 3 Learning Station: Writing (p. 554G)

Direct students to the Writing Learning Station for opportunities to explore and extend the lesson concept.

Option 4 Problem-Solving Practice

Reinforce problem-solving skills and strategies with the Problem-Solving Practice worksheet.

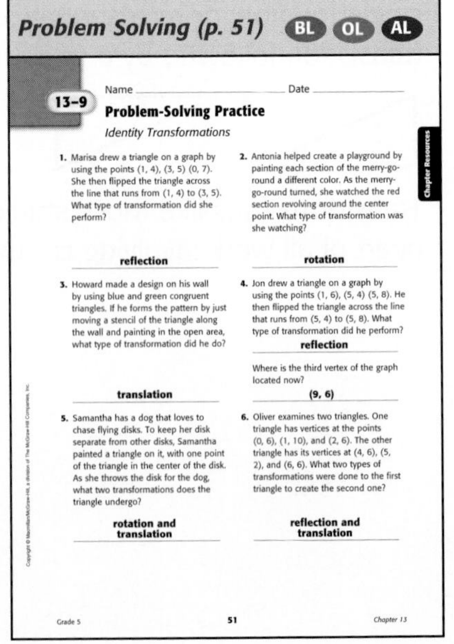

Problem Solving (p. 51) BL OL AL

13–9 Name ______ Date ______

Problem-Solving Practice

Identity Transformations

1. Marisa drew a triangle on a graph by using the points (1, 4), (3, 5) (0, 7). She then flipped the triangle across the line that runs from (1, 4) to (3, 5). What type of transformation did she perform?
reflection

2. Antonia helped create a playground by painting each section of the merry-go-round a different color. As the merry-go-round turned, she watched the red section revolving around the center point. What type of transformation was she watching?
rotation

3. Howard made a design on his wall by using blue and green congruent triangles. If he forms the pattern by just moving a stencil of the triangle along the wall and painting in the open area, what type of transformation did he do?
translation

4. Jon drew a triangle on a graph by using the points (1, 6), (5, 4) (5, 8). He then flipped the triangle across the line that runs from (5, 4) to (5, 8). What type of transformation did he perform?
reflection
Where is the third vertex of the graph located now?
(9, 6)

5. Samantha has a dog that loves to chase flying disks. To keep her disk separate from other disks, Samantha painted a triangle on it, with one point of the triangle in the center of the disk. As she throws the disk for the dog, what two transformations does the triangle undergo?
rotation and translation

6. Oliver examines two triangles. One triangle has vertices at the points (0, 6), (1, 10), and (2, 6). The other triangle has its vertices at (4, 6), (5, 2), and (6, 6). What two types of transformations were done to the first triangle to create the second one?
reflection and translation

Chapter Resources

Grade 5 51 Chapter 13

13-9 Identify Transformations

MAIN IDEA

I will identify transformations.

Math Online

macmillanmh.com

- Extra Examples
- Personal Tutor
- Self-Check Quiz

GET READY to Learn

Many decorative patterns are made using translations, reflections, or rotations. The pattern at the right could be made by reflecting or rotating the portion of the design in the black triangle.

EXAMPLE Identify a Transformation

1 **Determine whether the transformation shown below is a *translation*, *reflection*, or *rotation*.**

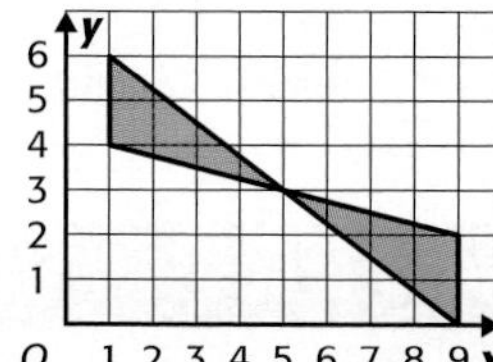

The triangle has been turned about the point at (4, 3) to a new position.

So, this is a rotation.

Real-World EXAMPLE Identify a Transformation

2 **ART** **What transformation could be used to create the design?**

The top and bottom half are mirror images of each other. So, a reflection across a horizontal line is one way to create the design.

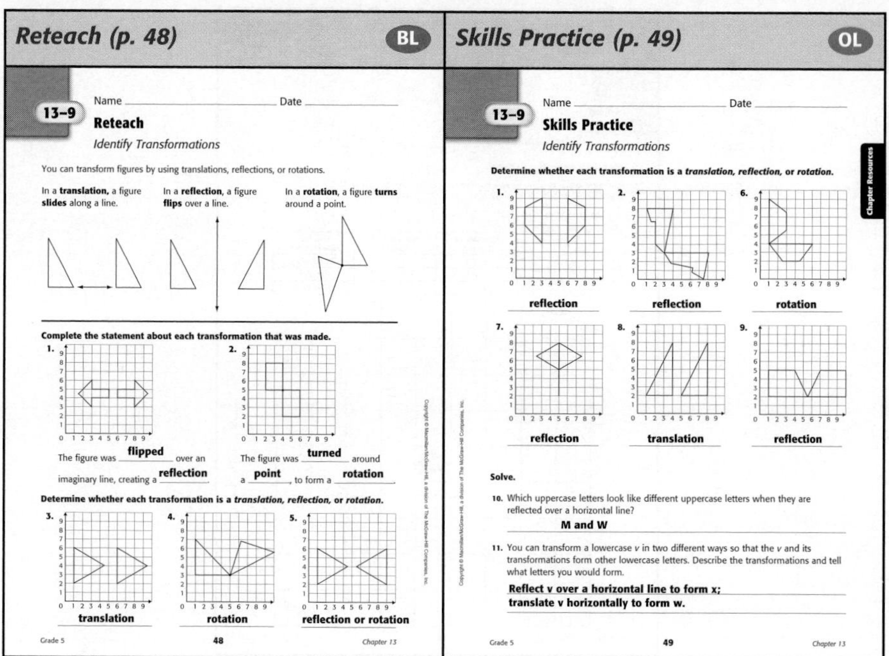

Reteach (p. 48) BL

13-9 Name ______ Date ______

Reteach

Identify Transformations

You can transform figures by using translations, reflections, or rotations.

In a **translation,** a figure **slides** along a line.

In a **reflection**, a figure **flips** over a line.

In a **rotation**, a figure **turns** around a point.

Complete the statement about each transformation that was made.

1. The figure was **flipped** over an imaginary line, creating a **reflection**.

2. The figure was **turned** around a **point** to form a **rotation**.

Determine whether each transformation is a *translation, reflection,* or *rotation*.

3. **translation**
4. **rotation**
5. **reflection or rotation**

Grade 5 | 48 | *Chapter 13*

Skills Practice (p. 49) OL

13-9 Name ______ Date ______

Skills Practice

Identify Transformations

Determine whether each transformation is a *translation, reflection,* or *rotation*.

1. **reflection**
2. **reflection**
6. **rotation**
7. **reflection**
8. **translation**
9. **reflection**

Solve.

10. Which uppercase letters look like different uppercase letters when they are reflected over a horizontal line?
M and W

11. You can transform a lowercase *v* in two different ways so that the *v* and its transformations form other lowercase letters. Describe the transformations and tell what letters you would form.
Reflect v over a horizontal line to form x; translate v horizontally to form w.

Grade 5 | 49 | *Chapter 13*

Chapter Resources

13-9 Identify Transformations

1 Introduce

Activity Choice 1 • Hands-On

- Ask students to graph the following ordered pairs (1, 3), (3, 1), (4, 3) and connect on a coordinate plane. **What would the translation of the triangle up 4 units look like?** It has the same shape and size with the vertices of the image 4 units up from the original figure.
- **Sketch the triangle reflected across a horizontal line drawn at 3 on the *y*-axis. Describe the image.** A triangle with vertices at (1, 3), (3, 5), and (4, 3).
- **Compare the two transformed figures.** They are in different places. They are reflections of each other.
- **Sketch a 90° clockwise rotation of the original figure. Describe the image.** The longer side of the image is perpendicular to the longer side of the original triangle. It has vertices at (2, 4), (4, 3), and (4, 6).

Activity Choice 2 • Literature

Introduce the lesson with *Geometry* by Lucille Caron and Philip M. St. Jacques. For a related math activity, see p. TR58.

2 Teach

Scaffolding Questions

Sketch a right triangle with vertices at (2, 4), (2, 1), and (4, 1) on a coordinate grid.

- **Describe an example of a translation of the triangle.** Sample answer: an image of the triangle having vertices at (5, 4), (5, 1), and (7, 1)
- **How can you tell if the triangle was translated or reflected?** It is translated when the image looks exactly like the original. It is reflected when it is a mirror image of the original.

GET READY to Learn

Have students open their books and read the information in **Get Ready to Learn**. Review **transformations, translations, reflection** and **rotation**. As a class, work through **Examples 1 and 2.**

Identify a Transformation

Example 1 Be sure students understand that either triangle can be used as the figure in the beginning position. Encourage students to think about what movement would be required in order to move one triangle to cover the other triangle.

ADDITIONAL EXAMPLES

1 Determine whether the transformation is a *translation*, *reflection*, or *rotation*. reflection

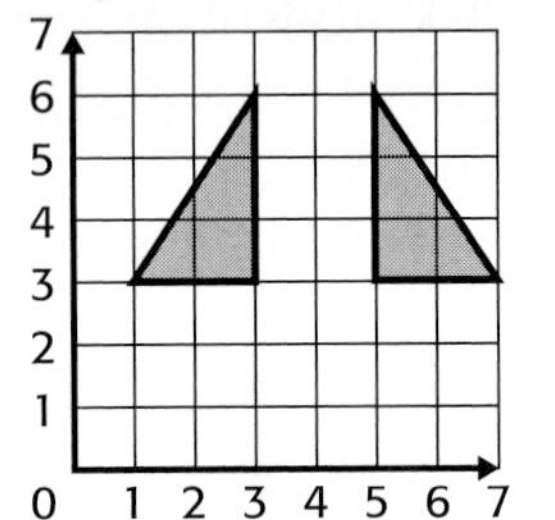

2 What transformation could be used to create the design? rotation

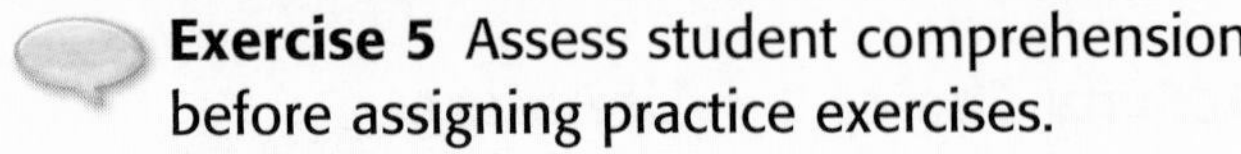

As a class, have students complete Exercises 1–5 in **Check What You Know** as you observe their work.

Exercise 5 Assess student comprehension before assigning practice exercises.

BL Alternate Teaching Strategy

If students have trouble identifying transformations...

Then use one of these reteach options:

1. CRM **Daily Reteach Worksheet** (p. 48)
2. Have students trace one figure on tracing paper and move the paper until it matches the second figure on the grid. Ask them what they had to do to match the figures. **Did you slide the tracing to match the figure? What kind of transformation is a slide? If you flipped the paper to match, what kind of transformation is that?** reflection **If you turned the tracing to match, what kind of transformation is that?** rotation

COMMON ERROR!

Exercise 13 Students may have trouble identifying transformations when more than one was used to create the image. Encourage students to sketch the possible transformation to see if they yield the final figure.

CHECK What You Know

Determine whether each transformation is a *translation, reflection,* or *rotation.* See Examples 1, 2 (p. 591)

1. 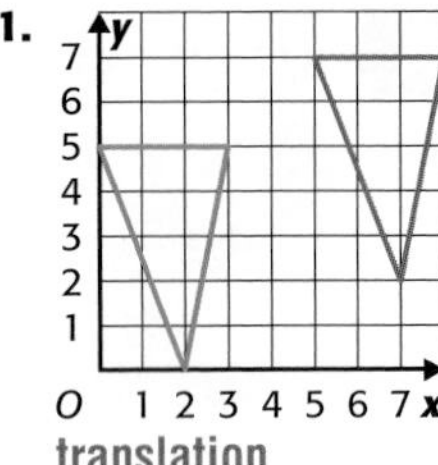
translation

2. 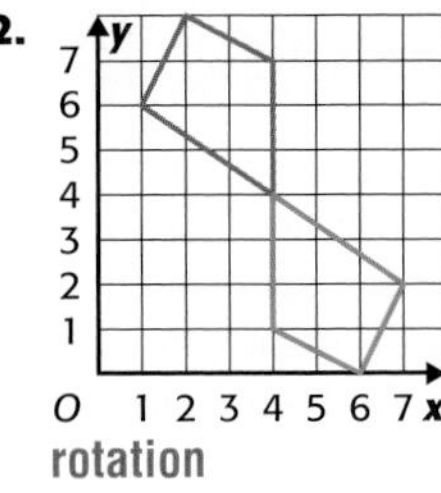
rotation

3. 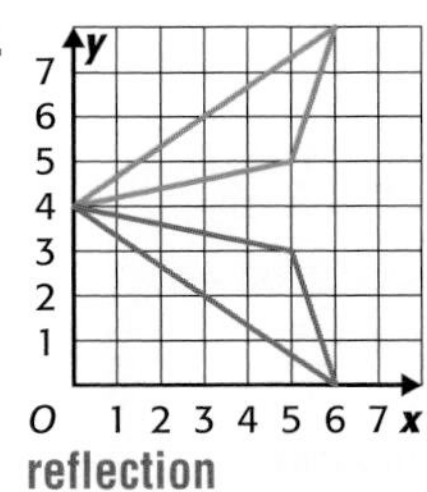
reflection

4. Which transformations appear in the pattern of bricks shown at the right? Sample answer: translations and rotations

5. **Talk About It** Describe how you could use a symmetrical shape on grid paper to show a translation, reflection, and rotation.
See Ch. 13 Answer Appendix.

Practice and Problem Solving

Determine whether each transformation is a *translation, reflection,* or *rotation.* See Examples 1, 2 (p. 591)

6. 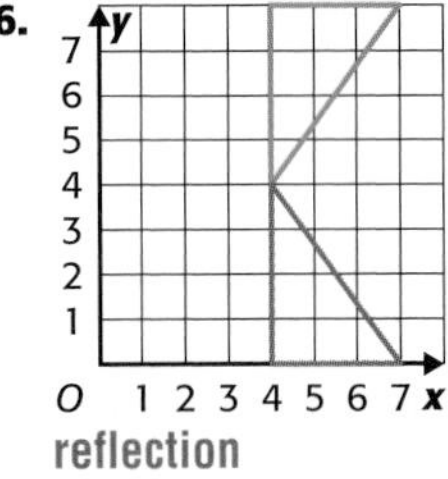
reflection

7. 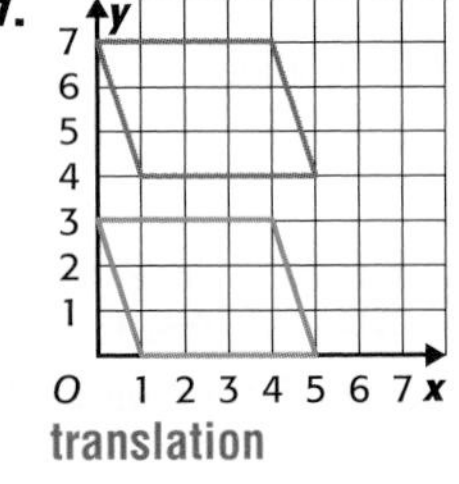
translation

8. 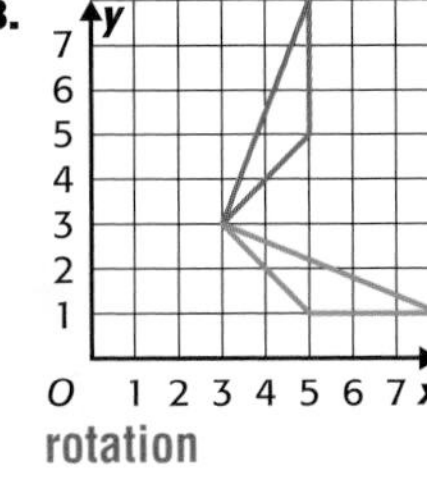
rotation

9. 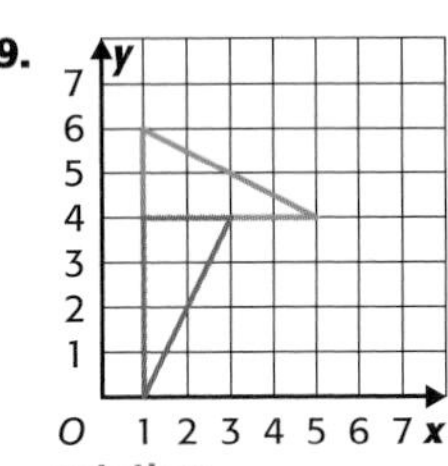
rotation

10. 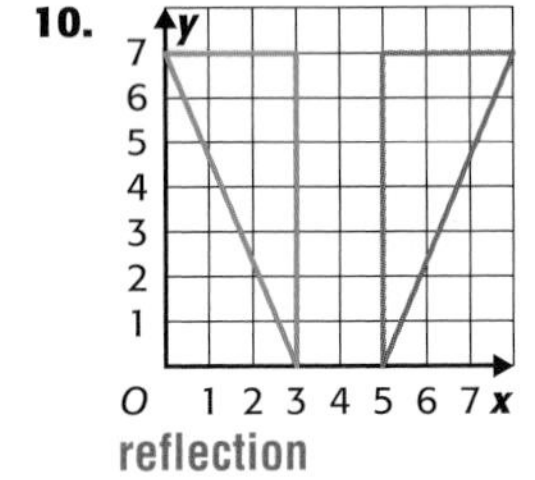
reflection

11. 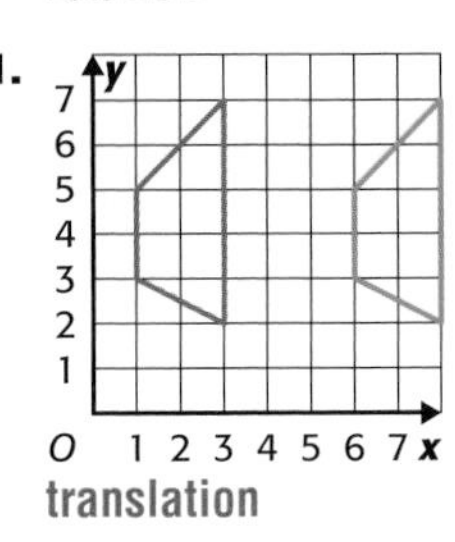
translation

Enrich (p. 52) AL

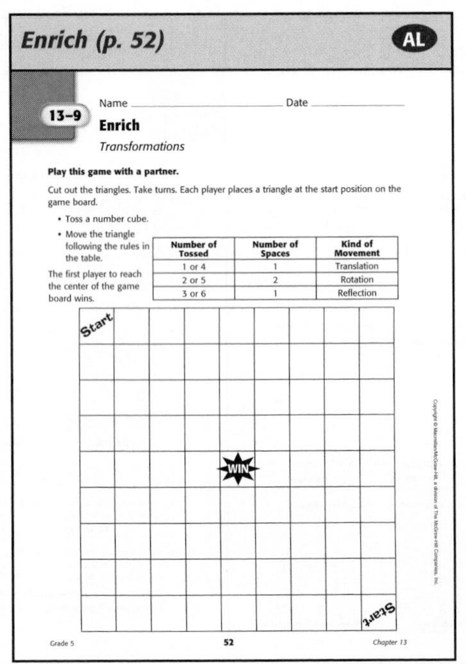

Name ________ Date ________

13-9 **Enrich**
Transformations

Play this game with a partner.

Cut out the triangles. Take turns. Each player places a triangle at the start position on the game board.

- Toss a number cube.
- Move the triangle following the rules in the table.

The first player to reach the center of the game board wins.

Number of Tossed	Number of Spaces	Kind of Movement
1 or 4	1	Translation
2 or 5	2	Rotation
3 or 6	1	Reflection

Grade 5 52 Chapter 13

12. Was a translation, reflection, or rotation used to create the pattern below? reflection

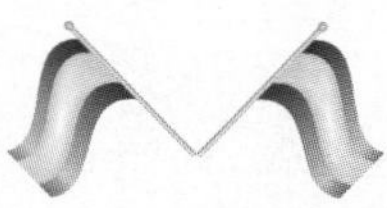

13. Two different transformations were used to change figure *A* to figure *B*. Describe them. Sample answer: A was translated to the right and reflected over a horizontal line.

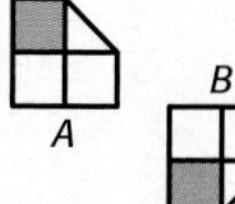

14. Analyze the pattern below. Which transformations could be used to create the design?

Sample answer: translations or reflections

15. Describe how you could use a transformation to complete the figure below.

Draw a reflection of the figure across a vertical line.

Data File

At the Michigan International Speedway, race car drivers travel around the 2-mile track at speeds of 200 miles per hour. Flags like the ones below are used in the race.

For Exercises 16–18, describe the transformations found in the patterns. 16–18. See Ch. 13 Answer Appendix.

16. End of Race

17. Faster Car is Approaching

18. Track is Slippery

H.O.T. Problems

19. **OPEN ENDED** Create a pattern using translations, reflections, and rotations. Describe the basic shape that you used and the transformations that you used. See students' work.

20. WRITING IN ▶MATH Write about a real-world situation that involves transformations. Describe the transformation that is used. Sample answer: When laying floor tile, translations and sometimes rotations may be used to form the pattern.

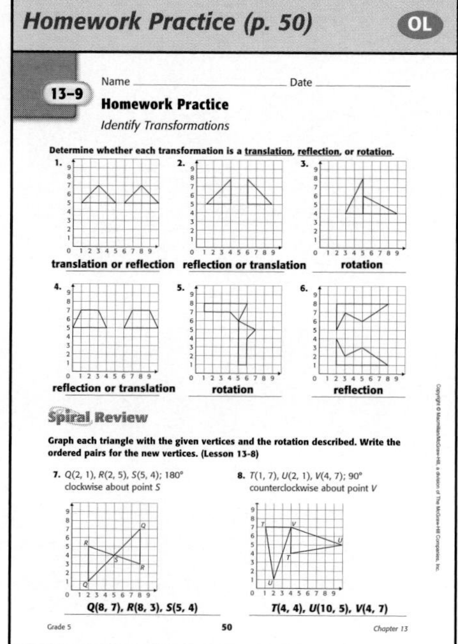

Homework Practice (p. 50) OL

13–9 Name ______ Date ______

Homework Practice

Identify Transformations

Determine whether each transformation is a translation, reflection, or rotation.

1. translation or reflection
2. reflection or translation
3. rotation
4. reflection or translation
5. rotation
6. reflection

Spiral Review

Graph each triangle with the given vertices and the rotation described. Write the ordered pairs for the new vertices. (Lesson 13-8)

7. *Q*(2, 1), *R*(2, 5), *S*(5, 4); 180° clockwise about point *S*

Q(8, 7), R(8, 3), S(5, 4)

8. *T*(1, 7), *U*(2, 1), *V*(4, 7); 90° counterclockwise about point *V*

T(4, 4), U(10, 5), V(4, 7)

Grade 5 50 Chapter 13

Copyright © Macmillan/McGraw-Hill, a division of The McGraw-Hill Companies, Inc.

3 Practice

Differentiate practice using these leveled assignments for Exercises 6–20.

Level	Assignment
BL Below/ Approaching Level	6–8, 12–13, 14, 20
OL On Level	8–17, 20
AL Above/Beyond Level	6–18 even, 19–20

Have students discuss and complete the Higher Order Thinking problems. For Exercise 19, encourage students to use one or two shapes of pattern blocks to create their design, being aware of the transformations they used.

WRITING IN ▶MATH Have students complete Exercise 20 in their Math Journals. You may choose to use this exercise as an optional formative assessment.

4 Assess

Formative Assessment

Present the following figures to students:

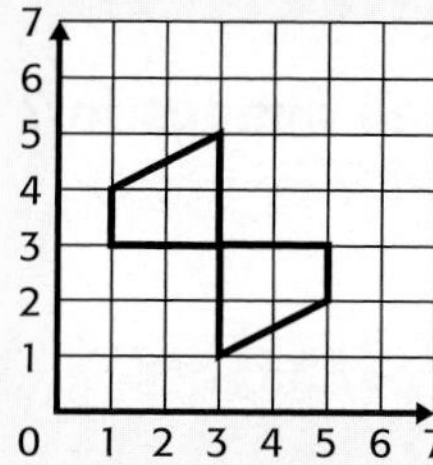

- **What type of transformation is illustrated in the figure? Explain.** Rotation; the first figure turned on a point to make the second figure.

Quick Check **Are students continuing to struggle with identifying transformations?**

If Yes → CRM Reteach Worksheet (p. 48)

If No → Independent Work Options (p. 591B)
CRM Skills Practice Worksheet (p. 49)
CRM Enrich Worksheet (p. 52)

Ticket Out the Door Write (2, 2), (4, 1), (5, 2) on the board. Graph the coordinate pairs, and sketch the triangle. Use red to sketch a translation, green to sketch a reflection, and blue to sketch a rotation.

Problem Solving

Lesson Planner

Objective

Interpret information and data from visual arts to solve problems.

National Standard 

Students will describe and place a variety of art objects in historical and cultural contexts.

Resources

Materials: paper, pencils

Activate Prior Knowledge

Before you turn students' attention to the pages, ask them to discuss Pompeii.

- **What happened in Pompeii?** A volcano buried the city.
- **What is Pompeii famous for?** People were buried frozen in their tracks.

Use the Student Page

Ask students to read the information on p. 594 and answer these questions:

- **How many squares surround the hexagon in this design?** 6
- **What are the measurements of the angles found in the triangles?** 60°

Problem Solving in Art

POMPEII PATTERNS

Pompeii was a popular vacation spot for wealthy members of the ancient Roman Empire. The city had houses that were designed in classic Roman style. This style was characterized by using a variety of geometrical shapes and patterns. Many of the houses included murals painted on the walls, decorative fountains, and patterned mosaic floors. In the year 79, nearby Mount Vesuvius erupted violently, spewing lava and ash throughout Pompeii. For 1,600 years, the city and its residents were lost under Mount Vesuvius' ashes. Today, scientists continue to uncover buildings and artworks at the site.

Did You Know?

The city of Pompeii was accidentally rediscovered by an Italian architect named Fontana in 1599.

Real-World Math

Use the image above of the design on a Pompeii building to solve each problem. 1–6. See margin.

1. Identify all of the geometric figures in the design.
2. Where do you see acute angles in the design?
3. Where do you see obtuse angles in the design?
4. Are there any right angles in the design? If so, where?
5. Where in the design do you see parallel lines?
6. Where in the design do you see perpendicular lines?
7. What can you tell about the triangles in the design? The triangles are equilateral.
8. Identify any transformations that could have been used to create the design. rotations, translations, and reflections.

Additional Answers

1. The perimeter of the design is a circle; the central figure is a hexagon; and the surrounding shapes include squares, triangles, and rhombi.
2. Acute angles are formed by the part of each rhombus facing into and away from the central hexagon.
3. Obtuse angles are formed by the part of each rhombus where it touches an adjacent square and triangle.
4. Yes, each corner of the squares are right angles.
5. Parallel lines are found on opposite sides of the squares and rhombi.
6. Perpendicular lines are formed in the squares where two sides meet.

Real-World Math

Assign the exercises on p. 595. Encourage students to choose a problem-solving strategy before beginning each exercise. If necessary, review the strategies suggested in Lesson 13-5, p. 577.

Exercise 1 Tell students that they do not need to describe anything outside the design.

Exercise 5 Remind students that parallel lines can be found in more than one shape.

WRITING IN MATH Have students create a word problem that uses the information found in the text and in the picture on pp. 594–595.

Extend the Activity

Have students measure the sides of the design, recreate the shapes and make their own design.

Chapter 13 Study Guide and Review

FOLDABLES Dinah Zike's Foldables

Use these lesson suggestions to incorporate the Foldable during the chapter. Students can then use their Foldables to review for the test.

Have students make a Ten-tab Vocabulary Foldable using one sheet of 8.5 × 11 notebook paper and label as shown. Students provide definitions of the terms beneath the tabs. Students can group related words under 1 tab. Ask students to discover and supply a new vocabulary word related to geometry and record the definition on the last tab. The Foldable can be used as a self-checking study aid to improve vocabulary recall.

Key Vocabulary

The page references after each word denote where that term was first introduced. If students have difficulty answering Exercises 1–5, remind them they can use the page references to review the vocabulary terms.

Vocabulary Review

Review chapter vocabulary using one of the following options.

- **Visual Vocabulary Cards** (19, 29, 30, 33, 37, 41)
- **eGlossary** at macmillanmh.com

Chapter 13 Study Guide and Review

FOLDABLES Study Organizer GET READY to Study

Be sure the following Big Ideas are written in your Foldable.

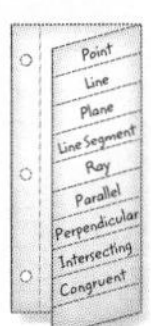

Key Concepts

Triangles

- Triangles can be classified by the lengths of their sides. (p. 566)

Triangle	Description
Isosceles	at least 2 sides congruent
Equilateral	all sides congruent
Scalene	no sides congruent

- Triangles can be classified by the measures of their angles. (p. 567)

Triangle	Description
Acute	3 acute angles
Right	1 right angle, 2 acute angles
Obtuse	1 obtuse angle, 2 acute angles

Quadrilaterals (p. 571)

- A parallelogram has both pairs of opposite sides parallel and congruent.
- Rectangles, rhombi, and squares are parallelograms.
- A trapezoid has exactly one pair of opposite sides parallel.

Transformations

- A **translation** is a slide. (p. 578)
- A **reflection** is a flip. (p. 582)
- A **rotation** is a turn. (p. 586)

Key Vocabulary

parallel lines (p. 558)
perpendicular lines (p. 558)
reflection (p. 582)
rotation (p. 586)
translation (p. 578)

Vocabulary Check

State whether each sentence is true or false. If false, replace the underlined word or number to make a true sentence.

1. In a rotation, a figure is moved without being turned or flipped. false; translation
2. Intersecting lines are lines that cross each other at right angles. false; perpendicular lines
3. Parallel lines always intersect. false; never
4. A rectangle has opposite sides congruent and parallel. true
5. A ray is a line that has one endpoint and goes on forever in one direction. true
6. Flipping a figure over a line to create a mirror image of the figure is called a reflection. true
7. A translation changes the size of the figure. false; does not change

 Chapter 13 Project

Identify It!

Alone, in pairs, or in small groups, have students discuss the results of their completed chapter project with the class. Assess their work using the Chapter Project rubric found in Chapter 13 Resource Masters, p. 63.

Lesson-by-Lesson Review

13-1 Geometry Vocabulary (pp. 557–560) 8. ray; $\overrightarrow{FG}$ 9. plane; plane *TUV*

Example 1
Identify the figure. Then name it using symbols.

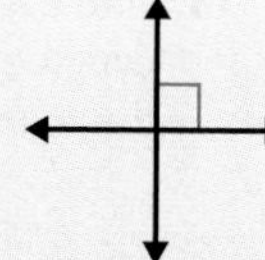

The figure is a line segment. In symbols, this is written as $\overline{LM}$ or $\overline{ML}$.

Example 2
Describe the pair of lines as *intersecting, perpendicular*, or *parallel*.

The lines intersect to form right angles. They are intersecting perpendicular lines.

Identify each figure. Then name it using symbols.

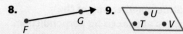

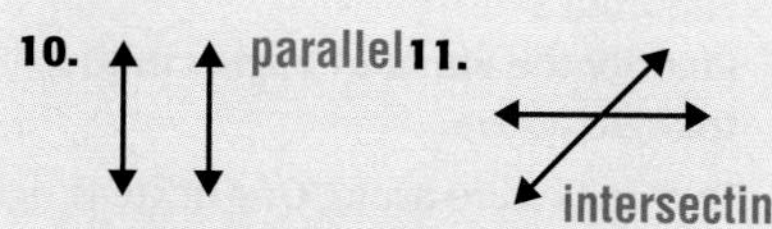

Describe each pair of lines as *intersecting, perpendicular*, or *parallel*.

10. parallel
11. intersecting

12. Draw a ray that can be used to show the direction north on a map. See margin.

13-2 Problem-Solving Strategy: Use Logical Reasoning (pp. 562–563)

Example 3
Angie, Carlo, and Camille each play a different sport: basketball, soccer, or football. Angie does not like soccer. Carlo's favorite sport is not played with a round ball. Who plays each sport?

Make a table to organize the information.

	Basketball	Soccer	Football
Angie	yes	X	X
Carlo	X	X	yes
Camille	X	yes	X

Angie likes basketball, Carlo likes football, and Camille likes soccer.

Solve. Use the *use logical reasoning* strategy.

13. Two walls intersect. Is the intersection an example of a point, line, ray, or line segment? line segment

14. Steve is taller than Lorena. Riley is shorter than Steve. Lorena is not the shortest. List the people from shortest to tallest. Riley, Lorena, Steve

15. Five dogs are getting groomed. Duke is groomed after Daisy and before Spike. Sadie is groomed after Duke and before Spike and Rusty. Spike is groomed immediately after Sadie. Which dog is groomed last? Rusty

Lesson-by-Lesson Review

Have students complete the Lesson-by-Lesson Review on pp. 596–600. Then you can use ExamView® Assessment Suite to customize another review worksheet that practices all the objectives of this chapter or only the objectives on which your students need more help.

Intervention If the given examples are not sufficient to review the topics covered by the questions, use the page references next to the exercises to review that topic in the Student Edition.

Additional Answer

12.

CHAPTER 13 Study Guide and Review

Additional Answer

22. The top two angles are congruent and the bottom two angles are congruent; 2 acute angles.

13-3 Triangles (pp. 566–569)

Example 4
Measure each side of the triangle. Then find the number of congruent sides. State whether any of the sides appear to be perpendicular.

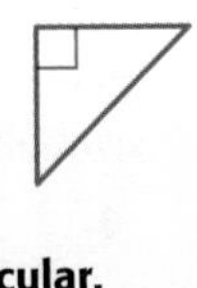

Two sides of the triangle are congruent. Two sides are perpendicular.

Example 5
Identify the kinds of angles in the triangle above.

Two angles are acute. One angle is right.

Measure the sides of each triangle. Then find the number of congruent sides. State whether any of the sides appear to be perpendicular. Write *yes* or *no*.

16. 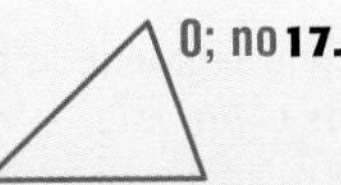 0; no **17.** 2; no

18. Find the number of congruent sides in the triangular sign. 3

13-4 Quadrilaterals (pp. 560–574)

19. Opposite sides are congruent and parallel.
20. Opposite sides are congruent and parallel. Adjacent sides are perpendicular.

Example 6
Describe the congruent sides in the quadrilateral. Then state whether any sides appear to be parallel or perpendicular.

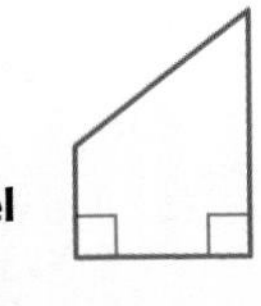

No sides are congruent. Two sides appear to be parallel. Two pairs of adjacent sides appear to be perpendicular.

Example 7
Refer to the figure in Example 6. Find the number of acute angles.

The figure has 1 acute angle.

Describe the sides that appear congruent in each quadrilateral. Then state whether any sides appear to be parallel or perpendicular.

19. **20.** 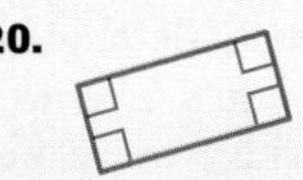

Find the number of acute angles in each quadrilateral.

21. 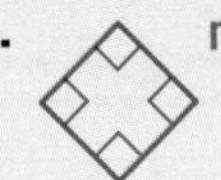 none **22.**  See margin.

23. Miss Cruz is cutting out a quadrilateral. It has four congruent sides and no right angles. What figure is it? rhombus

13-5 Problem-Solving Investigation: Choose a Strategy (pp. 576–577)

Example 8
Algebra Find the eighth number in the pattern below.

18, 19, 15, 16, 12, 13,...

Find the pattern in the list of numbers.

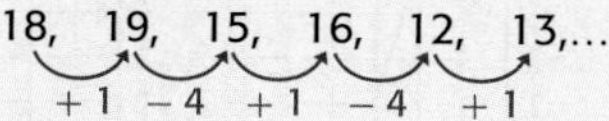

The pattern is to add 1, and then subtract 4.

So, the seventh number in the pattern is 13 − 4 or 9. The eighth number is 9 + 1 or 10.

Solve.

24. Holly is 6 years younger than her sister. Their mother is 44 years old, and her age is twice the sum of her two children's ages. How old is Holly? 8

25. How many 2-inch squares fit inside a rectangle 6 inches by 8 inches? 12 squares

26. Caden uses one pencil the first week of drawing class, and twice as many pencils each week as he did the week before. How many pencils does he use the fifth week? 16 pencils

13-6 Translations and Graphs (pp. 578–581) 27–28. See margin.

Example 9
A triangle has vertices $A(2, 2)$, $B(1, 4)$, and $C(5, 2)$. Graph the triangle. Then graph its translation image 1 unit right and 5 units up. Write the ordered pairs for the vertices of the image.

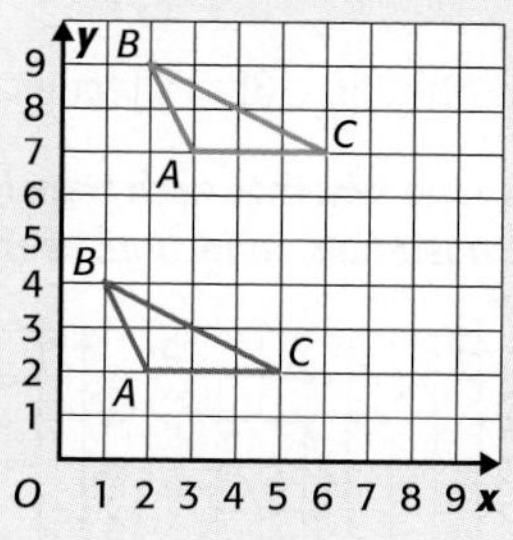

The new vertices are $A(3, 7)$, $B(2, 9)$, and $C(6, 7)$.

Graph each figure and the translation image described. Write the ordered pairs for the vertices of the image.

27. quadrilateral with vertices $F(2, 9)$, $G(7, 9)$, $H(8, 7)$, $J(5, 7)$; translated 6 units down

28. triangle with vertices $T(7, 3)$, $U(9, 8)$, $V(9, 4)$; translated 3 units left, 1 unit up

29. A triangular stool has legs at (5, 3), (9, 3), and (7, 6). It is moved 5 units to the right. What are the new coordinates? (10, 3), (14, 3), (12, 6)

Additional Answers

27.

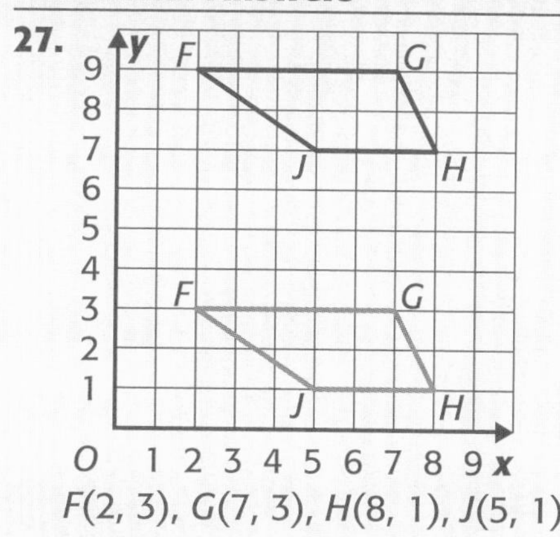

$F(2, 3)$, $G(7, 3)$, $H(8, 1)$, $J(5, 1)$

28.

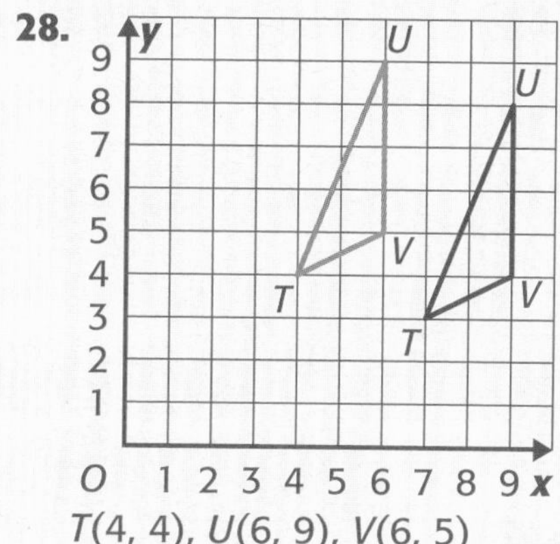

$T(4, 4)$, $U(6, 9)$, $V(6, 5)$

Chapter 13 Study Guide and Review 599

CHAPTER 13

Study Guide and Review

Additional Answers

30. 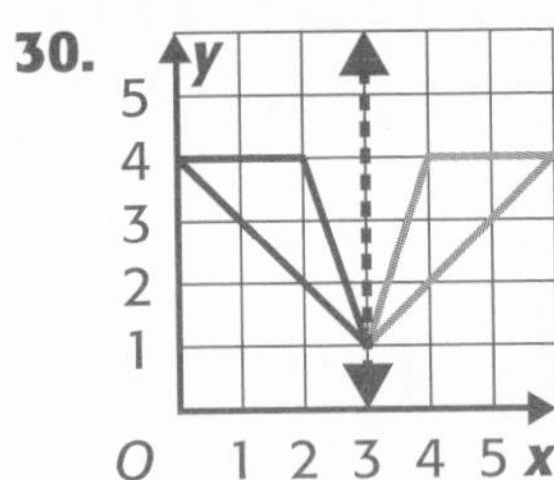

(3, 1), (4, 4), (6, 4)

31. 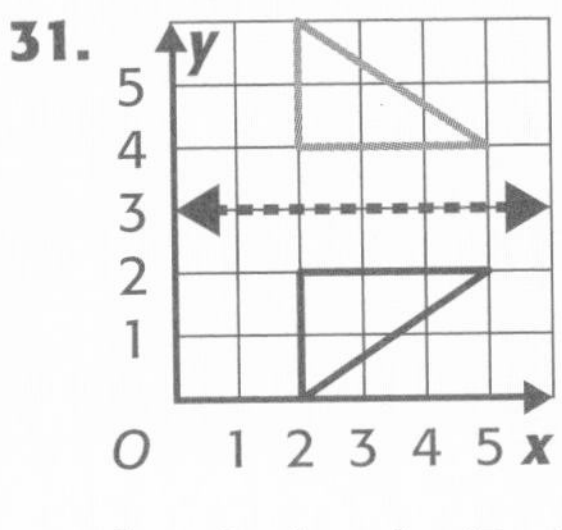

(2, 4), (2, 6), (5, 4)

32. 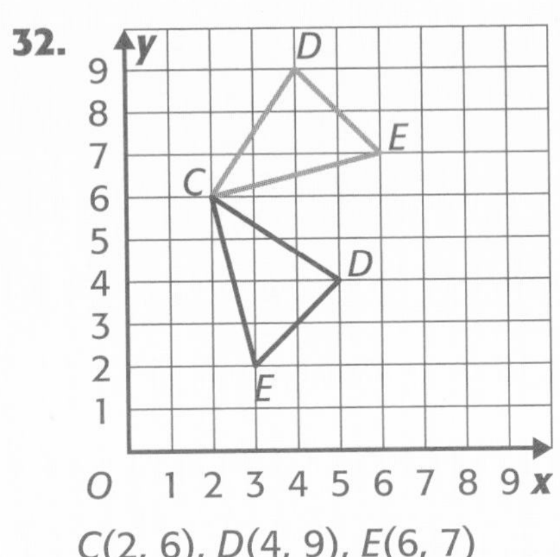

$C(2, 6)$, $D(4, 9)$, $E(6, 7)$

33. 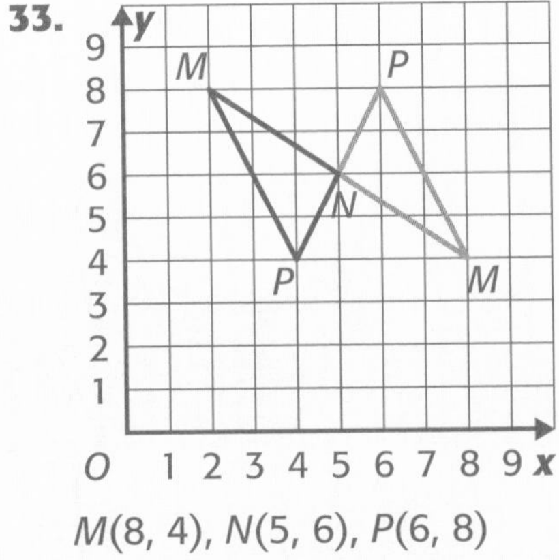

$M(8, 4)$, $N(5, 6)$, $P(6, 8)$

13-7 Reflections and Graphs (pp. 582–585) 30–33. See margin.

Example 10
Graph the figure after a reflection across the line. Then write the ordered pairs for the vertices of the image.

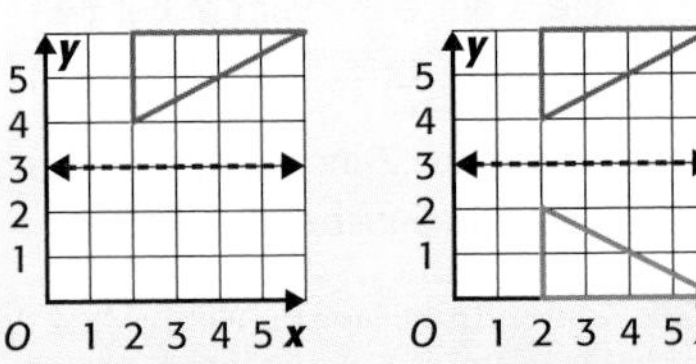

The ordered pairs for the new vertices are (2, 0), (2, 2), and (6, 0).

Graph each figure after a reflection across the line. Then write the ordered pairs for the vertices of the image.

30. **31.**

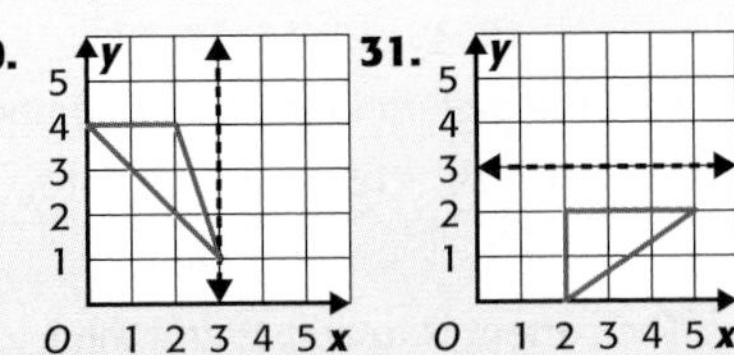

13-8 Rotations and Graphs (pp. 586–590)

Example 11
Graph the rotation of the triangle clockwise about point *W*. Write the ordered pairs for the new vertices.

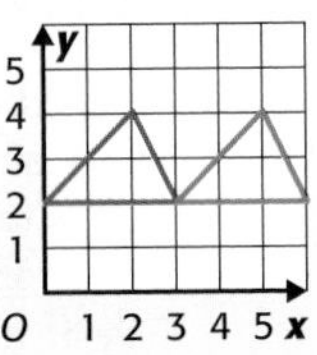

The ordered pairs for the new vertices are (3, 2), (3, 4), and (6, 4).

Graph each figure and the rotation described. Write the ordered pairs for the new vertices.

32. triangle with vertices $C(2, 6)$, $D(5, 4)$, $E(3, 2)$; rotated 90° counterclockwise about C

33. triangle with vertices $M(2, 8)$, $N(5, 6)$, $P(4, 4)$; rotated 180° clockwise about N

13-9 Identify Transformations (pp. 591–593) 34. rotation 35. reflection

Example 12
Determine whether the transformation is a *translation*, *reflection*, or *rotation*.

The triangle slid 3 units right. This is a translation.

Determine whether each transformation is a *translation*, *reflection*, or *rotation*.

34. **35.**

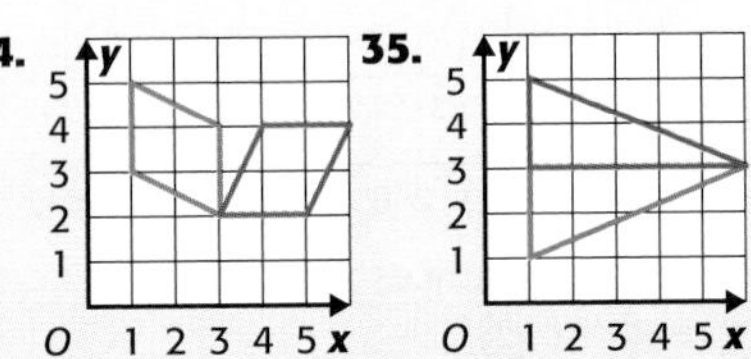

600 Chapter 13

Chapter Test

Math Online macmillanmh.com
• Chapter Test

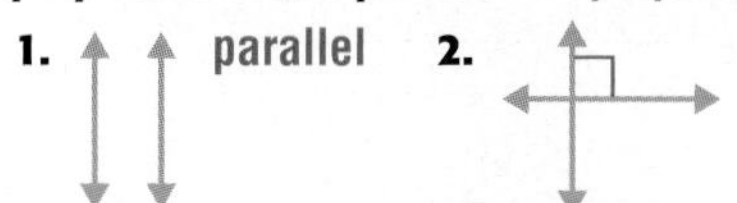

Describe each pair of lines as *intersecting*, *perpendicular*, or *parallel*. 2. perpendicular

1. 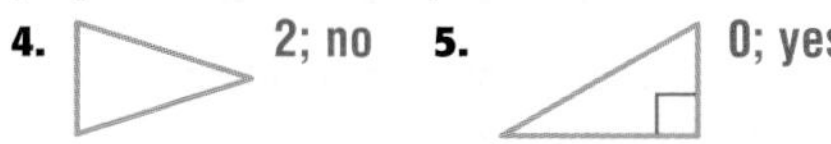 parallel 2.

3. Hiroshi has been at a baseball game for 1 hour 50 minutes. The time is 5:20 P.M. At what time did he arrive? 3:30 P.M.

Measure each side of the triangle. Then find the number of congruent sides. State whether any of the sides appear to be perpendicular. Write *yes* or *no*.

4.  2; no 5. 0; yes

Find the number of acute angles in each quadrilateral.

6. 2 7. 1

8. **MULTIPLE CHOICE** Wendy will show her friend an example of an acute angle. Which figure could she NOT use? C
   - **A** quadrilateral
   - **B** rhombus
   - **C** square
   - **D** trapezoid

9. Which single transformation is represented by the figure and its image? reflection

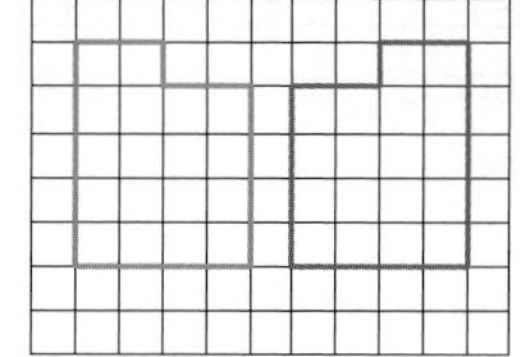

Graph the figure and the translation image described. Write the ordered pairs for the vertices of the image.

10. triangle with vertices $N(2, 2)$, $P(6, 3)$, $Q(4, 1)$; translated 5 units up
See Ch. 13 Answer Appendix.

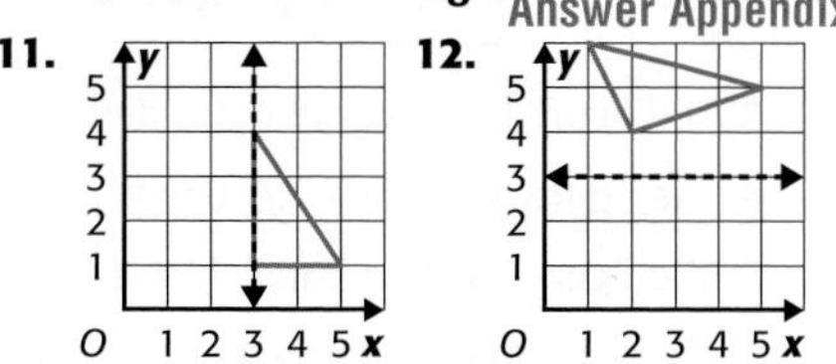

Graph each figure after a reflection across the line. Then write the ordered pairs for the vertices of the image. 11–13. See Ch. 13 Answer Appendix.

11. 12.

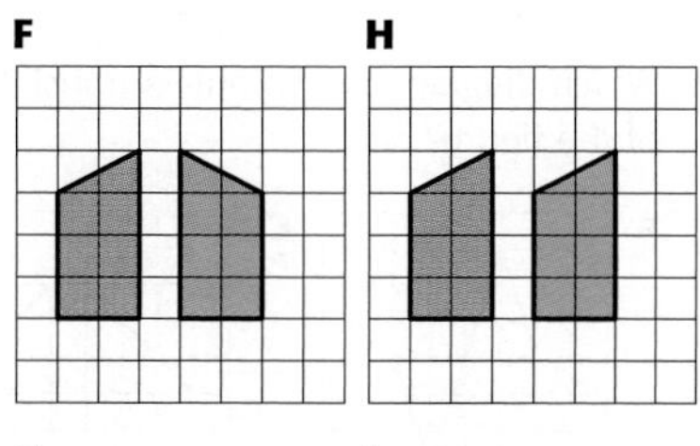

13. Graph a triangle with vertices $A(1, 4)$, $B(5, 4)$, and $C(5, 2)$. Sketch the triangle rotated 180° about point B. Write the ordered pairs for the new vertices.

14. **MULTIPLE CHOICE** Which pair of figures shows a translation? H

F H

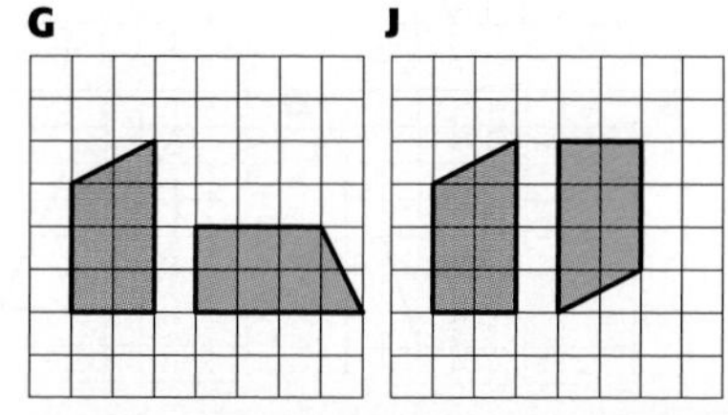

G J

Chapter 13 Chapter Test

Summative Assessment

Use these alternate leveled chapter tests to differentiate assessment for the specific needs of your students.

Leveled Chapter 13 Tests			
Form	Type	Level	CRM Pages
1	Multiple Choice	AL	65–66
2A	Multiple Choice	OL	67–68
2B	Multiple Choice	OL	69–70
2C	Free Response	AL	71–72
2D	Free Response	AL	73–74
3	Free Response	AL	75–76

BL = below/approaching grade level
OL = on grade level
AL = above/beyond grade level

Vocabulary Test

CRM **Chapter 13 Resource Masters** (p. 60)

ExamView Assessment Suite Customize and create multiple versions of your Chapter Test and the test answer keys.

Data-Driven Decision Making

Based on the results of the Chapter Test, use the following to review concepts that continue to present students with problems.

Exercises	State/Local Standards	What's the Math?	Error Analysis	Resources for Review
1–2		Identify types of lines (parallel, perpendicular, intersecting).	Does not understand "parallel," "perpendicular," and "intersecting."	Strategic Intervention Guide (pp. 126, 128) CRM Chapter 13 Resource Masters (Reteach Worksheets) pp. 8, 13–14, 18, 23, 28–29, 33, 38, 43, 48 Math Adventures My Math Zone Chapter 13 Math Online Extra Examples • Concepts in Motion
4–8		Identify characteristics of triangles and quadrilaterals.	Does not understand "congruent." Does not understand "acute." Does not know names or characteristics of basic quadrilaterals.	
9		Identify transformations on a grid.	Does not know what a transformation is. Does not know different names for transformations.	
10–14		Graph figures and their translations and reflections on a coordinate grid.	Does not understand "translation," "reflection," "rotation," "vertices." Reverses numbers when writing ordered pairs.	

Chapter 13 Test Practice

Formative Assessment

- Use Student Edition pp. 602–603 as practice and cumulative review. The questions are written in the same style as many state tests.
- You can also use these two pages to benchmark student progress, or as an alternate homework assignment.

Additional practice pages can be found in the Chapter 13 Resource Masters.

Chapter 13 Resource Masters
Cumulative Test Practice
- Multiple Choice format (pp. 65–70)
- Free Response format (pp. 71–76)

Create practice worksheets or tests that align to your state standards.

Math Online Have students visit macmillanmh.com for additional practice to reinforce your state standards.

Chapter 13 Test Practice
Cumulative, Chapters 1–13

Math Online macmillanmh.com
- Test Practice

PART 1 Multiple Choice

Read each question. Then fill in the correct answer on the answer sheet provided by the teacher or on a sheet of paper.

1. Which statement about the trapezoid shown below is true? C

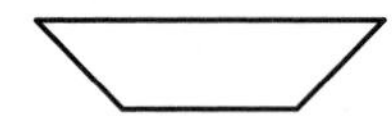

A The figure has 4 congruent sides.
B The figure contains 4 right angles.
C The figure has two parallel bases.
D The figure has a perimeter of 10 units.

2. Which of the following shapes could never have perpendicular sides? F

F circle
G rectangle
H square
J triangle

3. Which diagram shows only a translation of the figure? D

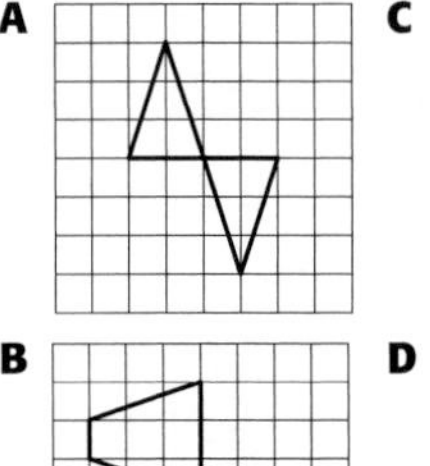

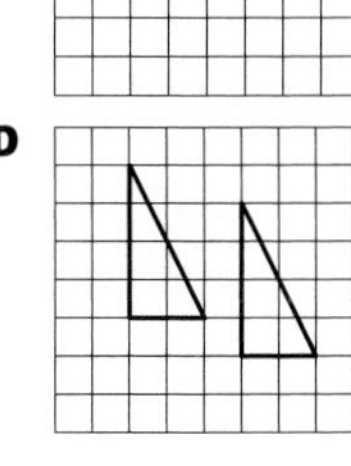

4. Which single transformation is shown below? H

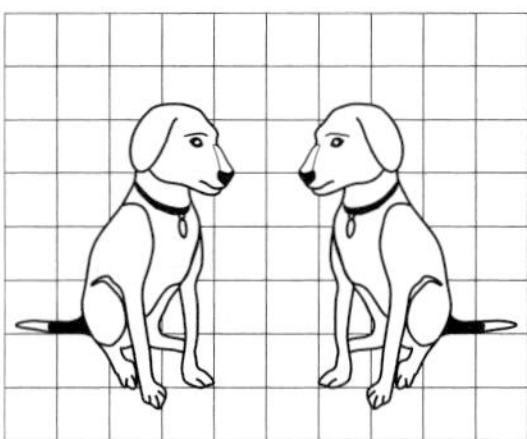

F rotation
G translation
H reflection
J not here

5. Which of these shapes could never have parallel opposite sides? D

A rectangle
B rhombus
C trapezoid
D triangle

6. What part of the model is shaded? G

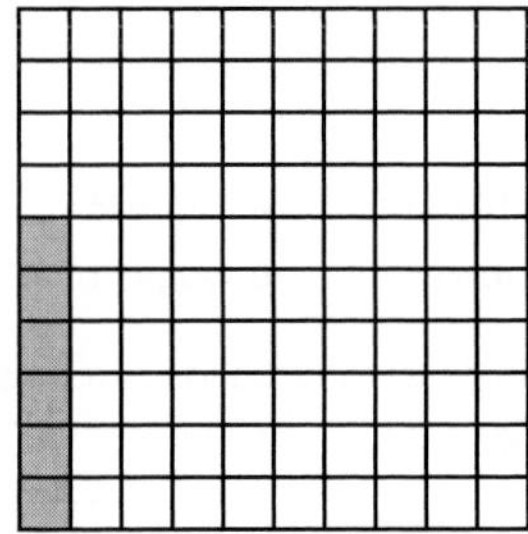

F 0.006
G 0.06
H 0.6
J 6

Test-Taking Tip

Remind students that to estimate the measure of an angle, they can compare it to an angle whose measure they know, such as a 90° angle.

Preparing for Standardized Tests
For test-taking strategies and practice, see pages R42–R55.

7. Mr. Cortez determined that the cost of renting a popcorn machine for 9 hours was $82. Which shows that his solution is NOT reasonable? C

Number of Hours	Cost ($)
1	32
3	47
5	62
7	77

A The terms are decreasing.

B The terms are multiples of 11.

C The terms are increasing by 15.

D The terms are multiples of 15.

8. An isosceles triangle is shown. Which statement about the triangle is true? H

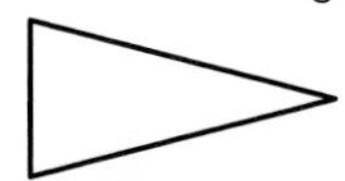

F None of the sides are congruent.

G All the angles are right angles.

H The triangle has only 2 sides that are congruent.

J Two of the sides are perpendicular.

9. What fraction is equivalent to 0.32? B

A $\frac{32}{1000}$ **C** $\frac{32}{10}$

B $\frac{32}{100}$ **D** $3\frac{2}{10}$

PART 2 Short Response

Record your answers on the answer sheet provided by your teacher or on a sheet of paper.

10. Julie practiced the piano one afternoon, as shown. Find the number of minutes she practiced the piano. See margin.

Start

Finish

11. What type of angle will the hands of a clock show at 1:15? acute angle

PART 3 Extended Response

Record your answers on the answer sheet provided by your teacher or on a sheet of paper. Show your work.

12. Use a Venn diagram to compare characteristics of perpendicular lines and intersecting lines. See margin.

13. Describe two ways to represent $1.76 using dollars and coins. You may NOT use more than 6 coins. See margin.

NEED EXTRA HELP?													
If You Missed Question...	1	2	3	4	5	6	7	8	9	10	11	12	13
Go to Lesson...	13–4	13–1	13–9	13–9	13–3	8–2	6–6	13–3	1–4	11–7	13–3	13–1	1–8

Answer Sheet Practice

Have students simulate taking a state test by recording their answers on a practice recording sheet.

CRM Chapter 13 Resource Masters
Student Recording Sheet (p. 81)

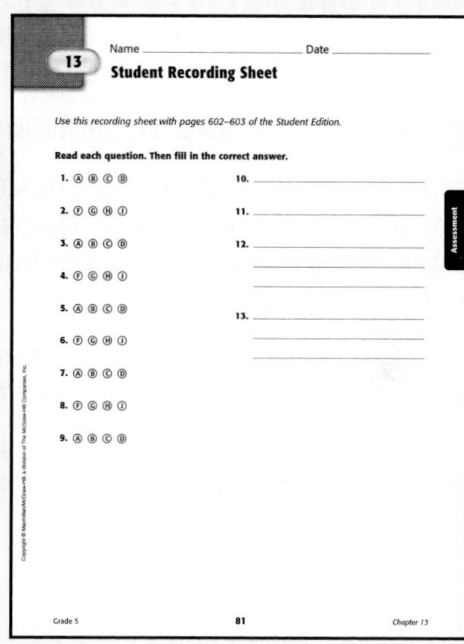
13
Name ______ Date ______
Student Recording Sheet

Use this recording sheet with pages 602–603 of the Student Edition.

Read each question. Then fill in the correct answer.

1. Ⓐ Ⓑ Ⓒ Ⓓ
2. Ⓕ Ⓖ Ⓗ Ⓙ
3. Ⓐ Ⓑ Ⓒ Ⓓ
4. Ⓕ Ⓖ Ⓗ Ⓙ
5. Ⓐ Ⓑ Ⓒ Ⓓ
6. Ⓕ Ⓖ Ⓗ Ⓙ
7. Ⓐ Ⓑ Ⓒ Ⓓ
8. Ⓕ Ⓖ Ⓗ Ⓙ
9. Ⓐ Ⓑ Ⓒ Ⓓ
10. ______
11. ______
12. ______
13. ______

Assessment

Grade 5 81 *Chapter 13*

Additional Answers

10. 75, Sample answer: one hour is 60 minutes, plus 15 more minutes is 75 minutes.

12. Characteristics of Perpendicular Lines — Characteristics of Intersecting Lines

form right angles | cross at a point | form 2 obtuse angles and 2 acute angles

13. Sample answer: 1 dollar bill, 3 quarters, and 1 penny; one dollar bill, 2 quarters, 2 dimes, 1 nickel, and 1 penny.

Page 556, Quick Check

6. Sample answer:

7–10.

Page 563, Lesson 13-2

1. No; Sample answer: That clue shows that girls have the purple and green notebooks and boys have the red and blue notebooks. Without that clue, it is impossible to determine who has each notebook.

2. Maggie: green; Sam: red; Aisha: purple; Nicolás: blue

3. No; sample answer: To find the area of a rectangle or a square, multiply the length by the width. The whole number factors of 16 are 1, 2, 4, 8, and 16. So, the garden may be a square 4 ft on each side. Or, it could be a rectangle 1 ft by 16 ft or 2 ft by 8 ft.

4. Sample answer: when you have a group of facts that can lead to a conclusion or when you can eliminate possibilities

5. Central Avenue and Main Street, Central Avenue and Park Street, Fletcher Avenue and Main Street, Fletcher Avenue and Park Street

11.

12. Sample answer: Since Ramon is not the teacher or the athlete, Charlotte and Nora must be the teacher and the athlete. Charlotte does not like sports and Nora likes to run, so Nora is the athlete and Charlotte is the teacher.

Page 575, Mid-Chapter Check

15. Yes; a parallelogram is a quadrilateral with 2 pairs of parallel sides.

Page 579–581, Lesson 13-6

1.

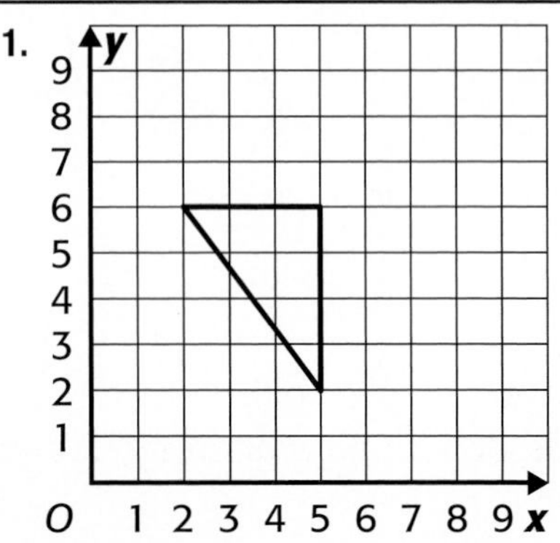

; (2, 6), (5, 6), (5, 2)

2.

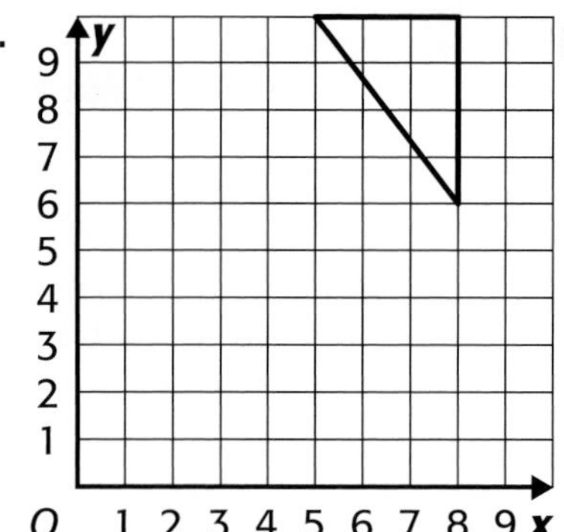

; (5, 10), (8, 10), (8, 6)

3.

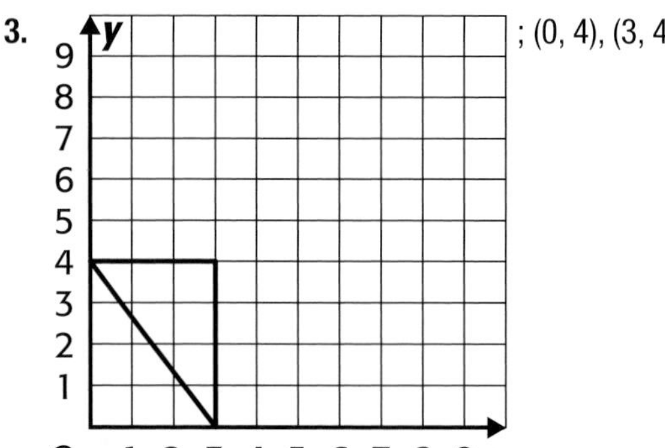

; (0, 4), (3, 4), (3, 0)

4.

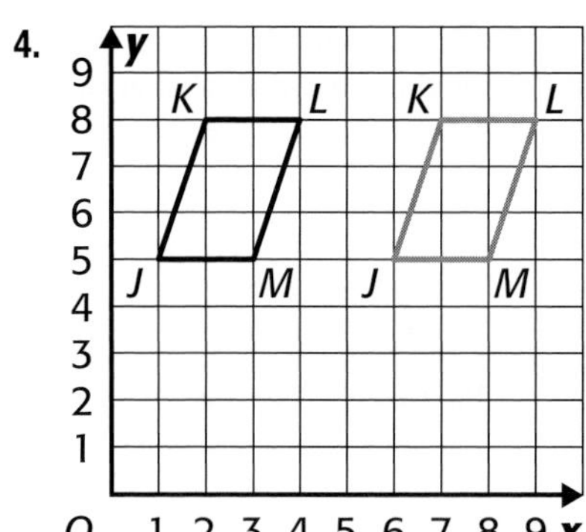

; *J*(6, 5), *K*(7, 8), *L*(9, 8), *M*(8, 5)

5.

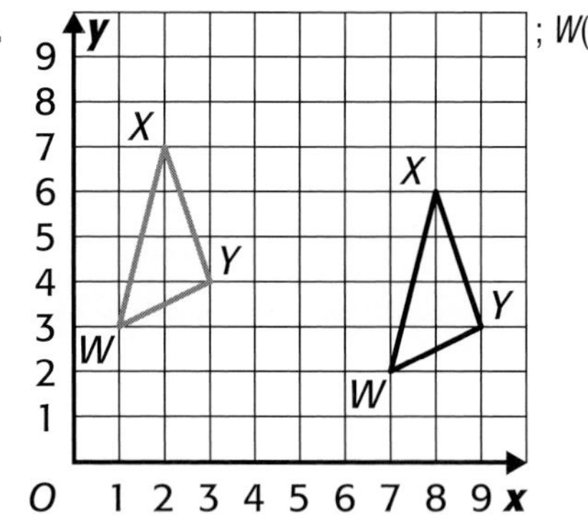

; *W*(1, 3), *X*(2, 7), *Y*(3, 4)

12.

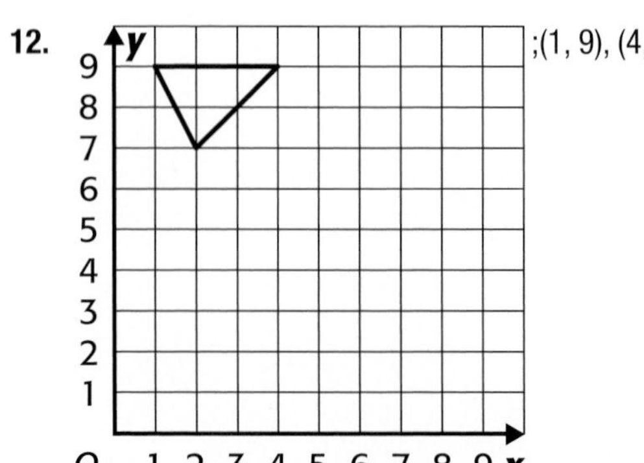

;(1, 9), (4, 9), (2, 7)

13. 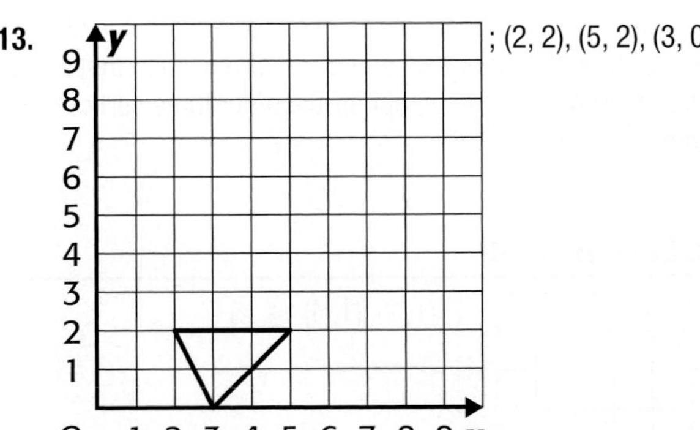 ; (2, 2), (5, 2), (3, 0)

14. 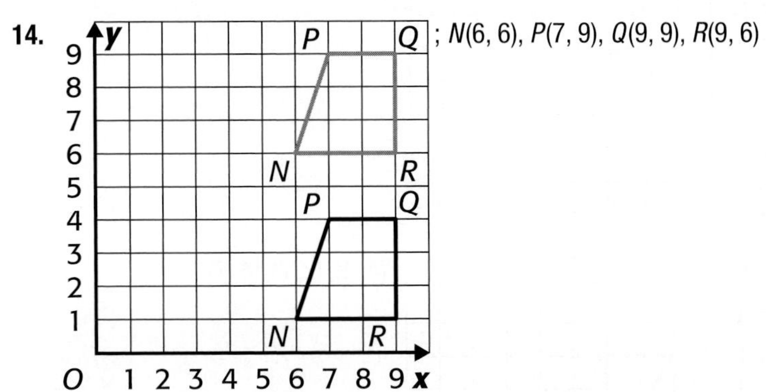 ; N(6, 6), P(7, 9), Q(9, 9), R(9, 6)

15. 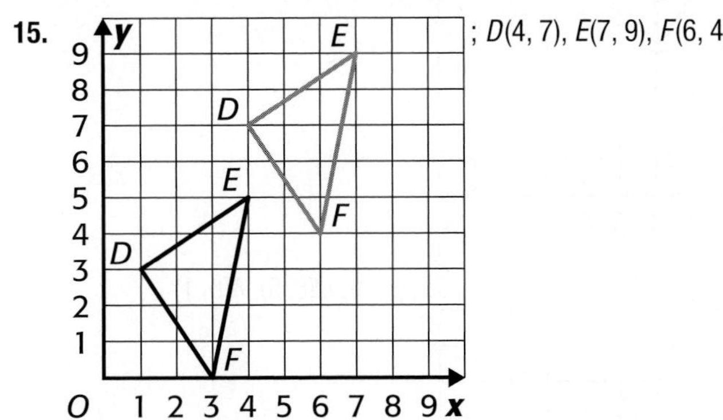 ; D(4, 7), E(7, 9), F(6, 4)

17. 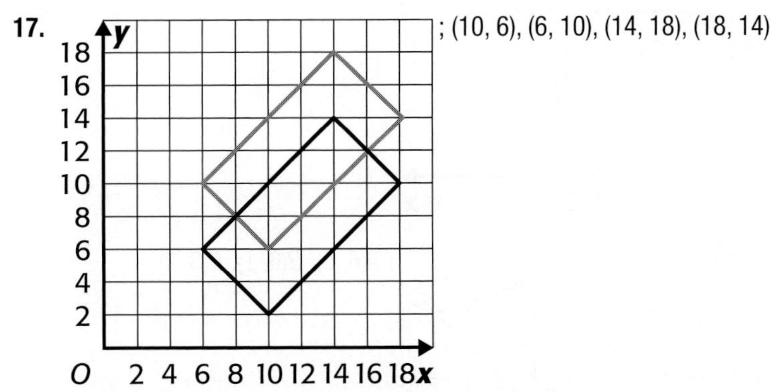 ; (10, 6), (6, 10), (14, 18), (18, 14)

20. 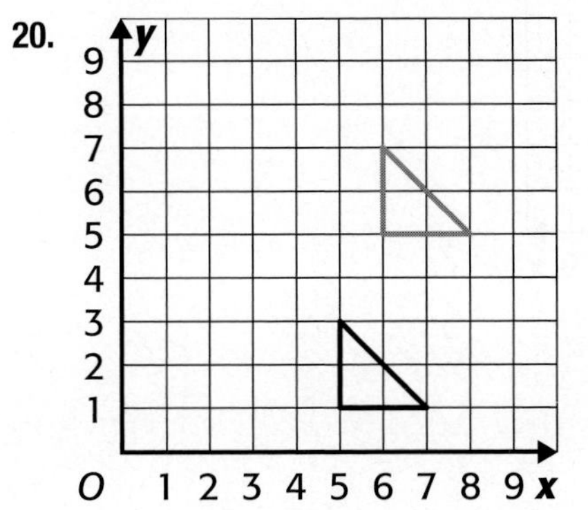

25. Opposite sides are congruent and parallel. Adjacent sides are perpendicular.

26. One pair of opposite sides is congruent. One pair of opposite sides is parallel.

27. Opposite sides are congruent and parallel.

Pages 583–585, Lesson 13-7

1. 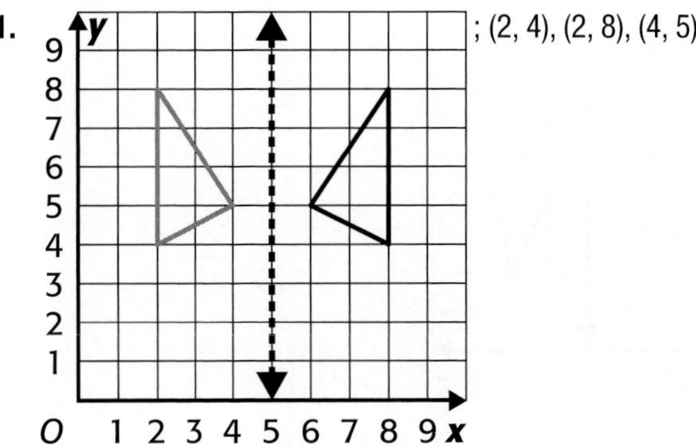 ; (2, 4), (2, 8), (4, 5)

2. 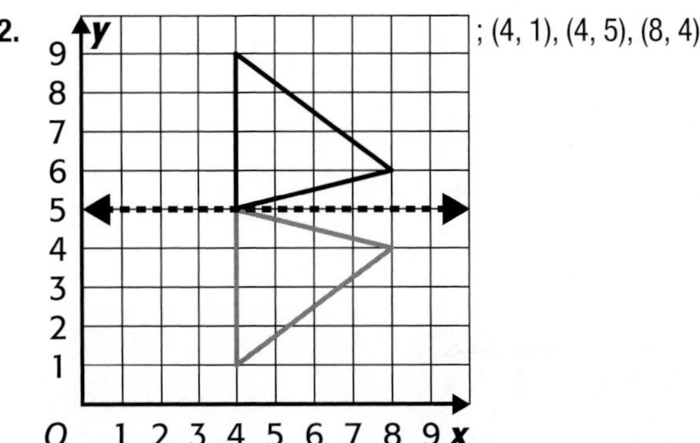 ; (4, 1), (4, 5), (8, 4)

3. 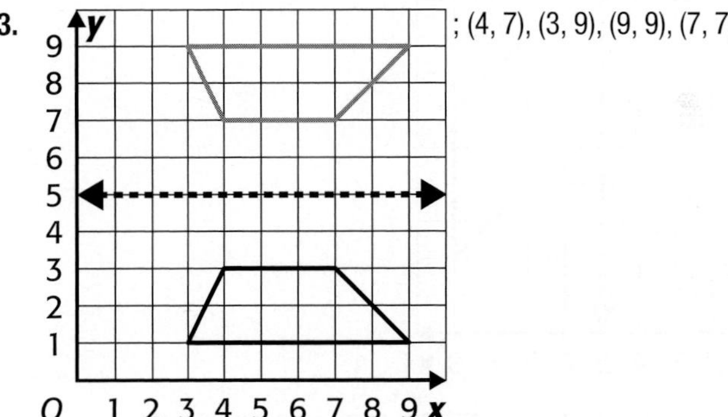 ; (4, 7), (3, 9), (9, 9), (7, 7)

5. Sample answer: Translations and reflections are both transformations that involve congruent figures. In a translation, a figure is moved from one place to another without being turned or flipped. In a reflection, a figure is moved from one place to another by being flipped.

6. 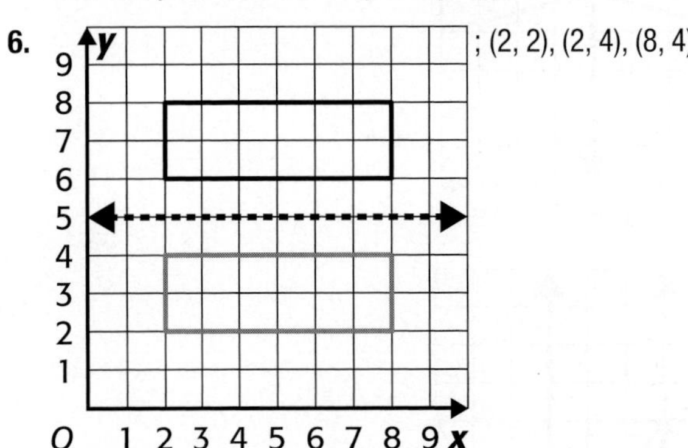 ; (2, 2), (2, 4), (8, 4), (8, 2)

7. 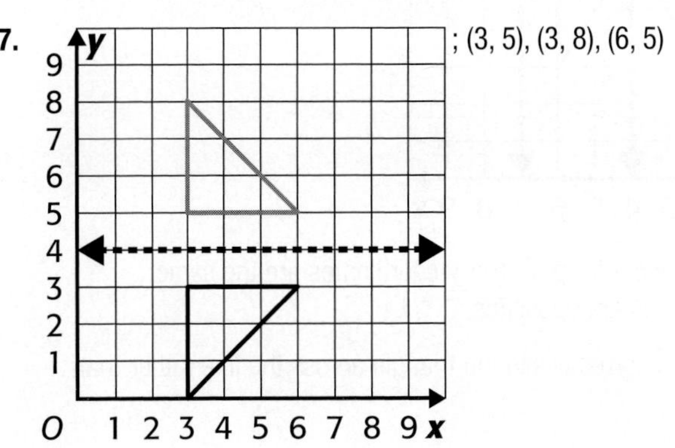 ; (3, 5), (3, 8), (6, 5)

8. 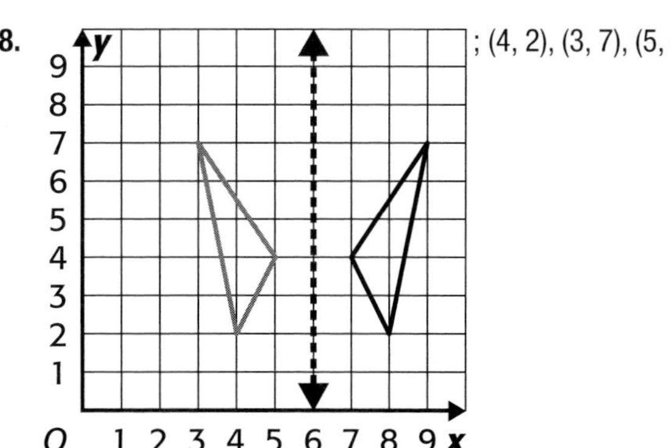
; (4, 2), (3, 7), (5, 4)

9. 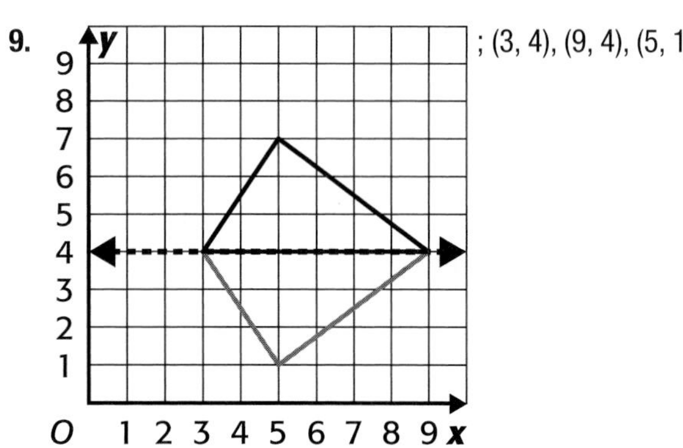
; (3, 4), (9, 4), (5, 1)

10. 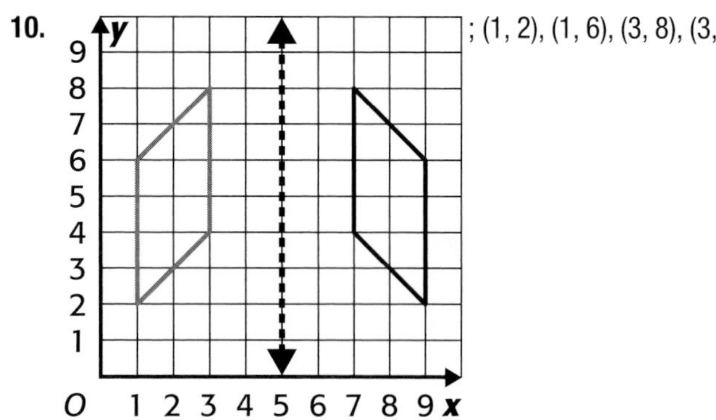
; (1, 2), (1, 6), (3, 8), (3, 4)

11. 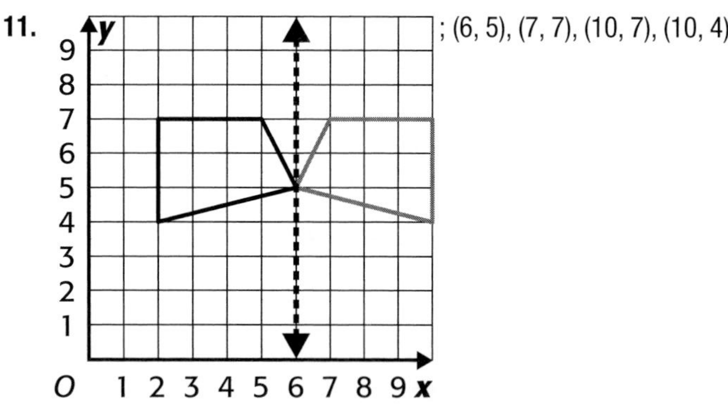
; (6, 5), (7, 7), (10, 7), (10, 4)

18. 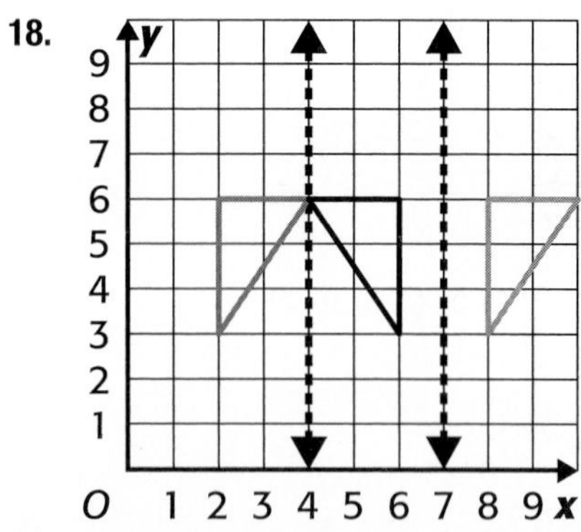

19. See students' work for grid. The *y*-coordinates are the same; the *x*-coordinates are opposites.

20. Alexis; Devon incorrectly slid the triangle across the line rather than reflect it.

21. Sample answer: Count the number of units a vertex is from the line of reflection. Draw a point on the other side of the line of reflection that is the same number of units from the line. Repeat for the other three vertices. Connect the points.

Pages 587–590, Lesson 13-8

1. 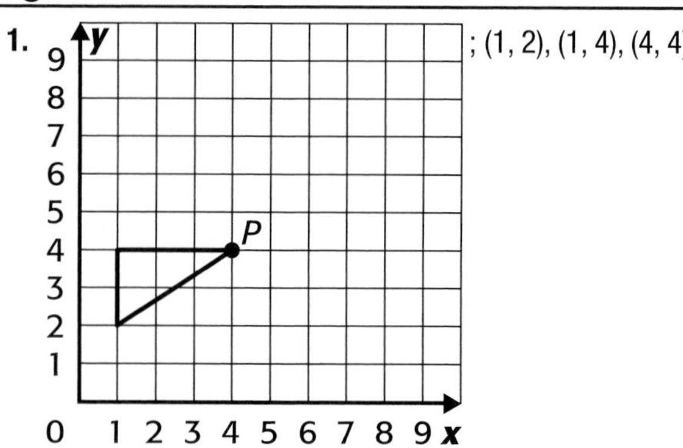
; (1, 2), (1, 4), (4, 4)

2. 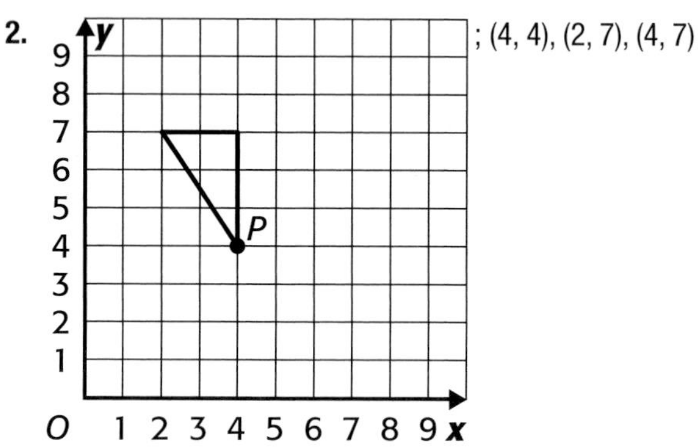
; (4, 4), (2, 7), (4, 7)

3. 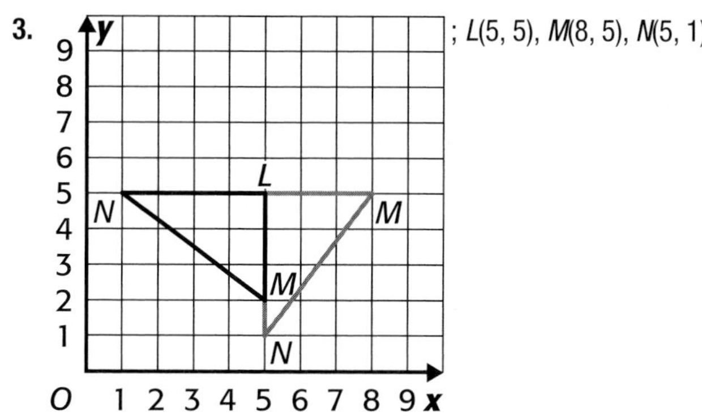
; *L*(5, 5), *M*(8, 5), *N*(5, 1)

4. 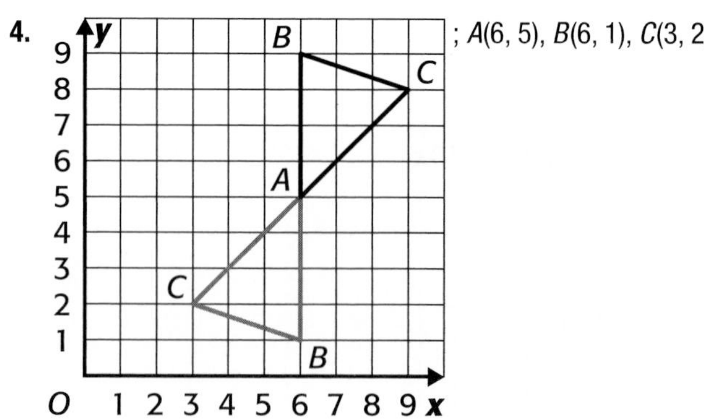
; *A*(6, 5), *B*(6, 1), *C*(3, 2)

11. 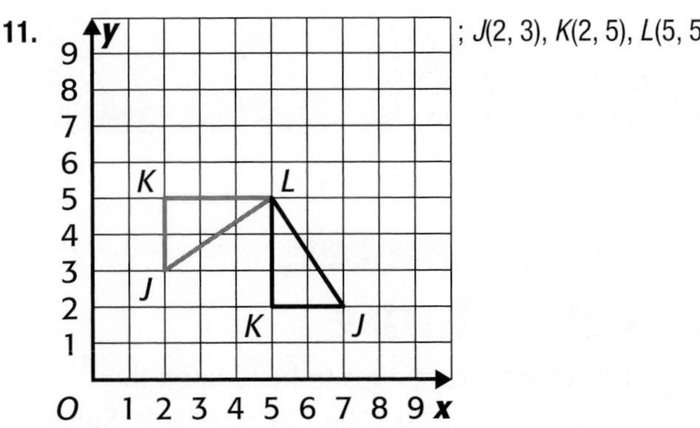

; $J(2, 3)$, $K(2, 5)$, $L(5, 5)$

12. 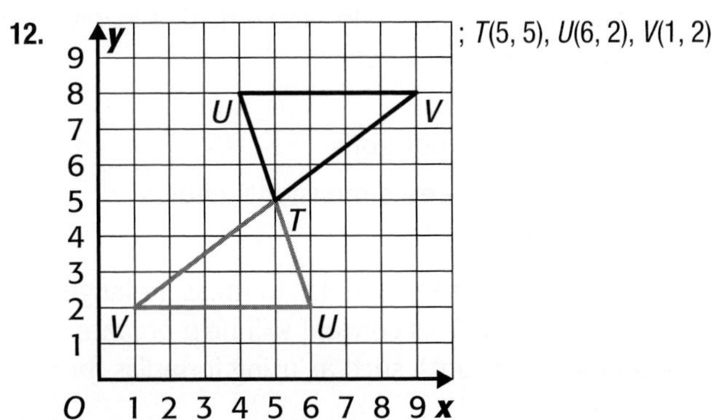

; $T(5, 5)$, $U(6, 2)$, $V(1, 2)$

13. 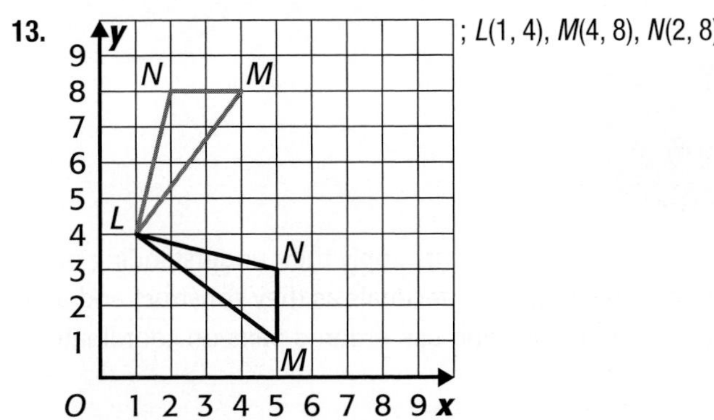

; $L(1, 4)$, $M(4, 8)$, $N(2, 8)$

14. 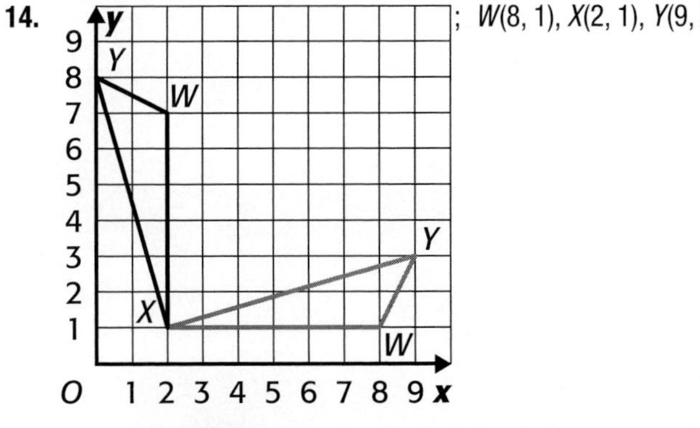

; $W(8, 1)$, $X(2, 1)$, $Y(9, 3)$

15. 

18. rotation; (7, 1), (2, 1)

Pages 592–593, Lesson 13-9

5. Sample answer: To show a translation, move all the vertices the same direction the same distance. To show a reflection, draw a horizontal or vertical line. Then plot the vertices the same distance from the line on the opposite side of the line. To show a rotation, use one of the vertices and turn the figure so that each pair of corresponding sides forms a 90 degree angle.

16. translations or reflections of the squares across vertical and horizontal lines

17. rotation of triangle across the diagonal line, then a translation of the triangle

18. translations or reflections of the stripes across vertical lines. See students' work for drawings.

Page 601, Chapter Test

10. 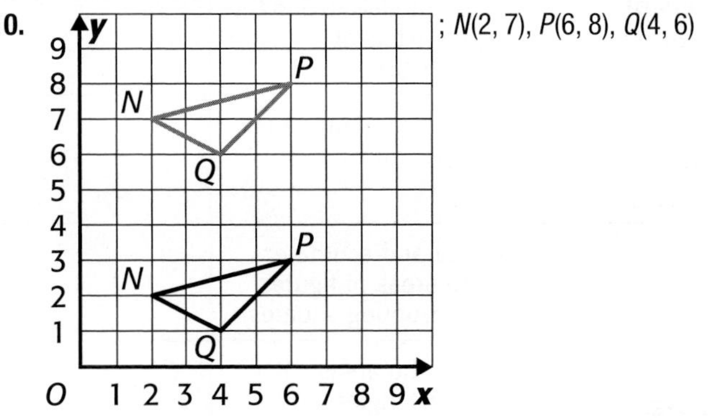

; $N(2, 7)$, $P(6, 8)$, $Q(4, 6)$

11. 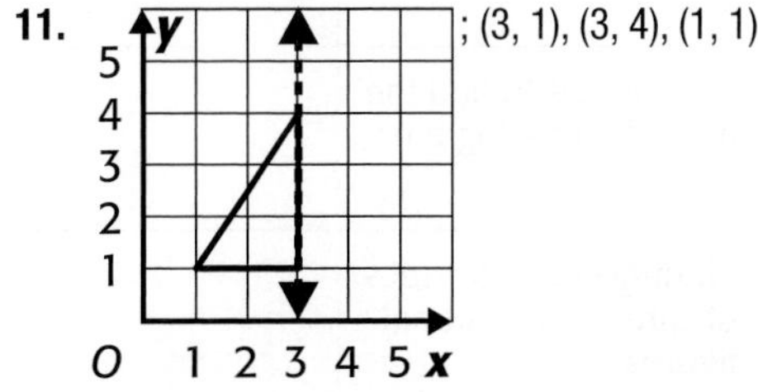

; (3, 1), (3, 4), (1, 1)

12. 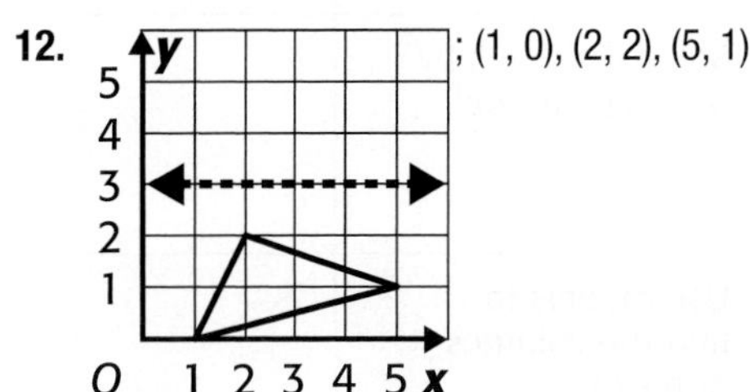

; (1, 0), (2, 2), (5, 1)

13. 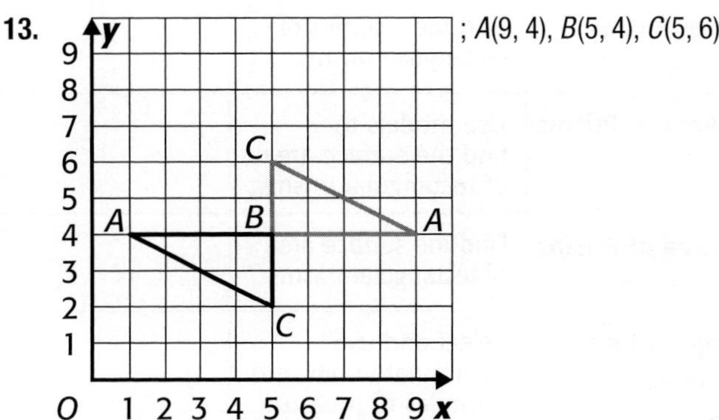

; $A(9, 4)$, $B(5, 4)$, $C(5, 6)$

Chapter Overview

Chapter-at-a-Glance

In Chapter 14, the emphasis is on measuring perimeter, area, and volume of geometric figures.

Lesson	Math Objective	State/Local Standards
EXPLORE 14-1 **Perimeters of Rectangles** (p. 607)	Use models to find the perimeters of rectangles.	
14-1 **Perimeters of Polygons** (pp. 608–611)	Find the perimeters of polygons.	
14-2 **Area** (pp. 612–615)	Find and estimate the areas of figures by counting squares.	
14-3 **Areas of Rectangles and Squares** (pp. 616–619)	Find the areas of rectangles.	
EXTEND 14-3 **Area of Parallelograms** (p. 620–621)	Use models to find the area of parallelograms.	
14-4 **Three-Dimensional Figures** (pp. 624–627)	Identify characteristics of three-dimensional figures.	
14-5 **Problem-Solving Strategy: Make a Model** (pp. 628–629)	Solve problems by making a model.	
EXPLORE 14-6 **Volumes of Prisms** (p. 630)	Use models to find the volumes of prisms.	
14-6 **Volumes of Prisms** (pp. 631–635)	Find the volumes of rectangular prisms.	
EXPLORE 14-7 **Surface Area of Prisms** (pp. 638–639)	Use models to find the surface area of rectangular prisms.	
14-7 **Surface Area of Prisms** (pp. 640–643)	Find the surface area of rectangular prisms.	
14-8 **Select Appropriate Measurement Formulas** (pp. 644–647)	Select and use appropriate units and formulas to measure length, perimeter, area, and volume.	
14-9 **Problem-Solving Investigation: Choose a Strategy** (pp. 648–649)	Choose the best strategy to solve a problem.	

Measure Perimeter, Area, and Volume

BIG Idea This chapter continues to build upon the measurement and geometry standards. Students apply their understanding to real world problems that involve the measurement of length, area, and volume.

Students learn to:

- find perimeter and area of polygons
- identify characteristics of three-dimensional figures
- find the volume of prisms

Measurement Students use formulas to measure length, perimeter, area, and volume. This concept will help prepare them for measurement concepts, such as using formulas for surface area. (Lesson 14-7)

G5-FP6C Data Analysis: Students apply their understanding of whole numbers, fractions, and decimals as they construct and analyze double-bar and line graphs and use ordered pairs on coordinate grids.

Skills Trace

Vertical Alignment

Fourth Grade

In fourth grade, students learned to:

- Find the perimeter of polygons, and the areas of rectangles and squares.
- Measure and estimate volume in cubic units.

Fifth Grade

During this chapter, students learn to:

- Identify characteristics of three-dimensional figures.
- Find and estimate the areas of figures by counting squares.
- Find the perimeters of polygons, areas of rectangles and volumes of rectangular prisms.
- Find the surface area of rectangular prisms.

After this chapter, students learn to:

- Use probability to make a prediction.

Sixth Grade

In sixth grade, students learn to:

- Find the perimeters of squares and rectangles, and the areas of parallelograms and triangles.
- Find volume of rectangular prisms.
- Estimate and find the circumference of circles.

Backmapping and Vertical Alignment **McGraw-Hill's *Math Connects*** program was conceived and developed with the final results in mind: student success in Algebra 1 and beyond. The authors, using the **NCTM Focal Points and Focal Connections** as their guide, developed this brand new series by backmapping from Algebra 1 concepts, and vertically aligning the topics so that they build upon prior skills and concepts and serve as a foundation for future topics.

Math Vocabulary

The following math vocabulary words for Chapter 14 are listed in the glossary of the ***Student Edition***. You can find interactive definitions in 13 languages in the ***eGlossary*** at macmillanmh.com.

area The number of square units needed to cover the inside of a region or plane figure. (p. 612A)

base The side on which a figure, shape, or 3-dimensional solid sits. (p. 624A)

cone A 3-dimensional figure with a curved surface, a circular base and one vertex. (p. 624A)

cylinder A 3-dimensional figure having two parallel congruent circular bases and a curved surface connecting the two bases. (p. 624A)

perimeter The distance around a shape or region. (p. 608A)

polygon A closed plane figure formed using line segments that meet only at their endpoints. (p. 608A)

polyhedron A 3-dimensional figure in which all of the surfaces are polygons. (p. 624A)

prism A 3-dimensional figure with two parallel, congruent polygons as bases and parallelograms for faces. (p. 624A)

rectangular prism A 3-dimensional figure with six faces that are rectangles. (p. 624A)

surface area The sum of all the faces of a prism. (p. 640A)

three-dimensional figure A figure that has length, width, and height. (p. 624A)

volume The number of cubic units needed to fill a 3-dimensional figure or solid figure. (p. 631A)

Visual Vocabulary Cards
Use Visual Vocabulary Cards 2, 32, 42, 45, and 48 to reinforce the vocabulary in this lesson. (The Define/Example/Ask routine is printed on the back of each card.)

Chapter Planner

Suggested Pacing		
Instruction	Review & Assessment	TOTAL
13 days	1 day	**14 days**

Diagnostic Assessment
Quick Check (p. 606)

	Explore 14-1 (Pacing: 1 day)	Lesson 14-1 (Pacing: 1 day)	Lesson 14-2 (Pacing: 1 day)
Lesson/ Objective	**Perimeters of Rectangles** (p. 607) **Objective:** Use models to find the perimeters of rectangles.	**Perimeters of Polygons** (pp. 608–611) **Objective:** Find the perimeters of polygons.	**Areas** (pp. 612–615) **Objective:** Find and estimate the areas of figures by counting squares.
State/Local Standards			
Math Vocabulary		**polygon, perimeter**	**area**
Lesson Resources	**Manipulatives** square tiles	**Materials** yardsticks **Manipulatives** square pattern blocks, base-ten blocks **Other Resources** CRM Leveled Worksheets (pp. 8–12) Daily Reteach • 5-Minute Check • Problem of the Day	**Materials** grid paper, overhead projector, colored pencils **Other Resources** CRM Leveled Worksheets (pp. 13–17) Daily Reteach • 5-Minute Check • Problem of the Day
Technology Math Online		Math Tool Chest Math Adventures Personal Tutor	Math Adventures Personal Tutor
Reaching All Learners		English Learners, p. 608B ELL Below Level, p. 608B BL Early Finishers, p. 608B OL	English Learners, p. 612B ELL Gifted and Talented, p. 612B AL Early Finishers, p. 612B OL
Alternate Lesson			*IMPACT Mathematics*: Unit I

KEY

BL Below/Approaching Level OL On Level AL Above/Beyond Level ELL English Learners
SE Student Edition TE Teacher Edition CRM Chapter 1 Resource Masters CD-Rom
Transparency Real-World Problem Solving Library

	Lesson 14-3 (Pacing: 1 day)	Extend 14-3 (Pacing: 1 day)	Lesson 14-4 (Pacing: 1 day)
Lesson/ Objective	**Areas of Rectangles and Squares** (pp. 616–619) **Objective:** Find the areas of rectangles.	**Areas of Parallelograms** (pp. 620–621) **Objective:** I will use models to find the area of parallelograms.	**Three-Dimensional Figures** (pp. 624–627) **Objective:** Identify characteristics of three-dimensional figures.
State/Local Standards			
Math Vocabulary		**net**	**three-dimensional figure, polyhedron, prism, base, face, edge, vertex, rectangular prism, triangular prism, cylinder, cone**
Lesson Resources	**Materials** grid paper **Manipulatives** geoboards, square tiles, base-ten blocks **Other Resources** CRM Leveled Worksheets (pp. 18–22) Daily Reteach • 5-Minute Check • Problem of the Day	**Materials** grid paper, scissors	**Materials** box of markers, jar, and objects representing rectangular and triangular prisms, cylinders, and cones **Manipulatives** geometric solids **Other Resources** CRM Leveled Worksheets (pp. 23–27) Daily Reteach • 5-Minute Check • Problem of the Day
Technology **Math Online**	Math Adventures Personal Tutor		Personal Tutor
Reaching All Learners	English Learners, p. 616B ELL Below Level, p. 616B BL Early Finishers, p. 616B AL		English Learners, p. 624B ELL Gifted and Talented, p. 624B AL Early Finishers, p. 624B OL AL
Alternate Lesson	*IMPACT Mathematics:* Unit I		

Game Time
What's the Area? (p. 622)

Formative Assessment
Mid-Chapter Check (p. 623)

Chapter Planner

	Lesson 14-5 (Pacing: 1 day)	Explore 14-6 (Pacing: 1 day)	Lesson 14-6 (Pacing: 1 day)
Lesson/ Objective	**Problem-Solving Strategy Make a Model** (pp. 628–629) **Objective:** Solve problems by making a model.	**Volumes of Prisms** (p. 630) **Objective:** Use models to find the volumes of prisms.	**Volumes of Prisms** (pp. 631–635) **Objective:** Find the volumes of rectangular prisms.
State/Local Standards			
Math Vocabulary			**volume**
Lesson Resources	**Materials** marbles, cans (optional) **Manipulatives** centimeter cubes, coins, square tiles, two-colored counters (optional) **Other Resources** CRM Leveled Worksheets (pp. 28–32) Daily Reteach • 5-Minute Check • Problem of the Day *Exploring the World by Sea*	**Manipulatives** centimeter cubes	**Manipulatives** rulers, centimeter cubes, connecting cubes **Other Resources** CRM Leveled Worksheets (pp. 33–37) Daily Reteach • 5-Minute Check • Problem of the Day
Technology Math Online			Math Adventures Personal Tutor • Concepts in Motion
Reaching All Learners	English Learners, p. 628B ELL Gifted and Talented, p. 628B AL Early Finishers, p. 628B OL AL		English Learners, p. 631B ELL Below Level, p. 631B BL Early Finishers, p. 631B OL AL
Alternate Lesson			*IMPACT Mathematics*: Unit J

Problem Solving in Science (p. 636)

	Explore 14-7 (Pacing: 1 day)	Lesson 14-7 (Pacing: 1 day)
Lesson/ Objective	**Surface Area of Prisms** (pp. 638–639) **Objective:** Use models to find the surface areas of rectangular prisms.	**Surface Area of Prisms** (pp. 640–643) **Objective:** Find the surface areas of rectangular prisms.
State/Local Standards		
Math Vocabulary	**net**	**surface area**
Lesson Resources	**Materials** grid paper, scissors	**Materials** grid paper **Other Resources** CRM Leveled Worksheets (pp. 38–42) Daily Reteach • 5-Minute Check • Problem of the Day
Technology Math Online		Personal Tutor
Reaching All Learners		English Learners, p. 640B ELL Gifted and Talented, p. 640B AL Early Finishers, p. 640B BL
Alternate Lesson		

Chapter Planner

	Lesson 14-8 (Pacing: 1 day)	Lesson 14-9 (Pacing: 1 day)
Lesson/ Objective	**Select Appropriate Measurement Formulas** (pp. 644–647) **Objective:** Select and use appropriate units and formulas to measure length, perimeter,	**Problem-Solving Investigation Choose a Strategy** (pp. 648–649) **Objective:** Choose the best strategy to solve a problem.
State/Local Standards		
Math Vocabulary		
Lesson Resources	**Manipulatives** ruler **Other Resources** CRM Leveled Worksheets (pp. 43–47) Daily Reteach • 5-Minute Check • Problem of the Day	**Manipulatives** centimeter cubes, pattern blocks, play money **Other Resources** CRM Leveled Worksheets (pp. 48–52) Daily Reteach • 5-Minute Check • Problem of the Day *Exploring the World by Sea*
Technology		
Math Online	Personal Tutor	
Reaching All Learners	English Learners, p. 644B ELL Gifted and Talented, p. 644B AL Early Finishers, p. 644B OL AL	English Learners, p. 648B ELL Gifted and Talented, p. 648B AL Early Finishers, p. 648B OL AL
Alternate Lesson	*IMPACT Mathematics:* Unit J	

Summative Assessment
- Study Guide and Review (p. 650)
- Chapter Test (p. 655)
- Test Practice (p. 656)

Assessment Options

Diagnostic Assessment

- SE *Option 1:* Quick Check (p. 606)
- *Option 2:* Online Quiz macmillanmh.com
- CRM *Option 3:* Diagnostic Test (p. 54)
- CRM *Option 4:* Chapter Pretest (p. 55)

Formative Assessment

- TE Alternate Teaching Strategies (every lesson)
- SE Talk About It (every lesson)
- SE Writing in Math (every lesson)
- SE Check What You Know (every lesson)
- TE Into the Future (p. 615)
- TE Yesterday's News (pp. 619, 634)
- SE Mid-Chapter Check (p. 623)
- CRM Lesson Quizzes (pp. 56–58)
- CRM Mid-Chapter Test (p. 59)

Summative Assessment

- SE Chapter Test (p. 655)
- SE Test Practice (p. 656)
- CRM Vocabulary Test (p. 60)
- CRM Leveled Chapter Tests (pp. 65–77)
- CRM Cumulative Test Practice (pp. 78–80)
- CRM Oral Assessment (pp. 61–62)
- ExamView® Assessment Suite
- Advance Tracker

Mc Graw Hill Professional Development

Targeted professional development has been articulated throughout **McGraw-Hill's *Math Connects*** program. The **McGraw-Hill Professional Development Video Library** provides short videos that support the **NCTM Focal Points and Focal Connections.** For more information, visit **macmillanmh.com**.

Model Lessons

Instructional Strategies

Teacher Notes

Learning Stations

Cross-Curricular Links

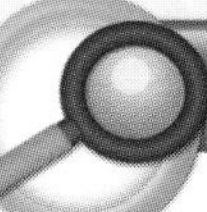

Science

pair

LOGICAL

Amoeba Area

An amoeba is a single-celled organism that looks like a blob. They are so small that they are measured in micrometers, or thousandths of millimeters.

- Each person draws the outline of an amoeba on graph paper. Imagine that each square on the graph paper represents a micrometer. You can estimate the area of the amoeba in the same way you estimate figures in centimeters or meters using graph paper.
- Now give your amoeba to your partner and race to see who estimates the area of the other partner's amoeba first.

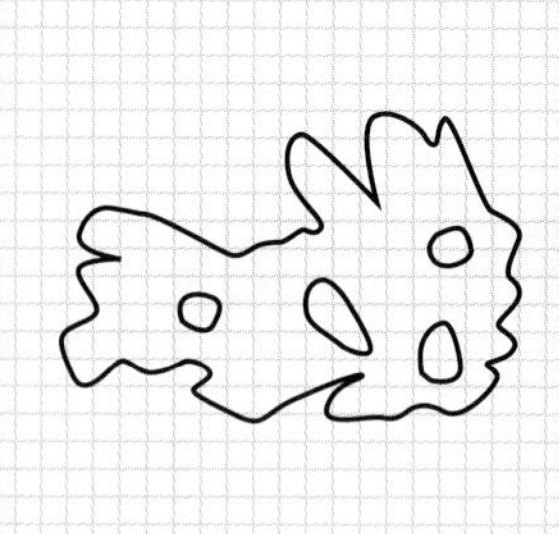

Materials:
- graph paper
- paper
- pencils

Art

individual

SPATIAL

Measure a Masterpiece

- Find a painting you like in an artbook. Usually, the dimensions of the painting are given.
- Using the dimensions you find, calculate the area of the painting.
- What if you had to ship this painting to another museum for a special exhibition? You will need to build a box to ship the painting in.
- Starting with the paintings dimensions, add six inches to both the width and height for extra room for the frame and padding.
- If the depth of the box is eight inches, what is the box's volume?

27 inches by 20 inches

Materials:
- art books
- paper
- pencils

Writing

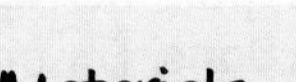

pair

LOGICAL

Poetry Perimeter

Make a perimeter of poetry around your classroom.

- Calculate the length of your paper you will need to cover your classroom's perimeter. Then estimate how many lines of poetry you think will fit on the paper using two inch letters.
- Write a poem with that number of lines with your partner, then alternate, line by line, to transfer it onto the paper roll.
- Once you have transferred the poem onto the paper roll, add more lines if necessary to fill up the paper. When you have finished, hang the poem along the perimeter of the classroom.

Materials:
- classroom dimensions
- 3" wide roll of paper
- paper
- pencils

Reading

pair | LOGICAL

Perimeter Mystery

- Read *Math Mini-Mysteries* by Sandra Markle by yourself or with a partner.
- Each person makes a grid paper map, to scale, of the classroom using the provided measurements.
- Each person writes a series of six messages on index cards. On each index card, write a piece of a mystery story. Place the cards along the perimeter, and mark them on your map. Exchange maps with the other person.
- The first person to find all six of the pieces of the story wins.

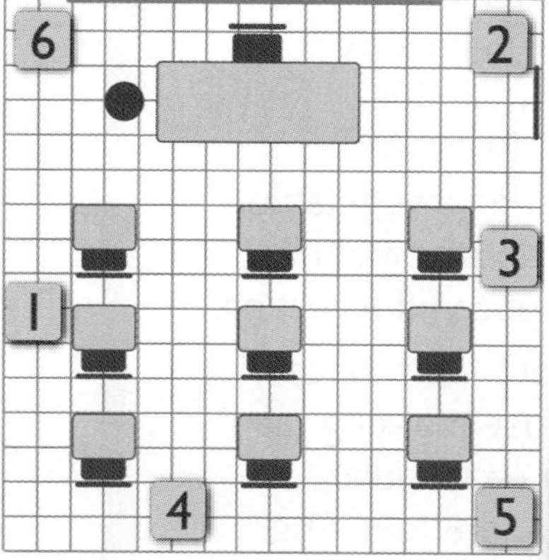

Materials:
- *Math Mini-Mysteries* by Sandra Markle
- centimeter rulers
- index cards
- pencils

Health

individual | SPATIAL

Cartons Speak Volumes

It is recommended that the average person drink 64 ounces of water a day. Find which carton will hold that much.

- Starting from least to greatest, measure each container. Using your measurements, calculate the volume of each container and compare.
- Fill the measuring cup to the 16-ounce level, then fill the smallest carton with water until you reach the top. Remember to keep track of the amount of ounces you poured. Repeat the process for each carton.
- Which carton held 64 ounces? What was the volume of that carton?

Materials:
- empty pint, quart, half gallon orange juice cartons with the top cut off and carton size covered up
- 2 cup measuring cup
- access to water

Social Studies

pair | LOGICAL

Farming Fields

How much farmland can you accumulate?

- Take turns rolling the number cubes to use as measurements of a cornfield in acres. Model your fields on grid paper.
- After ten rounds, calculate how much area of land in total each person has. What is the difference between the two total areas?
- Each person draws a line from one corner of the field to the opposite corner, then draws another line between the other corners.
- Estimate what the area would be for one triangle, or parcel, of the field. Who has the bigger parcel of farmland?

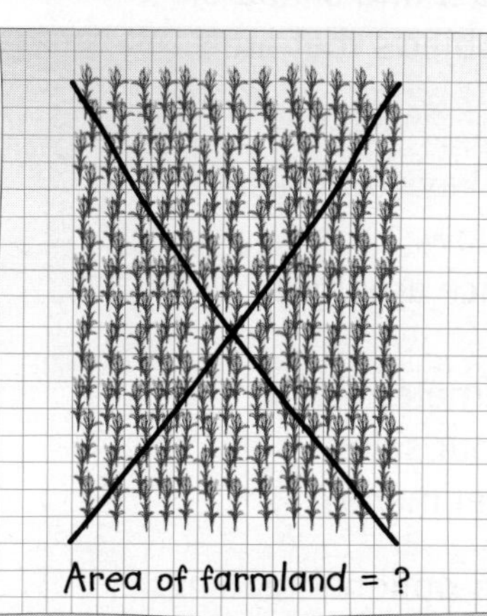

Materials:
- two number cubes
- pencils
- grid paper

CHAPTER 14

Introduce the Chapter

Real World: Fence It In

Materials: masking tape, yardstick

Remind students what they have learned about in the past several chapters: customary and metric units of measure and geometric figures. Tell students that they will learn more about measurement and geometry in this lesson.

- Ask students to imagine planting a vegetable garden in the middle of the classroom. Tell them that they will need to fence off a section.
- Clear a space on the classroom floor. Have students work together and use masking tape and a yardstick to mark off a rectangular "garden" that is 5 feet wide and 6 feet long.
- **How many feet of fencing will we need to completely surround our garden?** 22 feet
- Have students brainstorm different ways to find the distance around the garden.

Direct students to Student Edition p. 604. Have students read the paragraph at the top of the page.

- **What is the total surface of the woods?** 6 acres **What kind of unit is an acre?** a unit of area
- **What are some units you might use to measure the perimeter of the woods?** sample answers: yards, feet, meters

WRITING IN ▸MATH

Starting the Chapter

Ask students to name some three-dimensional figures they remember learning about in fourth grade. Then have them choose one figure and write a paragraph describing it. Ask students to include information on the number and shape of faces and talk about real-world objects that are shaped like the figure.

Key Vocabulary Introduce the key vocabulary in the chapter using the routine below.

Define: Perimeter is the distance around a shape or region.
Example: We can find the perimeter of the chalkboard by measuring all four sides.
Ask: What is the formula for perimeter?

Read-Aloud Anthology For an optional reading activity to introduce this chapter's math concepts, see the Read-Aloud Anthology on p. TR24.

Measure Perimeter, Area, and Volume

BIG Idea What are perimeter and area?

Perimeter is the distance around a closed figure. **Area** is the number of square units needed to cover a surface.

Example A Kentucky farm has 6 acres of woods with horseback riding trails. The perimeter is the distance around the woods. The area is the total surface of the woods, 6 acres.

What will I learn in this chapter?

- Find perimeters of polygons.
- Find and estimate the areas of figures by counting squares and using formulas.
- Identify characteristics of three-dimensional figures.
- Select and use appropriate units and formulas to measure length, perimeter, area, and volume.
- Solve problems by using the *make a model* strategy.

Key Vocabulary

area
perimeter
polygon
prism
three-dimensional figure

Math Online Student Study Tools at macmillanmh.com

Chapter 14 Project

It's Your Area

Students take what they've learned in measuring the area of shapes and scale it up to real life.

- Students choose a building in their town to measure. They identify the shapes used in creating the floor plan of the building, and get the measurements from an authority figure. They should also get the measurement for the height of the building or heights of each part of the building.
- Students calculate the total area of the floor plan of their chosen building. They can also calculate the total surface area of the building by calculating the area of each side of the building, using its length and height, and adding the areas of all of the surfaces.

Refer to Chapter 14 Resource Masters, p. 58, for a rubric to assess students' progress on this project.

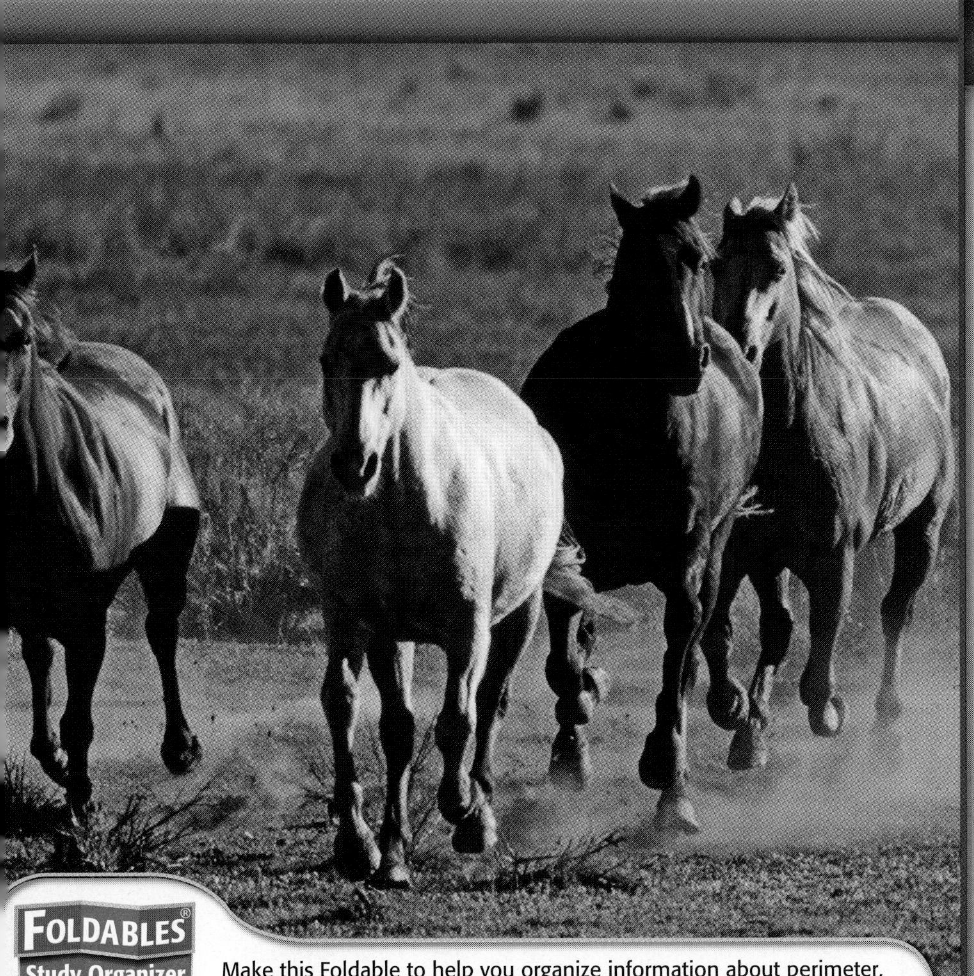

FOLDABLES® Study Organizer

Make this Foldable to help you organize information about perimeter, area, and volume. Begin with a sheet of 11″ × 17″ paper and six index cards.

1. **Fold** the paper lengthwise about 3″ from the bottom.

2. **Fold** in thirds. Open and staple the edges on either side to form three pockets.

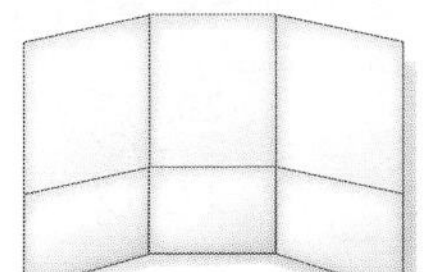

3. **Label** each pocket as shown. Place two index cards in each pocket.

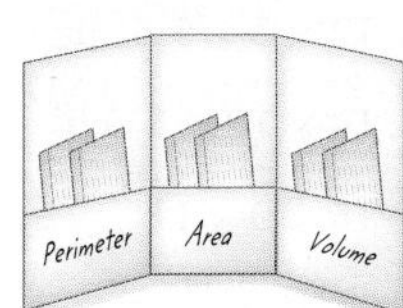

ELL National ESL Standards Alignment for Chapter 14

Lesson, Page	ESL Standards	Modality	Level
14-1, p. 608B	Goal 2, Standard 2, i	Spatial, Kinesthetic	Beginning
14-2, p. 612B	Goal 2, Standard 2, f	Logical, Visual/Spatial	Intermediate
14-3, p. 616B	Goal 1, Standard 3, e	Visual, Linguistic	Intermediate
14-4, p. 624B	Goal 1, Standard 3, k	Visual, Linguistic	Beginning
14-5, p. 628B	Goal 2, Standard 1, c	Linguistic, Logical	Advanced
14-6, p. 631B	Goal 2, Standard 2, g	Visual/Spatial, Kinesthetic	Intermediate
14-7, p. 640B	Goal 2, Standard 1, f	Linguistic, Logical	Intermediate
14-8, p. 644B	Goal 2, Standard 3, h	Kinesthetic, Logical	Advanced
14-9, p. 648B	Goal 2, Standard 1, g	Kinesthetic	Advanced

The National ESL Standards can be found in the Teacher Reference Handbook.

FOLDABLES® Dinah Zike's Foldables

Guide students through the directions on p. 605 to create their own Foldable graphic organizers for fractions. Students may also use their Foldables to study and review chapter assessments.

When to Use It Lessons 14-1, 14-2, 14-3, 14-4, 14-5, 14-6 and 14-7 (Additional instructions for using the Foldables with these lessons are found on pp. 623 and 649.)

Chapter 14 Literature List

Lesson	Book Title
14-1	**Geometry** Lucille Caron and Philip M. St. Jacques
14-2	**Sir Cumference and the Sword in the Cone** Cindy Neuschwander
14-3	**Sir Cumference and the Isle of Immeter** Cindy Neuschwander
14-4	**Sir Cumference and the Sword in the Cone** Cindy Neuschwander
14-5	**How Tall How Short How Faraway?** David A. Adler
14-6	**Geometry** Lucille Caron and Philip M. St. Jacques
14-7	**Sir Cumference and the Sword in the Cone** Cindy Neuschwander
14-8	**Sir Cumference and the Sword in the Cone** Cindy Neuschwander

- Read the Math at Home letter found on Chapter 14 Resource Master, p. 4, with the class and have each student sign it. (A Spanish version is found on p. 5.)
- Send home copies of the Math at Home letter with each student.

Diagnostic Assessment

Check for students' prerequisite skills before beginning the chapter.

- **Option 1:** ***Quick Check***

  SE Student Edition, p. 606

- **Option 2:** ***Online Assessment***

  Math Online macmillanmh.com

- **Option 3:** ***Diagnostic Test***

  CRM Chapter 14 Resource Masters, p. 54.

RTI (Response to Intervention)

Apply the Results Based on the results of the diagnostics assessment on Student Edition p. 606, use the chart below to address individual needs before beginning the chapter.

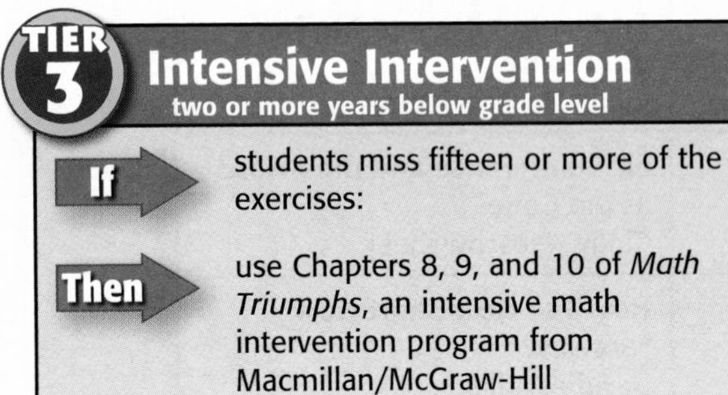

TIER 3 Intensive Intervention
two or more years below grade level

If students miss fifteen or more of the exercises:

Then use Chapters 8, 9, and 10 of *Math Triumphs*, an intensive math intervention program from Macmillan/McGraw-Hill

ARE YOU READY for Chapter 14?

You have two ways to check prerequisite skills for this chapter.

Option 2

Math Online Take the Chapter Readiness Quiz at macmillanmh.com.

Option 1

Complete the Quick Check below.

QUICK Check

Add. (Lessons 2-4, 2-6, and 10-7) (Used in Lesson 14-7)

1. $15 + 20 + 25 + 7$ 67

2. $9\frac{1}{2} + 11 + 14\frac{1}{2}$ 35

3. $8\frac{1}{4} + 12 + 12$ $32\frac{1}{4}$

4. $5 + 13 + 19$ 37

5. $16.3 + 16.3 + 16.3$ 48.9

6. $4 + 9.1 + 3.2 + 8$ 24.3

7. The amount of money that Tyrese spent shopping is shown in the table. Find the total amount that he spent. $46.49

Item	Amount ($)
CD	14.99
T-shirt	26.30
Snack	5.20

Multiply. (Lessons 3-4 and 3-6) (Used in Lesson 14-3)

8. 10×26 260

9. 12×14 168

10. 75×2 150

11. 25×48 1,200

12. 25×6 150

13. 5×32 160

14. 132×13 1,716

15. 45×45 2,025

16. Mrs. Ohlin sold 3 handmade bookshelves for $160 each. How much money did she earn in all? $480

Multiply. (Lessons 3-4 and 3-6) (Used in Lesson 14-6)

17. $12 \times 3 \times 5$ 180

18. $8 \times 6 \times 4$ 192

19. $14 \times 10 \times 3$ 420

20. $15 \times 9 \times 6$ 810

21. $13 \times 9 \times 11$ 1,287

22. $12 \times 7 \times 14$ 1,176

606 **Chapter 14** Measure Perimeter, Area, and Volume

TIER 2 Strategic Intervention below/approaching grade level	**TIER 1 On-Level**	**Above/Beyond-Level**
If students miss seven to fourteen in: **Exercises 1–22**	**If** students miss three to six in: **Exercises 1–22**	**If** students miss two or less in: **Exercises 1–22**
Then choose a resource	**Then** choose a resource	**Then** choose a resource
TE Start Smart 5: Measurement (p. 10) **Math Online** Extra Examples • Personal Tutor • Concepts in Motion	TE Learning Stations (pp. 604G–604H) TE Chapter Project (p. 604) CRM Game: Pentomino Madness Math Adventures **Math Online** Fact Dash	TE Learning Stations (pp. 604G–604H) TE Chapter Project (p. 604) Real-World Problem Solving Reader: *Exploring the World by Sea* My Math Zone Chapter 13, 14 **Math Online** Games

Measurement Activity for 14-1

Perimeters of Rectangles

MAIN IDEA

I will use models to find the perimeters of rectangles.

New Vocabulary

perimeter

The **perimeter** of a figure is the distance around the figure. Perimeter is a measure of length. The perimeter of the rectangle at the right is 6 + 4 + 6 + 4 or 20 centimeters.

6 cm

4 cm

ACTIVITY Copy and complete the table.

Rectangle	Length (ℓ)	Width (w)	2ℓ	$2w$	Perimeter (P)
	2	1	4	2	$2 + 1 + 2 + 1 = 6$
	3	1	6	2	$3 + 1 + 3 + 1 = 8$
	3	2	6	4	$3 + 2 + 3 + 2 = 10$
	4	1	8	2	$4 + 1 + 4 + 1 = 10$
	4	2	8	4	$4 + 2 + 4 + 2 = 12$

CHECK What You Know

1. WRITING IN ▸MATH Refer to the table above. How are ℓ and w related to the perimeter of the rectangles? Then use P, ℓ, and w to write an equation for the perimeter of a rectangle. **The perimeter is the sum of the sides; $P = \ell + \ell + w + w$**
2. Use the formula you wrote in Exercise 1 to find the perimeter of the rectangle. Select and use appropriate units. **26 in.**

   8 in.

   5 in.
3. In Exercise 2, only two sides of the rectangle are labeled. Explain why this is enough information to find the perimeter. **Opposite sides of a rectangle are congruent. So, the measures of opposite sides are equal.**
4. Find $2\ell + 2w$ for the rectangle in Exercise 2. Then write an equation to describe the relationship between P, ℓ, and w. **26; $P = 2(\ell + w)$**

Measurement Activity for 14-1

Lesson Planner

Objective

Use models to find the perimeters of rectangles.

Resources

Manipulatives: square tiles

1 Introduce

- Ask students to find various classroom objects shaped like rectangles, such as workbook covers or the tops of their desks. Help them identify lengths and widths.
- Choose one object. **Which two sides show length? Which show width? What do you notice about each pair of sides?** Sample answer: The two lengths are equal and parallel and the two widths are equal and parallel.

2 Teach

Activity Distribute square tiles. Model the rectangle in the first row for students. Go over how to identify the length and width and fill in each column of the table. Have students complete the table.

3 Assess

Formative Assessment

Use the Check What You Know exercises 1–4 to assess whether students understand how to use models to find the perimeters of rectangles.

Perimeters of Polygons

Lesson Planner

Objective

Find the perimeters of polygons.

Vocabulary

polygon, perimeter

Resources

Materials: yardsticks
Manipulatives: square pattern blocks, base-ten blocks
Literature Connection: *Geometry* by Lucille Caron and Philip M. St. Jacques
Teacher Technology
TeacherWorks • Interactive Classroom

Focus on Math Background

In previous grade levels, students learned to find the perimeter of any polygon by adding the lengths of all of the sides of the figure. Students will now use what they learned about evaluating expressions to find the perimeter of squares and rectangles. Patterns seen in the relationship between the perimeter and the side lengths can be written as a rule or formula for finding the perimeter of any square ($P = 4s$) or rectangle ($P = 2\ell + 2w$). It should be noted that because of the Commutative Property it does not matter which dimension is considered the length or the width.

11 in.

4 in.

$$P = 2\ell + 2w$$
$$P = 2(11) + 2(4)$$
$$= 22 + 8$$
$$= 30 \text{ in.}$$

Daily Routine

Use these suggestions before beginning the lesson on p. 608.

5-Minute Check

(Reviews Lesson 13-9)

Determine whether the transformation is a *translation*, *reflection*, or *rotation*.

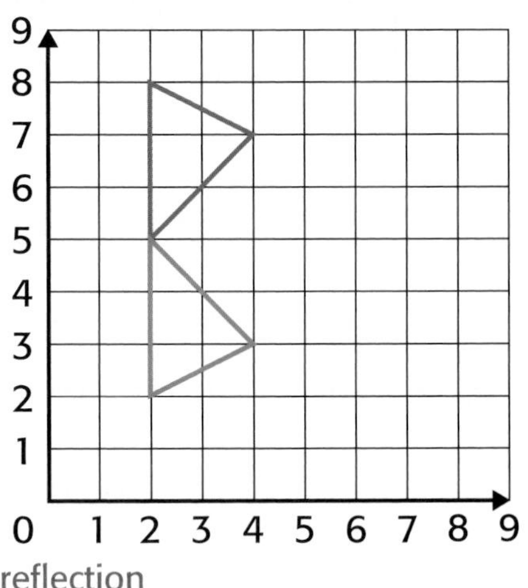

reflection

Problem of the Day

Mackenzie has 25 pages to read for homework. She read $14\frac{2}{4}$ pages then took a break. She read another $5\frac{1}{4}$ pages before dinner. How many pages does she have left to read? $5\frac{1}{4}$ pages

Building Math Vocabulary

Write the lesson vocabulary words and their definitions on the board.

Have students use paperclips to build various polygons, including rectangles and squares. Then have them count the number of paperclips around the outside of each polygon to find its perimeter.

Visual Vocabulary Cards

Use Visual Vocabulary Card 32 to reinforce the vocabulary in this lesson. (The Define/Example/Ask routine is printed on the back of each card.)

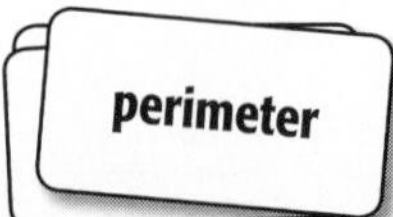

Differentiated Instruction

Small Group Options

Option 1 Below Level BL

SPATIAL

Materials: connecting cubes

- Help students model perimeter using connecting cubes to represent a fence around a figure.
- Tell students that they need to find the amount of fencing they will need for a rectangular fence that is 22 feet by 10 feet.

Option 2 English Language Learners ELL

SPATIAL, KINESTHETIC

Materials: tape measure, ruler, pencil, paper, box
Core Vocabulary: around, sides, perimeter
Common Use Verb: contain

See Math This strategy helps students comprehend that the perimeter contains the shape and that the sum of the sides equals around the whole perimeter.

- Say, "The **perimeter contains** the shape" as you model measuring the sides with a ruler.
- Record each measurement in centimeters
- Have students add or multiply to get the perimeter.
- Wrap a tape measure around the top of the box to measure its perimeter.
- Have students check their previous results with this measurement.

Use this worksheet to provide additional support for English Language Learners.

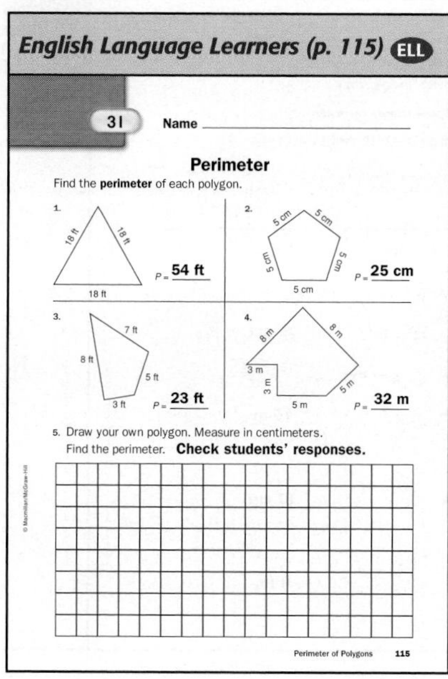

English Language Learners (p. 115) ELL

31 Name ______

Perimeter

Find the **perimeter** of each polygon.

1. 18 ft, 18 ft, 18 ft — $P =$ **54 ft**
2. 5 cm, 5 cm, 5 cm, 5 cm, 5 cm — $P =$ **25 cm**
3. 7 ft, 8 ft, 5 ft, 3 ft — $P =$ **23 ft**
4. 8 m, 8 m, 3 m, 3 m, 5 m, 5 m — $P =$ **32 m**
5. Draw your own polygon. Measure in centimeters. Find the perimeter. **Check students' responses.**

© Macmillan/McGraw-Hill

Perimeter of Polygons 115

Independent Work Options

Option 1 Early Finishers OL

KINESTHETIC

Materials: rulers, yardsticks, meter sticks

- Have students use customary and metric tools to measure the perimeter of common classroom objects, such as notebook covers and tabletops.
- Ask students to explain how they calculated the perimeters of different objects and tell how they decided upon units for each measurement.

Option 2 Student Technology

Math Online macmillanmh.com

Personal Tutor • Extra Examples

 Math Adventures

 Math Tool Chest, Attributes

Option 3 Learning Station: Science (p. 604G)

Direct students to the Science Learning Station for opportunities to explore and extend the lesson concept.

Option 4 Problem-Solving Practice

Reinforce problem-solving skills and strategies with the Problem-Solving Practice worksheet.

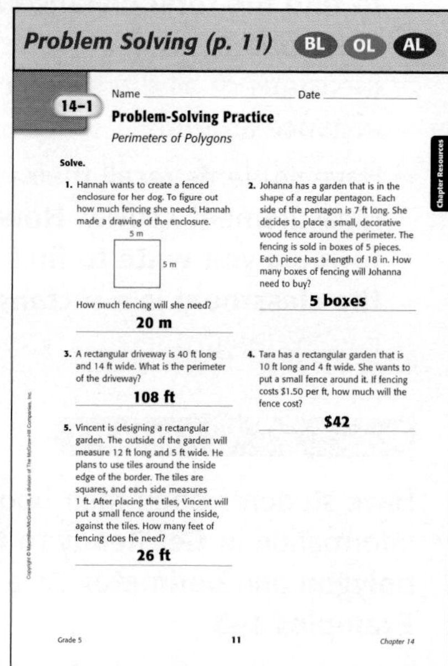

Problem Solving (p. 11) BL OL AL

14–1 Name ______ Date ______

Problem-Solving Practice

Perimeters of Polygons

Chapter Resources

Solve.

1. Hannah wants to create a fenced enclosure for her dog. To figure out how much fencing she needs, Hannah made a drawing of the enclosure.
   5 m, 5 m
   How much fencing will she need?
   20 m
2. Johanna has a garden that is in the shape of a regular pentagon. Each side of the pentagon is 7 ft long. She decides to place a small, decorative wood fence around the perimeter. The fencing is sold in boxes of 5 pieces. Each piece has a length of 18 in. How many boxes of fencing will Johanna need to buy?
   5 boxes
3. A rectangular driveway is 40 ft long and 14 ft wide. What is the perimeter of the driveway?
   108 ft
4. Tara has a rectangular garden that is 10 ft long and 4 ft wide. She wants to put a small fence around it. If fencing costs $1.50 per ft, how much will the fence cost?
   $42
5. Vincent is designing a rectangular garden. The outside of the garden will measure 12 ft long and 5 ft wide. He plans to use tiles around the inside edge of the border. The tiles are squares, and each side measures 1 ft. After placing the tiles, Vincent will put a small fence around the inside, against the tiles. How many feet of fencing does he need?
   26 ft

Copyright © Macmillan/McGraw-Hill, a division of The McGraw-Hill Companies, Inc.

Grade 5 11 Chapter 14

14-1 Perimeters of Polygons

1 Introduce

Activity Choice 1 • Hands-On

- **Is our classroom shaped like a rectangle, a square, or another shape? How do you know?** Sample answer: a rectangle, because there are four sides and four right angles, and the opposite sides are equal and parallel.
- Have small groups of students each use a yardstick to measure a different side of the classroom to the nearest foot. Then make a sketch on the board to model the classroom floor. Have students help you label the measurements of each side.

Activity Choice 2 • Literature

Introduce the lesson with *Geometry* by Lucille Caron and Philip M. St. Jacques. For a related math activity, see p. TR59.

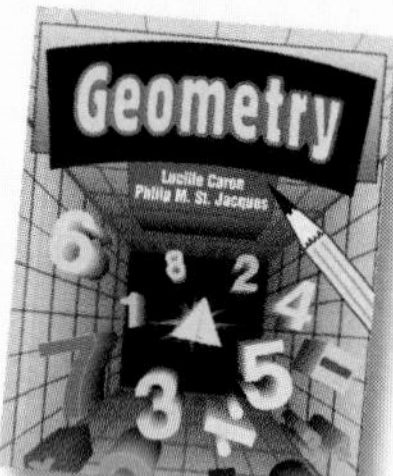

2 Teach

Scaffolding Questions

Use the classroom measurements and diagram from Activity Choice 1.

- **How did measuring the sides of the classroom help confirm that the room is a rectangle, square, or other shape?** Sample answer: Since the opposite parallel sides have the same measure and adjacent sides form square corners, the room is a rectangle.
- **How can you use the measures of the sides to find the total distance around the classroom?** Sample answer: Add the measures of all the sides to find the total distance around.
- Have students recall their work in the Explore Measurement Activity. **How can you use the formula you write to find the perimeter if the classroom is a rectangle?** The perimeter is $(2 \times \text{length}) + (2 \times \text{width})$.

GET READY to Learn

Have students open their books and read the information in **Get Ready to Learn**. Introduce **polygon** and **perimeter**. As a class, work through **Examples 1–3**.

14-1 Perimeters of Polygons

MAIN IDEA
I will find perimeters of polygons.
New Vocabulary
polygon
Math Online
macmillanmh.com
• Extra Examples
• Personal Tutor
• Self-Check Quiz

GET READY to Learn

A city park is building a fence around a dog run. They need to know the *perimeter*, or distance around the run, to determine how much fencing they will need.

A **polygon** is a closed figure made up of line segments that do not cross each other.

Polygons | **Not Polygons**

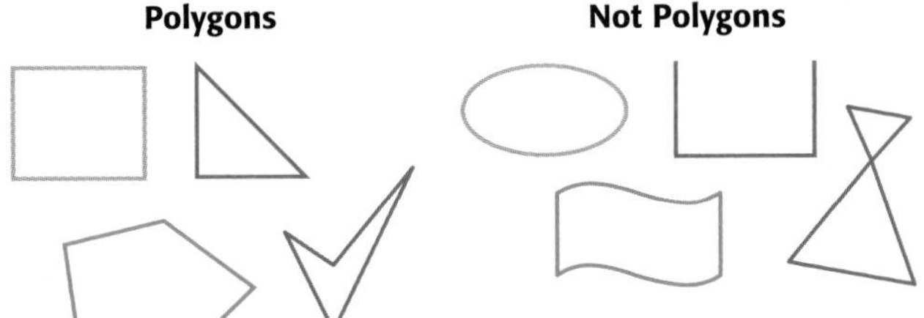

The perimeter of a polygon is measured in units of length, such as inches, feet, meters, or yards.

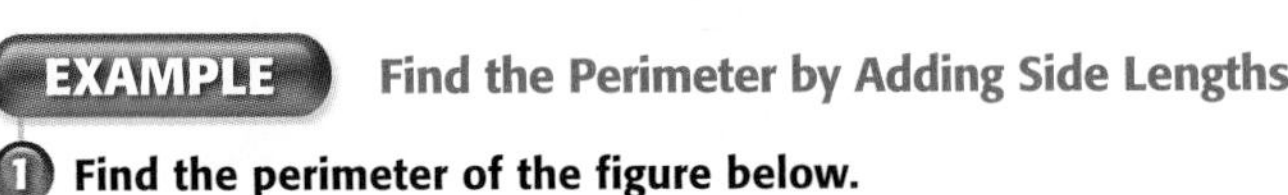

EXAMPLE Find the Perimeter by Adding Side Lengths

1 **Find the perimeter of the figure below.**

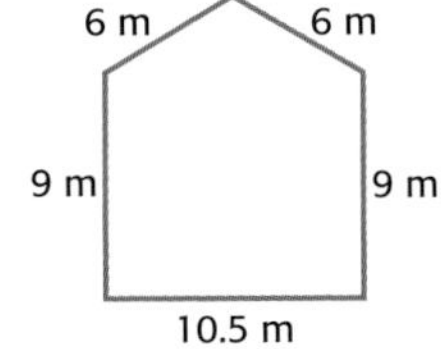

Estimate $10 + 10 + 10 + 10 + 10 = 50$ m

$P = 6 + 6 + 9 + 10.5 + 9$ Add the length of each side.
$= 40.5$

The perimeter is 40.5 meters. This is close to the estimate, so the answer is reasonable.

608 Chapter 14 Measure Perimeter, Area, and Volume

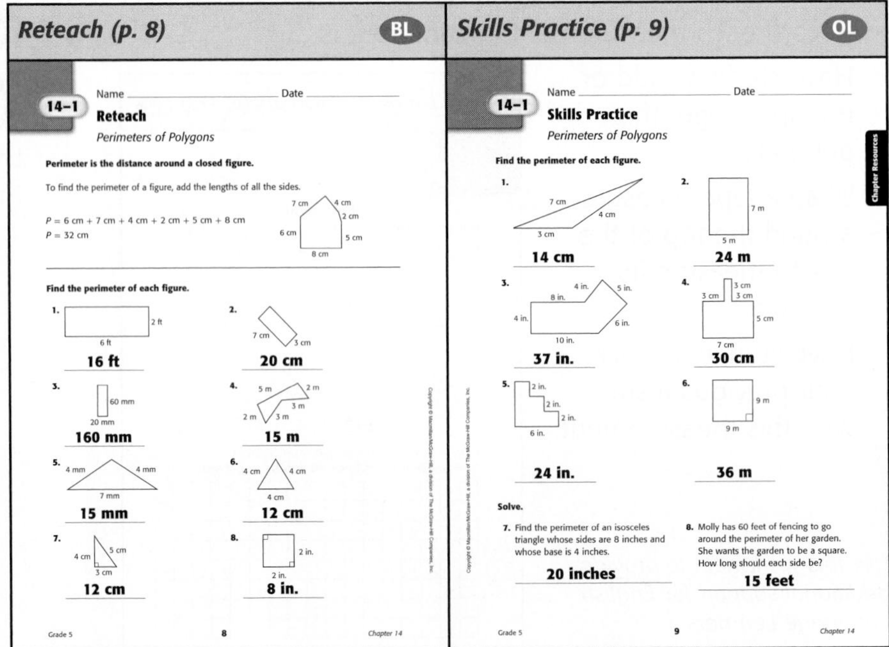

Reteach (p. 8) BL

14-1 Name ______ Date ______

Reteach

Perimeters of Polygons

Perimeter is the distance around a closed figure.

To find the perimeter of a figure, add the lengths of all the sides.

$P = 6\text{ cm} + 7\text{ cm} + 4\text{ cm} + 2\text{ cm} + 5\text{ cm} + 8\text{ cm}$
$P = 32\text{ cm}$

Find the perimeter of each figure.

1. 2 ft, 6 ft — **16 ft**
2. 7 cm, 3 cm — **20 cm**
3. 60 mm, 20 mm — **160 mm**
4. 5 m, 2 m, 3 m, 2 m, 3 m — **15 m**
5. 4 mm, 4 mm, 7 mm — **15 mm**
6. 4 cm, 4 cm, 4 cm — **12 cm**
7. 4 cm, 5 cm, 3 cm — **12 cm**
8. 2 in., 2 in. — **8 in.**

Grade 5 8 Chapter 14

Skills Practice (p. 9) OL

14-1 Name ______ Date ______

Skills Practice

Perimeters of Polygons

Find the perimeter of each figure.

1. 7 cm, 4 cm, 3 cm — **14 cm**
2. 7 m, 5 m — **24 m**
3. 4 in., 5 in., 8 in., 4 in., 6 in., 10 in. — **37 in.**
4. 3 cm, 3 cm, 3 cm, 5 cm, 7 cm — **30 cm**
5. 2 in., 2 in., 2 in., 6 in. — **24 in.**
6. 9 m, 9 m — **36 m**

Solve.

7. Find the perimeter of an isosceles triangle whose sides are 8 inches and whose base is 4 inches. **20 inches**
8. Molly has 60 feet of fencing to go around the perimeter of her garden. She wants the garden to be a square. How long should each side be? **15 feet**

Grade 5 9 Chapter 14

Chapter Resources

Remember

A square has all sides congruent. All angles are right angles.

A rectangle has both pairs of opposite sides parallel and congruent. All angles are right angles.

Hands-On Mini Activity

Copy and complete the table.

Square	1	2	3	4
Side Length (s)	1	2	3	4
Perimeter (P)	4	8	12	16

Describe the relationship between the perimeter of a square and side length. Then write an equation using P and s. The perimeter is four times the side length; $P = 4s$

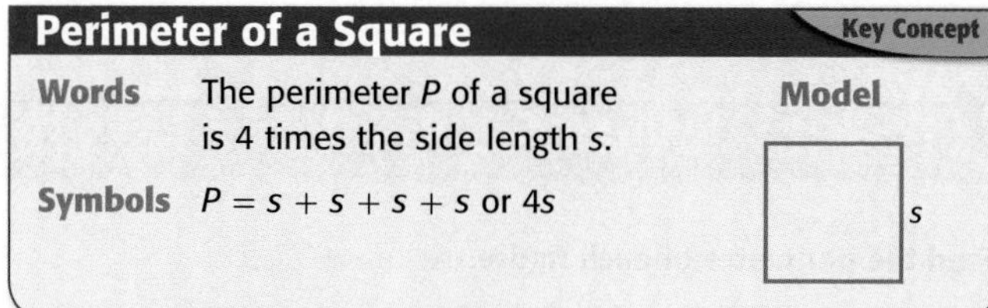

Perimeter of a Square — Key Concept

Words The perimeter P of a square is 4 times the side length s.

Symbols $P = s + s + s + s$ or $4s$

Model

Real-World EXAMPLE — Perimeter of a Square

2 ART **Hai and his uncle tiled the kitchen floor using square tiles like the one shown at the right. What is the perimeter of the tile?**

2 ft

$P = 4s$ Perimeter of a square

$P = 4(2)$ Replace s with 2.

$P = 8$ Multiply.

The perimeter of the tile is 8 feet.

Remember

You can always find the perimeter of a rectangle or square by adding the lengths of the four sides.

Perimeter of a Rectangle — Key Concept

Words The perimeter P of a rectangle is two times the length ℓ plus two times the width w.

Symbols $P = \ell + \ell + w + w$ or $2\ell + 2w$

Model

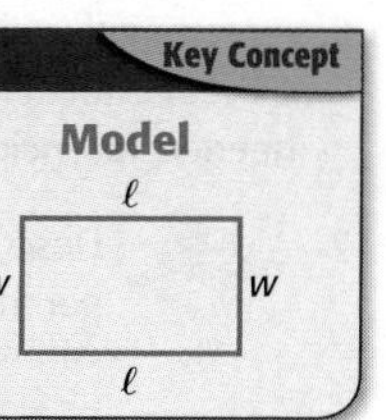

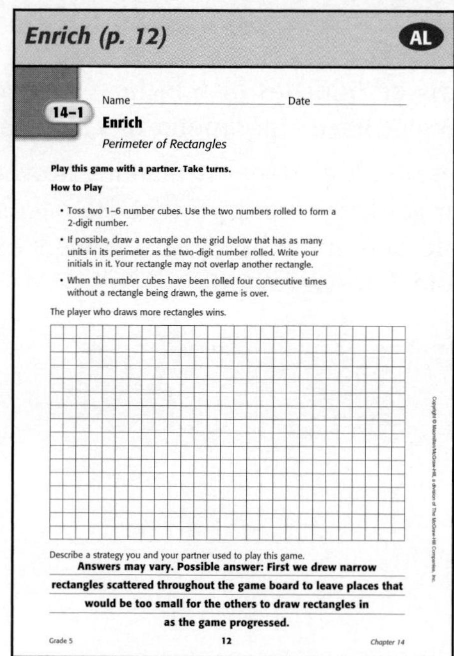

Enrich (p. 12) AL

14-1 Name ________ Date ________

Enrich

Perimeter of Rectangles

Play this game with a partner. Take turns.

How to Play

- Toss two 1–6 number cubes. Use the two numbers rolled to form a 2-digit number.
- If possible, draw a rectangle on the grid below that has as many units in its perimeter as the two-digit number rolled. Write your initials in it. Your rectangle may not overlap another rectangle.
- When the number cubes have been rolled four consecutive times without a rectangle being drawn, the game is over.

The player who draws more rectangles wins.

Describe a strategy you and your partner used to play this game. **Answers may vary. Possible answer: First we drew narrow rectangles scattered throughout the game board to leave places that would be too small for the others to draw rectangles in as the game progressed.**

Grade 5 12 Chapter 14

Hands-On Mini Activity

Remind students that when they work with measurements, they must be sure to include units in their answers. If specific units are not mentioned, the lengths are 1 unit, 2 units, etc.

Perimeter of a Square

Real-World Example 2 Remind students that the four sides of a square are equal. Help students make the connection between adding all of the sides to find the distance around a figure and the formula for finding the perimeter of square: $P = s + s + s + s = 4 \times s = 4s$.

ADDITIONAL EXAMPLES

1 Find the perimeter of the figure below.

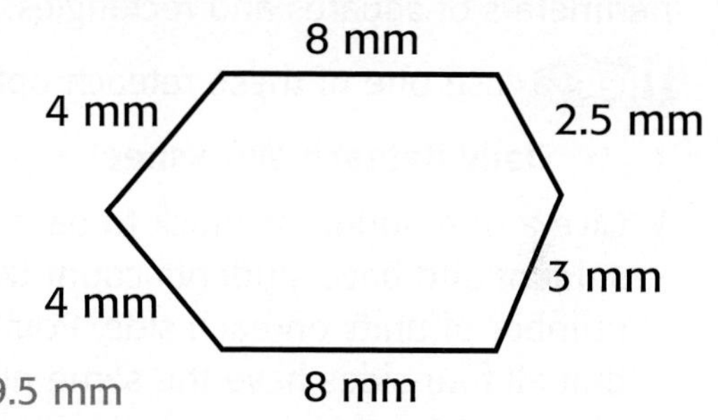

29.5 mm

2 Dyani created a collage for art class using square tiles like the one shown below. What is the perimeter of the tile?

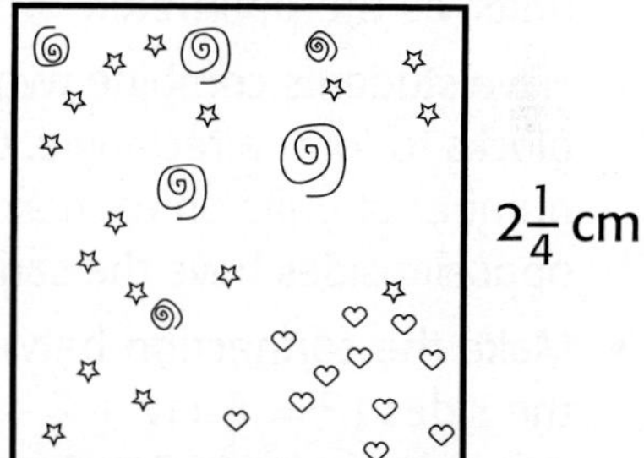

9 cm

ADDITIONAL EXAMPLE

3 Kaleb is building a fence around his rectangular garden. The garden is 8 feet long and 6 feet wide. How many feet of fencing will Kaleb need? 28 ft

CHECK What You Know

As a class, have students complete Exercises 1–7 in **Check What You Know** as you observe their work.

Exercise 7 Assess student comprehension before assigning practice exercises.

BL Alternate Teaching Strategy

If students have trouble finding the perimeters of squares and rectangles…

Then use one of these reteach options:

1. CRM **Daily Reteach Worksheet** (p. 8)
2. Give a one hundreds block to each student and have students count the number of units on each side. Point out that all four sides have the same number of units, 10.
   - Show students how adding all four sides and multiplying one side by four will produce the same measure, 40 units, as the perimeter.
   - Have students combine two hundreds blocks to form a rectangle. Count the number of units on each side. Show that opposite sides have the same length.
   - Make the connection between adding the sides ($P = \ell + w + \ell + w$) and using the formula $P = 2\ell + 2w$.
3. Tech Link Have students use Math Tool Chest to help complete the perimeter exercises.

COMMON ERROR!

Exercises 8–10 Students may accidentally leave out a side measurement when they add to calculate the perimeter of a polygon that is not a rectangle or square. Have students trace the figure on a separate sheet of paper and label the measure of each side. Then have them check off each side measure in their drawing as they write it as an addend.

Real-World EXAMPLE — Perimeter of a Rectangle

3 CRAFTS **Christa is sewing a lace border around the edges of her scrapbook. How many inches of lace will Christa need?**

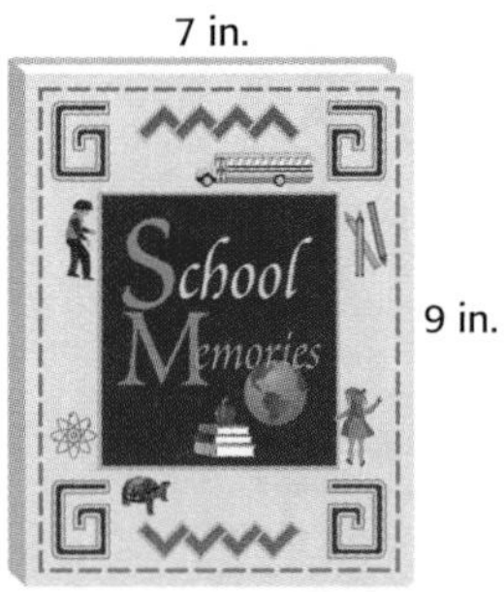

Find the perimeter of the scrapbook.

$P = 2\ell + 2w$	Perimeter of a rectangle
$P = 2(7) + 2(9)$	$\ell = 7$ and $w = 9$
$P = 14 + 18$	Multiply.
$P = 32$	Add.

So, Christa will need 32 inches of lace.

CHECK What You Know

Find the perimeter of each figure. See Example 1 (p. 608)

1. 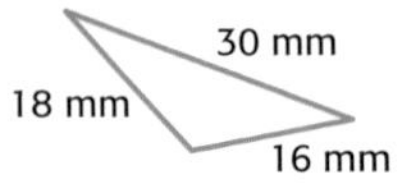

64 mm

2. 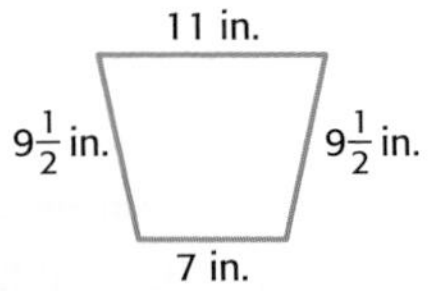

37 in.

Find the perimeter of each square or rectangle. See Examples 2, 3 (pp. 609–610)

3. 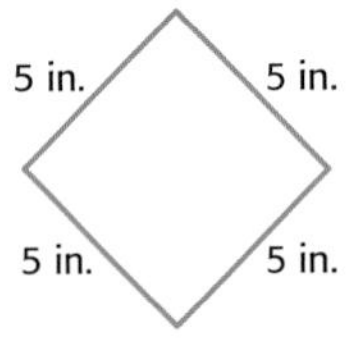

20 in.

4. 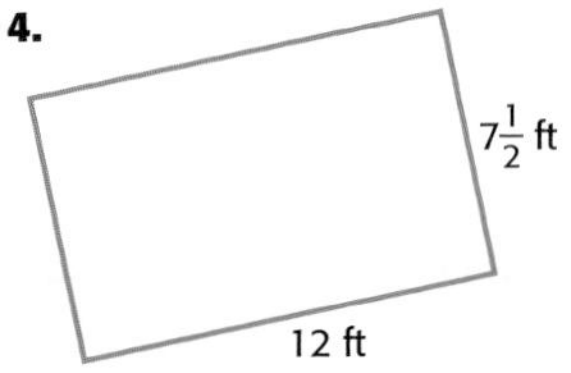

39 ft

5. 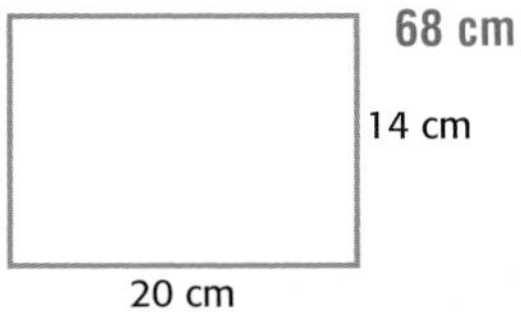

68 cm

6. A rectangular playground is 32 feet long and 14 feet wide. How many feet of edging are needed to enclose the playground? 92 ft

7. Talk About It Describe two ways to find the perimeter of a rectangle. Sample answer: Add the side measures or use the formula $P = 2\ell + 2w$.

Additional Answers

20. Sample answer: 5 inches by 6 inches; 4 inches by 7 inches; both rectangles have a perimeter of 22 inches.

21. Sample answer: A gardener is planting flowers around a rectangular garden 8 feet by 5 feet. He needs to find the perimeter to determine how many flowers to buy. What is the perimeter? Answer: 26 ft

★ indicates multi-step problem

Practice and Problem Solving

See page R37.

Find the perimeter of each figure. See Example 1 (p. 608)

8.

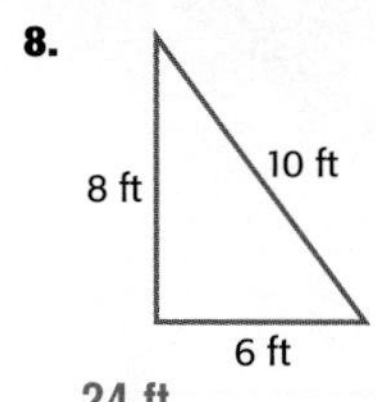

24 ft

9.

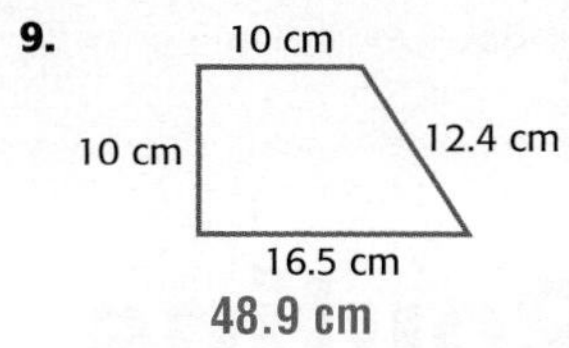

48.9 cm

10.

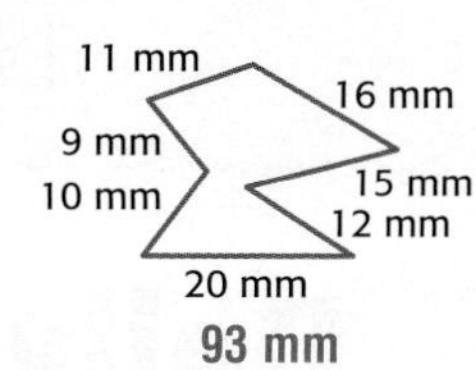

93 mm

Find the perimeter of each square or rectangle. See Examples 2, 3 (pp. 609–610) 13. $94\frac{2}{3}$ yd

11. 42 in. **12.** 32 cm **13.**

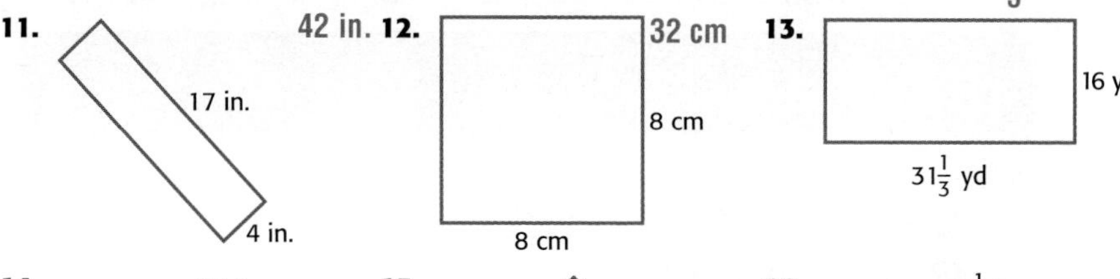

14.

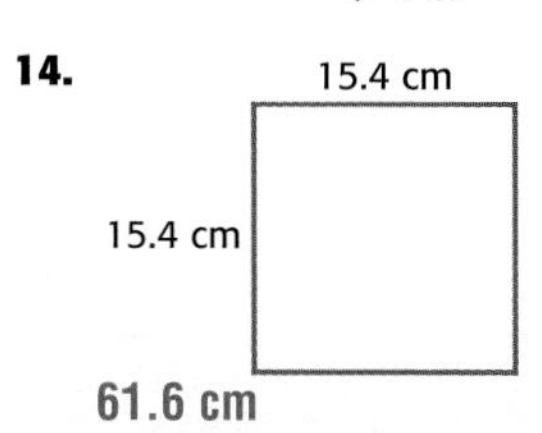

61.6 cm

15.

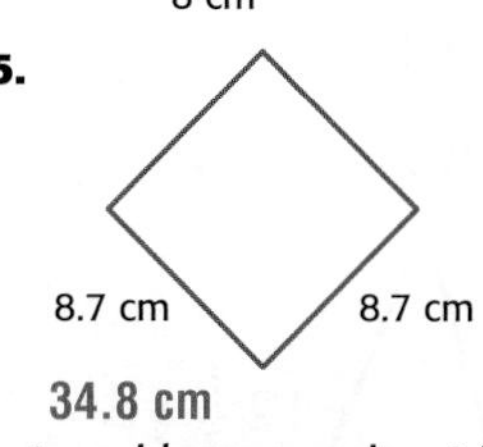

34.8 cm

16.

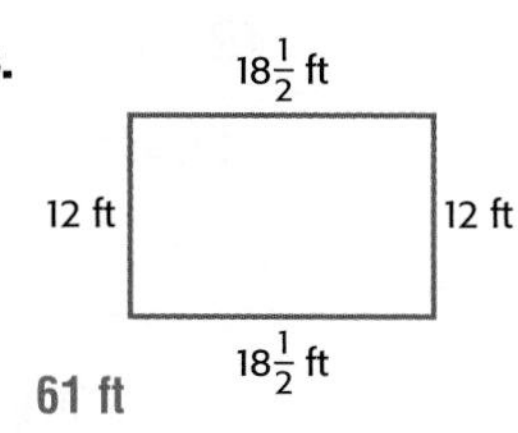

61 ft

17. An octagon-shaped table has two sides measuring 4 feet and the other sides each measuring 1 foot each. What is the perimeter of the table? 14 ft

★**18.** A billiards table is twice as long as it is wide. If the perimeter of a billiards table is 24 feet, what is the length and width of the table? 8 ft; 4 ft

19. Use a centimeter ruler to measure the side lengths rectangle shown at the right. Select and use appropriate units to find the perimetter of the rectangle. 10 cm

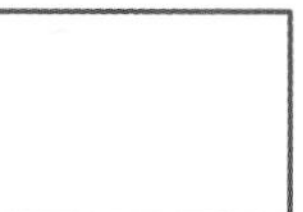

H.O.T. Problems

20–21. See margin.

20. OPEN ENDED Use a ruler to draw two different rectangles that have the same perimeter.

21. WRITING IN ▶MATH Write a real-world problem that can be solved by finding the perimeter. Then solve the problem.

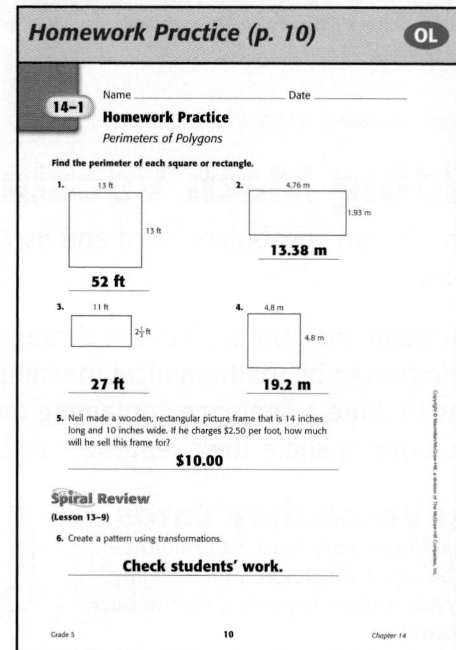

Homework Practice (p. 10) OL

14–1 Name ________ Date ________

Homework Practice

Perimeters of Polygons

Find the perimeter of each square or rectangle.

1. 13 ft; 13 ft — **52 ft**

2. 4.76 m; 1.93 m — **13.38 m**

3. 11 ft; $2\frac{1}{2}$ ft — **27 ft**

4. 4.8 m; 4.8 m — **19.2 m**

5. Neil made a wooden, rectangular picture frame that is 14 inches long and 10 inches wide. If he charges $2.50 per foot, how much will he sell this frame for? **$10.00**

Spiral Review

(Lesson 13–9)

6. Create a pattern using transformations. **Check students' work.**

Grade 5 10 Chapter 14

3 Practice

Differentiate practice using these leveled assignments for Exercises 8–21.

Level	Assignment
BL Below/ Approaching Level	8, 9, 13–15, 19–20
OL On Level	8–16, 19–22
AL Above/Beyond Level	8–19 even, 20–21

Have students discuss and complete the Higher Order Thinking problems. For Exercise 20, it may be helpful for students to begin by sketching and labeling the sides of the figures.

WRITING IN ▶MATH Have students complete Exercise 21 in their Math Journals. You may choose to use this as an optional formative assessment.

4 Assess

Formative Assessment

- **How can you find the perimeter of any kind of polygon?** Add the measures of all of the sides.
- **How can you use multiplication to find the perimeter of a rectangle?** Multiply the length by 2 and the width by 2, then add.
- **How can you use multiplication to find the perimeter of a square?** Multiply the length of one side by 4.

Quick Check **Are students continuing to struggle with finding perimeters of polygons?**

If Yes → Small Group Options (p. 608B)

If No → Independent Work Options (p. 608B)

CRM Skills Practice Worksheet (p. 9)

CRM Enrich Worksheet (p. 12)

Name the Math Sketch a rectangle with a length of 7.4 cm and width of 1.8 cm. Have students find the perimeter of the rectangle and tell what procedures they used to do so.

LESSON
14-2 Areas

Lesson Planner

Objective

Find and estimate the areas of figures by counting squares.

Vocabulary

area

Resources

Materials: grid paper, overhead projector, colored pencils
Literature Connection: *Sir Cumference and the Sword in the Cone* by Cindy Neuschwander
Teacher Technology
TeacherWorks • Interactive Classroom
Alternate Lesson: Use *IMPACT Mathematics*: Unit I to provide practice with area.

Focus on Math Background

Area gives a two-dimensional measure to a region enclosed by a shape. The area of a region describes the number of square units it takes to *cover* the region without any gaps or overlaps, and it is always expressed by a numerical value and a square unit of measure. Although some triangular and hexagonal units can cover a plane region without gaps or overlaps, the square provides the most convenient unit for area measure. Note that as students find area by counting squares, the size of the square unit determines the precision of the measurement, especially for irregular figures. For example, grid paper with 1-millimeter squares will produce a more precise value for an area than will grid paper with $\frac{1}{4}$-inch squares.

Daily Routine

Use these suggestions before beginning the lesson on p. 598.

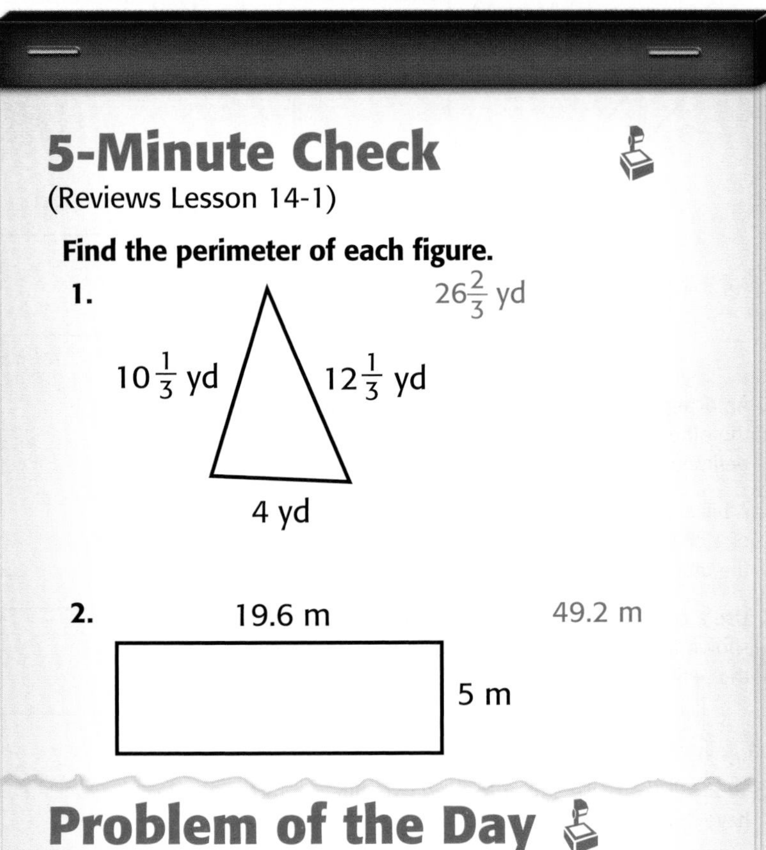

5-Minute Check

(Reviews Lesson 14-1)

Find the perimeter of each figure.

1. $26\frac{2}{3}$ yd

2. 49.2 m

Problem of the Day

The triangular banner Inez is making has three sides of equal length. She wants to put lace around the outside of the banner. If the perimeter of the banner is 3.6 feet, how much lace does she need for one side? 1.2 ft

Building Math Vocabulary

Write the lesson vocabulary word and its definition on the board.

Have students look up *area* in the dictionary and relate this definition to its mathematical meaning. Then ask students to write a sentence containing the word *area*. Have volunteers share their sentences with the class.

Visual Vocabulary Cards

Use Visual Vocabulary Card 2 to reinforce the vocabulary in this lesson. (The Define/Example/Ask routine is printed on the back of each card.)

Differentiated Instruction

Small Group Options

Option 1 LOGICAL, SPATIAL

Gifted and Talented AL

Materials: centimeter graph paper, pencils

- Review the formula for area of a rectangle.
- Draw a right triangle of any size on the graph paper.
- **How can you figure the area of this figure?** Accept any reasonable answer but you are looking for someone to realize that every triangle is $\frac{1}{2}$ of a rectangle.
- Using a dotted line, trace the other triangle, completing the rectangle.
- Now the area of the first triangle is easy to determine, since it is $\frac{1}{2}$ the area of the rectangle.
- Try this with a different triangle.

Option 2 LOGICAL, VISUAL/SPATIAL

English Language Learners ELL

Materials: 24 color tiles per student
Core Vocabulary: same, different, inside
Common Use Verb: form
Talk Math This strategy visually illustrates area as the space inside a shape.

- Review the definition of a rectangle. Draw several on the board. Use 12 tiles and ask: "Can I ***form*** a **rectangle** with these tiles?" yes, 3×4
- Give each student 24 tiles. Say: "Without talking to anyone, ***form*** a **rectangle** with these tiles." Students should make different looking rectangles (1×24; 2×12; 3×8; 4×6).
- Discuss how the rectangles are different. Draw them on the board with dimensions.
- Discuss how they are the same. Same number of tiles. Say: "The shape is **different**, but the area inside each one is the **same**."

Independent Work Options

Option 1 VISUAL/SPATIAL

Early Finishers OL

Materials: grid paper

- Have students draw four figures on grid paper: two polygons and two other figures of their choice.
- Ask students to find or estimate the area of each figure they drew in square units.
- You may extend the activity by having students exchange drawings with a partner and find or estimate the area of their partner's drawings.

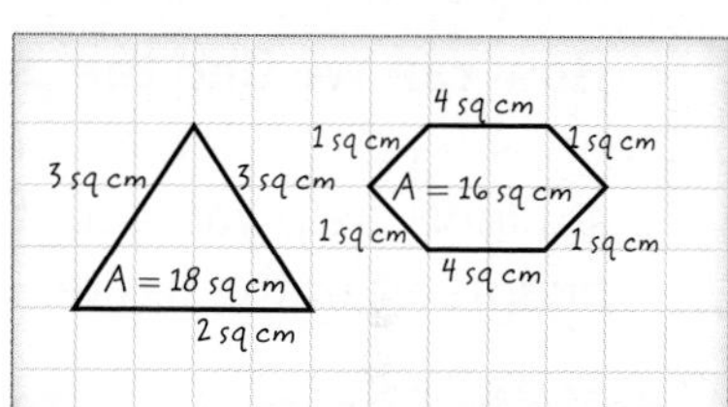

Option 2

Student Technology

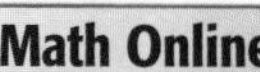

Math Online macmillanmh.com

Personal Tutor • Extra Examples

Math Adventures

Option 3

Learning Station: Social Studies (p. 604H)

Direct students to the Social Studies Learning Station for opportunities to explore and extend the lesson concept.

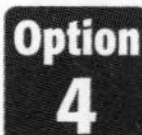

Option 4

Problem-Solving Practice

Reinforce problem-solving skills and strategies with the Problem-Solving Practice worksheet.

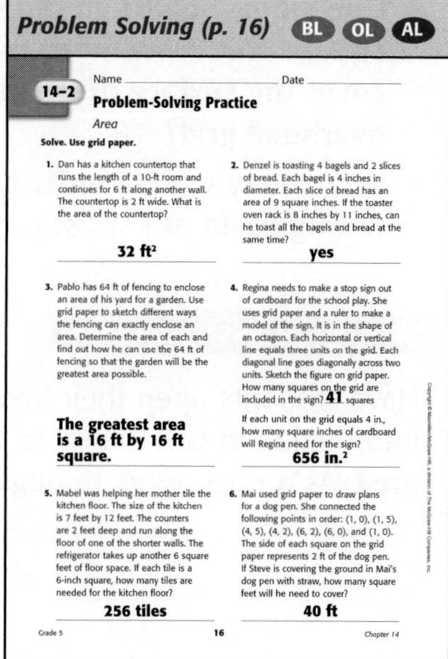

Problem Solving (p. 16) BL OL AL

14–2 Name ______ Date ______

Problem-Solving Practice

Area

Solve. Use grid paper.

1. Dan has a kitchen countertop that runs the length of a 10-ft room and continues for 6 ft along another wall. The countertop is 2 ft wide. What is the area of the countertop?
   32 ft²

2. Denzel is toasting 4 bagels and 2 slices of bread. Each bagel is 4 inches in diameter. Each slice of bread has an area of 9 square inches. If the toaster oven rack is 8 inches by 11 inches, can he toast all the bagels and bread at the same time?
   yes

3. Pablo has 64 ft of fencing to enclose an area of his yard for a garden. Use grid paper to sketch different ways the fencing can exactly enclose an area. Determine the area of each and find out how he can use the 64 ft of fencing so that the garden will be the greatest area possible.
   The greatest area is a 16 ft by 16 ft square.

4. Regina needs to make a stop sign out of cardboard for the school play. She uses grid paper and a ruler to make a model of the sign. It is in the shape of an octagon. Each horizontal or vertical line equals three units on the grid. Each diagonal line goes diagonally across two units. Sketch the figure on grid paper. How many squares on the grid are included in the sign? **41** squares

   If each unit on the grid equals 4 in., how many square inches of cardboard will Regina need for the sign?
   656 in.²

5. Mabel was helping her mother tile the kitchen floor. The size of the kitchen is 7 feet by 12 feet. The counters are 2 feet deep and run along the floor of one of the shorter walls. The refrigerator takes up another 6 square feet of floor space. If each tile is a 6-inch square, how many tiles are needed for the kitchen floor?
   256 tiles

6. Mai used grid paper to draw plans for a dog pen. She connected the following points in order: (1, 0), (1, 5), (4, 5), (4, 2), (6, 2), (6, 0), and (1, 0). The side of each square on the grid paper represents 2 ft of the dog pen. If Steve is covering the ground in Mai's dog pen with straw, how many square feet will he need to cover?
   40 ft

Grade 5 16 Chapter 14

14-2 Areas

1 Introduce

Activity Choice 1 • Hands-On

- Review perimeter with students. **What do you call the distance around a figure?** perimeter
- **What are some ways that you can calculate perimeter?** Add all the side lengths of a figure; use a formula for the perimeter of a rectangle or square.
- Draw a "L" hexagon on grid paper with side lengths of 6, 2, 4, 3, 2, and 5 units and show it to the class on the overhead projector. Point to the side of one square on the grid and remind students that it represents 1 unit.
- **How can we find the perimeter?** Count the units on each side of the shape and add. Have students help you count units and find the perimeter of the figure. 22 units

Activity Choice 2 • Literature

Introduce the lesson with *Sir Cumference and the Sword in the Cone* by Cindy Neuschwander. For a related math activity, see p. TR59.

2 Teach

Scaffolding Questions

Use the hexagon on the overhead projector from Activity Choice 1.

- **What is the measure of one side of a square in this grid?** 1 unit
- **One whole square in the grid is called a square unit. How many whole squares cover the surface of the figure on the overhead grid?** 18
- **How many square units cover the surface of the figure in all?** 18 square units

GET READY to Learn

Have students open their books and read the information in **Get Ready to Learn**. Introduce **area**. As a class, work through **Examples 1-3**.

14-2 Areas

MAIN IDEA

I will find and estimate the areas of figures by counting squares.

New Vocabulary

area

Math Online

macmillanmh.com

- Extra Examples
- Personal Tutor
- Self-Check Quiz

GET READY to Learn

A checkerboard is made up of sixty-four 1-inch squares. You can describe the board by saying that it has an *area* of 64 square inches.

Area is the number of square units that cover the surface of a closed figure.

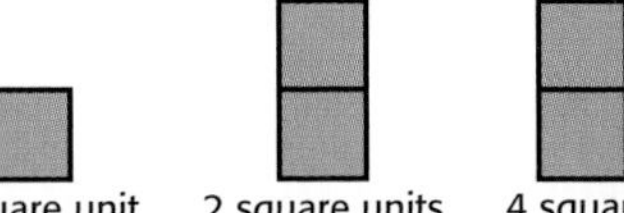

If the figure is not a square or a rectangle, count the number of whole squares and the number of half squares.

EXAMPLE Estimate Areas

1 **Find the area of the figure at the right.**

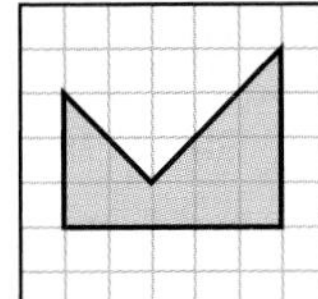

Step 1 Count the number of whole squares in the figure.

9 whole squares = 9 square units

Step 2 Count the number of half squares in the figure.

5 half squares = $2\frac{1}{2}$ square units

Step 3 Add the number of whole and half squares.

9 square units + $2\frac{1}{2}$ square units = $11\frac{1}{2}$ square units

So, the area of the figure is $11\frac{1}{2}$ square units.

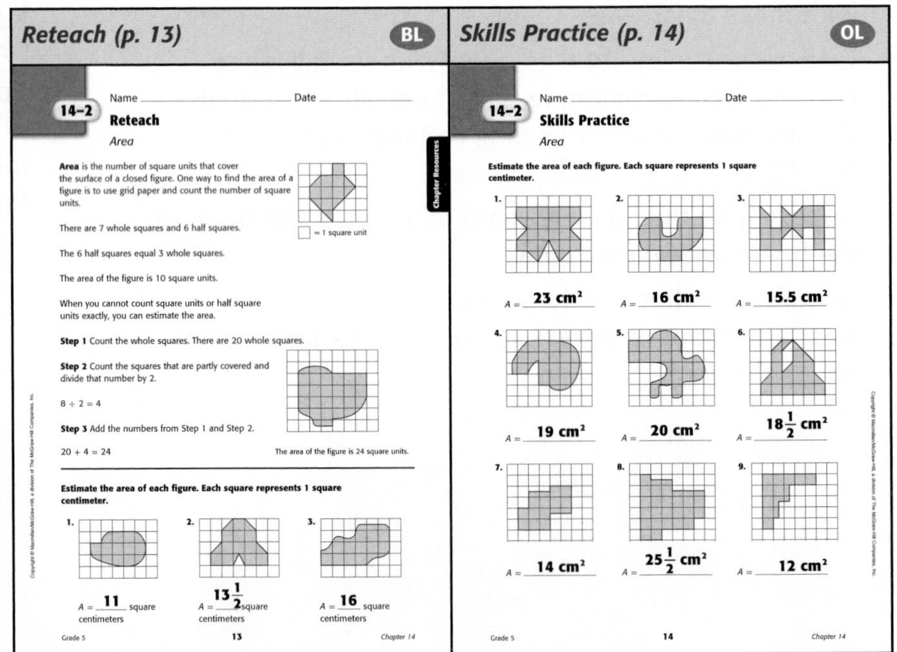

Reteach (p. 13) BL

14-2 Name ________ Date ________

Reteach

Area

Area is the number of square units that cover the surface of a closed figure. One way to find the area of a figure is to use grid paper and count the number of square units.

□ = 1 square unit

There are 7 whole squares and 6 half squares.

The 6 half squares equal 3 whole squares.

The area of the figure is 10 square units.

When you cannot count square units or half square units exactly, you can estimate the area.

Step 1 Count the whole squares. There are 20 whole squares.

Step 2 Count the squares that are partly covered and divide that number by 2.

8 ÷ 2 = 4

Step 3 Add the numbers from Step 1 and Step 2.

20 + 4 = 24

The area of the figure is 24 square units.

Estimate the area of each figure. Each square represents 1 square centimeter.

1. A = **11** square centimeters
2. A = $13\frac{1}{2}$ square centimeters
3. A = **16** square centimeters

Grade 5 13 Chapter 14

Chapter Resources

Skills Practice (p. 14) OL

14-2 Name ________ Date ________

Skills Practice

Area

Estimate the area of each figure. Each square represents 1 square centimeter.

1. A = **23 cm²**
2. A = **16 cm²**
3. A = **15.5 cm²**
4. A = **19 cm²**
5. A = **20 cm²**
6. A = $18\frac{1}{2}$ cm²
7. A = **14 cm²**
8. A = $25\frac{1}{2}$ cm²
9. A = **12 cm²**

Grade 5 14 Chapter 14

Remember

Some common units of area are *square inch*, *square foot*, *square yard*, *square mile*, *square centimeter*, and *square meter*.

When you cannot count square units or half square units exactly, you can estimate the area.

Real-World EXAMPLES — Estimate Areas

2 **TREE HOUSES The diagram shows the floor plan for a tree house. One square on the grid represents 1 square foot. About how many square feet is the area of the floor?**

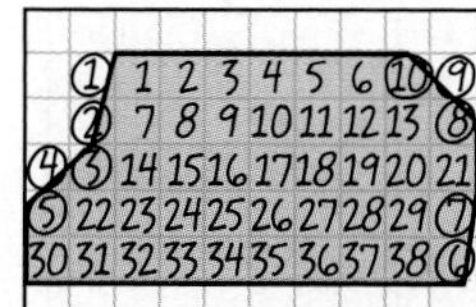

Step 1 Count the number of whole squares in the diagram.

38 whole squares = 38 square feet

Step 2 Count the partial squares circled in the diagram.

10 partial squares is about 5 square feet

Step 3 Add the number of whole and partial squares.

38 + 5 = 43 square feet

The tree house floor has an area of about 43 square feet.

3 **LANDSCAPING A landscape architect designed the pond at the right. Each square represents 1 square meter. Estimate the area of the pond.**

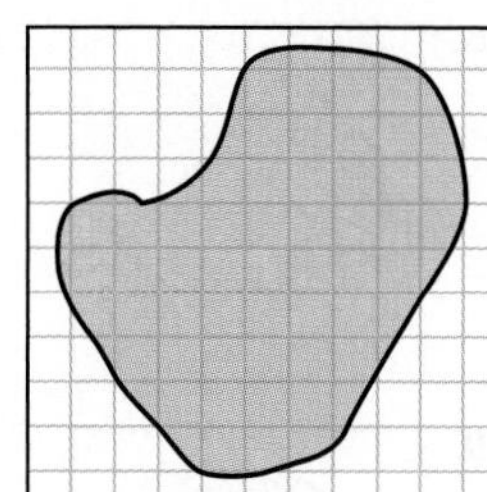

Step 1 Count the number of whole squares. There are 44 whole squares which is 44 square meters.

Step 2 Count the partial squares.

26 partial squares is about 13 square meters.

Step 3 Add the whole squares and partial squares.

44 + 13 = 57 square meters

The area of the pond is about 57 square meters.

Remember

The area of the figure on the previous page is exact. The areas of the figures in Examples 2 and 3 are estimates.

Enrich (p. 17) AL

14–2 Name ______ Date ______

Enrich

Perimeter and Area of Irregular Figures

You are a landscape designer. Your most recent project is a yard that measures 40 meters by 50 meters. You will include the features below.

- an irregularly-shaped pond that is between 100 and 200 square meters
- an irregularly-shaped vegetable garden that is between 50 and 100 square meters
- an irregularly-shaped flower garden that is between 50 and 100 square meters
- fences for the gardens
- a patio that is between 200 and 300 square meters.

Sketch your design on the grid below. Include a scale that explains what each square represents. **Check students' drawings.**

How many feet of fencing do you need for the gardens? Explain how you found your answers.

Check students' answers.

Chapter Resources

Grade 5 17 Chapter 14

Estimate Areas

Example 2 Go over this example carefully, paying particular attention to counting partial squares in Step 2. Point out that, since the figure does not have straight sides some partial squares will cover more than half of a square, and some less. Hence an estimate is needed.

ADDITIONAL EXAMPLES

1 Find the area of the figure at the right. about $9\frac{1}{2}$

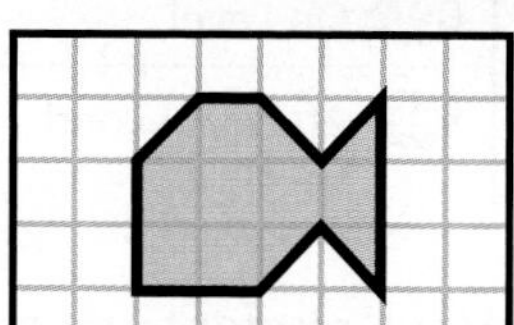

2 The diagram at the right shows the floor plan for a shed. One square on the grid represents 1 square foot. About how many square feet is the area of the shed floor? about 39 ft^2

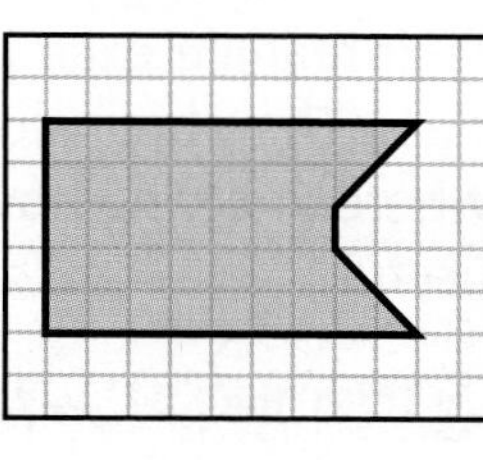

3 A lake is shown at the right. Each square represents 1 square mile. Estimate the area of the lake. Answers will vary: About 21 mi^2

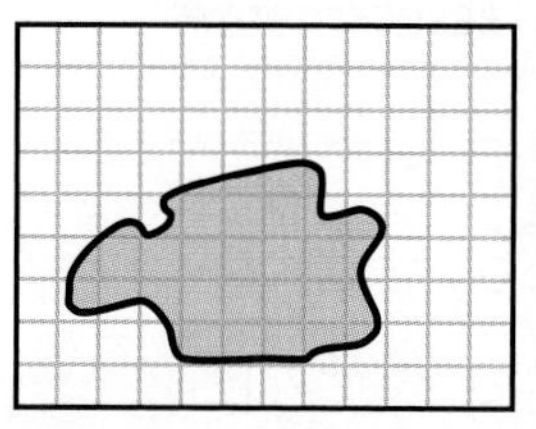

CHECK What You Know

As a class, have students complete Exercises 1–5 in **Check What You Know** as you observe their work.

Exercise 5 Assess student comprehension before assigning practice exercises.

BL Alternate Teaching Strategy

If students have trouble estimating the area of a figure…

Then use one of these reteach options:

1. CRM **Daily Reteach Worksheet** (p. 13)
2. Have students carefully trace or redraw the figure on grid paper. Tell them to shade in all of the whole squares using one colored pencil. Then have them mark off each whole square with a check mark or X as they count it. Have students use a second colored pencil to shade the partial squares and check each off after it is counted.

3 Practice

Differentiate practice using these leveled assignments for Exercises 6–15.

Level	Assignment
BL Below/ Approaching Level	6–10, 12
OL On Level	6–13, 15
AL Above/Beyond Level	6–12 even, 14–15

Have students discuss and complete the Higher Order Thinking problems. Have students share their real-life examples from Exercise 15 with the class. Then brainstorm additional situations where knowing how to estimate area would be useful.

WRITING IN ▶MATH Have students complete Exercise 15 in their Math Journals. You may choose to use this as an optional formative assessment.

COMMON ERROR!

Students may leave out the units when writing their answers. Tell students that an answer to a measurement problem is not complete without the units. To remember this important step, you may suggest that students write the units *before* estimating the area. Point out that it does not matter if units are abbreviated or written out (for example, ft^2 or square feet) as long as the correct units are part of the answer.

CHECK What You Know

Estimate the area of each figure. Each square represents 1 square centimeter. See Examples 1-3 (pp. 612–613) 1–5. Sample answers are given.

1. 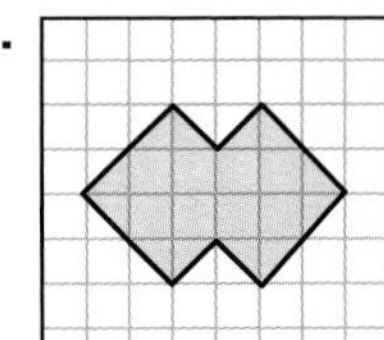 14 cm^2

2. 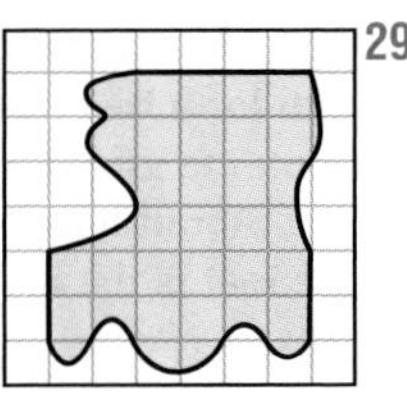 29 cm^2

3. 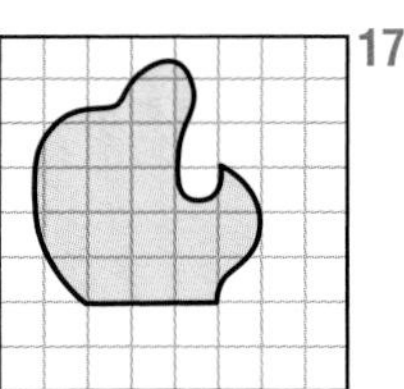 17 cm^2

4. A cake decorator is drawing a heart on a cake. Each square represents 1 square inch. Estimate the area of the heart. 28 in^2

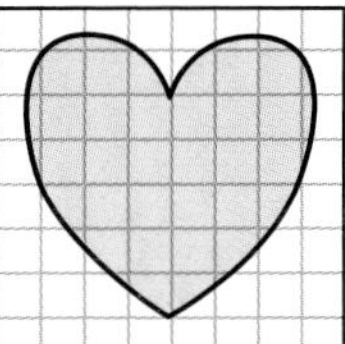

5. Talk About It Describe one way to estimate the area of an irregular figure that is drawn on grid paper. Count the number of whole squares. Then count the partial squares and divide by 2. Add the two numbers.

Practice and Problem Solving

EXTRA PRACTICE See page R37.

Estimate the area of each figure. Each square represents 1 square centimeter. See Examples 1-3 (pp. 612–613) 6–11. Sample answers are given. 10. 42 cm^2

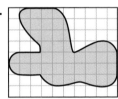

6. 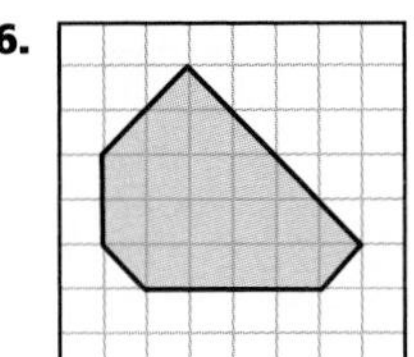 19 cm^2

7. 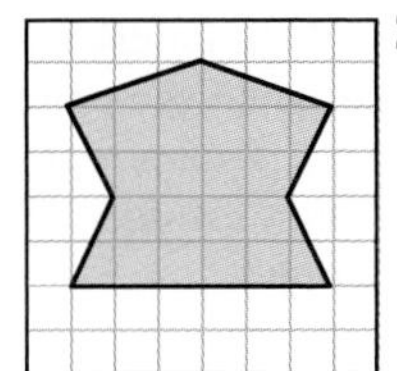 23 cm^2

8. 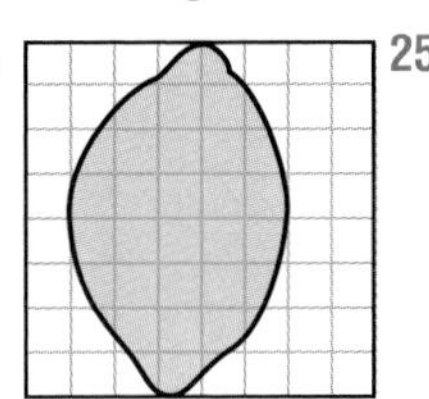 25 cm^2

9. 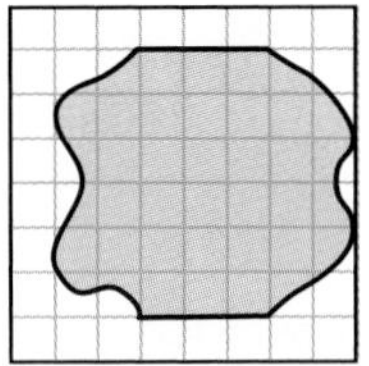 33 cm^2

10.

11. 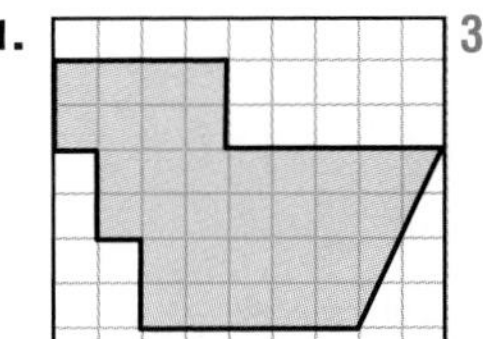 35 cm^2

12. Isaiah made a sign for his yard sale shown at the right. If each square represents 1 square inch, estimate the area of the sign. 15 in^2

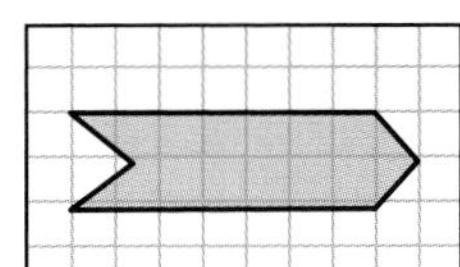

13. The flower patch at the right is on Cindy's backpack. One square represents 1 square centimeter. Estimate the total area of the patch. **Sample answer: 40 cm^2**

H.O.T. Problems

14. OPEN ENDED Draw a figure on grid paper with an approximate area of 38 square units. **See margin.**

15. WRITING IN ▸MATH Describe some real-life examples of when it would be useful to know how to estimate the area of figures. **Sample answer: finding area of cities and states; fertilizing irregular shaped gardens.**

TEST Practice

16. The student council is making a sign 8 feet long and 3 feet wide. They want to glue a colorful border around the four edges of the sign. How many feet of border will be needed? (Lesson 14-1) **B**

A 24 ft

B 22 ft

C 19 ft

D 14 ft

17. Which is the best estimate for the area of the figure? (Lesson 14-2) **H**

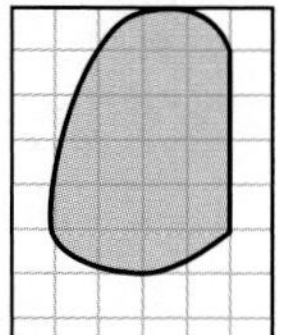

F 12 square units

G 15 square units

H 18 square units

J 24 square units

Spiral Review

Find the perimeter of each figure. (Lesson 14-1)

18. 11 ft, 11 ft **44 ft**

19.

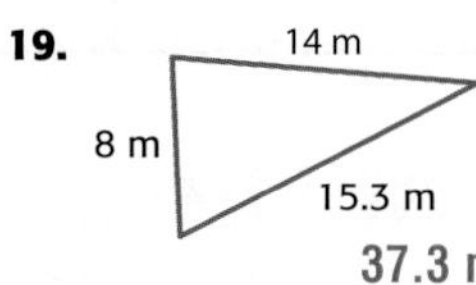

37.3 m

20. **87 in.**

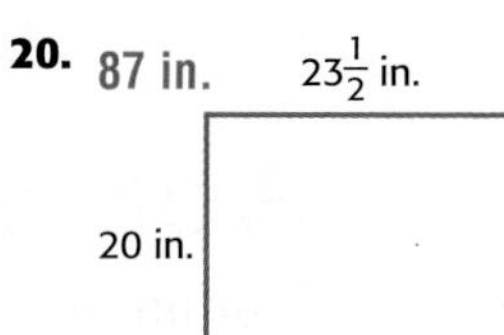

21. Triangle ABC has vertices at $A(1, 1)$, $B(4, 1)$, and $C(3, 5)$. After a transformation, the vertices are at $A(4, 1)$, $B(7, 1)$, and $C(6, 5)$. Determine whether the transformation is a translation, reflection, or rotation. (Lesson 13-9) **translation**

22. The temperature was 54°F at 3:00. Three hours later, the temperature was 48°F. Use an integer to represent the change. (Lesson 12-6) **−6**

Homework Practice (p. 15) OL

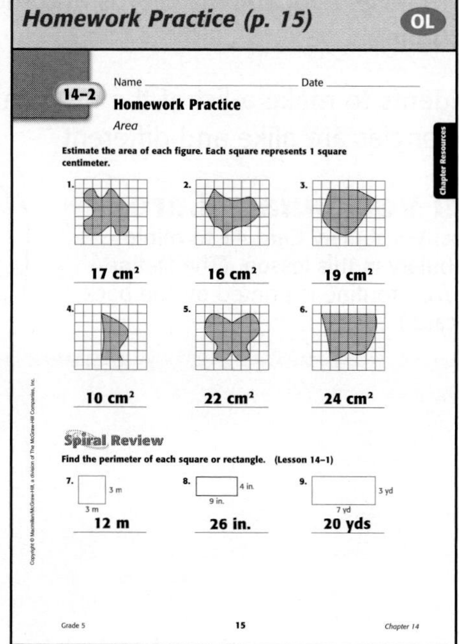

Name ______ Date ______

14-2 **Homework Practice**

Area

Estimate the area of each figure. Each square represents 1 square centimeter.

1. 17 cm²
2. 16 cm²
3. 19 cm²
4. 10 cm²
5. 22 cm²
6. 24 cm²

Spiral Review

Find the perimeter of each square or rectangle. (Lesson 14–1)

7. 3 m, 3 m — 12 m
8. 4 in., 9 in. — 26 in.
9. 3 yd, 7 yd — 20 yds

Grade 5 | 15 | Chapter 14

4 Assess

Formative Assessment

Draw a figure that is not a polygon on grid paper and show it to students on the overhead projector. Ask students to estimate the area of the figure and explain each step that they took to estimate. First, count the whole squares. Then count the partial squares and divide by 2. Add the whole squares and partial squares to estimate the total area.

Quick Check **Are students continuing to struggle with finding and estimating the areas of figures by counting squares?**

If Yes → CRM Reteach Worksheet (p. 13)

If No → Independent Work Options (p. 612B)
CRM Skills Practice Worksheet (p. 14)
CRM Enrich Worksheet (p. 17)

Into the Future Ask students to think about what they have learned so far in this chapter. Then have them write a sentence or two predicting what they think they might learn about next.

TEST Practice

Reviews Lessons 14-1 and 14-2

Assign the Test Practice problems to provide daily reinforcement of test-taking skills.

Spiral Review

Reviews Lessons 12-6, 13-9, and 14-1

Review and assess mastery of skills and concepts from previous chapters.

Additional Answer

14. Sample answer:

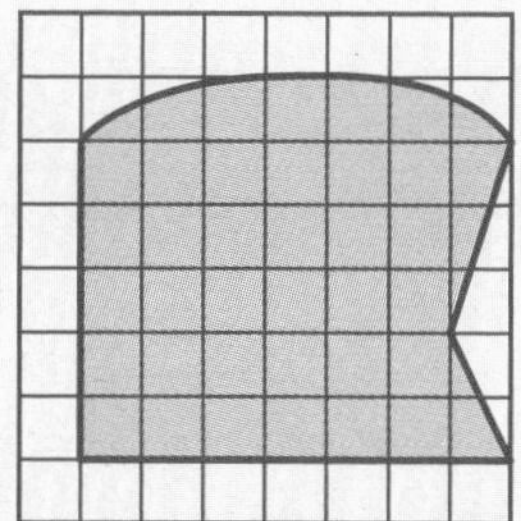

LESSON 14-3

Areas of Rectangles and Squares

Lesson Planner

Objective

Find the areas of rectangles.

Review Vocabulary

rectangle, square

Resources

Materials: grid paper
Manipulatives: geoboards, square tiles, base-ten blocks
Literature Connection: *Sir Cumference and the Isle of Immeter* by Cindy Nueschwander
Teacher Technology
TeacherWorks • Interactive Classroom
Alternate Lesson: Use *IMPACT Mathematics:* Unit I to provide practice with area.

Focus on Math Background

After finding areas of many rectangular regions by counting squares, students should be able to use their knowledge of expressions and equations to discover a formula for the area of any such region: $A = \ell \cdot w$. As with the formula for perimeter of a rectangle, it does not matter which dimension is identified as length and which as width, since multiplication is commutative. Indeed, there are many real situations in which the longer dimension of an object is referred to as its width and the shorter dimension is referred to as its length; examples include television screens, some airplanes, classrooms, etc.

Exponent notation is used to abbreviate the names of many area units: e.g., in^2, ft^2, cm^2, m^2. (Older notations, such as sq. in. for square inch, are no longer used.)

Daily Routine

Use these suggestions before beginning the lesson on p. 616.

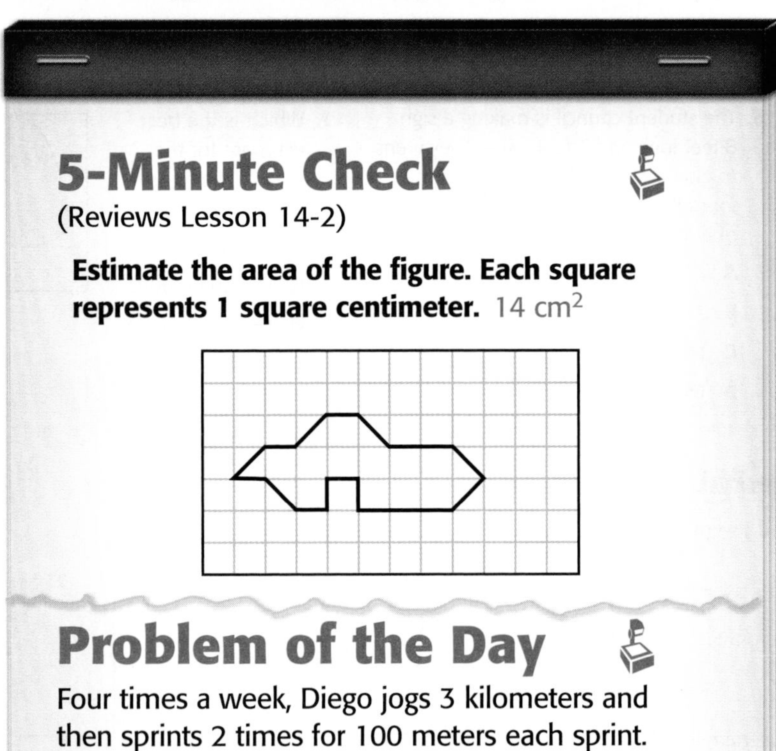

5-Minute Check

(Reviews Lesson 14-2)

Estimate the area of the figure. Each square represents 1 square centimeter. 14 cm^2

Problem of the Day

Four times a week, Diego jogs 3 kilometers and then sprints 2 times for 100 meters each sprint. What is the total number of kilometers Diego travels in his workouts each week? 12.8 km

Review Math Vocabulary

Write the review vocabulary words and their definitions on the board.

Ask students to make a list of the ways that squares and rectangles are alike and different.

Visual Vocabulary Cards

Use Visual Vocabulary Card 41 to reinforce the vocabulary in this lesson. (The Define/Example/Ask routine is printed on the back of each card.)

Differentiated Instruction

Small Group Options

Option 1 Below Level BL

SPATIAL

Materials: rulers and metersticks

- Ask students to use customary or metric units to measure the area of objects in the classroom, such as desktops and tabletops.

Option 2 English Language Learners ELL

VISUAL, LINGUISTIC

Materials: pictures of quadrilaterals, transparent grids
Core Vocabulary: syllables, to the beat, at the same time
Common Use Verb: moved

See Math This strategy helps students see how quadrilateral shapes can belong to different categories of quadrilaterals and still have the same area.

- On the board or wall, put columns headed rectangle and square.
- Review descriptions of each, and write these on the board.
- Have students place a grid over the picture and count and write the area underneath. Place each shape in the appropriate column and discuss.

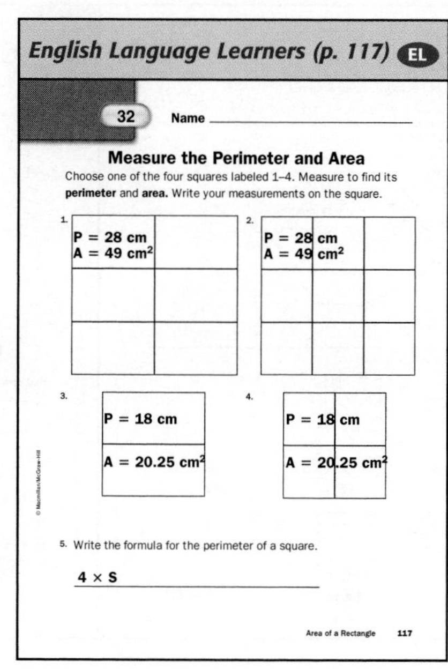

English Language Learners (p. 117) EL

32 Name ____________

Measure the Perimeter and Area

Choose one of the four squares labeled 1–4. Measure to find its **perimeter** and **area.** Write your measurements on the square.

1. P = 28 cm
A = 49 cm²

2. P = 28 cm
A = 49 cm²

3. P = 18 cm
A = 20.25 cm²

4. P = 18 cm
A = 20.25 cm²

5. Write the formula for the perimeter of a square.

4 × S

Area of a Rectangle 117

Use this worksheet to provide additional support for English Language Learners.

Independent Work Options

Option 1 Early Finishers AL

VISUAL/SPATIAL

Materials: grid paper, pencils

- Have each student draw a design using rectangles and squares.
- Have partners exchange designs, determine the dimensions, and find the area of each square or rectangle in the design.
- Students return the designs and agree that the areas given are correct.
- Suggest that each student colors his or her design.
- Display students' colored designs.

Option 2 Student Technology

Math Online macmillanmh.com

Personal Tutor • Extra Examples

Math Adventures

Option 3 Learning Station: Art (p. 604G)

Direct students to the Art Learning Station for opportunities to explore and extend the lesson concept.

Option 4 Problem-Solving Practice

Reinforce problem-solving skills and strategies with the Problem-Solving Practice worksheet.

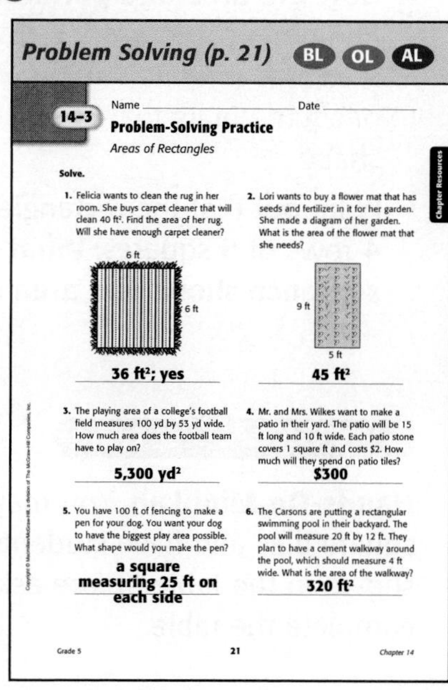

Problem Solving (p. 21) BL OL AL

14–3 Name ____________ Date ____________

Problem-Solving Practice

Areas of Rectangles

Chapter Resources

Solve.

1. Felicia wants to clean the rug in her room. She buys carpet cleaner that will clean 40 ft². Find the area of her rug. Will she have enough carpet cleaner?
6 ft, 6 ft
36 ft²; yes

2. Lori wants to buy a flower mat that has seeds and fertilizer in it for her garden. She made a diagram of her garden. What is the area of the flower mat that she needs?
9 ft, 5 ft
45 ft²

3. The playing area of a college's football field measures 100 yd by 53 yd wide. How much area does the football team have to play on?
5,300 yd²

4. Mr. and Mrs. Wilkes want to make a patio in their yard. The patio will be 15 ft long and 10 ft wide. Each patio stone covers 1 square ft and costs $2. How much will they spend on patio tiles?
$300

5. You have 100 ft of fencing to make a pen for your dog. You want your dog to have the biggest play area possible. What shape would you make the pen?
a square measuring 25 ft on each side

6. The Carsons are putting a rectangular swimming pool in their backyard. The pool will measure 20 ft by 12 ft. They plan to have a cement walkway around the pool, which should measure 4 ft wide. What is the area of the walkway?
320 ft²

Grade 5 21 Chapter 14

Areas of Rectangles and Squares

1 Introduce

Activity Choice 1 • Hands-On

- Distribute geoboards to individuals or pairs of students. Guide students to make a 3-unit-by-4 unit rectangle on the geoboard.
- **What is the length of one side of the rectangle?** 4 units **What is the width?** 3 units
- Have students calculate the perimeter of the rectangle. 14 units **What are two ways to find the perimeter?** Add the lengths of all the sides or use the formula $P = 2\ell + 2w$.
- Have students construct a square on the geoboard. **What formula can you use to find the perimeter of your square?** Use $P = 4s$.

Activity Choice 2 • Literature

Introduce the lesson with *Sir Cumference and the Isle of Immeter* by Cindy Neuschwander. For a related math activity, see p. TR59.

2 Teach

Scaffolding Questions

Have students construct a 4-unit-by-5-unit rectangle on their geoboards.

- **What is the length of the rectangle?** 5 units **the width?** 4 units **the perimeter?** 18 units
- **How many square units cover the surface of the rectangle?** 20 square units **What measurement does this represent?** area
- **How are area and perimeter different?** Perimeter measures the distance around the rectangle in units. Area measures the number of square units that cover the surface of the shape.
- Point out that the rectangle is an array with 4 rows of 5 squares. **What multiplication sentence shows the area of this rectangle?** $4 \times 5 = 20$

GET READY to Learn

Hands-On Mini Lab You may wish to distribute square tiles and have students make the figures shown in the table *before* asking students to complete the table.

14-3 Areas of Rectangles and Squares

MAIN IDEA

I will find the areas of rectangles.

Math Online

macmillanmh.com
- Extra Examples
- Personal Tutor
- Self-Check Quiz

GET READY to Learn

The largest flying American Flag is located in Gaston, North Carolina. The flag is 114 feet long and 65 feet wide. What is the area of the flag?

Hands-On Mini Activity

Copy and complete the table below. Use centimeter cubes to create and measure the rectangles shown.

Rectangle				
Length (ℓ)	3	3	4	4
Width (w)	1	2	2	3
Area (A)	3	6	8	12

a. Study the pattern in the table. How are the length and width of the rectangles related to the areas? length times width equals area

b. Use A, ℓ, and w to write a formula for the area of a rectangle. $A = \ell w$

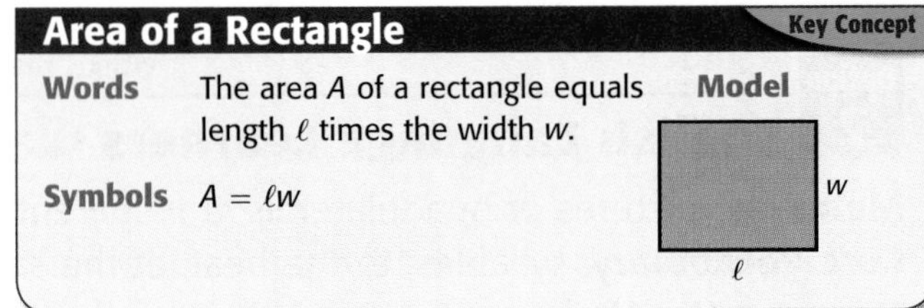

Area of a Rectangle — Key Concept

Words The area A of a rectangle equals length ℓ times the width w.

Symbols $A = \ell w$

Model

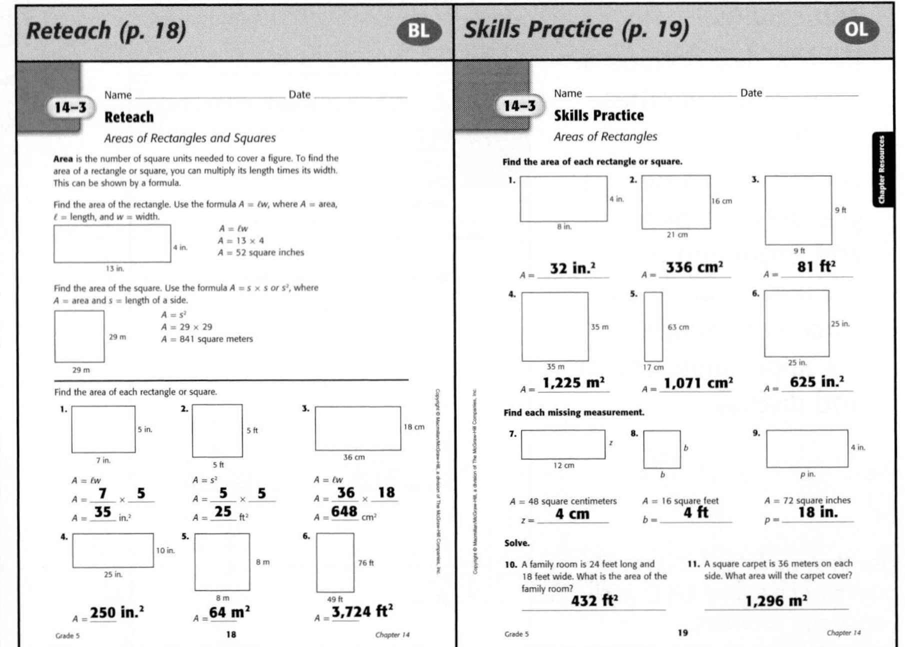

Reteach (p. 18) BL

14-3 Name ______ Date ______

Reteach

Areas of Rectangles and Squares

Area is the number of square units needed to cover a figure. To find the area of a rectangle or square, you can multiply its length times its width. This can be shown by a formula.

Find the area of the rectangle. Use the formula $A = \ell w$, where A = area, ℓ = length, and w = width.

13 in. × 4 in.

$A = \ell w$
$A = 13 \times 4$
$A = 52$ square inches

Find the area of the square. Use the formula $A = s \times s$ or s^2, where A = area and s = length of a side.

29 m × 29 m

$A = s^2$
$A = 29 \times 29$
$A = 841$ square meters

Find the area of each rectangle or square.

1. 7 in. × 5 in. $A = \ell w$; $A =$ **7** × **5**; $A =$ **35** in.^{2}
2. 5 ft × 5 ft $A = s^2$; $A =$ **5** × **5**; $A =$ **25** ft^2
3. 36 cm × 18 cm $A = \ell w$; $A =$ **36** × **18**; $A =$ **648** cm^2
4. 25 in. × 10 in. $A =$ **250 in.^{2}**
5. 8 m × 8 m $A =$ **64 m^2**
6. 49 ft × 76 ft $A =$ **3,724 ft^2**

Grade 5 18 Chapter 14

Skills Practice (p. 19) OL

14-3 Name ______ Date ______

Skills Practice

Areas of Rectangles

Find the area of each rectangle or square.

1. 8 in. × 4 in. $A =$ **32 in.^{2}**
2. 21 cm × 16 cm $A =$ **336 cm^2**
3. 9 ft × 9 ft $A =$ **81 ft^2**
4. 35 m × 35 m $A =$ **1,225 m^2**
5. 17 cm × 63 cm $A =$ **1,071 cm^2**
6. 25 in. × 25 in. $A =$ **625 in.^{2}**

Find each missing measurement.

7. 12 cm × z; $A = 48$ square centimeters; $z =$ **4 cm**
8. b × b; $A = 16$ square feet; $b =$ **4 ft**
9. p in. × 4 in.; $A = 72$ square inches; $p =$ **18 in.**

Solve.

10. A family room is 24 feet long and 18 feet wide. What is the area of the family room? **432 ft^2**
11. A square carpet is 36 meters on each side. What area will the carpet cover? **1,296 m^2**

Grade 5 19 Chapter 14

Chapter Resources

Real-World EXAMPLE — Area of a Rectangle

Remember

Different shapes have different formulas for area.

1 FLAGS Refer to the information at the beginning of the lesson. Find the area of the flag that is described.

The rectangle at the right represents the flag. The flag is 114 feet long and 65 feet wide.

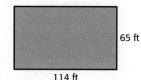

$A = \ell w$	Formula for area of a rectangle
$A = 114 \times 65$	Replace ℓ with 114 and w with 65.
$A = 7{,}410$	Multiply.

The area of the flag is 7,410 square feet.

Recall that a square is a rectangle with four congruent sides. Each side length is represented by s. So, you can replace ℓ and w in the formula $A = \ell w$ with s.

Remember

The expression s^2 is read *s squared* because its model forms a square with side s.

Area of a Square — Key Concept

Words The area A of a square equals the square of the side length s.

Symbols $A = s \times s$ or $A = s^2$

Model

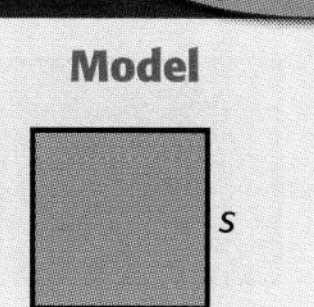

Real-World EXAMPLE — Area of a Square

2 SPORTS A baseball diamond is actually a square. Find the area of the baseball diamond at the right.

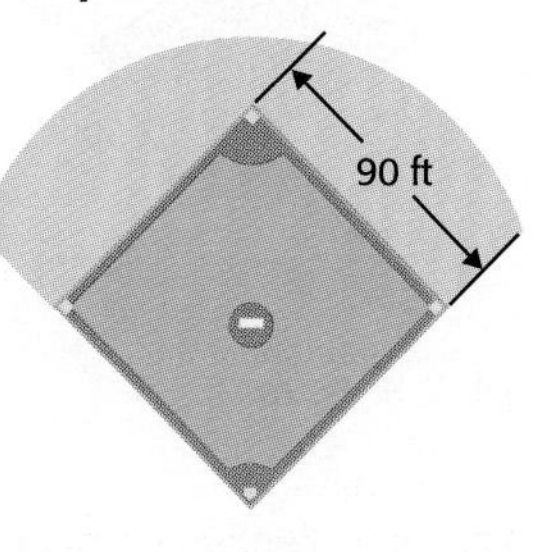

$A = s^2$	Formula for area of a square
$A = 90 \times 90$	Replace s with 90.
$A = 8{,}100$	Simplify.

The area of the baseball diamond is 8,100 square feet.

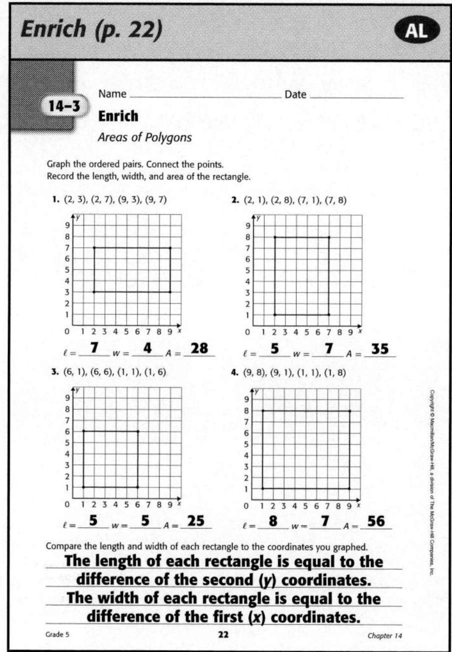

Enrich (p. 22) AL

14–3 Name ______ Date ______

Enrich

Areas of Polygons

Graph the ordered pairs. Connect the points.
Record the length, width, and area of the rectangle.

1. (2, 3), (2, 7), (9, 3), (9, 7)
ℓ = **7** w = **4** A = **28**

2. (2, 1), (2, 8), (7, 1), (7, 8)
ℓ = **5** w = **7** A = **35**

3. (6, 1), (6, 6), (1, 1), (1, 6)
ℓ = **5** w = **5** A = **25**

4. (9, 8), (9, 1), (1, 1), (1, 8)
ℓ = **8** w = **7** A = **56**

Compare the length and width of each rectangle to the coordinates you graphed.
The length of each rectangle is equal to the difference of the second (*y*) coordinates. The width of each rectangle is equal to the difference of the first (*x*) coordinates.

Grade 5 22 Chapter 14

Area of a Square

Example 2 Students may be confused by the exponent in the formula for the area of a square, $A = s^2$. Emphasize that s^2 simply means $s \times s$, or side $\times$ side.

ADDITIONAL EXAMPLES

1 A rectangular flag is 18 inches long and 12 inches wide. Find the area of the flag. 216 in^2

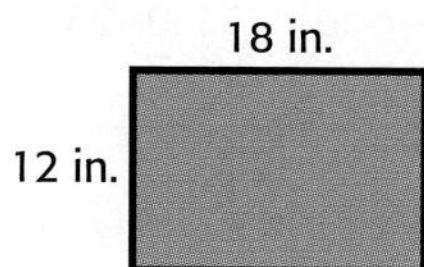

2 Find the area of the square parking lot shown below. 529 yd^2

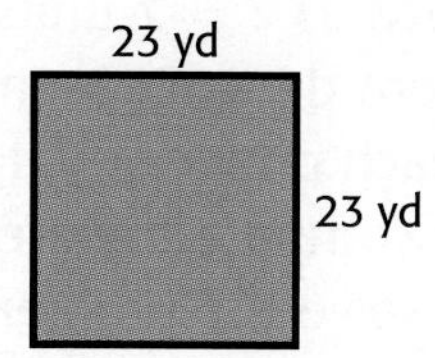

CHECK What You Know

As a class, have students complete Exercises 1–7 in **Check What You Know** as you observe their work.

Exercise 7 Assess student comprehension before assigning practice exercises.

BL Alternate Teaching Strategy

If students have trouble using formulas to find the areas of squares and rectangles …

Then use one of these reteach options:

1 CRM **Daily Reteach Worksheet** (p. 18)

2 Give a one hundreds block to each student and ask them how they might find the area. Point out that there are 10 rows with 10 squares in each row. Help students understand that, they may multiply the number of rows by the number of squares in each row to find the total number of squares, 100.

- Next, have students combine two hundreds blocks to form a rectangle. **How could you use multiplication to find the area of this rectangle?** Multiply the number of rows by the number of squares in each row.
- Have students develop a rule for finding the area of rectangles and squares.

3 Practice

Differentiate practice using these leveled assignments for Exercises 8–28.

Level	Assignment
BL Below/ Approaching Level	8–10, 14–16, 18, 20–22, 26–28
OL On Level	8–22, 28
AL Above/Beyond Level	9–25 odd, 26–28

Have students discuss and complete the Higher Order Thinking problems. For Exercise 27, encourage students to start by drawing a rectangle and labeling it with a simple length and width, such as $\ell = 2$ units and $w = 3$ units. Then have them draw a second larger rectangle and double each dimension. Have them calculate and compare the areas of the two rectangles to solve the problem.

WRITING IN MATH Have students complete Exercise 28 in their Math Journals. You may choose to use this as an optional formative assessment.

COMMON ERROR!

Students may not write areas in square units. For example, they may write that the area of a 2 ft-by-7 ft rectangle is 14 ft instead of 14 ft^2. Remind students that units of area are always square units. To illustrate this have students sketch rectangles and squares from the lesson exercises on grid paper to help them visualize area as "squares."

CHECK What You Know

Find the area of each rectangle or square. See Examples 1, 2 (p. 617)

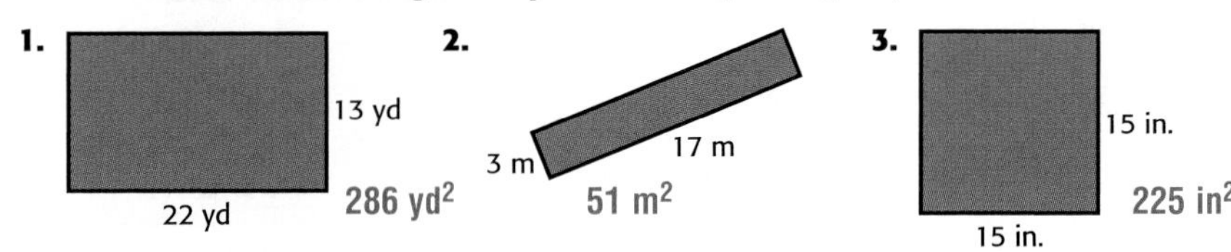

1. $286\ yd^2$
2. $51\ m^2$
3. $225\ in^2$

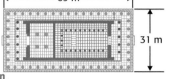

4. $\ell = 9$ km, $w = 1$ km $9\ km^2$
5. $\ell = 8$ cm, $w = 6$ cm $48\ cm^2$
6. The Parthenon of ancient Greece had the rectangular floor plan shown at the right. How much area does the building cover? $2{,}139\ m^2$

69 m
31 m

7. **Talk About It** Write the formulas for the area of a rectangle and a square. Explain what each variable represents. See margin.

★ indicates multi-step problem

Practice and Problem Solving

Find the area of each rectangle or square. See Examples 1, 2 (p. 617)

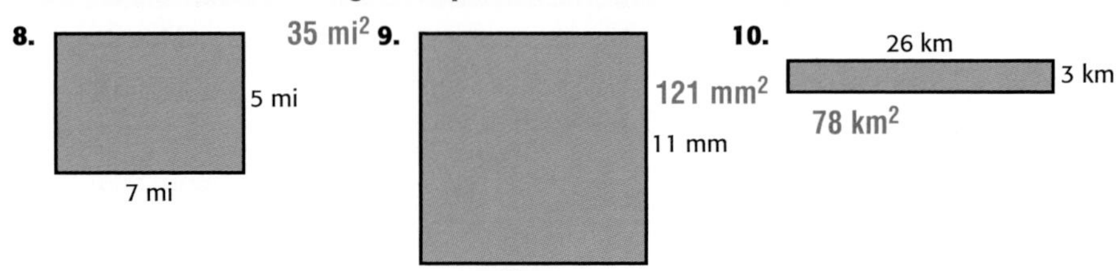

8. $35\ mi^2$
9. $121\ mm^2$
10. $78\ km^2$

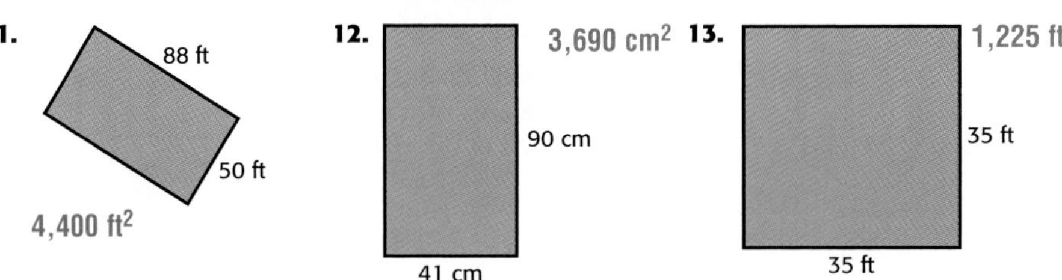

11. $4{,}400\ ft^2$
12. $3{,}690\ cm^2$
13. $1{,}225\ ft^2$

14. $\ell = 18$ m, $w = 5$ m $90\ m^2$
15. $\ell = 24$ m, $w = 37$ m $888\ m^2$
16. $\ell = 12$ cm, $w = 10$ cm $120\ cm^2$
17. Use a centimeter ruler to draw two different rectangles and one square that each have an area of 16 square centimeters. See students' work.

Additional Answer

7. rectangle: $A = \ell \times w$, where A = area, ℓ = length, and w = width; square: $A = s^2$, where A = area and s = side length

18. Use a centimeter ruler to measure the side lengths of the figures shown. Select and use appropriate formulas and units to find the area. **See margin.**

19. A square has an area of 196 square inches. What is the side length? **14 in.**

★20. The four boxes whose bases are described in the table are being used as props for the school's spring play. They can not take up more than 90 square feet of area on the stage. Can all the boxes be used? Explain. **See margin.**

Box	Length (ft)	Width (ft)
1	4	3
2	5	4
3	6	2
4	2	8

★21. A soccer field has to be 100 to 130 yards long and 50 to 100 yards wide. Find the least and greatest areas for the soccer field. **5,000 yd^2; 13,000 yd^2**

★22. The door of a new building measures 7 feet by 3 feet. It is to be covered with 12-inch square metal tiles that cost $15 each. How much will it cost to cover the door? Explain. **See margin.**

Data File

All of the license plates in the United States may have a different design, but they all come in one standard size.

License Plate Size	
Customary Units	Metric Units
12 in. × 6 in.	300 mm × 150 mm

Find the area of the license plate using each type of unit.

23. square inches **72 in^2**

24. square millimeters **45,000 mm^2**

25. square centimeters **450 cm^2**

H.O.T. Problems

26. **OPEN ENDED** Give the dimensions of a rectangle whose area is between 100 and 200 square centimeters. Find the area. **Sample answer: 10 cm by 11 cm; 110 cm^2**

27. **CHALLENGE** Suppose you double the length and the width of a rectangle. Would the area also double? Explain. **No; the area is 4 times as great.**

28. **WRITING IN ▶MATH** Write about a real-life situation that can be solved by finding the area of a rectangle. Then solve. **See margin.**

Homework Practice (p. 20) OL

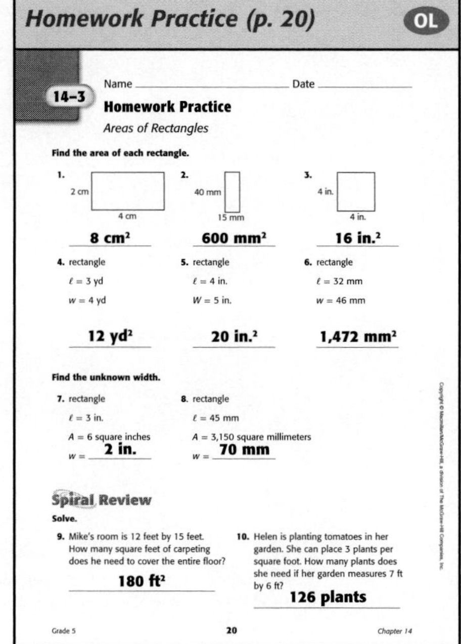

14-3 Name ____ Date ____

Homework Practice

Areas of Rectangles

Find the area of each rectangle.

1. 2 cm, 4 cm — **8 cm²**
2. 40 mm, 15 mm — **600 mm²**
3. 4 in., 4 in. — **16 in.²**
4. rectangle ℓ = 3 yd, w = 4 yd — **12 yd²**
5. rectangle ℓ = 4 in., w = 5 in. — **20 in.²**
6. rectangle ℓ = 32 mm, w = 46 mm — **1,472 mm²**

Find the unknown width.

7. rectangle ℓ = 3 in., A = 6 square inches, w = **2 in.**
8. rectangle ℓ = 45 mm, A = 3,150 square millimeters, w = **70 mm**

Spiral Review

Solve.

9. Mike's room is 12 feet by 15 feet. How many square feet of carpeting does he need to cover the entire floor? **180 ft²**
10. Helen is planting tomatoes in her garden. She can place 3 plants per square foot. How many plants does she need if her garden measures 7 ft by 6 ft? **126 plants**

Grade 5 20 Chapter 14

4 Assess

Formative Assessment

- **What could be the lengths and widths of two different rectangles with an area of 36 square inches?** Sample answers: $\ell = 4$ in., $w = 9$ in.; $\ell = 3$ in., $w = 12$ in.
- **What is the side length of a square with an area of 36 square inches?** 6 in.
- **How are finding the area of a rectangle and finding the area of a square alike and different?** You multiply length times width for both a square and a rectangle, but the length and the width are equal in measure for a square.

Quick Check **Are students continuing to struggle with finding the areas of rectangles?**

If Yes → Small Group Options (p. 616B)

If No → Independent Work Options (p. 616B)
CRM Skills Practice Worksheet (p. 19)
CRM Enrich Worksheet (p. 22)

Yesterday's News Ask students to write about how estimating the areas of figures by counting squares in Lesson 14-2 helped them with today's lesson on finding the areas of rectangles.

Additional Answers

18. rectangle: 3 cm × 4 cm = 12 cm; square: 3 cm × 3 cm = 9 cm
20. Yes; the sum of the four base areas is 12 ft^2 + 20 ft^2 + 12 ft^2 + 16 ft^2 or 60 ft^2. So, the boxes take up less than 90 ft^2.
22. $315; 7 × 3 = 21 ft^2. Since 12-inch squares are the same as 1-ft squares, 21 tiles are needed; 21 × $15 = $315.
28. Sample answer: A wall 8 feet high and 14 feet wide is to be painted. How many square feet need to be painted? Answer: 112 ft^2

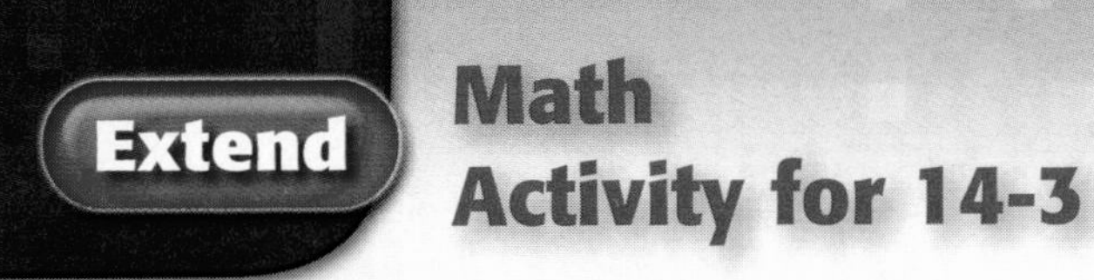

Lesson Planner

Objective

To use models to find the area of parallelograms.

Resources

Materials: grid paper, scissors

1 Introduce

Introduce the Concept

- Have students draw a 4-cm by 3-cm rectangle on grid paper.
- **What is the area of the rectangle?** 12 cm^2
- Have them draw and find the area of a 7-cm by 3-cm rectangle. 21 cm^2
- **How can you find the area of a rectangle that is 8 cm long and 5 cm wide without counting the squares inside the figure?** Multiply 8 by 5.
- **Find the area.** 40 cm^2

2 Teach

Activity 1 and 2 Emphasize to students that the shape has changed but the area stayed the same.

Activity 3 This Activity requires that students do the reverse of what was done in Activities 1 and 2.

Extend

Math Activity for 14-3

Areas of Parallelograms

MAIN IDEA

I will use models to find the area of parallelograms.

You Will Need
graph paper

You can create a parallelogram from a rectangle. The area of the parallelogram will be the same as the area of the rectangle.

ACTIVITY

1 Step 1 Cut out a rectangle using grid paper like the one shown below. The area is 8 square units.

Step 2 Cut a triangle from one side of the rectangle and move it to the other side to form a parallelogram.

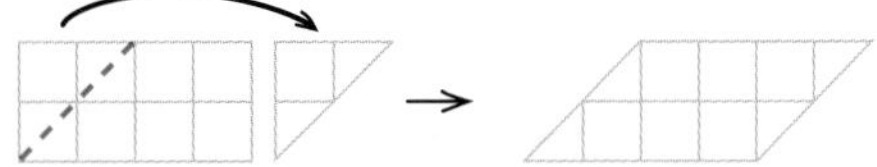

The area is still 8 square units.

ACTIVITY

2 Step 1 Cut out a rectangle using graph paper like the one shown below. The area is 12 square units.

Step 2 Cut a triangle from one side of the rectangle and move it to the other side to form a parallelogram.

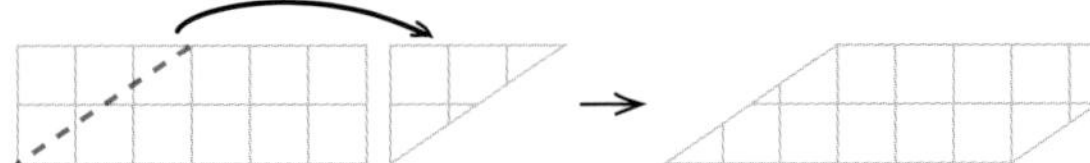

The area is still 12 square units.

ACTIVITY

3 Find the area of the parallelogram to the right by using a model.

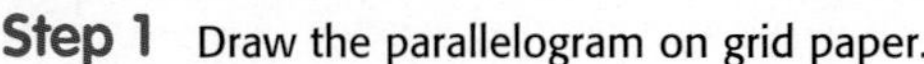

Step 1 Draw the parallelogram on grid paper.

Step 2 Fold and cut along the dotted line.

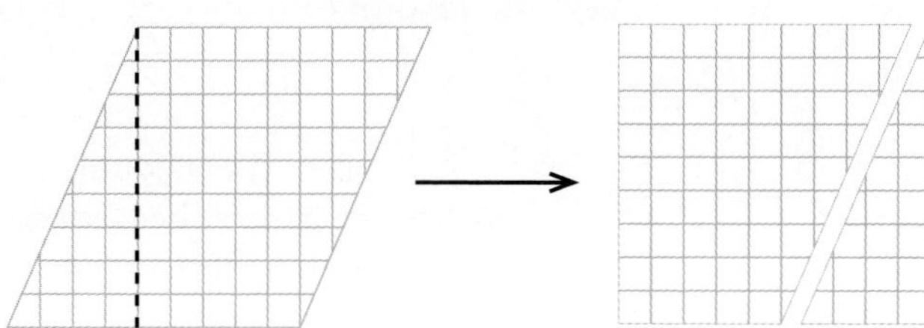

Step 3 Move the triangle to the right to make a square.

Step 4 Count up the number of units in the square or use the formula $A = \ell w$.
$A = 81$ square units

Think About It

1. Explain how to use a model to find the area of a parallelogram. **1. Sample answer: Cut one side of a parallelogram and move it to the opposite side to make a rectangle.**

CHECK What You Know

Use a model to find the area of each parallelogram.

2. 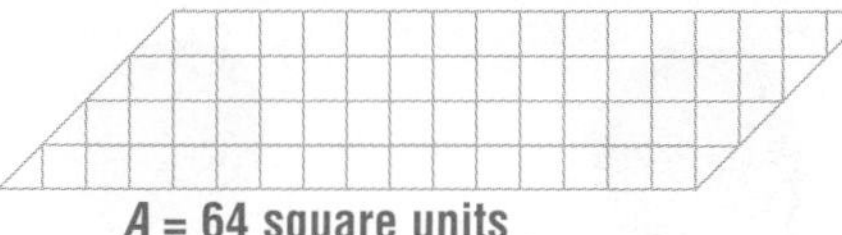 $A = 64$ square units

3.  $A = 12$ square units

4. 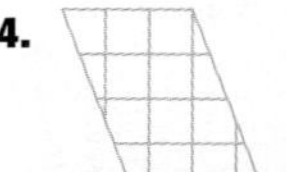 $A = 15$ square units

5. 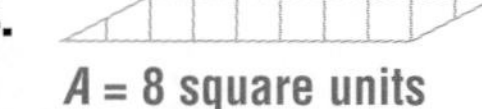 $A = 8$ square units

6. **WRITING IN ▶MATH** The formula for finding the area of a rectangle is $A = \ell w$. Can the same formula be used to find the area of a parallelogram? **Sample answer: No, the sides of a parallelogram are not perpendicular.**

3 Assess

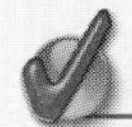

Formative Assessment

Use the **Check What You Know** exercises to assess whether students comprehend how to find the area of a parallelogram using models.

Extending the Concept

Have students use a straightedge to draw and label a rectangular parallelogram with a base of 4 squares and a height of 5 squares on graph paper. They can estimate the area by counting the squares and partial squares within the parallelogram.

- Ask students to count the full squares first and then figure out ways to count the partial squares. Discuss the strategies students used. Use the idea of combining partial squares to form whole squares.

From Concrete to Abstract Use Exercise 6 to link using a model to using a formula to find the area of a parallelogram.

What's The Area?

Math Concept: Measuring Areas

Materials: 18 index cards with sketches of different sized rectangles, centimeter ruler, paper, pencils

Introduce the game on p. 632 to your students to play as a class, in small groups, or at a learning workstation to review concepts introduced in this chapter.

Instructions

- Students play in groups of 2 to 4 players. They shuffle the cards and place them facedown in a pile on the table.
- Player 1 turns the first card face up. Players take turns turning over the cards for each round.
- All players estimate the area of the rectangle on the card in square centimeters, record it on their own paper. Then players work together to measure the rectangle and calculate its actual area. They need to select and use appropriate units and formulas.
- All players compare their estimates with the actual area. The player or players with the closest estimate earns 1 point.
- Play continues until all the cards have been used up. The player with the most points wins.

Extend the Game

Have students make the game using cards they make themselves. Have them trade decks with other teams so that they are not using the deck they created.

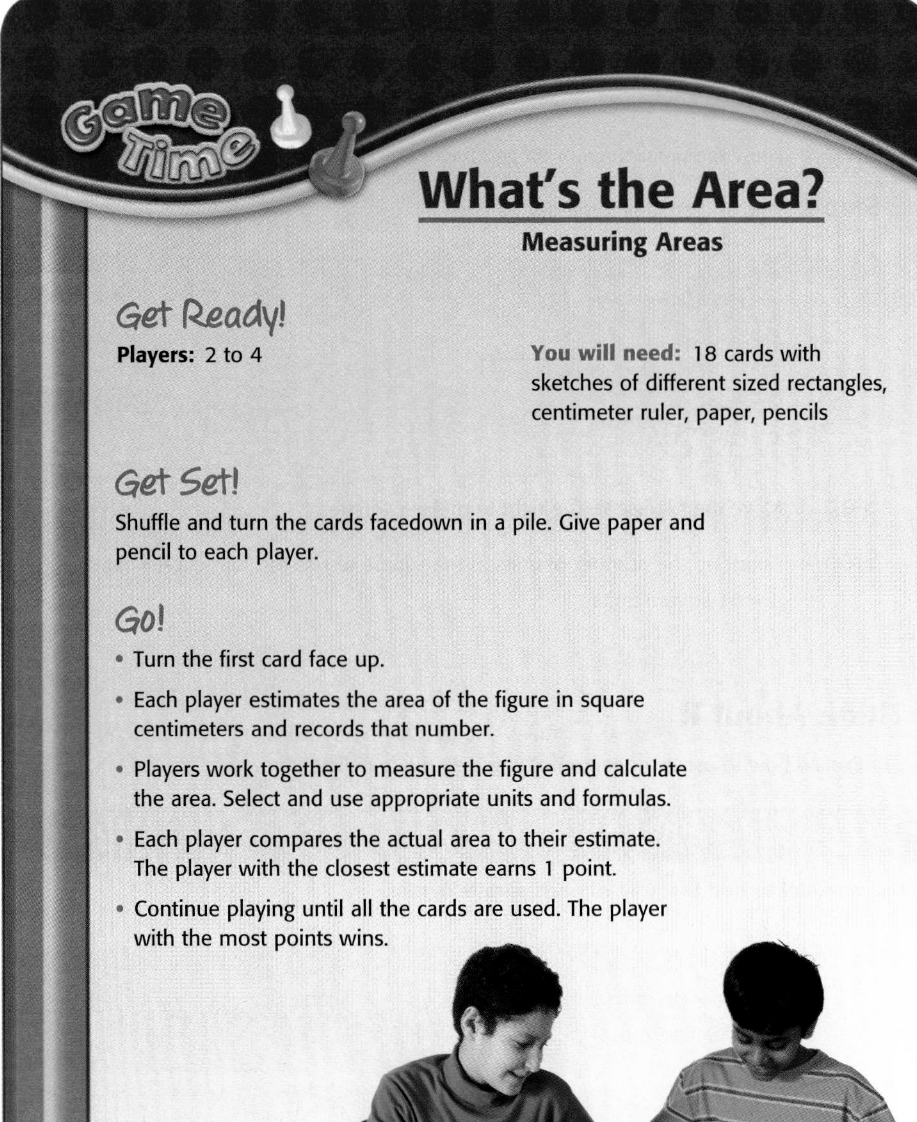

Game Time

What's the Area?

Measuring Areas

Get Ready!

Players: 2 to 4

You will need: 18 cards with sketches of different sized rectangles, centimeter ruler, paper, pencils

Get Set!

Shuffle and turn the cards facedown in a pile. Give paper and pencil to each player.

Go!

- Turn the first card face up.
- Each player estimates the area of the figure in square centimeters and records that number.
- Players work together to measure the figure and calculate the area. Select and use appropriate units and formulas.
- Each player compares the actual area to their estimate. The player with the closest estimate earns 1 point.
- Continue playing until all the cards are used. The player with the most points wins.

622 **Chapter 14** Measure Perimeter, Area, and Volume

Differentiated Practice

Use these leveled suggestions to differentiate the game for all learners.

Level	Assignment
BL Below/ Approaching Level	Students measure one side of a shape and use that hint to help them estimate the area.
OL On Level	Have students play the game with the rules as written.
AL Above/Beyond Level	Students calculate the area alone first, and get a point only if their calculation of the exact area is correct.

Mid-Chapter Check

Lessons 14-1 through 14-3

Find the perimeter of each square or rectangle. (Lesson 14-1)

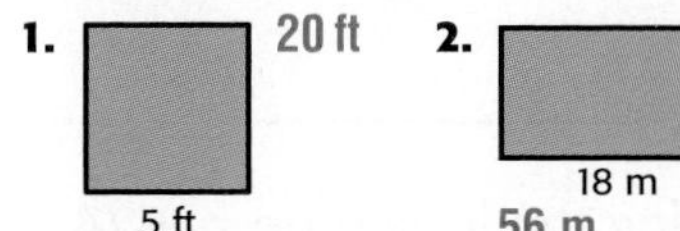

1. 20 ft
2. 56 m

3. **MULTIPLE CHOICE** Chelsea wants to plant flowers around her triangle-shaped garden. The sides of the garden measure 2 yards, 3 yards 2 feet, and 8 feet. What is the perimeter of the garden in feet? (Lesson 14-1) B
   - **A** 15 ft
   - **B** 25 ft
   - **C** 41 ft
   - **D** 47 ft

4. A horse stall is a square with a side length of 12 feet. What is the perimeter of the stall? (Lesson 14-1) 48 ft

5. A doghouse is a rectangle that measures $2\frac{1}{3}$ feet by 3 feet. What is the perimeter of the doghouse? (Lesson 14-1) $10\frac{2}{3}$ ft

Estimate the area of each figure. Each square represents 1 square foot. (Lesson 14-2) 6–7. Sample answers are given.

6. 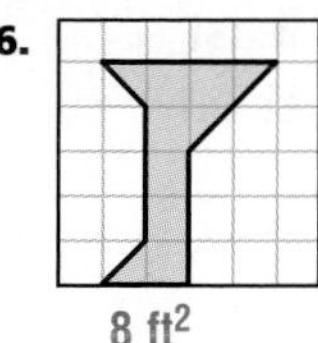
   8 ft²

7. 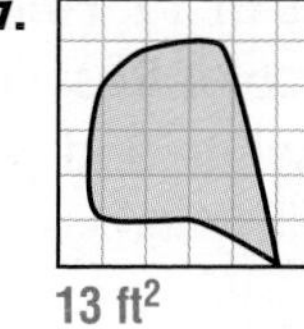
   13 ft²

8. Estimate the area of the stop sign below. (Lesson 14-2) about 41 units²

Find the area of each rectangle or square. (Lesson 14-3)

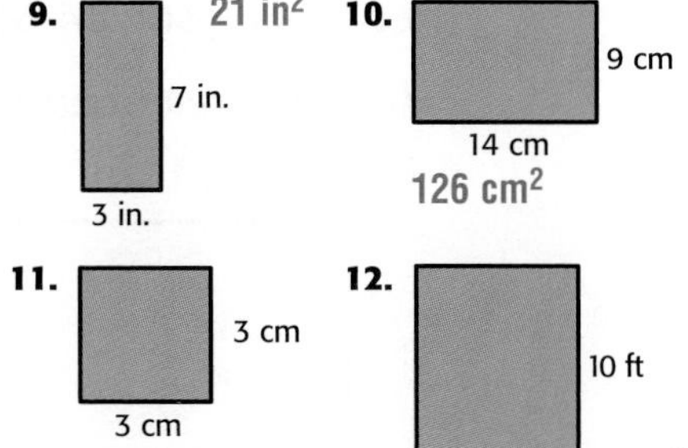

9. 21 in²
10. 126 cm²
11. 9 cm²
12. 80 ft²

13. **MULTIPLE CHOICE** A square has a length of 20 inches. What is the area? (Lesson 14-3) J
    - **F** 40 square inches
    - **G** 80 square inches
    - **H** 200 square inches
    - **J** 400 square inches

14. **WRITING IN MATH** Describe how to estimate the area of the figure in Exercise 7. (Lessons 14-1 and 14-3) See Ch. 14 Answer Appendix.

Formative Assessment 623

Chapter 14 Mid-Chapter Check

Lessons 14-1 through 14-3

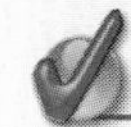

Formative Assessment

Use the Mid-Chapter Check to assess students' progress in the first half of the chapter.

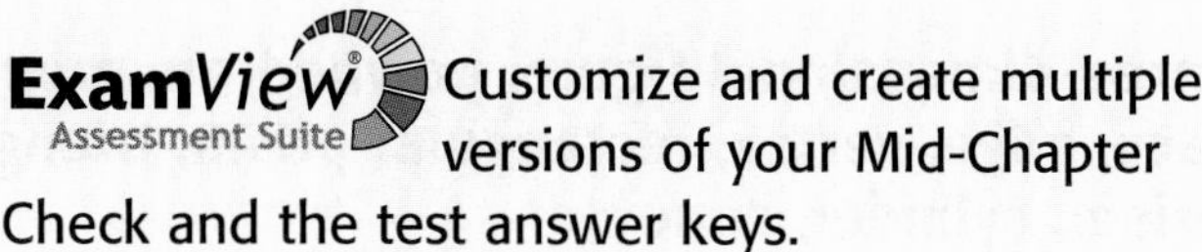

Customize and create multiple versions of your Mid-Chapter Check and the test answer keys.

FOLDABLES Dinah Zike's Foldables

Use these lesson suggestions to incorporate the Foldables during the chapter.

Lesson 14-1 Students use the left column of the Pocket Chart Foldable to record formulas for calculating perimeters of polygons. Examples of student work on quarter sheets of paper or index cards should be stored in the left side pocket.

Lessons 14-2, 14-3 Students use the right column of the Pocket Chart Foldable to record formulas for calculating the areas of rectangles, parallelograms, and composite figures. Examples of student work on quarter sheets of paper or index cards should be stored in the right side pocket.

Data-Driven Decision Making

Based on the results of the Mid-Chapter Check, use the following to review concepts that continue to present students with problems.

Exercises	State/Local Standards	What's the Math?	Error Analysis	Resources for Review
1–5 Lesson 14-1		Find the perimeters of polygons.	Does not add accurately. Does not add all sides. Does not know how to find perimeter.	CRM Chapter 14 Resource Masters (Reteach Worksheets) pp. 8, 13, 18 Math Adventures My Math Zone Chapter 14 Math Online Extra Examples • Concepts in Motion
9–13 Lesson 14-3		Find the area of a polygon.	Adds sides, not multiplies. Does not know how to multiply with fractions. Does not know square characteristics to find sides for area.	
6–8, 14 Lesson 14-2		Estimate the area of an irregular figure. Explain how to find areas with curved edges.	Adds only the whole squares and ignores parts of squares in irregular figures when finding areas. Does not understand "estimate."	

Three-Dimensional Figures

Lesson Planner

Objective

Identify characteristics of three-dimensional figures.

Vocabulary

three-dimensional figure, polyhedron, prism, base, face, edge, vertex, rectangular prism, triangular prism, cylinder, cone

Resources

Materials: box of markers, jar, and other common objects representing rectangular prisms, triangular prisms, cylinders, and cones
Manipulatives: geometric solids
Literature Connection: *Sir Cumference and the Sword in the Cone* by Cindy Neuschwander
Teacher Technology
TeacherWorks • Interactive Classroom

Focus on Math Background

Three-dimensional figures are so named because they have three dimensions: length, width, and height. They are also known as solid figures or space figures, as they enclose a region of space. A *face* is a flat side of a solid figure, two faces meet at an *edge*, and three or more edges meet at a *vertex*. A solid with faces that are polygons is called a *polyhedron* (meaning "many faces"). If two of the faces are congruent polygons (bases) and the others are rectangles, the solid is called a *prism*. The shape of the bases determines the name of a prism. For example, if the bases are rectangles, the prism is a *rectangular prism*; if the bases are triangles, the prism is a *triangular prism*, etc.

Daily Routine

Use these suggestions before beginning the lesson on p. 624.

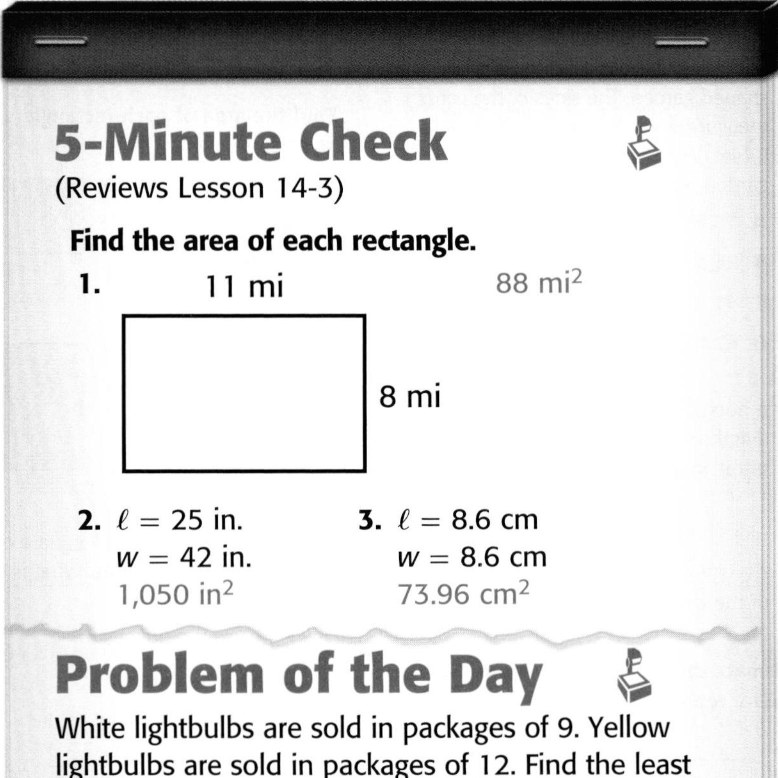

5-Minute Check

(Reviews Lesson 14-3)

Find the area of each rectangle.

1. 11 mi, 8 mi — 88 mi^2

2. $\ell = 25$ in.
$w = 42$ in.
1,050 in^2

3. $\ell = 8.6$ cm
$w = 8.6$ cm
73.96 cm^2

Problem of the Day

White lightbulbs are sold in packages of 9. Yellow lightbulbs are sold in packages of 12. Find the least number of lightbulbs of each color Rosario must buy to have the same number of white and yellow lightbulbs. Explain. 36 lightbulbs; see students' explanations.

Building Math Vocabulary

Write the lesson vocabulary words and their definitions on the board.

Have pairs of students look through an art book or a magazine and locate a rectangular prism, a triangular prism, a cylinder, and a cone.

Using the picture of the rectangular prism, students should identify a base, a face, an edge, and a vertex.

Visual Vocabulary Cards

Use Visual Vocabulary Cards 42 and 45 to reinforce the vocabulary in this lesson. (The Define/Example/Ask routine is printed on the back of each card.)

Differentiated Instruction

Small Group Options

Option 1 Gifted and Talented AL

SPATIAL

Materials: research books, newspapers, magazines

- Ask students to find pictures of famous buildings, such as the Pentagon, Eiffel Tower, and Empire State Building.
- Have them draw front, side, and top views.

Option 2 English Language Learners ELL

VISUAL, SPATIAL, LINGUISTIC

Materials: everyday objects, posterboard
Core Vocabulary: identify, front to back, turn
Common Use Verb: toss

Hear Math This strategy allows students to practice vocalizing the name of solid figures and associate solid figure vocabulary and forms with everyday objects.

- Have students practice saying the name of solid figures.
- Show them everyday objects, and work with students to practice and pronounce the names of these objects.
- Help students make a poster with the solid figure categories and shapes, like the example.

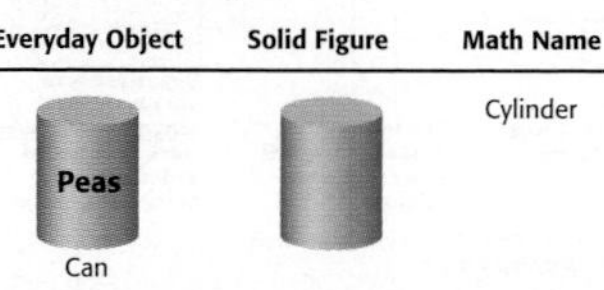

Everyday Object
Solid Figure
Math Name
Cylinder
Peas
Can

- Add additional everyday objects in that column as students discover more of them.

Use this worksheet to provide additional support for English Language Learners.

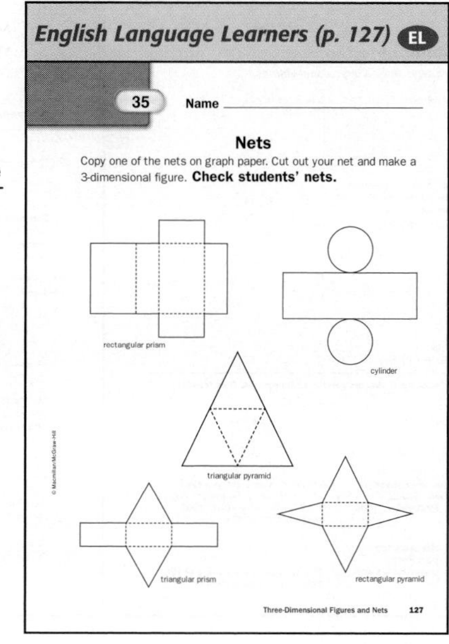

English Language Learners (p. 127) EL

35 Name ______

Nets

Copy one of the nets on graph paper. Cut out your net and make a 3-dimensional figure. **Check students' nets.**

rectangular prism

cylinder

triangular pyramid

triangular prism

rectangular pyramid

Three-Dimensional Figures and Nets 127

Independent Work Options

Option 1 Early Finishers OL AL

LOGICAL, SPATIAL

Materials: chart paper

- Challenge students to create a chart and fill in the following information for a cone, cylinder, triangular prism, and rectangular prism: number of faces, number of vertices, number of edges, number of pairs of parallel faces, number of pairs of parallel edges.
- Have students use their charts to compare and contrast the figures.

Option 2 Student Technology

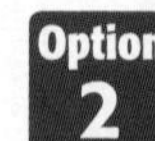

Math Online macmillanmh.com

Personal Tutor • Extra Examples

Option 3 Learning Station: Health (p. 604H)

Direct students to the Health Learning Station for opportunities to explore and extend the lesson concept.

Option 4 Problem-Solving Practice

Reinforce problem-solving skills and strategies with the Problem-Solving Practice worksheet.

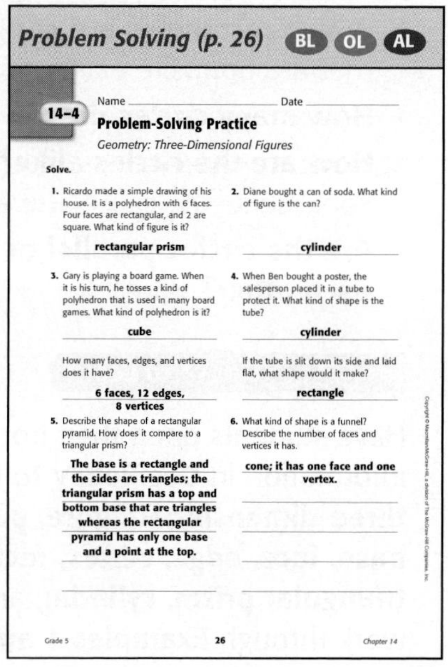

Problem Solving (p. 26) BL OL AL

14–4 Name ______ Date ______

Problem-Solving Practice

Geometry: Three-Dimensional Figures

Solve.

1. Ricardo made a simple drawing of his house. It is a polyhedron with 6 faces. Four faces are rectangular, and 2 are square. What kind of figure is it?
   rectangular prism
2. Diane bought a can of soda. What kind of figure is the can?
   cylinder
3. Gary is playing a board game. When it is his turn, he tosses a kind of polyhedron that is used in many board games. What kind of polyhedron is it?
   cube
   How many faces, edges, and vertices does it have?
   6 faces, 12 edges, 8 vertices
4. When Ben bought a poster, the salesperson placed it in a tube to protect it. What kind of shape is the tube?
   cylinder
   If the tube is slit down its side and laid flat, what shape would it make?
   rectangle
5. Describe the shape of a rectangular pyramid. How does it compare to a triangular prism?
   The base is a rectangle and the sides are triangles; the triangular prism has a top and bottom base that are triangles whereas the rectangular pyramid has only one base and a point at the top.
6. What kind of shape is a funnel? Describe the number of faces and vertices it has.
   cone; it has one face and one vertex.

Grade 5 26 Chapter 14

Three-Dimensional Figures

1 Introduce

Activity Choice 1 • Hands-On

- Have students point out various examples of two-dimensional figures in the classroom, such as circles, squares, rectangles, and triangles. Ask them to identify characteristics of each figure for you to write on the board. For example, a triangle has three sides and three vertices.
- Review the terms *parallel*, *perpendicular*, and *congruent* with students. **Which of these plane figures have parallel sides?** squares, rectangles
- **Which have perpendicular sides?** squares, rectangles, and right triangles Have students point to the parallel and perpendicular sides.
- Ask students to identify two congruent figures in the classroom or draw them on the board.

Activity Choice 2 • Literature

Introduce the lesson with *Sir Cumference and the Sword in the Cone* by Cindy Neuschwander. For a related math activity, see p. TR59.

2 Teach

Scaffolding Questions

Show students real-world three-dimensional objects, such as a box of markers and a can.

- **What plane figures do you see in these objects?** Sample answers: rectangles, circles
- **How many rectangles are on this box?** 6
- **Which rectangles are congruent?** rectangles that are opposite each other
- **How many circles do you see in this can?** 2
- **How are the circles alike?** They are congruent—the same size and shape.
- **Are the circles parallel or perpendicular to each other?** parallel

GET READY to Learn

Have students open their books and read the information in **Get Ready to Learn**. Introduce **three-dimensional figure, polyhedron, prism, base, face, edge, vertex, rectangular prism, triangular prism, cylinder,** and **cone**. As a class, work through **Examples 1 and 2**.

14-4 Three-Dimensional Figures

MAIN IDEA

I will identify characteristics of three-dimensional figures.

New Vocabulary

- three-dimensional figure
- polyhedron
- prism
- base
- face
- edge
- vertex
- rectangular prism
- triangular prism
- cylinder
- cone

Math Online

macmillanmh.com

- Extra Examples
- Personal Tutor
- Self-Check Quiz

GET READY to Learn

The building at the right is made up of shapes called *rectangular prisms*.

A two-dimensional figure is a plane figure that has length and width. A **three-dimensional figure** has length, width, and height. A three-dimensional figure with faces that are polygons is called a **polyhedron**. A **prism** is a polyhedron with two parallel congruent faces, called **bases**.

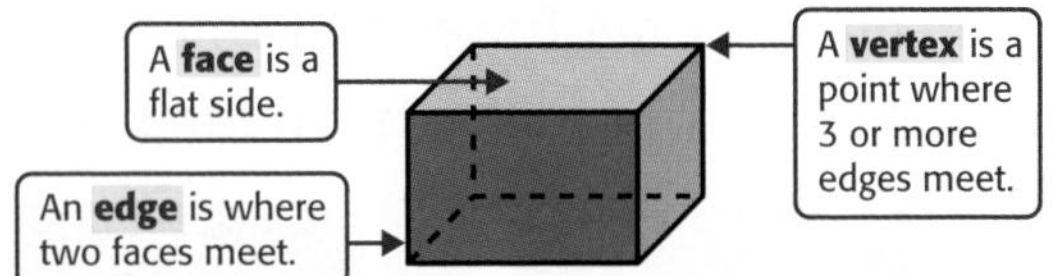

Three-dimensional Figures (Key Concepts)

Figure	Example	Characteristics
rectangular prism		a prism with six rectangular faces including two rectangular bases
triangular prism		a prism that has triangular bases
cylinder		a solid with two parallel congruent circular bases; a curved surface connects the bases
cone		a solid that has a circular base and one curved surface from the base to a vertex

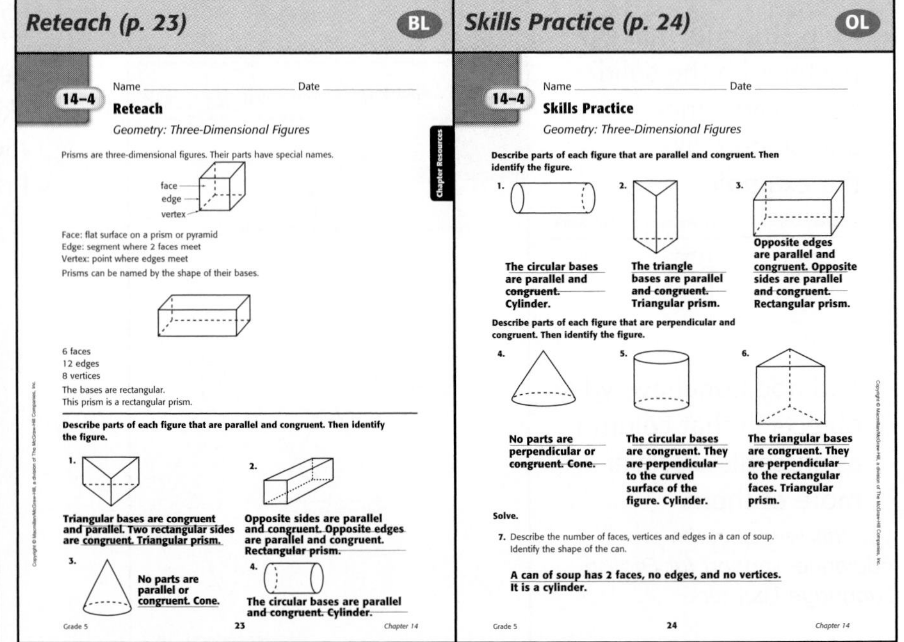

Reteach (p. 23) BL

14-4 Name ______ Date ______

Reteach

Geometry: Three-Dimensional Figures

Prisms are three-dimensional figures. Their parts have special names.

Face: flat surface on a prism or pyramid
Edge: segment where 2 faces meet
Vertex: point where edges meet
Prisms can be named by the shape of their bases.

6 faces
12 edges
8 vertices
The bases are rectangular.
This prism is a rectangular prism.

Describe parts of each figure that are parallel and congruent. Then identify the figure.

1. **Triangular bases are congruent and parallel. Two rectangular sides are congruent. Triangular prism.**
2. **Opposite sides are parallel and congruent. Opposite edges are parallel and congruent. Rectangular prism.**
3. **No parts are parallel or congruent. Cone.**
4. **The circular bases are parallel and congruent. Cylinder.**

Grade 5 23 Chapter 14

Chapter Resources

Skills Practice (p. 24) OL

14-4 Name ______ Date ______

Skills Practice

Geometry: Three-Dimensional Figures

Describe parts of each figure that are parallel and congruent. Then identify the figure.

1. **The circular bases are parallel and congruent. Cylinder.**
2. **The triangle bases are parallel and congruent. Triangular prism.**
3. **Opposite edges are parallel and congruent. Opposite sides are parallel and congruent. Rectangular prism.**

Describe parts of each figure that are perpendicular and congruent. Then identify the figure.

4. **No parts are perpendicular or congruent. Cone.**
5. **The circular bases are congruent. They are perpendicular to the curved surface of the figure. Cylinder.**
6. **The triangular bases are congruent. They are perpendicular to the rectangular faces. Triangular prism.**

Solve.

7. Describe the number of faces, vertices and edges in a can of soup. Identify the shape of the can.

A can of soup has 2 faces, no edges, and no vertices. It is a cylinder.

Grade 5 24 Chapter 14

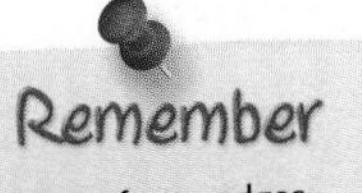

Remember

Bases, faces, edges, and vertices are all parts of three-dimensional figures.

EXAMPLE Characteristics of Solids

1 **Describe parts of the figure that are parallel and congruent. Then identify the figure.**

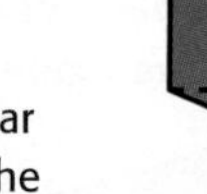

faces This figure has 5 faces. The triangular bases are parallel and congruent. The rectangular faces appear to be congruent.

edges There are 9 edges. The edges that form the vertical sides of the rectangles are parallel and congruent.

vertices This figure has 6 vertices.

So, the figure is a triangular prism.

Real-World EXAMPLE Characteristics of Solids

2 **SPORTS** **Describe parts of the tennis ball container that are perpendicular and congruent. Then identify the shape of the container.**

faces The circular bases are congruent. They are perpendicular to the curved surface of the container.

edges The container has no edges. So the container is a cylinder.

1–3. See Ch. 14 Answer Appendix.

CHECK What You Know

1. Describe parts of the figure that are parallel and congruent. Then identify the figure. See Examples 1, 2 (p. 625)

2. Describe parts of the hamster cage that are perpendicular and congruent. Then identify the shape of the cage.

3. **Talk About It** Describe the differences between a cylinder and a rectangular prism.

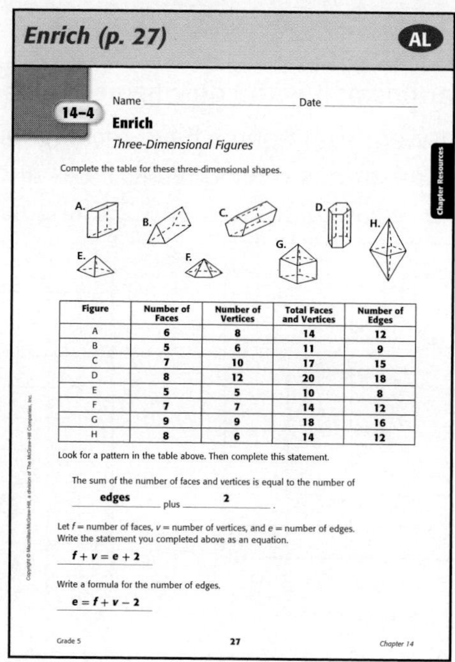

Enrich (p. 27) AL

14–4 Name ____________ Date ____________

Enrich

Three-Dimensional Figures

Complete the table for these three-dimensional shapes.

A. B. C. D. E. F. G. H.

Figure	Number of Faces	Number of Vertices	Total Faces and Vertices	Number of Edges
A	6	8	14	12
B	5	6	11	9
C	7	10	17	15
D	8	12	20	18
E	5	5	10	8
F	7	7	14	12
G	9	9	18	16
H	8	6	14	12

Look for a pattern in the table above. Then complete this statement.

The sum of the number of faces and vertices is equal to the number of **edges** plus **2**.

Let f = number of faces, v = number of vertices, and e = number of edges. Write the statement you completed above as an equation.

$f + v = e + 2$

Write a formula for the number of edges.

$e = f + v - 2$

Chapter Resources

Grade 5 27 Chapter 14

Characteristics of Solids

Example 1 Have students first identify all of the faces and edges in the triangular prism. Make sure students understand why the triangular bases are parallel. Explain that the term *base* can be used to describe one flat side of a cone or any pair of congruent opposite faces in a cylinder or prism.

ADDITIONAL EXAMPLES

1 Describe parts of the figure below that are parallel and congruent. Then identify the figure.

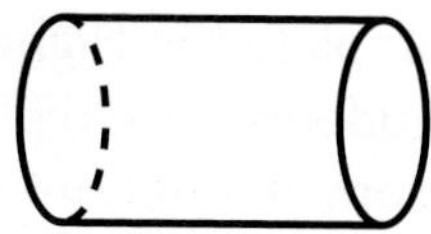

The circular bases are parallel and congruent; cylinder

2 Describe parts of the cereal box that are perpendicular and congruent. Then identify the shape of the box.

each face is perpendicular to the four adjacent faces; the opposite faces and edges are congruent; rectangular prism

CHECK What You Know

As a class, have students complete Exercises 1–3 in **Check What You Know** as you observe their work.

Exercise 3 Assess student comprehension before assigning practice exercises.

BL Alternate Teaching Strategy

If students have trouble identifying characteristics of three-dimensional figures…

Then use one of these reteach options:

1 CRM **Daily Reteach Worksheet** (p. 23)

2 Provide students with objects representing a variety of three-dimensional figures. Next have them sort the objects into groups of rectangular prisms, triangular prisms, cylinders, and cones. Ask students to describe how the objects in each group are alike and different. Encourage students to identify parallel, perpendicular, and congruent parts.

3 Practice

Differentiate practice using these leveled assignments for Exercises 4–17.

Level	Assignment
BL Below/ Approaching Level	5–6, 9–10, 13–14, 15
OL On Level	4–11, 13–15, 17
AL Above/Beyond Level	4–14 even, 15–17

Have students discuss and complete the Higher Order Thinking problems. If students have difficulty with Exercise 16, have them copy the net onto a separate sheet of paper, cut it out along the outside edges, and fold it on the dotted lines to make the three-dimensional figure.

WRITING IN MATH Have students complete Exercise 17 in their Math Journals. You may choose to use this as an optional formative assessment.

Additional Answers

4. No parts are parallel or congruent; cone.
5. Sample answer: The triangular bases are parallel and congruent. The edges that form the opposite sides of the rectangular faces are parallel and congruent; triangular prism.
6. Sample answer: The circular bases are parallel and congruent; cylinder.
7. Sample answer: Opposite sides are parallel and congruent. Opposite edges are parallel and congruent; rectangular prism.
8. Sample answers: All faces are congruent and all edges congruent. Adjacent faces are perpendicular and adjacent edges are perpendicular; cube
9. Sample answer: The circular bases are congruent. They are perpendicular to the curved surface of the container; cylinder.
10. No parts are perpendicular or congruent; cone.
11. Sample answer: The triangular bases are congruent. They are perpendicular to the rectangular faces. The adjacent edges of the rectangular faces are perpendicular. The opposite edges of the rectangular faces are congruent; triangular prism.

COMMON ERROR!

Some students may confuse the terms *parallel* and *perpendicular* when describing figures. Help them remember the meanings of these terms by using the following mnemonic device: the two ls in para*ll*el are parallel line segments.

Practice and Problem Solving

Describe parts of each figure that are parallel and congruent. Then identify the figure. See Examples 1, 2 (p. 625) 4–7. See margin.

4. 
5. 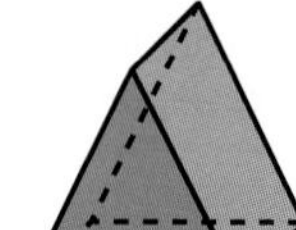
6. 
7. 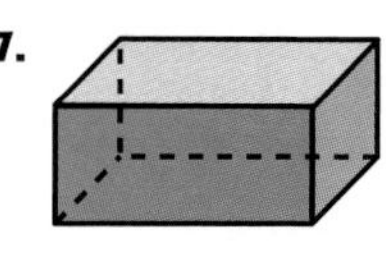

Describe parts of each figure that are perpendicular and congruent. Then identify the figure. See Examples 1, 2 (p. 625) 8–11. See margin.

8. 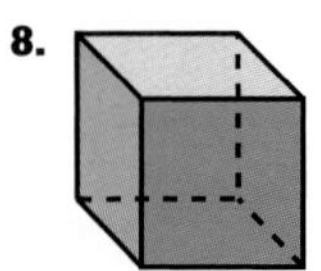
9. 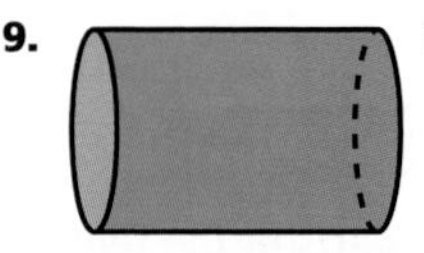
10. 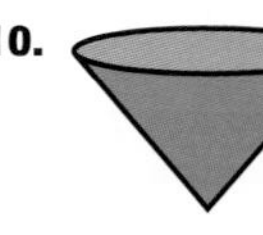
11. 

12. What kind of figure is the tomato soup can at the right? cylinder
13. Describe the number of vertices and edges in a closed book. Identify the shape of the book. 8 vertices; 12 edges; rectangular prism
14. Vera's closet is in the shape of a rectangular prism. Describe the pairs of parallel planes that make up her closet. floor and ceiling, front and back walls, side walls

H.O.T. Problems 15, 17. See margin.

15. **WHICH ONE DOESN'T BELONG?** Which figure does not belong with the other three? Explain your reasoning.

  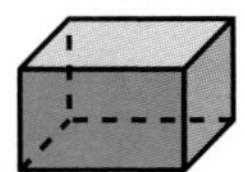 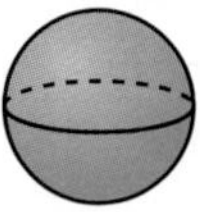

16. **CHALLENGE** Suppose the figure is folded on the dashed lines. What three-dimensional figure is formed? rectangular prism
17. **WRITING IN MATH** Describe the similarities and differences of a rectangular prism and a triangular prism.

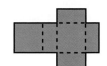

626 Chapter 14 Measure Perimeter, Area, and Volume

Additional Answers

15. Rectangular prism; it is the only figure that is a polyhedron.
17. Sample answer: Both figures have rectangular faces. A rectangular prism has 6 rectangular faces and a triangular prism has 3 rectangular faces and 2 triangular faces.

25. 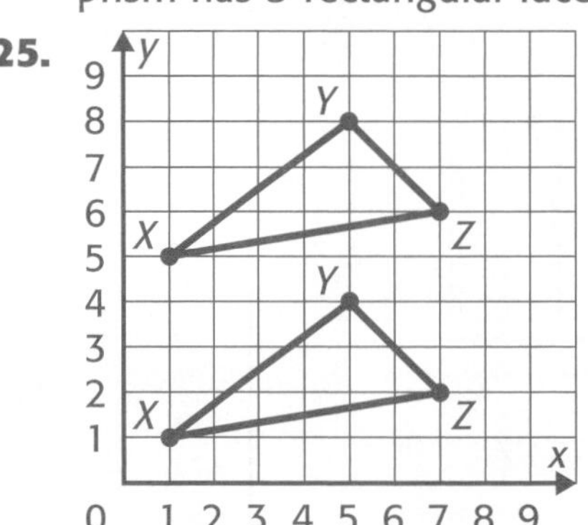

$x(1, 1), y(5, 4), z(7, 2)$

26. 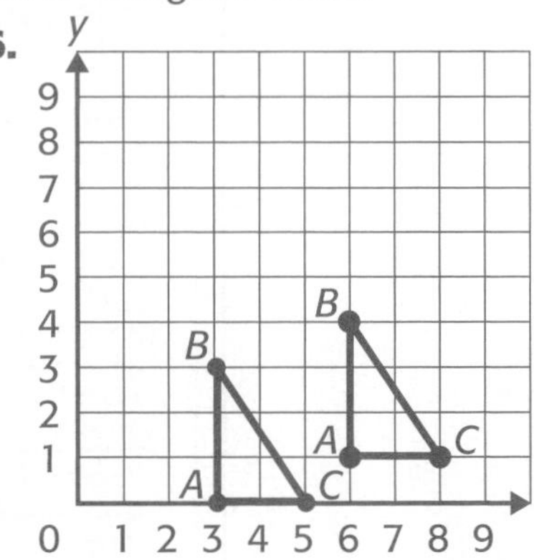

$A(6, 1), B(6, 4), C(8, 1)$

18. A rectangular fish tank is shown below.

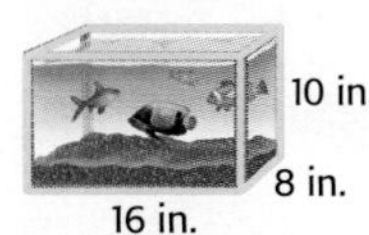

What is the area of the bottom of the fish tank? **(Lesson 14-3)** D

A 24 square inches

B 56 square inches

C 80 square inches

D 128 square inches

19. Look at the figure below.

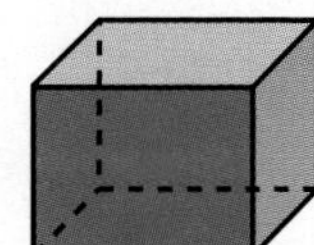

Which statement is true? **(Lesson 14-4)** G

F The figure has a triangular base.

G The figure has exactly 3 pairs of parallel faces.

H The figure has exactly 2 pairs of parallel faces.

J The figure has no perpendicular sides.

Spiral Review

Find the area of each rectangle or square. **(Lesson 14-3)**

20.

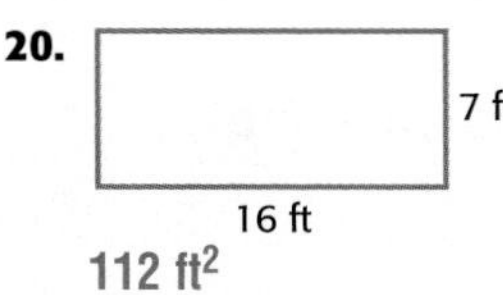

112 ft^2

21.

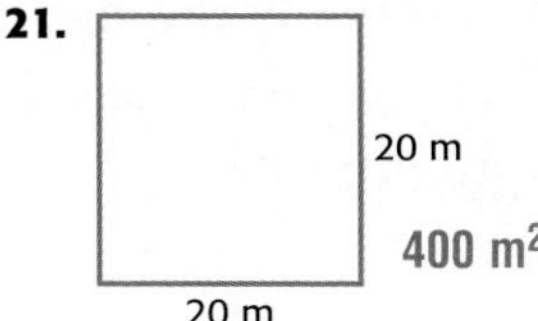

400 m^2

22.

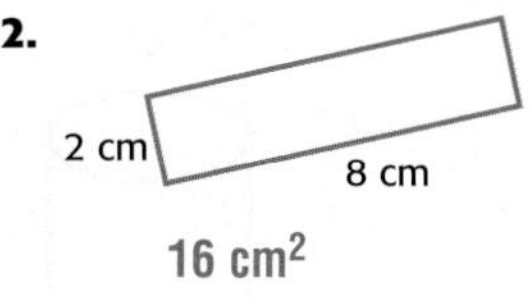

16 cm^2

23. Estimate the area of the figure at the right. Each square represents 1 square centimeter. **(Lesson 14-2)** Sample answer: 18 cm^2

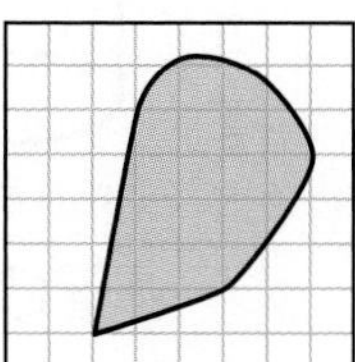

24. What is the perimeter of a rectangular building measuring 42 feet by 30 feet? **(Lesson 14-1)** 144 ft

Graph each figure and the translation described. Write the ordered pairs for the new vertices. **(Lessons 13-6 and 13-8)** 25, 26. See margin.

25. triangle *XYZ* with vertices *X*(1, 5), *Y*(5, 8), *Z*(7, 6); translated 4 units down

26. triangle *ABC* with vertices *A*(3, 0), *B*(3, 3), *C*(5, 0); translated up 1 unit and to the right 3 units.

Complete. **(Lesson 12-4)**

27. 40 L = ■ mL 40,000

28. 2 L = ■ mL 2,000

29. 16,000 mL = ■ L 16

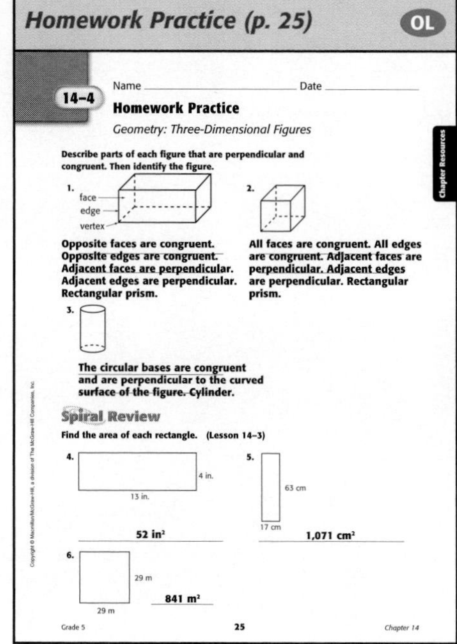

Homework Practice (p. 25) OL

Name ________ Date ________

14-4 Homework Practice

Geometry: Three-Dimensional Figures

Describe parts of each figure that are perpendicular and congruent. Then identify the figure.

1. face, edge, vertex

Opposite faces are congruent. Opposite edges are congruent. Adjacent faces are perpendicular. Adjacent edges are perpendicular. Rectangular prism.

2. All faces are congruent. All edges are congruent. Adjacent faces are perpendicular. Adjacent edges are perpendicular. Rectangular prism.

3. The circular bases are congruent and are perpendicular to the curved surface of the figure. Cylinder.

Spiral Review

Find the area of each rectangle. (Lesson 14-3)

4. 4 in., 13 in. — 52 in^2

5. 63 cm, 17 cm — $1{,}071 \text{ cm}^2$

6. 29 m, 29 m — 841 m^2

Grade 5 25 Chapter 14

Chapter Resources

4 Assess

Formative Assessment

Show students models or drawings of a rectangular prism and a cylinder and have them name each figure.

- **How are these figures alike? Describe as many similarities as you can.** Sample answers: They are both three-dimensional figures with plane figures as faces. They each contain at least one pair of congruent parallel faces.
- **How are these figures different? Describe as many differences as you can.** Sample answers: The rectangular prism is a polyhedron and the cylinder is not. The cylinder is not a prism. The rectangular prism has perpendicular faces and the cylinder does not.

Quick Check **Are students continuing to struggle with identifying characteristics of three-dimensional figures?**

If Yes → CRM Reteach Worksheet (p. 23)

If No → Independent Work Options (p. 624B)
CRM Skills Practice Worksheet (p. 24)
CRM Enrich Worksheet (p. 27)

Ticket Out the Door Sketch a cone on the board. Have students write the name of the figure and describe its characteristics on a sheet of paper to give you as they leave class for the day.

Reviews Lessons 14-3 and 14-4

Assign the Test Practice problems to provide daily reinforcement of test-taking skills.

Reviews Lessons 12-4, 13-6, 13-8, 14-1, 14-2, and 14-3

Review and assess mastery of skills and concepts from previous chapters.

14-5 Problem-Solving Strategy
Make a Model

Lesson Planner

Objective

Solve problems by making a model.

Resources

Materials: marbles, cans (optional)
Manipulatives: centimeter cubes, coins, square tiles, two-colored counters (optional)
Literature Connection: *How Tall How Short How Faraway?* by David A. Adler
Teacher Technology
TeacherWorks • Interactive Classroom

Real-World Problem Solving Library
Math and Social Studies: *Exploring the World by Sea*
Use these leveled books to reinforce and extend problem-solving skills and strategies.

Leveled for:

- OL On Level
- ELL Sheltered English
- SP Spanish

For additional support, see the Real-World Problem Solving Teacher's Guide.

Daily Routine

Use these suggestions before beginning the lesson on p. 628.

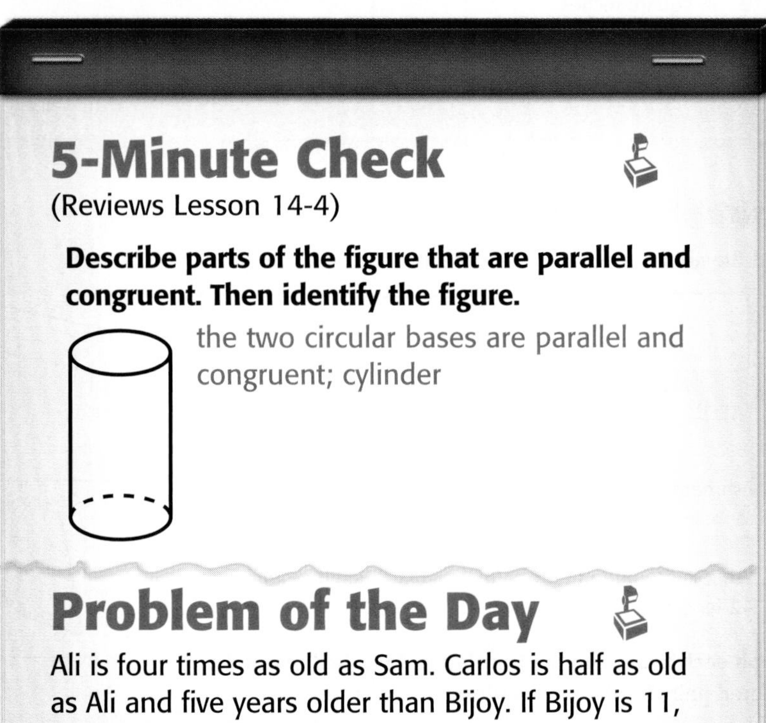

5-Minute Check

(Reviews Lesson 14-4)

Describe parts of the figure that are parallel and congruent. Then identify the figure.

the two circular bases are parallel and congruent; cylinder

Problem of the Day

Ali is four times as old as Sam. Carlos is half as old as Ali and five years older than Bijoy. If Bijoy is 11, how old is Sam? 8 years old

Differentiated Instruction

Small Group Options

Option 1 VISUAL, LOGICAL

Gifted and Talented AL

Materials: chart paper, markers, black and red checkers–four of each for each student or 2-color counters

- Copy the following problem on chart paper:

  Arrange 4 black checkers and 4 red checkers so that there are 6 straight lines of checkers with exactly 2 red checkers in each line, and there are exactly 2 black checkers in 2 of those 6 straight lines.

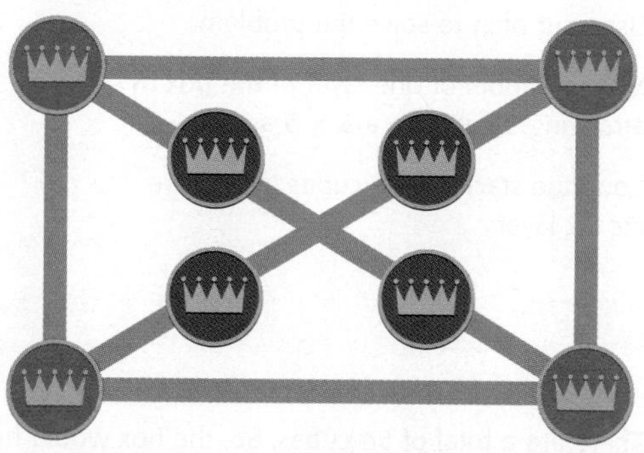

- Encourage students to try many ways and to work with a partner if necessary. Once a student finds a solution, it should be shared with another student to check to see that all of it works for this problem

Option 2 LINGUISTIC, LOGICAL

English Language Learners ELL

Materials: model car, airplane, dollhouse, Solar System model (if available), chart paper

Core Vocabulary: model, real things, help

Common Use Verb: use instead of

See Math This strategy helps students understand and vocalize the advantages and limitations of models.

- Display models and prompt names.
- Say, "These are "**models**" that we can ***use instead of*** the real things."
- Prompt good things about models: help us see larger things, can carry, and can help us understand.
- Repeat prompt for bad things about models: different function/size/material.
- Display a problem and have groups decide on a type of model to solve it.

Independent Work Options

Option 1 LINGUISTIC, KINESTHETIC

Early Finishers OL AL

Materials: various classroom objects or manipulatives

- Have students write a word problem that can be solved using the *make a model* strategy.
- Ask students to present their problems to another student or to the class and demonstrate how to solve the problem.

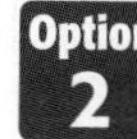

Option 2

Student Technology

Math Online macmillanmh.com

Personal Tutor • Extra Examples

Option 3

Learning Station: Reading (p. 604H)

Direct students to the Reading Learning Station for opportunities to explore and extend the lesson concept.

1 Introduce

Activity Choice 1 • Review

- Present students with the following problem: *Kaitlyn bought $8\frac{1}{2}$ pounds of potatoes, $4\frac{1}{4}$ pounds of corn, and $9\frac{3}{4}$ pounds of chicken for a barbecue. About how many pounds of food did she buy?*
- **What problem-solving strategy could you use?** use the *four-step plan*
- Ask students to decide if they should use paper and pencil, mental math, estimation, or a calculator to solve the problem and have them explain why they chose that method. Sample answer: about 23 pounds; Estimation, because an exact answer is not needed.

Activity Choice 2 • Literature

Introduce the lesson with *How Tall How Short How Faraway?* by David A. Adler. For a related math activity, see p. TR60.

2 Teach

Have students read the problem on the number of cubes needed to fill the box. Guide them through the problem-solving steps.

Understand Using the questions, review what students know and need to find.

Plan Have them discuss their strategy.

Solve Guide students to make a model to solve.

- How many cubes are in one layer? 9
- How many layers are there? 6
- How many cubes altogether? 54

Check Have students look back at the problem to make sure that the answer fits the facts given.

COMMON ERROR!

Exercise 5 Students may have trouble using the *make a model* strategy to solve problems involving larger units of measure, such as 150 feet. Have students either substitute smaller units for larger ones when modeling these problems (i.e., use inches instead of feet), or use numbers only in their models.

14-5 Problem-Solving Strategy

MAIN IDEA I will solve problems by making a model.

Nick is helping his younger sister put away her alphabet blocks. She has already put away one layer of blocks. To fill up one layer it takes nine blocks. If the box is filled with six layers of blocks, how many blocks would be in the box?

Understand	**What facts do you know?** • The number of blocks in one layer of a box. • The number of layers in the box. **What do you need to find?** • The number of blocks in the box when there are six layers.
Plan	Solve the problem by making a model.
Solve	Use your plan to solve the problem. Make a model of one layer of the box by arranging 9 cubes in a 3 × 3 array. Continue stacking the cubes until there are six layers. 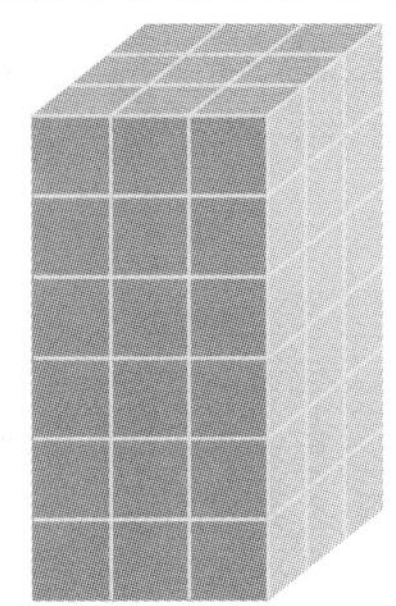 There are a total of 54 cubes. So, the box would have 54 blocks.
Check	Look back. Use logical reasoning and multiplication. There are 6 layers and each layer has 9 cubes. So, the total number of cubes is 6 × 9 or 54. The answer is correct. ✓

628 Chapter 14 Measure Perimeter, Area, and Volume

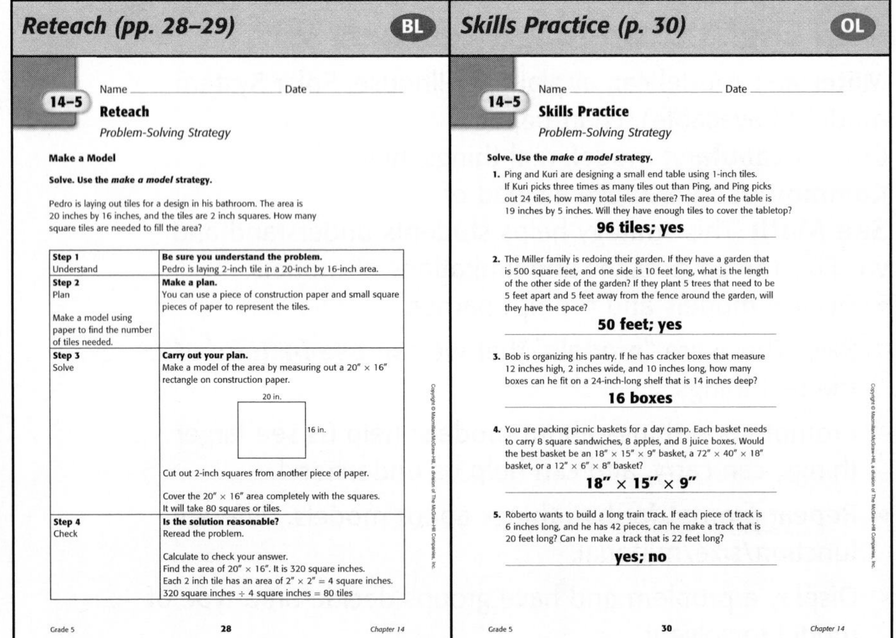

Reteach (pp. 28–29) BL

14-5 Name ______ Date ______

Reteach

Problem-Solving Strategy

Make a Model

Solve. Use the *make a model* strategy.

Pedro is laying out tiles for a design in his bathroom. The area is 20 inches by 16 inches, and the tiles are 2 inch squares. How many square tiles are needed to fill the area?

Step 1 Understand	**Be sure you understand the problem.** Pedro is laying 2-inch tile in a 20-inch by 16-inch area.
Step 2 Plan Make a model using paper to find the number of tiles needed.	**Make a plan.** You can use a piece of construction paper and small square pieces of paper to represent the tiles.
Step 3 Solve	**Carry out your plan.** Make a model of the area by measuring out a 20″ × 16″ rectangle on construction paper. 20 in. / 16 in. Cut out 2-inch squares from another piece of paper. Cover the 20″ × 16″ area completely with the squares. It will take 80 squares or tiles.
Step 4 Check	**Is the solution reasonable?** Reread the problem. Calculate to check your answer. Find the area of 20″ × 16″. It is 320 square inches. Each 2 inch tile has an area of 2″ × 2″ = 4 square inches. 320 square inches ÷ 4 square inches = 80 tiles

Grade 5 28 Chapter 14

Skills Practice (p. 30) OL

14-5 Name ______ Date ______

Skills Practice

Problem-Solving Strategy

Solve. Use the *make a model* strategy.

1. Ping and Kuri are designing a small end table using 1-inch tiles. If Kuri picks three times as many tiles out than Ping, and Ping picks out 24 tiles, how many total tiles are there? The area of the table is 19 inches by 5 inches. Will they have enough tiles to cover the tabletop?
   96 tiles; yes
2. The Miller family is redoing their garden. If they have a garden that is 500 square feet, and one side is 10 feet long, what is the length of the other side of the garden? If they plant 5 trees that need to be 5 feet apart and 5 feet away from the fence around the garden, will they have the space?
   50 feet; yes
3. Bob is organizing his pantry. If he has cracker boxes that measure 12 inches high, 2 inches wide, and 10 inches long, how many boxes can he fit on a 24-inch-long shelf that is 14 inches deep?
   16 boxes
4. You are packing picnic baskets for a day camp. Each basket needs to carry 8 square sandwiches, 8 apples, and 8 juice boxes. Would the best basket be an 18″ × 15″ × 9″ basket, a 72″ × 40″ × 18″ basket, or a 12″ × 6″ × 8″ basket?
   18″ × 15″ × 9″
5. Roberto wants to build a long train track. If each piece of track is 6 inches long, and he has 42 pieces, can he make a track that is 20 feet long? Can he make a track that is 22 feet long?
   yes; no

Grade 5 30 Chapter 14

ANALYZE the Strategy

Refer to the problem on the previous page.

1. How many blocks would the box contain if it had only five layers of blocks? **45 blocks**
2. If you stacked two boxes of the original size on top of each other, what would be the total number of blocks in the boxes? **108 blocks**
3. What are the advantages of the *make a model* strategy? **3. Sample answer: Using a model helps make the problem more concrete.**
4. List some objects that you could use to make a model. **Sample answer: blocks, coins, counters**

PRACTICE the Strategy

Solve. Use the *make a model* strategy.

5. **Measurement** On an assembly line that is 150 feet long, there is a work station every 15 feet. The first station is at the beginning of the line. How many work stations are there? **11 stations**
6. A store is stacking cans of food into a pyramid-shaped display. The bottom layer has 9 cans. There are 5 layers. If there are two less cans in each layer, how many cans are in the display? **25**
7. **Measurement** The distance around the center ring at the circus is 80 feet. A clown stands every 10 feet along the circle. How many clowns are there? **8 clowns**

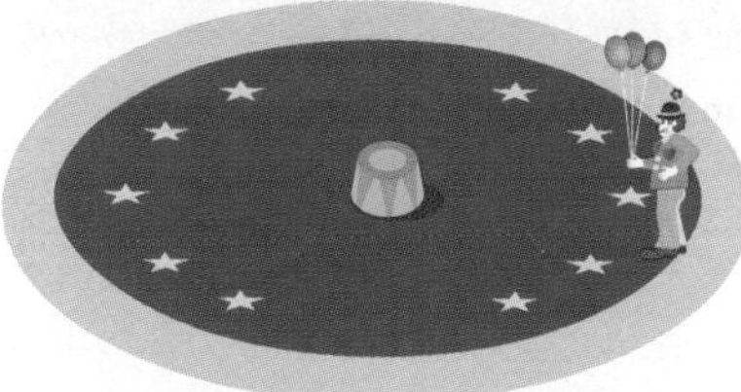

8. **Measurement** Martino wants to arrange 18 square tiles into a rectangular shape with the least perimeter possible. How many tiles will be in each row? **6 tiles**
9. In the figure below, there are 22 marbles in Box A. To go from Box A to Box B, four marbles can pass through the triangular machine at a time. Five marbles can pass through the square machine at a time. Describe how to move all the marbles from Box A to Box B in the fewest moves possible. **See Ch. 14 Answer Appendix.**

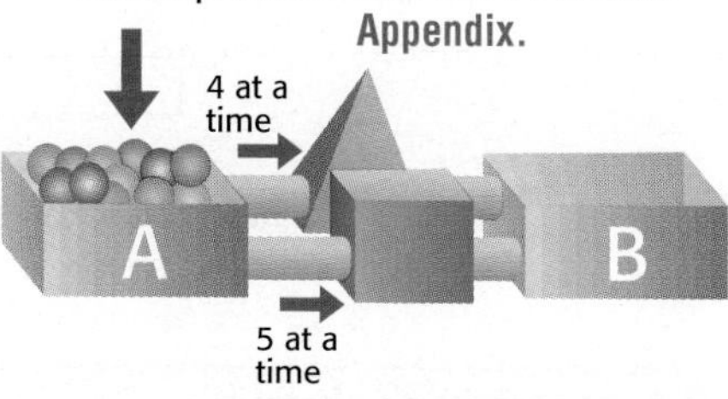

10. Drake lined up 15 pennies on his desk. He replaced every third penny with a nickel. Then he replaced every fourth coin with a dime. Finally, he replaced every fifth coin with a quarter. What is the value of the remaining 15 coins on his desk? Explain. **See Ch. 14 Answer Appendix.**
11. **WRITING IN MATH** Describe when you would use the *make a model* strategy. **Sample answer: When you cannot act it out.**

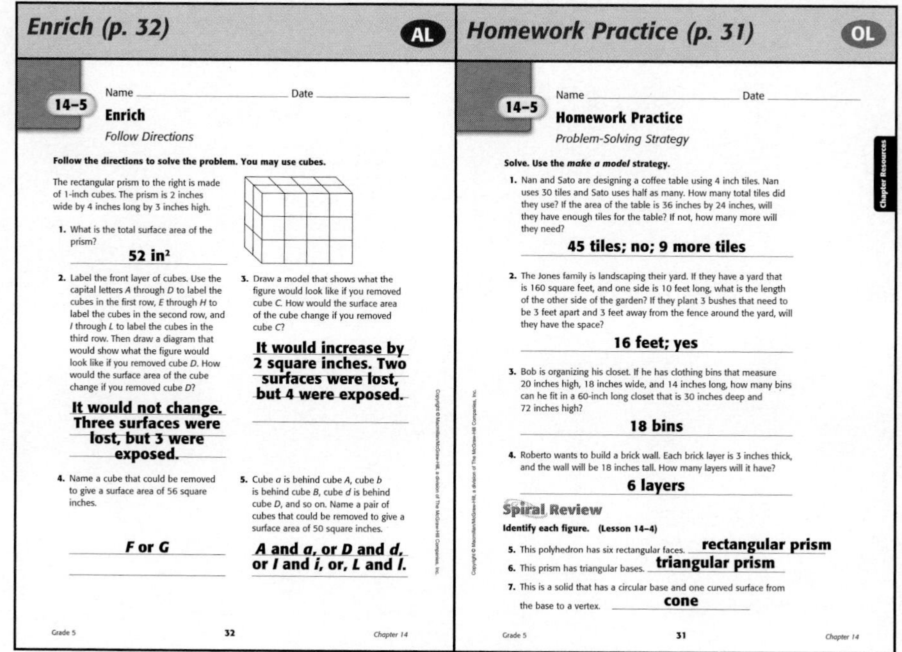

Enrich (p. 32) AL

14–5

Name ______________ Date ______________

Enrich

Follow Directions

Follow the directions to solve the problem. You may use cubes.

The rectangular prism to the right is made of 1-inch cubes. The prism is 2 inches wide by 4 inches long by 3 inches high.

1. What is the total surface area of the prism? **52 in^2**
2. Label the front layer of cubes. Use the capital letters *A* through *D* to label the cubes in the first row, *E* through *H* to label the cubes in the second row, and *I* through *L* to label the cubes in the third row. Then draw a diagram that would show what the figure would look like if you removed cube *D*. How would the surface area of the cube change if you removed cube *D*? **It would not change. Three surfaces were lost, but 3 were exposed.**
3. Draw a model that shows what the figure would look like if you removed cube C. How would the surface area of the cube change if you removed cube C? **It would increase by 2 square inches. Two surfaces were lost, but 4 were exposed.**
4. Name a cube that could be removed to give a surface area of 56 square inches. ***F* or *G***
5. Cube *a* is behind cube *A*, cube *b* is behind cube *B*, cube *d* is behind cube *D*, and so on. Name a pair of cubes that could be removed to give a surface area of 50 square inches. ***A* and *a*, or *D* and *d*, or *I* and *i*, or, *L* and *l*.**

Grade 5 32 Chapter 14

Homework Practice (p. 31) OL

14–5

Name ______________ Date ______________

Homework Practice

Problem-Solving Strategy

Solve. Use the *make a model* strategy.

1. Nan and Sato are designing a coffee table using 4 inch tiles. Nan uses 30 tiles and Sato uses half as many. How many total tiles did they use? If the area of the table is 36 inches by 24 inches, will they have enough tiles for the table? If not, how many more will they need? **45 tiles; no; 9 more tiles**
2. The Jones family is landscaping their yard. If they have a yard that is 160 square feet, and one side is 10 feet long, what is the length of the other side of the garden? If they plant 3 bushes that need to be 3 feet apart and 3 feet away from the fence around the yard, will they have the space? **16 feet; yes**
3. Bob is organizing his closet. If he has clothing bins that measure 20 inches high, 18 inches wide, and 14 inches long, how many bins can he fit in a 60-inch long closet that is 30 inches deep and 72 inches high? **18 bins**
4. Roberto wants to build a brick wall. Each brick layer is 3 inches thick, and the wall will be 18 inches tall. How many layers will it have? **6 layers**

Spiral Review

Identify each figure. (Lesson 14–4)

5. This polyhedron has six rectangular faces. **rectangular prism**
6. This prism has triangular bases. **triangular prism**
7. This is a solid that has a circular base and one curved surface from the base to a vertex. **cone**

Chapter Resources

Grade 5 31 Chapter 14

Analyze the Strategy Use Exercises 1–4 to analyze and discuss the problem-solving strategy.

BL Alternate Teaching Strategy

If students have trouble working with objects to make a model...

Then use one of these reteach options:

1 CRM **Daily Reteach Worksheet** (pp. 28–29)

2 Point out that a drawing can often be used to model a problem. Have students make a model by drawing and labeling parts of a picture instead of using objects.

3 Practice

Using the Exercises

Exercise 6 Define *pyramid* for students. Provide small groups of students with cans or encourage them to stack other objects, such as cubes, to model the problem.

Exercise 8 Provide students with square tiles. Encourage them to make arrays using all of the factor pairs for 18. This way, they will be sure to construct every rectangle possible with 18 tiles and identify the one with the least perimeter.

4 Assess

Formative Assessment

Have students explain how they would solve this problem using the *make a model* strategy: *Anna wants to arrange 24 square tiles into a rectangular shape with the greatest perimeter possible.* **How many tiles will be in each row?** 24

Quick Check **Are students continuing to struggle with solving problems by making a model?**

If Yes → CRM Reteach Worksheet (pp. 28–29)

If No → Independent Work Options (p. 628B)
CRM Skills Practice Worksheet (p. 30)
CRM Enrich Worksheet (p. 32)

Measurement Activity for 14-6

Lesson Planner

Objective

Use models to find the volumes of prisms.

Resources

Manipulatives: centimeter cubes

1 Introduce

- Ask students to locate rectangular prisms in the classroom, such as books or boxes. Review the terms *base* and *edge* from Lesson 14-4 and help students identify a base for one of the objects.
- Have students point to an edge of the base that shows its width and an edge that shows length. Help students identify an edge that shows the height of the prism.

2 Teach

Activity Distribute centimeter cubes. Model one rectangular prism for students (Prism A). Have the class help you fill in the row for Prism A in the table. Then have them make their own models and complete the table.

3 Assess

Formative Assessment

Use the **Check What You Know** Exercises 1–3 to assess whether students understand how to find the volumes of prisms.

Measurement Activity for 14-6

Volumes of Prisms

MAIN IDEA

I will use models to find the volumes of prisms.

You can use centimeter cubes to build rectangular prisms like the ones shown at the right.

ACTIVITY

Step 1 Use centimeter cubes to build four different rectangular prisms.

Step 2 For each prism, record the dimensions and the number of cubes used in a table like the one below.

Prism	Length (ℓ)	Width (w)	Height (h)	Area of Base (B)	Number of Cubes
A					
B					
C					
D					

Since volume can be measured using cubes, volume is measured in cubic units.

CHECK What You Know

1. Describe the relationship between the dimensions of the prism and number of cubes. The product of the length, width, and height equals the number of cubes.
2. Use ℓ, w, and h to write a formula for the volume V of a rectangular prism. $V = \ell wh$
3. Use the formula you wrote in Exercise 2 to find the volume of the prism at the right in appropriate units. Verify your solution by counting the number of cubes. 24 units^3

630 **Chapter 14** Measure Perimeter, Area, and Volume

LESSON 14-6

Volumes of Prisms

Lesson Planner

Objective

Find the volumes of rectangular prisms.

Vocabulary

volume

Resources

Manipulatives: rulers, centimeter cubes, connecting cubes
Literature Connection: *Geometry* by Lucille Caron and Philip M. St. Jacques
Teacher Technology
TeacherWorks • Interactive Classroom • Concepts in Motion
Alternate Lesson: Use *Impact Mathematics*: Unit J to provide practice with volume.

Focus on Math Background

Prior to this lesson, students have identified three-dimensional figures but have not yet found the volumes of those figures. Volume is the number of cubic units that fit inside a solid. A cubic unit is a cube that is 1 unit of length, 1 unit of width, and 1 unit of height. Only solid figures have volume. At this level, only the volumes of cubes and rectangular prisms are considered. Students need experience making rectangular prisms by stacking cubes and counting the number of cubes within the figure. To determine the volume of a solid, ask: How many *cubes fill the base* and how many *layers of cubes* are there in the given figure?

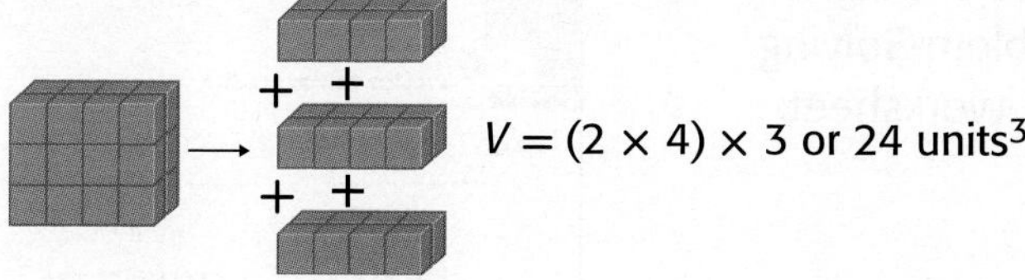

$V = (2 \times 4) \times 3$ or 24 units^3

As with area, units for volume are abbreviated with exponents: in^3, cm^3, etc.

Daily Routine

Use these suggestions before beginning the lesson on p. 631.

5-Minute Check

(Reviews Lesson 14-5)

Solve. Use the *make a model* strategy.
A picture frame is 4 inches wide and 12 inches long. It has yellow stars every inch and one at each corner. How many stars are there on the frame? 32 stars

Problem of the Day

A rectangle is 8 centimeters long and 4 centimeters wide. It has the same perimeter as a square. How much less area does it have? Draw a picture and explain. 4 cm^2 less; see students' work.

Building Math Vocabulary

Write the lesson vocabulary word and its definition on the board.

Have students discuss how they would explain the term *volume* to a third- or fourth-grade student.

Visual Vocabulary Cards

Use Visual Vocabulary Card 48 to reinforce the vocabulary in this lesson. (The Define/Example/Ask routine is printed on the back of each card.)

Differentiated Instruction

Small Group Options

Option 1 Below Level (BL)

SPATIAL

Materials: one-inch cubes for each student

- Review the properties of a rectangular prism.
- Have students build rectangular prisms that measure 2 cubes wide, 3 cubes deep, and 2 cubes high. **How many cubes do you need to build this prism?** 12
- Have students build rectangular prisms that measure 3 cubes wide, 2 cubes deep, and 2 cubes high. **How many cubes did it take to build this prism?** 12
- **What do you notice about these answers and why?** The answer is the same because the Commutative Property of Multiplication states that the order of the factors does not change the product.

Option 2 English Language Learners (ELL)

VISUAL/SPATIAL

Materials: blocks, index cards
Core Vocabulary: build, layers, diagram
Common Use Verb: follow instructions

Do Math Say: "Today we will ***build*** rectangular prisms ***following instructions*** on a **diagram**."

- Draw a diagram.

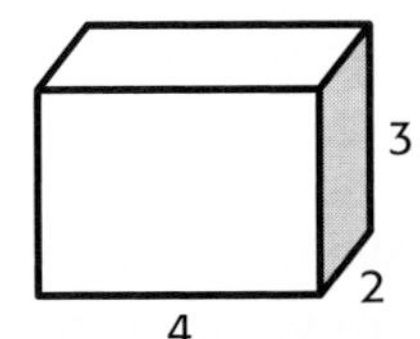

- Say: "According to this **diagram**, I have to put 2 rows each of 4 blocks on the bottom, and then do 3 more **layers** of it."
- Model how to follow the diagram.
- Students draw their own diagrams on an index card with up to 6 blocks on either side and exchange with someone in their group. They build one according to the diagram.
- Ask, **"How many blocks did you use to make your prism?"**

Use this worksheet to provide additional support for English Language Learners.

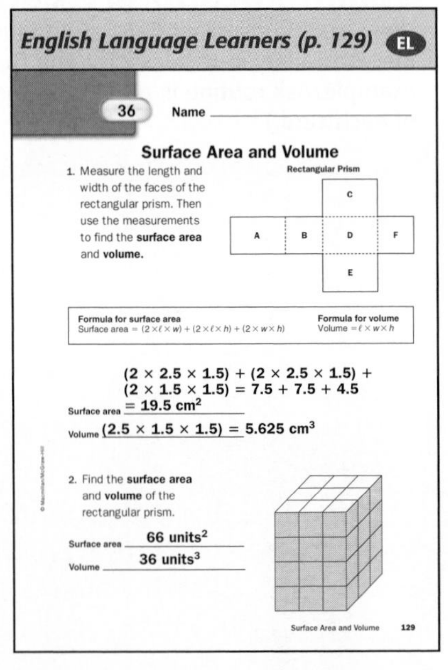

English Language Learners (p. 129) (EL)

36 Name ______

Surface Area and Volume

1. Measure the length and width of the faces of the rectangular prism. Then use the measurements to find the **surface area** and **volume**.

Rectangular Prism: A, B, C, D, E, F

Formula for surface area: Surface area = (2 × ℓ × w) + (2 × ℓ × h) + (2 × w × h)
Formula for volume: Volume = ℓ × w × h

Surface area: (2 × 2.5 × 1.5) + (2 × 2.5 × 1.5) + (2 × 1.5 × 1.5) = 7.5 + 7.5 + 4.5 = 19.5 cm²

Volume: (2.5 × 1.5 × 1.5) = 5.625 cm³

2. Find the **surface area** and **volume** of the rectangular prism.

Surface area: 66 units²

Volume: 36 units³

Surface Area and Volume 129

Independent Work Options

Option 1 Early Finishers (OL) (AL)

KINESTHETIC

Materials: rulers

- Challenge students to measure to the nearest inch the lengths, widths, and heights of several classroom objects that are rectangular prisms.
- Have students calculate the volume for each object they measured.
- You may extend the activity by having students remeasure the same objects to the nearest centimeter and calculate each new volume.

Option 2 Student Technology

Math Online macmillanmh.com

Personal Tutor • Extra Examples

 Math Adventures

Option 3 Learning Station: Writing (p. 604G)

Direct students to the Writing Learning Station for opportunities to explore and extend the lesson concept.

Option 4 Problem-Solving Practice

Reinforce problem-solving skills and strategies with the Problem-Solving Practice worksheet.

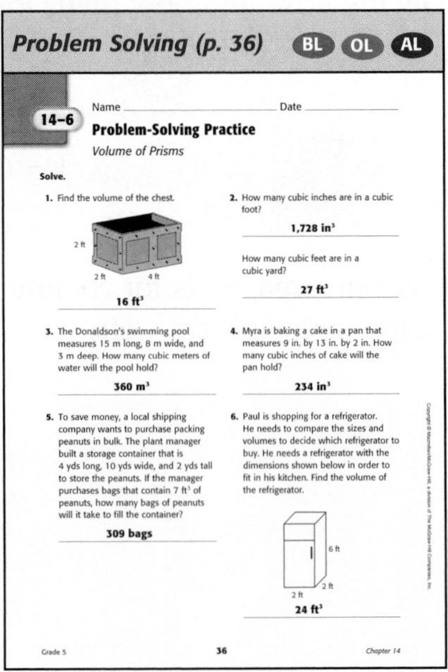

Problem Solving (p. 36) (BL) (OL) (AL)

Name ______ Date ______

14–6 **Problem-Solving Practice**
Volume of Prisms

Solve.

1. Find the volume of the chest. (2 ft, 2 ft, 4 ft) **16 ft³**
2. How many cubic inches are in a cubic foot? **1,728 in³**
   How many cubic feet are in a cubic yard? **27 ft³**
3. The Donaldson's swimming pool measures 15 m long, 8 m wide, and 3 m deep. How many cubic meters of water will the pool hold? **360 m³**
4. Myra is baking a cake in a pan that measures 9 in. by 13 in. by 2 in. How many cubic inches of cake will the pan hold? **234 in³**
5. To save money, a local shipping company wants to purchase packing peanuts in bulk. The plant manager built a storage container that is 4 yds long, 10 yds wide, and 2 yds tall to store the peanuts. If the manager purchases bags that contain 7 ft³ of peanuts, how many bags of peanuts will it take to fill the container? **309 bags**
6. Paul is shopping for a refrigerator. He needs to compare the sizes and volumes to decide which refrigerator to buy. He needs a refrigerator with the dimensions shown below in order to fit in his kitchen. Find the volume of the refrigerator. (6 ft, 2 ft, 2 ft) **24 ft³**

Grade 5 36 Chapter 14

14-6 Volumes of Prisms

GET READY to Learn

Armando makes sand paintings by filling clear plastic cases with colored sand. The amount of sand he uses depends on the amount of space in the cases.

MAIN IDEA

I will find the volumes of rectangular prisms.

New Vocabulary

volume

Math Online

macmillanmh.com

- Extra Examples
- Personal Tutor
- Self-Check Quiz

Volume is the amount of space that a three-dimensional figure contains. Volume is measured in cubic units. A cubic unit has length, width, and height.

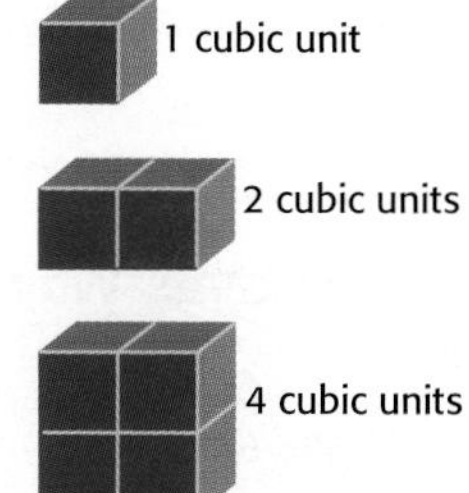

Some common units of volume are *cubic inch, cubic foot, cubic yard, cubic centimeter,* and *cubic meter.*

You can find the volume of a rectangular prism by using models or a formula.

Volume of a Rectangular Prism — Key Concept

Words The volume V of a rectangular prism is length ℓ times width w times height h.

Symbols $V = \ell wh$

Model

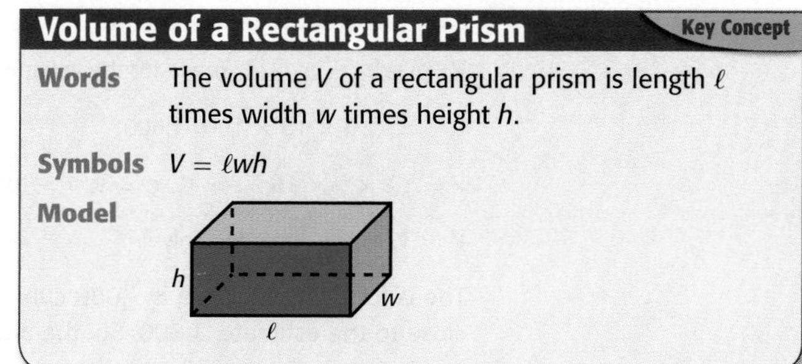

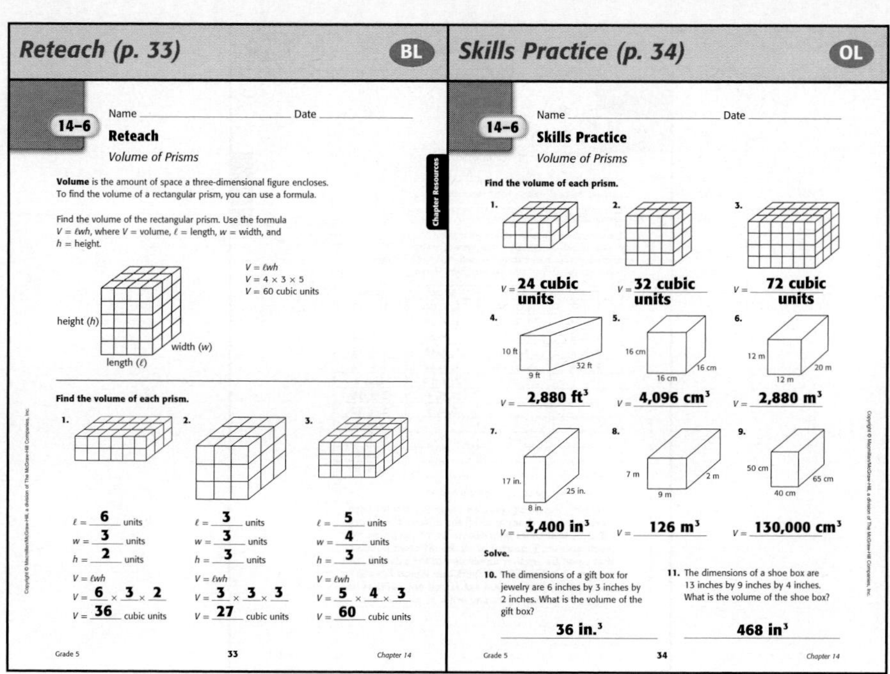

Reteach (p. 33) BL

14–6 Name ________ Date ________

Reteach

Volume of Prisms

Volume is the amount of space a three-dimensional figure encloses. To find the volume of a rectangular prism, you can use a formula.

Find the volume of the rectangular prism. Use the formula $V = \ell wh$, where V = volume, ℓ = length, w = width, and h = height.

height (h), width (w), length (ℓ)

$V = \ell wh$
$V = 4 \times 3 \times 5$
$V = 60$ cubic units

Find the volume of each prism.

1. ℓ = **6** units, w = **3** units, h = **2** units; $V = \ell wh$; V = **6** × **3** × **2**; V = **36** cubic units
2. ℓ = **3** units, w = **3** units, h = **3** units; $V = \ell wh$; V = **3** × **3** × **3**; V = **27** cubic units
3. ℓ = **5** units, w = **4** units, h = **3** units; $V = \ell wh$; V = **5** × **4** × **3**; V = **60** cubic units

Grade 5 33 Chapter 14

Skills Practice (p. 34) OL

14–6 Name ________ Date ________

Skills Practice

Volume of Prisms

Find the volume of each prism.

1. V = **24 cubic units**
2. V = **32 cubic units**
3. V = **72 cubic units**
4. 10 ft, 9 ft, 32 ft — V = **2,880 ft³**
5. 16 cm, 16 cm, 16 cm — V = **4,096 cm³**
6. 12 m, 12 m, 20 m — V = **2,880 m³**
7. 17 in., 8 in., 25 in. — V = **3,400 in³**
8. 7 m, 9 m, 2 m — V = **126 m³**
9. 50 cm, 40 cm, 65 cm — V = **130,000 cm³**

Solve.

10. The dimensions of a gift box for jewelry are 6 inches by 3 inches by 2 inches. What is the volume of the gift box? **36 in.³**
11. The dimensions of a shoe box are 13 inches by 9 inches by 4 inches. What is the volume of the shoe box? **468 in³**

Grade 5 34 Chapter 14

14-6 Volumes of Prisms

1 Introduce

Activity Choice 1 • Hands-On

- Review linear and square units of measure.
- Provide students with rulers and have them draw a line segment that is 1 centimeter long. **What kinds of things can you measure in centimeters?** Answers will vary.
- Sketch a rectangle on the board. **What can you measure about this rectangle using centimeters?** length, width, perimeter
- Next, have students use their rulers to draw a square that is 1 centimeter on each side. **What unit does the square show?** 1 square cm
- **What can you measure about the rectangle using square centimeters?** its area

Activity Choice 2 • Literature

Introduce the lesson with *Geometry* by Lucille Caron and Philip M. St. Jacques. For a related math activity, see p. TK60.

2 Teach

Scaffolding Questions

Give each student a centimeter cube and a ruler.

- **Is a centimeter cube a plane figure or a three-dimensional figure? How do you know?** three-dimensional; it has length, width, and height.
- **What do you notice about the edges and faces of the cube?** The faces are congruent squares, and the edges are all the same length.
- Have students measure one edge. **What is the length?** 1 cm **width?** 1 cm **height?** 1 cm
- Tell students that the cube represents 1 cubic centimeter or 1 cm^3.
- **How can you use cubic units to measure three-dimensional figures?** Count the number of cubic units that fill a three-dimensional figure.

GET READY to Learn

Have students open their books and read the information in **Get Ready to Learn**. Introduce **volume**. As a class, work through **Examples 1 and 2**.

Volume of a Prism

Example 2 Remind students of the procedure for multiplying three factors: multiply two factors first, then multiply that product by the third factor.

Remind students of the difference between *capacity* and *volume*. Volume refers to the space taken up by an object itself. Capacity refers to the amount of liquid or other substance a container can or does hold.

ADDITIONAL EXAMPLES

1. What is the volume of a fish tank that is 4 inches long, 4 inches wide, and 6 inches tall? 96 in^3
2. Find the volume of the rectangular prism. 480 m^3

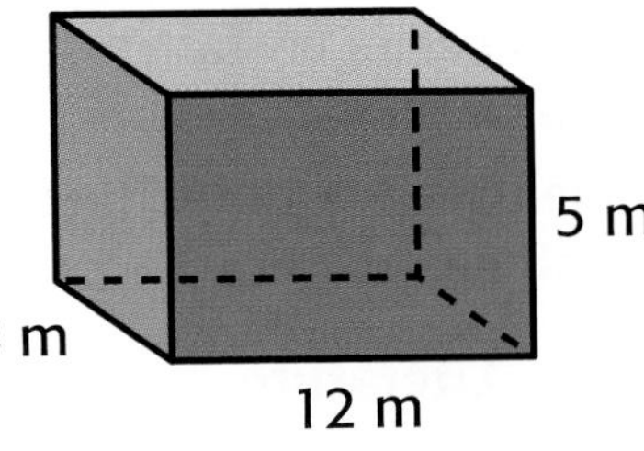

CHECK What You Know

As a class, have students complete Exercises 1–7 in **Check What You Know** as you observe their work.

Exercise 7 Assess student comprehension before assigning practice exercises.

BL Alternate Teaching Strategy

If students have trouble understanding the concept of volume…

Then use one of these reteach options:

1. CRM **Daily Reteach Worksheet** (p. 33)
2. Have each student make one rectangular prism using exactly 36 connecting cubes. Then ask students to show their prisms to the class and write the length, width, and height of the prism in units in a table you create on the board.
   - Next, have students use the formula $V = \ell \times w \times h$ to find the volume of each prism in the table.
   - Discuss how the different prisms all have the same volume of 36 cubic units. Have students explore how volume is related to length, width, and height.

Remember

A cube with 1 unit on an edge is a standard unit for measuring volume. When cubes are placed in a prism to determine volume, there are no gaps or overlaps between the cubes.

Real-World EXAMPLE Volume of a Prism

1. **GAMES What is the volume of a video game system that is 6 inches long, 4 inches wide, and 4 inches tall?**

One Way: Use a Model

Count the number of 1-inch cubes that will fill the bottom of the rectangular prism. The prism is 6 cubes long and 4 cubes wide. There are 24 cubes on the bottom.

There are 4 layers of cubes. So, there are 4 × 24 or 96 cubes.

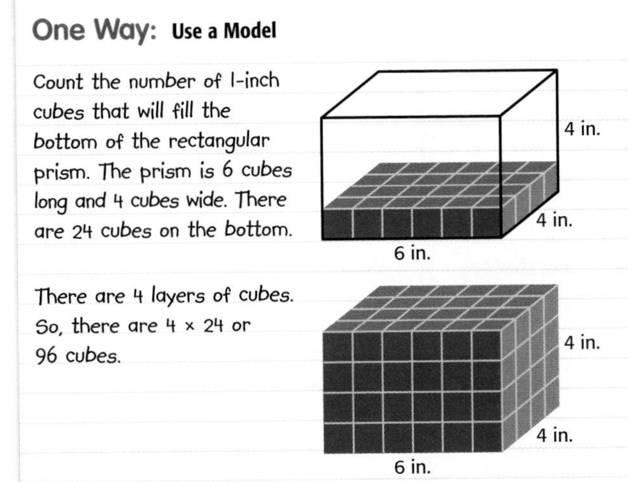

Another Way: Select and Use a Formula

$V = \ell wh$	Formula for the volume of a rectangular prism
$V = 6 \times 4 \times 4$	$\ell = 6, w = 4, h = 4$
$V = 96$	Multiply.

The volume of the video game system is 96 cubic inches.

EXAMPLE Volume of a Prism

2. **Find the volume of the prism.**

9 cm
10 cm
12 cm

$V = \ell wh$	Formula for the volume
Estimate $10 \times 10 \times 10 = 1{,}000$	
$V = \mathbf{12} \times \mathbf{9} \times \mathbf{10}$	$\ell = 12, w = 9, h = 10$
$V = 1{,}080$	Multiply.

The volume of the prism is 1,080 cubic centimeters. This is close to the estimate, 1,000. So, the answer is reasonable.

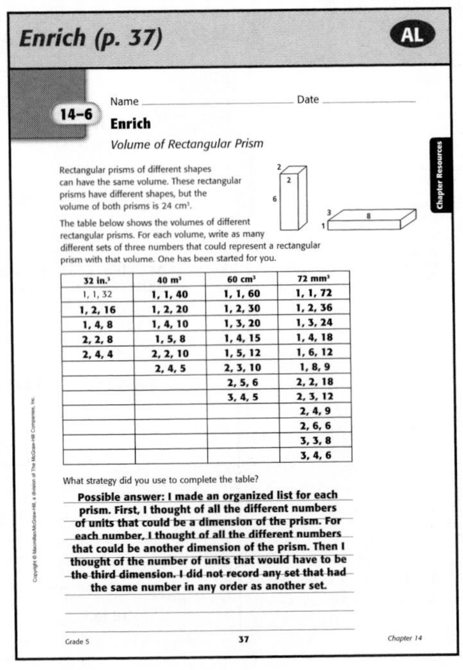

Enrich (p. 37) AL

Name ____________ Date ____________

14–6 **Enrich**

Volume of Rectangular Prism

Rectangular prisms of different shapes can have the same volume. These rectangular prisms have different shapes, but the volume of both prisms is 24 cm^3.

The table below shows the volumes of different rectangular prisms. For each volume, write as many different sets of three numbers that could represent a rectangular prism with that volume. One has been started for you.

32 in.^{3}	40 m^3	60 cm^3	72 mm^3
1, 1, 32	1, 1, 40	1, 1, 60	1, 1, 72
1, 2, 16	1, 2, 20	1, 2, 30	1, 2, 36
1, 4, 8	1, 4, 10	1, 3, 20	1, 3, 24
2, 2, 8	1, 5, 8	1, 4, 15	1, 4, 18
2, 4, 4	2, 2, 10	1, 5, 12	1, 6, 12
	2, 4, 5	2, 3, 10	1, 8, 9
		2, 5, 6	2, 2, 18
		3, 4, 5	2, 3, 12
			2, 4, 9
			2, 6, 6
			3, 3, 8
			3, 4, 6

What strategy did you use to complete the table?

Possible answer: I made an organized list for each prism. First, I thought of all the different numbers of units that could be a dimension of the prism. For each number, I thought of all the different numbers that could be another dimension of the prism. Then I thought of the number of units that would have to be the third dimension. I did not record any set that had the same number in any order as another set.

Grade 5 37 Chapter 14

Chapter Resources

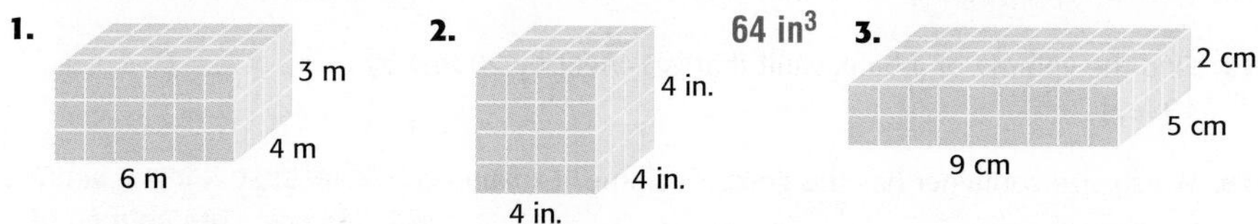

CHECK What You Know

Find the volume of each prism. See Examples 1, 2 (p. 632) 1. 72 m^3 3. 90 cm^3

1. 2. 64 in^3 3.

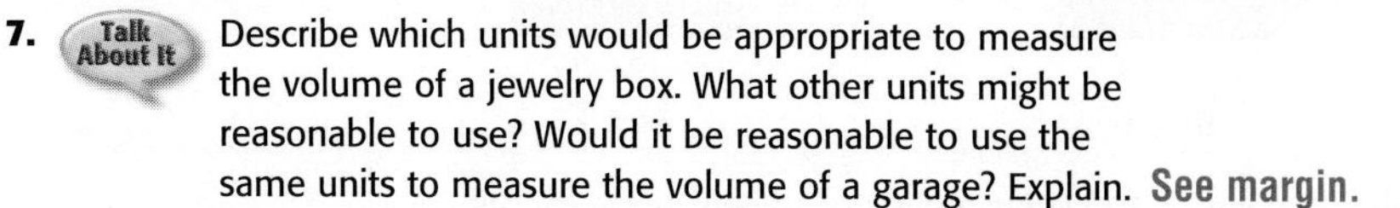

4. $\ell = 21$ cm, $w = 8$ cm, $h = 4$ cm 672 cm^3 5. $\ell = 19$ ft, $w = 9$ ft, $h = 16$ ft 2,736 ft^3

6. Find the cubic feet of air in a room that is 13 feet long, 10 feet high, and 11 feet wide. 1,430 ft^3

7. Talk About It Describe which units would be appropriate to measure the volume of a jewelry box. What other units might be reasonable to use? Would it be reasonable to use the same units to measure the volume of a garage? Explain. See margin.

★ indicates multi-step problem

Practice and Problem Solving

EXTRA PRACTICE See page R39.

Find the volume of each prism. See Examples 1, 2 (p. 632)

8. 990 ft^3 9. 936 cm^3 10. 1,331 in^3 11. 3,312 m^3

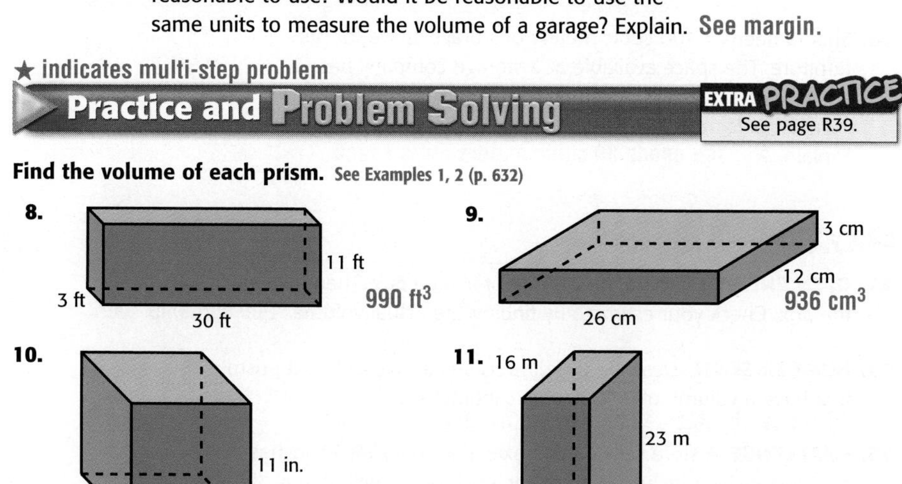

12. 1,071 cm^3 ★13. 24 in^3

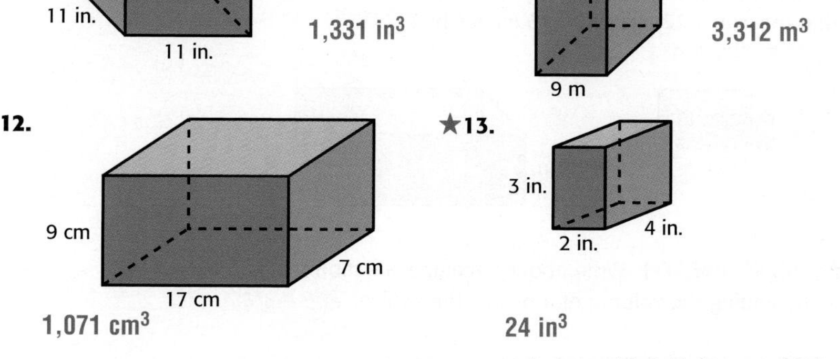

Additional Answer

7. Sample answer: Cubic centimeters would be appropriate, because a jewelry box is small. Cubic inches would also be appropriate. It would not be reasonable to use cubic centimeters or cubic inches to measure the volume of a garage because a garage is so large. It would be more reasonable to use cubic feet or cubic yards.

3 Practice

Differentiate practice using these leveled assignments for Exercises 8–24.

Level	Assignment
BL Below/Approaching Level	8–10, 14–15, 18–19, 21–22
OL On Level	8–12, 14–22, 24
AL Above/Beyond Level	9–19 odd, 21–24

Have students discuss and complete the Higher Order Thinking problems. If students have difficulty describing a real-life situation for Exercise 24, encourage them to think about rectangular prisms that can be filled with something. Have students share their examples with the class.

WRITING IN MATH Have students complete Exercise 24 in their Math Journals. You may choose to use this as an optional formative assessment.

COMMON ERROR!

Students may make multiplication errors when multiplying length × width × height. Remind students of the Commutative Property of Multiplication, which states that the order in which numbers are multiplied does not change the product. This means that the formula $V = \ell \times w \times h$ could also be written as $V = w \times \ell \times h$ or $V = h \times w \times \ell$, etc., and still produce the same volume. If students consistently make multiplication errors, suggest that they look carefully at the three factors (length, width, height) and arrange them in a new order that would make it easier to multiply.

4 Assess

Formative Assessment

Tell students they have a box with a length of 8 cm, a width of 6 cm, and a height of 12 cm.

- **How could you use a model to find the volume of box?** Sample answer: Fill the bottom of the box with centimeter cubes and count or multiply to find the number of cubes in that layer: 48. Fill the box with 12 layers and multiply 12 × 48 to find the number of cubes, 576.
- **How could you use a formula to find the volume?** Use the formula $V = \ell \times w \times h$ and substitute, $V = 8 \text{ cm} \times 6 \text{ cm} \times 12 \text{ cm}$. Multiply to get a volume of 576 cm^3.
- **Which method do you prefer to use? Why?** Answers will vary. Sample answer: I prefer to use the formula because it is the fastest method, and I can do it with pencil and paper.

Quick Check **Are students continuing to struggle with finding the volumes of rectangular prisms?**

If Yes → Small Group Options (p. 631B)

If No → Independent Work Options (p. 631B)
CRM Skills Practice Worksheet (p. 34)
CRM Enrich Worksheet (p. 37)

Yesterday's News Have students write about or discuss how the problem-solving strategy *make a model* helped them with today's lesson on volumes of prisms.

Additional Answers

23. 8 lunch boxes will fit. The length of the box is twice the length of a lunch box and the width of the box is more than twice the width of a lunch box. So, 4 lunch boxes will fit on the bottom of the box. Since the height of the box is twice the height of a lunchbox, two layers of 4 lunch boxes will fit.

24. Sample answer: A fish tank is 2 feet long, 1 foot wide, and 1.5 feet high. What is the volume of water that the tank can hold? Answer: 3 ft^3

Find the volume of each prism. See Examples 1, 2 (p. 632)

14. $\ell = 5$ yd, $w = 16$ yd, $h = 6$ yd **480 yd^3**

15. $\ell = 2$ m, $w = 8$ m, $h = 10$ m **160 m^3**

16. $\ell = 13$ in., $w = 3$ in., $h = 2$ in. **78 in^3**

17. $\ell = 13$ cm, $w = 8$ cm, $h = 10$ cm **1,040 cm^3**

18. Find the volume of a bank vault that is 14 feet by 20 feet by 19 feet. **5,320 ft^3**

★**19.** Which size container has the greater volume? Explain. **Box 1 because it has a volume of 2,744 cm^3. The volume of Box 2 is 2,730 cm^3.**

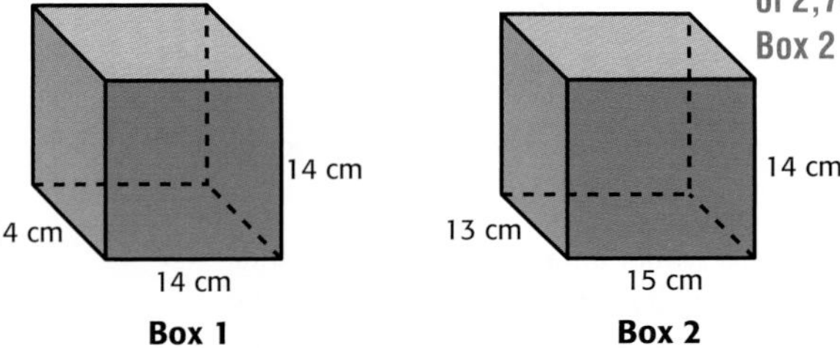

★**20.** Sherita needs 1,400 cubic meters of storage space for her furniture. The space available at a storage company has a length of 11 meters, width of 10 meters, and height of 12 meters. Is the space large enough for Sherita's furniture? Explain. **No; she needs 80 cubic meters more space.**

H.O.T. Problems

21. OPEN ENDED Estimate the volume of a shoe box. Then measure the box. Check your estimate by finding the actual volume. **See students' work.**

22. NUMBER SENSE Describe the dimensions of two different prisms that have a volume of 2,400 cubic centimeters. **Sample answers: 10 cm by 20 cm by 12 cm; 10 cm by 10 cm by 24 cm**

23. CHALLENGE A store sells lunch boxes that measure 11 inches by 7 inches by 4 inches. How many lunch boxes will fit in a box that measures 22 inches by 15 inches by 8 inches? Explain. **See margin.**

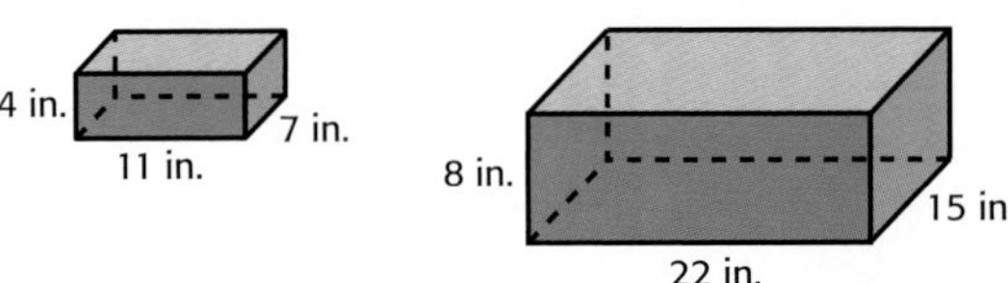

24. WRITING IN ▶MATH Write about a real-life situation that can be solved by finding the volume of a prism. Then solve. **See margin.**

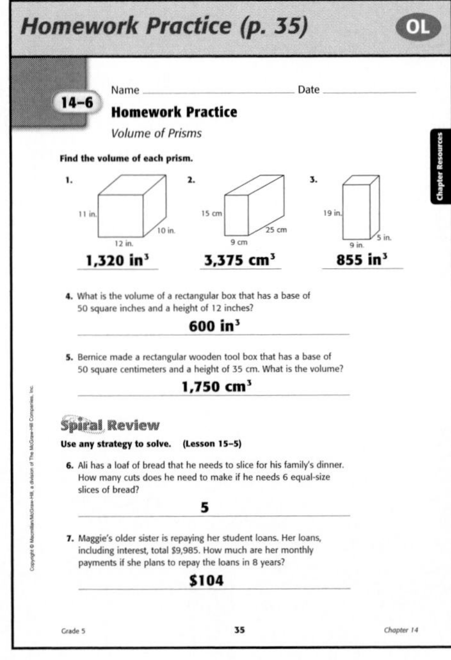

Homework Practice (p. 35) OL

Name ________ Date ________

14–6 **Homework Practice**

Volume of Prisms

Find the volume of each prism.

1. 11 in., 12 in., 10 in. **1,320 in^3**
2. 15 cm, 9 cm, 25 cm **3,375 cm^3**
3. 19 in., 9 in., 5 in. **855 in^3**

4. What is the volume of a rectangular box that has a base of 50 square inches and a height of 12 inches? **600 in^3**

5. Bernice made a rectangular wooden tool box that has a base of 50 square centimeters and a height of 35 cm. What is the volume? **1,750 cm^3**

Spiral Review

Use any strategy to solve. (Lesson 15–5)

6. Ali has a loaf of bread that he needs to slice for his family's dinner. How many cuts does he need to make if he needs 6 equal-size slices of bread? **5**

7. Maggie's older sister is repaying her student loans. Her loans, including interest, total $9,985. How much are her monthly payments if she plans to repay the loans in 8 years? **$104**

Chapter Resources

Grade 5 35 Chapter 14

25. Popcorn tins are stacked in a display so that there are 12 tins in the bottom row. There are 10 tins in the next row, and 8 tins in the row above that. There are five rows of tins. If the pattern continues, how many popcorn tins are there in all? (Lesson 14-5) C

A 22

B 30

C 40

D 42

26. **SHORT RESPONSE** Find the volume in cubic inches of a rectangular prism with length 8 inches, width 5 inches, and height 11 inches. (Lesson 14-6) 440

27. Which of these rectangular prisms has a volume of 20 cubic units? (Lesson 14-6) J

F

G

H

J

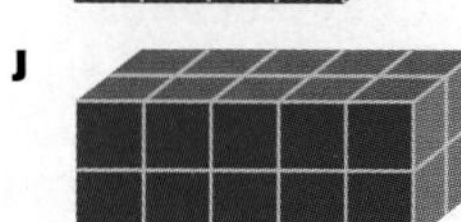

Spiral Review

28. Estimate the volume of one of your textbooks in cubic centimeters. Explain how you could make a model to test your estimate. (Lesson 14-5) See students' work.

29. What kind of three-dimensional shape is shown below? (Lesson 14-4) triangular prism

30. Estimate the area of the figure shown below. (Lesson 14-2)

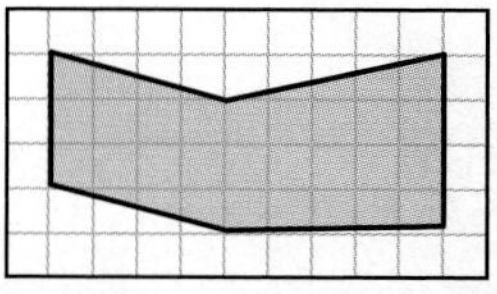

Sample answer: 30 units^2

Identify whether each group of objects represents a prime number or a composite number. (Lesson 9-2)

31. composite

32. prime

Reviews Lessons 14-5 and 14-6

Assign the Test Practice problems to provide daily reinforcement of test-taking skills.

Reviews Lessons 9-2, 14-2, 14-4, and 14-5

Review and assess mastery of skills and concepts from previous chapters.

Lesson Planner

Objective

Interpret information and data from science to solve problems.

National Standard 

Students should develop an understanding of science and technology in society.

Activate Prior Knowledge

Before you turn students' attention to the pages, ask them to discuss frozen foods.

- **What frozen foods have you eaten?** Sample answers: pizza, vegetables, ice cream
- **Who invented flash freezing?** Clarence Birdseye

Use the Student Page

Ask students to read the information on p. 621 and answer these questions:

- **What is the volume of a package of frozen vegetables?** 60 in^3
- **What is the volume of a package of frozen fish sticks?** 135 in^3

Birdseye View

You probably eat packaged frozen food every day. Frozen food might seem like a simple concept, but there's more to it than just putting a container of food in the freezer.

Clarence Birdseye is sometimes called "the father of frozen food" because he was the first to develop a practical way to preserve food by flash freezing.

Birdseye experimented with freezing fruits and vegetables, as well as fish and meat. His method of freezing food preserved the food's taste, texture, and appearance. He also was the first to package food in waxed cardboard packages that could be sold directly to consumers.

Did You Know?

148 patents were issued that related to Clarence Birdseye's flash-freezing method, his type of packaging, and the packaging materials he used.

Dimensions of Frozen Food Packages in Inches			
Item	**Length**	**Width**	**Height**
Pizza	12	12	2
Vegetables	5	6	2
Frozen Dinner	11	8	2
Fish Sticks	9	5	3
Hamburger Patties	9	10	4

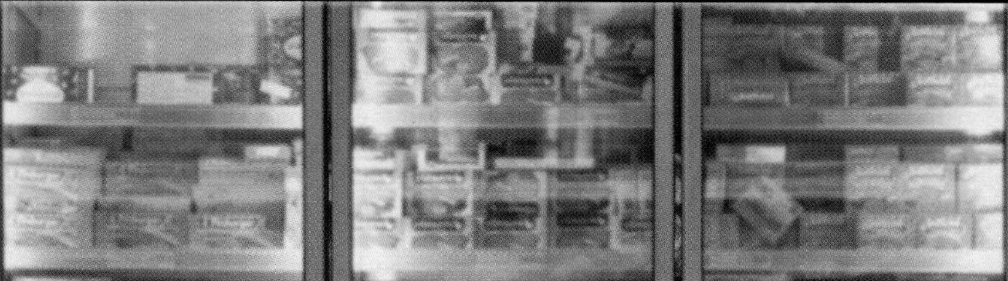

Real-World Math

Use the information above to solve each problem.

1. What is the volume of a frozen pizza package? 288 in^3
2. How much more space does a package of fish sticks occupy than a package of vegetables? 75 in^3
3. Is 175 cubic inches a reasonable estimate for the volume of a frozen dinner package? Explain. Yes; $V \approx 11 \times 8 \times 2$ or 176 in^3
4. A freezer has 2,600 cubic inches of available space. After seven packages of hamburger patties are placed inside, how much available freezer space is left? 80 in^3
5. A larger package of frozen vegetables has the same length and width but twice the height. What is the volume of this package? 120 in^3
6. Use an inch ruler to measure the length, width, and height of an actual frozen food package to the nearest whole unit. Then find the volume of the package. Sample answer: 4,860 in^3
7. WRITING IN ▶MATH Explain the differences between area and volume and the units used to represent them. See margin.

Additional Answer

7. Sample answer: For two-dimensional objects, area is found by multiplying the length and width and is expressed in square units. For three-dimensional objects, volume is the product of the length, width, and height and is expressed in cubic units.

Real-World Math

Assign the exercises on p. 637. Encourage students to choose a problem-solving strategy before beginning each exercise. If necessary, review the strategies suggested in Lesson 14-5, pp. 628–629.

Exercise 1 Remind students that they need to multiply all three measurements to get volume.

Exercise 4 Tell students that they need to figure out the volume of the hamburger patties and then use division to find out how many will fit into the freezer.

WRITING IN ▶MATH Have students create a word problem that uses the information found in the text and in the chart on p. 637.

Extend the Activity

Have students calculate how much freezer space one of each of these items will take up.

Math Activity for 14-7

Lesson Planner

Objective

Use models to find the surface area of rectangular prisms.

Vocabulary Resources

Materials: grid paper, scissors

Introduce

Introduce the Concept

- Pass out a number cube or connecting cube to each pair of students. **What solid figure is this?** a cube
- Have students cut a sheet of paper into pieces so they have enough pieces to cover each face of the number cube. Then tape the pieces together to form a cube. **How many pieces of paper did you cut?** 6 pieces
- **What shape is each piece of paper?** a square

2 Teach

Activity After Step 2, have students compare their nets. Have students think about whether all prisms formed by the same net have to be alike.

Math Activity for 14-7

Surface Area of Prisms

MAIN IDEA

I will use models to find the surface area of rectangular prisms.

You Will Need
graph paper
scissors

New Vocabulary

net

To find the *surface area* of a rectangular prism, you add the areas of all the faces of the prism.

All six faces can be seen by using a *net*. A **net** is a two dimensional pattern of a three dimensional figure.

ACTIVITY

1 Create a net to find the surface area of the prism.

Step 1 Draw and cut out the net below.

Step 2 Fold along the dotted lines.
Tape the edges together to form a prism.

Step 3 Find the area of each of the six faces of the prism.

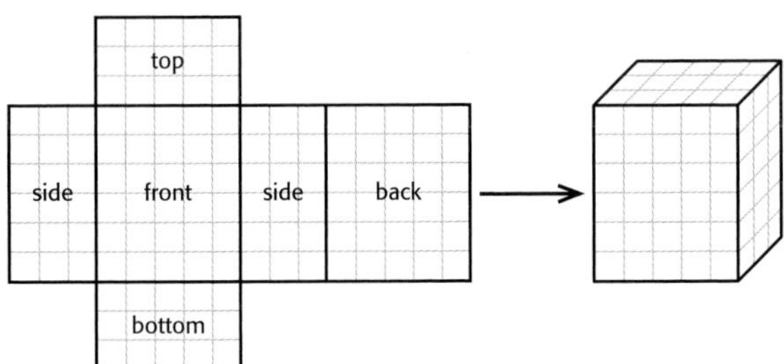

Face	front and back	top and bottom	two sides
Model			
Area (cm^2)	30	15	18

Step 4 Find the sum of the areas.

$A = 30 + 30 + 18 + 18 + 15 + 15$

$A = 126\ cm^2$ Surface area has square units because it measures area.

2 **Find the surface area of the rectangular prism.**

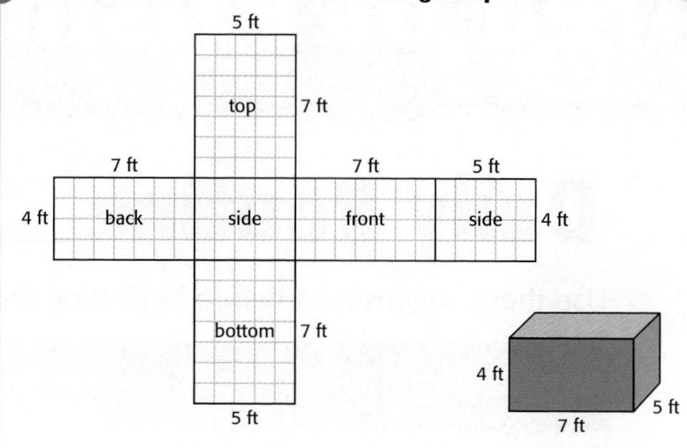

4 ft 7 ft 5 ft

Find the area of each face. Then add.

Face	front and back	top and bottom	two sides
Model			
Area (cm^2)	28	35	20

$A = 28 + 28 + 35 + 35 + 20 + 20$ or 166 square feet

Think About It

1. Explain how to find the surface area of a prism by using a net. Sample answer: Create the net. Find the area of all six faces. Find the sum of the areas.

Make a net to find the surface area of each rectangular prism.

2. 9 m, 4 m, 3 m — $150m^2$

3.

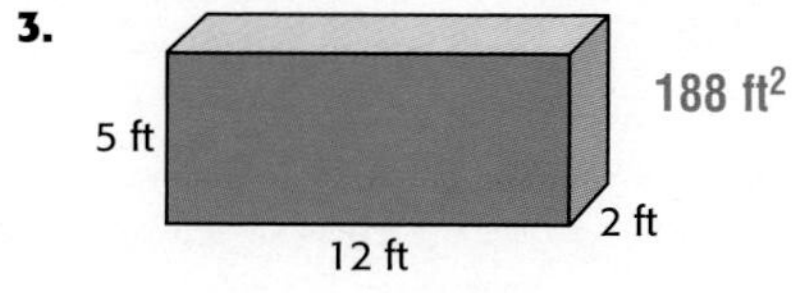

5 ft, 12 ft, 2 ft — 188 ft^2

4. WRITING IN ▶MATH Will the top side of a rectangular prism always have the same area as the bottom side? Explain. yes; Sample answer: the top and bottom, the front and back, and the two sides will always have the same area in a rectangular prism.

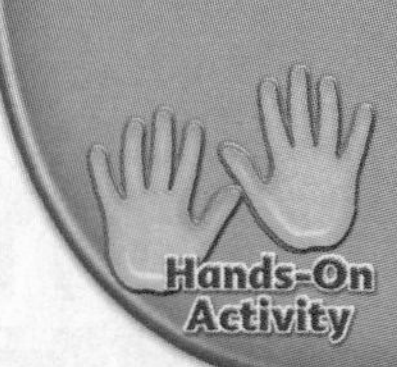

3 Assess

Formative Assessment

Use the *Check What You Know* exercises to assess whether students comprehend how to make a net to find the surface area of a rectangle prism.

From Concrete to Abstract Use Exercise 4 to bridge the idea of using a model to use a formula to find the surface area of a rectangular prism.

LESSON 14-7

Surface Area of Prisms

Lesson Planner

Objective

Find the surface areas of rectangular prisms.

Vocabulary

surface area

Resources

Literature Connection: *Sir Cumference and the Sword in the Cone* by Cindy Neuschwander
Teacher Technology
TeacherWorks • Interactive Classroom

Focus on Math Background

Prior to this lesson, students have found the area of rectangles but not yet found the surface area of rectangular prisms. Surface area of a solid is the sum of the areas of all surfaces (faces) of the figure. In the case of rectangular prisms, this would be the sum of 6 rectangular surfaces.

Students should note that a rectangular prism has 3 pairs of congruent faces. Surface area is always expressed using a numerical value and a square unit of measure.

There are two ways to determine the surface area of a rectangular prism: one involves "unfolding" the solid into its 6 faces, finding the area of each and then adding to find the total area; and the other is to use the formula for the surface area of rectangular prisms ($S = 2\ell w + 2\ell h + 2wh$). To determine the surface area of a prism, ask: How many *faces* and what is the *area of each face* in the given figure?

Daily Routine

Use these suggestions before beginning the lesson on p. 640.

5-Minute Check

(Reviews Lesson 14-6)

Find the volume of each prism.

1. length 8 yd, width 7 yd, height 3 yd 168 yd^3
2. length 12 cm, width 8 cm, height 5 cm 480 cm^3
3. length $5\frac{1}{4}$ ft, width 3 ft, height 9 ft $141\frac{3}{4}$ ft^3

Problem of the Day

Find the perimeter and the area of a rectangular driveway 40 m long and 30 m wide.
perimeter: 140 m; area: 1,200 m^2

Building Math Vocabulary

Write the lesson vocabulary word and its definition on the board. Have students give three or four examples of surface area.

Differentiated Instruction

Small Group Options

Option 1 Gifted and Talented AL

SPATIAL, KINESTHETIC

Materials: paper and pencil

Explore what happens to the surface area of a rectangular prism when the dimensions double.

- **Will the surface area also double? Why or why not?** No; it will quadruple because the area of each face will double.
- **What happens if only the height is doubled?** The new surface area will be less than double.
- **How does doubling all the dimensions affect the volume?** The new volume is 8 times greater than that of the original prism.

Option 2 English Language Learners ELL

LINGUISTIC, LOGICAL

Materials: different sized cardboard boxes, markers
Core Vocabulary: back, front, top, bottom
Common Use Verb: locate

Do Math This strategy helps students vocalize the locations of specific surface area.

- Give each student a box. Ask one student to hold his or her box in front of his or her body.
- Have another student hold his or her box on *top* of the first box.
- Another student holds his or her box on the *bottom* (under) of the first one.
- Another student holds his or her box in *front* of the original box.
- The last student holds his or her box in *back* of the original box.
- As they hold their box each says, "My box is of the first box".
- Students label all the sides of their boxes.

Independent Work Options

Option 1 Early Finishers AL

SOCIAL

Materials: grid paper, colored pencils

- Students draw the net of a rectangular prism on grid paper.
- They should then find the surface area of their prism. Have students show their work on each face.
- Next, students color each set of congruent faces on the prism, using different colors for different sets.
- Students cut out their nets, fold them, and tape the sides together to form the prism.
- Have students share their nets with the class.

Option 2 Student Technology

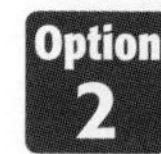

Math Online macmillanmh.com

Personal tutor • Extra Examples

Option 3 Learning Station: (p. 604I)

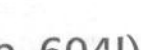

Direct students to the Art Learning Station for opportunities to explore and extend the lesson concept.

Option 4 Problem-Solving Practice

Reinforce problem-solving skills and strategies with the Problem-Solving Practice worksheet.

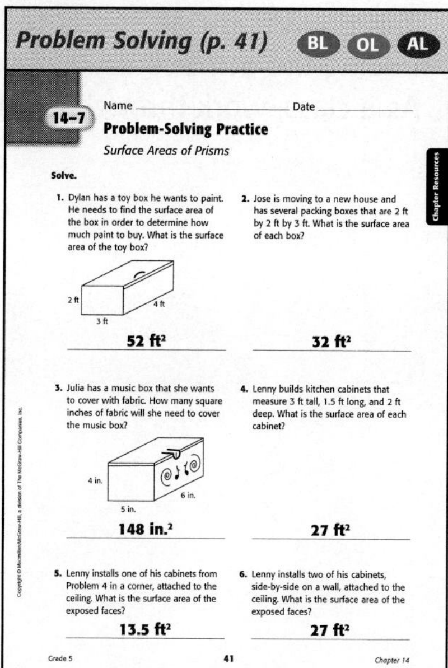

Problem Solving (p. 41) BL OL AL

14–7 Name ______ Date ______

Problem-Solving Practice

Surface Areas of Prisms

Solve.

1. Dylan has a toy box he wants to paint. He needs to find the surface area of the box in order to determine how much paint to buy. What is the surface area of the toy box?

52 ft²

2. Jose is moving to a new house and has several packing boxes that are 2 ft by 2 ft by 3 ft. What is the surface area of each box?

32 ft²

3. Julia has a music box that she wants to cover with fabric. How many square inches of fabric will she need to cover the music box?

148 in.²

4. Lenny builds kitchen cabinets that measure 3 ft tall, 1.5 ft long, and 2 ft deep. What is the surface area of each cabinet?

27 ft²

5. Lenny installs one of his cabinets from Problem 4 in a corner, attached to the ceiling. What is the surface area of the exposed faces?

13.5 ft²

6. Lenny installs two of his cabinets, side-by-side on a wall, attached to the ceiling. What is the surface area of the exposed faces?

27 ft²

Chapter Resources

Grade 5 41 Chapter 14

14-7 Surface Areas of Prisms

1 Introduce

Activity Choice 1 • Hands-On 

Provide grid paper.

- Have students draw a 6-unit by- 6-unit square. **What is the area of this square?** 36 units^2
- **How many faces does a cube have?** 6
- **Suppose each face has an area of 36 square units. What would be the area of all 6 faces?** 216 units^2

Activity Choice 2 • Literature

Introduce the lesson with *Sir Cumference and the Sword in the Cone* by Cindy Newschwander. For a related math activity see p. TR60

2 Teach

Scaffolding Questions

Have students measure the length, the width, and the height of their math books to the nearest half-inch.

- **Which dimensions would you use to find the area of the front and back covers?** length and width
- **Which dimensions would you use to find the area of the book's spine?** length and width

GET READY to Learn

Have students open their books and read the information in **Get Ready to Learn.** Introduce finding the **surface area** of rectangular prisms. As a class, work through **Examples 1–2.**

14-7 Surface Areas of Prisms

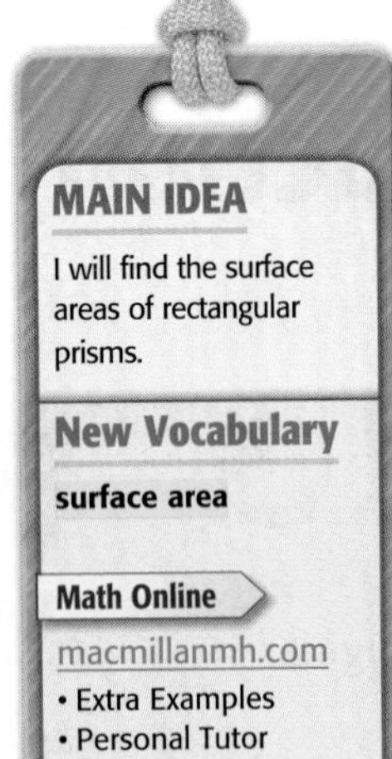

MAIN IDEA
I will find the surface areas of rectangular prisms.
New Vocabulary
surface area
Math Online
macmillanmh.com
• Extra Examples
• Personal Tutor
• Self-Check Quiz

GET READY to Learn

Wrapping paper is used to cover the surface area of a box.

The sum of the areas of all the faces of a prism is called the **surface area** of the prism.

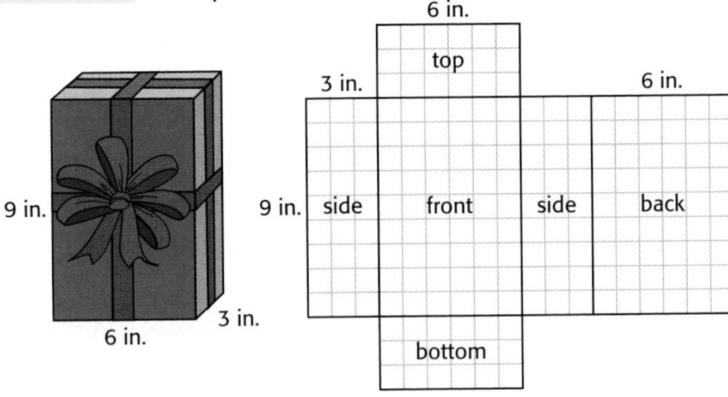

To find the surface area, you could add the areas of all six faces.

In the diagram above each face has a congruent opposite face. The front is congruent to the back, the top is congruent to the bottom, and the two sides are congruent.

So, the following formula can also be used to find surface area.

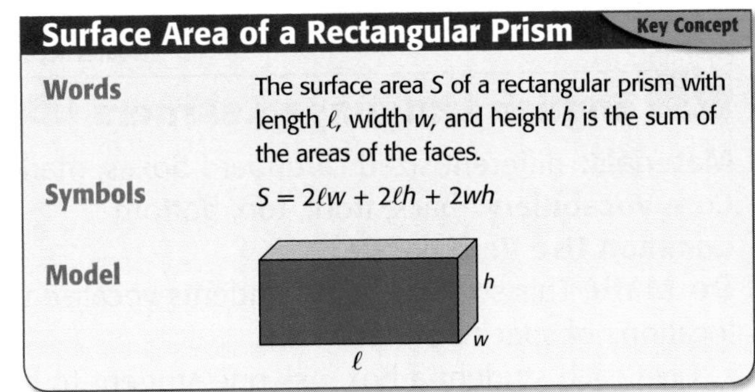

Surface Area of a Rectangular Prism — Key Concept

Words	The surface area S of a rectangular prism with length ℓ, width w, and height h is the sum of the areas of the faces.
Symbols	$S = 2\ell w + 2\ell h + 2wh$
Model	(figure: h, w, ℓ)

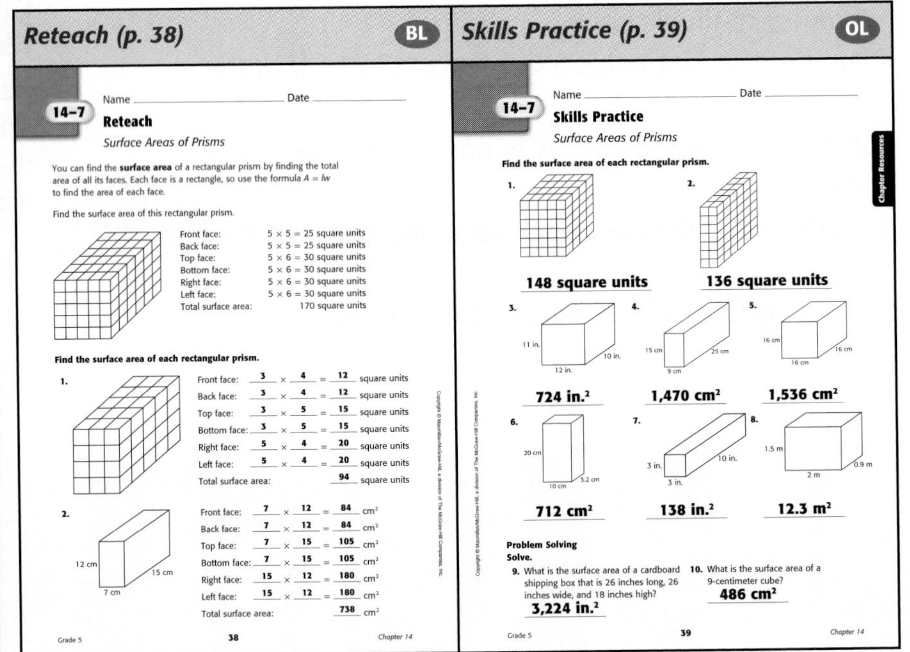

Reteach (p. 38) BL

14-7 Name ______ Date ______

Reteach

Surface Areas of Prisms

You can find the **surface area** of a rectangular prism by finding the total area of all its faces. Each face is a rectangle, so use the formula $A = lw$ to find the area of each face.

Find the surface area of this rectangular prism.

Front face:	5 × 5 = 25 square units
Back face:	5 × 5 = 25 square units
Top face:	5 × 6 = 30 square units
Bottom face:	5 × 6 = 30 square units
Right face:	5 × 6 = 30 square units
Left face:	5 × 6 = 30 square units
Total surface area:	170 square units

Find the surface area of each rectangular prism.

1.

Front face:	**3** × **4** = **12** square units
Back face:	**3** × **4** = **12** square units
Top face:	**3** × **5** = **15** square units
Bottom face:	**3** × **5** = **15** square units
Right face:	**5** × **4** = **20** square units
Left face:	**5** × **4** = **20** square units
Total surface area:	**94** square units

2. 12 cm, 15 cm, 7 cm

Front face:	**7** × **12** = **84** cm^2
Back face:	**7** × **12** = **84** cm^2
Top face:	**7** × **15** = **105** cm^2
Bottom face:	**7** × **15** = **105** cm^2
Right face:	**15** × **12** = **180** cm^2
Left face:	**15** × **12** = **180** cm^2
Total surface area:	**738** cm^2

Grade 5 38 Chapter 14

Skills Practice (p. 39) OL

14-7 Name ______ Date ______

Skills Practice

Surface Areas of Prisms

Find the surface area of each rectangular prism.

1. **148 square units**
2. **136 square units**
3. 11 in., 10 in., 12 in. **724 in.^{2}**
4. 15 cm, 25 cm, 9 cm **1,470 cm^2**
5. 16 cm, 16 cm, 16 cm **1,536 cm^2**
6. 20 cm, 5.2 cm, 10 cm **712 cm^2**
7. 3 in., 10 in., 3 in. **138 in.^{2}**
8. 1.5 m, 0.9 m, 2 m **12.3 m^2**

Problem Solving

Solve.

9. What is the surface area of a cardboard shipping box that is 26 inches long, 26 inches wide, and 18 inches high? **3,224 in.^{2}**
10. What is the surface area of a 9-centimeter cube? **486 cm^2**

Grade 5 39 Chapter 14

Chapter Resources

Real-World EXAMPLE — Find the Surface Area

1 GIFTS Find the surface area for the amount of wrapping paper needed to cover the gift on page 640.

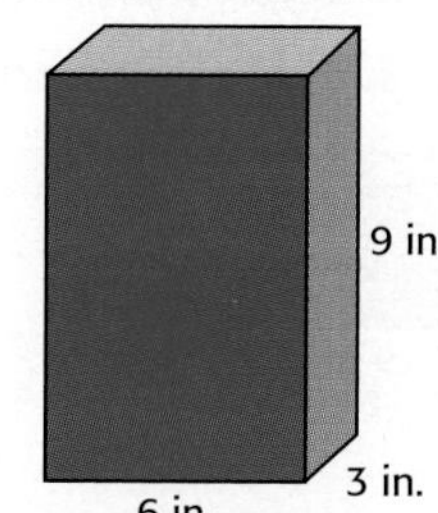

Find the area of each face.

top and bottom:
$2(\ell w) = 2(6 \times 3)$ or 36

front and back:
$2(\ell h) = 2(6 \times 9)$ or 108

two sides:
$2(wh) = 2(3 \times 9)$ or 54

Add to find the surface area.

The surface area is 36 + 108 + 54 or 198 square inches.

Remember

The top face has the same area as the bottom face. The front face has the same area as the back face. Both side faces have the same area.

Real-World EXAMPLE — Find the Surface Area

2 CAMERAS Digital cameras are made small enough to fit in a pocket. This camera is shaped like a rectangular prism. Find the surface area of the camera.

Find the area of each face.

top and bottom: $2(\ell w) = 2(6 \times 2)$ or 24

front and back: $2(\ell h) = 2(6 \times 4)$ or 48

two sides: $2(wh) = 2(2 \times 4)$ or 16

Add to find the surface area.

The surface area is 24 + 48 + 16 or 88 square inches.

ADDITIONAL EXAMPLES

1. Find the surface area of the rectangular prism. 136 cm^2

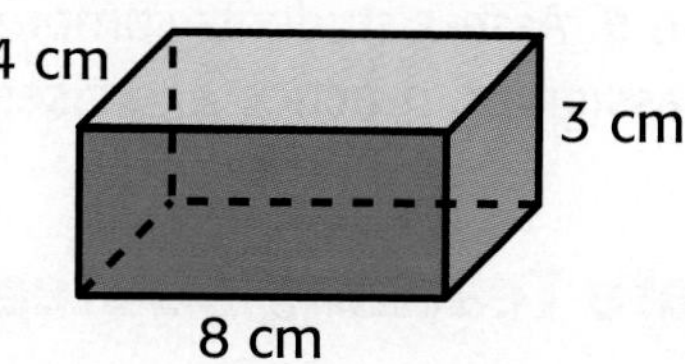

2. A box measures 13 inches long, 7 inches wide, and 4 inches deep. What is the surface area of the box? 342 in^2

As a class, have students complete Exercises 1–5 in **Check What You Know** as you observe their work.

Exercise 5 Assess students comprehension before assigning practice exercises.

BL Alternate Teaching Strategy

If students have trouble with surface area of rectangular prisms...

Then use one of these reteach options:

1 CRM **Daily Reteach Worksheet p. 38**

2 Provide an empty cereal box that has been sealed with tape along its edges. Have students cut it open and unfold it to form a net.

- **How many faces does the carton have?** 6
- **What kind of shape is each face?** rectangle
- **How can you find the total amount of surface area of cardboard?** Sample answer: Find the sum of the areas of the six rectangular faces.

3 Practice

Differentiate practice using these leveled assignments for Exercises 6–18.

Level	Assignment
BL Below/ Approaching Level	6–8, 13–14, 18
OL On Level	8–12, 14, 16–18
AL Above/Beyond Level	6–10 even, 12–14, 15–18

Have students discuss and complete the Higher-Order Thinking problems.

WRITING IN MATH Have students complete Exercise 18 in their Math Journals. You may choose to use this exercise as an optional formative assessment.

Additional Answer

5. Sample answer: A rectangular prism has 6 faces. Since you are only finding the area of 3 of the faces you need to double each face.

CHECK What You Know

Find the surface area of each rectangular prism. See Example 1 (p. 641)

1.
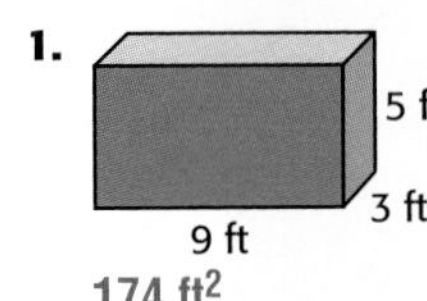

174 ft^2

2.
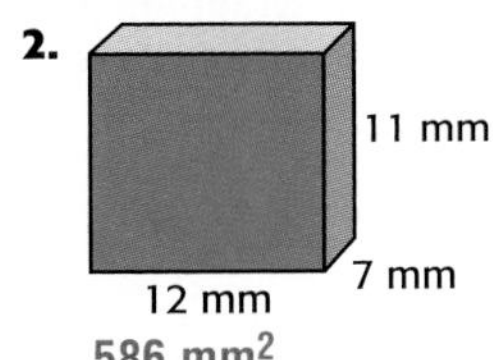

586 mm^2

3.
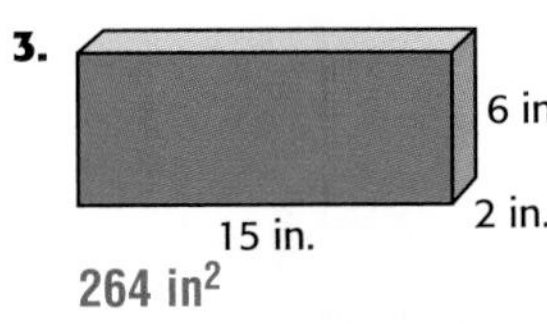

264 in^2

4. A box of animal crackers is shaped like a rectangular prism. What is the surface area of the box of crackers? 166 cm^2

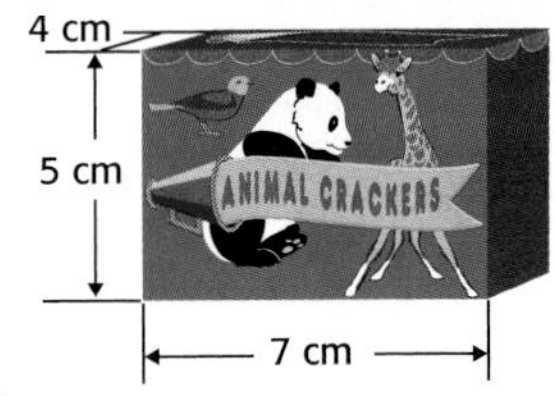

5. Talk About It The formula for the surface area of a rectangular prism is $S = 2\ell w + 2\ell h + 2wh$. Explain why there are three 2s in the formula. See margin.

Practice and Problem Solving

EXTRA PRACTICE See page R39

Find the surface area of each rectangular prism. See Example 1 (p. 641)

6.
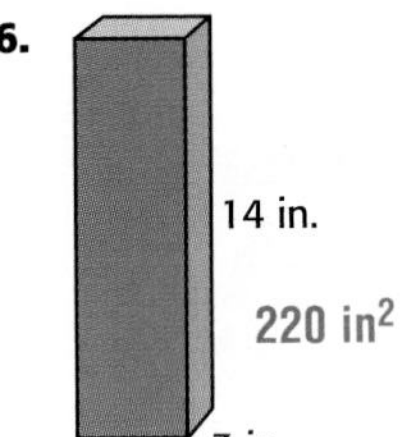

220 in^2

7.
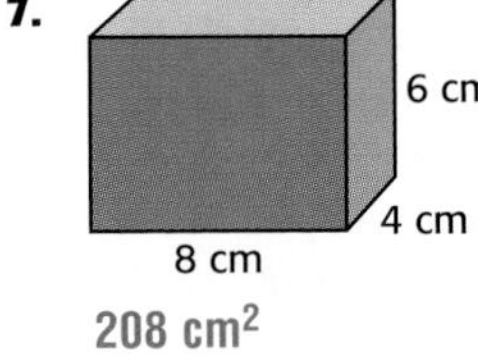

208 cm^2

8.
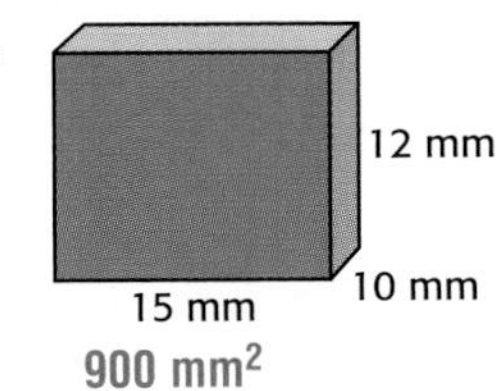

900 mm^2

9.
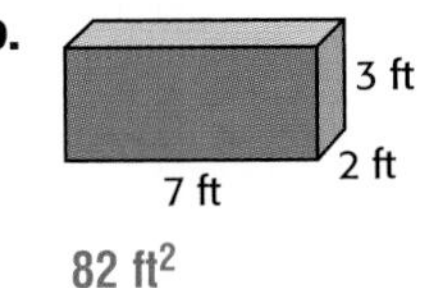

82 ft^2

10.
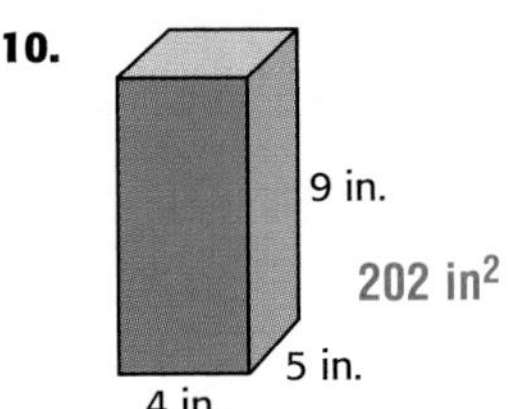

202 in^2

11.
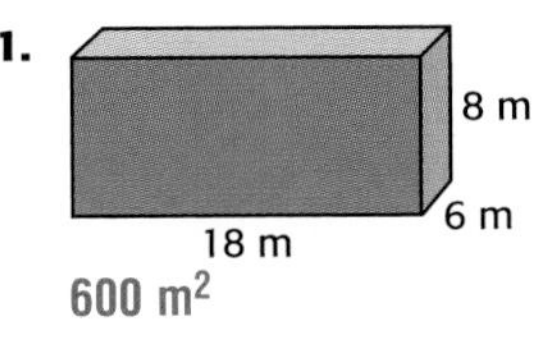

600 m^2

12. Alyssa owns a toolbox that is 16 inches by 22 inches by 5 inches. What is the surface area of the toolbox? 1,084 in^2

Homework Practice (p. 40) OL

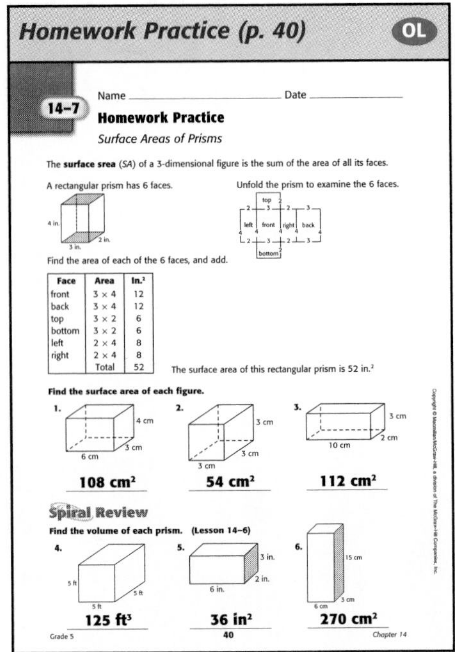

Name ______ Date ______

14–7 **Homework Practice**

Surface Areas of Prisms

The **surface srea** (*SA*) of a 3-dimensional figure is the sum of the area of all its faces.

A rectangular prism has 6 faces. Unfold the prism to examine the 6 faces.

Find the area of each of the 6 faces, and add.

Face	Area	In.^{2}
front	3 × 4	12
back	3 × 4	12
top	3 × 2	6
bottom	3 × 2	6
left	2 × 4	8
right	2 × 4	8
	Total	52

The surface area of this rectangular prism is 52 in.^{2}

Find the surface area of each figure.

1. 108 cm^2
2. 54 cm^2
3. 112 cm^2

Spiral Review

Find the volume of each prism. (Lesson 14–6)

4. 125 ft^3
5. 36 in^2
6. 270 cm^2

Grade 5 40 Chapter 14

13. Michelle put her sister's birthday present in a box with a length of 13 mm, a width of 4 mm, and a height of 8 mm. How many square millimeters of wrapping paper will Michelle need to completely cover the box? **376 mm^2**

14. A package of three golf balls comes in the box shown. What is the surface area of the box? **64 in^2**

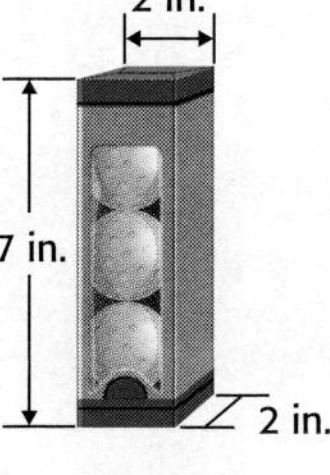

H.O.T. Problems

15. **OPEN ENDED** What is the possible length, width, and height of a rectangular prism with the surface area of 110 square centimeters? **Sample answer: 5 cm by 5 cm by 3 cm**

CHALLENGE For Exercises 16 and 17, use the rectangular prism shown.

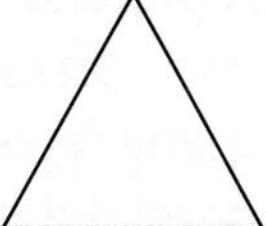

16. How many rectangles and how many squares would the net of the prism make? **4 rectangles and 2 squares**

17. Find the surface area of the rectangular prism. **$52\frac{1}{2}$ ft^2**

18. **WRITING IN MATH** Write a real-world problem about a time when you would need to find the surface area of a rectangular prism. **Sample answer: wrapping a gift**

TEST Practice

19. A shoebox has a length of 10 inches, a width of 5 inches, and a height of 6 inches. What is the surface area of the shoebox? (Lesson 14-7) **B**

A 220 in^2 **C** 325 in^2

B 280 in^2 **D** 340 in^2

20. **SHORT RESPONSE** If the surface area of the top of a rectangular prism is 16 square centimeters, what is the surface area of the bottom? (Lesson 14-7) **16 square centimeters**

Spiral Review

21. Find the volume of a cube that has a length, width, and height of 7 inches. (Lesson 14-6) **343 in^3**

22. Identify the kinds of angles in the triangle shown at the right. (Lesson 13-3) **3 acute angles**

4 Assess

Formative Assessment

- **Describe the steps you would use to find the surface area of a rectangular prism.** Sample answer: Find the area of the front and back, top and bottom, and two sides. Add the areas of the faces together.
- **Explain what $2\ell w$ means.** Sample answer: Since the top and bottom of the rectangular prism are congruent, find the area of one and multiply by 2 to get the area of both.

Ticket Out the Door Select a classroom object and give its measurements. Have students determine the size of the box in which it would fit and the least amount of paper they would need to wrap that box.

Quick Check **Are students continuing to struggle with surface area of rectangular prisms?**

If Yes → Small Group Options (p. 640B)

If No → Independent Work Options (p. 434B)

Skills Practice Worksheet (p. 39)

Enrich Worksheet (p. 42)

COMMON ERROR!

Exercises 13–14 Students may have trouble finding the area of all the faces of the rectangular prism without a diagram. Have them make a drawing of the prism and label the dimensions. Have them count to see that they have included all six faces.

Reviews Lessons 14-7

Assign the Test Practice problems to provide daily reinforcement of test-taking skills.

Reviews Lessons 14-6 and 13-3

Review and assess mastery of skills and concepts from previous chapters.

LESSON 14-8

Select Appropriate Measurement Formulas

Lesson Planner

Objective

Select and use appropriate units and formulas to measure length, perimeter, area, and volume.

Review Vocabulary

formula

Resources

Manipulatives: ruler
Literature Connection: *Sir Cumference and the Sword in the Cone* by Cindy Neuschwander
Teacher Technology
TeacherWorks • Interactive Classroom
Alternate Lesson: Use *Impact Mathematics*: Unit J to provide practice with mesurement formulas.

Focus on Math Background

Contextual situations can be used to good effect in helping students learn when to use perimeter, area, or volume as measurements. For example, suppose a classroom is being renovated. A person installing floor molding around the edges of the room would need to know the room's perimeter. A painter or carpet layer would need to know area. A heating and air conditioning engineer would need to know the volume of air contained in the room. Once the quantity of interest is identified, an appropriate computational formula can be selected. Students should always be urged to include correct units with all measurements or results of computation based on measurement.

Daily Routine

Use these suggestions before beginning the lesson on p. 643.

(Reviews Lesson 14-7)

Find the surface area of each rectangular prism.

1. 102 m^2

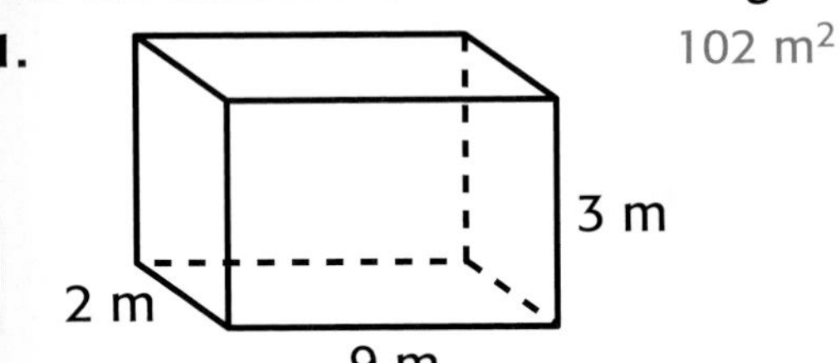

2. $\ell = 5$ ft, $w = 18$ ft, $h = 11$ ft 686 ft^2

3. $\ell = 14$ cm, $w = 6$ cm, $h = 8$ cm 488 cm^2

Problem of the Day

A pizzeria decreased the amount of pepperoni on each pizza from 7.6 ounces to 6.8 ounces. How many fewer *pounds* of pepperoni will the pizzeria need if it usually sells 795 pepperoni pizzas in a month? $39\frac{3}{4}$ lb

Review Math Vocabulary

Write the lesson vocabulary word and its definition on the board.

Have volunteers write various formulas they have learned in this chapter on the board. For example, $P = 2\ell + 2w$, $P = 4s$, $A = \ell \times w$, $A = s^2$, $V = \ell \times w \times h$. For each formula, have students tell what each variable stands for and when they might use the formula to solve a problem.

Visual Vocabulary Cards

Use Visual Vocabulary Card 13 to reinforce the vocabulary in this lesson. (The Define/Example/Ask routine is printed on the back of each card.)

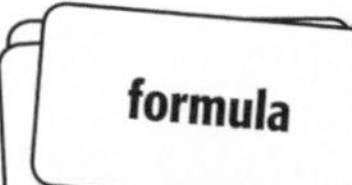

Differentiated Instruction

Small Group Options

Option 1 LOGICAL

Gifted and Talented AL

Materials: rulers and meter sticks, pencils of different lengths, other classroom objects to measure

- Review with students metric measure from smallest (mm) to longest (km).
- Discuss with students the need to find the most appropriate unit to use. Take out some objects to measure and arrange them according to length.
- Ask students to measure the shortest one and decide which unit is best. A small coin, such as a dime, is best measured in mm.
- Continue in this manner. Ask students to measure the objects and discuss the appropriate unit.

Option 2 KINESTHETIC, LOGICAL

English Language Learners ELL

Materials: picture of a painting with the frame traced, table or book surface with the surface covered with lines, container with liquid; magazines, scissors, glue, three posters

Core Vocabulary: real, example
Common Use Verb: locate

Do Math This strategy reviews *volume*, *perimeter*, and *area* with students and how each are used to measure.

- Show three pictures and ask: "On which poster can I glue the picture?" (Container with liquid on volume poster, painting with frame traced on perimeter poster, book or table surface on area poster).
- Working in groups, students decide who is going to locate a real life example of something we can measure with volume, perimeter or area to cut out and glue on the appropriate poster. Students confer before gluing.

Independent Work Options

Option 1 LINGUISTIC

Early Finishers OL AL

- Challenge students to write and solve three word problems: one where they will calculate perimeter, one where they will calculate area, and one where they will calculate volume.
- You may have students share their word problems with the class or exchange them with a partner to solve.

Option 2

Student Technology

Math Online macmillanmh.com

Personal Tutor • Extra Examples

Option 3

Learning Station: Social Studies (p. 604H)

Direct students to the Social Studies Learning Station for opportunities to explore and extend the lesson concept.

Option 4

Problem-Solving Practice

Reinforce problem-solving skills and strategies with the Problem-Solving Practice worksheet.

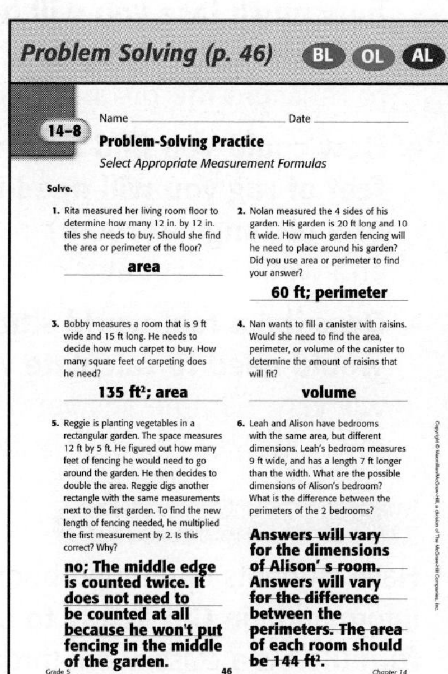

Problem Solving (p. 46) BL OL AL

14–8 Name ______ Date ______

Problem-Solving Practice

Select Appropriate Measurement Formulas

Solve.

1. Rita measured her living room floor to determine how many 12 in. by 12 in. tiles she needs to buy. Should she find the area or perimeter of the floor?
   area
2. Nolan measured the 4 sides of his garden. His garden is 20 ft long and 10 ft wide. How much garden fencing will he need to place around his garden? Did you use area or perimeter to find your answer?
   60 ft; perimeter
3. Bobby measures a room that is 9 ft wide and 15 ft long. He needs to decide how much carpet to buy. How many square feet of carpeting does he need?
   135 ft^2; area
4. Nan wants to fill a canister with raisins. Would she need to find the area, perimeter, or volume of the canister to determine the amount of raisins that will fit?
   volume
5. Reggie is planting vegetables in a rectangular garden. The space measures 12 ft by 5 ft. He figured out how many feet of fencing he would need to go around the garden. He then decides to double the area. Reggie digs another rectangle with the same measurements next to the first garden. To find the new length of fencing needed, he multiplied the first measurement by 2. Is this correct? Why?
   no; The middle edge is counted twice. It does not need to be counted at all because he won't put fencing in the middle of the garden.
6. Leah and Alison have bedrooms with the same area, but different dimensions. Leah's bedroom measures 9 ft wide, and has a length 7 ft longer than the width. What are the possible dimensions of Alison's bedroom? What is the difference between the perimeters of the 2 bedrooms?
   Answers will vary for the dimensions of Alison' s room. Answers will vary for the difference between the perimeters. The area of each room should be 144 ft^2.

Grade 5 46 Chapter 14

14-8 Select Appropriate Measurement Formulas

1 Introduce

Activity Choice 1 • Hands-On

- Have students locate an object shaped like a rectangular prism.
- **What are some different things you can measure on this object?** length, width, height, perimeter of a face, area of a face, volume Write responses on the board.
- Review the meanings of *perimeter*, *area*, and *volume* with students. Then have them examine the object and describe how they would find each measure. **What units might you use to measure the perimeter of a face? the area of a face? the volume of the object?** Sample answers: perimeter: inches; area: square inches; volume: cubic inches
- You may extend the activity by having students use a ruler to measure dimensions and calculate perimeter, area, and volume.

Activity Choice 2 • Literature

Introduce the lesson with *Sir Cumference and the Sword in the Cone* by Cindy Newschwander. For a related math activity, see p.TR60.

2 Teach

Scaffolding Questions

Ask students to suppose they want to put a lace border around a rectangular photograph.

- **What measurement could you use to find how much lace you will need: perimeter, area, or volume? Explain.** Perimeter; I need to measure the distance around the photo.
- **How could you find the number of square feet of rug you will need to cover the floor of a rectangular room?** measure the length and width in feet and multiply to find the area
- **Describe a real-world situation where you would need to calculate volume.** Answers will vary. Sample answer: I want to find out if my computer will fit in a certain box.

GET READY to Learn

Have students open their books and read the information in **Get Ready to Learn**. Review **formula**. As a class, work through **Examples 1–3**.

14-8 Select Appropriate Measurement Formulas

MAIN IDEA

I will select and use appropriate units and formulas to measure length, perimeter, area, and volume.

Math Online

macmillanmh.com
- Extra Examples
- Personal Tutor
- Self-Check Quiz

GET READY to Learn

The 2007 Women's World Cup was played in China. The field at Chengdu Stadium is 109 meters long by 75 meters wide.

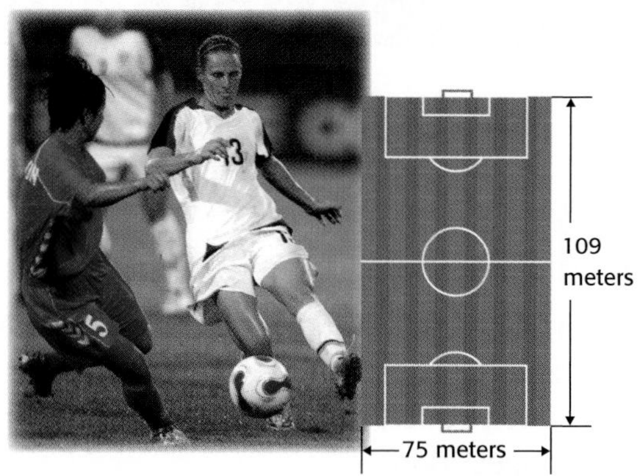

You have learned to find the perimeter, area, and volume of figures. It is important to be able to choose the appropriate measurement for a given situation.

Measurement Formulas — Key Concept

Measure	Used to Find	Model	Formula
Perimeter	distance around a figure	rectangle, w, ℓ	$P = 2\ell + 2w$
Area	space covered by a figure	shaded rectangle, w, ℓ	$A = \ell w$
Volume	space enclosed by a figure	rectangular prism, h, w, ℓ	$V = \ell wh$

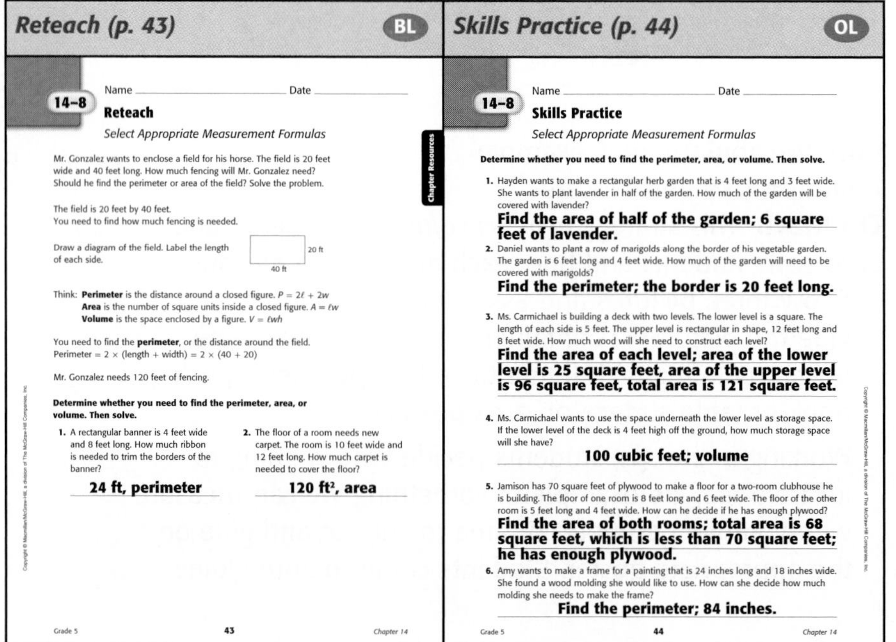

Reteach (p. 43) BL

14-8 Name ________ Date ________

Reteach

Select Appropriate Measurement Formulas

Mr. Gonzalez wants to enclose a field for his horse. The field is 20 feet wide and 40 feet long. How much fencing will Mr. Gonzalez need? Should he find the perimeter or area of the field? Solve the problem.

The field is 20 feet by 40 feet.
You need to find how much fencing is needed.

Draw a diagram of the field. Label the length of each side. (20 ft, 40 ft)

Think: **Perimeter** is the distance around a closed figure. $P = 2\ell + 2w$
Area is the number of square units inside a closed figure. $A = \ell w$
Volume is the space enclosed by a figure. $V = \ell wh$

You need to find the **perimeter**, or the distance around the field.
Perimeter = 2 × (length + width) = 2 × (40 + 20)

Mr. Gonzalez needs 120 feet of fencing.

Determine whether you need to find the perimeter, area, or volume. Then solve.

1. A rectangular banner is 4 feet wide and 8 feet long. How much ribbon is needed to trim the borders of the banner? **24 ft, perimeter**
2. The floor of a room needs new carpet. The room is 10 feet wide and 12 feet long. How much carpet is needed to cover the floor? **120 ft², area**

Grade 5 43 Chapter 14

Chapter Resources

Skills Practice (p. 44) OL

14-8 Name ________ Date ________

Skills Practice

Select Appropriate Measurement Formulas

Determine whether you need to find the perimeter, area, or volume. Then solve.

1. Hayden wants to make a rectangular herb garden that is 4 feet long and 3 feet wide. She wants to plant lavender in half of the garden. How much of the garden will be covered with lavender? **Find the area of half of the garden; 6 square feet of lavender.**
2. Daniel wants to plant a row of marigolds along the border of his vegetable garden. The garden is 6 feet long and 4 feet wide. How much of the garden will need to be covered with marigolds? **Find the perimeter; the border is 20 feet long.**
3. Ms. Carmichael is building a deck with two levels. The lower level is a square. The length of each side is 5 feet. The upper level is rectangular in shape, 12 feet long and 8 feet wide. How much wood will she need to construct each level? **Find the area of each level; area of the lower level is 25 square feet, area of the upper level is 96 square feet, total area is 121 square feet.**
4. Ms. Carmichael wants to use the space underneath the lower level as storage space. If the lower level of the deck is 4 feet high off the ground, how much storage space will she have? **100 cubic feet; volume**
5. Jamison has 70 square feet of plywood to make a floor for a two-room clubhouse he is building. The floor of one room is 8 feet long and 6 feet wide. The floor of the other room is 5 feet long and 4 feet wide. How can he decide if he has enough plywood? **Find the area of both rooms; total area is 68 square feet, which is less than 70 square feet; he has enough plywood.**
6. Amy wants to make a frame for a painting that is 24 inches long and 18 inches wide. She found a wood molding she would like to use. How can she decide how much molding she needs to make the frame? **Find the perimeter; 84 inches.**

Grade 5 44 Chapter 14

Determine the Appropriate Measurement

Remember

Perimeter is given in units, area is given in square units, and volume is given in cubic units.

1 SOCCER A grounds crew will be cutting the grass on the field at Chengdu stadium. Determine whether they will be cutting the perimeter, area, or volume of the grass. Then solve.

The field is a rectangle that is 109 meters long and 75 meters wide.

They need to find the area to determine the size of the surface that needs to be cut.

$A = \ell w$	Formula for area of a rectangle
$A = 109 \times 75$	$\ell = 109$ and $w = 75$
$A = 8{,}175$	Multiply.

The area of the field is 8,175 square meters.

2 SWIMMING Mr. Clive needs to install a rubber strip around the edge of the swimming pool shown below. Determine whether he should find the perimeter, area, or volume of the swimming pool. Then solve.

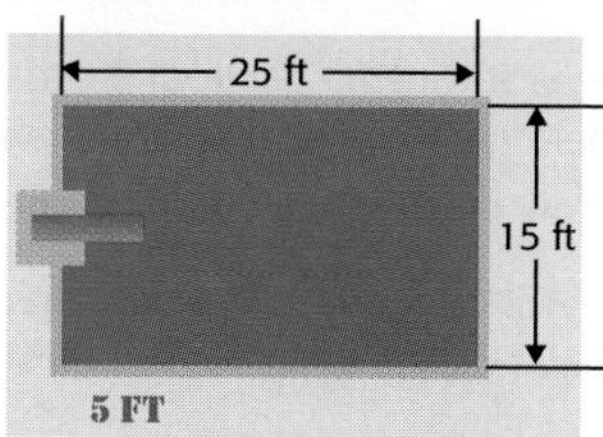

Mr. Clive needs to know the distance around the pool. So, he needs to find the perimeter.

$P = 2\ell + 2w$	Formula for perimeter of a rectangle
$P = 2(25) + 2(15)$	$\ell = 25$ and $w = 15$
$P = 80$	Simplify.

The distance around the pool is 80 feet.

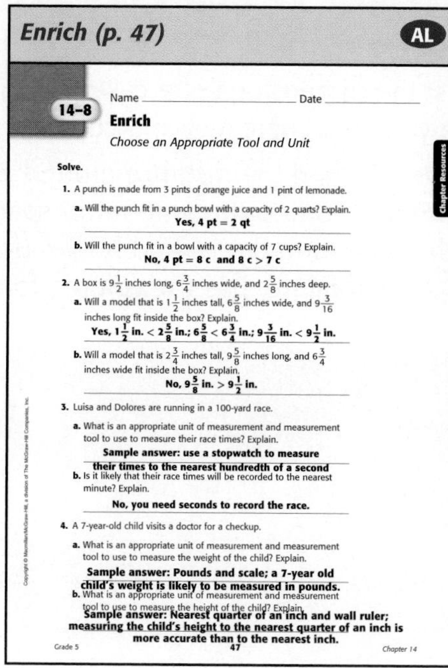

Enrich (p. 47) AL

14-8 Name ______________ Date ______________

Enrich

Choose an Appropriate Tool and Unit

Solve.

1. A punch is made from 3 pints of orange juice and 1 pint of lemonade.
   a. Will the punch fit in a punch bowl with a capacity of 2 quarts? Explain.
      Yes, 4 pt = 2 qt
   b. Will the punch fit in a bowl with a capacity of 7 cups? Explain.
      No, 4 pt = 8 c and 8 c > 7 c
2. A box is $9\frac{1}{2}$ inches long, $6\frac{3}{4}$ inches wide, and $2\frac{5}{8}$ inches deep.
   a. Will a model that is $1\frac{1}{2}$ inches tall, $6\frac{5}{8}$ inches wide, and $9\frac{3}{16}$ inches long fit inside the box? Explain.
      Yes, $1\frac{1}{2}$ in. < $2\frac{5}{8}$ in.; $6\frac{5}{8}$ < $6\frac{3}{4}$ in.; $9\frac{3}{16}$ in. < $9\frac{1}{2}$ in.
   b. Will a model that is $2\frac{3}{4}$ inches tall, $9\frac{5}{8}$ inches long, and $6\frac{3}{4}$ inches wide fit inside the box? Explain.
      No, $9\frac{5}{8}$ in. > $9\frac{1}{2}$ in.
3. Luisa and Dolores are running in a 100-yard race.
   a. What is an appropriate unit of measurement and measurement tool to use to measure their race times? Explain.
      Sample answer: use a stopwatch to measure their times to the nearest hundredth of a second
   b. Is it likely that their race times will be recorded to the nearest minute? Explain.
      No, you need seconds to record the race.
4. A 7-year-old child visits a doctor for a checkup.
   a. What is an appropriate unit of measurement and measurement tool to use to measure the weight of the child? Explain.
      Sample answer: Pounds and scale; a 7-year old child's weight is likely to be measured in pounds.
   b. What is an appropriate unit of measurement and measurement tool to use to measure the height of the child? Explain.
      Sample answer: Nearest quarter of an inch and wall ruler; measuring the child's height to the nearest quarter of an inch is more accurate than to the nearest inch.

Chapter Resources

Grade 5 47 Chapter 14

Determine the Appropriate Measurement

Example 1 Point out that the entire surface of the scoreboard will be cleaned, so students need to calculate the area of the surface. Emphasize choosing and including the correct units.

ADDITIONAL EXAMPLES

1 Badriya wants to buy a blanket that will cover the top of her bed. Her bed is 78 inches long and 36 inches wide. Determine whether she should find the perimeter, area, or volume. Then solve. area; 2,808 in^2

2 Hector wants to put wood trim around the top edge of his fish tank shown below. Determine whether he should find the perimeter, area, or volume. Then solve. perimeter: 78 in.

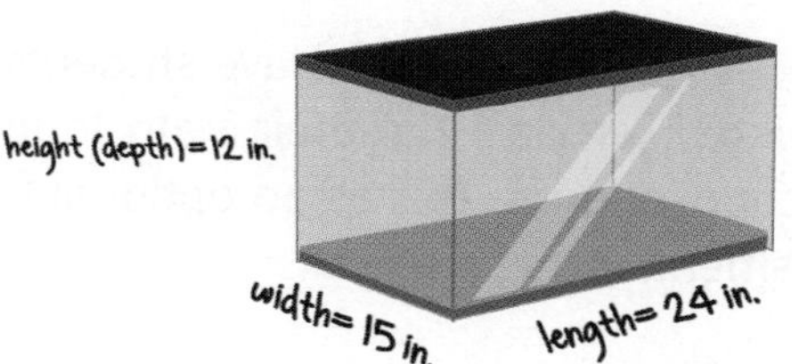

3 Jonah wants to calculate how much cereal he needs to refill an empty cereal box. Determine whether he should find the perimeter, area, or volume. Then solve. volume: 140 in^3

CHECK What You Know

As a class, have students complete Exercises 1–6 in **Check What You Know** as you observe their work.

Exercise 6 Assess student comprehension before assigning practice exercises.

BL Alternate Teaching Strategy

If students have trouble choosing the correct measurement needed to solve a problem…

Then use one of these reteach options:

1. CRM **Daily Reteach Worksheet** (p. 43)
2. For any given problem, have students begin by drawing and labeling a picture for the situation described. Then ask them to reread the problem carefully and look at their labeled picture to help them decide which measurement solves the problem: perimeter, area, or volume.

3 Practice

Differentiate practice using these leveled assignments for Exercises 7–14.

Level	Assignment
BL Below/ Approaching Level	7–9, 11, 13
OL On Level	7–14
AL Above/Beyond Level	8–12 even, 13–14

Have students discuss and complete the Higher Order Thinking problems. For Exercise 13, suggest that students calculate the volume of the prism *before* trying to find the error.

WRITING IN MATH Have students complete Exercise 14 in their Math Journals. You may choose to use this as an optional formative assessment.

COMMON ERROR!

Students may write the correct numbers in their answers but use incorrect units. Remind them that:

unit + unit = unit

unit × unit = unit^2

unit × unit × unit = unit^3

Real-World EXAMPLE Determine the Appropriate Measurement

3 DESIGN An architect needs to calculate how much cement to use for a decorative column. The figure represents the column. Determine whether she should find the perimeter, area, or volume of the column. Then solve.

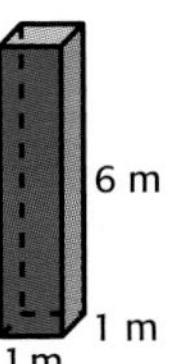

The architect needs to know how much space the column encloses. So, she needs to find the volume.

$V = \ell wh$	Formula for volume of a rectangular prism
$V = 1 \times 1 \times 6$	$\ell = 1$, $w = 1$, and $h = 6$
$V = 6$	Simplify.

So, 6 cubic meters of cement are needed.

CHECK What You Know

Determine whether you need to find the perimeter, area, or volume. Then solve. See Examples 1–3 (pp. 644–645)

1. Carmella is making a rectangular flower garden in her backyard. The space she wants to use is 4 meters in length and 2 meters wide. How much space will she have in her garden? **area; 8 m^2**
2. Mrs. Hernandez is sewing fringe around curtains that are used in a school play. There are four rectangular panels, each 3 feet wide and $5\frac{1}{2}$ feet long. How much fringe does she need to buy? **perimeter; 68 ft**
3. How much water is needed to fill a pool that is 50 meters long, 25 meters wide, and 3 meters deep? **volume; 3,750 m^3**
4. Which units would be most appropriate to measure the volume of a cake pan: cubic inches, cubic feet, or cubic yards? Explain. **See margin.**
5. A basketball court that is 50 feet wide and 84 feet long needs to be refinished. The cost for refinishing is $6.00 per square foot. What will be the total cost? **area; $25,200**

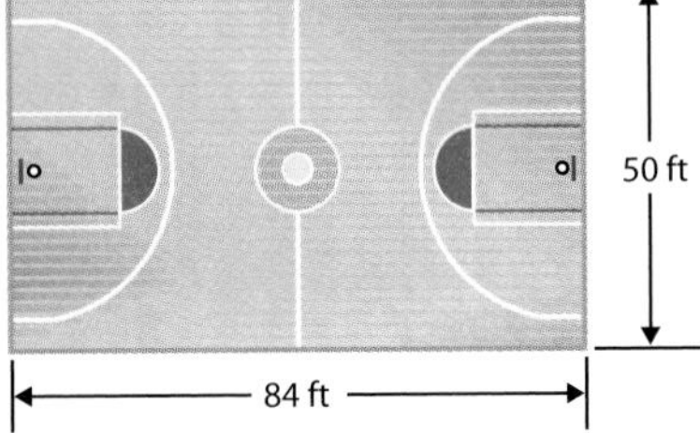

6. Talk About It Explain how you determine whether to use the formula for perimeter, area, or volume for a given situation. **See margin.**

646 Chapter 14 Measure Perimeter, Area, and Volume

Additional Answers

4. Cubic inches; the dimensions of a cake pan are less than both a foot and a yard. So, cubic feet and cubic yards are too large.
6. Sample answer: To find the distance around a figure, use the perimeter formula. To find the amount of space covered by a figure, use the area formula. To find how much space is enclosed by a solid figure, use the volume formula.

★ indicates multi-step problem

Practice and Problem Solving

EXTRA PRACTICE See page R39.

Determine whether you need to find the perimeter, area, or volume. Then solve. See Examples 1–3 (pp. 644–645)

7. A path is 3 feet wide and 14 feet long. How much gravel will Mr. James need if he wants to add 2 inches of gravel over the entire path? **volume; 7 ft^3**

8. A room is 8 meters by 16 meters. How much carpet is needed? **area; 128 m^2**

Refer to the pool shown at the right for Exercises 9 and 10.

25 ft, 8 ft, 10 ft, 7 ft

★**9.** Decorative tiles 6 inches long are to be placed around the edges of the pool. How many tiles will be needed? **perimeter; 160 tiles**

★**10.** What size tarp would be needed to cover the pool? **area; 305 ft^2**

Real-World PROBLEM SOLVING

Measurement In a fish tank, 30 square centimeters of water surface are needed for each centimeter of fish length. So, two fish that are 6 centimeters long need 360 square centimeters of water.

11. An angelfish is 12 centimeters long. How many angelfish could be placed in Tank B? **3**

12. A fancy guppy is 5 centimeters long. Which tank could hold 2 angelfish and 4 fancy guppies? **Tank C**

Tank	Size (cm)
A	$\ell = 24, w = 12, h = 12$
B	$\ell = 45, w = 25, h = 25$
C	$\ell = 60, w = 30, h = 38$

H.O.T. Problems

13. FIND THE ERROR Martin and Ryan are finding the volume of a prism with length 3 meters, height 8 meters, and width 17 meters. Who is correct? Explain your reasoning. **Ryan; Martin used the formula for the perimeter of a rectangle.**

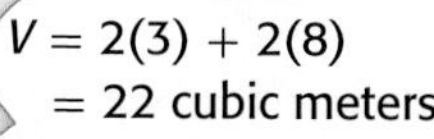

Martin
$V = 2(3) + 2(8)$
$= 22$ cubic meters

Ryan
$V = 3 \times 8 \times 17$
$= 408$ cubic meters

14. WRITING IN MATH Describe the steps you would take to find the area of your bedroom floor. **See margin.**

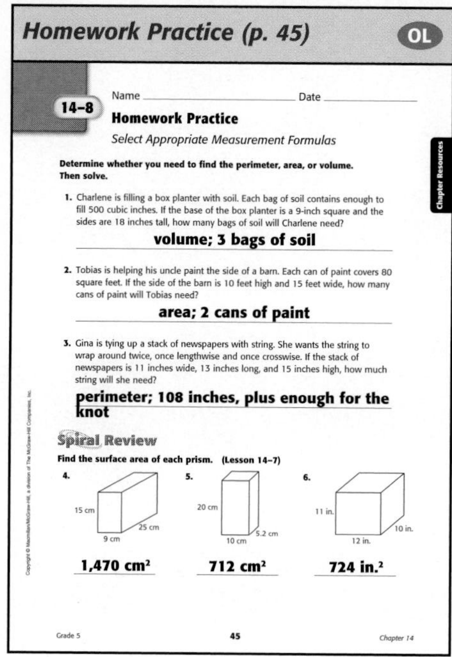

Homework Practice (p. 45) OL

14-8 Name ______ Date ______

Homework Practice

Select Appropriate Measurement Formulas

Determine whether you need to find the perimeter, area, or volume. Then solve.

1. Charlene is filling a box planter with soil. Each bag of soil contains enough to fill 500 cubic inches. If the base of the box planter is a 9-inch square and the sides are 18 inches tall, how many bags of soil will Charlene need?

volume; 3 bags of soil

2. Tobias is helping his uncle paint the side of a barn. Each can of paint covers 80 square feet. If the side of the barn is 10 feet high and 15 feet wide, how many cans of paint will Tobias need?

area; 2 cans of paint

3. Gina is tying up a stack of newspapers with string. She wants the string to wrap around twice, once lengthwise and once crosswise. If the stack of newspapers is 11 inches wide, 13 inches long, and 15 inches high, how much string will she need?

perimeter; 108 inches, plus enough for the knot

Spiral Review

Find the surface area of each prism. (Lesson 14-7)

4. 15 cm, 9 cm, 25 cm — **1,470 cm^2**

5. 20 cm, 10 cm, 5.2 cm — **712 cm^2**

6. 11 in., 12 in., 10 in. — **724 $in.^2$**

Chapter Resources

Grade 5 45 Chapter 14

4 Assess

Formative Assessment

- **How do you know when to calculate perimeter to solve a problem?** sample answer: when the problem asks for a measurement of the distance around something
- **When might you use the formula for the area of a rectangle to solve a problem?** sample answer: when I need to know the measure that covers a rectangular surface
- **Can you ever find the volume of a rectangle to solve a problem? Why or why not?** No, I can only find the volume of a three-dimensional figure. A rectangle is not a three-dimensional figure–it only has length and width. It has no height.

Quick Check **Are students continuing to struggle with selecting and using appropriate units and formulas to measure length, perimeter, area, and volume?**

If Yes → CRM Reteach Worksheet (p. 43)

If No → Independent Work Options (p. 643B)
CRM Skills Practice Worksheet (p. 44)
CRM Enrich Worksheet (p. 47)

Ticket Out the Door Sketch a rectangular prism on the board with measures labeled for length, width, and height. Label one face of the prism *A*. Have students calculate the perimeter and area of face *A* and the volume of the prism. Ask them to write their answers on a piece of paper and give them to you as they leave class for the day.

Additional Answer

14. Sample answer: Use a measuring tape to find the length and width in feet. Then multiply the length and the width to find the area. The units in the solution will be square feet.

14-9 Problem-Solving Investigation
Choose a Strategy

Lesson Planner

Objective

Choose the best strategy to solve a problem.

Resources

Manipulatives: centimeter cubes, pattern blocks, play money

Teacher Technology

TeacherWorks • Interactive Classroom

Real-World Problem Solving Library
Math and Social Studies: *Exploring the World by Sea*
Use these leveled books to reinforce and extend problem-solving skills and strategies.

Leveled for:

- OL On Level
- ELL Sheltered English
- SP Spanish

For additional support, see the Real-World Problem Solving Teacher's Guide.

Daily Routine

Use these suggestions before beginning the lesson on p. 647.

5-Minute Check

(Reviews Lesson 14-8)

Determine whether you need to find the perimeter, area, or volume. Then solve.

1. Kerry wants to install wood trim around the border of the floor in her rectangular-shaped bedroom. Her bedroom is 21 ft long and 15 ft wide. How much wood trim will she need? perimeter; 72 ft
2. How much water is needed to fill a fish tank with a length of 34 centimeters, a width of 20 centimeters, and a height of 28 centimeters? volume; 19,040 cm^3

Problem of the Day

The sum of three consecutive odd numbers less than 20 is one-seventh their product. What are the numbers? 3, 5, 7; $3 + 5 + 7 = 15$, $3 \times 5 \times 7 = 105$, $\frac{1}{7} \times 105 = 15$

Differentiated Instruction

Small Group Options

LOGICAL

Option 1 Gifted and Talented AL

Materials: paper and pencil

Hand students this problem written on paper: 7.5 hours of actual practice

Chad participates in softball 2 hours per weekday in the summer. There is a 20-minute stretching warm-up and a 10-minute cool down for each practice. How much time is actually spent playing ball each week? Remember there are 60 minutes in an hour.

KINESTHETIC

Option 2 English Language Learners ELL

Materials: scissors, paper, 2 in. by 2 in. cube

Core Vocabulary: fill out, identify, properties

Common Use Verb: build

Write Math This strategy allows students to choose the best strategy for building a 3-D shape from flat paper.

- Give the students paper and a 2 inch by 2 inch cube.
- Allow time for students to translate the dimensions and angles to build a paper cube of about the same size.
- Have students present their solutions and designs to the class.

Independent Work Options

LINGUISTIC

Option 1 Early Finishers OL AL

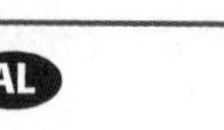

- Challenge students to write a word problem that can be solved using each of the problem-solving strategies listed on p. 627.
- Have students present their problems to the class or exchange them with a partner to solve.

Option 2 Student Technology

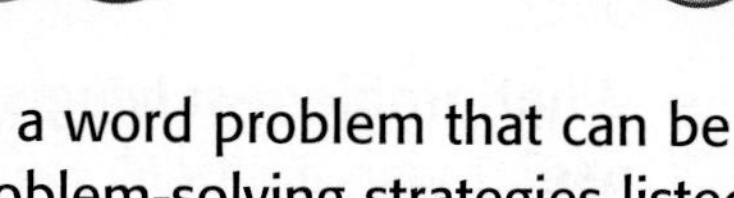

Math Online macmillanmh.com

Personal Tutor • Extra Examples

Option 3 Learning Station: Science (p. 604I)

Direct students to the Science Learning Station for opportunities to explore and extend the lesson concept.

1 Introduce

Activity • Review

- Present students with the following problem:

  A box can be completely filled with 6 layers of centimeter cubes. One layer is made of 2 rows of 2 cubes. How many cubes will fill the box?

- **What problem-solving strategy could you use?** make a model
- Provide pairs or small groups of students with centimeter cubes and guide them to make a model to solve the problem. 24 cubes

2 Teach

Have students read the problem on covering the swing set area. Guide them through the problem-solving steps.

Understand Using the questions, review what students know and need to find.

Plan Have them discuss their strategy.

Solve Guide students to draw a diagram to solve the problem.

- **Why do you add 1 meter two times to the length and two times to the width?** because the area extends an extra 1 meter on the top and the bottom of the widths and to the left and the right of the lengths
- **What is the total length of the rectangle?** 6 m **What is the total width of the rectangle?** 4 m

Check Have students look back at the problem to make sure that the answer fits the facts given.

- **Does your diagram match the word problem?** Check students' diagrams.

COMMON ERROR!

Exercise 5 Students may write a number sentence using addition only and accidentally leave out one of the seven addends. Encourage students to look for equal lengths of time within the table. Point out that they can use multiplication, then addition to find the total number of minutes.

14-9 Problem-Solving Investigation

MAIN IDEA I will choose the best strategy to solve a problem.

P.S.I. TEAM +

JACINDA: I am helping my mom cover the swing set area with mulch. The base of the swing set is rectangular in shape and measures 4 meters by 2 meters. The area we want to cover extends 1 meter in each direction from the edge of the swing set.

YOUR MISSION: Find the area of the space covered with mulch.

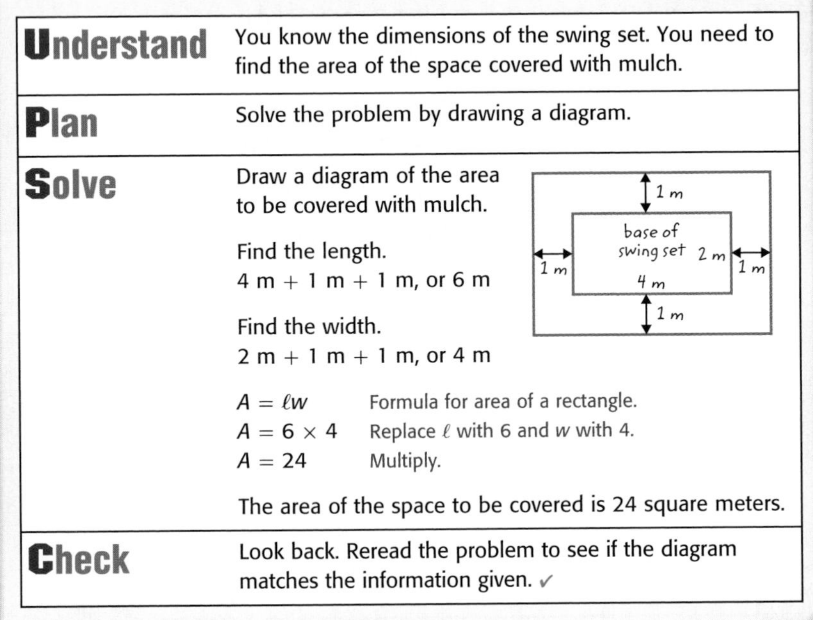

Understand	You know the dimensions of the swing set. You need to find the area of the space covered with mulch.
Plan	Solve the problem by drawing a diagram.
Solve	Draw a diagram of the area to be covered with mulch. Find the length. 4 m + 1 m + 1 m, or 6 m Find the width. 2 m + 1 m + 1 m, or 4 m $A = \ell w$ Formula for area of a rectangle. $A = 6 \times 4$ Replace ℓ with 6 and w with 4. $A = 24$ Multiply. The area of the space to be covered is 24 square meters.
Check	Look back. Reread the problem to see if the diagram matches the information given. ✓

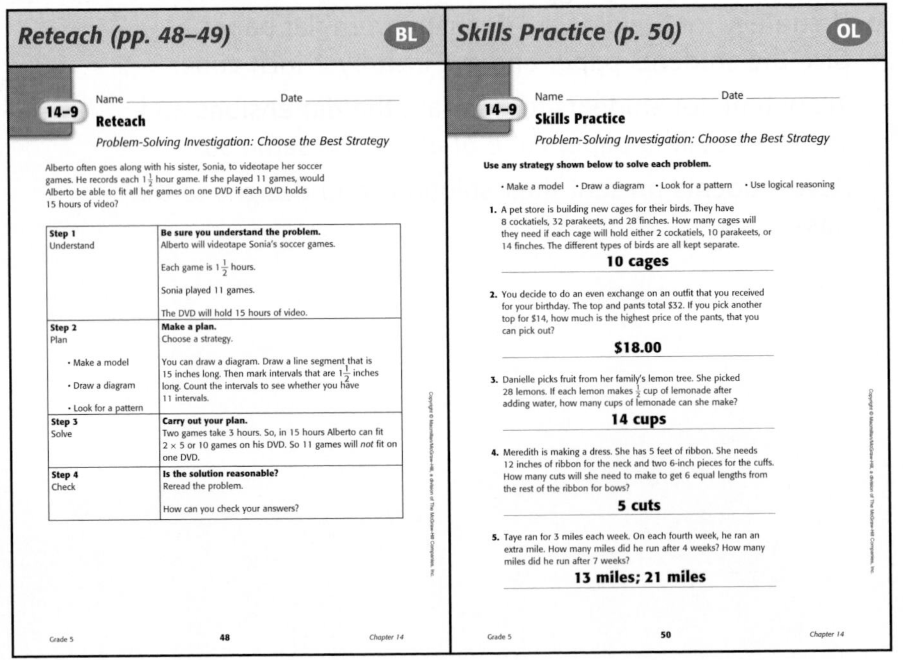

Reteach (pp. 48–49) BL

Name ______________ Date ______________

14-9 **Reteach**

Problem-Solving Investigation: Choose the Best Strategy

Alberto often goes along with his sister, Sonia, to videotape her soccer games. He records each $1\frac{1}{2}$ hour game. If she played 11 games, would Alberto be able to fit all her games on one DVD if each DVD holds 15 hours of video?

Step 1 Understand	**Be sure you understand the problem.** Alberto will videotape Sonia's soccer games. Each game is $1\frac{1}{2}$ hours. Sonia played 11 games. The DVD will hold 15 hours of video.
Step 2 Plan • Make a model • Draw a diagram • Look for a pattern	**Make a plan.** Choose a strategy. You can draw a diagram. Draw a line segment that is 15 inches long. Then mark intervals that are $1\frac{1}{2}$ inches long. Count the intervals to see whether you have 11 intervals.
Step 3 Solve	**Carry out your plan.** Two games take 3 hours. So, in 15 hours Alberto can fit 2×5 or 10 games on his DVD. So 11 games will *not* fit on one DVD.
Step 4 Check	**Is the solution reasonable?** Reread the problem. How can you check your answers?

Grade 5 48 *Chapter 14*

Skills Practice (p. 50) OL

Name ______________ Date ______________

14-9 **Skills Practice**

Problem-Solving Investigation: Choose the Best Strategy

Use any strategy shown below to solve each problem.

• Make a model • Draw a diagram • Look for a pattern • Use logical reasoning

1. A pet store is building new cages for their birds. They have 8 cockatiels, 32 parakeets, and 28 finches. How many cages will they need if each cage will hold either 2 cockatiels, 10 parakeets, or 14 finches. The different types of birds are all kept separate.

   10 cages

2. You decide to do an even exchange on an outfit that you received for your birthday. The top and pants total $32. If you pick another top for $14, how much is the highest price of the pants, that you can pick out?

   $18.00

3. Danielle picks fruit from her family's lemon tree. She picked 28 lemons. If each lemon makes $\frac{1}{2}$ cup of lemonade after adding water, how many cups of lemonade can she make?

   14 cups

4. Meredith is making a dress. She has 5 feet of ribbon. She needs 12 inches of ribbon for the neck and two 6-inch pieces for the cuffs. How many cuts will she need to make to get 6 equal lengths from the rest of the ribbon for bows?

   5 cuts

5. Taye ran for 3 miles each week. On each fourth week, he ran an extra mile. How many miles did he run after 4 weeks? How many miles did he run after 7 weeks?

   13 miles; 21 miles

Grade 5 50 *Chapter 14*

Mixed Problem Solving

See page R40.

Use any strategy shown below to solve each problem.

PROBLEM-SOLVING STRATEGIES
- Guess and check.
- Look for a pattern.
- Make a table.
- Draw a diagram.

1. **Geometry** Mariana stacked 8 cubes on top of each other to make a tower 8 cubes high. How many of the cubes' faces can Mariana see? **33 faces**

2. **Measurement** A hexagon that has each side equal to 1 inch has a perimeter of 6 inches.

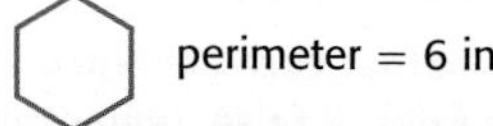

Two hexagons placed side by side have a perimeter of 10 inches. Three hexagons have a perimeter of 14 inches.

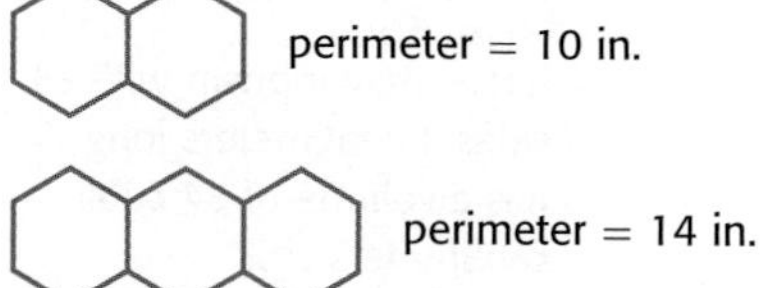

What would be the perimeter of five hexagons placed side by side? **22 in.**

3. Five friends are standing in a circle and playing a game where they toss a ball of yarn to one another. If each person tosses the yarn to each other only once, how many lines of yarn will be between them? **10 lines**

4. Pedro has $42 in his pocket. He has only $5 and $1 bills. He has a total of 14 bills. What combination of bills does he have? **7 $5-bills, 7 $1-bills**

5. **Algebra** The table below shows the number of minutes Danielle spent practicing the trumpet over the last 7 days. If she continues this pattern of practicing, in how many days will she have practiced 555 minutes? **24 days**

Day	Time (min)
1	20
2	20
3	35
4	20
5	20
6	35
7	20

For Exercises 6 and 7, use the following information.

Marita wants to make a rectangle with a perimeter of 20 inches.

6. How many rectangles can Marita make if she only uses whole numbers for the side lengths? List the dimensions. **See Ch. 14 Answer Appendix.**

7. Which rectangle has the greatest area? **5 × 5 rectangle**

8. **WRITING IN ▶MATH** One wall of a building is 80 feet long and 16 feet high. A one-gallon can of paint covers up to 450 square feet. If each can of paint costs $22.50, find the total cost of paint for the wall. Explain the steps you used to solve the problem. **See Ch. 14 Answer Appendix.**

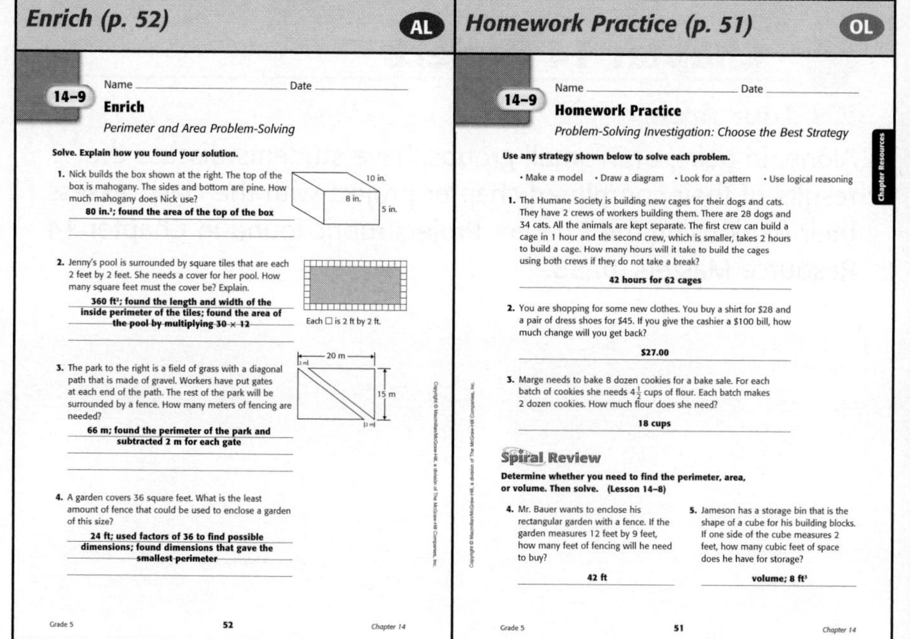

Enrich (p. 52) AL

14–9 Name ____________ Date ____________

Enrich

Perimeter and Area Problem-Solving

Solve. Explain how you found your solution.

1. Nick builds the box shown at the right. The top of the box is mahogany. The sides and bottom are pine. How much mahogany does Nick use?
80 in.²; found the area of the top of the box

2. Jenny's pool is surrounded by square tiles that are each 2 feet by 2 feet. She needs a cover for her pool. How many square feet must the cover be? Explain.
360 ft²; found the length and width of the inside perimeter of the tiles; found the area of the pool by multiplying 30 × 12

Each ☐ is 2 ft by 2 ft.

3. The park to the right is a field of grass with a diagonal path that is made of gravel. Workers have put gates at each end of the path. The rest of the park will be surrounded by a fence. How many meters of fencing are needed?
66 m; found the perimeter of the park and subtracted 2 m for each gate

4. A garden covers 36 square feet. What is the least amount of fence that could be used to enclose a garden of this size?
24 ft; used factors of 36 to find possible dimensions; found dimensions that gave the smallest perimeter

Homework Practice (p. 51) OL

14–9 Name ____________ Date ____________

Homework Practice

Problem-Solving Investigation: Choose the Best Strategy

Chapter Resources

Use any strategy shown below to solve each problem.

• Make a model • Draw a diagram • Look for a pattern • Use logical reasoning

1. The Humane Society is building new cages for their dogs and cats. They have 2 crews of workers building them. There are 28 dogs and 34 cats. All the animals are kept separate. The first crew can build a cage in 1 hour and the second crew, which is smaller, takes 2 hours to build a cage. How many hours will it take to build the cages using both crews if they do not take a break?
42 hours for 62 cages

2. You are shopping for some new clothes. You buy a shirt for $28 and a pair of dress shoes for $45. If you give the cashier a $100 bill, how much change will you get back?
$27.00

3. Marge needs to bake 8 dozen cookies for a bake sale. For each batch of cookies she needs $4\frac{1}{2}$ cups of flour. Each batch makes 2 dozen cookies. How much flour does she need?
18 cups

Spiral Review

Determine whether you need to find the perimeter, area, or volume. Then solve. (Lesson 14–8)

4. Mr. Bauer wants to enclose his rectangular garden with a fence. If the garden measures 12 feet by 9 feet, how many feet of fencing will he need to buy?
42 ft

5. Jameson has a storage bin that is the shape of a cube for his building blocks. If one side of the cube measures 2 feet, how many cubic feet of space does he have for storage?
volume; 8 ft³

BL Alternate Teaching Strategy

If students have trouble choosing a strategy...

Then use one of these reteach options:

1 CRM **Daily Reteach Worksheet** (pp. 48–49)

2 Have the class brainstorm different problem-solving strategies they have learned about and write them on the board. Have volunteers briefly describe each strategy. Keep the full list on the board for students to refer to when choosing a strategy to solve problems.

3 Practice

Using the Exercises

Exercise 2 Students may use hexagon pattern blocks and *make a model* to solve this problem.

Exercise 4 You may provide students with play money to help them solve this problem.

Exercises 6 and 7 Students may either *draw a picture* or *make a model* to solve these problems.

4 Assess

Formative Assessment

- **When might you check for reasonableness to solve a problem?** Sample answer: when an answer is given and the problem asks if the answer is correct
- **How can estimation help you with these kinds of problems?** Sample answer: An estimate might tell me quickly if the answer given is reasonable or not.

Quick Check **Are students continuing to struggle with choosing the best strategy to solve a problem?**

If Yes → CRM Reteach Worksheet (pp. 48–49)

If No → Independent Work Options (p. 647B)
CRM Skills Practice Worksheet (p. 50)
CRM Enrich Worksheet (p. 52)

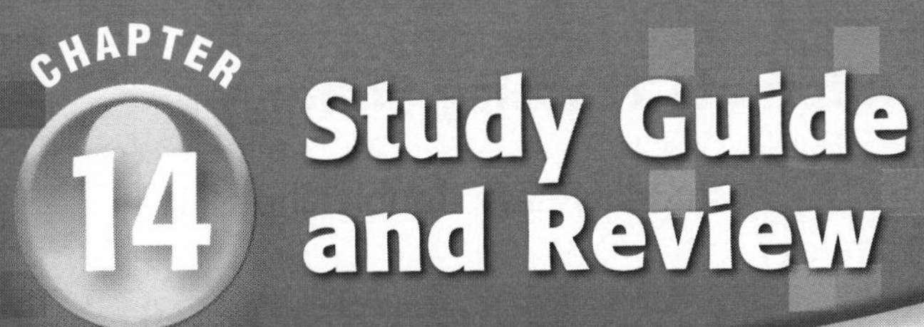

Study Guide and Review

 Dinah Zike's Foldables

Use these lesson suggestions to incorporate the Foldable during the chapter. Students can then use their Foldables to review for the test.

Lesson 14-8 Students use the right column of the Pocket Chart Foldable to record formulas for measuring length, perimeter, area, and volume. Examples of student work on quarter sheets of paper or index cards should be stored in the right side pocket.

Key Vocabulary

The page references after each word denote where that term was first introduced. If students have difficulty answering Exercises 1–5, remind them they can use the page references to review the vocabulary terms.

Vocabulary Review

Review chapter vocabulary using one of the following options.

- **Visual Vocabulary Cards** (2, 13, 32, 41, 42, 45, 48)
- **eGlossary** at macmillanmh.com

Study Guide and Review

FOLDABLES Study Organizer GET READY to Study

Be sure the following Big Ideas are written in your Foldable.

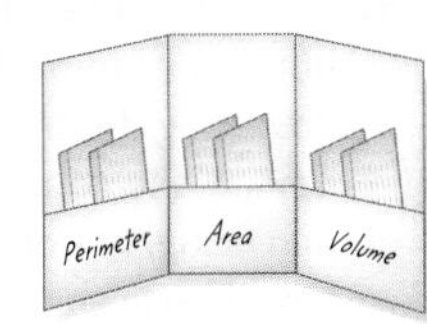

Key Concepts

Perimeters of Polygons

- The perimeter P of a square is 4 times the side length s. (p. 609)

$$P = s + s + s + s \quad \text{or} \quad 4s$$

- The perimeter P of a rectangle is two times the length ℓ plus two times the width w. (p. 609)

$$P = \ell + \ell + w + w \quad \text{or} \quad 2\ell + 2w$$

Areas of Rectangles

- The area A of a rectangle is the length ℓ times the width w. (p. 616)

$$A = \ell w$$

- The area A of a square is the square of the side length s. (p. 617)

$$A = s^2 \quad \text{or} \quad s \times s$$

Surface Areas of Rectangular Prisms

- The surface area S of a rectangular prism is the sum of the areas of the faces. (p. 640)

$$S = 2\ell w + 2\ell h + 2wh$$

Volumes of Prisms

- The volume V of a rectangular prism is length ℓ times width w times height h. (p. 631)

$$V = \ell wh$$

Key Vocabulary

area (p. 612)
cone (p. 624)
cylinder (p. 624)
perimeter (p. 607)
polygon (p. 608)
prism (p. 624)
rectangular prism (p. 624)
surface area (p. 640)
triangular prism (p. 624)
volume (p. 631)

Vocabulary Check

State whether each sentence is *true* or *false*. If false, replace the underlined word or number to make a true sentence.

1. The perimeter of a rectangle is the length times the width. false; area
2. A rectangular prism with all sides 4 centimeters long has a volume of 64 cubic centimeters. true
3. The area of a square with a side length of 8 inches is 32 square inches. false; 64
4. A three-dimensional figure with faces that are polygons is called a polyhedron. true
5. A cylinder has two parallel congruent circular bases. true

 Chapter 14 Project

It's Your Area

Alone, in pairs, or in small groups, have students discuss the results of their completed chapter project with the class. Assess their work using the Chapter Project rubric found in Chapter 14 Resource Masters, p. 58.

Lesson-by-Lesson Review

14-1 Perimeters of Polygons (pp. 608–611)

Example 1
Find the perimeter of the rectangle.

9 in.
16 in.

$P = 2\ell + 2w$ Perimeter of rectangle

$P = 2(16) + 2(9)$ $\ell = 16, w = 9$

$P = 50$ in. Simplfiy.

The perimeter is 50 inches.

Find the perimeter of each figure.

6.

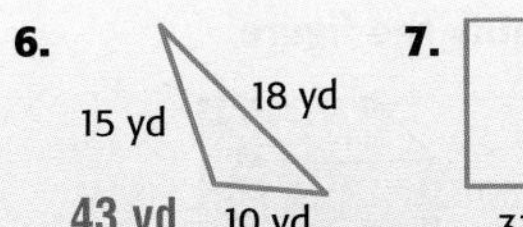

43 yd

7. 124 cm

31 cm
31 cm

8. A garden in the shape of a square is 15 feet on each side. What is the perimeter? 60 ft

14-2 Areas (pp. 612–615)

Example 2
Estimate the area of the figure. Each square represents 1 square inch.

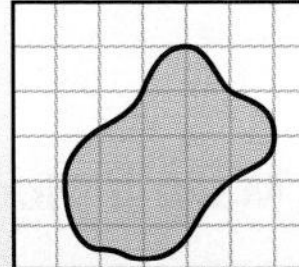

7 whole squares = 7 square inches

11 partial squares is about $5\frac{1}{2}$ square inches

The area is about $7 + 5\frac{1}{2} = 12\frac{1}{2}$ square centimeters.

Estimate the area of each figure. Each square represents 1 square centimeter. 9. 14 cm^2 10. 19.5 cm^2

9.

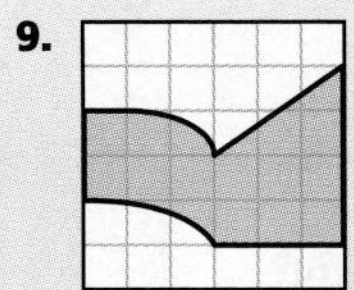

10.

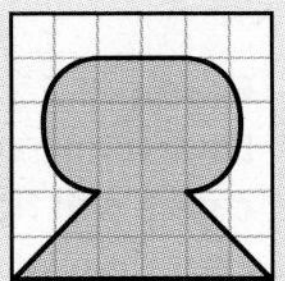

14-3 Areas of Rectangles and Squares (pp. 616–619)

Example 3
Find the area of the rectangle.

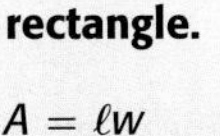

$A = \ell w$

$A = 8 \times 4$ $\ell = 8, w = 4$

$A = 32$ square centimeters

Find the area of each rectangle or square.

11.

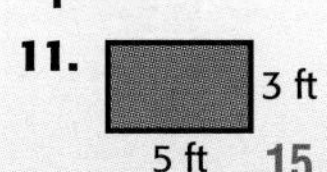

15 ft^2

12. 10 m^2

2 m
5 m

13. A new building measures 42 feet by 30 feet. How much land does it cover? 1,260 ft^2

Lesson-by-Lesson Review

Have students complete the Lesson-by-Lesson Review on pp. 651–654. Then you can use ExamView® Assessment Suite to customize another review worksheet that practices all the objectives of this chapter or only the objectives on which your students need more help.

Intervention If the given examples are not sufficient to review the topics covered by the questions, use the page references next to the exercises to review that topic in the Student Edition.

Additional Answers

14. Sample answer: The triangular bases are parallel and congruent. The edges that form the opposite sides of the rectangular faces are parallel and congruent. The adjacent edges of the rectangular faces are perpendicular. The opposite edges of the rectangular faces are congruent; triangular prism.

15. No parts are parallel, perpendicular, or congruent; cone.

16. The circular bases are parallel and congruent; cylinder.

19. Sample answer: 6 ft × 6 ft, 8 ft × 4 ft, 9 ft × 3 ft

14-4 Three-Dimensional Figures (pp. 624–627) 14–16. See margin.

Example 4
Describe parts of the figure that are parallel, perpendicular and congruent. Then identify the figure.

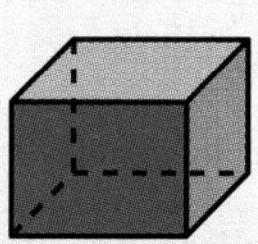

Opposite faces are parallel and congruent. Adjacent faces form right angles, so they are perpendicular.

The figure is a rectangular prism.

Describe parts of each figure that are parallel, perpendicular, and congruent. Then identify the figure.

14.  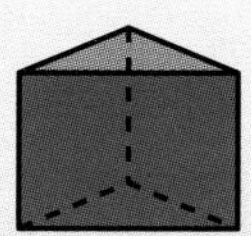

15. 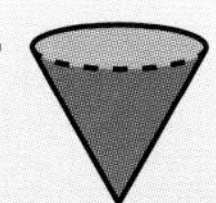

16. Describe parts of the vase that are parallel and congruent. Then identify the shape of the vase.

14-5 Problem-Solving Strategy: Make a Model (pp. 628–629)

Example 5
How many centimeter cubes will fit in the container at the right?

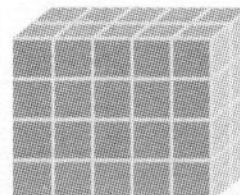

You can use cubes to model the situation.

First, arrange 2 rows of 5 cubes.

Next, add three more layers of cubes.

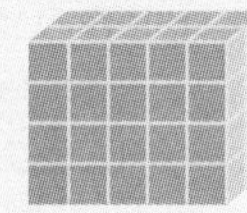

The total number of cubes used is 40. So, 40 centimeter cubes will fit in the container.

Solve by making a model.

17. A box is filled with 48 cubes that measure 1 inch on each side. The cubes completely fill the box. What are possible dimensions of the box? **Sample answer: 8 in. by 2 in. by 3 in.**

18. Haley is making a bracelet by placing beads and charms on a 6-inch chain. She places a charm at 1 inch from each end, and at every $\frac{1}{2}$ inch in between. How many charms does she use? **9 charms**

19. Destiny has 24 feet of fencing material to make a pet enclosure. Describe three different rectangular areas that can be enclosed by the fencing. **See margin.**

14-6 Volumes of Prisms (pp. 631–635)

Example 6
Find the volume of the prism.

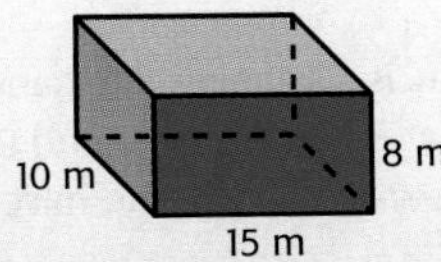

$V = \ell wh$	Volume of a prism
$V = 15 \times 10 \times 8$	$\ell = 15, w = 10, h = 8$
$V = 1{,}200$	Multiply.

The volume of the prism is 1,200 cubic meters.

Find the volume of each prism.

20. 6 ft, 8 ft, 2 ft **96 ft³**

21. 3 in., 3 in., 3 in. **27 in³**

22.

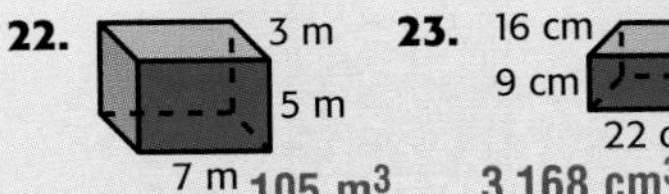

22. **105 m³** **23.** **3,168 cm³**

24. Victoro keeps his pet rabbit in a cage that is shaped like a rectangular prism. The cage measures 2 feet by 3 feet by 2 feet. What is the volume of the cage? **12 ft³**

14-7 Surface Area of Prisms (pp. 640-643)

Example 7
Find the surface area of the rectangular prism.

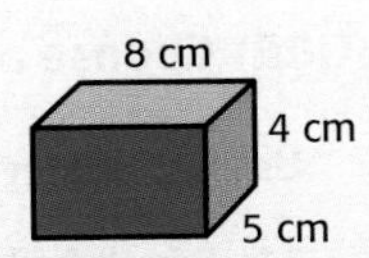

$S = 2\ell w + 2\ell h + 2wh$

top and bottom: $2(\ell w) = 2(8 \times 5)$ or 80

front and back: $2(\ell h) = 2(8 \times 4)$ or 64

two sides: $2(wh) = 2(5 \times 4)$ or 40

The surface area is 80 + 64 + 40 or 184 square centimeters.

Find the surface area of each rectangular prism.

25. **26.**

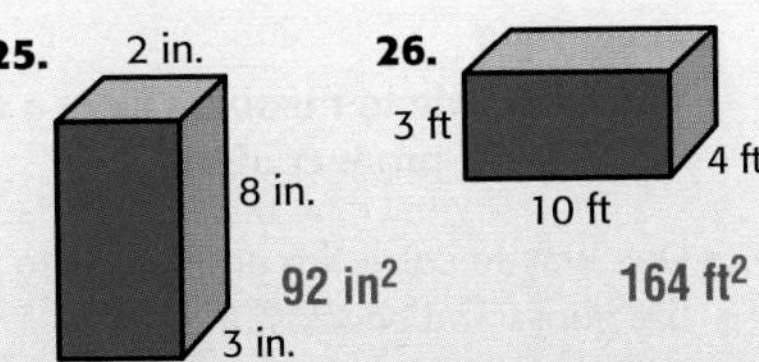

25. **92 in²** **26.** **164 ft²**

27. A DVD player measures 17 inches by 15 inches by 3 inches. What is the minimum surface area of a box to hold the DVD player? **702 in²**

Chapter 14 Study Guide and Review **653**

Chapter 14 Study Guide and Review

14-8 Select Appropriate Measurement Formulas (pp. 644–647)

Example 8
The park shown below is to be covered with new sod. How much sod is needed? Determine whether you need to find the perimeter, area, or volume. Then solve.

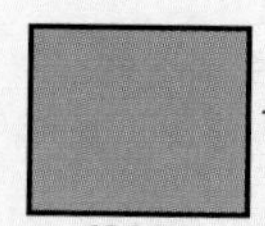

The sod is to cover the entire surface of the park, so the area needs to be found.

$A = \ell w$ Area of a rectangle

$A = 120 \times 100$ $\ell = 120, w = 100$

$A = 12{,}000$ Multiply.

The area that needs to be covered with sod is 12,000 square meters.

Determine whether you need to find the perimeter, area, or volume. Then solve.

28. Ray is sweeping a rectangular floor that is 12 feet long and 9 feet wide. How much does he have to sweep? area; 108 ft^2

29. A gym mat measures 8 feet by 4 feet. The edges of the mat need to be repaired. What is the total length of the edges? perimeter; 24 ft

30. Planters that are 16 inches long, 7 inches wide, and 5 inches high are to be placed around a restaurant patio. How much soil is needed to fill 8 planters? volume; 4,480 in^3

32. Yes; Sample answer: $1.49 + $1.09 + $2.25 = $4.83. Since $4.83 < $5.00, he has enough money.

14-9 Problem-Solving Investigation: Choose a Strategy (pp. 648–649)

Example 9
What two whole numbers have a sum of 12 and a product of 32?

One way to solve the problem is to use the guess and check strategy.

Guess: 3 and 9
Check: $3 + 9 = 12, 3 \times 9 = 27 \neq 32$

Guess: 4 and 8
Check: $4 + 8 = 12, 4 \times 8 = 32$ ✓

The whole numbers are 4 and 8.

Use any strategy to solve.

31. Barrett has 18 sports cards. He collects football and baseball cards. He has twice as many baseball cards. How many of each kind does he have? 6 football, 12 baseball

32. Leon has $5 to buy a bottle of water that costs $1.49, a granola bar for $1.09, and a newspaper for $2.25. Does he have enough money? Explain.

Chapter Test

Math Online macmillanmh.com
• Chapter Test

Find the perimeter of each rectangle or square.

1. 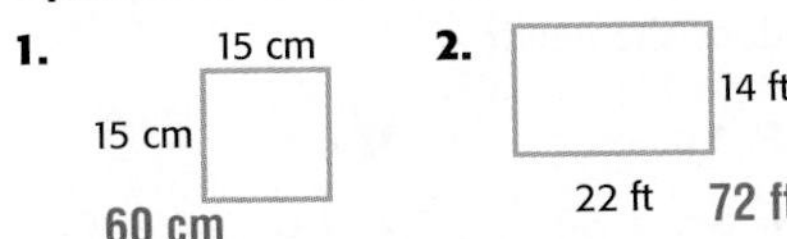

60 cm

2. 14 ft, 22 ft 72 ft

3. **MULTIPLE CHOICE** A rectangular picture frame is 10 inches by 12 inches. Jodie wants to add a lace border around the frame. Which length would fit around the frame with the least amount left? C

A 1 foot C 4 feet
B 2 feet D 5 feet

Find the area of each rectangle or square.

4. 5 ft, 8 ft $40\ ft^2$
5. 6 m, 6 m $36\ m^2$

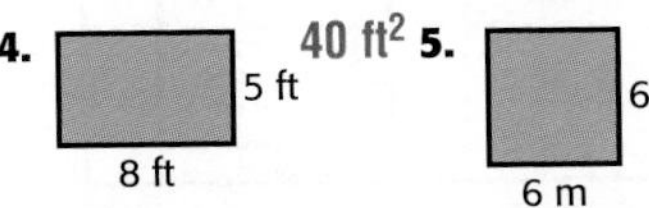

6. Estimate the area of the figure. Each square represents 1 square centimeter. Sample answer: $15\ cm^2$

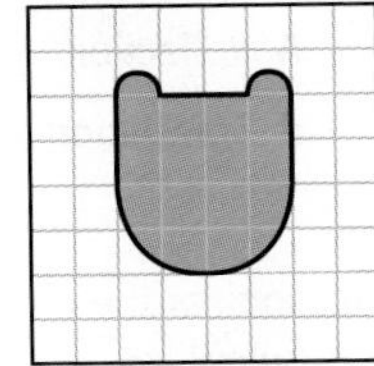

7. If you place one cube on a table, you can see 5 faces of the cube. If you place a second cube on top of the first, you can see 9 faces. How many faces can you see in a stack of 6 cubes? 25 faces

8. A backyard is in the shape of a right triangle. The sides measure 30 feet, 40 feet, and 50 feet. How much fencing is needed to enclose the entire backyard? 120 ft

9. **MULTIPLE CHOICE** Which figure below has 3 more edges than faces? G

F 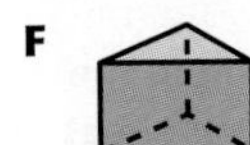
H 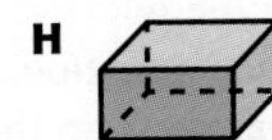
G 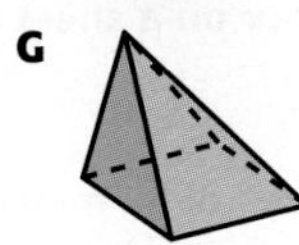
J 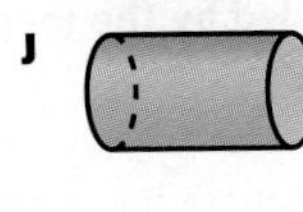

Find the volume of each prism.

10. 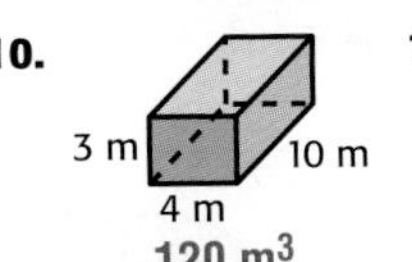

$120\ m^3$

11. 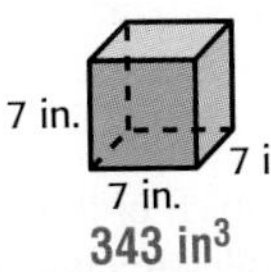

$343\ in^3$

A pool is 50 meters long, 20 meters wide, and 3 meters deep. For each problem, determine whether you need to find the perimeter, area, or volume. Then solve.

12. The bottom of the pool needs to be painted. How much paint is needed? area; $1{,}000\ m^3$

13. How many lifeguards are needed if they are posted every 35 meters? perimeter; 4 lifeguards

14. Find the surface area of the rectangular prism.

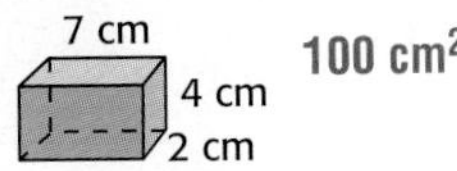

$100\ cm^2$

15. WRITING IN MATH Describe the difference between finding the area of a rectangle and finding the volume of a rectangular prism. See Ch.14 Answer Appendix.

CHAPTER 14

Chapter Test

Summative Assessment

Use these alternate leveled chapter tests to differentiate assessment for the specific needs of your students.

Leveled Chapter 14 Tests			
Form	**Type**	**Level**	**CRM Pages**
1	Multiple Choice	BL	65-66
2A	Multiple Choice	OL	67-68
2B	Multiple Choice	OL	69-70
2C	Free Response	AL	71-72
2D	Free Response	AL	73-74
3	Free Response	AL	75-76

BL = below/approaching grade level
OL = on grade level
AL = above/beyond grade level

Vocabulary Test

CRM **Chapter 14 Resource Masters** (p. 60)

ExamView Assessment Suite Customize and create multiple versions of your Chapter Test and the test answer keys.

Data-Driven Decision Making

Based on the results of the Chapter Test, use the following to review concepts that continue to present students with problems.

Exercises	State/Local Standards	What's the Math?	Error Analysis	Resources for Review
1–3 **8, 13**		Find the perimeter of figures.	Does not add accurately. Adds only two sides with given measurement. Does not know inches to foot relationship.	CRM Chapter 14 Resource Masters (Reteach Worksheets) pp. 8, 13, 18, 23, 28, 33, 38, 43, 48 Math Adventures My Math Zone Chapter 14 Math Online Extra Examples • Concepts in Motion
4–6 **12–14**		Find the area or surface area of figures.	Uses wrong numbers to find area. Does not multiply accurately. Does not add parts of squares to find total area.	
7, 9		Use geometric vocabulary or models to problem solve.	Does not understand "faces," "vertices," "parallel," "congruent," "edges," to identify parts or create model to solve problems.	
10–11, 15		Find the volume of figures.	Adds three figures instead of multiplying them. Does not understand "prism." Cannot draw picture or visualize to find volume.	

CHAPTER 14 Test Practice

Formative Assessment

- Use Student Edition pp. 656–657 as practice and cumulative review. The questions are written in the same style as many state tests.
- You can also use these two pages to benchmark student progress, or as an alternate homework assignment.

Additional practice pages can be found in the Chapter 14 Resource Masters.

Chapter 14 Resource Masters
Cumulative Test Practice

- Multiple Choice format (pp. 78–80)
- Free Response format (pp. 77)

Create practice worksheets or tests that align to your state standards.

Math Online Have students visit macmillanmh.com for additional practice to reinforce your state standards.

CHAPTER 14 Test Practice
Cumulative, Chapters 1–14

PART 1 Multiple Choice

Read each question. Then fill in the correct answer on the answer sheet provided by the teacher or on a sheet of paper.

1. A square has a perimeter of 36 meters. What is the area of the square? A

A 81 m^2 **C** 9 m^2
B 72 m^2 **D** 6 m^2

2. Which of the following would you use to find the volume of the figure shown? H

F $V = \ell \times w$
G $V = 2\ell + 2w$
H $V = \ell \times w \times h$
J $V = 2\ell \times 2w \times 2h$

3. How many faces, edges, and vertices does the figure have? A

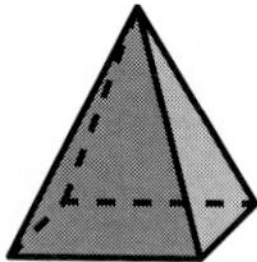

A 5 faces, 8 edges, 5 vertices
B 5 faces, 6 edges, 8 vertices
C 5 faces, 8 edges, 6 vertices
D 6 faces, 10 edges, 6 vertices

4. Bansi needs 48 ounces of buttermilk for a recipe. How many cups of buttermilk does she need? H

F 4 c **H** 6 c
G 5 c **J** 7 c

5. Which transformation is represented in the diagram? C

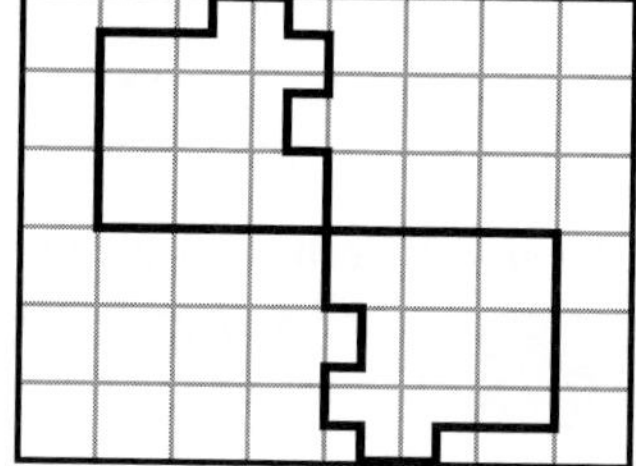

A Reflection **C** Rotation
B Translation **D** Not here

6. Look at the pattern of numbers shown below. F

7, ___, 17, 22, 27, 32

Which expression could be used to find the missing number in the pattern?

F (27 − 18) + 3
G (7 + 12) − 5
H (17 − 12) + 5
J (28 − 23) + 3

Test-Taking Tip

Tell students to read each question carefully to determine which formula to use.

Preparing for Standardized Tests
For test-taking strategies and practice, see pages R42–R55.

7. Which statement about the figures shown below is true? D

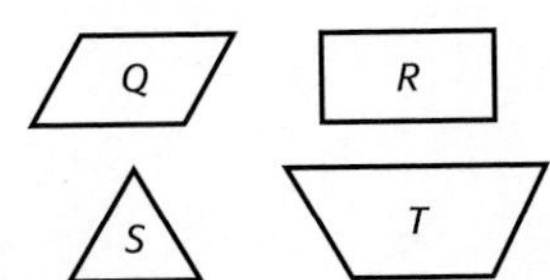

A Figures *Q* and *R* are congruent.

B Figures *S* and *T* are squares.

C Figures *S* and *R* have the same number of sides.

D Figures *Q* and *T* each have at least two acute angles.

8. The drawing below represents a parking lot at a pet store.

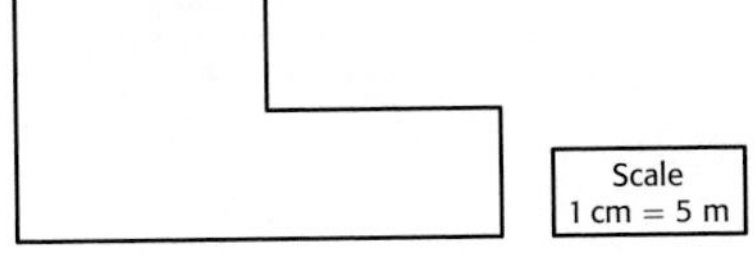

Use the ruler on the Mathematics Chart to measure the dimensions of the parking lot to the nearest tenth of centimeter. Which is the closest to the perimeter of the parking lot in meters? G

F 125 m

G 100 m

H 75 m

J 18 m

PART 2 Short Response

Record your answers on the answer sheet provided by your teacher or on a sheet of paper.

9. A rectangular driveway measures 16 feet by 12 feet. What is the area of the driveway in square feet? $192\ ft^2$

10. Find the number of millimeters that are equivalent to 50 centimeters.
1cm = 10mm, so 50cm = 500mm

PART 3 Extended Response

Record your answers on the answer sheet provided by your teacher or on a sheet of paper.

11. Derrick is painting a toy chest that is 14 inches tall, 9 inches wide, and 11 inches long. Draw a diagram of Derrick's toy chest. Then, find the surface area and volume of the chest. See margin.

12. It takes 3 feet of wood to make 1 birdhouse. If you have 23 feet of wood, can you make 8 birdhouses? Explain. See margin.

NEED EXTRA HELP?												
If You Missed Question...	1	2	3	4	5	6	7	8	9	10	11	12
Go to Lesson...	14-3	14-6	14-4	12-4	13-9	6-6	13-1	14-1	14-3	12-1	14-6	4-6

Summative Assessment 657

Answer Sheet Practice

Have students simulate taking a state test by recording their answers on a practice recording sheet.

CRM Chapter 14 Resource Masters
Student Recording Sheet (p. 81)

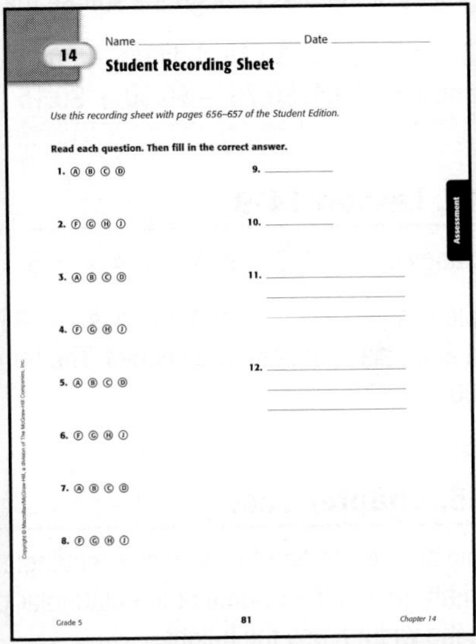
Name ______ Date ______

14 **Student Recording Sheet**

Use this recording sheet with pages 656–657 of the Student Edition.

Read each question. Then fill in the correct answer.

1. Ⓐ Ⓑ Ⓒ Ⓓ
2. Ⓕ Ⓖ Ⓗ Ⓙ
3. Ⓐ Ⓑ Ⓒ Ⓓ
4. Ⓕ Ⓖ Ⓗ Ⓙ
5. Ⓐ Ⓑ Ⓒ Ⓓ
6. Ⓕ Ⓖ Ⓗ Ⓙ
7. Ⓐ Ⓑ Ⓒ Ⓓ
8. Ⓕ Ⓖ Ⓗ Ⓙ
9. ______
10. ______
11. ______
12. ______

Assessment

Copyright © Macmillan/McGraw-Hill, a division of The McGraw-Hill Companies, Inc.

Grade 5 81 Chapter 14

Addtional Answers

11. $S = 758\ in^2$ $V = 1{,}386\ in^3$

14 in.
9 in.
11 in.

12. Sample answer: No; It takes 3 feet of wood for each birdhouse. $8 \times 3 = 24$. You have only 23 feet of wood.

Page 623, Mid-Chapter Check

14. Sample answer: $20 \times 20 = 400$ in^2

Page 625, Lesson 14-4

1. Sample answer: The circular bases are parallel and congruent; cylinder.

2. Sample answer: Each side of the cage is perpendicular to the four adjacent sides. The opposite sides are congruent. The opposite edges are congruent; rectangular prism.

3. Sample answer: A cylinder has a curved surface and a rectangular prism has polygonal sides. The bases of a cylinder are circles and the bases of a rectangular prism are rectangles.

Page 629, Lesson 14-5

9. Move three groups of marbles through the triangular machine and move two groups of marbles through the square machine.

10. \$1.26; 3 quarters = \$0.75, 3 dimes = \$0.30, 3 nickels = \$0.15, and 6 pennies = \$0.06. \$0.75 + \$0.30 + \$0.15 + \$0.06 = \$1.26.

Page 649, Lesson 14-9

6. 5 rectangles; 1×9, 2×8, 3×7, 4×6, 5×5

8. Sample answer: The area of the wall is 1,258 ft^2. Since $1{,}258 \div 450$ is about 2.8, 3 cans of paint are needed. The total cost is $3 \times \$22.50$ or about \$67.50.

Page 655, Chapter Test

15. Sample answer: To find the area of a rectangle, multiply the length times the width. To find the volume of a rectangular prism, multiply the length times the width times the height.

NOTES

Chapter Overview

Chapter-at-a-Glance

In Chapter 15, the emphasis is on expressing probabilities and using probabilities to make predictions.

Lesson	Math Objective	State/Local Standards
15-1 Probability (pp. 661–663)	Determine the likelihood of an event.	
EXPLORE **15-2 Make a Prediction** (pp. 666–667)	Use probability to make a prediction.	
15-2 Probability as a Fraction (pp. 668–672)	Use fractions to describe probability.	
EXTEND **15-2 Probability Experiment** (p. 673)	Use technology to describe probability as a fraction.	
15-3 Problem-Solving Strategy: Make an Organized List (pp. 674–675)	Solve problems by making an organized list.	
15-4 Counting Outcomes (pp. 677–680)	List outcomes of a probability experiment.	
15-5 Problem-Solving Investigation: Choose the Best Strategy (pp. 682–683)	Choose the best strategy to solve a problem.	

Use Probability to Make Predictions

BIG Idea In this chapter, students develop and apply concepts and skills of probability through exploration of familiar settings. Students will:

- review and extend their intuitive qualitative notions of probability
- determine fraction representations to quantify probability statements
- develop methods for determining possible outcomes to experiments
- analyze outcomes to experiments and other data-collection activities, using the results to generate quantitative probability statements
- make predictions based on results of experiments

Algebra Students use tree diagrams to list possible outcomes of a probability experiment. This concept will help prepare them for algebra concepts, such as using formulas to determine combinations and permutations. (Lesson 15-4)

G5-FP6C Data Analysis: Students apply their understanding of whole numbers, fractions, and decimals as they construct and analyze double-bar and line graphs and use ordered pairs on coordinate grids.

Skills Trace
Vertical Alignment

Fourth Grade

In fourth grade, students learned to:

- Find the probability of outcomes using a grid.

Fifth Grade

During this chapter, students learn to:

- Use probability to make a prediction.
- Determine the likelihood of an event and use fractions to describe probability.

Sixth Grade

In sixth grade, students learn to:

- Find and interpret the probability of a simple event.
- Predict the actions of a larger group using a sample.

Backmapping and Vertical Alignment **McGraw-Hill's *Math Connects*** program was conceived and developed with the final results in mind: student success in Algebra 1 and beyond. The authors, using the **NCTM Focal Points and Focal Connections** as their guide, developed this brand new series by backmapping from Algebra 1 concepts, and vertically aligning the topics so that they build upon prior skills and concepts and serve as a foundation for future topics.

Math Vocabulary

The following math vocabulary words for Chapter 15 are listed in the glossary of the ***Student Edition***. You can find interactive definitions in 13 languages in the ***eGlossary*** at macmillanmh.com.

certain Will definitely happen. (p. 661A)

equally likely Having the same chance of occurring. (p. 661A)
Example: in a coin toss you are equally likely to flip a head or a tail.

favorable outcome Desired results in a probability experiment. (p. 668A)

impossible An outcome or event is impossible if it has a probability of 0. (p. 661A)

outcome A possible result of an experiment. (p. 661A)

probability A number between 0 and 1 that measures the likelihood of an event happening. (p. 661A)

tree diagram A diagram of all the possible outcomes of an event or series of events or experiments. (p. 677A)

Chapter Planner

Suggested Pacing		
Instruction	Review & Assessment	TOTAL
6 days	1 day	**7 days**

Diagnostic Assessment
Quick Check (p. 660)

	Lesson 15-1 (Pacing: 1 day)	Explore 15-2 (Pacing: $\frac{1}{2}$ day)	Lesson 15-2 (Pacing: $\frac{1}{2}$ day)
Lesson/ Objective	**Probability** (pp. 661–663) **Objective:** Determine the likelihood of an event.	**Make a Prediction** (pp. 666–667) **Objective:** Use probability to make a prediction.	**Probability as a Fraction** (pp. 668–672) **Objective:** Use fractions to describe probability.
State/Local Standards			
Math Vocabulary	**probability, certain, impossible, equally likely, outcome, probability experiment**		**favorable outcome**
Lesson Resources	**Manipulatives** connecting cubes, pennies (one per student) **Other Resources** CRM Leveled Worksheets (pp. 8–12) Daily Reteach • 5-Minute Check • Problem of the Day	**Materials** paper bags **Manipulatives** connecting cubes	**Materials** paper bag **Manipulatives** connecting cubes **Other Resources** CRM Leveled Worksheets (pp. 13–17) Daily Reteach • 5-Minute Check • Problem of the Day
Technology			Math Adventures
Math Online	Personal Tutor		Personal Tutor • Concepts in Motion
Reaching All Learners	English Learners, p. 661B ELL Below Level, p. 661B BL Early Finishers, p. 661B AL		English Learners, p. 668B ELL Gifted and Talented, p. 668B AL Early Finishers, p. 668B AL
Alternate Lesson	*IMPACT Mathematics:* Unit G		*IMPACT Mathematics:* Unit G

Problem Solving in Science
(p. 664)

Use Probability to Make Predictions

	Extend 15-2 (Pacing: 1 day)	Lesson 15-3 (Pacing: 1 day)	Lesson 15-4 (Pacing: 1 day)
Lesson/Objective	**Probability as a Fraction** (p. 673) Tech Link **Objective:** Use technology to describe probability as a fraction.	**Problem-Solving Strategy Make an Organized List** (pp. 674–675) **Objective:** Solve problems by making an organized list.	**Counting Outcomes** (pp. 677–680) **Objective:** List outcomes of a probability experiment.
State/Local Standards			
Math Vocabulary			**tree diagram**
Lesson Resources		**Other Resources** CRM Leveled Worksheets (pp. 18–22) Daily Reteach • 5-Minute Check • Problem of the Day *The Shifting Nature of Weather*	**Manipulatives** number cube labeled 1–6, spinner **Other Resources** CRM Leveled Worksheets (pp. 23–27) Daily Reteach • 5-Minute Check • Problem of the Day
Technology / **Math Online**	Math Tool Chest		Personal Tutor
Reaching All Learners		English Learners, p. 674B ELL Gifted and Talented, p. 674B AL Early Finishers, p. 674B OL AL	English Learners, p. 677B ELL Below Level, p. 677B BL Early Finishers, p. 677B AL
Alternate Lesson			

Formative Assessment
Mid-Chapter Check (p. 676)

Game Time
Bean Game
(p. 681)

Chapter Planner

Lesson 15-5

Pacing: 1 day

	Lesson 15-5
Lesson/ Objective	**Problem-Solving Investigation** **Choose a Strategy** (pp. 682–683) **Objective:** Choose the best strategy to solve a problem.
State/Local Standards	
Math Vocabulary	
Lesson Resources	**Other Resources** CRM Leveled Worksheets (pp. 28–32) Daily Reteach • 5-Minute Check • Problem of the Day *The Shifting Nature of Weather*
Technology **Math Online**	
Reaching All Learners	English Learners, p. 682B ELL Below Level, p. 682B BL Early Finishers, p. 682B OL AL
Alternate Lesson	

Summative Assessment

- Study Guide and Review (p. 684)
- Chapter Test (p. 687)
- Test Practice (p. 688)

Teacher Notes

Assessment Options

Diagnostic Assessment

- SE *Option 1:* Quick Check (p. 661)
- *Option 2:* Online Quiz macmillanmh.com
- CRM *Option 3:* Diagnostic Test (p. 34)
- CRM *Option 4:* Chapter Pretest (p. 35)

Formative Assessment

- TE Alternate Teaching Strategies (every lesson)
- SE Talk About It (every lesson)
- SE Writing in Math (every lesson)
- SE Check What You Know (every lesson)
- TE Ticket Out the Door (p. 663)
- SE Mid-Chapter Check (p. 676)
- CRM Lesson Quizzes (pp. 36–38)
- CRM Mid-Chapter Test (p. 39)

Summative Assessment

- SE Chapter Test (p. 687)
- SE Test Practice (p. 686)
- CRM Vocabulary Test (p. 40)
- CRM Leveled Chapter Tests (pp. 45–56)
- CRM Cumulative Test Practice (pp. 59–61)
- CRM Oral Assessment (pp. 41–42)
- ExamView® Assessment Suite
- Advance Tracker

Mc Graw Hill Professional Development

Targeted professional development has been articulated throughout **McGraw-Hill's *Math Connects*** program. The **McGraw-Hill Professional Development Video Library** provides short videos that support the **NCTM Focal Points and Focal Connections.** For more information visit macmillanmh.com.

Model Lessons

Instructional Strategies

Learning Stations

Cross-Curricular Links

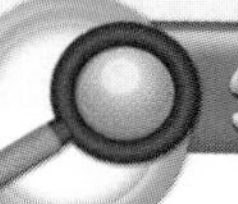

Science

pair | LOGICAL

Blood Types

Blood is classified by type. Here is how many people out of every hundred Americans that have each blood type:

$O+ = \frac{38}{100}$ $A+ = \frac{34}{100}$ $B+ = \frac{9}{100}$ $AB+ = \frac{3}{100}$

$O- = \frac{7}{100}$ $A- = \frac{6}{100}$ $B- = \frac{2}{100}$ $AB- = \frac{1}{100}$

- Organize a blood drive. Each person rolls a number cube to see how many hundreds of units of blood you get people to donate (multiply one hundred times the number you roll).
- Using the information about blood types, how many units of each type are each of you likely to get? How many of each type if you join forces?

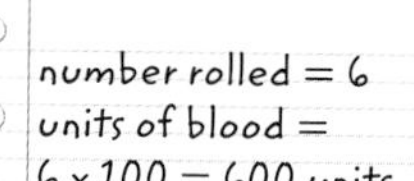

number rolled = 6
units of blood =
6 x 100 = 600 units

O+ = 228 O− = 42
A+ = 204 A− = 36
B+ = 54 B− = 12
AB+ = 18 AB− = 6

Materials:
- number cube
- pencils
- paper

Art

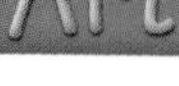

pair | LOGICAL

Museum Search

- Use a museum guide to search the National Gallery for a particular artist.
- Count the number of works of art the museum has by this artist.
- How many pieces are paintings? How many are drawings? Are there any print or sculpture pieces by this artist in the collection? Express each type of work as a fraction of the total works of this artist for each medium.
- What is the probability that the museum will sell a painting by this artist?

Auguste Renoir

43 Paintings = $\frac{11}{20}$

7 Drawings = $\frac{9}{100}$

3 Sculptures = $\frac{1}{25}$

25 Prints = $\frac{8}{25}$

Materials:
- National Gallery museum guide
- pencils
- paper

Writing

individual | LINGUISTIC

The Same Old Story

- Many events in daily life are repeated. Writers often use the idea of repetition in stories. In fairy tales, for example, the same action often happens over and over again, to reinforce an idea.
- You can use this repetition to make predictions. Write a story about a character who has to make a prediction using repetition. Show how your main character looks at his or her daily surroundings and notices the same things happening over and over again. You can write your story in the form of a fairy tale, if you wish.

The third time Joseph walked down the path, he met the same wise man...

Materials:
- paper
- pencils

Health

Healthy Choices

Make a sandwich menu, and use an illustrated tree chart to show all of your healthy choices.

- Think of three choices of healthy breads for your sandwiches, four healthy fillings, and three possible additions to the sandwich. Healthy choices for bread include whole wheat or oatmeal, and fillings can be lean deli meats, grilled chicken or vegetables, or low-fat cheeses. Additions might be lettuce, mustard, tomatoes, or other healthy additions. Be creative.
- Now make a tree diagram on a poster, showing all the kinds of sandwiches you can offer from your menu.

Materials:
- poster board
- paper
- pencils
- markers

Music

individual | LOGICAL

Musical Cube

- Using paper, scissors, and tape, cut out and fold a cube using the net found at this Learning Station. Then, using markers, label each side of the cube with the name of an orchestral instrument. Illustrate it by drawing the actual instrument if you wish.
- Create a 10-person band by rolling the cube ten times and recording which instrument it lands on each time.
- Predict what would happen if you rolled 100 times to create an entire orchestra. How many of each instrument would your orchestra contain?

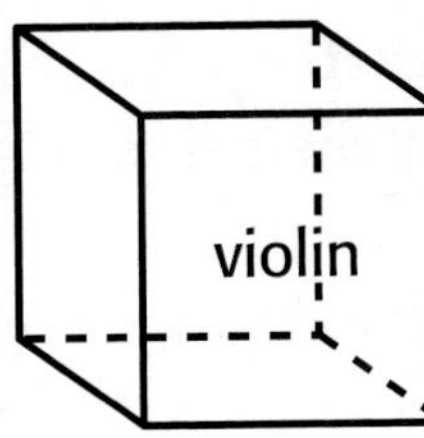

Materials:
- net of cube
- scissors
- markers
- tape
- paper
- pencils

Social Studies

Twirling the World

Close your eyes, spin the globe, and see where your finger lands.

- You and your partner take turns spinning the globe. One of you spins and the other stops the globe from spinning by placing a finger on it. Did your finger land on a continent or on an ocean? Keep a count of where you land.
- Count the number of times in twenty spins that your finger lands on a continent or on an ocean.
- Express your outcome as a fraction. What is the likelihood that on the 21st spin, your finger will land on a continent or on an ocean?

Materials:
- pencils
- paper
- globe

Introduce the Chapter

Real World: Likely or Not?

Materials: number cubes labeled 1–6, paper, pencil

Share with students that they will be learning about probability in this chapter.

- Have students work in pairs, each pair using 2 number cubes. Tell students to roll both number cubes, add the numbers rolled, and tally their results on a chart labeled with the sums 1–12.
- After students have rolled 25 times and tallied their results, compile the data on a class chart.
- Discuss the results. Ask them about the impossible likelihood of rolling numbers that add to one.
- Discuss why it is more likely that the sums 6, 7 and 8 appear than any of the other sums.

Direct students to Student Edition p. 658. Have students read the paragraph at the top of the page.

- **What is the probability that Jeremy will take a New Jersey quarter from his pocket?** $\frac{1}{3}$; There are 3 quarters and only one of them is a New Jersey quarter.

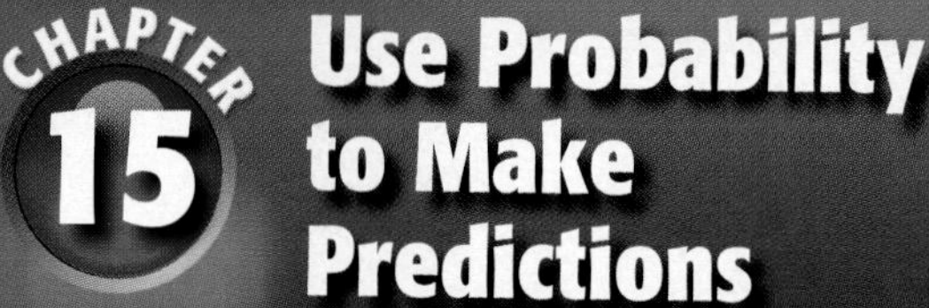

Use Probability to Make Predictions

BIG Idea What is probability?

Probability is the chance that a given event will happen.

Example In his pocket, Jeremy has the three state quarters shown below. If he takes a quarter from his pocket without looking, what is the probability that it is the New Jersey quarter?

The probability is **1 out of 3**, or $\frac{1}{3}$, that it will be the New Jersey quarter.

What will I learn in this chapter?

- Determine the likelihood of an event.
- Use fractions to describe the results of an experiment.
- Use experimental results to make a prediction.
- List outcomes of a probability experiment.
- Solve problems by *making an organized list.*

Key Vocabulary

probability
outcome
probability experiment
tree diagram

Student Study Tools at macmillanmh.com

WRITING IN MATH

Starting the Chapter

Have students write a paragraph about probability statements used in the real world. Prompt them by referring to weather reports and games they may have played. Encourage them to use such phrases as "likely," "unlikely," and "equally likely."

Key Vocabulary Introduce the key vocabulary in the chapter using the routine below.

Define: An outcome is a possible result in a probability experiment.

Example: If I have 4 marbles and 2 are blue, 1 is yellow, and 1 is red, there are 3 possible outcomes when I pull one out of a bag: blue, red, yellow.

Ask: When have you used outcomes?

Read-Aloud Anthology For an optional reading activity to introduce this chapter's math concepts, see the Read-Aloud Anthology on p. TR32.

Chapter 15 Project

Probability Preferences

Students figure out the probability of a song being played on a class-run radio station.

- Students list several types of music on the board, including hard rock, pop, blues, jazz, folk, alt-rock, country, and classical. Students record the number of hands raised for each type of music as a fraction of the number of students in the class.
- Students plan a requests-only radio show that will please the entire class, using the data collected. They decide on a total number of songs to play, and use the fractions to calculate the probability of getting an audience request for each type of music. They use this information to predict how many songs from each genre of music they will most likely play on their radio show.

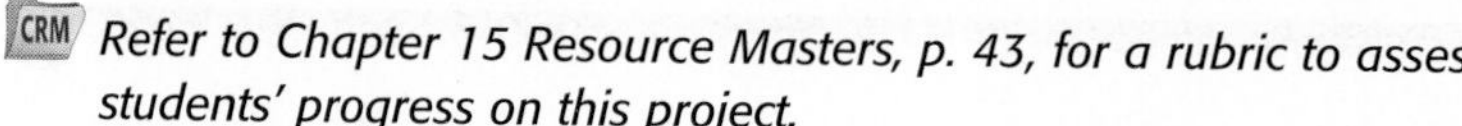

Refer to Chapter 15 Resource Masters, p. 43, for a rubric to assess students' progress on this project.

FOLDABLES Study Organizer

Make this Foldable to help you organize information about probability. Begin with a sheet of 11″ × 17″ paper.

1. **Fold** the short sides toward the middle.
2. **Fold** the top to the bottom.
3. **Open.** Cut as shown to make four tabs.
4. **Label** each tab as shown.

Chapter 15 Use Probability to Make Predictions 659

FOLDABLES Dinah Zike's Foldables

Guide students through the directions on p. 659 to create their own Foldable graphic organizers for probability. Students may also use their Foldables to study and review for chapter assessments.

When to Use It Lessons 15-1, 15-2, and 15-3. (Additional instructions for using the Foldables with these lessons are found on pp. 676 and 684.)

Chapter 15 Literature List

Lesson	Book Title
15-1	**Do You Wanna Bet?: Your Chance to Find Out About Probability** Jean Cushman
15-2	**Do You Wanna Bet?: Your Chance to Find Out About Probability** Jean Cushman
15-3	**Polar Bear Math** Ann Whitehead Nagda and Cindy Bickel
15-4	**Odds and Chances for Kids** Manfred G. Riedel
Any	**What Do You Mean by "Average"?: Means, Medians, and Modes** Elizabeth James
Any	**Hottest, Coldest, Highest, Deepest** Steve Jenkins

ELL National ESL Standards Alignment for Chapter 15

Lesson, Page	ESL Standards	Modality	Level
15-1, p. 661B	Goal 1, Standard 3, k	Kinesthetic, Linguistic	Intermediate
15-2, p. 668B	Goal 2, Standard 2, j	Visual/Spatial	Beginning
15-3, p. 674B	Goal 2, Standard 2, f	Visual, Logical	Advanced
15-4, p. 677B	Goal 1, Standard 1, a	Auditory	Beginning
15-5, p. 682B	Goal 2, Standard 1, f	Social	Advanced

The National ESL Standards can be found in the Teacher Reference Handbook.

- Read the Math at Home letter found on Chapter 15 Resource Masters, p. 4, with the class and have each student sign it. (A Spanish version is found on p. 5.)
- Send home copies of the Math at Home letter with each student.

Diagnostic Assessment

Check for students' prerequisite skills before beginning the chapter.

- **Option 1:** ***Quick Check***

  SE Student Edition, p. 658

- **Option 2:** ***Online Assessment***

  Math Online macmillanmh.com

- **Option 3:** ***Diagnostic Test***

  CRM Chapter 15 Resource Masters, p. 34

RTI (Response to Intervention)

Apply the Results Based on the results of the diagnostics assessment on Student Edition p. 660, use the chart below to address individual needs before beginning the chapter.

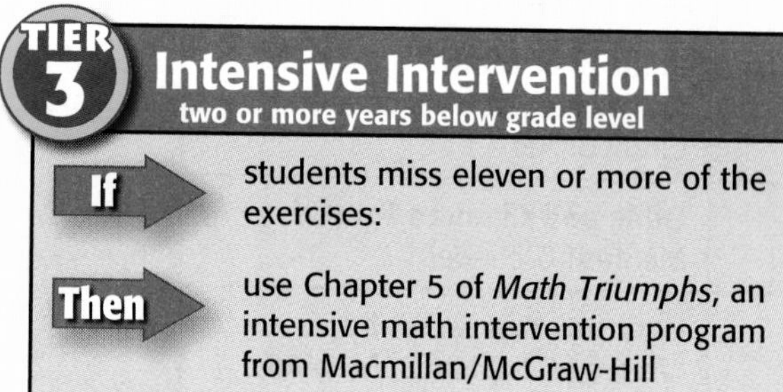

TIER 3 Intensive Intervention
two or more years below grade level

If students miss eleven or more of the exercises:

Then use Chapter 5 of *Math Triumphs*, an intensive math intervention program from Macmillan/McGraw-Hill

ARE YOU READY for Chapter 15?

You have two ways to check prerequisite skills for this chapter.

Option 2

Math Online Take the Chapter Readiness Quiz at macmillanmh.com.

Option 1

Complete the Quick Check below.

QUICK Check

Choose from *certain, impossible, likely,* or *unlikely* to describe each probability. (Prior Grade) (Used in Lessons 15-1 and 15-2)

1. If you choose a letter from the word EAR, it will be a vowel. likely
2. If you spin the spinner at the right, the number will be 8. impossible
3. If you spin the spinner at the right, the number will be 5. unlikely
4. If you choose a letter from the word MATHEMATICS, it will be Q. impossible
5. If you toss a coin, it will come up either heads or tails. certain

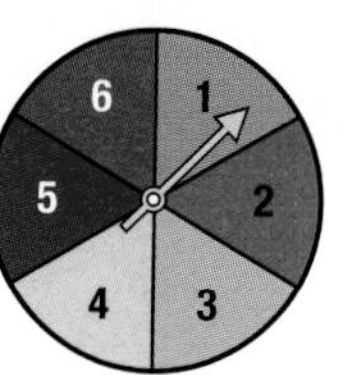

Write each fraction in simplest form. (Lesson 9-4) (Used in Lesson 15-2)

6. $\frac{10}{12}$ $\frac{5}{6}$
7. $\frac{4}{8}$ $\frac{1}{2}$
8. $\frac{5}{15}$ $\frac{1}{3}$
9. $\frac{14}{21}$ $\frac{2}{3}$
10. $\frac{6}{10}$ $\frac{3}{5}$
11. $\frac{9}{24}$ $\frac{3}{8}$
12. $\frac{12}{16}$ $\frac{3}{4}$
13. $\frac{28}{36}$ $\frac{7}{9}$

14. Paloma goes to school 20 out of the 30 days in April. Write the number of days out of the month that she goes to school as a fraction in simplest form. (Lesson 9-4) (Used in Lesson 15-2) $\frac{2}{3}$
15. Daryl is meeting his friends on either Saturday or Sunday. They are either going to lunch or going to see a movie. Describe two different situations that could happen. (Prior Grade) (Used in Lesson 15-4) Sample answer: go to lunch on Saturday or see a movie on Sunday
16. Manning is choosing a sandwich and a beverage from the table at the right. Describe three different choices. (Prior Grade) (Used in Lesson 15-4) Sample answer: cheese and iced tea, tuna and lemonade, turkey and iced tea

Sandwich	Beverage
Cheese	Iced tea
Tuna	Lemonade
Turkey	

TIER 2 Strategic Intervention below/approaching grade level	**TIER 1 On-Level**	**Above/Beyond-Level**
If students miss five to ten in: **Exercises 1–16**	**If** students miss three or four in: **Exercises 1–16**	**If** students miss two or less: **Exercises 1–16**
Then choose a resource:	**Then** choose a resource:	**Then** choose a resource:
TE Start Smart 6: Probability and Statistics (p. 12) **Math Online** Extra Examples • Personal Tutor • Concepts in Motion	TE Learning Stations (pp. 658G–658H) TE Chapter Project (p. 658) CRM Game: Predict Math Adventures My Math Zone Chapter 14 **Math Online** Fact Dash	TE Learning Stations (pp. 658G–658H) TE Chapter Project (p. 658) Real-World Problems Solving Reader: *The Shifting Nature of Weather* Math Adventures My Math Zone Chapter 14, 15 **Math Online** Games

LESSON

15-1 Probability

Lesson Planner

Objective

Determine the likelihood of an event.

Vocabulary

probability, certain, impossible, equally likely, outcome, probability experiment

Resources

Manipulatives: connecting cubes, pennies (one per student)
Literature Connection: *Do You Wanna Bet?: Your Chance to Find Out About Probability* by Jean Cushman
Teacher Technology
TeacherWorks • Interactive Classroom
Alternate Lesson: Use *IMPACT Mathematics:* Unit G to provide practice with probability

Focus on Math Background

This lesson focuses on identifying outcomes for a probability experiment. A *probability experiment* is a well-defined procedure that produces identifiable results, and an *outcome* is any one of the possible results. Although, not defined in the lesson, an *event* consists of one or more outcomes. A *simple event* is just one outcome. For example, there are six possible outcomes when a number cube is rolled. Rolling a 2 is a simple event; another event is rolling an even number, but it is not a simple event.

Informal and qualitative descriptions of likelihood are the main concern here. Of special importance is the concept of *equally likely* events, as several key uses of probability and statistics depend upon randomness, meaning that all outcomes of a particular probability experiment are equally likely. The six possible outcomes of rolling a number cube are equally likely, but the possible sums when rolling two number cubes are not.

Daily Routine

Use these suggestions before beginning the lesson on p. 661.

5-Minute Check

(Reviews Lesson 14-9)

Use any strategy to solve.

Rahman is 5 years older than twice Julieta's age. If Rahman is 27, how old is Julieta? 11 years old

Problem of the Day

What is the product of the three prime numbers between 40 and 50? Explain how you know the three numbers are prime. $41 \times 43 \times 47 = 82{,}861$; the only factors of each prime number are 1 and the number itself.

Building Math Vocabulary

Write the lesson vocabulary words and their definitions on the board.

Ask students to write the words and definitions in their Math Journals. Have them contribute ideas of real world events to their lists titled "certain," "impossible," and "equally likely."

Differentiated Instruction

Small Group Options

SPATIAL, INTERPERSONAL

Option 1 Below Level BL

Materials: spinner, paper, markers or colored pencils

- Have students construct and use a spinner to understand the concepts of *equally likely, likely,* and un*likely*.
- The spinner should have four sections, two of which take up $\frac{1}{8}$ of the spinner each.
- Have students write three sentences to describe the probabilities for the colors in the spinner. The first sentence should use *equally likely*. The second should use *likely*. The third uses *unlikely*.
- Students test the accuracy of their sentences by spinning the spinner 20 times.

KINESTHETIC, LINGUISTIC

Option 2 English Language Learners ELL

Core Vocabulary: certain, likely/unlikely, possible/impossible
Common Use Verb: will/won't

Hear Math This strategy helps students understand negating prefixes and the relationship between certain, likely/unlikely, and possible/impossible.

- Draw vocabulary words appropriately on the continuum.
- **Ask:** "Will it snow in Hawaii in July?" unlikely
- Point to unlikely on the continuum and write "snow in July" underneath it. Say: "It is **unlikely** that it ***will*** snow in July in Hawaii." Emphasize the negating prefixes.
- Repeat with more situations. When students demonstrate understanding, allow them to create and place additional sentences.

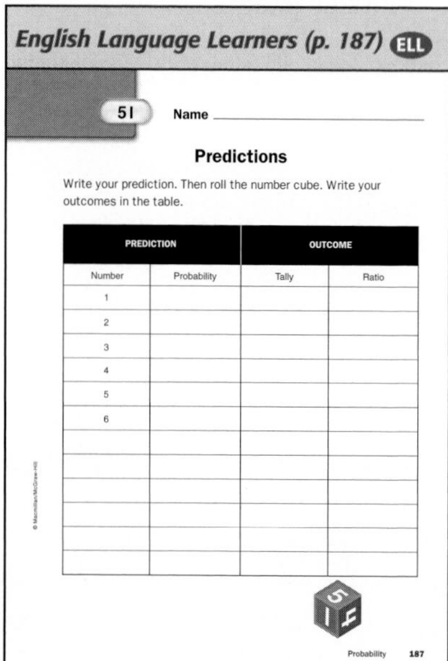

English Language Learners (p. 187) ELL

51 Name

Predictions

Write your prediction. Then roll the number cube. Write your outcomes in the table.

PREDICTION		OUTCOME	
Number	Probability	Tally	Ratio
1			
2			
3			
4			
5			
6			

Probability 187

Use this worksheet to provide additional support for English Language Learners.

Independent Work Options

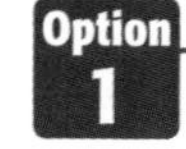

LOGICAL

Option 1 Early Finishers AL

Materials: paper bag, 10 connecting cubes (various colors)

- Set up bags prior to this activity so that the contents are not known to students. Have students work in pairs.
- Have one partner draw a cube from the bag, record the color, and place the cube back in the bag. Have partners write a probability statement about the color drawn.
- Draw another cube, record, and place it back in the bag. Have partners write a second probability statement about the cubes drawn. Have students continue drawing, recording, replacing, and writing statements until they have drawn 10 times. Based on the 10 draws, ask students to guess the contents of the bag. They may then open the bag to check their results.

Option 2 Student Technology

Math Online macmillanmh.com

Personal Tutor • Extra Examples

Option 3 Learning Station: Health (p. 658H)

Direct students to the Health Learning Station for opportunities to explore and extend the lesson concept.

Option 4 Problem-Solving Practice

Reinforce problem-solving skills and strategies with the Problem-Solving Practice worksheet.

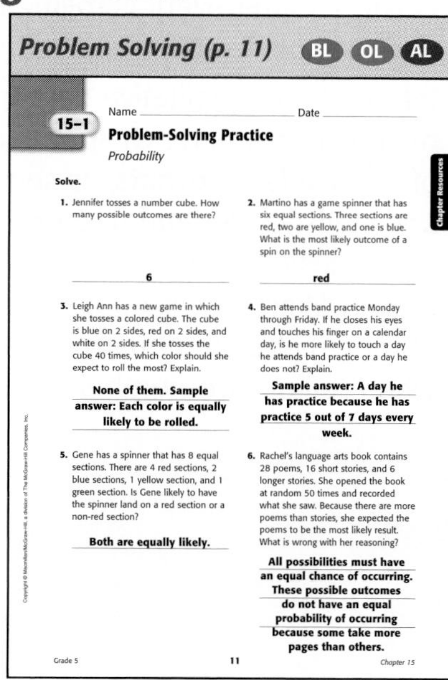

Problem Solving (p. 11) BL OL AL

15–1 Name ______ Date ______

Problem-Solving Practice

Probability

Chapter Resources

Solve.

1. Jennifer tosses a number cube. How many possible outcomes are there?

   6

2. Martino has a game spinner that has six equal sections. Three sections are red, two are yellow, and one is blue. What is the most likely outcome of a spin on the spinner?

   red

3. Leigh Ann has a new game in which she tosses a colored cube. The cube is blue on 2 sides, red on 2 sides, and white on 2 sides. If she tosses the cube 40 times, which color should she expect to roll the most? Explain.

   None of them. Sample answer: Each color is equally likely to be rolled.

4. Ben attends band practice Monday through Friday. If he closes his eyes and touches his finger on a calendar day, is he more likely to touch a day he attends band practice or a day he does not? Explain.

   Sample answer: A day he has practice because he has practice 5 out of 7 days every week.

5. Gene has a spinner that has 8 equal sections. There are 4 red sections, 2 blue sections, 1 yellow section, and 1 green section. Is Gene likely to have the spinner land on a red section or a non-red section?

   Both are equally likely.

6. Rachel's language arts book contains 28 poems, 16 short stories, and 6 longer stories. She opened the book at random 50 times and recorded what she saw. Because there are more poems than stories, she expected the poems to be the most likely result. What is wrong with her reasoning?

   All possibilities must have an equal chance of occurring. These possible outcomes do not have an equal probability of occurring because some take more pages than others.

Grade 5 11 Chapter 15

15-1 Probability

GET READY to Learn

One cube is drawn from each bag without looking. Write *certain, impossible,* or *equally likely* to make each a true sentence.

Bag 1

It is __?__ that a black cube will be drawn. **equally likely**

Bag 2

It is __?__ that a yellow cube will be drawn. **certain**

Bag 3

It is __?__ that a yellow cube will be drawn. **impossible**

MAIN IDEA

I will determine the likelihood of an event.

New Vocabulary

probability
certain
impossible
equally likely
outcome
probability experiment

Math Online

macmillanmh.com
- Extra Examples
- Personal Tutor
- Self-Check Quiz

Probability is the chance that an event will happen.

Probability		
Description	**Meaning**	**Example**
Certain	The event will definitely happen.	Drawing a yellow cube from Bag 2.
Impossible	There is no chance the event will happen.	Drawing a yellow cube from Bag 3.
Equally likely	There is an equal chance the event will happen.	Drawing a black cube from Bag 1.

An **outcome** is a possible result in a **probability experiment**. So, when drawing a cube from Bag 1 above, the possible outcomes are a black cube and a green cube.

EXAMPLE List Outcomes

1 **Cole spins the spinner at the right. List the possible outcomes.**

The spinner could land on the red space, the blue space, or the orange space.

outcomes: red, blue, orange

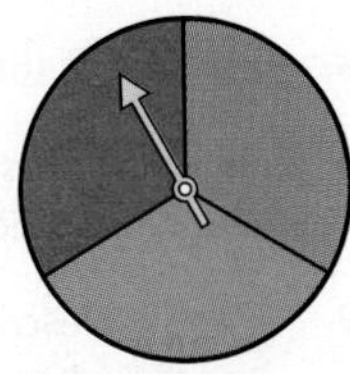

15-1 Probability

1 Introduce

Activity Choice 1 • Hands-On

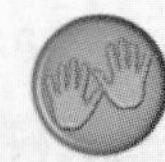

- Have students work in pairs. Give each student a penny. **How many tosses out of 50 do you think will be heads? tails?** Answers will vary.
- Tell partners to keep a tally of heads and tails as they each toss the penny 50 times. **How many tosses out of 50 were heads? tails?** Answers will vary; should be about 25 each.
- Have students discuss why a coin toss is often used to make fair decisions.
- Record the results of several tallies on the board. **Why are about half of the tosses heads and half tails?** There is an equal chance that the coin will land heads up or tails up.
- **Technology Link** Students could also use the probability feature from Math Tool Chest to do the coin toss activity.

Activity Choice 2 • Literature

Introduce the lesson with *Do You Wanna Bet?: Your Chance to Find Out About Probability* by Jean Cushman. For a related math activity, see p. TR61.

2 Teach

Scaffolding Questions

Place 12 connecting cubes in a paper bag: 4 red, 4 purple, 2 yellow, 1 green, and 1 orange.

- **If it is more likely for someone to draw a red cube than a green cube from the bag, what would you expect about the red cubes?** There are more red than green cubes.
- **If it is equally likely to draw a green cube or an orange cube, what would you expect?** There is the same number of green and orange.
- **There are no blue cubes in the bag. How would you describe the possibility of drawing a blue cube?** impossible

GET READY to Learn

Have students open their books and read the information in **Get Ready to Learn.** Introduce the vocabulary. As a class, work through **Examples 1 and 2.**

List Outcomes

Example 1 Be sure students understand that every possible outcome should be listed not just those that are most probable. If the orange section were much larger than the red and blue, red, orange, and blue would still be the outcomes.

ADDITIONAL EXAMPLES

1. Janessa rolls a number cube labeled 1–6. List the possible outcomes. 1, 2, 3, 4, 5. 6
2. There are 1 green, 8 blue, 2 red and 4 yellow marbles in a bag. One marble is chosen at random. Describe the probability of choosing a blue marble. Write *certain, impossible, likely, unlikely,* or *equally likely*. likely

CHECK What You Know

As a class, have students complete Exercises 1–9 in **Check What You Know** as you observe their work.

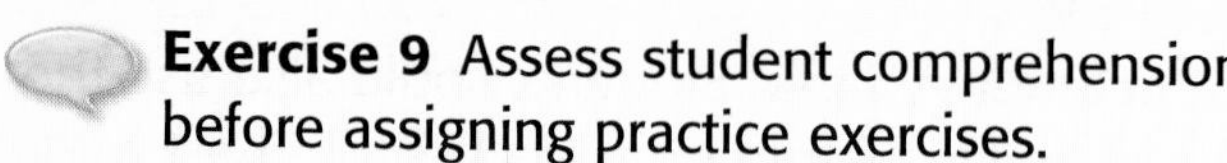

Exercise 9 Assess student comprehension before assigning practice exercises.

BL Alternate Teaching Strategy

If students have trouble describing the likelihood of an event…

Then use one of these reteach options:

1 CRM **Daily Reteach Worksheet** (p. 8)

2 Have students sort a bag of 16 cubes of which 6 are red, 4 are yellow, 4 are green, and 2 are purple.

- Direct students to draw a picture of the sorted cubes and write a series of statements such as "More red → Likely" and "Less purple → Unlikely", "Equal yellow and green → Equally likely".

COMMON ERROR!

Exercises 10–20 Students may have trouble with determining the number of possible outcomes when there is more than one of each kind of object in a group. Have students group like objects before determining that each group of like objects is a possible outcome as opposed to each individual item being a possible outcome.

If the probability that an event will occur is *more* than equally likely, use the phrase *likely*. If the probability is *less* than equally likely, use the phrase *unlikely* to describe it.

Remember

At random or *randomly* means choosing a marble without looking. Each marble is equally likely to be chosen.

EXAMPLE Describe Probability

2 **One marble is chosen at random. Describe the probability of choosing a green marble. Write *certain, impossible, likely, unlikely*, or *equally likely*.**

event: choosing a green marble

outcomes: red, blue, green, yellow

There is only 1 green marble, compared to 9 other marbles. So, the probability of choosing a green marble is *unlikely*.

CHECK What You Know

List the possible outcomes in each probability experiment. See Example 1 (p. 661)

1. spinning the spinner

4, 5, 6, 7, 8, 9

2. tossing a quarter

heads, tails

3. choosing a card at random

red, blue, yellow

One disc is randomly drawn from the bag. Describe the probability of drawing each disc. Write *certain, impossible, likely, unlikely,* or *equally likely.* See Example 2 (p. 662)

4. blue likely
5. red unlikely
6. green impossible
7. blue, red, or yellow certain
8. How many possible outcomes are there for choosing a letter in the word CERTAIN? 7
9. Talk About It Describe outcomes that are likely and unlikely to occur when a number cube labeled 1 to 6 is tossed. Explain. Sample answer: The likely outcomes are 1, 2, 3, 4, 5, and 6. The unlikely outcomes are 0 and numbers greater than 6.

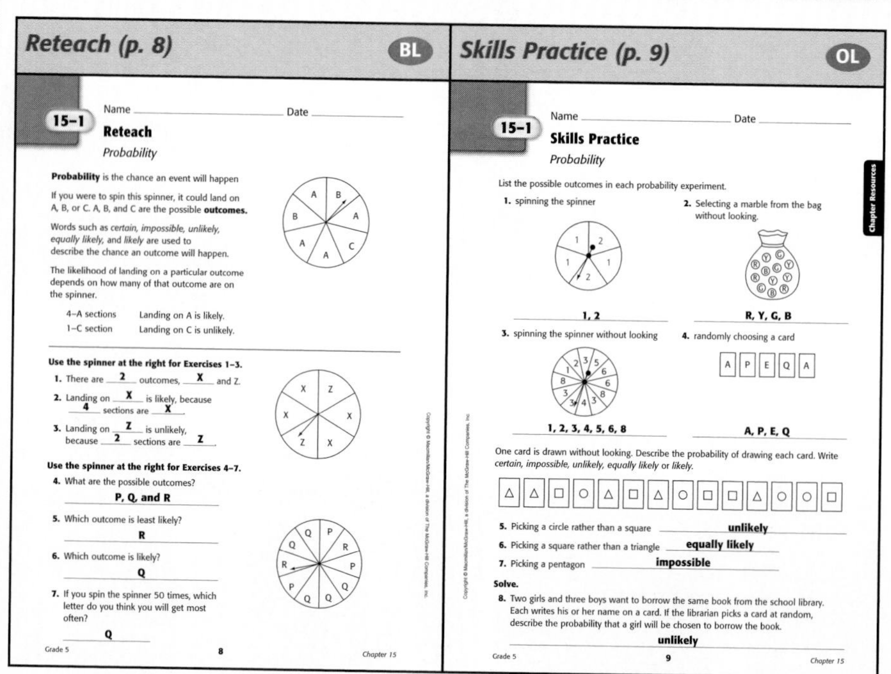

Reteach (p. 8) BL

15–1 Name ________ Date ________

Reteach

Probability

Probability is the chance an event will happen

If you were to spin this spinner, it could land on A, B, or C. A, B, and C are the possible **outcomes.**

Words such as *certain, impossible, unlikely, equally likely,* and *likely* are used to describe the chance an outcome will happen.

The likelihood of landing on a particular outcome depends on how many of that outcome are on the spinner.

4–A sections	Landing on A is likely.
1–C section	Landing on C is unlikely.

Use the spinner at the right for Exercises 1–3.

1. There are **2** outcomes, **X** and Z.
2. Landing on **X** is likely, because **4** sections are **X**.
3. Landing on **Z** is unlikely, because **2** sections are **Z**.

Use the spinner at the right for Exercises 4–7.

4. What are the possible outcomes? **P, Q, and R**
5. Which outcome is least likely? **R**
6. Which outcome is likely? **Q**
7. If you spin the spinner 50 times, which letter do you think you will get most often? **Q**

Grade 5 8 Chapter 15

Skills Practice (p. 9) OL

15–1 Name ________ Date ________

Skills Practice

Probability

List the possible outcomes in each probability experiment.

1. spinning the spinner **1, 2**
2. Selecting a marble from the bag without looking. **R, Y, G, B**
3. spinning the spinner without looking **1, 2, 3, 4, 5, 6, 8**
4. randomly choosing a card **A, P, E, Q**

One card is drawn without looking. Describe the probability of drawing each card. Write *certain, impossible, unlikely, equally likely* or *likely.*

△ △ □ ○ △ □ △ ○ □ □ △ ○ ○ □

5. Picking a circle rather than a square **unlikely**
6. Picking a square rather than a triangle **equally likely**
7. Picking a pentagon **impossible**

Solve.

8. Two girls and three boys want to borrow the same book from the school library. Each writes his or her name on a card. If the librarian picks a card at random, describe the probability that a girl will be chosen to borrow the book. **unlikely**

Grade 5 9 Chapter 15

Chapter Resources

Practice and Problem Solving

See page R40.

List the possible outcomes in each probability experiment. See Example 1 (p. 661)

10. choosing one coin at random

quarter, nickel, dime

11. randomly choosing one can of soup

tomato, chicken noodle

12. choosing one cube without looking red

13. spinning the spinner 1, 2, 3, 4, 5

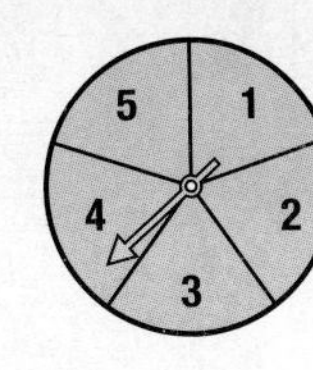

14. randomly choosing one letter from the word EVENT E, V, N, T

One card is drawn without looking. Describe the probability of drawing each card. Write *certain, impossible, likely, unlikely,* or *equally likely.* See Example 2 (p. 662)

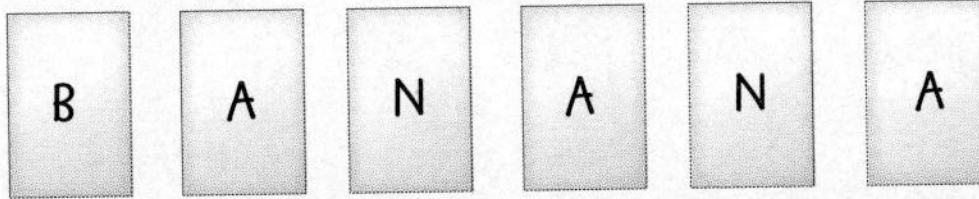

15. B less likely

16. A equally likely

Suppose you spin the spinner at the right. Describe the probability of landing on each color. Write *certain, impossible, likely, unlikely,* or *equally likely.* See Example 2 (p. 662)

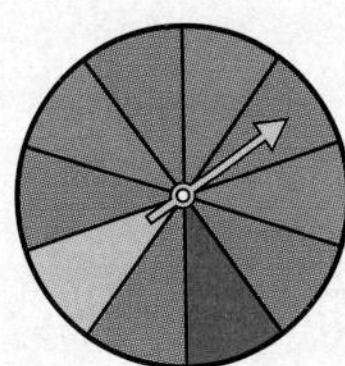

17. orange rather than red likely

18. green impossible

19. orange rather than blue unlikely

20. *not* purple certain

H.O.T. Problems

21. CHALLENGE Describe a group of 10 cubes that have the following characteristics. Sample answer: 1 red, 1 blue, 3 yellow, 5 green
- There are 4 different colors.
- When a cube is drawn, one color is more likely to be drawn than any other.
- Exactly two of the remaining colors are equally likely to be drawn.

22. WRITING IN MATH Write a real-world problem that can be solved by describing its probability. Then solve the problem. See Ch.15 Answer Appendix.

Enrich (p. 12) AL

15-1 Name ______ Date ______

Enrich

Explore Probability

1. Suppose you were to toss two number cubes and find their sum. Complete the table to show all the possible outcomes.

	1	2	3	4	5	6
1	2	3	4	5	6	7
2	3	4	5	6	7	8
3	4	5	6	7	8	9
4	5	6	7	8	9	10
5	6	7	8	9	10	11
6	7	8	9	10	11	12

2. How many different outcomes are possible? 11 outcomes
3. Is each outcome equally likely to happen? Explain. No; some sums occur only once, and other sums occur more than once.
4. Which sums are least likely to happen? 2 or 12
5. Which sum is most likely to happen? 7
6. Conduct an experiment. Toss two number cubes and record their sum in the table below. Repeat 25 times. Results will vary.

Sum	2	3	4	5	6	7	8	9	10	11	12
Tally											
Frequency											

7. Do the results of your experiment match the results of problems 4 and 5? Why or why not? Results may or may not match.

Grade 5 12 Chapter 15

Homework Practice (p. 10) OL

15-1 Name ______ Date ______

Homework Practice

Probability

Suppose you spin the spinner at right. Describe the probability of landing on each pattern. Write *certain, impossible, unlikely, equally likely,* or *likely.*

1. striped, plain, or speckled certain
2. striped likely
3. speckled unlikely

One cube is drawn without looking. Describe the probability of choosing a pattern. Write *certain, impossible, unlikely, equally likely,* or *likely.*

4. five-star impossible
5. spots unlikely
6. two star likely

Spiral Review

Determine whether you need to find the perimeter, area, or volume. Then solve. (Lesson 14-7)

7. Elizabeth is planting a garden. She wants to use a space that is 5 yards long and 3 yards wide. How much space will she have in her garden? area; 15 yd²
8. Which units would be most appropriate to measure the volume of a pool: cubic inches, cubic feet, or cubic yards? Explain. cubic yards because it is the largest unit

Grade 5 10 Chapter 15

3 Practice

Differentiate practice using these leveled assignments for Exercises 10–22.

Level	Assignment
BL Below/ Approaching Level	10–13, 16–17, 18–20
OL On Level	12–18, 22
AL Above/Beyond Level	11–21 odd, 21–22

Have students discuss and complete the Higher Order Thinking problems.

WRITING IN MATH Have students complete Exercise 22 in their Math Journals. You may choose to use this exercise as an optional formative assessment.

4 Assess

Formative Assessment

Present students with a group of 8 cubes: 4 red, 2 yellow, 1 green, 1 purple.

- **What are the possible outcomes in this experiment?** red, yellow, green, purple
- **Describe the probability of drawing a red cube if you were to draw randomly from this group? Explain.** likely, because there are more red cubes
- **Describe the probability of drawing a green rather than a purple cube?** equally likely

Quick Check **Are students continuing to struggle with determining the likelihood of an event?**

If Yes → Small Group Options (p. 661B)

If No → Independent Work Options (p. 661B)
CRM Skillls Practice Worksheet (p. 9)
CRM Enrich Worksheet (p. 12)

Ticket Out the Door Draw the following on the board: 6 blue squares, 3 green squares, and 1 red square in a bag. Have students write three different probability statements on a card about drawing one square at random using such terms as *likely, unlikely, equally likely, impossible,* and *certain.*

Lesson Planner

Objective

Interpret information and data from science to solve problems.

National Standard 

Students should develop an understanding of the diversity and adaptations of organisms.

Resources

Materials: paper, pencils

Activate Prior Knowledge

Before you turn students' attention to the pages, ask them to discuss wildflowers.

- **What kinds of wildflowers do you know?** Sample answer: clover
- **Why should people grow wildflowers?** Sample answer: because they provide a habitat for wildlife

Use the Student Page

Ask students to read the information on pp. 664–665 and answer these questions:

- **Which wildflower makes up the most part of the Wildflower Habitat mix?** grasses **the least?** clovers
- **The amount of perennial flowers and grains is about equal to which single category or wildflower?** grasses

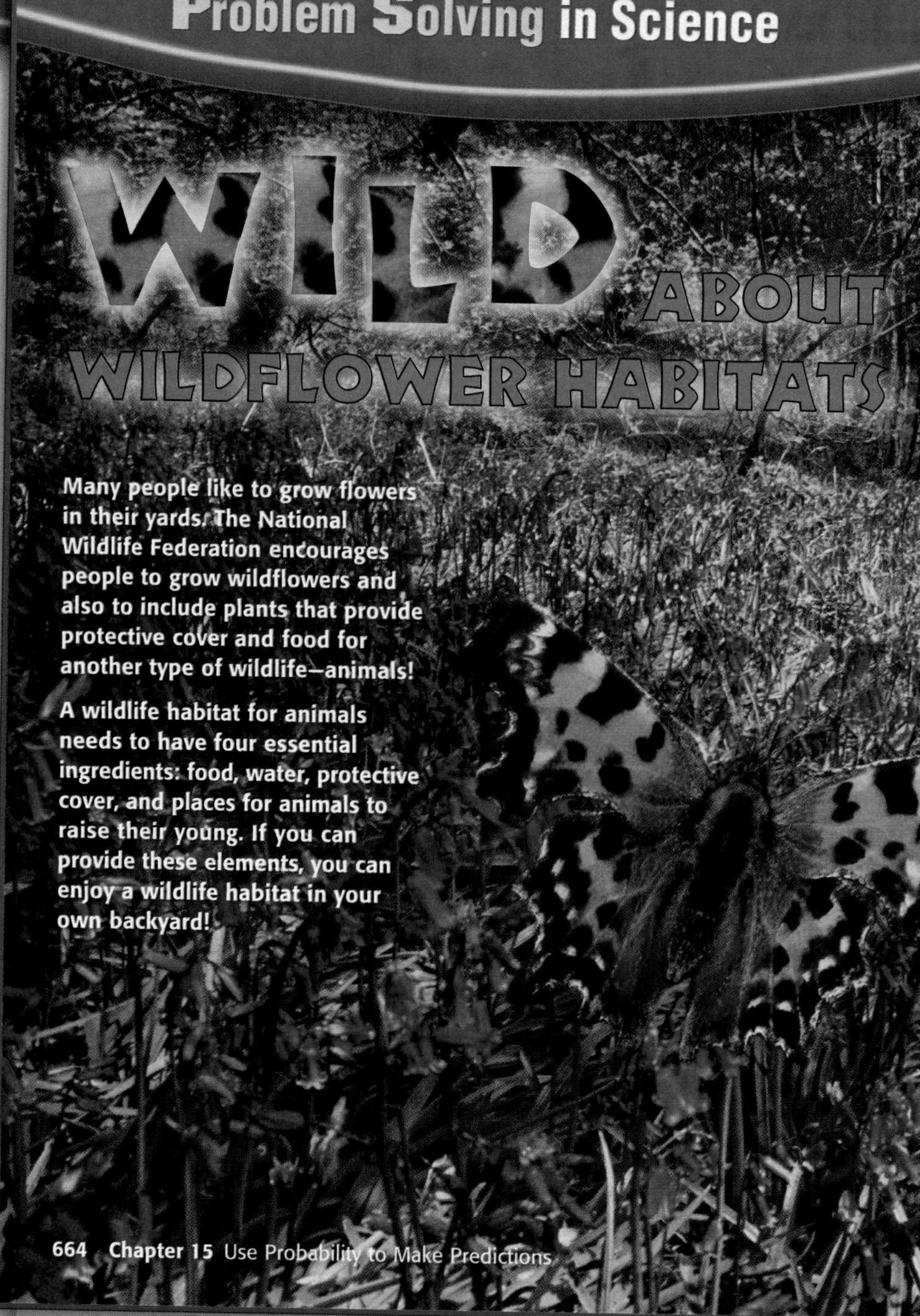

Problem Solving in Science
WILD ABOUT WILDFLOWER HABITATS
Many people like to grow flowers in their yards. The National Wildlife Federation encourages people to grow wildflowers and also to include plants that provide protective cover and food for another type of wildlife—animals!
A wildlife habitat for animals needs to have four essential ingredients: food, water, protective cover, and places for animals to raise their young. If you can provide these elements, you can enjoy a wildlife habitat in your own backyard!
664 Chapter 15 Use Probability to Make Predictions

Real-World Math

Use the table below to solve each problem.

1. Suppose you pick one seed at random from the packet of wildflower habitat mix. Is the probability of picking a grain *greater than* or *less than* picking a grass? less than

2. If you pick one seed at random from the packet of wildflower habitat mix, is the probability of picking a clover *likely* or *unlikely*? unlikely

3. If there are 700 seeds in the wildflower habitat mix, how many would be annual flowers? 175

4. Suppose you pick one seed at random from the packet of wildflower habitat mix. What is the probability that you would pick a flower seed? Write your answer as a fraction. $\frac{1}{2}$

5. Describe your answer for Exercise 4 as *certain, impossible,* or *equally likely.* equally likely

6. WRITING IN ▶MATH Explain how the fraction of seeds in the wildlife habitat mix will result in a well-balanced wildlife habitat. See margin.

WILDFLOWER HABITAT MIX

Grasses	$\frac{7}{20}$
Clovers	$\frac{1}{20}$
Grains	$\frac{1}{10}$
Annual flowers	$\frac{1}{4}$
Perennial flowers	$\frac{1}{4}$

Did You Know?
A lawn costs about $700 per acre each year. A wildflower meadow costs about $30 per acre each year.

Additional Answer

6. Sample answer: Since the seeds are mixed together randomly, the seeds will also be scattered in a random arrangement. Since 50% of the seeds are wildflowers, it is likely that wildflowers will dominate the habitat, and that wildflowers will be fairly evenly mixed with grasses, grains, and clovers.

Real-World Math

Assign the exercises on p. 665. Encourage students to choose a problem-solving strategy before beginning each exercise. If necessary, review the strategies suggested in Lesson 15-5, p. 683.

Exercises 3–4 Remind students to refer to the chart.

Exercise 5 Remind students to use the fractions to figure out probability.

WRITING IN ▶MATH Have students create a word problem that uses the information found in the text and in the chart on pp. 664–665.

Extend the Activity

Have students come up with examples of each wildflower and write them next to each category.

Math Probability Activity for 15-2

Lesson Planner

Objective

Use probability to make a prediction.

Resources

Materials: paper bags
Manipulatives: connecting cubes

1 Introduce

- Have students place 5 blue cubes, 3 yellow cubes, and 2 red cubes in front of them on their desks.
- Review with students how to name each color as a fractional part of the group. **What fraction of the cubes is blue? yellow? red?** $\frac{5}{10}$ or $\frac{1}{2}$ are blue, $\frac{3}{10}$ are yellow, and $\frac{2}{10}$ or $\frac{1}{5}$ are red
- Tell students that they can use what they know about fractional parts of a group to make predictions about outcomes in probability.

2 Teach

Activity Copy the table from the student page on the board and have students draw their own on paper. Distribute small paper bags. Have students place their cubes in the bags. Then have them draw cubes from the bag, replacing them after recording in the tally column. Make sure students understand that the cubes are to be chosen randomly, meaning without looking, so that every cube has equal chance of being drawn.

Probability Activity for 15-2

Make a Prediction

MAIN IDEA

I will use probability to make a prediction.

You Will Need
centimeter cubes
bag

ACTIVITY

Step 1 Place 5 blue cubes, 3 yellow cubes, and 2 red cubes in a bag.

What fraction of the cubes is blue? yellow? red? Write each fraction in a table like the one below.

Outcome	Fraction	Prediction	Tally	Number
Blue	$\frac{1}{2}$			
Yellow	$\frac{3}{10}$			
Red	$\frac{1}{5}$			

Step 2 Suppose you draw a cube and then return it to the bag. If you do this 40 times, predict the number of times a blue, a yellow, and a red cube will be drawn. Record your predictions in the table.

Step 3 Without looking, draw a cube from the bag. Record the color in the Tally column of your table.

Step 4 Replace the cube and repeat Step 3 for a total of 40 times. Add the tally marks and record the numbers in the table.

Think About It

1. Explain how you predicted the number of blue, yellow, and red cubes that would be drawn. See margin.
2. Compare your predictions in Step 2 with the actual number of cubes that were drawn. Describe any differences. 2–4. See students' work.
3. In your experiment, what fraction of the cubes drawn is blue? yellow? red? How do these compare to the actual fractions? Explain any differences.
4. Suppose this experiment was performed an additional 20 times for a total of 60 times. Based on the experimental results, predict the number of times you would draw a red cube.

CHECK What You Know

5. Perform this experiment an additional 20 times for a total of 60 times. Copy and complete the table below with your predictions and results. See students' work.

Outcome	Fraction	Prediction	Tally	Number
Blue	$\frac{1}{2}$			
Yellow	$\frac{3}{10}$			
Red	$\frac{1}{5}$			

A bag has 6 marbles. One marble is drawn and replaced 30 times. The results are shown in the table.

Color	Number of Times Drawn
Red	25
White	5

6. Predict the number of red marbles in the bag. Explain. 6–9. See margin.
7. Based on the experiment, describe the likelihood that there is a blue marble in the bag. Explain.
8. Predict the number of white marbles in the bag. Explain.
9. WRITING IN MATH The same experiment was performed with a bag containing 18 marbles and the same results were achieved. Predict the number of red marbles in the bag. Explain.

Think About It

Assign Exercises 1–4 in the Think About It section to assess student comprehension of the concepts presented in the Activities.

3 Assess

Formative Assessment

Use the **Check What You Know** Exercises 6, 8 and 9 to assess whether students understand how to use probability to make a prediction.

From Concrete to Abstract Use Exercise 6 to bridge the gap between knowing what an experimental group consists of and determining an unknown quantity of items for each possible outcome.

Extending the Concept What would you expect to happen in 60 draws if there were equal numbers of 3 colors of cubes in a bag?

Additional Answers

1. Sample answer: 5 out of 10 or one half of the cubes in the bag are blue. So, one half of the 40 draws, or 20, can be expected to result in a blue cube. In the same way, 12 draws can be expected to be yellow and 8 draws can be expected to be red.
6. Sample answer: In the experiment a red marble was drawn 25 times out of 30 times, or $\frac{5}{6}$ of the time. If there are 6 marbles in the bag and $\frac{5}{6}$ of them are red, there would be 5 red marbles.
7. Sample answer: 0; In the experiment, no blue marbles were drawn.
8. Sample answer: In the experiement, a white marble was drawn 5 times out of 30 times, or $\frac{1}{6}$ of the time. If there are 6 marbles in the bag and $\frac{1}{6}$ of them are white, there would be one white marble.
9. Sample answer: There are three times as many marbles in the bag; if 5 out of 6 marbles is predicted to be red, then 5×3, or 15 out of 18 marbles would be red.

LESSON 15-2

Probability as a Fraction

Lesson Planner

Objective

Use fractions to describe probability.

Vocabulary

favorable outcome

Resources

Materials: paper bag
Manipulatives: connecting cubes
Literature Connection: *Do You Wanna Bet?: Your Chance to Find Out About Probability* by Jean Cushman
Teacher Technology
Interactive Classroom • TeacherWorks
Alternate Lesson: Use *IMPACT Mathematics:* Unit G to provide practice with probability as a fraction.

Focus on Math Background

Students now use their knowledge of fractions to attach numerical values to probabilities. If all possible outcomes of an experiment have been identified and are equally likely, then:

$$P(\text{event}) = \frac{\text{number of favorable outcomes}}{\text{number of possible outcomes}}$$

Here the standard notation P(event) is used to mean the probability of an event. Thus P(heads) stands for the probability that the toss of a coin will result in heads facing upward. A *favorable outcome*, often called a *success*, is defined by the context of the situation, and does not necessarily mean "desirable." For example, an industrial quality control calculation may use "success" to describe finding a defective item.

Daily Routine

Use these suggestions before beginning the lesson on p. 668.

5-Minute Check

(Reviews Lesson 15-1)

One card is drawn without looking. Describe the probability of drawing each card. Write *certain, impossible, likely, equally likely* or *unlikely.*

1. an even number rather than an odd number likely
2. 5 rather than 8 unlikely
3. 2 rather than 7 equally likely
4. 9 impossible
5. even and odd numbers certain

Problem of the Day

A number is divided by 8. When the quotient is multiplied by 7, the product is 224. What is the number? Explain how you would find the answer. 256; work backward, $224 \div 7 = 32$, $32 \times 8 = 256$

Building Math Vocabulary

Write the lesson vocabulary words and their definitions on the board.

Have students write the phrase and its definition in their Math Journal. Ask students to write two sentences using the phrase for situations they may have experienced.

Differentiated Instruction

Small Group Options

Option 1 Gifted and Talented AL

LOGICAL

Materials: 2 number cubes labeled 1–6 for each student

- Distribute 2 number cubes to each student.
- **What is the probability of rolling an even number with one number cube?** $\frac{3}{6}$ or $\frac{1}{2}$
- **If you used both number cubes, how many even two-digit numbers can you roll?** 18
- **What is the probability of rolling an even two-digit number?** $\frac{18}{36}$ or $\frac{1}{2}$
- **What is the probability of rolling an even sum of these two number cubes?** $\frac{18}{36}$ or $\frac{1}{2}$

Option 2 English Language Learners

VISUAL/SPATIAL

Materials: 5 clear labeled bags with color tiles in the following manner: Bag 1: 10 red tiles, Bag 2: 8 red tiles, 2 blue tiles; Bag 3: 5 red tiles, 5 blue tiles; Bag 4: 2 red tiles, 8 blue tiles; Bag 5: 10 blue tiles
Core Vocabulary: likely, certain, impossible
Common Use Verb: study
See Math This strategy connects vocabulary to probability and fractional amounts.

- Write the words *likely, certain, impossible* on the board to discuss meaning.
- Show bags and say: "***Study*** each bag. Each one has 10 tiles, but they are not the same."
- Say: "If I stick my hand without looking in Bag 1, would it be **likely, certain**, or **impossible** to pick a red tile?" certain
- Say: "If I pick from Bag 2, what would my chances be to pick a red tile?" likely
- Say: "If I pick from bag 5, what would my chances be to pick a red tile?" impossible

Independent Work Options

Option 1 Early Finishers AL

LOGICAL

Materials: number cube labeled 1–6, pencil, paper

- Have students make a table with 5 columns labeled as the following: 1; 2 or 3; 4, 5 or 6; even; odd.
- Students roll the number cube 30 times and keep a tally of their rolls in the correct columns.
- Ask students to calculate the probability of rolling the numbers in each column. Then have them determine the fraction of the total rolls in each column that actually appeared. Note that the theoretical probability that was calculated may not be the same as the experimental fraction.

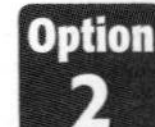

Option 2 Student Technology

Math Online macmillanmh.com

Personal Tutor • Extra Examples

Math Adventures

Option 3 Learning Station: Music (p. 658A)

Direct students to the Music Learning Station for opportunities to explore and extend the lesson concept.

Option 4 Problem-Solving Practice

Reinforce problem-solving skills and strategies with the Problem-Solving Practice worksheet.

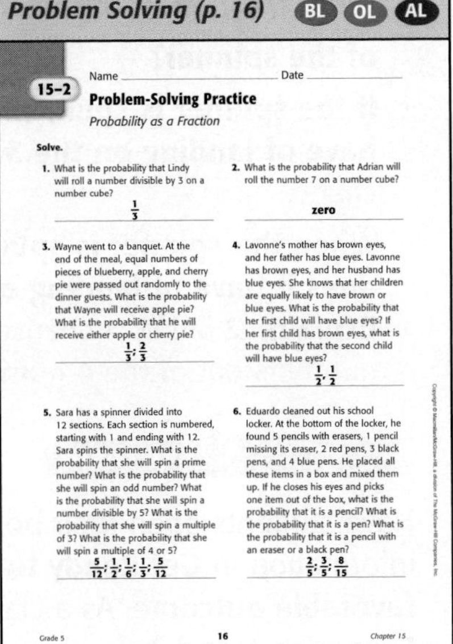

Problem Solving (p. 16) BL OL AL

15–2 Name ______ Date ______

Problem-Solving Practice

Probability as a Fraction

Solve.

1. What is the probability that Lindy will roll a number divisible by 3 on a number cube? $\frac{1}{3}$
2. What is the probability that Adrian will roll the number 7 on a number cube? **zero**
3. Wayne went to a banquet. At the end of the meal, equal numbers of pieces of blueberry, apple, and cherry pie were passed out randomly to the dinner guests. What is the probability that Wayne will receive apple pie? What is the probability that he will receive either apple or cherry pie? $\frac{1}{3}$; $\frac{2}{3}$
4. Lavonne's mother has brown eyes, and her father has blue eyes. Lavonne has brown eyes, and her husband has blue eyes. She knows that her children are equally likely to have brown or blue eyes. What is the probability that her first child will have blue eyes? If her first child has brown eyes, what is the probability that the second child will have blue eyes? $\frac{1}{2}$, $\frac{1}{2}$
5. Sara has a spinner divided into 12 sections. Each section is numbered, starting with 1 and ending with 12. Sara spins the spinner. What is the probability that she will spin a prime number? What is the probability that she will spin an odd number? What is the probability that she will spin a number divisible by 5? What is the probability that she will spin a multiple of 3? What is the probability that she will spin a multiple of 4 or 5? $\frac{5}{12}$; $\frac{1}{2}$; $\frac{1}{6}$; $\frac{1}{3}$; $\frac{5}{12}$
6. Eduardo cleaned out his school locker. At the bottom of the locker, he found 5 pencils with erasers, 1 pencil missing its eraser, 2 red pens, 3 black pens, and 4 blue pens. He placed all these items in a box and mixed them up. If he closes his eyes and picks one item out of the box, what is the probability that it is a pencil? What is the probability that it is a pen? What is the probability that it is a pencil with an eraser or a black pen? $\frac{2}{5}$; $\frac{3}{5}$; $\frac{8}{15}$

Grade 5 16 Chapter 15

15-2 Probability as a Fraction

1 Introduce

Activity Choice 1 • Hands-On

- Show students a bag of 12 cubes of the following colors: 8 red, 2 green, and 2 yellow. **How likely is it that we will draw a yellow cube? a red cube? a purple cube?** yellow cube: unlikely; red cube: likely; purple cube: impossible
- List the possible outcomes of an experiment in which a cube is drawn from the bag.
- **Are there any outcomes that are equally likely?** Drawing a green is equally as likely as drawing a yellow.

Activity Choice 2 • Literature

Introduce the lesson with *Do You Wanna Bet? Your Chance to Find Out About Probability* by Jean Cushman. For a related math activity, see p. TR61.

2 Teach

Scaffolding Questions

Draw a spinner on the board with four equal sections labeled 1–4.

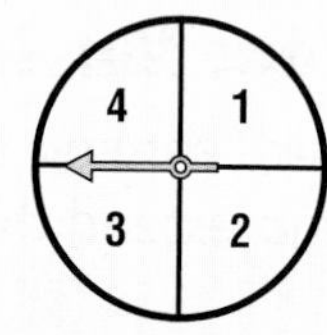

- **How many possible outcomes are on the spinner?** 4 possible outcomes
- **What fraction describes one of the sections of the spinner?** $\frac{1}{4}$
- **If the spinner is spun, what chance does it have of landing on the 3?** a 1 out of 4 chance
- **When the spinner is spun, what chance does it have of landing on an odd number? Explain.** 2 out of 4 chance; There are 2 odd numbers out of the 4 numbers on the spinner.

GET READY to Learn

Have students open their books and read the information in **Get Ready to Learn.** Introduce **favorable outcome**. As a class, work through **Examples 1 and 2.**

15-2 Probability as a Fraction

MAIN IDEA

I will use fractions to describe probability.

New Vocabulary

favorable outcome

Math Online

macmillanmh.com

- Extra Examples
- Personal Tutor
- Self-Check Quiz

GET READY to Learn

When the spinner shown is spun, what is the probability that it will land on G?

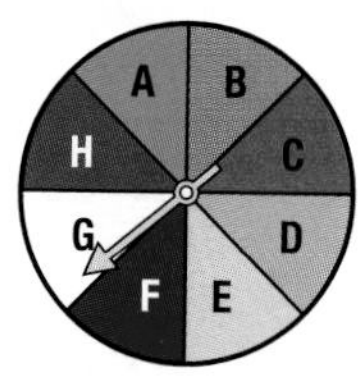

The probability that the spinner above will land on G can be described using a fraction.

$$P(G) = \frac{1}{8} \quad \begin{array}{l} \leftarrow \text{number of ways to land on G} \\ \leftarrow \text{number of possible outcomes} \end{array}$$

Since you are finding the probability of landing on G, the outcome of landing on G is called a **favorable outcome**.

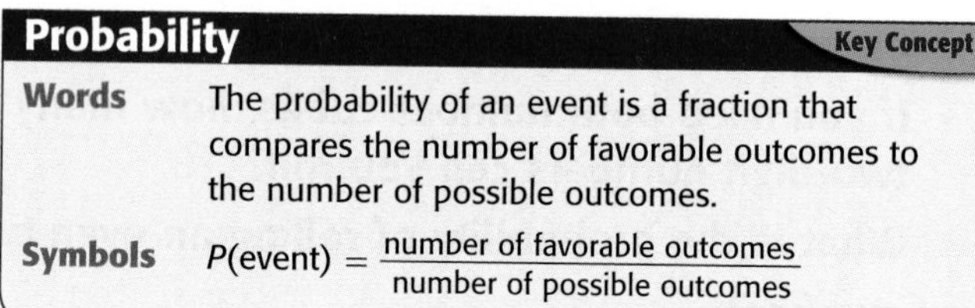

Probability — Key Concept

Words	The probability of an event is a fraction that compares the number of favorable outcomes to the number of possible outcomes.
Symbols	$P(\text{event}) = \dfrac{\text{number of favorable outcomes}}{\text{number of possible outcomes}}$

The probability of an event can be described by a number from 0 to 1.

- An event that is *impossible* has a probability of 0.
- An event that is *certain* to happen has a probability of 1.

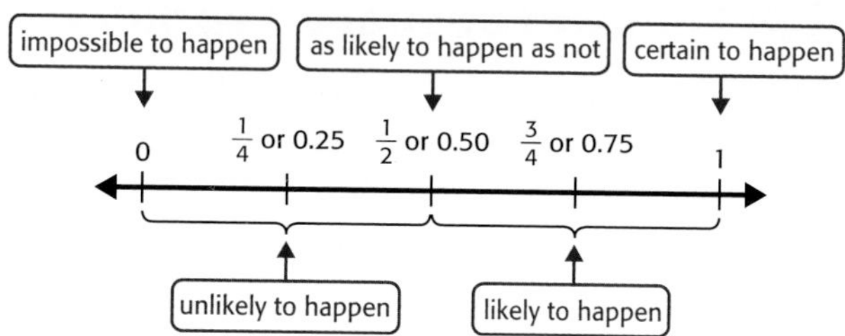

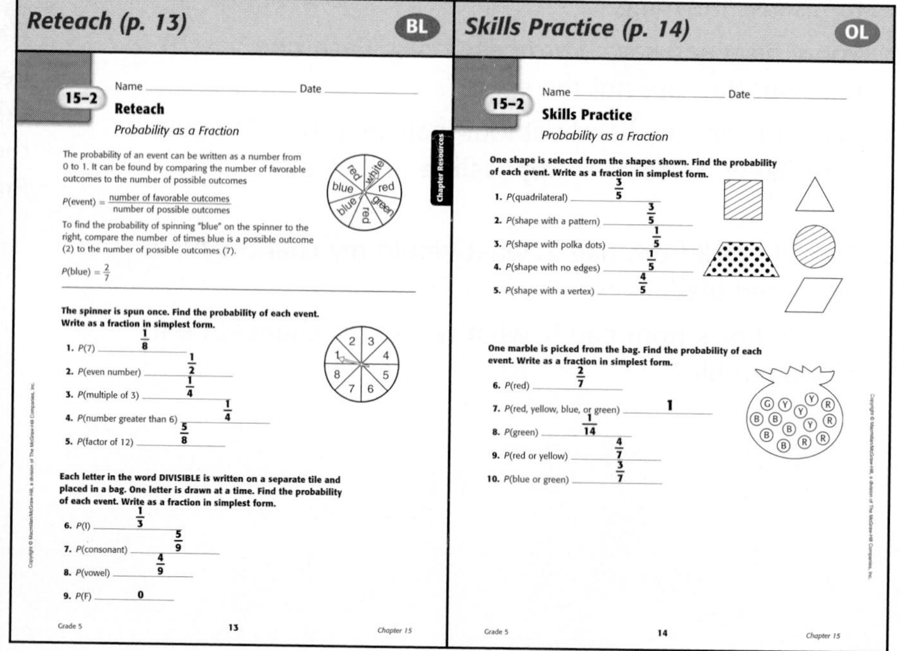

Reteach (p. 13) BL

15-2 Name ______ Date ______

Reteach

Probability as a Fraction

The probability of an event can be written as a number from 0 to 1. It can be found by comparing the number of favorable outcomes to the number of possible outcomes

$P(\text{event}) = \dfrac{\text{number of favorable outcomes}}{\text{number of possible outcomes}}$

To find the probability of spinning "blue" on the spinner to the right, compare the number of times blue is a possible outcome (2) to the number of possible outcomes (7).

$P(\text{blue}) = \frac{2}{7}$

The spinner is spun once. Find the probability of each event. Write as a fraction in simplest form.

1. $P(7)$ $\frac{1}{8}$
2. $P(\text{even number})$ $\frac{1}{2}$
3. $P(\text{multiple of 3})$ $\frac{1}{4}$
4. $P(\text{number greater than 6})$ $\frac{1}{4}$
5. $P(\text{factor of 12})$ $\frac{5}{8}$

Each letter in the word DIVISIBLE is written on a separate tile and placed in a bag. One letter is drawn at a time. Find the probability of each event. Write as a fraction in simplest form.

6. $P(\text{I})$ $\frac{1}{3}$
7. $P(\text{consonant})$ $\frac{5}{9}$
8. $P(\text{vowel})$ $\frac{4}{9}$
9. $P(\text{F})$ 0

Grade 5 — 13 — Chapter 15

Skills Practice (p. 14) OL

15-2 Name ______ Date ______

Skills Practice

Probability as a Fraction

One shape is selected from the shapes shown. Find the probability of each event. Write as a fraction in simplest form.

1. $P(\text{quadrilateral})$ $\frac{3}{5}$
2. $P(\text{shape with a pattern})$ $\frac{3}{5}$
3. $P(\text{shape with polka dots})$ $\frac{1}{5}$
4. $P(\text{shape with no edges})$ $\frac{1}{5}$
5. $P(\text{shape with a vertex})$ $\frac{4}{5}$

One marble is picked from the bag. Find the probability of each event. Write as a fraction in simplest form.

6. $P(\text{red})$ $\frac{2}{7}$
7. $P(\text{red, yellow, blue, or green})$ 1
8. $P(\text{green})$ $\frac{1}{14}$
9. $P(\text{red or yellow})$ $\frac{4}{7}$
10. $P(\text{blue or green})$ $\frac{3}{7}$

Grade 5 — 14 — Chapter 15

EXAMPLE Use Fractions to Describe Probability

Remember

P(blue) means the probability of choosing blue.

1 One marble is randomly chosen from the bag. Find the probability that a blue marble is chosen.

Use a fraction to describe the probability that a blue marble is chosen.

$P(\text{event}) = \dfrac{\text{number of favorable outcomes}}{\text{number of possible outcomes}}$

$P(\text{blue}) = \dfrac{4}{12}$ ← number of blue marbles / ← total number of marbles

$P(\text{blue}) = \dfrac{1}{3}$ Simplify.

So, the probability of choosing a blue marble is $\frac{1}{3}$.

Real-World EXAMPLE

2 BALLOONS Latanya has a bag of different colored balloons, as shown in the table. If she takes one balloon without looking, what is the probability that she gets a pink or white balloon?

Color	Number of Balloons
Pink	6
White	8
Orange	3
Green	4

There are 6 + 8 + 3 + 4 or 21 balloons in all. There are 6 + 8 or 14 balloons that are either pink or white.

$P(\text{event}) = \dfrac{\text{number of favorable outcomes}}{\text{number of possible outcomes}}$

$P(\text{pink or white}) = \dfrac{6 + 8}{6 + 8 + 3 + 4}$ ← pink or white balloons / ← total number of balloons

$= \dfrac{14}{21}$ Add.

$= \dfrac{2}{3}$ Simplify.

So, the probability that Latanya gets a pink or white balloon is $\frac{2}{3}$.

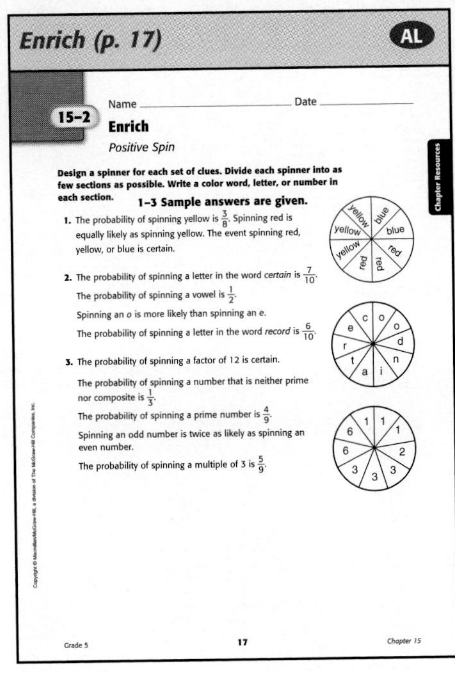

Enrich (p. 17) AL

15-2 Name ______ Date ______

Enrich

Positive Spin

Design a spinner for each set of clues. Divide each spinner into as few sections as possible. Write a color word, letter, or number in each section.

1–3 Sample answers are given.

1. The probability of spinning yellow is $\frac{3}{8}$. Spinning red is equally likely as spinning yellow. The event spinning red, yellow, or blue is certain.
2. The probability of spinning a letter in the word *certain* is $\frac{7}{10}$. The probability of spinning a vowel is $\frac{1}{2}$. Spinning an *o* is more likely than spinning an e. The probability of spinning a letter in the word *record* is $\frac{6}{10}$.
3. The probability of spinning a factor of 12 is certain. The probability of spinning a number that is neither prime nor composite is $\frac{1}{3}$. The probability of spinning a prime number is $\frac{4}{9}$. Spinning an odd number is twice as likely as spinning an even number. The probability of spinning a multiple of 3 is $\frac{5}{9}$.

Grade 5 17 Chapter 15

Use Fractions to Describe Probability

Example 2 Be sure students understand the difference between a favorable outcome and a possible outcome. Remind them that the number of favorable outcomes is a specific part of the total group and must be less than or equal to the number of possible outcomes.

ADDITIONAL EXAMPLES

1 One marble is chosen from the bag. Find the probability that a red marble is chosen. $\frac{3}{8}$

2 Jamal is making a beaded belt. Each packet of beads comes in the colors shown in the table. If Jamal takes one bead without looking, what is the probability that he gets a blue or green bead? $\frac{7}{10}$

Color	Number of Beads
Red	12
Blue	18
Green	24
Yellow	6

CHECK What You Know

As a class, have students complete Exercises 1–8 in **Check What You Know** as you observe their work.

Exercise 8 Assess student comprehension before assigning practice exercises.

BL Alternate Teaching Strategy

If students have trouble describing probability using fractions…

Then use one of these reteach options:

1 CRM **Daily Reteach Worksheet** (p. 13)

2 Give students 12 connecting cubes of which 6 are red, 4 are yellow, and 2 are green. Have students sort the cubes by color and connect them in a row. **What fraction of the cubes is red? yellow? green?** $\frac{1}{2}, \frac{1}{3}, \frac{1}{6}$ **If you put your 12 cubes in a bag and draw several times without looking, what color would you expect to choose about $\frac{1}{2}$ of the draws? $\frac{1}{3}$ of the draws? $\frac{1}{6}$ of the draws?** red; yellow; green

3 Practice

Differentiate practice using these leveled assignments for Exercises 9–31.

Level	Assignment
BL Below/ Approaching Level	9–12, 15–18, 21–22, 24
OL On Level	11–20, 22–28, 30
AL Above/Beyond Level	10–28 even, 29–31

Have students discuss and complete the Higher Order Thinking problems. For Exercise 30, encourage students to write the numbers 1–6 on their papers and circle groups of 2 numbers that have something in common before they describe their events.

WRITING IN ▸MATH Have students complete Exercise 31 in their Math Journals. You may choose to use this as an optional formative assessment.

Additional Answer

8. Sample answer: Suppose a number cube is rolled. If you want to find the probability of rolling a 2, then 2 is a favorable outcome. The numbers 1, 3, 4, 5, and 6 are outcomes that are not favorable.

COMMON ERROR!

Exercise 12 Students may have trouble identifying and determining the probability of impossible events. Have students identify if each event could possibly occur. If the event is impossible, help students to see that there are zero favorable outcomes and that 0 is the probability.

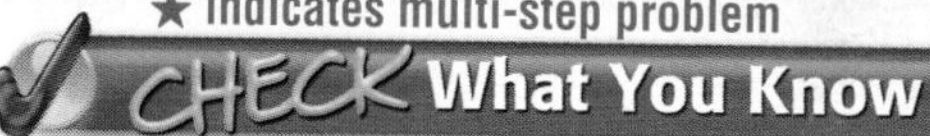

CHECK What You Know

The spinner is spun once. Find the probability of each event. Write as a fraction in simplest form. See Examples 1, 2 (p. 669)

1. $P(4)$ $\frac{1}{6}$
2. $P(\text{odd number})$ $\frac{1}{2}$
3. $P(\text{number less than 6})$ $\frac{5}{6}$
4. $P(1 \text{ or } 6)$ $\frac{1}{3}$
5. $P(9)$ 0
6. $P(\text{positive number})$ 1

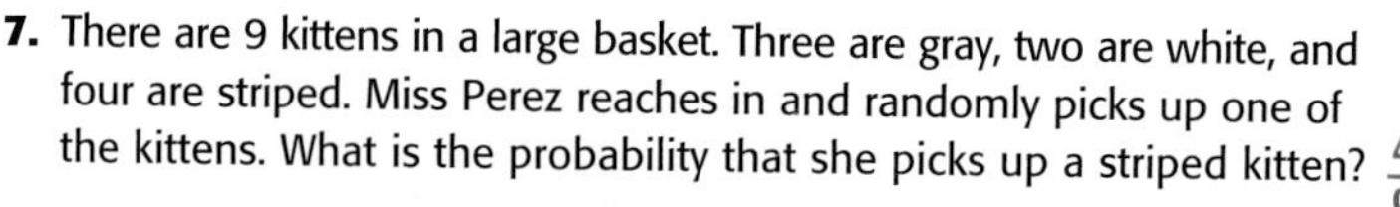

7. There are 9 kittens in a large basket. Three are gray, two are white, and four are striped. Miss Perez reaches in and randomly picks up one of the kittens. What is the probability that she picks up a striped kitten? $\frac{4}{9}$
8. **Talk About It** Use an example to describe the difference between a favorable outcome and an outcome that is not favorable. See margin.

Practice and Problem Solving

See page R40.

A number cube labeled 1 through 6 is rolled. Find the probability of each event. Write as a fraction in simplest form. See Examples 1, 2 (p. 669)

9. $P(6)$ $\frac{1}{6}$
10. $P(\text{even number})$ $\frac{1}{2}$
11. $P(\text{a number less than 5})$ $\frac{2}{3}$
12. $P(\text{a negative number})$ 0
13. $P(\text{a number less than 13})$ 1
14. $P(\text{a prime number})$ $\frac{1}{2}$

One block is drawn from the blocks shown. Find the probability of each event. Write as a fraction in simplest form. See Examples 1, 2 (p. 669)

15. $P(\text{red})$ $\frac{7}{10}$
16. $P(\text{blue})$ $\frac{1}{5}$
17. $P(\textit{not}\text{ yellow})$ $\frac{9}{10}$
18. $P(\text{yellow, red, or blue})$ 1
19. $P(\text{white})$ 0
20. $P(\text{red or yellow})$ $\frac{4}{5}$
21. A letter is chosen at random from the word FRACTION. What is the probability that the letter chosen is a consonant? $\frac{5}{8}$
22. An amusement park has a ride with 20 cars numbered 1 through 20. Leroy chooses a car at random. What is the probability that he chooses an even-numbered car? $\frac{1}{2}$

★23. Dawn has 16 pennies, 19 nickels, and 15 dimes in a piggy bank. If she turns the bank over and a coin falls out, what is the probability that it will be a dime? $\frac{3}{10}$

★**24.** A band has a drummer, 2 guitar players, a keyboard player, and a lead singer. One of their names is randomly chosen. What is the probability that it is the name of the drummer or lead singer? $\frac{2}{5}$

★**25.** Darius has a magnetic construction set that has plastic pieces in different geometric shapes, as shown in the table. If he chooses one piece from the box without looking, what is the probability that he chooses a square or pentagon? $\frac{2}{5}$

Shape	Number of Pieces
Triangle	26
Square	16
Rhombus	16
Pentagon	12

Real-World PROBLEM SOLVING

Science When one pea plant fertilizes another pea plant, a seed forms that can grow into an offspring plant. Each pea plant has two genes, one from each parent. Whether the plant grows to be tall or short depends on which pair of genes the plant has.

- If the plant has the genes TT, then it will be tall.
- If the plant has the genes Tt, then it will be tall.
- If the plant has the genes tt, then it will be short.

The table shows the possible outcomes for the offspring of two plants that each have Tt genes. Each of the four outcomes is equally likely.

Pea Plant 1 (columns), Pea Plant 2 (rows)

Genes	T	t
T	TT tall	Tt tall
t	Tt tall	tt short

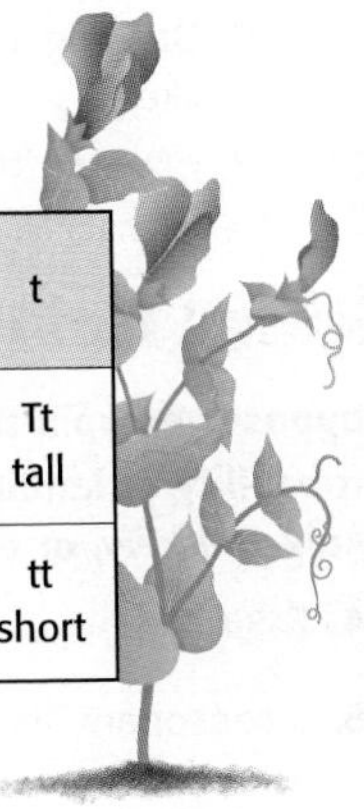

Find each probability.

26. The offspring will have the genes TT. $\frac{1}{4}$

27. The offspring will be tall. $\frac{3}{4}$

28. The offspring will have the genes Tt. $\frac{1}{2}$

H.O.T. Problems

29. OPEN ENDED Create a spinner so that the probability of landing on red is less than the probability of landing on any other single color. Use red and at least two other colors. State the probability of each color using a fraction. **29–31. See margin.**

30. CHALLENGE Suppose a 6-sided number cube is rolled. Describe two different events that have a probability of $\frac{1}{3}$.

31. WRITING IN MATH Write a real-world problem that can be solved by finding the probability. Then solve the problem.

Homework Practice (p. 15) OL BL AL

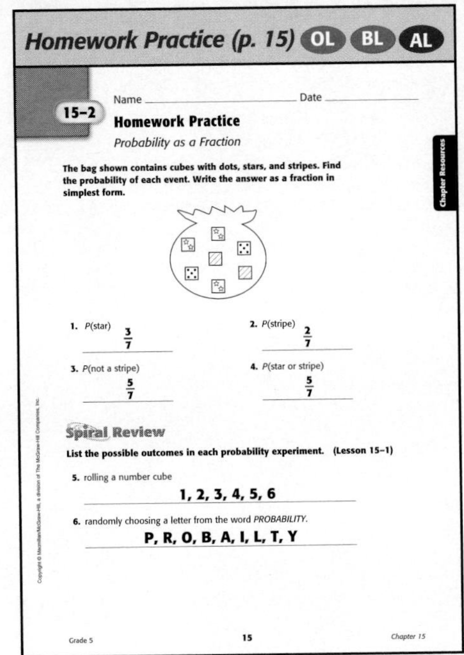
15-2 Name ____ Date ____

Homework Practice

Probability as a Fraction

The bag shown contains cubes with dots, stars, and stripes. Find the probability of each event. Write the answer as a fraction in simplest form.

1. P(star) $\frac{3}{7}$
2. P(stripe) $\frac{2}{7}$
3. P(not a stripe) $\frac{5}{7}$
4. P(star or stripe) $\frac{5}{7}$

Spiral Review

List the possible outcomes in each probability experiment. (Lesson 15–1)

5. rolling a number cube **1, 2, 3, 4, 5, 6**
6. randomly choosing a letter from the word *PROBABILITY.* **P, R, O, B, A, I, L, T, Y**

Grade 5 15 Chapter 15

4 Assess

Formative Assessment

Draw on the board: a bag with 2 squares, 8 triangles, 12 circles, and 2 ovals inside.

- **What is the probability of drawing a square? Write as a fraction in simplest form.** $\frac{1}{12}$
- **Explain how would you find the probability of drawing a triangle at random.** There are 8 triangles and 24 shapes in all. So the probability of drawing a triangle is $\frac{8}{24}$ or $\frac{1}{3}$.

Quick Check **Are students continuing to struggle with using fractions to describe probability?**

If Yes → Small Group Options (p. 668B)

If No → Independent Work Options (p. 668B)
CRM Skills Practice Worksheet (p. 14)
CRM Enrich Worksheet (p. 17)

Name the Math Have students write all of the steps of finding the probability of rolling a number less than 3 on a number cube labeled 1–6. Encourage them to use the terms favorable outcomes and possible outcomes in their explanations.

Additional Answers

29. Sample answer:

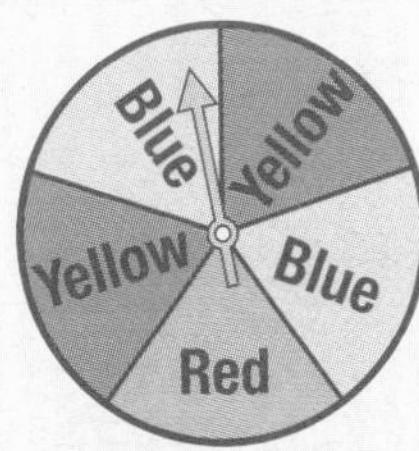

$P(\text{red}) = \frac{1}{5}$, $P(\text{blue}) = \frac{2}{5}$, $P(\text{yellow}) = \frac{2}{5}$

30. Sample answer: $P(1 \text{ or } 2) = \frac{2}{6}$ or $\frac{1}{3}$ and $P(\text{a number greater than } 4) = \frac{2}{6}$ or $\frac{1}{3}$

31. Sample answer: Ali, Bart, Celia, Daphne, and Erica are trying to decide at whose house they will study. They put their names into an envelope and randomly draw one name. What is the probability that the name drawn is Celia? Answer: $\frac{1}{5}$

Reviews Lessons 15-1 and 15-2

Assign the Test Practice problems to provide daily reinforcement of test-taking skills.

Reviews Lessons 14-3, 14-8, and 15-1

Review and assess mastery of skills and concepts from previous chapters.

32. One cube is drawn at random from the bag. Which is a true statement? (Lesson 15–1) C

A Drawing a red cube is impossible.

B Drawing an orange cube is certain.

C Drawing a red cube is unlikely.

D Drawing an orange cube is equally likely.

33. Ronada has a bag of coins, as shown in the table.

Coin	Number of Coins
Penny	10
Nickel	8
Dime	6
Quarter	3

If she takes one coin without looking, what is the probability that she will pick a dime or quarter? (Lesson 15-2) G

F $\frac{1}{4}$ **H** $\frac{1}{2}$

G $\frac{1}{3}$ **J** $\frac{3}{4}$

Spiral Review

Suppose you spin the spinner at the right. Describe the probability of landing on each letter. Write *certain, impossible, likely, unlikely,* or *equally likely*. (Lesson 15–1)

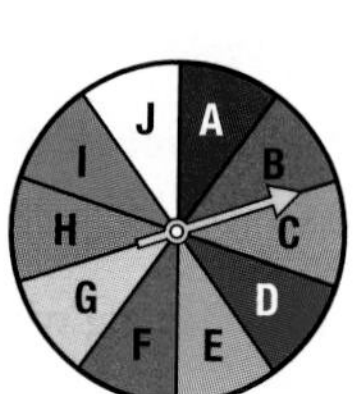

34. F unlikely

35. M impossible

36. a consonant likely

37. *not* Z certain

Determine whether you need to find the perimeter, area, or volume. Then solve. (Lesson 14-8)

38. Measurement A wall 12 feet long and 8 feet high is being painted with chalkboard paint. How much space is to be painted? area; 96 ft^2

39. Measurement Elijah is making a rectangular wooden picture frame that is $5\frac{1}{2}$ inches wide and 7 inches long. What length of wood does he need? perimeter; 25 in.

Find the area of each rectangle. (Lesson 14–3)

40. $\ell = 16$ cm, $w = 13$ cm 208 cm^2

41. $\ell = 12$ m, $w = 8$ m 96 m^2

42. $\ell = 18$ yd, $w = 16$ yd 288 yd^2

43. $\ell = 15$ ft, $w = 19$ ft 285 ft^2

Technology Activity for 15-2
Probability Experiment

MAIN IDEA

I will use technology to describe probability as a fraction.

Juana and Chad are playing a game that uses a spinner. The spinner is divided into 4 equal sections. Each section is a different color. If they spin the spinner 40 times, predict how many times the outcome would be green.

You can use the Math Tool Chest™ to conduct an experiment.

- Choose Spinner.
- Increase the number of trials to 40.
- Set speed to spin slow and click go.
- Click on the Link button in the bottom right-hand corner.
- Select table.

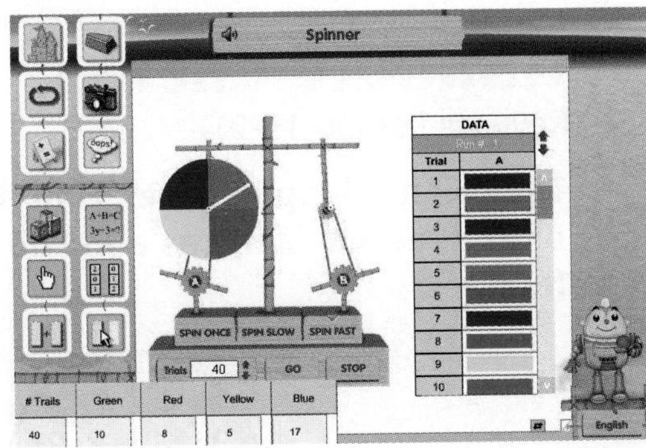

In this experiment, green was the outcome 10 times.

CHECK What You Know

1. How many times out of 40 spins would you have expected the outcome to be green? Explain. 10; $\frac{1}{4}$ of the spins should be green.
2. If you were to spin the spinner 100 times, how many outcomes would you predict to be green? 1,000 times? 25, 250
3. If you were to spin the spinner 100 times, what would you predict to be the probability for green, yellow, or blue? 75
4. WRITING IN ➤MATH Write your own real-world probability problem. Use the spinner from Math Tool Chest.™ See margin.

Using Math Tool Chest

Find Probability

- For the experiment, students may not receive an answer of exactly 10. However, their answers should be closer to 10 than 20. If not, have students repeat the activity.

Additional Answer

4. Will and Hillary are playing a game with a spinner. Will gets a point if the arrow lands on an even number. Hillary gets a point if the arrow lands on an odd number. Who has the better chance of winning? Hillary

Technology Activity for 15-2

Lesson Planner

Objective

Use technology to describe probability as a fraction.

Resources

Math Online macmillanmh.com

 Math Tool Chest

Getting Started

- The activities and exercises on p. 673 use the Spinner Tool in Math Tool Chest. They may be completed as a class, in pairs, or individually.
- Have students read each example on p. 673.
- As a class, work through the each activity in each example following the instructions on the page.

Exercise 4 Assess student comprehension using the Writing in Math question.

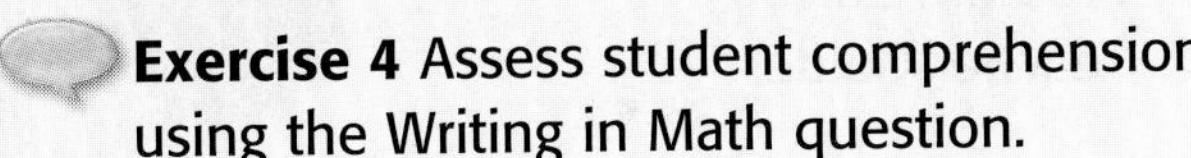

Extending the Link

- After students complete Exercises 1–4, challenge them to test each answer by using the Math Tool Chest spinner.

15-3 Problem-Solving Strategy
Make an Organized List

Lesson Planner

Objective

Solve problems by making an organized list.

Resources

Literature Connection: *Polar Bear Math* by Ann Whitehead Nagda and Cindy Bickel

Teacher Technology

Interactive Classroom • TeacherWorks

Real-World Problem Solving Library
Math and Science: *The Shifting Nature of Weather*

Use these leveled books to reinforce and extend problem-solving skills and strategies.

Leveled for:

- OL On Level
- ELL Sheltered English
- SP Spanish

For additional support, see the Real-World Problem Solving Teacher Guide.

Daily Routine

Use these suggestions before beginning the lesson on p. 674.

5-Minute Check

(Reviews Lesson 15-2)

The spinner is spun once. Find the probability of each event. Write as a fraction in simplest form.

1. $P(3)$ $\frac{1}{4}$
2. P(a number less than 3) 0
3. P(an even number) $\frac{5}{8}$
4. P(a number less than 7) 1
5. P(3 or 4) $\frac{3}{4}$

Problem of the Day

The Delicious Nut Company uses $1\frac{1}{8}$ pounds of peanuts in a recipe. The Yummy Nut Company uses 5 times as many peanuts in their recipe. How many more pounds of peanuts does Yummy Nut Company use? $4\frac{1}{2}$ lb

Differentiated Instruction

Small Group Options

VISUAL, PAIR

Option 1 Gifted and Talented AL

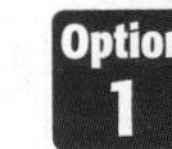

Materials: paper and pencil

- Hand students the following problem:
- *A new ice cream shop is opening and has the selection of frozen yogurt, cones, and toppings shown on the sign.* How many different one yogurt flavor, one topping cones are possible? 42

VISUAL, LOGICAL

Option 2 English Language Learners ELL

Materials: pictures of 4 shirts, 3 shorts, 4 pairs of shoes, 2 pairs of socks (cut out from magazine or drawn)
Core Vocabulary: put together, combinations, wear
Common Use Verb: to mix
Write Math This strategy helps students make an organized list of possibilities.

- Show pictures of clothes and allow students to mix them.
- Say: "How can we remember what outfits we have **put together**?" Prompt students to make a list.
- Have the students write their list in their notebook, discussing how many possible combinations can be put together.
- Repeat with other things as time permits.

Independent Work Options

LOGICAL

Option 1 Early Finishers OL AL

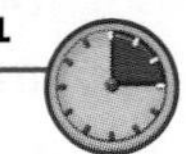

Materials: small cards, pencil and paper

- Ask students to write a number from 1–5 on each of five cards.
- Have students make an organized list as they use their cards to find all possible orders for the five numbers.
- After completing their lists, have students count and compare their orders of numbers with other students. Discuss strategies for making the list and discrepancies in the total number of orders listed.

Option 2 Student Technology

Math Online macmillanmh.com

Personal Tutor • Extra Examples

Option 3 Learning Station: Health (p. 658G)

Direct students to the Health Learning Station for opportunities to explore and extend the lesson concept.

15-3 Problem-Solving Strategy

1 Introduce

Activity Choice 1 • Review

- Pose the following problem:

  Kelsey's family drove 2,376 miles on 100 gallons of gas. How many miles per gallon is this? 23.76 miles per gallon

- **What strategy would you use to solve the problem?** *Solve a simpler problem*

Activity Choice 2 • Literature

Introduce this lesson with *Polar Bear Math* by Ann Whitehead Nagda and Cindy Bickel. For a related math activity, see p. TR61.

2 Teach

Have students read the problem. Guide them through the problem-solving steps.

Understand Using the questions, review what students know and need to find.

Plan Have them discuss their strategy.

Solve Guide students to *make an organized list* to solve the problem.

- **Why is the batting glove listed twice in the organized list?** There are two combinations of the glove and other items that cost about $15
- **How many combinations of items are there that cost about $15?** 5 combinations

Check Have students look back at the problem to make sure that the answer fits the facts given.

- **How do you know you have found all possible combinations that cost about $15?** List each item and find all possible combinations that cost $15 with that item.

COMMON ERROR!

Exercise 6 Students may "double count" items in situations where the order of the items does not matter. Have students write an organized list to show all of the combinations and then circle those that use the same items but in a different order. Students can cross off the repeated combinations and then count.

15-3 Problem-Solving Strategy

MAIN IDEA I will solve problems by making an organized list.

Edgar saw the following items at a store: a batting glove for $8.95, inline skates for $39.75, weights for $5.50 each, and a can of tennis balls for $2.75. Which items can Edgar buy and spend about $15?

Understand

What facts do you know?

- The cost of the items and that Edgar has $15 to spend.

What do you need to find?

- You need to find which items Edgar can buy and spend about $15.

Plan

One way to solve the problem is by making an organized list.

Solve

Since the inline skates cost more than $15, eliminate the inline skates as an option. Round the other costs to the nearest dollar.

Batting glove: $8.95 ≈ $9
Weights: $5.50 ≈ $6
Can of tennis balls: $2.75 ≈ $3

Start with the batting glove:

- 1 glove + 1 weight ≈ $9 + $6, or $15
- 1 glove + 2 cans of tennis balls ≈ $9 + $6, or $15

List other combinations that contain the weights:

- 2 weights + 1 can of tennis balls ≈ $12 + $3, or $15
- 1 weight + 3 cans of tennis balls ≈ $6 + $9, or $15

List any remaining combination that contain the tennis balls:

- 5 cans of tennis balls ≈ $15

Check

Check the list to be sure that all of the possible combinations of sporting good items that total no more than $15 are included. ✓

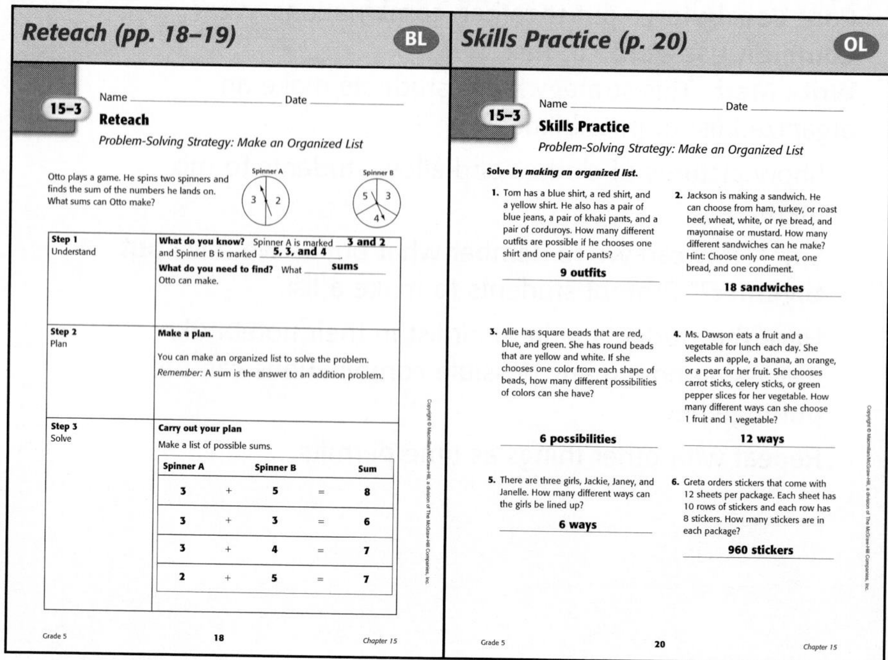

Reteach (pp. 18–19) BL

15-3 Name ______ Date ______

Reteach

Problem-Solving Strategy: Make an Organized List

Otto plays a game. He spins two spinners and finds the sum of the numbers he lands on. What sums can Otto make?

Step 1 Understand	**What do you know?** Spinner A is marked **3 and 2** and Spinner B is marked **5, 3, and 4**. **What do you need to find?** What **sums** Otto can make.
Step 2 Plan	**Make a plan.** You can make an organized list to solve the problem. *Remember:* A sum is the answer to an addition problem.
Step 3 Solve	**Carry out your plan** Make a list of possible sums.

Spinner A		Spinner B		Sum
3	+	5	=	8
3	+	3	=	6
3	+	4	=	7
2	+	5	=	7

Grade 5 18 Chapter 15

Skills Practice (p. 20) OL

15-3 Name ______ Date ______

Skills Practice

Problem-Solving Strategy: Make an Organized List

Solve by *making an organized list*.

1. Tom has a blue shirt, a red shirt, and a yellow shirt. He also has a pair of blue jeans, a pair of khaki pants, and a pair of corduroys. How many different outfits are possible if he chooses one shirt and one pair of pants? **9 outfits**
2. Jackson is making a sandwich. He can choose from ham, turkey, or roast beef, wheat, white, or rye bread, and mayonnaise or mustard. How many different sandwiches can he make? Hint: Choose only one meat, one bread, and one condiment. **18 sandwiches**
3. Allie has square beads that are red, blue, and green. She has round beads that are yellow and white. If she chooses one color from each shape of beads, how many different possibilities of colors can she have? **6 possibilities**
4. Ms. Dawson eats a fruit and a vegetable for lunch each day. She selects an apple, a banana, an orange, or a pear for her fruit. She chooses carrot sticks, celery sticks, or green pepper slices for her vegetable. How many different ways can she choose 1 fruit and 1 vegetable? **12 ways**
5. There are three girls, Jackie, Janey, and Janelle. How many different ways can the girls be lined up? **6 ways**
6. Greta orders stickers that come with 12 sheets per package. Each sheet has 10 rows of stickers and each row has 8 stickers. How many stickers are in each package? **960 stickers**

Grade 5 20 Chapter 15

ANALYZE the Strategy

Refer to the problem on the previous page. 1, 4. See Ch. 15 Answer Appendix.

1. Which items can Edgar buy and spend between $20 and $25?
2. What is the least amount of money Edgar would need if he wanted to buy the inline skates and one other item? $42.50
3. What strategy is similar to *making an organized list*? Sample answer: make a table
4. Describe how making an organized list is helpful in solving a problem.

PRACTICE the Strategy

Solve by *making an organized list*.

5. How many different products are possible using the digits 1, 3, 5, and 7? 12 products

   ▢.▢
   × ▢.▢

6. Lawrence has $0.20 in his pocket. How many different possibilities of coins could he have? List the possibilities. See Ch. 15 Answer Appendix.
7. Laura hit the dartboard shown below with 3 darts. How many total scores are possible? 10 scores

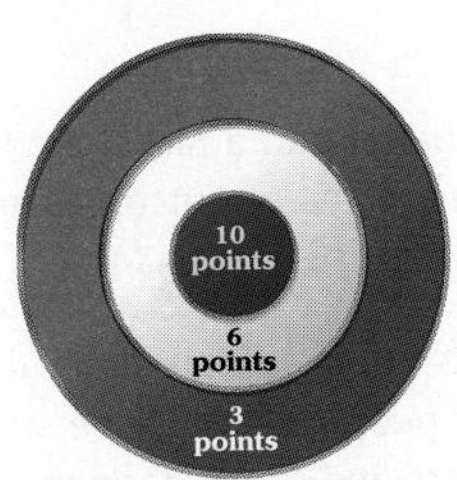

8. Awenita is selecting 2 charms for her charm bracelet. She has 4 charms to choose from. How many different arrangements of 2 charms can she choose? Describe the possibilities. See Ch. 15 Answer Appendix.
9. A red marble, a blue marble, a green marble, and a yellow marble are placed in a brown paper bag. Suppose if you take one marble out of the bag at a time. How many different orders can all four marbles be removed from the bag? List all possibilities.
   9–10. See Ch. 15 Answer Appendix.
10. Sean has the three cards shown below. How many different ways can he arrange the three letters? List them.

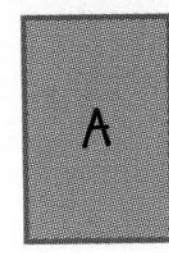

11. The following four numbers are used for employee identification at a small company: 1, 2, 3, and 4. How many different employee identification numbers can be made if 1 is always the first number? 6
    12. See Ch. 15 Answer Appendix.
12. **WRITING IN ▶MATH** Mrs. Glover has four pictures to display in a row on her desk. Explain how to use the *make an organized list* strategy to find the different ways she can display the pictures.

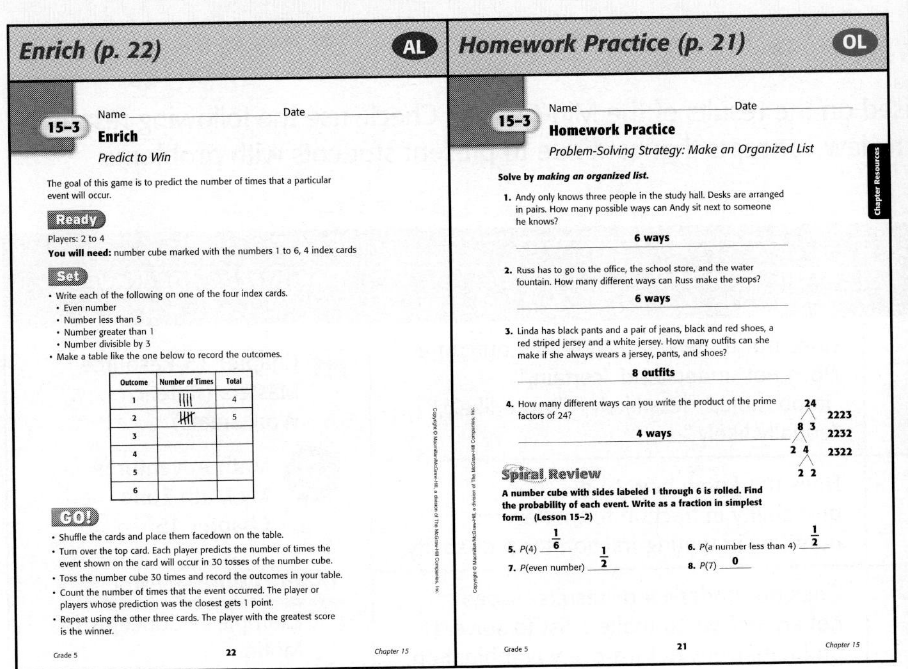

Enrich (p. 22) AL

15–3 Name ________ Date ________

Enrich

Predict to Win

The goal of this game is to predict the number of times that a particular event will occur.

Ready

Players: 2 to 4

You will need: number cube marked with the numbers 1 to 6, 4 index cards

Set

- Write each of the following on one of the four index cards.
  - Even number
  - Number less than 5
  - Number greater than 1
  - Number divisible by 3
- Make a table like the one below to record the outcomes.

Outcome	Number of Times	Total
1	||||	4
2	~~||||~~	5
3		
4		
5		
6		

GO!

- Shuffle the cards and place them facedown on the table.
- Turn over the top card. Each player predicts the number of times the event shown on the card will occur in 30 tosses of the number cube.
- Toss the number cube 30 times and record the outcomes in your table.
- Count the number of times that the event occurred. The player or players whose prediction was the closest gets 1 point.
- Repeat using the other three cards. The player with the greatest score is the winner.

Grade 5 22 Chapter 15

Homework Practice (p. 21) OL

15–3 Name ________ Date ________

Homework Practice

Problem-Solving Strategy: Make an Organized List

Chapter Resources

Solve by *making an organized list*.

1. Andy only knows three people in the study hall. Desks are arranged in pairs. How many possible ways can Andy sit next to someone he knows? **6 ways**
2. Russ has to go to the office, the school store, and the water fountain. How many different ways can Russ make the stops? **6 ways**
3. Linda has black pants and a pair of jeans, black and red shoes, a red striped jersey and a white jersey. How many outfits can she make if she always wears a jersey, pants, and shoes? **8 outfits**
4. How many different ways can you write the product of the prime factors of 24? **4 ways**

   24 → 8, 3; 8 → 2, 4; 4 → 2, 2
   2223
   2232
   2322

Spiral Review

A number cube with sides labeled 1 through 6 is rolled. Find the probability of each event. Write as a fraction in simplest form. (Lesson 15–2)

5. $P(4)$ $\frac{1}{6}$
6. $P(\text{a number less than 4})$ $\frac{1}{2}$
7. $P(\text{even number})$ $\frac{1}{2}$
8. $P(7)$ 0

Grade 5 21 Chapter 15

Analyze the Strategy Use Exercises 1–4 to analyze and discuss the problem-solving strategy.

BL Alternate Teaching Strategy

If students have trouble making an organized list…

Then use one of these reteach options:

1. CRM **Daily Reteach Worksheet** (pp. 18–19)
2. Help students use connecting cubes to show all possible orders using four colors. Have them build one row of four colors. Then, using four more cubes, set up a second row, making only one change in the order of the colors. Have students list each order as they build each row.

3 Practice

Using the Exercises

Exercises 5 and 7 ask students to determine the total number of different combinations without consideration as to order. In Exercise 5, the product of 13×57 is the same as 57×13.

4 Assess

Formative Assessment

Write the following on the board:

The names of 3 students are written on cards and placed in a box. What are all of the possible orders that the names can be drawn? ABC, ACB, BAC, BCA, CAB, CBA

- **How would you use an organized list to solve the problem?** Use different initials to represent each student and then make one change for each addition to the list.
- **Does the order of the cards matter?** yes

Quick Check **Are students continuing to struggle with using an organized list to solve problems?**

If Yes → Small Group Options (p. 674B)

If No → Independent Work Options (p. 674B)
CRM Skills Practice Worksheet (p. 20)
CRM Enrich Worksheet (p. 22)

Mid-Chapter Check

Lessons 15-1 through 15-3

Formative Assessment

Use the Mid-Chapter check to assess students' progress in the first half of the chapter.

Customize and create multiple versions of your Mid-Chapter Check and the test answer keys.

FOLDABLES Dinah Zike's Foldables

Use these lesson suggestions to incorporate the Foldables during the chapter.

Lesson 15-1 Have students conduct a probability experiment and list likely outcomes beneath the top left tab.

Lesson 15-2 Beneath the bottom left tab, have students use fractions to describe the results of the experiment.

Lesson 15-3 Have students list outcomes of the probability experiment beneath the bottom right tab. Student work, vocabulary, and notes taken during the experiment can be stored in the middle pocket of the Foldable.

Mid-Chapter Check

Lessons 15-1 through 15-3

List the possible outcomes in each probability experiment. (Lesson 15-1)

1. choosing one card without looking

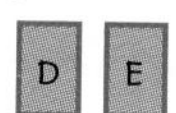

D, E, F, G

2. spinning the spinner
red, green, yellow

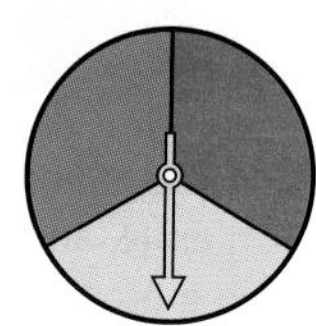

One marble is randomly drawn from the bag. Describe the probability of drawing each marble. Write *certain, impossible, likely, unlikely,* or *equally likely*. (Lesson 15-1)

3. blue unlikely

4. purple impossible

5. red, blue, green, or yellow certain

6. yellow or green likely

7. **MULTIPLE CHOICE** Desiree has 4 red pens, 6 blue pens, and 2 purple pens in her desk drawer. If she takes 1 pen from her drawer without looking, what is the probability that it will be a blue pen? (Lesson 15-2) B

A $\frac{2}{5}$ **C** $\frac{6}{11}$

B $\frac{1}{2}$ **D** $\frac{3}{4}$

One cube is drawn from the bag. Find the probability of each event. Write as a fraction in simplest form. (Lesson 15-2) 10. $\frac{1}{2}$

8. P(green) $\frac{1}{3}$ **9.** P(blue) 0

10. P(green or black) **11.** P(*not* black) $\frac{5}{6}$

12. **MULTIPLE CHOICE** The table shows the results of 20 spins on a spinner. Based on these results, what is the probability that the spinner will land on green? (Lesson 15-2) G

Color	Number of Spins
Red	7
Orange	2
Green	8
Blue	3

F $\frac{4}{5}$ **H** $\frac{1}{4}$

G $\frac{2}{5}$ **J** $\frac{1}{9}$

13. A quarter and a nickel are tossed. How many different outcomes are possible? Make a list. (Lesson 15-3)
13–15. See Ch. 15 Answer Appendix.

14. Pete's Pizza offers thin or thick crust and pepperoni, sausage, mushroom, onion, and green peppers as toppings. How many different 1-topping pizzas are possible? Make a list. (Lesson 15-3)

15. WRITING IN MATH Explain why one event may be more likely to occur than another event in an experiment.

676 Chapter 15

Data-Driven Decision Making

Based on the results of the Mid-Chapter Check, use the following resources to review concepts that continue to present students with problems.

Exercises	State/Local Standards	What's the Math?	Error Analysis	Resources for Review
1–6 Lesson 15-1		Describe the probability of an event.	Does not understand "possible outcomes." Does not understand "certain," "impossible," "less likely," "more likely," "equally likely."	CRM Chapter 15 Resource Masters (Reteach Worksheets) Math Adventures My Math Zone Chapter 15 Math Online Extra Examples • Concepts in Motion
7–12, 15 Lesson 15-2		Use fractions and probability to make a prediction.	Does not know how to describe probability in fraction form. Reverses numbers in writing fraction for probability.	
13–14 Lesson 15-3		Solve problems by making a list.	Does not understand "results." Does not know how to make a list to solve a problem. Does not list every combination.	

LESSON 15-4 Counting Outcomes

Lesson Planner

Objective

List outcomes of a probability experiment.

Vocabulary

tree diagram

Resources

Manipulatives : number cube labeled 1–6, spinner
Literature Connection: *Odds and Chances for Kids* by Manfred G. Riedel
Teacher Technology
Interactive Classroom • TeacherWorks

Focus on Math Background

It is often helpful to list all possible outcomes of an experiment, called the *sample space*, in order to compute probabilities accurately. A tree diagram is one systematic way to create such a list. For example, the following two-stage tree diagram can be used to identify the outcomes of tossing a coin and rolling a number cube: There are 12 possible outcomes when tossing a coin and rolling a number cube, each having probability $\frac{1}{12}$. The sum of the probabilities for all outcomes in a sample space must be 1.

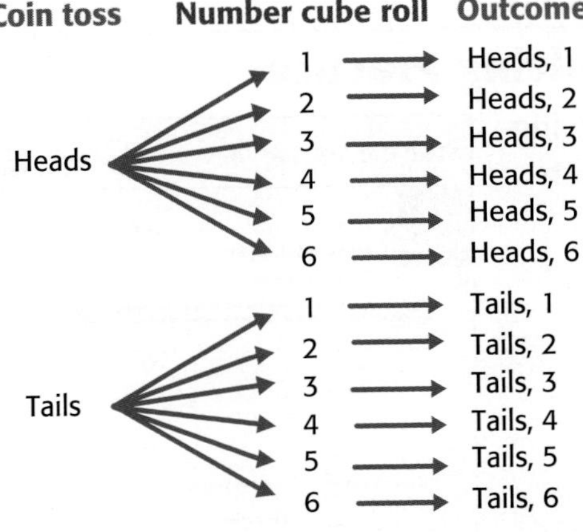

Daily Routine

Use these suggestions before beginning the lesson on p. 677.

5-Minute Check

(Reviews Lesson 15-3)

Solve by making an organized list.

A bagel shop is having a buy one, get one free special. They have cranberry, blueberry, strawberry, raisin, and pizza bagels. What are all of the possible two bagel combinations that you can buy on special? cc, cb, cs, cr, cp, bb, bs, br, bz, ss, sr, sp, rr, rp, pp

Problem of the Day

The fifth grade swim team has won $\frac{2}{3}$ of its meets and the fourth grade swim team has won $\frac{3}{5}$ of its meets. If each team attended 15 meets, how many meets have they won altogether? Show how you got your answer. 19 meets

Building Math Vocabulary

Write the lesson vocabulary words and their definitions on the board.

Ask students to write the word and its definition in their Math Journals. Have them discuss why tree diagrams are used as organizational tools in such contexts as a family tree.

Differentiated Instruction

Small Group Options

Option 1 SOCIAL, LOGICAL

Below Level BL

Materials: paper and pencil

- Have students write down one color and one number from the following chart without showing their partner.

Red	1
Blue	2
Yellow	3

- Partners work together to find all the possible outcomes of the chart.
- Ask students if it is likely or unlikely that they wrote down the same outcome.
- Students show their papers. unlikely

Option 2 AUDITORY

English Language Learners ELL

Core Vocabulary: maybe, whether or not, future
Common Use Verb: will happen

Do Math This strategy asks students questions about events in their life to introduce the concept of probability.

- Tell students probability is about something that will or will not happen. Ask them questions about their life and prompt them to answer yes, no, or maybe.
- Demonstrate to students to use thumbs up for yes, thumbs down for no, and thumb sideways for maybe.
- Ask: "Who is going to eat lunch? Who is going to go to college? Who is going to sleep after school?", etc.
- Remind students probability is whether or not something will happen.

Use this worksheet to provide additional support for English Language Learners.

English Language Learners (p. 189) ELL

52 Name ______

Tree Diagrams

Fill in the tree diagram. Use the first letter of each color.

Spinner 1 — r, b

Spinner 2 — y, g

Check students' responses.

Compound Events 189

Independent Work Options

Option 1 VISUAL, SPATIAL

Early Finishers AL

Materials: 3 pennies, pencil, paper

- Ask students to determine the probability of tossing the three coins once and landing on 3 heads, 3 tails, 2 heads and 1 tail, and 2 tails and 1 head by making a tree diagram.
- Have students make a tally chart with the headings: 3 heads, 3 tails, 2 heads and 1 tail, 2 tails and 1 head.
- Students then toss the three coins 40 times and tally their results in the correct column. After 40 tosses, have them write the fraction for the number of outcomes in each column and compare them with the probability as determined earlier.

Option 2 Tech Link

Student Technology

Math Online macmillanmh.com

Personal Tutor • Extra Examples

Option 3

Learning Station: Music (p. 658H)

Direct students to the Music Learning Station for opportunities to explore and extend the lesson concept.

Option 4

Problem-Solving Practice

Reinforce problem-solving skills and strategies with the Problem-Solving Practice worksheet.

Problem Solving (p. 26) BL OL AL

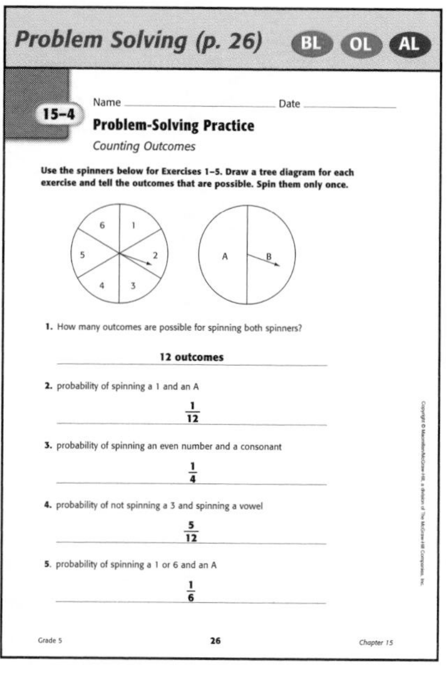

15-4 Name ______ Date ______

Problem-Solving Practice

Counting Outcomes

Use the spinners below for Exercises 1–5. Draw a tree diagram for each exercise and tell the outcomes that are possible. Spin them only once.

1. How many outcomes are possible for spinning both spinners? **12 outcomes**
2. probability of spinning a 1 and an A $\frac{1}{12}$
3. probability of spinning an even number and a consonant $\frac{1}{4}$
4. probability of not spinning a 3 and spinning a vowel $\frac{5}{12}$
5. probability of spinning a 1 or 6 and an A $\frac{1}{6}$

Grade 5 26 Chapter 15

15-4 Counting Outcomes

GET READY to Learn

The stone shown is made from topaz. Topaz stones come in different colors, such as blue, pink, or clear. They can have different cuts such as a regular cut or a star cut.

MAIN IDEA

I will list outcomes of a probability experiment.

New Vocabulary

tree diagram

Math Online

macmillanmh.com

- Extra Examples
- Personal Tutor
- Self-Check Quiz

You can use a tree diagram to show all possible color-cut combinations of topaz. A **tree diagram** is a diagram that shows all possible outcomes of an event.

Real-World EXAMPLE Use Tree Diagrams to List Outcomes

1 **GEMSTONES Refer to the information above. Make a tree diagram to show all possible color-cut combinations of the topaz described.**

The colors are blue, pink, and clear. List the colors. The cuts are a regular cut and a star cut. For each color, list the cuts.

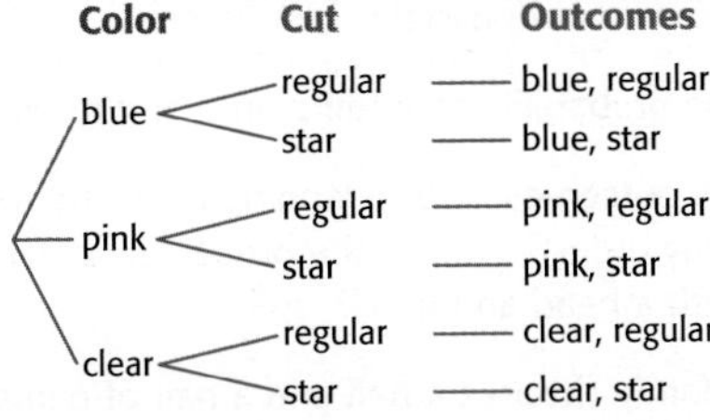

There are six possible combinations. These are listed as outcomes on the tree diagram.

Toss	Spinner
1	red
	blue
2	red
	blue
3	red
	blue
4	red
	blue
5	red
	blue
6	red
	blue

15-4 Counting Outcomes

1 Introduce

Activity Choice 1 • Hands-On

- Make and post a chart showing the following: One Topping Pizza Special: Choose Size: Small, Medium, Large; Choose Crust: Thick, Thin; Choose Topping: Veggie, Meat.
- Have students meet in small groups. Ask them to find all possible pizza combinations using the information from the chart. **How many different types of pizzas are possible?** 12
- Discuss ways students organized their data. **How did you make sure that you included all of the pizzas possible?** Answers will vary.

Activity Choice 2 • Literature

Introduce the lesson with *Odds and Chances for Kids* by Manfred G. Riedel. For a related math activity, see p. TR61.

2 Teach

Scaffolding Questions

Show students a 1–6 number cube and a spinner with 2 equal sections marked red and blue.

- **How many possible outcomes are there in rolling the number cube once? What are they?** 6; 1, 2, 3, 4, 5, 6
- **How many possible outcomes in spinning the spinner? What are they?** 2; blue and red
- **If you were to toss the number cube and spin the spinner, what would each outcome have?** a number and a color
- Draw a tree diagram on the board, omitting the outcomes. (See bottom margin at left.)
- **How can you use the diagram to find all of the possible outcomes? What are they?** Follow the arrows to find all outcomes for the tosses and spins together; 1, red; 1, blue; 2, red; 2, blue; 3, red; 3, blue; 4, red; 4, blue; 5, red; 5, blue; 6, red; 6, blue.

GET READY to Learn

Have students open their books and read the information in **Get Ready to Learn.** Introduce **tree diagram.** As a class, work through **Examples 1 and 2.**

Find Probability

Example 2 Be sure students understand that they must determine both the number of favorable outcomes and the number of all of the possible outcomes before they can determine the probability of an event.

ADDITIONAL EXAMPLES

1 Four of the coasters at Wonderland Park are Tornado, Free Fall, Big Coaster, and Cyclone. Two of the water rides are Thunder Jet Racer and Shoot the Chute. Make a tree diagram to show all possible 2-ride combinations if a person rides a coaster first and then a water ride.

Coasters	Water Rides	Outcomes
Tornado	Thunder Jet	T, TJ
	Shoot the Chute	T, SC
Free Fall	Thunder Jet	FF, TJ
	Shoot the Chute	FF, SC
Big Coaster	Thunder Jet	BC, TJ
	Shoot the Chute	BC, SC
Cyclone	Thunder Jet	C, TJ
	Shoot the Chute	C, SC

2 A spinner has 3 sections of equal size and each section is a different color. Suppose you spin a spinner two times. What is the probability of spinning the same color? $\frac{3}{9} = \frac{1}{3}$

CHECK What You Know

As a class, have students complete Exercises 1–8 in **Check What You Know** as you observe their work.

Exercise 8 Assess student comprehension before assigning practice exercises.

BL Alternate Teaching Strategy

If students have trouble drawing a tree diagram to show outcomes…

Then use one of these reteach options:

1 CRM **Daily Reteach Worksheet** (p. 23)

2 Have students use two 4-part spinners that are each labeled A, B, C, and D. Have them list all possible outcomes of spinning each spinner once. Have them list each possible outcome for A of one spinner by moving the arrow to each of the letters on the second spinner. Continue by doing the same for B, C, and D. Students can then count all of the possible outcomes.

Remember

Outcomes are written at branch ends.

EXAMPLE Find Probability

2 **Suppose you toss a penny, a nickel, and a dime. What is the probability of getting 3 heads?**

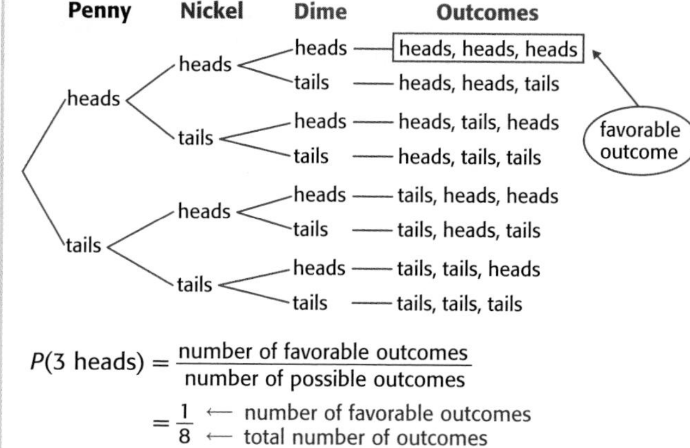

$P(3 \text{ heads}) = \frac{\text{number of favorable outcomes}}{\text{number of possible outcomes}}$

$= \frac{1}{8}$ ← number of favorable outcomes / ← total number of outcomes

CHECK What You Know

A coin is tossed twice. See Examples 1, 2 (pp. 677–678)

1. Make a tree diagram to show all possible outcomes. See margin.
2. What is the probability of tossing two tails? $\frac{1}{4}$
3. What is the probability of tossing one tail and one head? $\frac{1}{2}$

The spinner is spun and two coins are tossed. See Examples 1, 2 (pp. 677–678)

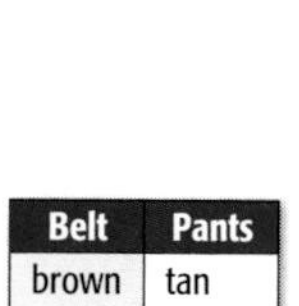

4. Make a tree diagram to show all possible outcomes. Tell how many outcomes are possible. See margin.
5. What is the probability of landing on 2 and tossing two tails? $\frac{1}{16}$
6. How many outcomes involve landing on 3 and tossing a head and a tail (in any order)? What is the probability of landing on 3 and tossing both a head and a tail? 2; $\frac{1}{8}$
7. Trent randomly chooses a belt and a pair of pants from his closet. What is the probability of choosing a black belt and black pants? $\frac{1}{6}$

Belt	Pants
brown	tan
black	black
	blue

8. Talk About It Describe the steps you take to make a tree diagram when there are two probability experiments involved. See margin.

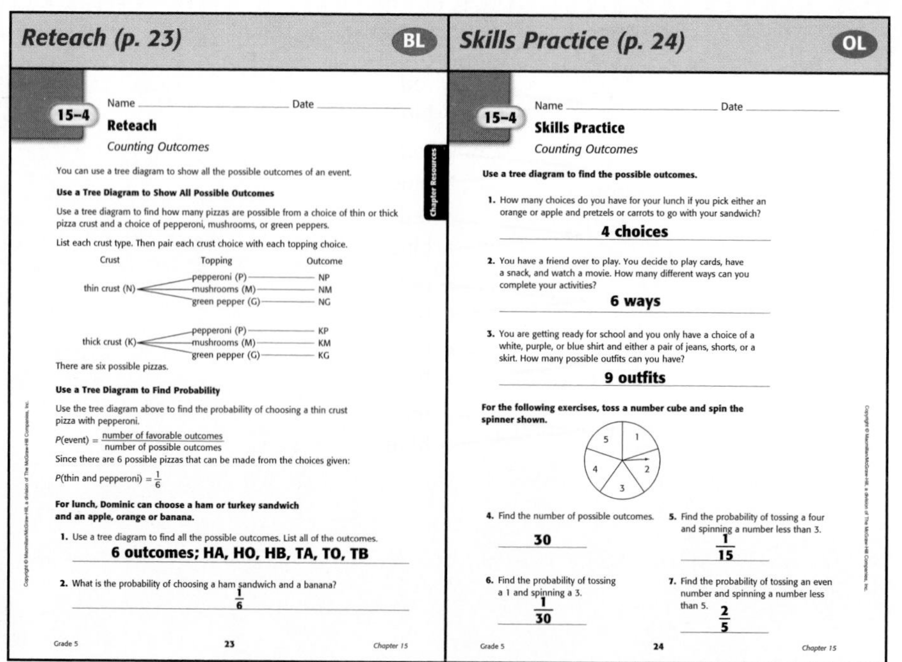

Reteach (p. 23) BL

15-4 Name ______ Date ______

Reteach

Counting Outcomes

You can use a tree diagram to show all the possible outcomes of an event.

Use a Tree Diagram to Show All Possible Outcomes

Use a tree diagram to find how many pizzas are possible from a choice of thin or thick pizza crust and a choice of pepperoni, mushrooms, or green peppers.

List each crust type. Then pair each crust choice with each topping choice.

Crust	Topping	Outcome
thin crust (N)	pepperoni (P)	NP
	mushrooms (M)	NM
	green pepper (G)	NG
thick crust (K)	pepperoni (P)	KP
	mushrooms (M)	KM
	green pepper (G)	KG

There are six possible pizzas.

Use a Tree Diagram to Find Probability

Use the tree diagram above to find the probability of choosing a thin crust pizza with pepperoni.

$P(\text{event}) = \frac{\text{number of favorable outcomes}}{\text{number of possible outcomes}}$

Since there are 6 possible pizzas that can be made from the choices given:

$P(\text{thin and pepperoni}) = \frac{1}{6}$

For lunch, Dominic can choose a ham or turkey sandwich and an apple, orange or banana.

1. Use a tree diagram to find all the possible outcomes. List all of the outcomes. **6 outcomes; HA, HO, HB, TA, TO, TB**
2. What is the probability of choosing a ham sandwich and a banana? $\frac{1}{6}$

Grade 5 23 Chapter 15

Skills Practice (p. 24) OL

15-4 Name ______ Date ______

Skills Practice

Counting Outcomes

Use a tree diagram to find the possible outcomes.

1. How many choices do you have for your lunch if you pick either an orange or apple and pretzels or carrots to go with your sandwich? **4 choices**
2. You have a friend over to play. You decide to play cards, have a snack, and watch a movie. How many different ways can you complete your activities? **6 ways**
3. You are getting ready for school and you only have a choice of a white, purple, or blue shirt and either a pair of jeans, shorts, or a skirt. How many possible outfits can you have? **9 outfits**

For the following exercises, toss a number cube and spin the spinner shown.

4. Find the number of possible outcomes. **30**
5. Find the probability of tossing a four and spinning a number less than 3. $\frac{1}{15}$
6. Find the probability of tossing a 1 and spinning a 3. $\frac{1}{30}$
7. Find the probability of tossing an even number and spinning a number less than 5. $\frac{2}{5}$

Grade 5 24 Chapter 15

18. See Ch. 15 Answer Appendix

Practice and Problem Solving

See page R41.

A 4-sided die, called a tetrahedron, numbered 1 through 4 is tossed and a coin is tossed. See Examples 1, 2 (pp. 677–678)

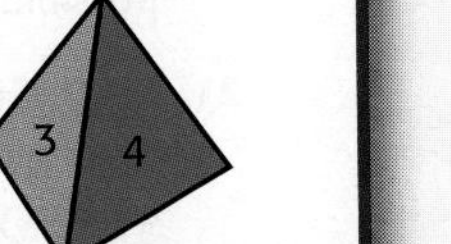

9. Make a tree diagram to show all possible outcomes. Tell how many outcomes are possible. See Ch. 15 Answer Appendix.
10. What is the probability of tossing an odd number and a tail? $\frac{1}{4}$

The two spinners at the right are spun. See Examples 1, 2 (pp. 677–678)

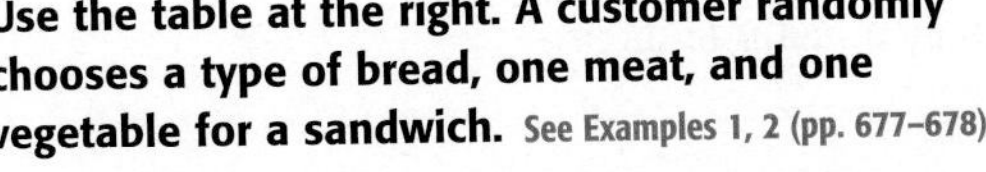

11. Make a tree diagram to show all possible outcomes. How many outcomes are possible? See Ch. 15 Answer Appendix.
12. What is the probability of spinning an A and a 1? $\frac{1}{6}$
13. What is the probability of spinning *not* C? $\frac{2}{3}$

Use the table at the right. A customer randomly chooses a type of bread, one meat, and one vegetable for a sandwich. See Examples 1, 2 (pp. 677–678)

Bread	Meat	Vegetable
white	turkey	lettuce
wheat	ham	tomato
	beef	

14. Make a tree diagram to show all possible outcomes. How many outcomes are possible? See Ch. 15 Answer Appendix.
15. How many sandwiches include wheat bread and turkey? 2
16. What is the probability that the sandwich has ham and tomato? $\frac{1}{6}$
17. A store has 6 different shades of blue paint. The paint can be either oil or latex. The shine can be gloss, semi-gloss, or flat. How many combinations include blue latex paint? 18

Data File

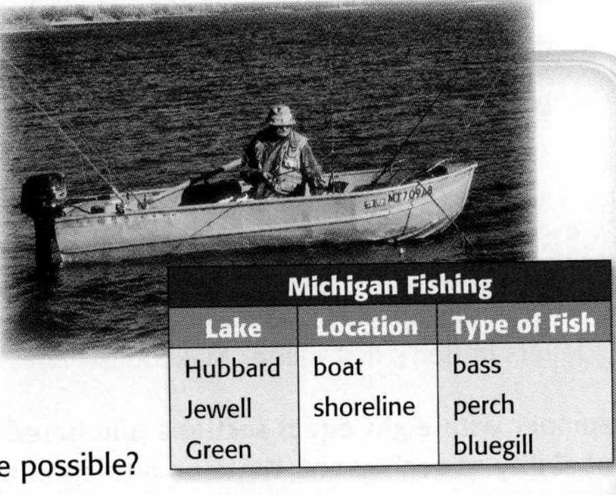

Fishing is a popular sport in Michigan. There are over 11,000 inland lakes and 3,126 miles of Great Lakes shoreline. The table shows some different fishing possibilities that people could choose when visiting a Michigan lake.

Michigan Fishing		
Lake	**Location**	**Type of Fish**
Hubbard	boat	bass
Jewell	shoreline	perch
Green		bluegill

18. Make a tree diagram to show all different fishing possibilities.
19. How many different ways to fish are possible? 18 ways

Additional Answers

1.

Toss 1	Toss 2	Outcomes
heads	heads	heads, heads
	tails	heads, tails
tails	heads	tails, heads
	tails	tails, tails

4 outcomes

Enrich (p. 27) AL

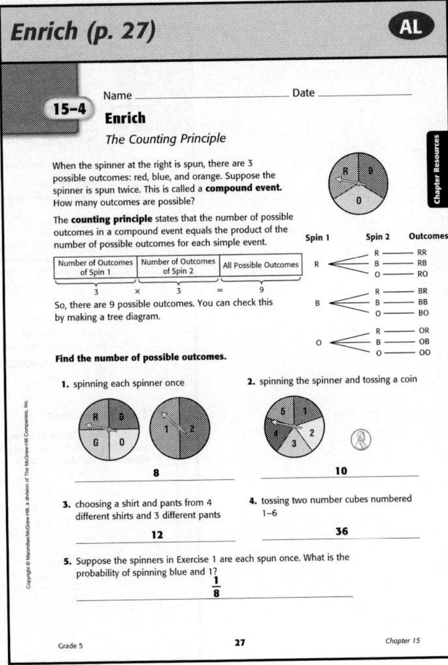
15-4 Name ______ Date ______

Enrich

The Counting Principle

When the spinner at the right is spun, there are 3 possible outcomes: red, blue, and orange. Suppose the spinner is spun twice. This is called a **compound event.** How many outcomes are possible?

The **counting principle** states that the number of possible outcomes in a compound event equals the product of the number of possible outcomes for each simple event.

Number of Outcomes of Spin 1	Number of Outcomes of Spin 2	All Possible Outcomes
3 ×	3 =	9

So, there are 9 possible outcomes. You can check this by making a tree diagram.

Spin 1	Spin 2	Outcomes
R	R, B, O	RR, RB, RO
B	R, B, O	BR, BB, BO
O	R, B, O	OR, OB, OO

Find the number of possible outcomes.

1. spinning each spinner once 8
2. spinning the spinner and tossing a coin 10
3. choosing a shirt and pants from 4 different shirts and 3 different pants 12
4. tossing two number cubes numbered 1–6 36
5. Suppose the spinners in Exercise 1 are each spun once. What is the probability of spinning blue and 1? $\frac{1}{8}$

Grade 5 27 Chapter 15

3 Practice

Differentiate practice using these leveled assignments for Exercises 9–22.

Level	Assignment
BL Below/Approaching Level	9–12, 14–17, 18–19
OL On Level	11–19, 21
AL Above/Beyond Level	10–18 even, 20–22

Have students discuss and complete the Higher Order Thinking problems. For Exercise 20, have students draw a tree diagram and determine the probability of each event before determining the probability of the event they have chosen.

WRITING IN MATH Have students complete Exercise 22 in their Math Journals. You may choose to use this exercise as an optional formative assessment.

4.

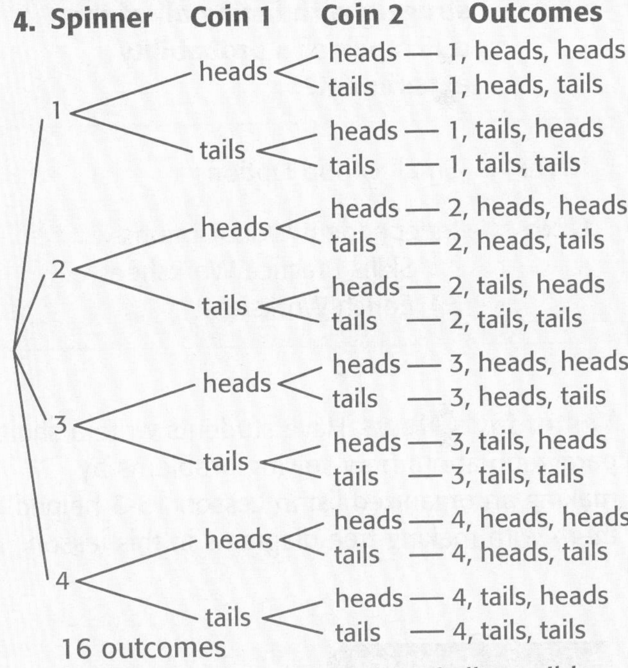

8. Sample answer: Make a list of all possible outcomes of the first experiment. Determine the number of possible outcomes of the second experiment. Draw that number of branches from each outcome in the first column. Write the outcomes of the second probability experiment next to each branch.

COMMON ERROR!

Exercises 14, 17, and 18 Students may struggle with drawing a correct tree diagram when there are three or more events. Encourage students to work in a step-by-step fashion as they determine all of the possible outcomes for each of the events, drawing lines on their tree diagram only when they are listing the possible outcomes.

4 Assess

Formative Assessment

Pose the following scenario: *Suppose you toss a penny three times.*

- **How would you find the probability of landing on two heads and one tail?** Make a tree diagram to show heads and tails for each coin toss to find the number of possible outcomes for the denominator, count the number of times there are two heads and one tail to find the number of favorable outcomes for the numerator and write the fraction in simplest form.
- **What is the probability of landing on two heads and one tail?** $\frac{3}{8}$

Quick Check

Are students continuing to struggle with listing all of the outcomes of a probability experiment?

If Yes → Small Group Options (p. 677B)

If No → Independent Work Options (p. 677B)
CRM Skills Practice Worksheet (p. 24)
CRM Enrich Worksheet (p. 27)

Yesterday's News Have students write a short paragraph about how solving problems by making an organized list in Lesson 15-3 helped them with making tree diagrams in this lesson.

TEST Practice

Reviews Lessons 15-3 and 15-4

Assign the Test Practice problems to provide daily reinforcement of test-taking skills.

Spiral Review

Reviews Lessons 15-2 and 15-3

Review and assess mastery of skills and concepts from previous chapters.

Additional Answer

21. Sample answer: Makayla; there are 4 outcomes possible and only one of those outcomes will have 2 heads.

H.O.T. Problems

20. **OPEN ENDED** Suppose two number cubes are rolled. Describe one possible event. What is the probability of the event occurring? Sample answer: rolling two 6s, the probability is $\frac{1}{36}$
21. **FIND THE ERROR** Jack and Makayla are finding the probability of tossing heads twice when a dime is tossed twice. Who is correct? Explain your reasoning. See margin.

Jack
$\frac{1}{2}$, since each toss has a probability of $\frac{1}{2}$.

Makayla
$\frac{1}{4}$, since there is one outcome out of four that has two heads.

22. **WRITING IN MATH** Describe how the number of possible outcomes changes if a spinner is spun twice rather than once. The number of outcomes increases by a factor of itself.

TEST Practice

23. The eye color of an Abyssinian cat can be green, blue, gold, or hazel. Their fur color can be brown or black. How many different eye and fur color combinations are possible? (Lessons 15-3 and 15-4) C

A 4
B 6
C 8
D 10

24. The spinners are spun once. What is the probability of spinning a 5 and a B? (Lesson 15-4) F

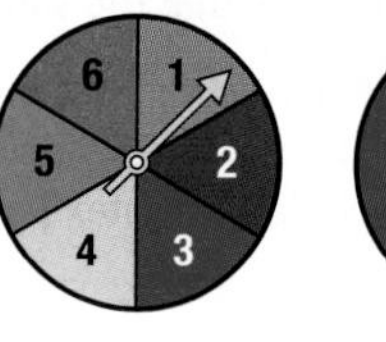

F $\frac{1}{12}$
G $\frac{1}{6}$
H $\frac{1}{5}$
J $\frac{2}{7}$

Spiral Review

25. How many different 3-letter arrangements can be made from the letters in Ben's first name? Make a list. (Lesson 15-3) 6; BEN, BNE, EBN, ENB, NEB, NBE

A spinner with eight equal sections numbered 1–8 is spun once. Find the probability of each event. Write as a fraction in simplest form. (Lesson 15-2)

26. $P(6)$ $\frac{1}{8}$
27. $P(10)$ 0
28. $P(7 \text{ or } 8)$ $\frac{1}{4}$

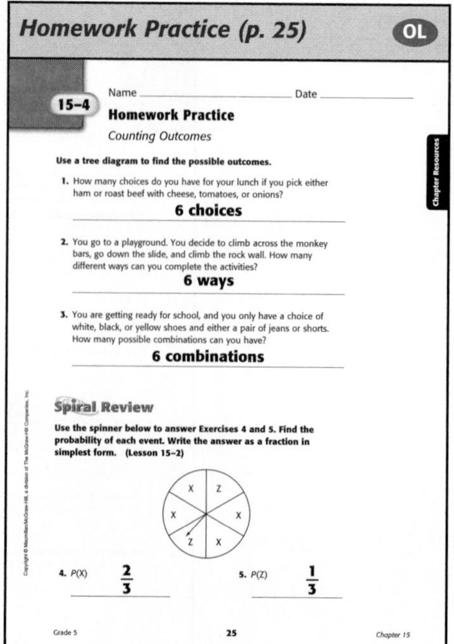

Homework Practice (p. 25) OL

Name ________________ Date ________

15-4 **Homework Practice**
Counting Outcomes

Chapter Resources

Use a tree diagram to find the possible outcomes.

1. How many choices do you have for your lunch if you pick either ham or roast beef with cheese, tomatoes, or onions? **6 choices**
2. You go to a playground. You decide to climb across the monkey bars, go down the slide, and climb the rock wall. How many different ways can you complete the activities? **6 ways**
3. You are getting ready for school, and you only have a choice of white, black, or yellow shoes and either a pair of jeans or shorts. How many possible combinations can you have? **6 combinations**

Spiral Review

Use the spinner below to answer Exercises 4 and 5. Find the probability of each event. Write the answer as a fraction in simplest form. (Lesson 15-2)

4. $P(X)$ $\frac{2}{3}$
5. $P(Z)$ $\frac{1}{3}$

Bean Game

Counting Outcomes

Get Ready!

Players: 2, 3, or 4

You will need: 6 dry beans
bowl
marker

Get Set!

Color one side of each bean with the marker.

Go!

The first player places the beans in the bowl, gently tosses the beans into the air, and catches them in the bowl. Points are scored as follows.

- If all of the beans land with the unmarked sides up, score 6 points.
- If all of the beans land with the marked sides up, score 4 points.
- If exactly one bean lands with the marked or unmarked side up, score 2 points.
- If three beans are marked and three beans are unmarked, score 1 point.

If a toss scores points, the player takes another turn. If a toss does not score any points, it is the next player's turn.

The winner is the player with the most points after a given number of rounds.

Game Time Bean Game **681**

Bean Game

Math Concept: Counting Outcomes

Materials: 6 dry lima beans, bowl, marker

Introduce the game on p. 681 to your students to play as a class, in small groups, or at a learning workstation to review concepts introduced in this chapter.

Instructions

- Students play in groups of 2, 3, or 4. They color one side of each bean with a marker, as shown on page 681.
- Player 1 places the beans in the bowl, gently tosses the beans into the air, and catches them in the bowl.
- The point system is as follows: 6 points for all beans landing with unmarked sides up, 4 points for all beans landing with marked sides up, 2 points if exactly one bean lands with marked or unmarked side up and the rest land in the opposite fashion, and 1 point if three beans land marked and three land unmarked.
- If Player 1 scores points, he or she takes another turn. If no points are scored, the next player takes a turn.
- Play continues for a given number of rounds. The player with the most points wins.

Extend the Game

Have students play more rounds, or have the winner of each group play the winner of another group.

Differentiated Practice

Use these leveled suggestions to differentiate the game for all learners.

Level	Assignment
BL Below/ Approaching Level	Students use a chart to help them count outcomes and calculate points.
OL On Level	Have students play the game with the rules as written.
AL Above/Beyond Level	Students take the outcomes of their turns and express them as fractions of the total number of turns they took.

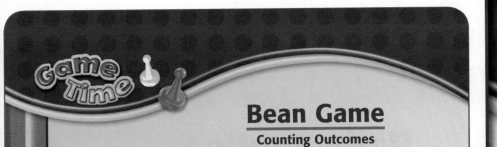

Choose a Strategy

Lesson Planner

Objective

Choose the best strategy to solve a problem.

Resources

Materials: pencil and paper

Teacher Technology

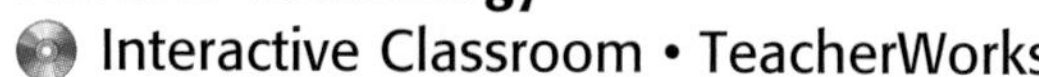
Interactive Classroom • TeacherWorks

Real-World Problem Solving Library
Math and Science: *The Shifting Nature of Weather*

Use these leveled books to reinforce and extend problem-solving skills and strategies.

Leveled for:

- OL On Level
- ELL Sheltered English
- SP Spanish

For additional support, see the Real-World Problem Solving Teacher Guide.

Daily Routine

Use these suggestions before beginning the lesson on p. 682.

5-Minute Check

(Reviews Lesson 15-4)

A restaurant offers several choices on their breakfast menu. For eggs the choices are scrambled, fried, or an omelet. The choices for breads are wheat toast or a croissant. Customers may choose either grape or tomato juice.

1. Make a tree diagram to show all of the different breakfasts possible if eggs, bread, and juice are ordered.

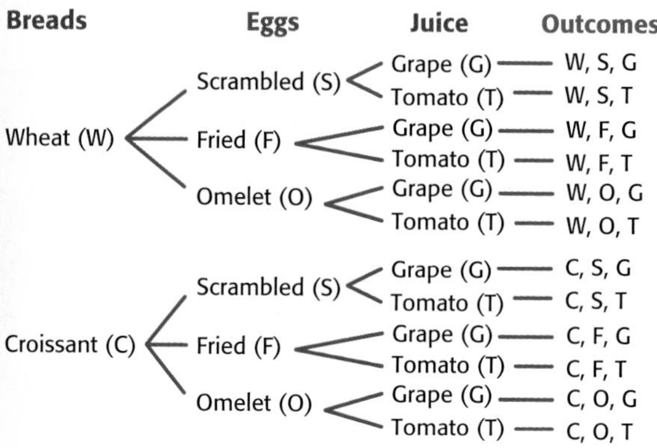

2. If a breakfast with a bread, an egg dish, and a juice was chosen at random, what is the probability that it would have wheat toast, an omelet, and grape juice? $\frac{1}{6}$

Problem of the Day

Two sides of an octagonal flower garden are each 3.8 meters long. The rest the sides measure 2.6 meters each. How much fencing material will be needed to enclose the garden? Show your work. 23.2 meters

Differentiated Instruction

Small Group Options

Option 1 VISUAL, PAIR

Below Level BL

Materials: paper and pencil

- Hand this problem to students to solve:

> Anna and her classmates are going on a Saturday field trip. So far Anna has earned $25 babysitting to help pay her way. The bus costs $9, the event ticket costs $10 and food will cost $7.

- **Has she earned enough to pay for the trip?** no
- **If the souvenirs cost $6, how much more must she earn for this trip?** $7

Option 2 SOCIAL

English Language Learners ELL

Materials: poster board
Core Vocabulary: different strategy, solve using, present
Common Use Verb: illustrates

Hear Math This strategy incorporates cooperative and visual learning to reference problem-solving strategies.

- Divide the class into four groups and assign a different strategy for each group.
- Show a problem from a previous lesson and prompt students to solve it using the assigned strategy.
- Have groups make a poster that illustrates their problem-solving steps.
- As time permits, ask the students to present their poster and explain the strategy process to the class.

Independent Work Options

Option 1 LINGUISTIC

Early Finishers OL 

Materials: index cards, pencils

- Have students choose a topic which includes at least three choices someone might have to make in the real world and write a word problem about the choices.
- Then have students exchange cards and solve the problem they received by making an organized list or a tree diagram. They may return the cards to the writers of the original problem for checking.

Option 2

Student Technology

Math Online macmillanmh.com

Personal Tutor • Extra Examples

Option 3

Learning Station: Social Studies (p. 658H)

Direct students to the Social Students Learning Station for opportunities to explore and extend the lesson concept.

1 Introduce

Activity • Review

- Present students with the following problem:
  For a class project, Cam has to choose two partners out of five of his friends: Alita, Wendy, Bao, Lily, and Patrick. How many possible groups can he make?
- Remind students how to make organized lists. Ask for 5 volunteers to each wear a nametag of one of Cam's friends. Show students the possible pairs Cam could work with.
- **How many groups can be made with Cam and two of his friends?** 10

2 Teach

Have students read the problem on making a class flag. Guide them through the problem-solving steps.

Understand Using the questions, review what students know and need to find.

Plan Have them discuss their strategy.

Solve Guide students to use the *draw a picture* strategy to solve the problem.

- **Where is the star placed in each flag?** in the center of the middle stripe
- **What other strategy do you need to use make sure that you have included all of the possible flags in your drawing? Explain.** Sample answer: *make an organized list*

Check Have students look back at the problem to make sure that the answer fits the facts given.

COMMON ERROR!

Exercise 3 Some students may have difficulty with visual discrimination. Have these students verbalize what they are seeing, and guide them in solving the problems.

15-5 Problem-Solving Investigation

MAIN IDEA I will choose the best strategy to solve a problem.

P.S.I. TEAM +

DREW: I am making a flag to represent our class at the school assembly. The flag must have three solid-colored horizontal stripes (one red, one blue, and one yellow) with a gray star in the center of the middle stripe.

YOUR MISSION: Find how many different flags Drew can make.

Understand	You know that the flag will have a red, blue, and yellow stripe and that a star will be in the center of the middle stripe. You need to find how many different flags Drew can make with three stripes and one star.
Plan	You can use the *make a picture* strategy.
Solve	Continue drawing flags until no more flags can be made. After drawing the flags, you find that 6 different flags can be made with 3 horizontal stripes with a star in the center of the middle stripe.
Check	Look back. Make a list of all the possible flags. RBY, RYB, YBR, YRB, BYR, BRY Since there are 6 items in the list and 6 different flags, the answer is correct. ✓

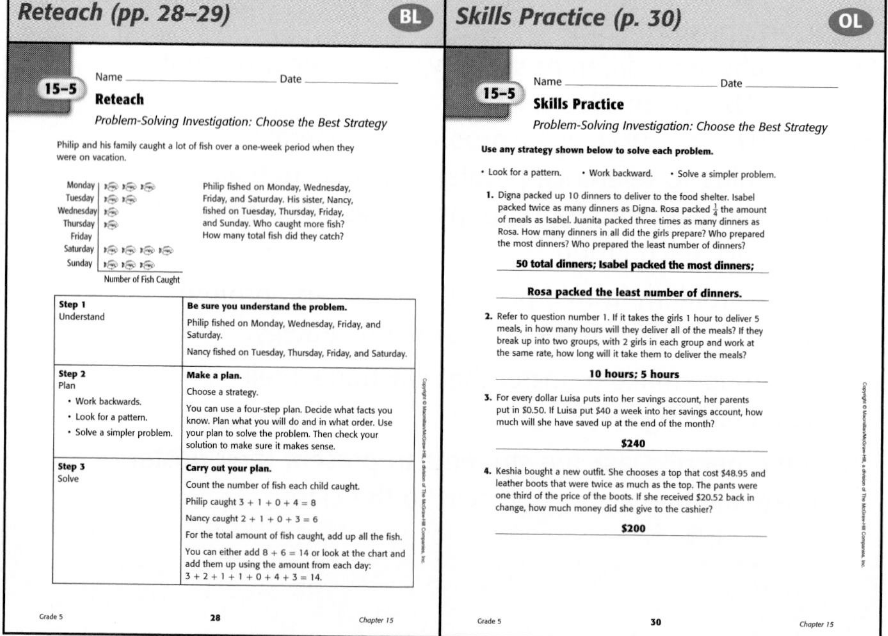

Reteach (pp. 28–29) BL

15-5 Name ______ Date ______

Reteach

Problem-Solving Investigation: Choose the Best Strategy

Philip and his family caught a lot of fish over a one-week period when they were on vacation.

Philip fished on Monday, Wednesday, Friday, and Saturday. His sister, Nancy, fished on Tuesday, Thursday, Friday, and Sunday. Who caught more fish? How many total fish did they catch?

Step 1 Understand	**Be sure you understand the problem.** Philip fished on Monday, Wednesday, Friday, and Saturday. Nancy fished on Tuesday, Thursday, Friday, and Saturday.
Step 2 Plan • Work backwards. • Look for a pattern. • Solve a simpler problem.	**Make a plan.** Choose a strategy. You can use a four-step plan. Decide what facts you know. Plan what you will do and in what order. Use your plan to solve the problem. Then check your solution to make sure it makes sense.
Step 3 Solve	**Carry out your plan.** Count the number of fish each child caught. Philip caught $3 + 1 + 0 + 4 = 8$ Nancy caught $2 + 1 + 0 + 3 = 6$ For the total amount of fish caught, add up all the fish. You can either add $8 + 6 = 14$ or look at the chart and add them up using the amount from each day: $3 + 2 + 1 + 1 + 0 + 4 + 3 = 14$.

Grade 5 28 Chapter 15

Skills Practice (p. 30) OL

15-5 Name ______ Date ______

Skills Practice

Problem-Solving Investigation: Choose the Best Strategy

Use any strategy shown below to solve each problem.

• Look for a pattern. • Work backward. • Solve a simpler problem.

1. Digna packed up 10 dinners to deliver to the food shelter. Isabel packed twice as many dinners as Digna. Rosa packed $\frac{1}{4}$ the amount of meals as Isabel. Juanita packed three times as many dinners as Rosa. How many dinners in all did the girls prepare? Who prepared the most dinners? Who prepared the least number of dinners?

   50 total dinners; Isabel packed the most dinners;

   Rosa packed the least number of dinners.

2. Refer to question number 1. If it takes the girls 1 hour to deliver 5 meals, in how many hours will they deliver all of the meals? If they break up into two groups, with 2 girls in each group and work at the same rate, how long will it take them to deliver the meals?

   10 hours; 5 hours

3. For every dollar Luisa puts into her savings account, her parents put in $0.50. If Luisa put $40 a week into her savings account, how much will she have saved up at the end of the month?

   $240

4. Keshia bought a new outfit. She chooses a top that cost $48.95 and leather boots that were twice as much as the top. The pants were one third of the price of the boots. If she received $20.52 back in change, how much money did she give to the cashier?

   $200

Grade 5 30 Chapter 15

682 Chapter 15 Use Probability to Make Predictions

Mixed Problem Solving

See page R40.

Use any strategy shown below to solve each problem.

PROBLEM-SOLVING STRATEGIES
- Make an organized list.
- Draw a picture.
- Solve a simpler problem.

1. Vince is ordering lunch from Taco Express. The choices are shown in the table below.

Tacos	Filling	Salsa
soft	beef	mild
hard	chicken	medium
	pork	hot
	vegetables	

How many different possibilities are there if Vince orders a taco with one filling and one type of salsa? **24 possibilities**

2. **Geometry** A window design is made from a rectangle divided by two diagonals. How many sections are there? What are their shapes? **4 sections; triangles**

3. Isabel is playing a game with the set of cards shown below. She takes one card from this set without looking. What is the probability that the card will have either a triangle or circle on it? $\frac{2}{3}$

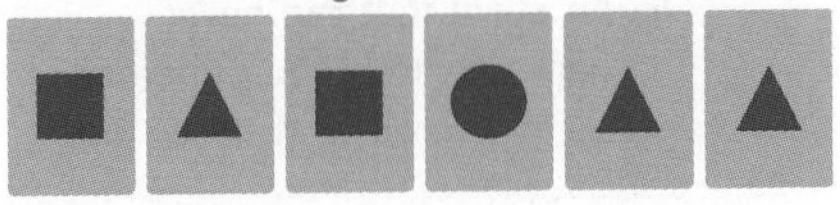

4. Monya has three different shirts and two pairs of pants. She wants to make different outfits, each with one pair of pants and one shirt. How many different outfits can she make? **6 outfits**

5. **Geometry** A student divides a triangle into sections by drawing a line from each vertex to the center of the opposite side. How many sections are there, and what are their shapes? **6 sections; triangles**

6. **Measurement** Three students can make 9 posters in 45 minutes. How many posters can 6 students make at the same rate in 90 minutes? **36 posters**

7. Logan is buying a digital music player. The choices are shown below.

Color	Capabilities
black	music
blue	music and photos
pink	music, photos, and movies
silver	
white	

How many different possibilities of color and capabilities are there? **15 possibilities**

8. **WRITING IN MATH** Jeff said that since 3 + 3 = 6, there are 6 different possibilities of cereal and juice for breakfast. Tell what mistake he made. Explain how to correct it. **See Ch. 15 Answer Appendix.**

Cereal	Juice
oatmeal	orange
corn flakes	apple
wheat squares	pineapple

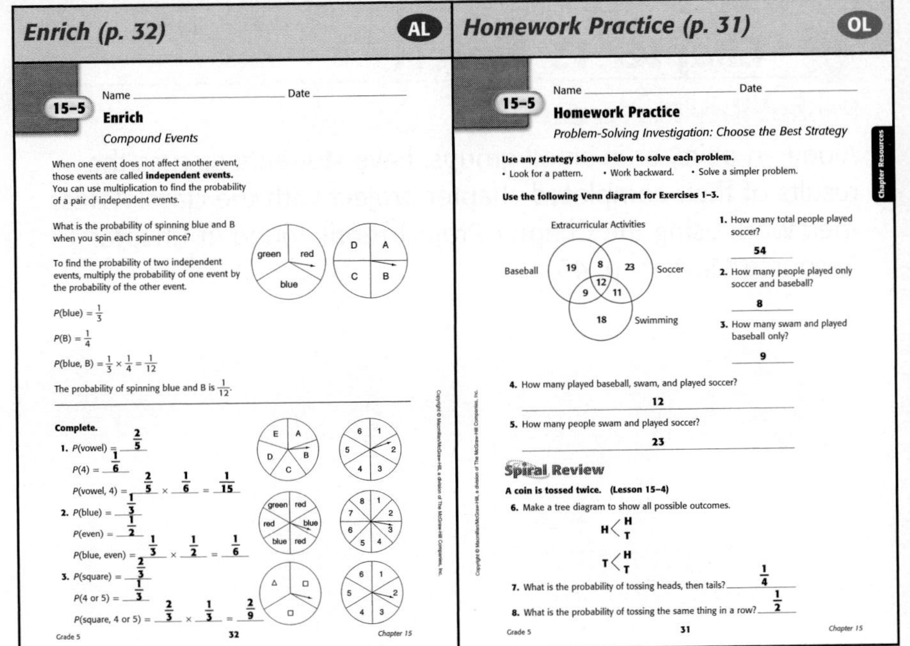

Enrich (p. 32) AL

15–5 Name ______ Date ______

Enrich

Compound Events

When one event does not affect another event, those events are called **independent events.** You can use multiplication to find the probability of a pair of independent events.

What is the probability of spinning blue and B when you spin each spinner once?

To find the probability of two independent events, multiply the probability of one event by the probability of the other event.

$P(\text{blue}) = \frac{1}{3}$

$P(\text{B}) = \frac{1}{4}$

$P(\text{blue, B}) = \frac{1}{3} \times \frac{1}{4} = \frac{1}{12}$

The probability of spinning blue and B is $\frac{1}{12}$.

Complete.

1. $P(\text{vowel}) = \frac{2}{5}$
   $P(4) = \frac{1}{6}$
   $P(\text{vowel, 4}) = \frac{2}{5} \times \frac{1}{6} = \frac{1}{15}$
2. $P(\text{blue}) = \frac{1}{3}$
   $P(\text{even}) = \frac{1}{2}$
   $P(\text{blue, even}) = \frac{1}{3} \times \frac{1}{2} = \frac{1}{6}$
3. $P(\text{square}) = \frac{2}{3}$
   $P(\text{4 or 5}) = \frac{1}{3}$
   $P(\text{square, 4 or 5}) = \frac{2}{3} \times \frac{1}{3} = \frac{2}{9}$

Grade 5 32 Chapter 15

Homework Practice (p. 31) OL

15–5 Name ______ Date ______

Homework Practice

Problem-Solving Investigation: Choose the Best Strategy

Use any strategy shown below to solve each problem.
- Look for a pattern.
- Work backward.
- Solve a simpler problem.

Use the following Venn diagram for Exercises 1–3.

1. How many total people played soccer? **54**
2. How many people played only soccer and baseball? **8**
3. How many swam and played baseball only? **9**
4. How many played baseball, swam, and played soccer? **12**
5. How many people swam and played soccer? **23**

Spiral Review

A coin is tossed twice. (Lesson 15–4)

6. Make a tree diagram to show all possible outcomes.
   H < H, T
   T < H, T
7. What is the probability of tossing heads, then tails? $\frac{1}{4}$
8. What is the probability of tossing the same thing in a row? $\frac{1}{2}$

Grade 5 31 Chapter 15

Chapter Resources

BL Alternate Teaching Strategy

If students have trouble choosing the best strategy...

Then use one of these reteach options:

1. CRM **Daily Reteach Worksheet** (pp. 28–29)
2. Have students write each of the strategies, *make an organized list, draw a picture* and *solve a simpler problem* at the top of a column on a paper. Ask them to write clue words that might be associated with each of the strategies. For example, clue words for *make an organized list* might include "combinations" or "probability." Encourage students to use and add to their lists as they solve word problems.

3 Practice

Using the Exercises

Exercise 2 requires students to know that a diagonal is a line segment drawn between two nonadjacent vertices in a polygon.

Exercises 1, 4, 7, and 8 Students may make an organized list or draw a tree diagram to find the total number of combinations.

4 Assess

Formative Assessment

Write the following on the board:

Maria has three colors of beads: red, green, and yellow. Each bead comes in two shapes, round and triangular, and two sizes, small and medium. How many different types of beads does she have? 12

- **How could you solve?** Make an organized list showing colors, shapes and sizes.

Quick Check **Are students continuing to struggle with choosing the best strategy to solve a problem?**

If Yes → Small Group Options (p. 682B)

If No → Independent Work Options (p. 682B)
CRM Skills Practice Worksheet (p. 30)
CRM Enrich Worksheet (p. 32)

CHAPTER 15 Study Guide and Review

FOLDABLES® Dinah Zike's Foldables

Use these lesson suggestions to incorporate the Foldables during the chapter. Students can then use their Foldables to review for the test.

If students have not completed their Foldables, guide them to create and fill in the appropriate information using the instructions on pp. 659 and 676.

You may choose to use the Foldables to help students review the concepts presented in this chapter and as a tool for studying for the Chapter Test.

Key Vocabulary

The page references after each word denote where that term was first introduced. If students have difficulty answering Exercises 1–6, remind them they can use the page references to review the vocabulary terms.

Vocabulary Review

Review chapter vocabulary using the following option.

- **eGlossary** at macmillanmh.com

FOLDABLES® Study Organizer GET READY to Study

Be sure the following Big Ideas are written in your Foldable.

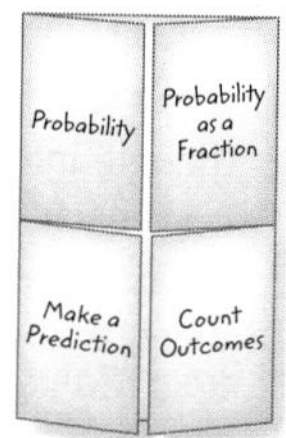

Key Concepts

Probability

- **Probability** is the chance that an event will happen. (p. 661)

Probability	Meaning
Certain	The event will definitely happen.
Impossible	There is no chance the event will happen.
Equally likely	There is an equal chance the event will happen.

- An **outcome** is a possible result in a **probability experiment.** (p. 661)

Describe Probability using Fractions

- The probability of an event can be described using a fraction. (p. 668)

$$P(\text{event}) = \frac{\text{number of favorable outcomes}}{\text{number of possible outcomes}}$$

- An event that is impossible has a probability of 0.
- An event that is certain to happen has a probability of 1.

Key Vocabulary

certain (p. 661)
impossible (p. 661)
outcome (p. 661)
probability (p. 661)
probability experiment (p. 661)
tree diagram (p. 677)

Vocabulary Check

Complete. Use a word from this Key Vocabulary list.

1. An event that will definitely happen is __?__ to happen. certain
2. When a coin is tossed, the two __?__ are heads and tails. outcomes
3. __?__ is the chance that an event will occur. Probability
4. An outcome is a possible result in a(n) __?__. probability experiment
5. A(n) __?__ shows all possible outcomes of an experiment. tree diagram
6. An event that can never happen can be described as __?__ to occur. impossible

Chapter 15 Project

Probability Preferences

Alone, in pairs, or in small groups, have students discuss the results of their completed chapter project with the class. Assess their work using the Chapter Project rubric found in Chapter 15 Resource Masters, p. 43.

Lesson-by-Lesson Review

15-1 Probability (pp. 661–663)

Example 1
Describe the probability of the spinner landing on 1.

The chance of landing on 1 is equally likely.

One letter is randomly chosen from the word OUTCOME. Describe the probability of choosing each letter. Write *certain, impossible, likely, unlikely,* or *equally likely.*

7. T unlikely **8.** E unlikely **9.** A impossible

15-2 Probability as a Fraction (pp. 668–672)

Example 2
One marble is randomly chosen from the bag. Find the probability that a green marble is chosen.

$P(\text{event}) = \frac{\text{number of favorable outcomes}}{\text{number of possible outcomes}}$

$P(\text{green}) = \frac{2}{7}$

So, the probability that a green marble is chosen is $\frac{2}{7}$.

The spinner is spun once. Find the probability of each event. Write as a fraction in simplest form.

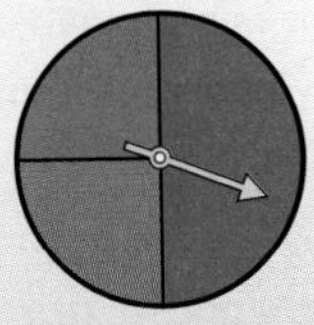

10. $P(\text{blue})$ $\frac{1}{4}$ **11.** $P(\text{red})$ $\frac{1}{2}$

12. $P(\text{green, red, or blue})$ 1

15-3 Problem-Solving Strategy: Make an Organized List (pp. 674–675)

Example 3
How many different sums are possible using the digits 1, 2, and 3?

■■ + ■

12 + 3 = 15	13 + 2 = 15
21 + 3 = 24	23 + 1 = 24
31 + 2 = 33	32 + 1 = 33

There are 3 possible sums.

Solve by *making an organized list.*

13. There are 2 movies that Bailey wants to see. Each movie is showing at 5 different times. How many choices does she have? 10 choices

Lesson-by-Lesson Review

Have students complete the Lesson-by-Lesson Review on pp. 685–686. Then you can use ExamView® Assessment Suite to customize another review worksheet that practices all the objectives of this chapter or only the objectives on which your students need more help.

Intervention If the given examples are not sufficient to review the topics covered by the questions, use the page references next to the exercises to review that topic in the Student Edition.

Chapter 15 Study Guide and Review

Additional Answer

14.

Coin	Cube	Outcome
H	1	H, 1
	2	H, 2
	3	H, 3
	4	H, 4
	5	H, 5
	6	H, 6
T	1	T, 1
	2	T, 2
	3	T, 3
	4	T, 4
	5	T, 5
	6	T, 6

12 outcomes

15-4 Counting Outcomes (pp. 677–680)

Example 4
A coin is tossed and the spinner is spun. What is the probability that the outcome is tails and red?

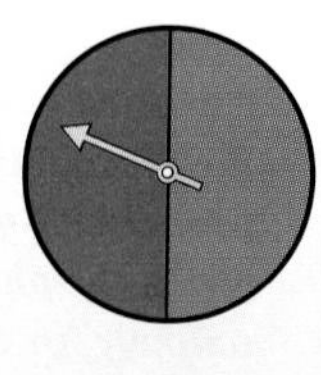

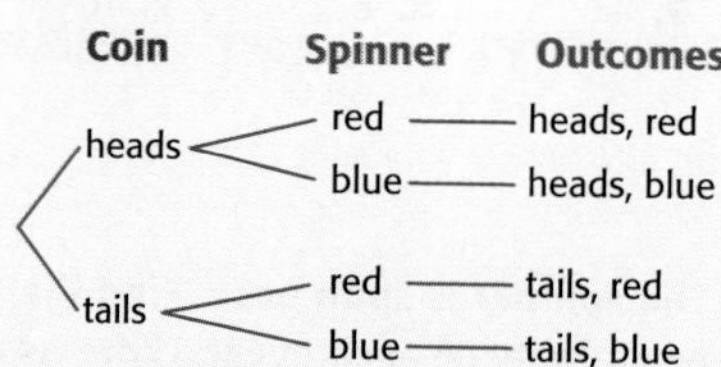

There are four possible outcomes. One outcome is tails and red. So, the probability of that outcome is $\frac{1}{4}$.

A number cube labeled 1 to 6 is rolled and a coin is tossed.

14. Make a tree diagram to show all possible outcomes. Tell how many outcomes are possible. See margin.

15. What is the probability of rolling the number 2 and tossing heads? $\frac{1}{12}$

16. What is the probability of rolling an even number and tossing tails? $\frac{1}{4}$

17. A store has roses, tulips, and carnations. They each come in red and yellow. How many outcomes are possible? 6 outcomes

15-5 Problem-Solving Investigation: Choose a Strategy (pp. 682–683)

Example 5
Miranda has a black purse and a tan purse. She has a black hat and a red hat. How many different purse-hat possibilities are there?

Make a list of the different possibilities.

black purse and black hat
black purse and red hat
tan purse and black hat
tan purse and red hat

So, there are 4 different purse-hat possibilities.

18. For lunch, Mazo can choose a soup or salad, a hamburger or grilled cheese, and a fruit cup or yogurt. How many different lunch possibilities are there? 8 possibilities

19. A student divides a hexagon into sections by drawing three diagonals from one vertex. How many sections are there? What are their shapes? 4 sections; triangles

686 Chapter 15 Use Probability to Make Predictions

macmillanmh.com
• Chapter Test

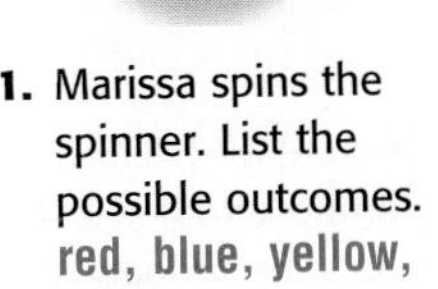

Chapter Test

1. Marissa spins the spinner. List the possible outcomes. red, blue, yellow, green

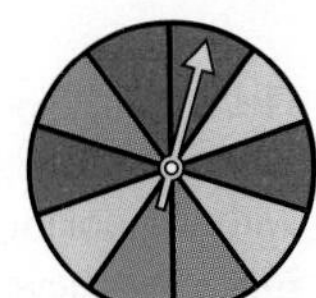

One block is randomly drawn from the bag. Describe the probability of drawing each marble. Write *certain*, *impossible*, *likely*, *unlikely*, or *equally likely*.

2. red likely
3. green unlikely
4. yellow impossible
5. not green likely

6. **MULTIPLE CHOICE** Each letter in the word HOMEWORK is written on a separate note card. If one card is picked without looking, what is the probability that it will have a vowel on it? B

   A $\frac{1}{4}$

   B $\frac{3}{8}$

   C $\frac{1}{2}$

   D $\frac{3}{4}$

7. **Geometry** Mrs. Hong has two sets of math shapes. One set has a square and a triangle. The other set has a circle, a rectangle, and a pentagon. If she chooses one shape from each set, how many possibilities are there? 6

8. **MULTIPLE CHOICE** Jana tossed a coin and a number cube marked 1 to 6. What is the probability that the results were tails and 3? J

   F $\frac{1}{4}$ **H** $\frac{1}{8}$

   G $\frac{1}{6}$ **J** $\frac{1}{12}$

Marlon grabs a pair of shoes and a pair of socks without looking. He has black, brown, and red shoes. He has four pairs of socks: white, blue, yellow, and red.

9. Make a tree diagram to show the possible outcomes. Tell how many outcomes are possible. See Ch. 15 Answer Appendix.
10. What is the probability that the shoes and socks are both red? $\frac{1}{12}$
11. What is the probability that the socks are *not* white? $\frac{3}{4}$

The spinner is spun once. Find the probability of each event. Write as a fraction in simplest form.

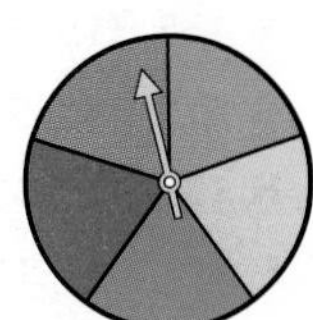

12. P(red) $\frac{1}{5}$
13. P(blue or yellow) 13. $\frac{2}{5}$
14. P(black) 0
15. P(*not* purple) 1

16. **WRITING IN MATH** Gabe is downloading 3 songs from a group of 5 songs. Explain how to find the different possibilities for downloading the 3 songs. See Ch. 15 Answer Appendix.

CHAPTER 15

Chapter Test

Summative Assessment

Use these alternate leveled chapter tests to differentiate assessment for the specific needs of your students.

Leveled Chapter 15 Tests			
Form	**Type**	**Level**	**CRM Pages**
1	Multiple Choice	BL	45–46
2A	Multiple Choice	OL	47–48
2B	Multiple Choice	OL	49–50
2C	Free Response	AL	51–52
2D	Free Response	AL	53–54
3	Free Response	AL	55–56

BL = below/approaching grade level
OL = on grade level
AL = above/beyond grade level

Vocabulary Test

CRM **Chapter 15 Resource Masters** (p. 40)

ExamView Assessment Suite Customize and create multiple versions of your Chapter Test and the test answer keys.

Data-Driven Decision Making

Based on the results of the Chapter Test, use the following to review concepts that continue to present students with problems.

Exercises	State/Local Standards	What's the Math?	Error Analysis	Resources for Review
1, 7, 9, 16 Lesson 15-4		List outcomes of a probability event. Make a list or use a tree diagram to tell how many outcomes are possible.	Does not understand "possible outcomes." Does not combine same parts to create one part for denominator total for all possible outcomes.	CRM Chapter 15 Resource Masters (Reteach Worksheets) Math Adventures My Math Zone Chapter 15 Math Online Extra Examples • Concepts in Motion
2–6 Lesson 15-1		Determine the likelihood/probability of an event.	Does not understand "randomly," "certain," "impossible," "less, equally, or more likely." Reverses numerator and denominator.	
8, 10–15 Lesson 15-2		Use fractions to describe probability.	Reverses numerator and denominator in writing probability. Does not use total different colors as denominator for fractions.	

Chapter 15 Test Practice

Formative Assessment

- Use Student Edition pp. 688–689 as practice and cumulative review. The questions are written in the same style as many state tests.
- You can also use these two pages to benchmark student progress, or as an alternate homework assignment.

Additional practice pages can be found in the Chapter 15 Resource Masters.

CRM **Chapter 15 Resource Masters**
Cumulative Test Practice

- Multiple Choice format (pp. 45–50)
- Free Response format (pp. 51–56)

End-of-Year Assessment

Use the **End-of-Year Test** to assess student comprehension of the skills and concepts presented in Grade 5.

CRM **Chapter 15 Resource Masters**
End-of-Year Test (p. 62)

Create practice worksheets or tests that align to your state standards.

Math Online Have students visit macmillanmh.com for additional practice to reinforce your state standards.

Chapter 15 Test Practice

Cumulative, Chapters 1–15

PART 1 Multiple Choice

Read each question. Then fill in the correct answer on the answer sheet provided by your teacher or on a sheet of paper.

1. The table shows the tips that Stella earned each week. Based on these results, what is the probability that Stella will earn more than \$100 in tips next week? D

Week	Tips Earned ($)
1	94
2	132
3	115
4	104

A $\frac{1}{4}$ **C** $\frac{1}{2}$

B $\frac{1}{3}$ **D** $\frac{3}{4}$

2. If each digit 1, 3, and 5 is used only once, which group shows all the possibilities of 3-digit numbers? J

F 135, 315, 531

G 315, 135, 513, 531

H 135, 315, 531, 153, 513

J 315, 351, 135, 153, 513, 531

3. The table shows the choices for frozen yogurt sundaes. From how many different combinations of 1 type of yogurt and 1 type of topping can a customer choose? A

Yogurt	Topping
Strawberry	Nuts
Vanilla	Granola
Lemon	Strawberry
	Pineapple

A 12 **C** 7

B 9 **D** 6

4. Eleven cards spell the word MATHEMATICS when put together. If one card is chosen without looking, what is the probability that it will have the letter M on it? G

F $\frac{1}{11}$ **H** $\frac{4}{11}$

G $\frac{2}{11}$ **J** $\frac{9}{11}$

5. A fifth grade class voted for the class mascot. Based on these results, which is the most reasonable prediction of the number of votes a bear would receive if 50 students voted? B

Mascot	Number of Students
Bear	7
Falcon	4
Panther	11
Ram	3

A 22 **C** 8

B 14 **D** 6

6. Look for the pattern in the sequence of numbers below.

5, 10, 7, 14, 11, 22, 19, ...

Which rule describes this pattern best? G

F Add 5, subtract 3.

G Multiply by 2, subtract 3.

H Add 5, multiply by 2.

J Multiply by 2, add 3.

Test-Taking Tip

Tell students to read the question carefully. They can break it into smaller parts to make it easier to solve.

Preparing for Standardized Tests
For test-taking strategies and practice, see pages R42–R55.

7. Teams are formed for a game so they each have 1 boy and 1 girl. There are 5 girls and 5 boys. How many different combinations are possible? C

A 5 **C** 25
B 10 **D** 50

8. The table shows the grades Jake earned on 13 tests. Based on these results, what is the probability that Jake will earn a B on his next spelling test? G

Spelling Tests	
Grade	Number
A	10
B	2
C	1

F $\frac{1}{13}$ **H** $\frac{3}{13}$
G $\frac{2}{13}$ **J** $\frac{10}{13}$

9. Five horses were in a race. They wore different colored blankets. Use the clues below to name a possible order of the horses from first to last. D

Blanket	Finish
Red	First
Orange	Between blue and yellow
Green	Fifth

A green, yellow, orange, blue, red
B red, green, yellow, blue, orange
C blue, red, orange, yellow, green
D red, blue, orange, yellow, green

PART 2 Short Response

Record your answers on the answer sheet provided by your teacher or on a sheet of paper.

10. The temperature outside at 6:45 A.M. was 56°F. By noon, the temperature was 62°F. Write an integer to represent this situation. +6

11. Name one object that would be measured using milligrams, one that would be measured using grams, and one that would be measured with kilograms. See margin.

PART 3 Extended Response

Record your answers on the answer sheet provided by your teacher or on a sheet of paper.

12. Write a real-world problem that can be solved using the equation $24 = 3p$. See margin.

13. Which shape would have a larger perimeter, an equilateral triangle with sides that are each 14 inches, or a square with sides that are each 1 foot? Explain. See margin.

NEED EXTRA HELP?													
If You Missed Question...	1	2	3	4	5	6	7	8	9	10	11	12	13
Go to Lesson...	15-2	15-4	15-4	15-2	15-2	9-6	15-4	15-2	15-3	12-5	12-3	6-2	13-3

Summative Assessment 689

Answer Sheet Practice

Have students simulate taking a state test by recording their answers on a practice recording sheet.

CRM Chapter 15 Resource Masters
Student Recording Sheet (p. 61)

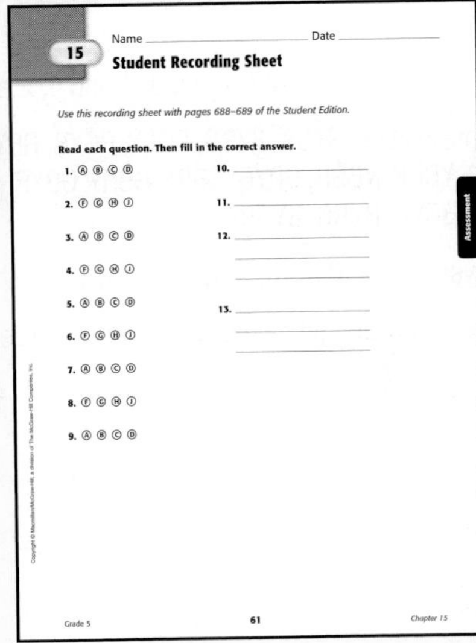

Additional Answers

11. Sample answer: milligrams- insect, grams- pen, kilograms- dog.

12. Sample answer: The Bulldogs scored 3 times as many points as the Tigers. If the Bulldogs scored 24 points, how many points did the Tigers score? 8

13. Sample answer: square; The perimeter of the square is 48 inches. The perimeter of the triangle is 42 inches.

Page 663, Lesson 15-1

22. Sample answer: There are 6 girls and 4 boys who put their names in a box. A name is drawn at random to choose a team leader. Is it more likely that a girl or a boy will be chosen? Answer: a girl, because there are more girls' names in the box than boys' names.

Page 675, Lesson 15-3

1. 2 batting gloves and 1 weight; 2 batting gloves and 2 cans of tennis balls; 1 batting glove and 2 weights; 1 batting glove and 4 cans of tennis balls; 4 weights; 3 weights and 2 cans of tennis balls; 3 weights and 1 can of tennis balls; 2 weights and 3 cans of tennis balls; 2 weights and 4 cans of tennis balls; 1 weight and 6 cans of tennis balls; 1 weight and 5 cans of tennis balls; 8 cans of tennis balls; and 7 cans of tennis balls

4. A list helps keep track of all the possibilities in a problem.

6. 9; 2 dimes; 1 dime 2 nickels; 1 dime 1 nickel 5 pennies; 1 dime 10 pennies; 4 nickels; 3 nickels 5 pennies; 2 nickels 10 pennies, 1 nickel 15 pennies; 20 pennies

8. 6 combinations; 1 and 2, 1 and 3, 1 and 4, 2 and 3, 2 and 4, 3 and 4

9. 24 possibilities; RYGB, RYBG, RGBY, RGYB, RBYG, RBGY, YRGB, YRBG, YGRB, YGBR, YBRG, YBGR, GRYB, GRBY, GBRY, GBYR, GYRB, GYBR, BRYG, BRGY, BGRY, BGYR, BYRG, BYGR

10. 6 ways; ABC, ACB, BAC, BCA, CAB, CBA

12. Sample answer: List all the ways you can order the pictures.

Page 676, Mid-Chapter Check

13. 4 results;
Q: head, N: head
Q: head, N: tails
Q: tails, N: head
Q: tails, N: tails

14. 10 different pizzas;
thin, pepperoni
thin, sausage
thin, mushroom
thin, onion
thin, green peppers
thick, pepperoni
thick, sausage
thick, mushroom
thick, onion
thick, green peppers

15. Sample answer: An event that has a greater number of favorable outcomes is more likely to occur than an event that has fewer favorable outcomes.

Page 679, Lesson 15-4

9.

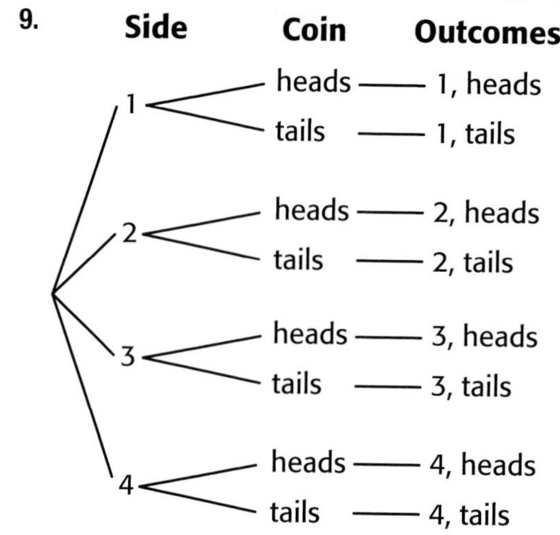

11.

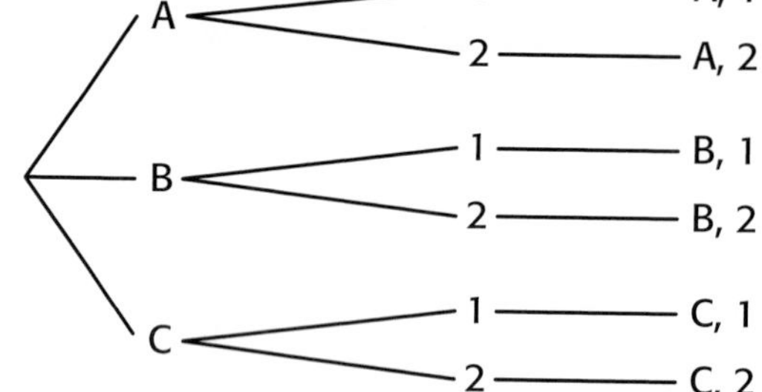

14.

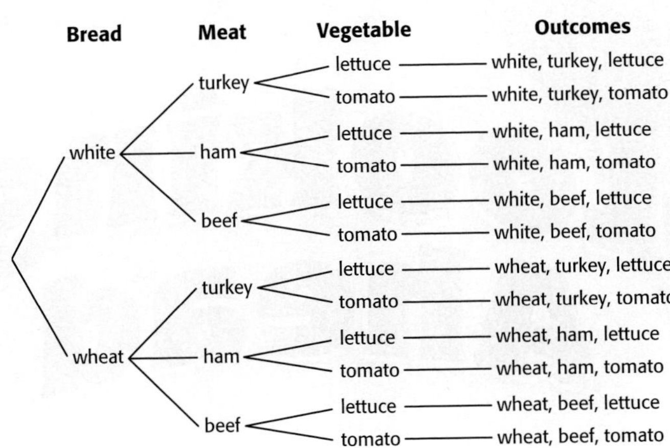

18.

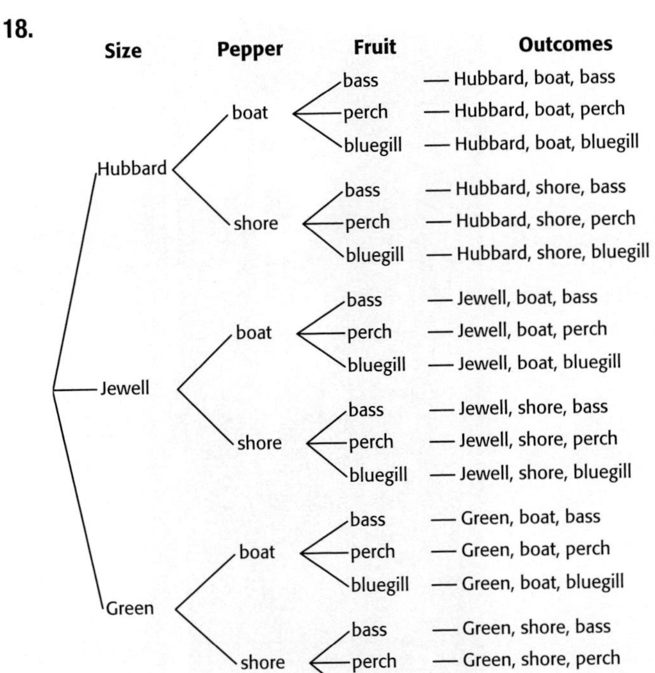

Page 683, Lesson 15-5

8. Sample answer: Jeff should have made a list or a tree diagram to find all the possible outcomes. By doing so, there are 9, not 6, different outcomes.

Page 687, Chapter Test

9.

Shoes	Socks	Outcomes
black	white	black, white
	blue	black, blue
	yellow	black, yellow
	red	black, red
brown	white	brown, white
	blue	brown, blue
	yellow	brown, yellow
	red	brown, red
red	white	red, white
	blue	red, blue
	yellow	red, yellow
	red	red, red

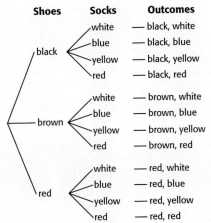

16. Sample answer: Gabe should make a tree diagram to show all the possible combinations he can choose from. By doing so, there are 60 possibilities.

Looking Ahead

The lessons in **Looking Ahead** can be used to extend concepts and skills present during the current year. Also, some lessons can be used at the end of the year after your state testing is completed. By presenting these important concepts and skills, you can help students be more successful.

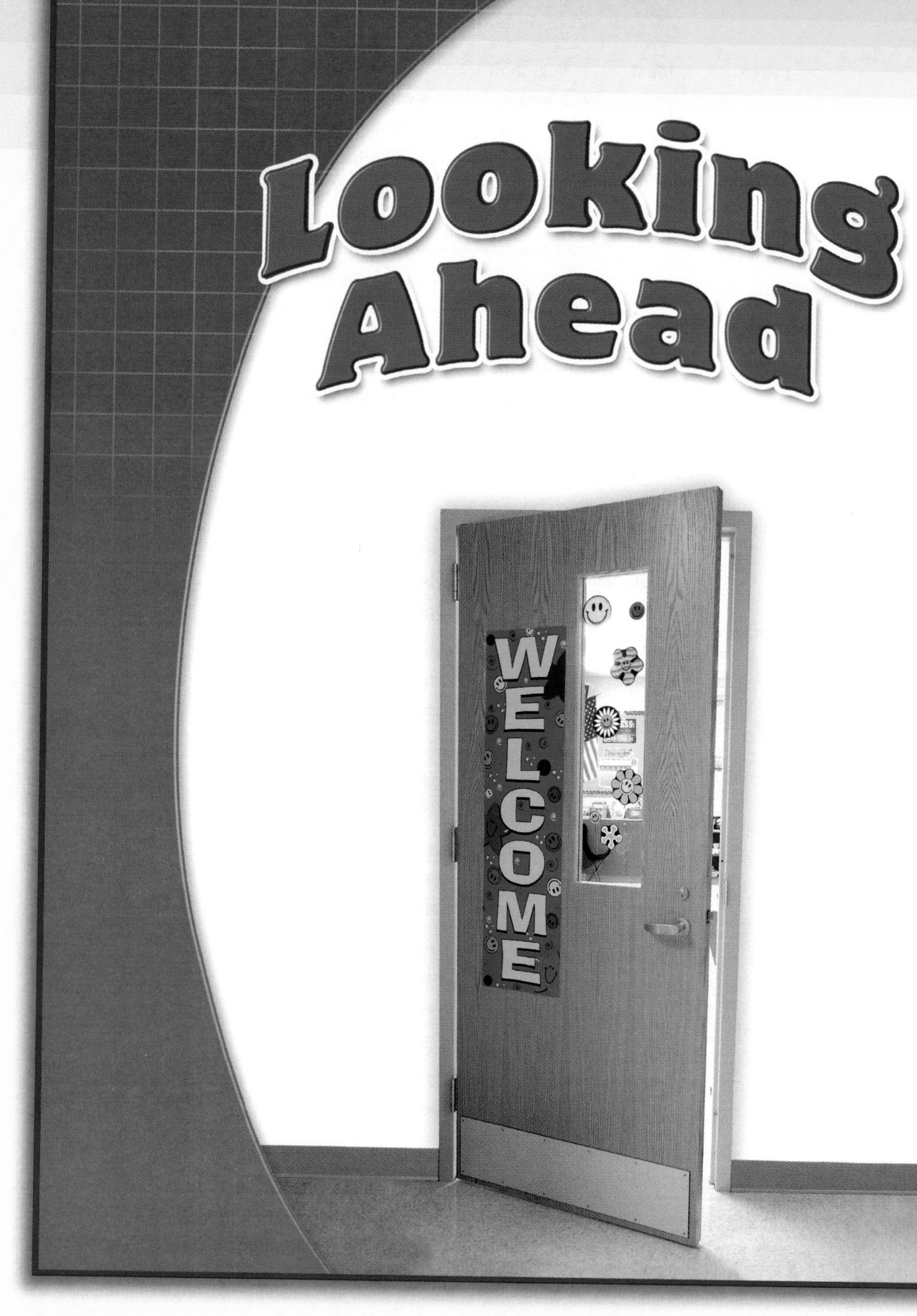

Let's Look Ahead!

Looking Ahead

Looking Ahead 1

Multiplying Decimals

Lesson Planner

Objective

Multiply decimals by decimals.

Review Vocabulary

factor, product

Resources

Materials: index cards, decimal models, highlighters

Teacher Technology

Interactive Classroom • TeacherWorks

Focus on Math Background

When students added and subtracted decimals in Chapter 2, they learned that they must align the decimal points in the addends or in the minuend and subtrahend before beginning their computations.

When multiplying decimals, the decimal points of the factors are *not* aligned, and the factors are *not* placed so that digits with the same place value are lined up one directly below the other. Instead, the decimal numbers are aligned on the right and then the decimals are multiplied as if they were whole numbers. The position of the decimal point in the product is based on the total number of places to the right of the decimal point in each factor. This total tells you how many places there will be to the right of the decimal point in the product. For example, to multiply 0.03×0.002

- Multiply as if the factors were whole numbers: $3 \times 2 = 6$
- Count the places to the right of the decimal point in each factor and find the total.
  $0.03 \rightarrow 2$ places; $0.002 \rightarrow 3$ places; $2 + 3 = 5$ places
- Count the same number of places from the right in the product and place the decimal point. 0.00006 (5 places)

Daily Routine

Use these suggestions before beginning the lesson on p. LA2.

5-Minute Check

(Reviews Lesson 15-5)

Use a problem-solving strategy to solve each problem.

1. Paula is making a sandwich. Her choice of bread is rye or wheat. Her choice of meat is ham, turkey, or roast beef. If she chooses one type of bread and one type of meat, how many different sandwiches does she have to choose from? 6
2. A square with side lengths of 8 ft is cut into fourths. What are the side lengths of the 4 smaller squares? 4 ft

Problem of the Day

Eli wants to buy three books at $5.79 each. Estimate how much change he will get back from two $10 bills. Explain how you solved the problem. $2; Explanations may vary.

Review Math Vocabulary

Write the review vocabulary words and their definitions on the board.

Have students review their definitions of the terms in their notebooks or Math Journals. Have them write a multiplication of a decimal by a whole number, and have them label the factors. Have them find the product and label it.

Visual Vocabulary Cards

Use Visual Vocabulary Card 12 to reinforce the vocabulary reviewed in this lesson. (The Define/Example/Ask routine is printed on the back of each card.)

Differentiated Instruction

Small Group Options

LOGICAL, SOCIAL 

Option 1 Below Level BL

Materials: chart paper, markers, paper, pencils

- Copy the following problems on the chart paper:
- Ask the students to copy these problems on their paper. Then work with a partner.
- Ask, "Where does the decimal point go in each product and why?"
- Encourage the students to talk with their partner to decide for each problem. Accept any reasonable answer, except the one that states the rule of counting decimal places. What you are looking for is an understanding that 4.1 is 4 and a little more and 3.2 is 3 and a little more and 4.9 is almost 5.

3.2 × 4.1 1312	5.3 × 2.6 1378
4.9 × 0.5 245	34.2 × .71 24282

LOGICAL 

Option 2 English Language Learners ELL

Materials: plastic coin money
Core Vocabulary: half
Common Use Verb: would rather have

See Math This strategy helps students realize that when multiplying with decimals, the product is lower than with whole numbers.

- Display a 50-cent coin. Ask its monetary value.
- Ask students if they multiply 0.50 by a whole number, will it always have a higher value than if they multiplied it by another decimal?
- Say: "Multiply it by a whole number. (0.50 × 5 = 2.50)
- Repeat for multiplying by a decimal. (0.50 × .5 = .25)
- ***Would*** you ***rather have*** $2.50 or 25¢?"
- Repeat using different coins.

Independent Work Options

LOGICAL, VISUAL 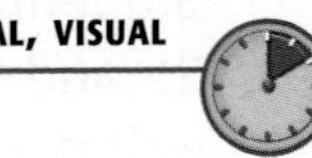

Option 1 Early Finishers OL AL

Materials: index cards, pencils

- Each student writes a multiplication expression on the front of an index card using decimals for both factors.
- Students exchange cards, find the product of the multiplication, and write the product on the back of the card.
- Partners must agree that the products are correct.
- Groups can combine all their cards and use them as flash cards for the class.

Option 2 Student Technology

Math Online macmillanmh.com

Personal Tutor • Extra Examples

 Math Adventures

Looking Ahead 1 Multiplying Decimals

1 Introduce

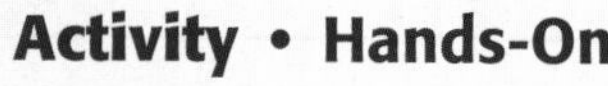

Activity • Hands-On

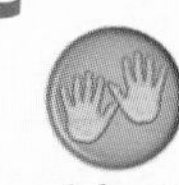

Assign groups of four. Provide 20 index cards per group.

- Student 1 writes 10 whole numbers between 25 and 99, one number to a card. Student 2 writes 10 decimals between 0.001 and 0.1, one number to a card.
- The decks of whole numbers and decimals are kept separate and placed facedown.
- Student 3 chooses a card from the decimal deck; Student 4 chooses a card from the whole number deck.
- Together the members estimate the product of the two factors and record the multiplication sentence.
- The used cards are replaced in the deck and the activity is repeated with members taking turns choosing the cards.

2 Teach

Scaffolding Questions

Write a table of deli meat prices on the board.

- **How could you estimate the cost of 3 pounds of salami?** Sample answer: Round \$3.99 to \$4, multiply by 3, for \$12.
- **How would you estimate the cost of 6 pounds of bologna?** Sample answer: Round \$2.89 to \$3, multiply by 6, for \$18.
- **How would you find the estimated cost of 2.5 pounds of ham?** Sample answer: Round one up and round one down and multiply: \$3 × 3. The price would be about \$9.

GET READY to Learn

Hands-On Mini Lab Students will use base-ten blocks to model multiplying decimals. Remind students that the flats represent 1 whole, rods represent tenths, and units represent hundredths.

Multiplying Decimals

MAIN IDEA

What You'll Learn
I will multiply a decimal by a whole number and by another decimal.

Materials:
grid paper
colored pencils
scissors

Math Online
macmillanmh.com
- Extra Examples
- Personal Tutor
- Self-Check Quiz

Hands-On Mini Lab

Recall that a 10-by-10 grid represents the number one.

ACTIVITY

1 Model 0.7 × 0.3 using decimal models.

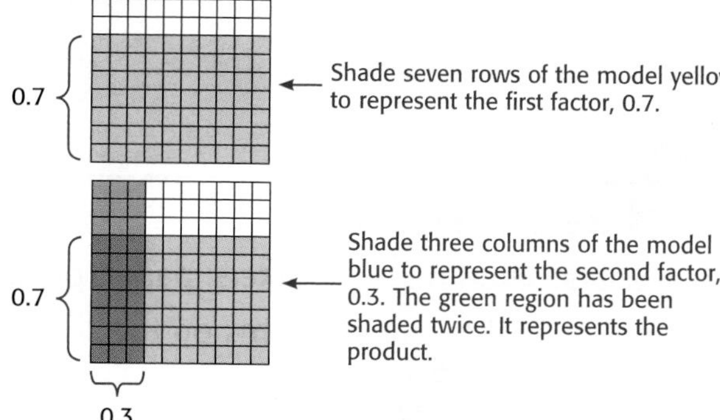
0.7
Shade seven rows of the model yellow to represent the first factor, 0.7.
0.7
Shade three columns of the model blue to represent the second factor, 0.3. The green region has been shaded twice. It represents the product.
0.3

There are 21 hundredths in the region where the colors overlap. So, 0.7 × 0.3 = 0.21.

Draw decimal models to show each product.

a-d See Answer Appendix for models.

a. 3 × 0.2 0.6 **b.** 2 × 0.5 1 **c.** 0.4 × 0.8 0.32 **d.** 0.6 × 0.4 0.24

2 Model 0.4 × 2 using decimal models.

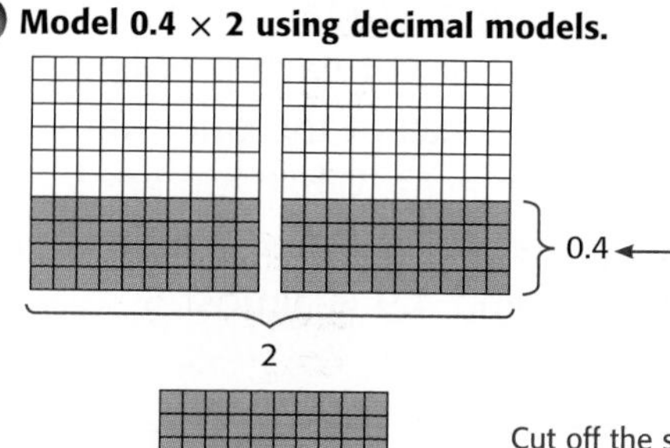
Shade four rows of each decimal model to represent 0.4.
0.4
2
Cut off the shaded rows and rearrange them to form as many 10-by-10 grids as possible. The product is eight tenths.

So, 0.4 × 2 = 0.8.

EXAMPLES Multiply Decimals by a Whole Number

1 **Find 7 × 0.96.**

One Way: **Use estimation.**

Round 0.96 to 1. $7 \times 0.96 \longrightarrow 7 \times 1$ or 7

```
   4
 0.96    Since the estimate is 7,
×   7    place the decimal point
 6.72    after the 6.
```

Another Way: **Count decimal places.**

```
   4
 0.96  ←  There are two places to the right of the decimal point.
×   7
 6.72  ←  Count two decimals places from right to left.
```

2 **Measurement** **Find the area of a board that is 4 feet by 3.62 feet.**

Estimate $4 \times 3.62 \longrightarrow 4 \times 4$ or 16

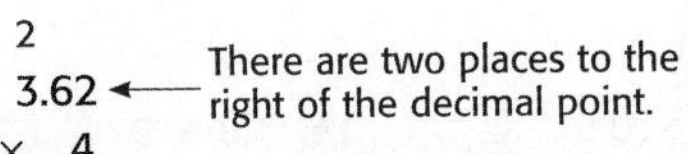

```
   2
 3.62  ←  There are two places to the right of the decimal point.
×   4
14.48  ←  Count two decimals places from right to left.
```

The area of the bulletin board is 14.48 feet.

EXAMPLE Multiply Decimals

3 **Find 5.2 × 3.4.** **Estimate** $5.2 \times 3.4 \longrightarrow 5 \times 3$ or 15

```
   5.2  ←  one decimal place
 × 3.4  ←  one decimal place
   208
 +156
 17.68  ←  two decimal places
```

The product is 17.68.

Check for Reasonableness Compare 17.68 to the estimate.

$17.68 \approx 15$ ✓

Multiplying Decimals

Example 3 Call attention to the fact that when students multiply decimals, the decimal points in the factors are not aligned. The position of the decimal point in the product is based on the sum of the number of decimal places in the factors.

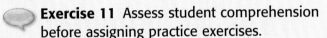

ADDITIONAL EXAMPLES

1. Find 8 × 2.9. 23.2
2. Carmen earns $14.60 per hour as a painter's helper. She worked a total of 15 hours one week. How much money did she earn? $219
3. Find 1.2 × 5.3. 6.36

CHECK What You Know

As a class, have students complete Exercises 1–11 in **Check What You Know** as you observe their work.

Exercise 11 Assess student comprehension before assigning practice exercises.

BL Alternate Teaching Strategy

If students have trouble multiplying decimals ...

Then use this reteach option:

Allow students to use decimal models, if necessary, when you discuss Example 3. Emphasize that two decimal factors are multiplied as if they were whole numbers. Have students use highlighters to mark each factor from the decimal point to the right.

- **How do you know where to place the decimal point in the product?** Go back and count the decimal places used in *both* factors.

Call attention to the fact that students must count places from *right to left* to place the decimal point correctly in the product.

3 Practice

Differentiate practice using these leveled assignments for Exercises 12–39.

Level	Assignment
BL Below/ Approaching Level	12–18 even, 24, 27, 32, 37
OL On Level	14–23, 28–30, 32, 35, 37–39
AL Above/Below Level	12–30 even, 32–39

Have students discuss and complete the Higher Order Thinking problems. Remind students to consider the order of operations when they are evaluating expressions.

WRITING IN ▸MATH Have students complete Exercise 39 in their Math Journals. You may choose to use this exercise as an optional formative assessment.

COMMON ERROR!

Exercise 16 When students multiply 4 × 0.02, they may forget to annex a zero in the product before inserting the decimal point. Emphasize the need to count the decimal places in *both* factors before counting off that number of places for the decimal point in the product.

CHECK What You Know

Multiply. See Examples 1–3, p. LA3

1. 6 × 0.5 3 **2.** 4 × 2.6 10.4 **3.** 7 × 0.89 6.23

4. 3 × 2.49 7.47 **5.** 52 × 2.1 109.2 **6.** 3.4 × 2.7 9.18

7. 5.4 × 0.9 4.86 **8.** 8.2 × 5.8 47.56 **9.** 5.7 × 0.6 3.42

10. A recipe for a cake calls for 3.5 cups of sugar. How many cups of sugar are needed for 4 cakes? 14 cups

11. Talk About It Is the product of 2.8 and 1.5 greater than 6 or less than 6? How do you know? Sample answer: less than; Use estimation 3 × 2 = 6. Both numbers are rounded up, so the estimate is larger than the exact.

★ indicates multi-step problem.

Practice and Problem Solving

Multiply. See Examples 1–3, p. LA3

12. 2 × 1.3 2.6 **13.** 3 × 0.5 1.5 **14.** 1.8 × 9 16.2

15. 2.4 × 8 19.2 **16.** 4 × 0.02 0.08 **17.** 0.66 × 5 3.3

18. 0.7 × 0.4 0.28 **19.** 1.5 × 2.7 4.05 **20.** 0.4 × 3.7 1.48

21. 0.8 × 7.3 5.84 **22.** 2.4 × 3.8 9.12 **23.** 6.2 × 0.3 1.86

Algebra Evaluate each expression if $x = 3$, $y = 0.2$, and $z = 4.5$.

24. xy 0.6 **25.** $7.3y$ 1.46 ★**27.** xyz 2.7

28. $(7 \times 2) \times y$ 2.8 **29.** xz 13.5 **30.** $(9 - x) \times y$ 1.2

★**31.** Miguel is trying to eat less than 750 Calories at dinner. A 4-serving, thin crust cheese pizza has 272.8 Calories per serving. A dinner salad has 150 Calories. Will Miguel be able to eat the salad and two pieces of pizza for under 750 Calories? Explain. Sample answer: Yes; 272.8 × 2 + 150 = 695.6.

Real-World PROBLEM SOLVING

Science **A panda spends about 0.5 of the day eating. They can eat up to 33 pounds of bamboo in a single day.**

32. How long will the panda spend eating in 7 days? **3.5 days**

33. How many pounds of bamboo will a panda eat in 30 days? **990 pounds**

Measurement **Find the area of each rectangle.**

34. **16.2 in.^{2}**

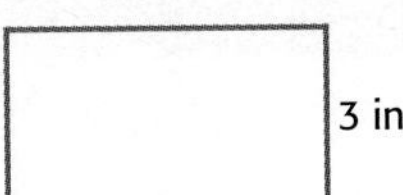

3 in.

5.4 in.

35. **58.28 ft^2**

6.2 ft

9.4 ft

H.O.T. Problems

36. **OPEN ENDED** Write a multiplication problem in which the product has two decimal places. **Sample answer $0.3 \times 0.9 = 0.27$**

37. **FIND THE ERROR** Armando and Kellis are finding the product of 0.52 and 21. Who is correct? Explain. **Sample Answer: Kellis is right because the product should have the decimal two places to the right.**

Armando

$$\begin{array}{r} 0.52 \\ \times\ 21 \\ \hline 1{,}092 \end{array}$$

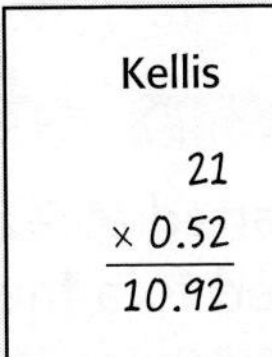

Kellis

$$\begin{array}{r} 21 \\ \times\ 0.52 \\ \hline 10.92 \end{array}$$

38. **NUMBER SENSE** Place the decimal point in the answer to make it correct. Explain your reasoning.
$4.98 \times 8.32 = 414336$ **41.4336**

39. **WRITING IN ▸MATH** Write a real-world problem that can be solved using multiplication. One factor should be a decimal. **Sample Answer: I bought three ice cream cones for $1.59 each. How much money did I spend? 3 × 1.59 = $4.77.**

4 Assess

Formative Assessment

- **If you multiply 0.062×0.005, how many places from right to left in the product will you insert the decimal point?** 6 places
- **Suppose there are only 4 digits in the product. What must you do?** Sample answer: Annex 2 zeros before inserting the decimal point so that there will be 6 digits to the right of the decimal point.

Quick Check **Are students continuing to struggle with multiplying decimals?**

If Yes → Strategic Intervention Guide (p. 115)

If No → Independent Work Options (p. LA2B)

Ticket Out the Door Have students write the answer to the following problem on a small piece of paper and hand it to the teacher as they leave the classroom. 0.47×0.04 0.0188

Looking Ahead 2

Multiplying Fractions

Lesson Planner

Objective

Multiply fractions.

Review Vocabulary

factor, **numerator**, **denominator**

Resources

Materials: grid paper, colored pencils

Manipulatives: counters

Teacher Technology

Interactive Classroom • TeacherWorks

Focus on Math Background

In this lesson, students will:

- Multiply two proper fractions by multiplying the numerators and the denominators.

$$\frac{a}{b} \times \frac{c}{d} = \frac{ac}{bd}$$

- Multiply a proper fraction by whole number by rewriting the whole number as an improper fraction with a denominator of 1, multiplying the fractions, and simplifying the answer by writing it as a mixed number.

$$\frac{a}{b} \times c = \frac{a}{b} \times \frac{c}{1} = \frac{ac}{b}$$

When multiplying fractions in this lesson, students should begin to understand that:

- The product of two proper fractions will always be less than either fraction because multiplying a fraction by a fraction is taking part of a part.
- The product of a whole number greater than 1 and a proper fraction will always be less than the whole number and greater than the fraction, i.e. whole number factor > product > proper fraction factor.

Daily Routine

Use these suggestions before beginning the lesson on p. LA6.

5-Minute Check

(Reviews Lesson LA1)

Multiply.

1. 3×0.5 1.5
2. 0.7×0.4 0.28
3. 0.32×1.8 0.576
4. 2.05×0.9 1.845

Problem of the Day

A movie started at 2:05 P.M. After the movie ended, Matías talked to a friend for 45 minutes. He left the theater at 4:30 P.M. What was the length of the movie? Explain your strategy. 1 h 40 min. or 100 min.; strategies may vary.

Review Math Vocabulary

Write the review vocabulary words and their definitions on the board.

Have students review the terms in their Math Journals. Give students an example of a fact family such as 3, 4, 12.

- **What multiplication and division facts can you make from this fact family?** $3 \times 4 = 12$; $4 \times 3 = 12$; $12 \div 4 = 3$; $12 \div 3 = 4$

Visual Vocabulary Cards

Use Visual Vocabulary Card 12 to reinforce the vocabulary reviewed in this lesson. (The Define/Example/Ask routine is printed on the back of each card.)

Differentiated Instruction

Small Group Options

SPATIAL, VISUAL

Option 1 Below Level BL

Materials: chart paper, colored pencils

Create a poster that explains how the area model works when multiplying fractions.

Model $\frac{1}{3} \times \frac{3}{4}$:

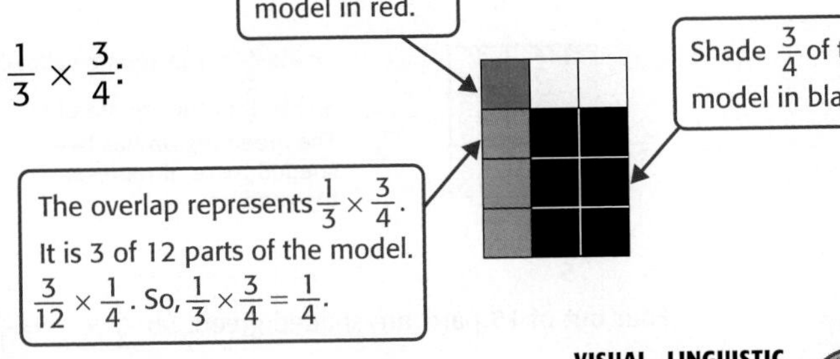

Shade $\frac{1}{3}$ of the model in red.
Shade $\frac{3}{4}$ of the model in black.
The overlap represents $\frac{1}{3} \times \frac{3}{4}$. It is 3 of 12 parts of the model. $\frac{3}{12} \times \frac{1}{4}$. So, $\frac{1}{3} \times \frac{3}{4} = \frac{1}{4}$.

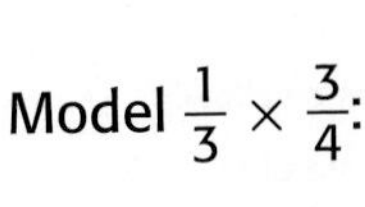

VISUAL, LINGUISTIC

Option 2 English Language Learners ELL

Core Vocabulary: value, more, less

Common Use Verb: is shown

See Math This strategy allows students to visualize multiplying fractions.

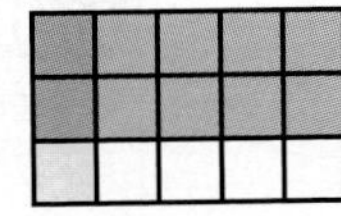

- Write "$\frac{1}{5} \times \frac{2}{3}$". Show a 3×5 grid.
- Ask students how they would solve this problem. Accept responses.
- Model coloring a column. Ask if this shows 1 out of the 5 columns.
- Color the column lightly in yellow.
- Repeat for 2 rows of 3, coloring them lightly in blue.
- Outline the green squares and write the fraction $\frac{2}{15}$.
- Discuss if $\frac{1}{5} \times \frac{2}{3}$ is the same as $\frac{2}{15}$.

Independent Work Options

TACTILE, LOGICAL

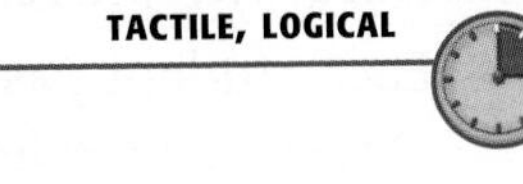

Option 1 Early Finishers OL AL

Materials: paper, pencil

Have students cut the following recipe in half and fourths.

Trail Mix

1 cup peanuts	$\frac{1}{2}$ cup	$\frac{1}{4}$ cup
$\frac{3}{4}$ cup pretzels	$\frac{3}{8}$ cup	$\frac{3}{16}$ cup
$\frac{1}{2}$ cup raisins	$\frac{1}{4}$ cup	$\frac{1}{8}$ cup
$\frac{2}{3}$ cup crackers	$\frac{1}{3}$ cup	$\frac{1}{6}$ cup

Option 2 Student Technology

Math Online macmillanmh.com

Personal Tutor • Extra Examples

 Math Adventures

Multiplying Fractions

Introduce

Activity • Hands-On 

Assign groups of four. Provide groups with grid paper.

- Have each student model $\frac{1}{2}$ of $\frac{3}{4}$. $\frac{3}{8}$
- Each student passes his or her model to the student on the left.
- Students check the model they received and determine if it is correct. If the model is incorrect, it is returned for corrections to the student who made it.
- Students, in turn, verbalize how they made the model.

2 Teach

Scaffolding Questions

Display 6 counters.

- **How could you find half of the counters?** Sample answer: Divide them into 2 equal groups and then count one group. Half of 6 is 3.
- **What fraction equation can you write to show half of 6?** $\frac{1}{2} \times 6 = 3$
- **How would you find two-thirds of the counters?** Sample answer: Divide the counters into 3 equal groups. $\frac{2}{3}$ of 6 is 4.
- **What fraction equation can you write to show two-thirds of 6?** $\frac{2}{3} \times 6 = 4$

GET READY to Learn

Have students open their books and read the information in **Get Ready to Learn**. Review **factor**, **numerator** and **denominator**. As a class, work through **Examples 1–3**.

Multiplying Fractions

MAIN IDEA

I will multiply fractions.

Math Online

macmillanmh.com

- Extra Examples
- Personal Tutor
- Self-Check Quiz

GET READY to Learn

Michael planted a vegetable garden. Two-thirds of the vegetables that he planted were green. Two-fifths of the green vegetables were peppers. The expression $\frac{2}{3} \times \frac{2}{5}$ represents the fraction of all the vegetables that Michael planted that were green peppers.

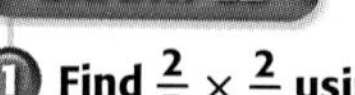

EXAMPLE Multiply Fractions

1 **Find $\frac{2}{3} \times \frac{2}{5}$ using a model. Write in simplest form.**

To find $\frac{2}{3} \times \frac{2}{5}$, find $\frac{2}{5}$ of $\frac{2}{3}$.

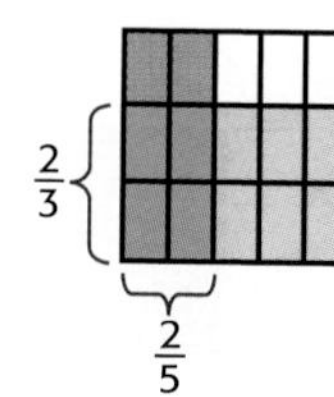

Shade $\frac{2}{3}$ of the square yellow.

Shade $\frac{2}{5}$ of the square blue.

The green region has been shaded twice. It represents the product.

Four out of 15 parts are shaded green. So, $\frac{2}{3} \times \frac{2}{5} = \frac{4}{15}$.

Multiplying Fractions — Key Concept

Words To multiply fractions, multiply the numerators and multiply the denominators.

Numbers $\frac{3}{5} \times \frac{1}{2} = \frac{3 \times 1}{5 \times 2}$

Algebra $\frac{a}{b} \times \frac{c}{d} = \frac{a \times c}{b \times d}$, where b and d are not 0.

You can simplify the fractions before or after you multiply them.

EXAMPLE **Multiply Fractions**

2 **Find $\frac{3}{4} \times \frac{5}{9}$.**

One Way: **Simplify after multiplying.**

$$\frac{3}{4} \times \frac{5}{9} = \frac{3 \times 5}{4 \times 9}$$

$$= \frac{15 \div 3}{36 \div 3} = \frac{5}{12} \quad \text{Simplify.}$$

Another Way: **Simplify before multiplying.**

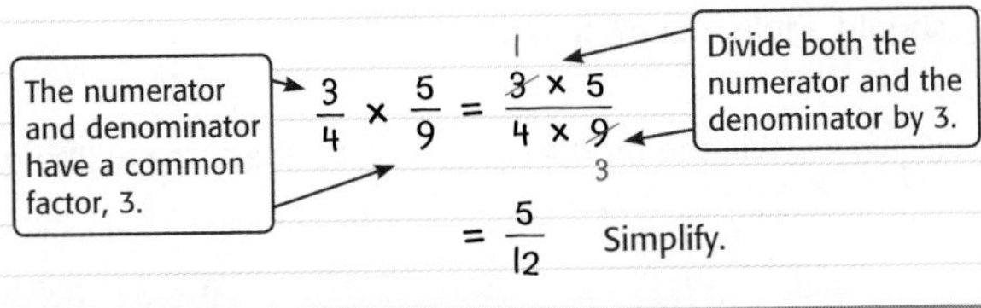

$$\frac{3}{4} \times \frac{5}{9} = \frac{\overset{1}{\cancel{3}} \times 5}{4 \times \underset{3}{\cancel{9}}}$$

$$= \frac{5}{12} \quad \text{Simplify.}$$

Real-World EXAMPLE

3 **FOOD The student council voted for the kind of food served at their school's year-end celebration. There are 10 council members, and $\frac{4}{8}$ of them voted for pizza. How many students voted for pizza?**

$\frac{4}{8} \times 10 = \frac{4 \times 10}{8 \times 1}$ Rewrite 10 as $\frac{10}{1}$.

$= \frac{40 \div 8}{8 \div 8} = \frac{5}{1}$ Simplify.

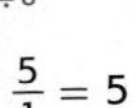

$\frac{5}{1} = 5$

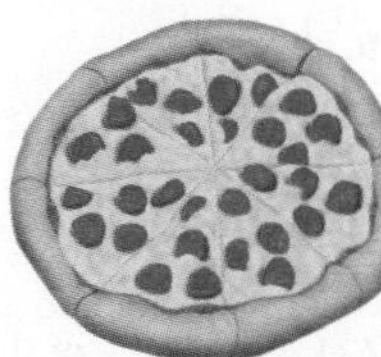

So, 5 of the students voted for pizza.

Simplifying Before Multiplying

Example 2 Explain that both strategies achieve the same product.

ADDITIONAL EXAMPLES

1 Find $\frac{1}{5} \times \frac{1}{6}$. $\frac{1}{30}$

2 Find $\frac{3}{7} \times \frac{2}{9}$. $\frac{2}{21}$

3 Twelve people order dessert, $\frac{3}{4}$ of them eat apple pie. How many people eat apple pie for dessert? $\frac{3}{4} \times 12 = 9$

CHECK What You Know

As a class, have students complete Exercises 1–12 in **Check What You Know** as you observe their work.

Exercise 12 Assess student comprehension before assigning practice exercises.

BL Alternate Teaching Strategy

If students have trouble multiplying fractions …

Then use this reteach option:

Have students draw an appropriately sized grid on paper, for example, $\frac{1}{6} \times \frac{3}{4}$. Students should draw a 6 by 4 grid. Have students shade the first column with red to show $\frac{1}{6}$. Have students shade the first three rows blue to represent $\frac{3}{4}$. The purple overlap represents the product, $\frac{3}{24}$.

3 Practice

Differentiate practice using these leveled assignments for Exercises 13–35.

Level	Assignment
BL Below/ Approaching Level	14–24 even, 30–34 even
OL On Level	13–23 odd, 25–35 odd
AL Above/Beyond Level	12–32 even, 33–35

Have students discuss and complete the Higher Order Thinking problems. For Exercises 32–33, students are asked to provide a counterexample if the statement is false. Explain that a counterexample is an example that shows a statement is *not* true.

WRITING IN MATH Have students complete Exercise 35 in their Math Journals. You may choose to use this exercise as an optional formative assessment.

CHECK What You Know

Multiply. Write in simplest form. **(See Examples 1–3, pp. LA6–LA7)**

1. $\frac{1}{7} \times \frac{1}{2}$ $\frac{1}{14}$
2. $\frac{4}{5} \times \frac{3}{4}$ $\frac{3}{5}$
3. $\frac{5}{6} \times \frac{3}{4}$ $\frac{5}{8}$
4. $\frac{3}{10} \times \frac{5}{6}$ $\frac{1}{4}$
5. $\frac{3}{4} \times \frac{2}{7}$ $\frac{3}{14}$
6. $\frac{3}{5} \times \frac{5}{6}$ $\frac{1}{2}$
7. $\frac{3}{4} \times \frac{5}{12}$ $\frac{5}{16}$
8. $\frac{2}{9} \times \frac{1}{3}$ $\frac{2}{27}$
9. $\frac{6}{7} \times \frac{3}{4}$ $\frac{9}{14}$

10. Melody is putting together a puzzle that has 50 pieces. She has $\frac{7}{10}$ of the puzzle complete. How many pieces does Melody have in place? 35 pieces

11. Adults should sleep $\frac{1}{3}$ of the day. How many hours of the day should adults sleep? 8 hours

12. Talk About It Will the product of $\frac{2}{9} \times \frac{1}{3}$ be the same as the product of $\frac{2}{9} \times \frac{2}{6}$? Explain. Sample answer: Yes, because $\frac{1}{3} = \frac{2}{6}$.

Practice and Problem Solving

Multiply. Write in simplest form. **(See Examples 1–3, pp. LA6–LA7)**

13. $\frac{2}{3} \times \frac{1}{4}$ $\frac{1}{6}$
14. $\frac{5}{6} \times \frac{2}{3}$ $\frac{5}{9}$
15. $\frac{3}{4} \times \frac{2}{5}$ $\frac{3}{10}$
16. $\frac{1}{3} \times \frac{2}{5}$ $\frac{2}{15}$
17. $\frac{3}{5} \times \frac{5}{7}$ $\frac{3}{7}$
18. $\frac{4}{9} \times \frac{3}{8}$ $\frac{1}{6}$
19. $\frac{3}{4} \times \frac{5}{8}$ $\frac{15}{32}$
20. $\frac{1}{8} \times \frac{3}{4}$ $\frac{3}{32}$
21. $\frac{1}{2} \times \frac{4}{9}$ $\frac{2}{9}$

22. Carrie ate $\frac{1}{5}$ of the oranges that her mother brought home from the grocery store. If there were 10 oranges, how many oranges did Carrie eat? 2 oranges

Algebra **Evaluate each expression if $a = \frac{3}{4}$, $b = \frac{2}{3}$, and $c = \frac{1}{6}$.**

23. ab $\frac{1}{2}$

24. cb $\frac{1}{9}$

25. ac $\frac{1}{8}$

26. $\frac{3}{5}a$ $\frac{9}{20}$

27. $\frac{5}{6}a$ $\frac{5}{8}$

28. abc $\frac{1}{12}$

29. Lydia is 63 inches tall. Her baby brother is $\frac{1}{3}$ of her height.

How many inches tall is Lydia's baby brother? 21 in.

30. Collin and his family are going on vacation for 6 days. They plan on spending $\frac{2}{3}$ of the days at the beach.

How many days will Collin and his family spend at the beach? 4 days

H.O.T. Problems

31. OPEN ENDED How can you determine if the product of $\frac{1}{2} \times \frac{4}{9}$ will be larger or smaller than $\frac{1}{2}$? Sample answer: Estimate $\frac{1}{2} \times \frac{1}{2} = \frac{1}{4}$

REASONING **State whether each statement is true or false. If the statement is false, provide a counterexample.**

32. The product of a whole number and a fraction is always a whole number. False; $1 \times \frac{1}{2} = \frac{1}{2}$

33. The product of two fractions that are each between 0 and 1 is also between 0 and 1. True

34. NUMBER SENSE If you toss a coin 20 times is it possible to land on heads $10\frac{1}{2}$ times? No. The number of times must be a whole number.

35. **WRITING IN ➤MATH** When multiplying $\frac{5}{6} \times \frac{3}{4}$, can you simplify before you multiply? Yes. 3 and 6 have a common factor of 3.

4 Assess

Formative Assessment

Write $\frac{2}{3} \times \frac{6}{16}$ on the board.

- **How do you multiply these fractions?** Multiply the numerators, 2 × 6; multiply the denominations 3 × 16; simplify the product, 0 $\frac{12}{48} = \frac{1}{4}$.
- **If you simplify before multiplying, how will that product compare to the product if you do not simplify first?** Sample answer: It will not make a difference because you can simplify before you multiply or simplify when you get the product.

Quick Check **Are students continuing to struggle with multiplying fractions?**

If Yes → Small Group Options (p. LA6B)
Strategic Intervention Guide (p. 110)

If No → Independent Work Options (p. LA6B)

Into the Future Have students write about how they think today's lesson on multiplying fractions will help them with tomorrow's lesson on multiplying mixed numbers.

COMMON ERROR!

Exercises 13–22 Remind students to simplify their answers whenever possible.

Ratios

Lesson Planner

Objective

Express ratios in fraction form.

Vocabulary

ratio

Resources

Teacher Technology

Interactive Classroom • TeacherWorks

Focus on Math Background

A ratio is a way of comparing two quantities that states their relative size, but not necessarily their specific values. Since a ratio involves division, and is often written as a fraction, students sometimes confuse ratios and fractions. Common fractions are used to represent parts of a whole or group while ratios frequently compare the number of objects in one set to the number of objects in a completely different set. The two sets may contain like or unlike things. Furthermore, ratios cannot be added, subtracted, multiplied, or divided like fractions can.

Ratios are presented in three forms, for example 2 to 6, 2:6, and $\frac{2}{6}$. The form involving a colon, 2:6, is not used as widely as it once was. A ratio can also be given as a decimal, such as 0.4, or 0.4 to 1. When a decimal is used to write a ratio, students may need to be reminded that it still compares two quantities.

Daily Routine

Use these suggestions before beginning the lesson on p. LA10.

5-Minute Check

(Reviews Looking Ahead 2)

Multiply. Write in simplest form.

1. $\frac{2}{3} \times \frac{1}{4}$ $\frac{1}{6}$
2. $\frac{4}{5} \times \frac{3}{4}$ $\frac{3}{5}$
3. $\frac{1}{2} \times \frac{1}{7}$ $\frac{1}{14}$
4. $\frac{1}{8} \times \frac{2}{3}$ $\frac{1}{12}$

Problem of the Day

Which ratio does not belong in this group? Explain your reasoning. $\frac{2}{6}, \frac{4}{12}, \frac{6}{18}, \frac{3}{9}, \frac{6}{9}, \frac{7}{21}$

$\frac{6}{9}$; All the other ratios in simplest form are equivalent to $\frac{1}{3}$.

Building Math Vocabulary

Write the lesson vocabulary words and their definitions on the board.

Have students write the new words in their Math Journals. Include an example for each term.

Visual Vocabulary Cards

Use Visual Vocabulary Card 38 to reinforce vocabulary introduced in this lesson. (The Define/Example/Ask routine is printed on the back of each card.)

ratio

Differentiated Instruction

Small Group Options

SPATIAL, LOGICAL

Option 1 Gifted and Talented 

Materials: paper and pencil

Give students problems involving ratios found on a state map. For example, pose the following problem: *What is the ratio of states beginning with a vowel to those beginning with a consonant?*

INTRAPERSONAL

Option 2 English Language Learners 

Materials: chalkboard
Core Vocabulary: answer, we, ratio
Common Use Verb: like

Talk Math This strategy helps students understand ratios and comparative language.

- Say: "Which sport do you ***like*** more, baseball or soccer?
- Write the ratio in simplest form that compares the number of students who like baseball better than soccer. Say: "This is called a **ratio**. Explain how a **ratio answers** our question: Which sport do **we *like*** more?"
- Repeat for the number of students who like dogs instead of cats as time permits.

Independent Work Options

AUDITORY, SOCIAL

Option 1 Early Finishers  

Materials: paper and pencil

- Have students find ratios in the classroom, such as 5 computers to 35 students, 2 wall maps to 18 students.

Option 2 Student Technology

Math Online macmillanmh.com

Personal Tutor • Extra Examples

Math Adventures

Ratios

1 Introduce

Activity • Hands-On

- Display 36 counters of different colors. Have students record their answers when you ask the following questions.
- **What fraction of the counters is red? blue? yellow?** Answers will vary.
- **What is the fraction of red and blue counters together? of yellow and green counters together?** Answers will vary.
- **Write each fraction in simplest form.** Answers will vary.

2 Teach

Scaffolding Questions

Count the number of girls and boys in the class and display these numbers on the board.

- **What fraction shows the part the girls represent in the class? What part are the boys?** Answers will vary.
- **Can these fractions be simplified?** Answers will vary.
- **How could you use a fraction to write a ratio to compare the number of girls and boys in this class?** Sample answer: I would write the number of girls as the numerator and the number of boys as the denominator.

GET READY to Learn

Have students open their books and read the information in **Get Ready to Learn**. Introduce **ratio** and **equivalent ratio**. As a class, work through **Examples 1–3**.

Ratios

MAIN IDEA

What You'll Learn
Express ratios and rates in fraction form.

New Vocabulary

ratio
equivalent ratios

Math Online
macmillanmh.com
- Extra Examples
- Personal Tutor
- Self-Check Quiz

GET READY to Learn

CLOTHES The table shows how many shirts of each color are on a shelf.

Shirts	
Color	**Number**
Black	6
Yellow	10
Blue	5
Red	4
Green	7

1. Write a sentence that compares the number of green shirts to the number of red shirts. Use the word *less* in your sentence. See margin.
2. Write a sentence that compares the number of blue shirts to the number of yellow shirts. Use the word *half* in your sentence. See margin.
3. Write a sentence comparing the number of black shirts to the total number of shirts. Use a fraction in your sentence. See margin.

There are many ways to compare numbers. A **ratio** is a comparison of two numbers by division. A ratio of 7 green shirts to 10 yellow shirts can be written in three ways.

Ratio	Using *to*	Using:	Using a *Fraction*
green shirts to yellow shirts	7 to 10	7:10	$\frac{7}{10}$

Real-World EXAMPLE Write a Ratio in Simplest Form

1 **VEGETABLES Write the ratio that compares the number of carrots to the pieces of broccoli.**

carrots → $\frac{4}{6} = \frac{2}{3}$ ← broccoli

The ratio of carrots to broccoli is $\frac{2}{3}$, 2 to 3, or 2:3. $\frac{4}{6}$ and $\frac{2}{3}$ are said to be **equivalent ratios** since $\frac{4}{6} = \frac{2}{3}$.

Additional Answers

1. There are 3 less red shirts than green shirts.
2. There are half as many blue shirts than there are yellow shirts.
3. Of the shirts on the shelf, $\frac{3}{16}$ are red shirts.

EXAMPLE Use Ratios to Compare Parts to a Whole

2 FLOWERS Write the ratio that compares the number of red flowers to the total number of flowers.

red flowers → $\frac{4}{12} = \frac{1}{3}$
total flowers →

The ratio of red flowers to the total number of flowers is $\frac{1}{3}$, 1 to 3, or 1:3. For every one red flower, there are three total flowers.

EXAMPLE Use Ratio Tables

3 FOOD To make 5 peach pies, you need 2 pounds of peaches. How many pounds of peaches do you need to make 20 pies?

Set up a ratio table.

Number of Pies	5		20
Pounds of Peaches	2		■

Label the rows with the two quantities being compared. Then fill in what is given.

Multiply to find the desired quantity.

Number of Pies	5	× 4	20
Pounds of Peaches	2	× 4	8

Multiply each quantity by 4.

So, use 8 pounds of peaches to make 20 pies.

CHECK What You Know

Write each ratio as a fraction in simplest form. **(See Examples 1–3 pp. LA10–LA11)**

1. 6 dogs to 8 cats $\frac{3}{4}$
2. 15 pens to 45 pencils $\frac{1}{3}$
3. 10 mosquitoes out of 30 insects $\frac{1}{3}$
4. 4 pretzels out of 24 snacks $\frac{1}{6}$
5. 14 dimes to 24 nickels $\frac{7}{12}$
6. 15 rubies to 25 emeralds $\frac{3}{5}$
7. 

Example 1 gave a part to part ratio, and Example 2 gave a part to whole ratio. Explain the difference between a ratio comparing part to part and a ratio comparing part to whole. See margin.

Additional Answer

7. Sample Answer: A ratio comparing part to part compares objects within a set. A ratio comparing part to whole compares an object to the entire set.

ADDITIONAL EXAMPLES

1. Write the ratio in simplest form that compares the number of scooters to the number of unicycles. $\frac{1}{4}$

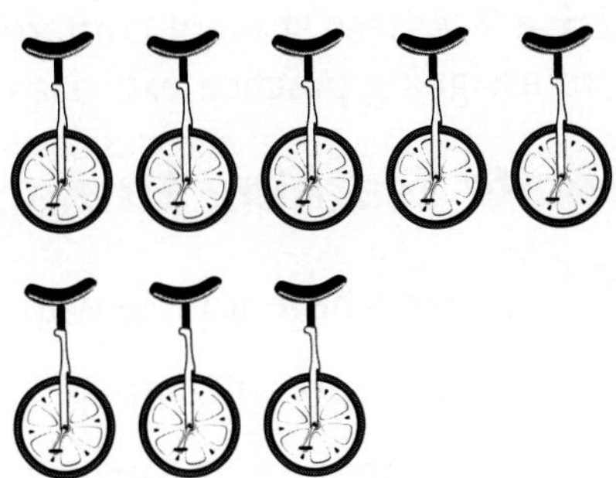

2. Refer to Additional Example 1. Write the ratio that compares the number of scooters to the total number of scooters and unicycles. $\frac{1}{5}$

3. To make 3 pans of lasagna, you need 4 pounds of ground beef. How many pounds of ground beef do you need to make 9 pans of lasagna? 12

CHECK What You Know

As a class, have students complete Exercises 1–7 in **Check What You Know** as you observe their work.

Exercise 7 Assess student comprehension before assigning practice exercises.

BL Alternate Teaching Strategy

If students have trouble with ratios …

Then use this reteach option:

Display classroom items, such as 6 pencils and 5 books.

- **How many items do you see in all?** 11 items
- **Write a ratio comparing pencils to all the items.** $\frac{6}{11}$

3 Practice

Differentiate practice using these leveled assignments for Exercises 8–32.

Level	Assignment
BL Below/ Approaching Level	8–28 even
OL On Level	8–22, 24, 26, 28
AL Above/Beyond Level	8–28 even, 29–32

Have students discuss and complete the Higher Order Thinking problems. Encourage students to draw pictures or make a table to help solve Exercise 31.

WRITING IN ▸MATH Have students complete Exercise 32 in their Math Journals. You may choose to use this exercise as an optional formative assessment.

Practice and Problem Solving

Write each ratio as a fraction in simplest form. (See Examples 1–3 pp. LA10–LA11)

8. 15 elm trees to 10 pine trees $\frac{3}{2}$

9. 8 circles to 22 squares $\frac{4}{11}$

10. 6 iguanas out of 21 lizards $\frac{2}{7}$

11. 4 cell phones out of 18 phones $\frac{2}{9}$

12. 10 girls out of 24 students $\frac{5}{12}$

13. 32 apples out of 72 pieces of fruit $\frac{4}{9}$

Write an equivalent ratio to each ratio given.

14. 2:3 Sample answer: 4:6

15. 4 to 7 Sample answer: 8 to 14

16. $\frac{5}{9}$ Sample answer: $\frac{10}{18}$

17. 5:6 Sample answer: 10:12

18. 3 to 11 Sample answer: 6 to 22

19. $\frac{3}{8}$ Sample answer: $\frac{6}{16}$

20. Draw a picture showing 4 pencils and a number of pens in which the ratio of pencils to pens is 2:3. See margin.

21. In a certain store, the ratio of high definition televisions sold to regular televisions is 1 to 4. Explain the meaning of this ratio. For every 4 televisions sold, one is high definition.

22. Find the ratio of the number of vowels in the word *Mississippi* to the number of consonants. Write as a fraction in simplest form. $\frac{4}{7}$

Real-World PROBLEM SOLVING

Social Studies There are 23 states in the United States that border an ocean. Only 5 of those states border the Pacific Ocean.

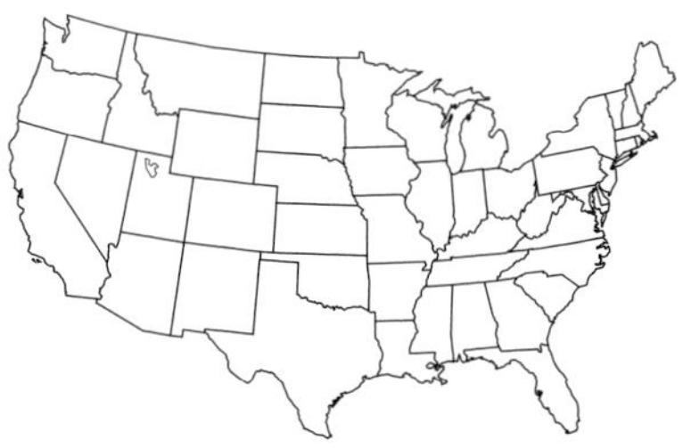

23. Write a ratio for the number of states bordering the Pacific Ocean to the number of states bordering any ocean. 5:23

24. Write a ratio for the number of states that border an ocean to the number of states in the United States. 23:50

Additional Answers

20.

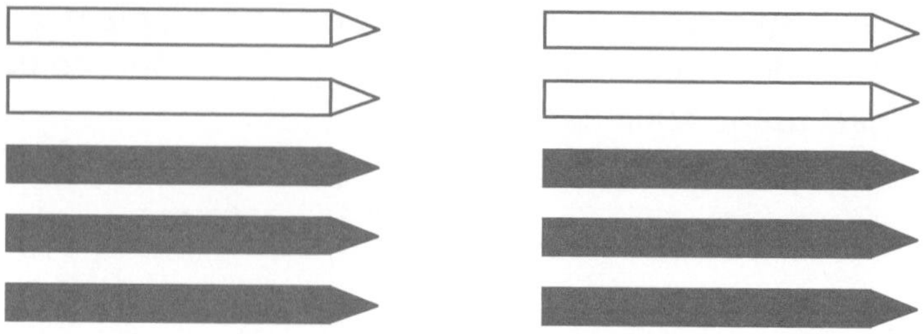

32. Sample Answer: There will be 7 quarters because $\frac{1}{3} = \frac{7}{21}$.

25. It is school policy that for field trips there is 1 adult to go along with every 8 students. How many adults will go on a field trip with 48 students? **6 adults**

Number of Adults	1	× ?	■
Number of Students	8	× ?	48

26. At a school cafeteria, 3 out of every 5 students order a hamburger. If 60 students are eating in the cafeteria, how many students order a hamburger? **36 students**

Number of Hamburgers	3	× ?	■
Number of Students	5	× ?	60

For Exercises 27 and 28, use the graphic at the right. Write each ratio in simplest form.

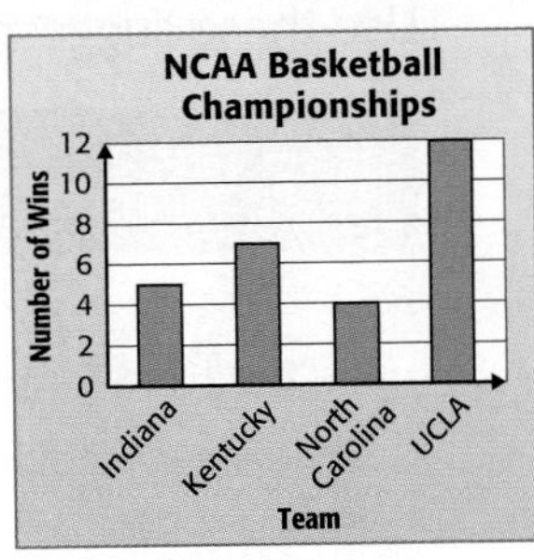

27. What ratio compares the number of wins for Indiana to the number of wins for Kentucky? $\frac{5}{7}$

28. What ratio compares the number of wins for North Carolina to the number of wins for UCLA? $\frac{1}{3}$

H.O.T. Problems

29. **NUMBER SENSE** Write the ratio 6 robins out of 15 birds in three different ways. **6:15, 6 to 15,** $\frac{6}{15}$

30. **CRITICAL THINKING** If 12 out of 40 students received above a 95% on the test, what ratio of students received a 95% or below? **28 out of 40**

31. **FIND THE ERROR** There are 6 red, 5 blue, 9 green, and 4 yellow marbles in a bag. Ivan and Martha are each writing a part to whole ratio for the number of blue marbles. Who is correct? Explain. **Sample answer: Martha is correct. Ivan did a part to part ratio, not a part to whole ratio.**

Ivan

$\frac{\text{blue}}{\text{red}} = \frac{5}{6}$

Martha

$\frac{\text{blue}}{\text{total marbles}} = \frac{5}{24}$

32. **WRITING IN ▸MATH** The ratio of quarters to pennies in a piggy bank is 1 to 3. Explain how to write an equivalent ratio showing the number of pennies in the bank if there are 7 quarters. **See margin.**

4 Assess

Formative Assessment

- Write **ten basketballs to 25 baseballs** as a ratio using a colon, as a fraction, and by using the word "to". 10:25, $\frac{10}{25}$, 10 to 25.
- Is $\frac{2}{5}$ an equivalent ratio to 10:25? yes

Ticket Out The Door Have students write the ratio of boys to girls on a small piece of paper and hand it to the teacher as they leave the classroom.

Looking Ahead 4

Rates

Lesson Planner

Objective

Express rates in fraction form.

Vocabulary

rate, **unit rate**

Resources

Teacher Technology

Interactive Classroom • TeacherWorks

Focus on Math Background

A rate is a ratio that compares two quantities with different kinds of units. When a rate is simplified so that it has a denominator of 1, it is called a unit rate. Students use unit rates in their everyday lives to measure and compare rates such as speed, price, and wage. Many real-world problems can be solved by extending or projecting a unit rate.

Daily Routine

Use these suggestions before beginning the lesson on p. LA14.

5-Minute Check

(Reviews Looking Ahead 3)

Write each ratio as a fraction in simplest form.

1. 6 tomatoes to 8 green peppers $\frac{3}{4}$
2. 14 girls to 16 boys $\frac{7}{8}$
3. 12 buttons to 20 paper clips $\frac{3}{5}$
4. 5 quarters to 15 pennies $\frac{1}{3}$

Problem of the Day

Which has the better unit price: a 8-ounce jar of salsa for $2.40 or a 10-ounce jar of salsa for $2.70? 10-ounce jar

Building Math Vocabulary

Write the lesson vocabulary words and their definitions on the board.

Have students write the new words in their Math Journals. Include an example for each term. Explain how *ratio*, *rate*, and *unit rate* are related.

Visual Vocabulary Cards

Use Visual Vocabulary Cards 38 and 39 to reinforce vocabulary introduced or reviewed in this lesson. (The Define/Example/Ask routine is printed on the back of each card.)

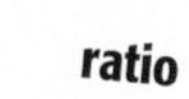

Differentiated Instruction

Small Group Options

SPATIAL, LOGICAL

Option 1 Gifted and Talented AL

Materials: paper and pencil

Give students problems involving gas mileage and ask them to solve. For example, pose the following problem: *If your car gets 30 miles to the gallon and holds 16 gallons, how many times would you fill up for a 2,000 mile trip?*

INTRAPERSONAL

Option 2 English Language Learners ELL

Materials: chalkboard
Core Vocabulary: answer, rate, drive
Common Use Verb: is faster
Talk Math This strategy helps students understand rates and comparative language.

- Say: "Is it ***faster*** to drive 55 miles per hour or 45 miles per hour?"
- Write both rates on the board. Say: "This is called a **rate**. Explain how a **rate answers** our question: "Which is **faster**?"

Independent Work Options

AUDITORY, SOCIAL

Option 1 Early Finishers OL AL

Materials: paper and pencil

- Have students calculate the rate it takes to perform several activities, such as sharpening 10 pencils, reading 2 pages in their textbook, etc.

Option 2 Student Technology

Math Online macmillanmh.com

Personal Tutor • Extra Examples

Math Adventures

Rates

1 Introduce

Activity • Hands-On

Have students work in pairs. Have them take turns reading as much as possible in 2 minutes from a written text. Count the number of words that each student read in 2 minutes. Ask the following questions.

- **Write the ratio of number of words read to number of minutes.** Answers will vary.
- **How many words could you read in one minute at this rate?** Answers will vary.

2 Teach

Scaffolding Questions

Ask:

- **What is the speed limit on the highway?** 60/65/70 mph
- **If you drive at that speed, how far will you travel in one hour?** 60/65/70 miles
- **If 4 pounds of tomatoes cost $8, how much would one pound cost?** $2

GET READY to Learn

Have students open their books and read the information in **Get Ready to Learn**. Introduce **rate** and **unit rate**. As a class, work through **Examples 1–3**.

Rates

MAIN IDEA

I will express rates in fraction form.

New Vocabulary

rate
unit rate

Math Online

macmillanmh.com
- Extra Examples
- Personal Tutor
- Self-Check Quiz

GET READY to Learn

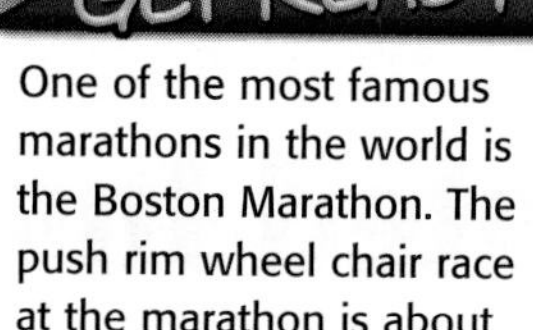

One of the most famous marathons in the world is the Boston Marathon. The push rim wheel chair race at the marathon is about 26 miles. Some athletes must have a qualifying time of 2 hours in order to race.

26 miles in 2 hours $= \frac{26 \text{ mi}}{2 \text{ h}} = \frac{13 \text{ mi}}{1 \text{ h}}$

The average rate, of the athlete must be 13 miles per hour.

A ratio that compares two quantities with different kinds of units is called a **rate**. The example above compares miles and hours.

When a rate is simplified so that it has a denominator of 1 unit, it is called a **unit rate**. The table shows common unit rates.

Ratio	Unit Rate	Name
$\frac{\text{number of miles}}{\text{1 hour}}$	miles per hour	speed
$\frac{\text{number of miles}}{\text{1 gallon}}$	miles per gallon	gas mileage
$\frac{\text{number of dollars}}{\text{1hour}}$	dollars per hour	hourly wage

EXAMPLE Find Unit Rates

1 **Write 300 feet in 30 seconds as a unit rate in feet per second.**

$= \frac{300 \text{ ft}}{30 \text{ s}}$ Write the rate as a fraction.

$= \frac{300 \text{ ft} \div 30}{30 \text{ s} \div 30}$ Divide the numerator and the denominator by 30.

$= \frac{10 \text{ ft}}{1 \text{ s}}$ Simplify.

So, the unit rate is 10 feet per second.

Real-World EXAMPLE

2 **A family of four attend a baseball game and want to eat hot dogs. Find the unit rate if it costs $12 for 4 hot dogs.**

$12 for 4 hot dogs $= \frac{\$12}{4 \text{ hot dogs}}$ Write the rate as a fraction.

$= \frac{\$12 \div 4}{4 \div 4}$ Divide the numerator and the denominator by 4.

$= \frac{\$3}{1 \text{ hot dog}}$ Simplify.

So, the unit rate is $3 per hot dog.

In Example 2, you found a special kind of unit rate, called the *unit price.* This is the price per unit and is useful when you want to compare the cost of an item that comes in different sizes.

EXAMPLE Choose the Best Buy Using Estimation

3 **The costs of different sized bags of sand used to fill a sandbox are shown. Which bag costs the least per pound?**

Size	Price
3 lb	$12.05
4 lb	$19.99
8 lb	$40.25

Find the unit price, or the cost per pound, of each bag. Divide the price by the number of pounds.

Estimated cost

3-pound bag $12 ÷ 3 pounds = $4 per pound
4-pound bag $20 ÷ 4 pounds = $5 per pound
8-pound bag $40 ÷ 8 pounds = $5 per pound

The 3-pound bag costs the least per pound.

CHECK What You Know

Find each unit rate. **(See Examples 1–3, pp. LA14–LA15)**

1. $36 for 12 gallons $3 per gallon

2. 1,500 words in 25 minutes 60 words per min

3. 55 pounds for $11 5 lbs per dollar

4. 28 cans of juice for $7 4 cans per dollar

5. A person jumps rope 36 times in 18 seconds. What is the unit rate? 2 jumps per s

6. Which has the better unit price: a 6-pack of soda for $3 or a 12-pack for $4? a 12-pack for $4

7. **WRITING IN MATH** Ethan can buy 4 DVDs for $72.12 at DVD World or 9 DVDs for $153.25 at Movie Town. Estimate to find which has the better unit price. Explain. Movie Town; $17/CD < $18/CD

ADDITIONAL EXAMPLES

1 Write 240 miles in 4 hours as a unit rate in miles per hour. 60 mph

2 Jared bought 8 movie tickets for a total of $72. Find the unit rate. $9 per ticket

3 The costs of different sizes of bags of dog food are shown in the table. Which bag costs the least per pound? Use estimation. 25-lb bag

Size	Price ($)
5 lb	2.65
10 lb	4.80
25 lb	10.25

Find a Unit Rate

Examples 1–3 Remind students that when they write a unit rate, it must have a denominator of 1.

CHECK What You Know

As a class, have students complete Exercises 1–7 in **Check What You Know** as you observe their work.

Exercise 7 Assess student comprehension before assigning practice exercises.

BL Alternate Teaching Strategy

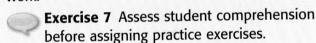

If students have trouble with rates ...

Then use this reteach option:

Display classroom items, such as 6 pencils and 5 books.

- **Suppose you could buy six pencils for 48¢. Use a ratio to find the unit rate.** $\frac{48¢}{6} = \frac{8¢}{1}$
- **Suppose you could buy five books for $60. Use a ratio to find the unit rate.** $\frac{\$60}{5} = \frac{\$12}{1}$

3 Practice

Differentiate practice using these leveled assignments for Exercises 8–34.

Level	Assignment
BL Below/ Approaching Level	8–28 even
OL On Level	8–13, 18, 20, 22, 24, 26, 28–30, 32–34
AL Above/Beyond Level	8–28 even, 30–34

Have students discuss and complete the Higher Order Thinking problems.

WRITING IN MATH Have students complete Exercise 34 in their Math Journals. You may choose to use this exercise as an optional formative assessment.

Practice and Problem Solving

Find each unit rate. (See Examples 1–3, pp. LA14–LA15)

8. $45 for 5 pounds $9 per lb

9. $96 for 8 ounces $12 per oz

10. 150 people for 5 classes 30 people per class

11. 420 miles in 6 hours 70 miles per h

12. 210 visitors in 35 days 6 visitors per day

13. 510 Calories in 3 servings 170 calories per serving

14. 40 meters in 4 seconds 10 m per s

15. 84 miles in 14 gallons 6 m per gal

16. 70 yards in 7 minutes 10 yards per min

17. $45 in 5 hours $9 per hr

Use estimation to choose the better value.

18. $47.99 for a 16-ounce bag or $23.60 for a 12-ounce bag
$23.60 for a 12-ounce bag

19. vitamins sold in bottles of 24 for $3.69, 50 for $5.49, 100 for $10.29, or 180 for $11.99 180 for $11.99

Use the table at the right for Exercises 20 and 21.

Container	Serving Size (oz)	Price
A	18	$5.80
B	16	$4.34
C	12	$3.72
D	10	$2.30

20. Estimate the cost of each container to the nearest dollar amount. Which container has the best value? Container D

21. Which two containers have about the same unit price? Container A and Container C

22. A fountain pumps 60,000 gallons of water every 15 minutes. What is the unit rate? 4,000 gal per min

23. Find the unit rate if 40 tickets are sold in 8 minutes. 5 tickets per minute

24. Rebecca blinks her eyes 60 times in 5 minutes. At this rate, how many times does she blink in one minute? 12

25. Luke can type 300 words in 5 minutes. At this rate, how many words can he type in one minute? 60 words

Use the table at the right for Exercises 26–27.

Job	Total Paid	Days Per Week
Server	$160	4
Valet	$168	3
Cashier	$144	2
Librarian	$256	4

26. Lannie is looking for a job that pays at least 64 dollars a day. However, she must work at least 3 days a week. Use the table to determine which job fits Lannie's needs the best. Explain. Librarian; It is the only job that is at least 3 days a week and pays $64 a day.

27. Which job pays the most money per day? Cashier

Real-World PROBLEM SOLVING

SHARKS **The Shortfin Mako uses its incredible speed to track down fish like the tuna or the sword fish. The Mako is the fastest shark in the ocean. It can travel as far as 60 miles in only 3 hours.**

28. How many miles can the Mako shark travel in one hour? 20 miles

29. How long would it take the Mako shark to travel 80 miles if were traveling at top speed? 4 hrs

H.O.T. Problems

30. **NUMBER SENSE** In which situation will the rate $\frac{x \text{ ft}}{y \text{ min}}$ increase? Explain your reasoning.

a. x increases, y is unchanged

b. x is unchanged, y increases

Situation a: Sample answer; because you are traveling more distance without increasing time

31. **CHALLENGE** A rate is always a ratio, but a ratio is not always a rate. Write a sentence or two to explain this statement, and give an example of when a ratio is not a rate. A ratio that compares two numbers with like units is not a rate. $\frac{4 \text{ ft}}{8 \text{ ft}}$

32. **WHICH ONE DOESN'T BELONG?** Identify the measurement that is different from the other three. Explain your reasoning. See margin.

8 ft per s	25 mi
6 cans per pack	$16 per lb

33. **CHALLENGE** The stationery store sold 6 boxes of colored notebook paper in 15 minutes. At this rate, how many boxes will they sell per hour? 24 boxes

34. **WRITING IN MATH** Write a sentence describing how unit price can help you spend less money at the grocery store. Sample answer: Unit price gives the cost of one item within a set. This enables you to compare the cost of items.

Additional Answer

32. 25 mi; It is the only measurement that is not a rate.

4 Assess

Formative Assessment

- Explain how to find the unit rate for the following: $50 for 5 pounds. Divide $50 and 5 pounds each by 5. $10 for 1 pound.

Ticket Out The Door Have students write the unit rate for 360 miles in 6 hours on a small piece of paper and hand it to the teacher as they leave the classroom. 60 mph

Looking Ahead 5

Order of Operations

Lesson Planner

Objective

Find the value of expressions using the order of operations.

Vocabulary

order of operations

Resources

Teacher Technology

Interactive Classroom • TeacherWorks

Focus on Math Background

Students already know how to add, subtract, multiply, and divide. As they learn to evaluate expressions that contain several different operations, they need guidelines as to the order in which the operations must be performed. Consider the expression $5 + 2 \times 8$. Do you add $5 + 2$ to get 7 and then multiply by 8 to get 56? Or do you multiply 2×8 to get 16 and then add 5 to get 21? To avoid confusion, mathematicians created the order of operations guidelines. These guidelines say that operations within parentheses are performed first, the values of powers are found second, then multiplications and divisions are performed from left to right, and lastly additions and subtractions are performed from left to right. If these guidelines are followed, the value of the expression $5 + 2 \times 8$ is $5 + 16$ or 21.

It should be noted that when there may be multiple operations within the parentheses, (e.g., $19 - (3 + 4)$), it is as if the operations within the parentheses are a mini-problem. When this occurs, the order of operations guidelines are followed within the parentheses before continuing on with the operations outside of the parentheses, e.g., $19 - (3 + 4)$ is $19 - 7$, which is equal to 12.

Daily Routine

Use these suggestions before beginning the lesson on p. LA18.

5-Minute Check

(Reviews Looking Ahead 4)

Find the unit rate.

1. \$34 for 2 feet \$17 per foot
2. 800 pounds for \$100 8 lbs per dollar
3. 42 times in 6 seconds 7 times per s

Problem of the Day

A store sells bottles of hand lotion for \$7 each and scented candles for \$8 each. Write an expression to find the total cost of four bottles of hand lotion and three scented candles. Then find the value of the expression. $4 \times \$7 + 3 \times \$8$; \$52

Building Math Vocabulary

Write the lesson vocabulary words and their definitions on the board.

Divide the class into small groups. Have each group make a poster showing the steps for the order of operations. Hang the posters on the wall.

Visual Vocabulary Cards

Use Visual Vocabulary Card 28 to reinforce the vocabulary introduced in this lesson. (The Define/Example/Ask routine is printed on the back of each card.)

order of operations

Differentiated Instruction

Small Group Options

SPATIAL

Option 1 Gifted and Talented AL

Materials: paper, pencil

- Present the following problems to students (see the sheet of paper to the right).
- Tell students to use the order of operations and the symbols ( ) × ÷ + − to create a true statement.

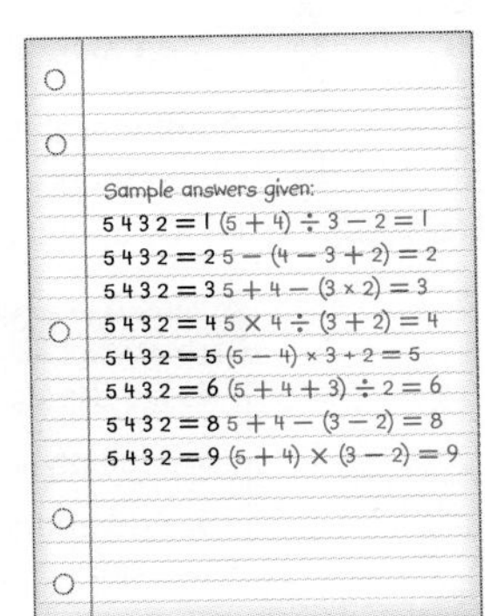

KINESTHETIC

Option 2 English Language Learners ELL

Materials: a hopscotch-looking poster on a playground against a brick wall, with: ( ), powers in the top 2 squares and ×, ÷ and +, − in side by side squares in the bottom 2 rows above chalk hopscotch that mimics the poster; whiteboard

Core Vocabulary: Where do you start? hop, then

Common Use Verb: follow

Do Math This strategy uses kinesthetic learning to help students follow the correct order of operations.

- Show poster and say: "This is the order you ***follow*** when doing a problem.
- Write "50 ÷ 5 − 3 + (3 × 12)" on the whiteboard. Say: "Where do you start?" Model solving the problem, hopping through sequential steps.
- Repeat as time permits, providing the solutions as necessary.

Independent Work Options

LOGICAL

Option 1 Early Finishers OL AL

Materials: a variety of advertisements and circulars for food and household items

- Ask students to create a short grocery list for a family (no more than 5 items).
- Then have students write expressions for the items on their list and use the order of operations to find the value of each expression.

Option 2 Student Technology

Math Online macmillanmh.com

Personal Tutor • Extra Examples

Order of Operations

1 Introduce

Activity • Hands-On

- Write $5 + 3 \times 2$ on the board.
- Divide the class into small groups. Have each group work the problem.
- Have the groups tell the order in which they performed the various operations and their answers. Answers will vary.
- Tell students it is necessary that everyone agrees on the answer when working a problem with several operations. As a result, it is agreed that everyone should follow the steps known as the order of operations.

2 Teach

Scaffolding Questions

Write the following problem on the board:

$6 + 2 \times 5 =$

- **What is the answer if you add and then multiply?** 40
- **What is the answer if you multiply and then add?** 16
- **Which answer is correct? How do you know?** Sample answer: 16; according to the order of operations, you must multiply before you add.

GET READY to Learn

Have students open their books and read the information in **Get Ready to Learn**. Introduce **order of operations**. As a class, work through **Examples 1–3**.

Order of Operations

MAIN IDEA

I will use the order of operations to find the value of expressions.

New Vocabulary

order of operations

Math Online

macmillanmh.com

- Extra Examples
- Personal Tutor
- Self-Check Quiz

GET READY to Learn

CHORES **The table shows the number of minutes Erica spends doing each activity after school.**

Activity	Time Spent (min)
walking the dog	25
watering plants	10

1. How many total minutes are spent if Erica walks the dog for five days after school? 125 min
2. How many total minutes are spent if Erica walks the dog and waters plants for four days after school? 140 min
3. What two operations did you use in Exercise 2? Explain how to find the answer to Exercise 2 using these operations. multiplication and addition; Sample answer: I multiplied 25 by 4 and 10 by 4. Then I added the products.

A numerical expression like $25 \times 4 + 10 \times 4$ is a combination of numbers and operations. The **order of operations** tells you which operation to perform to evaluate the expression.

Order of Operations — Key Concept

1. Do the operations in the parentheses first.
2. Multiply and divide in order from left to right.
3. Add and subtract in order from left to right.

EXAMPLES Use Order of Operations

1 **Find $25 \times 4 + 10 \times 4$.**

$25 \times 4 + 10 \times 4$	Write the expression.
$100 + 40$	Since there are no parentheses, multiply 25 by 4 and 10 by 4.
140	Add 100 and 40.

2 **Find $7 \times (9 - 3)$.**

$7 \times (9 - 3)$	Write the expression.
7×6	Find 9 – 3 first because it is in parentheses.
42	Multiply 7 and 6.

Real-World EXAMPLE — Write and Find the Value of Expressions

3 CHORES Refer to the lesson opener. Write an expression to find the total number of minutes Erica spends walking the dog and watering plants for three days after school. Then find the value of the expression.

First, write the expression.

Words	number of minutes spent walking the dog for three days.	+	number of minutes spent watering plants for three days.
Expression	25 × 3	+	10 × 3

$25 \times 3 + 10 \times 3 = 75 + 30$ — First, multiply 25 by 3 and 10 by 3.

$= 105$ — Add.

So, Erica spends a total of 105 minutes walking the dog and watering the plants for three days after school.

CHECK What You Know

Find the value of each expression. See Examples 1, 2 (p. LA18)

1. 8 + 3 × 2 14
2. 5 + 4 × 6 29
3. 10 ÷ 2 + 1 6
4. 13 + 16 ÷ 4 17
5. 4 × 3 + 3 × 9 39
6. 6 × 5 + 2 × 2 34
7. 8 + (7 × 3) 29
8. 20 – (3 × 5) 5
9. (4 + 2) × 8 48
10. 9 × (3 + 4) 63
11. 18 ÷ (3 + 3) 3
12. 1 + (15 ÷ 3) 6
13. Makayla and Samson are entered in a two-person relay race. Makayla will run 2 miles and Samson will bicycle 4 miles. Makayla can run one mile in 9 minutes and Samson can bicycle one mile in 4 minutes. Write an expression to find the total time to finish the race. Then find the value of the expression See Example 3 (p. LA19) 2 × 9 + 4 × 4; 34 min
14. A store sells DVDs for $18 each and CDs for $12 each. Write an expression to find the total cost of four DVDs and four CDs. Then find the value of the expression. See Example 3 (p. LA19) 4 × $18 + 4 × $12; $120.
15. Talk About It What operation would you perform first in evaluating the expression 8 – (3 × 4) + 5? Explain. Find 3 × 4 first; Sample answer: You should simplify all expressions inside parentheses first.

Use Order of Operations

Example 1 In problems such as this one, students are often tempted to add before they multiply. Remind them that multiplication is always performed before addition unless grouping symbols tell them otherwise.

ADDITIONAL EXAMPLES

Find the value of each expression.

1. 8 × 5 + 7 × 3 61
2. 4 × (6 – 2) 16
3. A DVD rental store rents new releases for $6 each and older releases for $4 each. Write an expression to find the total cost of renting two new releases and three older releases. Then find the value of the expression. 2 × $6 + 3 × $4; $24

Tips for New Teachers You may want to create a mnemonic device or have your students create one to help them remember the sequence for order of operations such as:

Please	**P**arentheses
Excuse	**E**xponents
My **D**ear	**M**ultiply/**D**ivide from left to right
Aunt **S**ally	**A**dd/**S**ubtract from left to right

As a class, have students complete Exercises 1–15 in **Check What You Know** as you observe their work.

Exercise 15 Assess student comprehension before assigning practice exercises.

BL Alternate Teaching Strategy

If students have trouble following the guidelines for the order of operations ...

Then use this reteach option:

Write the following expression on the board and have students copy it onto a piece of paper: 12 − (7 + 3) + 6 × 9. Tell students to leave room between the numbers and signs.

- Read out each number of the order of operations. In different colors, students write a 1 above the expression in parentheses, a 2 above the multiplication sign, a 3 above the minus sign, and a 4 above the plus sign in front of 6.
- Using the example they have just completed, students create a chart or list to keep in their notebooks to use as a reference.

3 Practice

Differentiate practice using these leveled assignments for Exercises 16–47.

Level	Assignment
BL Below/ Approaching Level	16–27, 35, 36, 42, 43, 47
OL On Level	17–47 odd, 47
AL Above/Beyond Level	17–41 odd, 42–47

Have students discuss and complete the Higher Order Thinking problems. Encourage them to perform only one operation at a time as they follow the order of operation steps.

WRITING IN ▸MATH Have students complete Exercise 47 in their Math Journals. You may choose to use this exercise as an optional formative assessment.

Practice and Problem Solving

Find the value of each expression. See Examples 1, 2 (p. LA18)

16. 7 + 5 × 4 27 **17.** 3 + 3 × 3 12 **18.** 14 + 2 × 6 26

19. 8 + 5 × 7 43 **20.** 25 ÷ 5 + 3 8 **21.** 12 ÷ 4 − 1 2

22. 28 ÷ 4 + 3 10 **23.** 18 ÷ 9 + 11 13 **24.** 5 × 7 + 3 × 4 47

25. 8 × 4 + 3 × 7 53 **26.** 9 × 3 + 3 × 2 33 **27.** 6 × 3 + 2 × 8 34

28. 3 + (6 × 3) 21 **29.** 17 − (2 × 3) 11 **30.** (7 + 3) × 4 40

31. 9 × (12 ÷ 4) 27 **32.** 25 (3 + 2) 5 **33.** 4 + (16 ÷ 8) 6

34. On Monday, Mrs. Hinderer drove at an average speed of 50 miles per hour. On Tuesday, she drove at an average speed of 55 miles per hour. Write an expression to find the total number of miles she drove if she drove for 4 hours on Monday and 2 hours on Tuesday. Then find the value of the expression. See Example 3 (p. LA19)
4 × 50 + 2 × 55; 310 mi

35. One apple contains 70 Calories and one pear contains 100 Calories. Write an expression to find the total number of Calories that are in 3 apples and 2 pears. Then find the value of the expression. See Example 3 (p. LA19)
4 × 3 × 70 + 2 × 100; 410 Calories.

70 calories

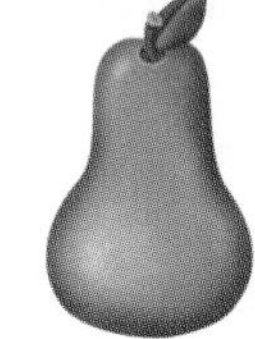
100 calories

36. Philip earns $12 an hour for mowing lawns and $9 an hour for raking leaves. Write an expression to find the total amount Philip would earn mowing and raking for 5 hours each. Then find the value of the expression. See Example 3 (p. LA19)
5 × $12 + 5 × $9; $105.

37. The table gives the price of each type of admission to the Museum of Natural History. Seven eleven-year olds and three adults will buy tickets for admission. Write an expression to find the total admission cost. Then find the value of the expression.
7 × $3 + 3 × $6; $39

Museum of Natural History Admission Prices

Type of Admission	Price ($)
Under 2 years	Free
2–12 years	3
over 12 years	6

Real-World PROBLEM SOLVING

Science A housecat spends about 16 hours a day asleep. It also spends about 4 hours grooming.

38. In 3 days, how long will a cat spend sleeping? grooming? **48 h; 12 h**

39. How much total time does a housecat spend sleeping and grooming in 7 days? **140 h**

40. Write an expression to find the total time a housecat spends sleeping and grooming in 30 days. **$16 \times 30 + 4 \times 30$**

H.O.T. Problems

41. OPEN ENDED Write a numerical expression involving parentheses for which you would use the order of operations to find its value. Then find the value of the expression.
Sample answer: $5 + (3 \times 6)$; 23

42. FIND THE ERROR Marty and Shenequa are finding the value of the expression $7 + (21 \div 7) - 4$. Who is correct? Explain. **Sample answer: Marty is correct. He first divided 21 by 7. Shenequa incorrectly added 7 and 21 first.**

Marty	Shenequa
$7 + (21 \div 7) - 4$ $= 7 + 3 - 4$ $= 10 - 4$ $= 6$	$7 + (21 \div 7) - 4$ $= 28 \div 7 - 4$ $= 4 - 4$ $= 0$

CHALLENGE For Exercises 43–46, use the order of operations to find the value of each expression.

43. $5 + (6 \times 2) - 3 + (4 \times 4)$ **30**

44. $30 - (3 \times 6) + (12 \div 4) - 2$ **13**

45. $24 \div (7 + 1) \times 2 + 11$ **17**

46. $9 + (49 \div 7) - 1 + (5 \times 3)$ **30**

47. WRITING IN MATH Write a real-world problem that can be solved by first writing a numerical expression and then by using the order of operations. Then solve.

Additional Answer

47. Sample answer: Five friends went to a restaurant. They each ordered a sandwich for $6 and a beverage for $2. Find the total cost. $5 \times \$6 + 5 \times \$2 = \$40$

4 Assess

Formative Assessment

- **Write an expression, involving multiplication, in which you have to subtract first in order to find its value. Explain why the subtraction has to come before the multiplication.**
  Sample answer: $9 \times (7 - 4)$; parentheses have to be done first.

Quick Check **Are students continuing to struggle with order of operations?**

If Yes → Small Group Options (p. LA18B)

If No → Independent Work Options (p. LA18B)

Name the Math Give students the following problem: $(18 - 7) \times 9 \div 3$. Ask them to tell how they would solve it.

Looking Ahead 6

Algebraic Expressions

Lesson Planner

Objective

Evaluate algebraic expressions.

Resources

Teacher Technology

Interactive Classroom • TeacherWorks

Focus on Math Background

It is extremely important for students to understand the algebraic language that is introduced in this lesson. Students should understand the concept of a variable and know what expressions are. They should also understand that the symbol chosen as the variable can be anything, as long as the symbol chosen has not already been defined as something else. Knowing what expressions are and are not will help them as they proceed in their study of algebra, as they will need to be able to distinguish between expressions and equations.

$7 + y - 2$	$9 + y = 4$
expression (no equals sign)	equation (equals sign)

Note that you *evaluate* expressions and you *solve* equations. Replacing the variable in an expression with a given value is sometimes described as *substituting* a value for the variable. After substituting the given values for the variables in an expression, you must pay attention to the order of operations. In this lesson and others, encourage students to use precise mathematical language as they talk about expressions and find the value of them.

Daily Routine

Use these suggestions before beginning the lesson on p. LA22.

5-Minute Check

(Reviews Looking Ahead 5)

Find the value of each expression.

1. $7 + 4 \times 6$ 31
2. $5 \times 3 + 8 \times 2$ 31
3. $54 - 36 \div 9$ 50
4. $9 \times (2 + 3)$ 45

Problem of the Day

Patrick and four of his friends will buy tickets to the museum for $11 each. It costs an additional $2 for the dinosaur exhibit. The expression $5 \times 11 + 2d$ gives the total cost for the five friends to go to the museum if only d friends see the dinosaur exhibit. Find the total cost if $d = 4$. $63

Building Math Vocabulary

Write the lesson vocabulary words and their definitions on the board.

Have each student write down their own algebraic expression and label the variable. They should write the definitions in their Math Journals.

Visual Vocabulary Cards

Use Visual Vocabulary Cards 1, 10 and 47 to reinforce the vocabulary used in this lesson. (The Define/Example/Ask routine is printed on the back of each card.)

algebraic expression

Differentiated Instruction

Small Group Options

SPATIAL, INTRAPERSONAL

Option 1 Below Level BL

Materials: two-color counters

- Have students draw pictures that help them remember how to solve algebraic expressions when the variable is a positive integer, such as $6 + x$, where $x = 4$. Provide two-color counters to help students set up their examples to be drawn.

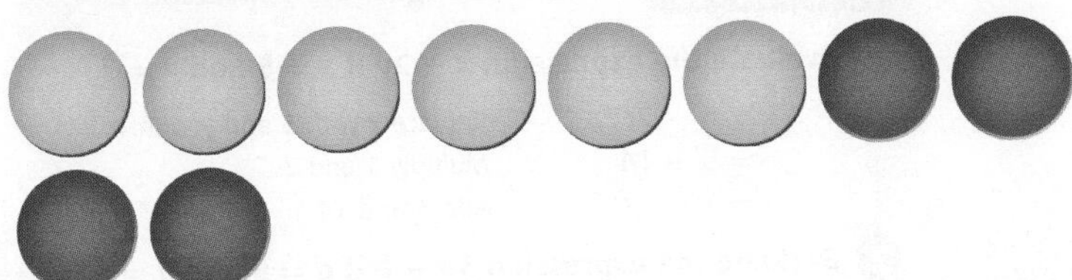

LOGICAL

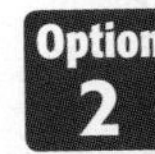

Option 2 English Language Learners ELL

Core Vocabulary: numbers, can be written, or
Common Use Verb: could be written
See Math This strategy helps students see variables (x) as a number representation distinct from "x" as a word or part of a word.

- Review different ways to show 5 (5 claps, 5 fingers, 5 blocks, or written as five, 3 + 2, 卌, etc.)
- Say: "5 can also be represented with a geometry shape." Write: "if $\Delta = 5$, then $\Delta + \Delta = 10$."
- Allow students to create simple equations using a Δ as a number 5.
- Repeat, changing the Δ to x. Practice variable equations as time permits.

Independent Work Options

LOGICAL

Option 1 Early Finishers AL

Materials: index cards, newspapers or magazines

- Give students examples of information that can be expressed algebraically. For example, an ad that gives "$5 off meal price if more than $20," can be written as the algebraic expression $p - 5$.
- Have students find an example of information that could be expressed algebraically and copy it on an index card.
- On the back of the card, they write the algebraic expression for the example.
- Students exchange cards and practice writing the expressions.

Option 2 Student Technology

Math Online macmillanmh.com

Personal Tutor • Extra Examples

Math Adventures

Algebraic Expressions

Introduce

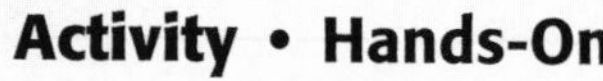

Activity • Hands-On 

- Have 2 students stand in front of the class. One holds a box whose contents cannot be seen and the other holds 5 cups.
- Ask the rest of the students to write down an expression showing the total number of cups the two students are holding. For example, some may draw a box and put + 5 next to it.
- Tell students that the box represents an unknown value and the 5 represents a known value. A variable, a letter, can be used for the unknown amount. The expression could be $b + 5$. The expression represents the sum of some number and 5.

Teach

Scaffolding Questions

Write the following algebraic expressions on the board:

$w - 5$	$4 \times a$
$7 + x$	$3 \times y - 4$

- **How would you read these algebraic expressions aloud?** w minus 5; 4 times a; 7 plus x; 3 times y minus 4
- **How could you find the value of each expression? Explain your answer.** You need to know a value for the variable in each expression in order to find the value of each expression.

GET READY to Learn

Have students open their books and read the information in **Get Ready to Learn**. As a class, work through **Examples 1–4**.

Algebraic Expressions

MAIN IDEA

I will use the order of operations to evaluate algebraic expressions.

Math Online

macmillanmh.com

- Extra Examples
- Personal Tutor
- Self-Check Quiz

GET READY to Learn

Tom is counting his money. His piggybank is full of quarters and dimes. He has four additional quarters.

1. Let x represent the number of quarters that are in Tom's piggybank. Write an expression to represent the total number of quarters that Tom has. $x + 4$
2. Let y represent the number of dimes in Tom's piggybank. Write an expression to represent the total number of coins that Tom has. $x + 4 + y$
3. If there are 37 quarters in Tom's piggybank and 15 dimes, how many total coins does he have? 56

In Chapter 5, you learned to evaluate simple algebraic expressions such as $x + 4$, $5x$, and $x - 9$. You can also use the order of operations to evaluate algebraic expressions when more than one operation is involved.

EXAMPLES Evaluate Algebraic Expressions

1 Evaluate the expression $x + 2y$ if $x = 5$ and $y = 7$.

$x + y = 5 + 2(7)$	Replace x with 5 and y with 7.
$= 5 + 14$	Multiply 2 and 7.
$= 19$	Add 5 and 14.

2 Evaluate the expression $3a - b$ if $a = 9$ and $b = 4$.

$3a - b = 3(9) - 4$	Replace a with 9 and b with 4.
$= 27 - 4$	Multiply 3 and 9.
$= 23$	Subtract 4 from 27.

3 Evaluate the expression $6w + 7(z - 2)$ if $w = 8$ and $z = 11$.

$6w + 7(z - 2) = 6(8) + 7(11 - 2)$	$w = 8$ and $z = 11$
$= 6(8) + 7(9)$	Subtract 2 from 11.
$= 48 + 63$	Multiply 6 by 8 and 7 by 9.
$= 111$	Add 48 and 63.

Real-World EXAMPLE

4 AMUSEMENT PARKS An amusement park has an admission cost of \$25. Paulo has a gift certificate for two free admissions. The expression $25(n - 2)$ represents the total admission cost in dollars for n friends to go to the park. Find the total cost of admission if $n = 6$.

$25(n - 2) = 25(6 - 2)$	Replace n with 6.
$= 25(4)$	Find $6 - 2$.
$= 100$	Multiply 25 by 4.

So, the total cost of admission for six friends is \$100.

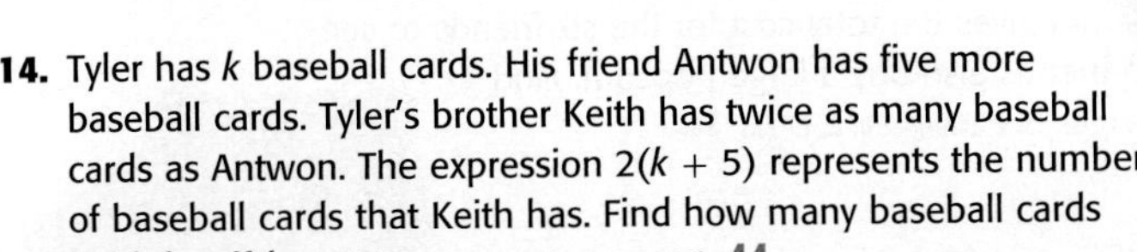

CHECK What You Know

Evaluate each expression if $m = 7$ and $n = 3$. (See Examples 1-3, p. LA22)

1. $m + 3n$ 16
2. $4m + n$ 31
3. $5m + 2n$ 41
4. $2m + 7n$ 35
5. $m - n$ 4
6. $6m - 2n$ 36
7. $m - 2n$ 1
8. $3m - n$ 18
9. $4m + 3(n - 1)$ 34
10. $3m + 2(n + 4)$ 35
11. $m + 5(n + 2)$ 32
12. $2m + 3(n - 3)$ 14
13. The cost of a large pizza at Papa Pepperoni's is \$9. Meghan has a coupon for a total of \$3 off any order. The expression $9p - 3$ represents the total cost in dollars for p large pizzas with Meghan's coupon. Find the total cost if $p = 4$. (See Example 4, p. LA23) \$33
14. Tyler has k baseball cards. His friend Antwon has five more baseball cards. Tyler's brother Keith has twice as many baseball cards as Antwon. The expression $2(k + 5)$ represents the number of baseball cards that Keith has. Find how many baseball cards Keith has if $k = 17$. (See Example 4, p. LA23) 44
15. 

When evaluating the expression $5h + 4(h + 3)$ for $h = 7$, which operation would you perform first? Explain. **evaluate $h + 3$; Sample answer: Simplify the expression inside parentheses first.**

Evaluate Algebraic Expressions

Example 1 Remind students that when a number is next to a variable, as in $2y$, this means to multiply 2 times the value of y.

ADDITIONAL EXAMPLES

1. Evaluate $a + 3b$ if $a = 5$ and $b = 4$. 17
2. Evaluate $7m - n$ if $m = 6$ and $n = 8$. 34
3. Evaluate $6x + 3(y - 2)$ if $x = 7$ and $y = 4$. 48
4. The expression $8x - 2$ represents the amount of money Nicholas will need to pay for 8 binders with a \$2 off coupon where x is the cost of each binder. How much will he pay if each binder is \$5? \$38

As a class, have students complete Exercises 1–15 in **Check What You Know** as you observe their work.

Exercise 15 Assess student comprehension before assigning practice exercises.

BL Alternate Teaching Strategy

If students have trouble evaluating expressions ...

Then use this reteach option:

Ask students to use grid paper to model and evaluate $k + 7$, for $k = 6$ through $k = 10$. For each value for k, students draw a box around a number of squares and lightly shade inside the box. They should write the value for k inside each set of boxed squares (for example, $k = 6$).

- Then students draw a box of seven squares. Inside the box, they should write "+ 7."
- At the end of each row, students should write the value of the expression. For example,

$$k + 7 = 6 + 7$$
$$= 13$$

3 Practice

Differentiate practice using these leveled assignments for Exercises 16–46.

Level	Assignment
BL Below/ Approaching Level	16–24, 35, 37, 38, 39
OL On Level	16–33, 34–37, 38–41, 46
AL Above/Beyond Level	16–40 even, 41–46

Have students discuss and complete the Higher Order Thinking problems. Exercises 41–45 require students to perform mathematical computations, while Exercise 46 requires written explanations.

WRITING IN ▸MATH Have students complete Exercise 46 in their Math Journals. You may choose to use this exercise as an optional formative assessment.

Practice and Problem Solving

Evaluate each expression if $c = 8$ and $d = 2$. (See Examples 1-3, p. LA22)

16. $c + 5d$ 18 **17.** $2c + d$ 18 **18.** $3c + 4d$ 32

19. $6c + 7d$ 62 **20.** $c - d$ 6 **21.** $5c - 3d$ 34

22. $c - 2d$ 4 **23.** $4c - d$ 30 **24.** $3(c + 2d)$ 36

25. $3(3c + d)$ 78 **26.** $2(c - d)$ 12 **27.** $4(3c - d)$ 88

28. $2(2c + 3d)$ 44 **29.** $2(3c + 4d)$ 64 **30.** $2c + 5(d - 1)$ 21

31. $4c + 2(d + 7)$ 50 **32.** $c + 3(d + 2)$ 20 **33.** $4c + 6(d + 1)$ 50

34. Measurement The perimeter of a rectangle is given by the expression $2\ell + 2w$. Find the perimeter of a rectangle if $\ell = 13$ centimeters and $w = 9$ centimeters. (See Example 4, p. LA23) 44 cm

35. Mrs. Hamilton's class is selling magazine subscriptions. The subscription costs are shown in the table. The expression $30a + 18b$ gives the total amount earned from selling a 12-month subscriptions and b 6-month subscriptions. Find the total amount earned if $a = 4$ and $b = 3$. (See Example 4, p. LA23) $174

Costs of Magazine Subscriptions

Type of Subscription	Cost per Month ($)
12 months	30
6 months	18

36. Movie tickets at Studio 19 cost $8 each. Celeste and five of her friends will buy tickets. The cost of a large popcorn is $3 each. The expression $6 \times 8 + 3m$ gives the total cost for the six friends to see a movie if m of the friends also buy a large popcorn. Find the total cost if $m = 4$. (See Example 4, p. LA23) $60

37. At a pet store, goldfish cost $2 each and hamsters cost $9 each. The expression $2g + 9h$ gives the total cost of g goldfish and h hamsters. Find the total cost if $g = 8$ and $h = 2$. (See Example 4, p. LA23) $34

Real-World PROBLEM SOLVING

Science An airplane is flying at an average speed of 500 miles per hour. A car below is traveling at an average speed of 60 miles per hour. The expression 500h gives the total distance in miles that the airplane will travel in h hours. The expression 60h gives the total distance in miles that the car will travel h hours.

38. How many total miles will the airplane travel in 4 hours? The car? 2,000 mi; 240 mi

39. The expression 500h – 60h gives the difference in the number of miles that the airplane and car have traveled after h hours. How many miles farther will the airplane travel in 6 hours than the car? 2,000 mi

40. Measurement The expression $\frac{1}{2}bh$ gives the area of a triangle, where b is the length of the base of the triangle and h is the height of the triangle. Find the area of a triangle if b = 12 inches and h = 10 inches. 60 in^2

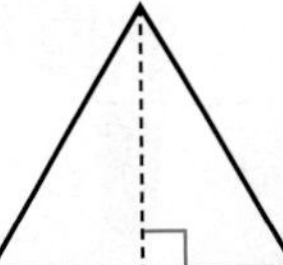

H.O.T. Problems

41. OPEN ENDED Write an algebraic expression for which x = 5 and y = 8. Then evaluate your expression. Sample answer: $9x - 3y$; 21

CHALLENGE For Exercises 42–45, use the order of operations to evaluate each expression if $a = 6$, $b = 3$, and $c = 9$.

42. $4a + 2(b + 7) - 3c$ 17

43. $a \times b + 36 \div 2c$ 20

44. $3c \div b + 5a \div b$ 19

45. $6a + 3b \div c + a$ 43

46. WRITING IN MATH You and a friend are each evaluating the expression $2(n - 1) + n$ if $n = 3$. Your friend says the answer is $2 \times 3 - 1 + 3$, or 8. Write one or two sentences explaining their error. Then find the correct answer.

Additional Answer

46. Sample answer: The expression inside the parentheses needs to be evaluated first. The friend incorrectly first multiplied 2 by 3. The first step should be 3–1. The correct answer is 2(3 –1) + 3, or 2(2) + 3, which is 7.

4 Assess

Formative Assessment

- **Explain the steps you would use to evaluate $5 + 7y$ if $y = 3$. Evaluate the expression.** Replace y with 3; multiply 7 and 3; add 5; 26

Quick Check **Are students continuing to struggle with variables and algebraic expression?**

If Yes → Small Group Options (p. LA22B)

If No → Independent Work Options (p. LA22B)

Name the Math Write the algebraic expression $5 + 3f$ on the board. Have students use a half sheet of paper to tell how they would evaluate the expression if $f = 9$.

Problem-Solving Projects

The **Problem-Solving Projects** apply the math skills that students have learned during the year. By completing the projects, the students will use and connect Grade 5 mathematics to everyday situations and activities.

End-of-Year Assessment

Use the **End-of-Year Test** to assess student comprehension of the skills and concepts presented in Grade 5.

CRM **Chapter 15 Resource Masters**
End-of-Year Test (p. 62)

Problem-Solving Projects

Problem-Solving Projects

PROJECT 1

Lesson Planner

Objective

Students learn about the Olympics, using measurement, estimation, fractions, and decimals. They also review median and mode using Olympic events.

Review Vocabulary

estimate, measurement, median, mode

Resources

Materials: tape measure, paper, pencil, stopwatches, large buckets of water, containers that hold 2 quarts of water, large sponges, ropes, Frisbees, labels reading $\frac{1}{4}$, $\frac{1}{2}$, and 1

Day 1

- Have students estimate how far they can jump, and then estimate how far the entire class can jump.
- Have students set up a long jump course either outside or in the gymnasium to test their estimates. Each person jumps once, and students measure and record the jumps, using a tape measure.
- Have students add up all of the distances to get the total distance the class jumped. See whose estimates came closest to the real measurements.

Day 2

- Students work in pairs. Have students mark off a 50-yard dash course outside, and time each other running the 50-yard dash using a stopwatch. Students record their times.
- Students find the median and mode of their race times. If you wish, you can have students display their data in a chart or graph.

The first Olympic Games with a recorded winner was in Greece in 776 BCE. In the beginning, there was only one event, a sprint. The winner received a wreath of olive branches to place on his head because olive trees were thought to be sacred.

Getting Started

Day 1 The Long Jump Challenge

- Many Olympic long jumpers are able to jump over 20 feet. Estimate how far you think you can jump. Suppose the lengths of all of the jumps of everyone in your class were added together. About how long do you think this would be?
- Go outside or in your gymnasium and set up a long jump site. Everyone should jump once. Record the exact measures.
- Add the distances to find the total length of jumps for the class. Then compare the actual amount to the estimate. Who had the closest estimate?

Day 2 On Your Mark, Get Set, GO!

- One Olympic event is the 100-meter dash. Today you will run the 50-yard dash. Go outside and mark off an area that is 50 yards long.
- Find a partner. Time each other running the 50-yard dash. Record your times.
- Find the median and mode of the times for everyone in your class.

Projects

Day 3 Sponge Relay

- Another Olympic event is the 4-by-400 meter relay. Today you will run a relay. Work in teams that have the same number of members. Each team has an equal-size empty container. Each team races to fill their container to the appropriate line by dunking the sponge into a large bucket, running to the empty container, and wringing the water into it. Record the times for each team to fill their container. Compare the times. Order the times from least to greatest.

Day 4 Frisbee Frenzy

The Olympic event, the discus, focuses on distance. Today you will throw a frisbee but will focus on accuracy.

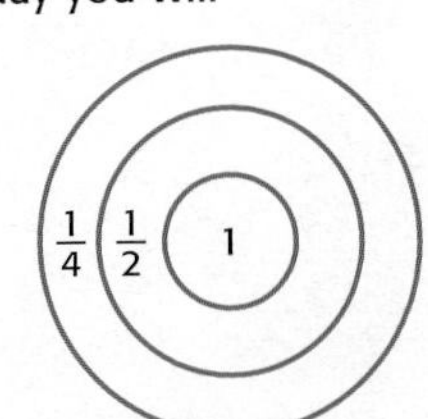

- Set up a Frisbee toss outside. Make a bull's-eye target like the one shown. The outer section is $\frac{1}{4}$, or 0.25, of a point. The middle section is $\frac{1}{2}$, or 0.5, of a point. The center circle or bull's-eye is worth 1 point. Each person gets three tosses.
- After your three tosses, add up your total points. Find the median and mode of total points for everyone in your class.

Day 5 Now You Are the Olympic Judge!

- Now it is time to take what you have learned and teach other classes. You may need to make a few adjustments for the younger grades.
- Divide your class into four groups of equal size. Each group is in charge of one of the activities.

Wrap-Up

- How did you use math in this project?
- Describe how you used measurement in the above events.
- Explain why exact measurements and not estimates are need for Olympic events.

Answers for Wrap-Up

Sample answers:

- Measuring length was used in the long jump activity and the 50-yard dash. Measuring volume was used in the sponge relay.
- Exact measurements are needed in the Olympics to determine records and winners.

Day 3

- Divide the class into equal teams.
- Have each team fill one container with 2 quarts of water and mark the 2-quart line on an empty container.
- One by one, members of each team run to dunk the sponge into the full container and wring it out into the empty container. The first team to fill the empty container to the 2-quart mark wins the relay race.

Day 4

- Students make a bull's-eye target with three circles on the ground outside. The outer circle is worth $\frac{1}{4}$, or 0.25 of a point. The middle circle is worth $\frac{1}{2}$, or 0.5 of a point. The bull's eye is worth 1 point.
- Students take turns making three tosses with a Frisbee onto the bull's-eye target.
- After each student's three tosses, they add up their points as fractions and then as decimals. At the end of the game, they add up the total points for the class.

Day 5

- Students hold a math Olympics using the events from Days 1–4, challenging other classes. Discuss how students might change the events for younger students.
- Divide the class into four groups, each one responsible for one event.

Wrap-Up

- Use the Wrap-Up questions to assess students' work:
- **What else do you know about the Olympics?** Answers will vary.
- **When will the next Olympic games be held? Where will it be?** Answers vary according to your current year.
- **What Olympic activity would you participate in?** Answers will vary.

Problem-Solving Projects

PROJECT 2

Lesson Planner

Objective

Students create floor plans and scaled drawings of the classroom and a dream home, using area, perimeter, and volume measurements.

Review Vocabulary

perimeter, area, volume, probability

Resources

Materials: pencils, paper, grid paper, rulers or yardsticks, magazines, catalogues, construction paper, markers, glue, scissors, small and large cardboard boxes, index cards

Day 1

- Students work in pairs to measure the perimeter and area of the classroom to the nearest yard. They convert their measurements to feet.
- Student pairs measure the furniture in the room and analyze its placement in the room.
- Student pairs create a scaled drawing of the classroom and the furniture in it, rearranged to their liking, on grid paper. Make sure students label the furniture.

Day 2

- Discuss with students the elements of a persuasive speech.
- Student pairs write a speech to explain to the class why their design to rearrange the classroom should be adopted. They present the speech to the class.

Do you know an interior designer? Some people go to college to learn how to arrange rooms in an appealing and practical fashion. Practice your design skills by rearranging your classroom and by creating a design of your own dream home.

Getting Started

Day 1 Measure and Map It

- Measure to find the perimeter and area of your classroom to the nearest yard. Then convert your measurements to feet.
- Measure the furniture and study its placement in the classroom. Could it be set up in a different way?
- Use graph paper to create a drawing of a rearrangement of the classroom furniture. Be sure to label everything.

Day 2 Persuading the Client

- Create a persuasive speech to explain to the class why your design should be used to rearrange the classroom. Tell why you decided to place objects where you did. Think about how your design might make it easier for the teacher to teach and your classmates to learn.
- Deliver your speech and share your design with the class.

Day 3 The Winning Model

- Walk around the room and look at all of the designs. Consider the speeches that were presented yesterday. Vote for the one that you think will work the best for your classroom.
- Discuss the probability of certain designs being selected.
- Record the votes of everyone in the class. Then rearrange the classroom to match the winning design.

Day 4 Dream Design

You will create a model of a dream house.

- Work with a group to glue smaller boxes inside of a larger box to create walls in your group's dream home.
- Find the perimeter and area of each room in your group's dream home.
- Cut out pictures of furniture, swimming pools, and other features you want in your group's dream home from magazines and catalogs and place them in the correct rooms in the box.

Day 5 Show it Off

- Use the Internet to find information and floor plans from real homes in your area.
- With your group, create a brochure highlighting all the amazing features your dream home has to offer. Make sure to include the home's dimensions.
- Have a "Tour of Homes" and invite other classes to visit.

Wrap-Up

- How did you use math to design your dream home?
- Explain why you needed exact measurements when designing your dream classrooms.
- Which type of graph would you use to display the number of votes for the best design? Explain why. Then make the graph.

Answers for Wrap-Up

Sample answers:

- An exact measurement was needed to ensure that there was enough space for the new arrangement.
- Bar graph; A bar graph is used to compare quantities.

Day 3

- Display student designs around the classroom and have students walk around to see the various classroom plans.
- Have a vote to see which design is the best, using index cards and a voting box.
- Before you look at the results, discuss what the probability of drawing one design from the box would be if that person got a certain number of votes.
- Have students create a bar graph of the voting results.
- Have the students rearrange the room according to the winning design.

Day 4

- Form student groups and have them design a dream home. Each group uses a large box and fills it with smaller boxes to represent rooms in the home.
- Students design floor plans for each room. They find the perimeter, area, and volume of each room.
- Students decorate the house with pictures from catalogues and other art supplies.

Day 5

- Students visit www.newhomes.com to see real floor plans of homes in their area.
- Students create a brochure to highlight all the features of their dream homes.
- Students have a "Tour of Homes" in the classroom to show off their designs.

Wrap-Up

- Use the Wrap-Up questions to assess students' work:
- **What was the most difficult part of your project? What did you enjoy the most?** Answers will vary.
- **After looking at other students' designs, what would you change about your dream home?** Answers will vary.

Problem-Solving Projects

PROJECT 3

Lesson Planner

Objective

Students will learn about the post office, using measurements, coordinate grids, and estimation.

Review Vocabulary

scale, coordinate grid, weight

Resources

Materials: United States maps, Internet access, pencil, paper, books about Pony Express, grid paper, fine point marker, world maps, scale, packages of different weights

Day 1

- Have students look at a United States map and use the scale to find out how far the Pony Express traveled from St. Joseph, Missouri to Sacramento, California. Ask students to estimate how long the trip might have taken the Pony Express.
- Have students write a journal entry as if they were Pony Express riders back in 1860. Students may visit www.ponyexpress.org on the Internet for more information to make their journal entries more realistic.

Day 2

- Discuss with students why mail carriers have specific routes.
- Have students draw a coordinate grid on grid paper and map their school on the grid. Have them include and label classrooms, the cafeteria, and other offices on their maps.
- Students work in pairs to say coordinates and find the matching areas on their maps.

One way people communicate with each other is through mail. Sending mail across the country today is easy. You just apply the proper postage and drop it off at the post office or in a mailbox.

Getting Started

Day 1 The Old Pony Express

- In 1860, there were no mail trucks or planes. But there was the Pony Express. The Pony Express was a team of horses and riders that carried mail from St. Joseph, Missouri, to Sacramento, California. Look at a United States map. Use the scale to find this approximate distance in miles. How long might it have taken them?
- If there was a Pony Express station every 20 miles along the route, how many stations were there in all?
- Write a journal entry as if you were a Pony Express rider back in 1860.

Day 2 Coordinate Your School

- Each day, many mail carriers walk their mail routes. Why do you think it is important to have specific routes?
- Draw a mail route for your school. Using grid paper, draw a coordinate grid labeled 0 to 20. Mark and label the coordinates of the classrooms you want on your mail route.

P6 Problem-Solving Projects

Projects

Day 3 Weighing In

- The price of sending packages through the United States Postal Service depends on the type of package, its weight, and how far it will be sent. Pick a city in the United States to send a 3-pound package. Use the Internet or another source to find the cost.
- Your teacher has set out different packages that need to be mailed. Based on what you have learned above, weigh each package, and calculate the cost of sending it to the city you selected.

Day 4 Overseas Friends

- If you were to send a package from your local post office to a friend overseas, it might travel in many ways. It might be sent in a truck, a plane, or via a mail carrier. Pick one city overseas in which you would like to send a 3-pound package. Track how many miles your package would have to travel from your school to that city. Then find the cost of sending the package.
- Suppose someone is sending you a 3-pound package from the same city you chose. Research the currency that is used in that country to find out how much it will cost to send the package.

Day 5 A Trip to the Post Office

- Using the Internet, find the cost of a stamp for the following years: 1950, 1960, 1970, 1980, 1990, and 2000. Make a table to display the data.
- What is the difference between the cost of a stamp from 1950 to 1960? 1960 to 1970? 1970 to 1980? 1980 to 1990? 1990 to 2000?
- Which years had the greatest increase in price? Which years had the least increase in price?

Wrap-Up

- Almost every year, the price of sending mail increases. Why do you think this happens?
- Why do you think it costs more to send mail overseas?
- Which type of graph would you use to best display the cost of a stamp from 1950 to 2000? Explain your reasoning.

Answers for Wrap-Up

Sample answers:

- As with all products, the price of stamps has risen over time due to many factors such as inflation, supply, and demand.
- There are more costs, such as fuel, to deliver mail overseas.
- Line graph; a line graph shows change over time.

Day 3

- Have students use the postage calculator at www.usps.com to calculate how much it would cost to send one package to any United States destination they choose.
- Provide students with packages of different weights to weigh on a scale.
- Students use the information they learned from the Web site plus the weight of each package to calculate the cost of sending the packages to their destination.

Day 4

- Students pick a city overseas and, using a world map and its scale, figure out how far this city is from their school.
- Students calculate how much it would cost to send a 3-pound package to that destination in United States dollars.
- Then students use www.x-rates.com on the Internet to find out how much it would cost in the currency of their chosen city to send a 3-pound package to their school.

Day 5

- After students have created their tables, extend the activity by having them create line graphs to show the cost of stamps over time.
- Based on the data, have students predict the cost of a stamp ten years from now.

Wrap-Up

- Use the Wrap-Up questions to assess students' work:
- **Why do you think postal charges increase?** Answers will vary.
- **Where could you go, besides a post office, to send a package?** a shipping company
- **Why does overseas mail cost more?** Transportation costs more.

Problem-Solving Projects

PROJECT 4

Lesson Planner

Objective

Students will collect, interpret, and display data on favorite pies, and work with fractions and measurements to create a recipe for a giant pie. They will bake a "mud pie," have a taste test, and display their results.

Review Vocabulary

data, tally chart, bar graph, pie chart, pictograph

Resources

Materials: pencils, paper, construction paper, posterboard, pumpkin pie recipe, cookbooks, grocery circulars, Internet access, ingredients for mud pie, recipe for mud pie, measuring and mixing tools, mixing bowls, pie pans

Day 1

- Students create a survey to find out favorite types of pie. They take the survey themselves and give the survey to at least five other people.
- Be sure that students do not take a survey more than once. Discuss why this is important for accurate results.
- Have students survey others in the school.

Day 2

- Students record their survey data on a tally chart.
- Have students work in small groups, creating bar graphs, pictographs, or pie charts on a poster board to display their tally-chart data.
- Student groups may use one or all three types of display methods. Discuss which method works the best for this data.

It's How Big?

This pie holds the Guinness World Record for the largest pumpkin pie. It was baked in October of 2005 in New Bremen, Ohio. How much do you think it weighs? How many people do you think it would serve?

Getting Started

Day 1 Find out the Favorite

- As a class, create a survey about favorite types of pie.
- Have the entire class take the survey and determine the results.
- Survey other students in the school to find their favorite type of pie.

Day 2 Chart the Results

- Record the data received from your surveys in a frequency table.
- Work in small groups to create bar graphs, pictographs, and line plots on poster board.

Day 3 Make the World's Largest Pie

- Look at the picture of the world record pie. Draw a large pie resembling the world's largest pumpkin pie on construction paper.
- Work in groups to convert a recipe for a normal sized pumpkin pie into this large sized pie. Determine the amount of ingredients needed for the largest pie. Then find the cost of making the largest pie using a calculator.
- Record all the information and display your pie for the school.

Day 4 Tell Everyone!

- Pretend that your class broke the record for the world's largest pie and write a newspaper article about it. Make sure to include all the information that was recorded about the pie yesterday.

Day 5 Magnificent Mud

- In small groups, use the Internet or cookbooks to find a recipe for "mud pie."
- Make the pie using the recipe.
- As a class, set up a taste test for teachers. Survey the teachers about the taste test.
- Record and display the taste test results in a bar graph.
- Discuss the results of the taste test.

Wrap-Up

- Explain why it was important to display the data about favorite types of pies.
- Explain which type of graph best displays this data.
- You used a calculator to find the cost of making the largest pie. Explain the benefits of using a calculator to find total costs.
- Explain how you use math to make your mud pie.

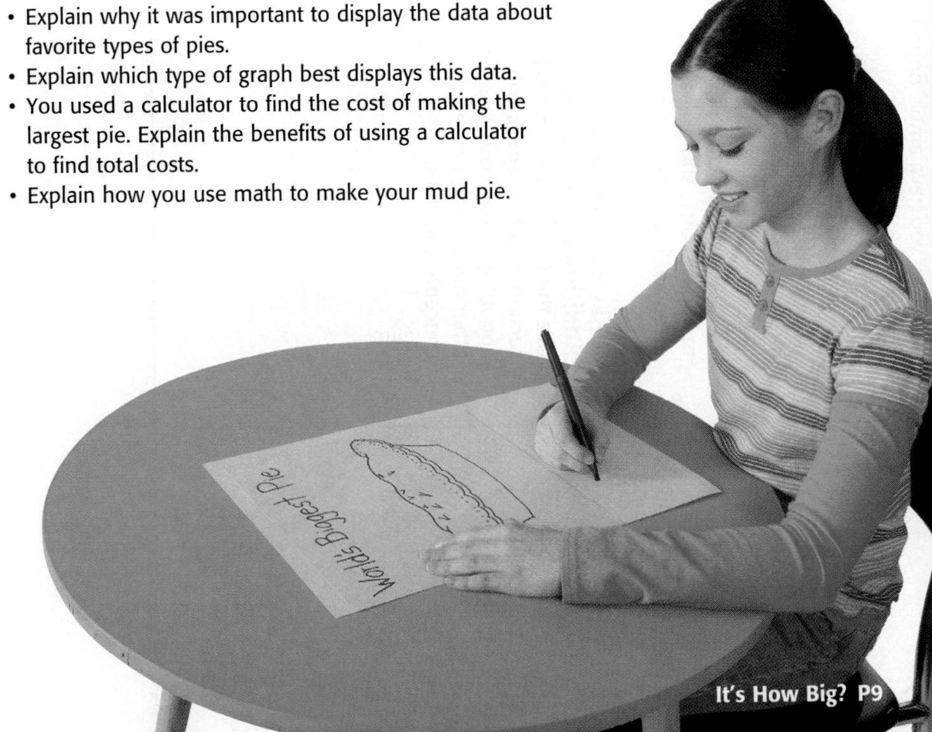

Answers for Wrap-Up

Sample answers:

- Displaying the data helps to show which type of pie is the favorite.
- Bar graph or pictograph should be used to display the data about pies.
- Technology can help us save time when calculating answers.

Day 3

- Students view the world's largest pie at http://pumpkinnook.com/giants/pumpkinpierecord.htm. The record-holding pie weighs 2,020 lbs. Students construct a pie of the same size on construction butcher paper.
- Divide students into three groups to take a pumpkin pie recipe, found at http://allrecipes.com/recipe/libbys-famous-pumpkin-pie/detail.aspx, and convert it to a giant-sized pie recipe.
- Each of the three student groups researches one of the following: the cost of the pie, the ingredients, and the calories. Students record this information and display it on their giant pie for the school to see.

Day 4

- Students pretend that they broke the record for the world's largest pie and write a newspaper article about it. They include the information recorded on their giant construction paper pie and display the article.

Day 5

- Groups of four students use cookbooks or the Internet to get a "mud pie" recipe. They make the pie and have a taste test. Other teachers may come to test the pies.
- Students record and display test results on a pie chart. They discuss how the same recipe could turn out differently.

Wrap-Up

- Use the Wrap-Up questions to assess students' work:
- **How did you use math to make your pie?** Answers will vary.
- **What was the most difficult part of your project?** Answers will vary.
- **What step of the project did you enjoy the most?** Answers will vary.
- **How do you think you could improve your mud pie?** Answers will vary.

Student Handbook

Built-In Workbook

Reference

How to Use the Student Handbook

The Student Handbook is the additional skill and reference material found at the end of books. The Student Handbook can help answer these questions.

What If I Need More Practice?

You, or your teacher, may decide that working through some additional problems would be helpful. The **Extra Practice** section provides these problems for each lesson so you have ample opportunity to practice new skills.

What If I Need to Prepare for a Standardized Test?

The **Preparing for Standardized Tests** section provides worked-out examples and practice problems for multiple-choice, short-response, and extended response questions.

What if I Want to Learn Additional Concepts and Skills?

Use the Concepts and Skills Bank section to either refresh your memory about topics you have learned in other math classes or learn new math concepts and skills.

What If I Forgot a Vocabulary Word?

The **English-Spanish Glossary** provides a list of important, or difficult, words used throughout the textbook. It provides a definition in English and Spanish as well as the page number(s) where the word can be found.

What If I Need to Find Something Quickly?

The **Index** alphabetically lists the subjects covered throughout the entire textbook and the pages on which each subject can be found.

What If I Forget Measurement Conversions, Multiplication Facts, or Formulas?

Inside the back cover of your math book is a list of measurement conversions and formulas that are used in the book. You will also find a multiplication table inside the back cover.

Extra Practice

Lesson 1-1
Pages 17–19

Name the place value of the underlined digit. Then write the number it represents. 1–6. See Extra Practice Answer Appendix.

1. 51,424 **2.** 324,856 **3.** 80,885,004

4. 65,080,050,000 **5.** 413,800,560,399 **6.** 79,707,010

Write each number in standard form.

7. 7 million, 760 thousand, 400 7,760,400

8. six billion, four hundred five million, three hundred 6,405,000,300

9–11. See Extra Practice Answer Appendix.

Write in expanded form. Then read and write in word form.

9. 850,120 **10.** 30,335,012 **11.** 61,850,002,050

Lesson 1-2
Pages 20–23

Replace each ● with <, >, or = to make a true sentence.

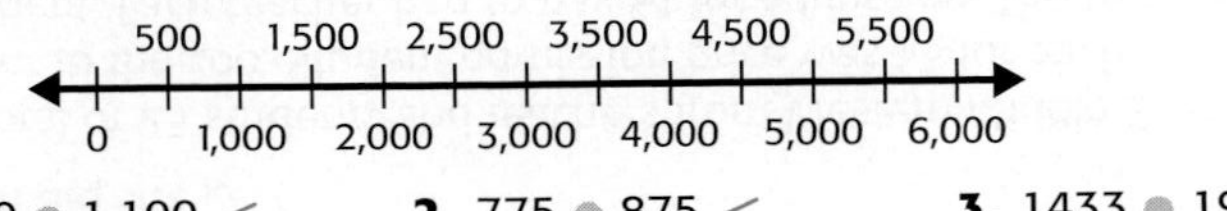

1. 600 ● 1,100 < **2.** 775 ● 875 < **3.** 1433 ● 1973 <

4. 5,551 ● 5,545 > **5.** 775 ● 775 = **6.** 205 ● 3,205 <

Replace each ● with <, >, or = to make a true sentence.

7. 890 ● 4,080 < **8.** 10,600 ● 340 > **9.** 7,500 ● 7,000 >

10. 105,706 ● 90,805 > **11.** 12 ● 1,200 < **12.** 7,900 ● 9,700 <

Lesson 1-3 1. See Extra Practice Answer Appendix.
Pages 24–25

Use the four-step plan to solve each problem.

1. A sprinter set three Olympic records. Her times were 2:02 minutes, 53.7 seconds, and 26.5 seconds. She competed in the 400-meter dash, the 800-meter run, and the 200-meter dash. What were her times for each event? Explain how you know.

2. Fernando gets out of school at 4:00 P.M. He goes to bed at 9:00 P.M. How much time does he have left if he spends 2 hours at football practice, 1 hour and 30 minutes on his homework, and 50 minutes eating? 40 min

3. Your mother agrees to triple whatever you put into a savings account at the bank. If you have deposited $25 each year for the last 3 years, how much money has been deposited? $300

Lesson 1-4
Pages 28–30

Use a model to write each fraction as a decimal.

1. $\frac{1}{2}$ 0.5 **2.** $\frac{8}{10}$ 0.8 **3.** $\frac{94}{100}$ 0.94

4. $\frac{34}{100}$ 0.34 **5.** $\frac{187}{1,000}$ 0.187 **6.** $\frac{333}{1,000}$ 0.333

7. $\frac{7}{100}$ 0.07 **8.** $\frac{17}{1,000}$ 0.017 **9.** $\frac{500}{1,000}$ 0.500

10. $\frac{775}{1,000}$ 0.775 **11.** $\frac{663}{1,000}$ 0.663 **12.** $\frac{250}{1,000}$ 0.250

13. The average snowfall in Amarillo, Texas is 15.4 inches. Write this decimal as a fraction. $15\frac{4}{10}$

14. In a survey, $\frac{56}{100}$ of the students preferred hamburgers to hot dogs. Write this fraction as a decimal. 0.56

Lesson 1-5
Pages 32–35

Name the place value of each underlined digit. Then write the number it represents.

1. 42.23 hundredths; 0.03 **2.** 7.35 tenths; 0.3

3. 1.096 thousandths; 0.006 **4.** 36.937 tenths; 0.9

Write each number in standard form. 6. 33.02

5. 16 and 7 tenths 16.7 **6.** thirty-three and two hundredths

7. 11 + 2 + 0.4 + 0.06 + 0.005 13.465 **8.** 9 + 0.09 + 0.001 9.091

Write each number in expanded form. Then read and write in word form. 10. 0.7 + 0.07 + 0.005; seven hundred seventy-five thousandths

9. 6.78 6 + 0.7 + 0.08 ; six and seventy-eight hundredths **10.** 0.775

11. 50.05 50 + 0.05; fifty and five hundreths **12.** 84.993 80 + 4 + 0.9 + 0.09 + 0.003; eighty-four and nine hundred ninety-three thousandths

Lesson 1-6
Pages 36–39

Replace each ● with <, >, or = to make a true sentence.

1. 2.2 ● 2.8 < **2.** 0.55 ● 0.66 < **3.** 0.27 ● 0.277 <

4. 9.456 ● 9.45 > **5.** 11.74 ● 10.25 > **6.** 4.55 ● 4.54 >

7. 0.09 ● 0.090 = **8.** 75.75 ● 75.70 > **9.** 5.8 ● 8.5 <

10. 25.5 ● 25.00 > **11.** 0.01 ● 0.010 = **12.** 82.02 ● 82.20 <

13. Roy can run the 100 meter dash in 11.04 seconds. Malik can run the same distance in 11.40 seconds. Who is faster, Roy or Malik? Roy

Lesson 1-7 3–10. See Extra Practice Answer Appendix. Pages 42–46

Order each set of numbers from least to greatest.

1. 55, 42, 43, 29 29, 42, 43, 55
2. 109, 167, 87, 99 87, 99, 109, 167
3. 2,984, 2,893, 4,367, 2,335, 4,387
4. 3.8, 5.9, 2.7, 1.9, 5.6
5. 59,033, 52,456, 59,999, 51,092
6. 63.09, 61.99, 68.47, 63.10
7. 44.4, 4.44, 0.444, 444, 0.044
8. 7.27, 7.79, 0.772, 77.5, 76.903
9. 7.5, 5.7, 7.55, 5.77
10. 9, 8.9, 8.96, 9.01, 9.001
11. Clara's cat weighs 9.72 pounds. Lucia's cat weighs 9.8 pounds. Write a sentence comparing the cats' weights.
    Sample answers: Clara's cat weighs less than Lucia's cat; $9.72 < 9.8$

Lesson 1-8 1, 3. See Extra Practice Answer Appendix. Pages 48–49

Solve. Use the *guess and check* strategy.

1. Hunter saw 16 wheels on a total of 5 cars and motorcycles at the store. How many cars and motorcycles are there at the store?
2. The sum of two numbers is 17. Their product is 72. What are the two numbers? 9 and 8
3. Shirley bought two hot dogs from a street vendor and received \$2.50 back in change. The vendor gave her the change in quarters and nickels. If she received 14 coins, how many of each coin did she get?
4. A total of 23 students and teachers from Western Middle School went to the zoo. Student admission price was \$3 for each student. Each teacher had to pay \$4 for admission. The total cost was \$71. How many students went to the zoo? 21 students

Lesson 2-1 Pages 61–63

Round each number to the underlined place.

1. 16 20
2. 823 820
3. 2,599 2,600
4. 4,999 5,000
5. 17,347 20,000
6. 409,168 409,170
7. 5,555 5,600
8. 333,225 330,000

Round each decimal to the place indicated.

9. 7.8; ones 8
10. 2.34; tenths 2.3
11. 0.928; hundredths 0.93
12. 56.10; ones 56
13. 4.298; tenths 4.3
14. 22.399; hundredths 22.40
15. 5.345; ones 5
16. 0.687; tenths 0.70
17. The thickness of a United States penny is 1.27 millimeter. Round this number to the nearest tenth. 1.3

Lesson 2-2 1–7. Sample answers are given. Pages 64–67

Estimate each sum or difference. Use rounding or compatible numbers. Show your work.

1. 44 − 21; $45 - 20 = 25$
2. 1,833 + 3,109; $2{,}000 + 3{,}000 = 5{,}000$
3. 472 − 268; $500 - 250 = 250$
4. 6.9 + 3.5; $7.0 + 4.0 = 11$
5. 299.5 + 700.3; $300 + 700 = 1{,}000$
6. 8,723 − 3,114; $9{,}000 - 3{,}000 = 6{,}000$
7. Shanti has 472 baseball cards. Her brother has 835 baseball cards. About how many baseball cards do they have altogether? Show your work. 1,300 cards; $500 + 800 = 1{,}300$

Lesson 2-3 Pages 68–69

Solve. Use the *work backward* strategy.

1. The local girl scout troop is selling cookies for a fundraiser. They sold all 30 of the boxes that cost \$3 and the rest of the boxes they sold were \$2 each. If they made \$170, how many boxes of cookies did they sell? 70 boxes
2. Calvin's mother gave him \$3.35 in change that was left over after she bought groceries. The grocery receipt was for \$32.23. How much money did Calvin's mother have before she went grocery shopping? \$35.58
3. Lola went to Chicago with friends. She wanted to be home no later than 9:00 P.M. on Sunday. It will take Lola 7 hours to ride the train home or 6 hours if she takes the bus. What time will she need to leave Chicago if she rides the bus home? 3:00 P.M.

Lesson 2-4 Pages 70–72

Add or subtract.

1. 45 + 18 = 63
2. 620 − 430 = 190
3. 4,320 + 6,109 = 10,429
4. 560 − 350 = 210
5. 17,700 + 13,356 = 31,056
6. 4,350 + 360 = 4,710
7. 934 − 275 = 659
8. 20,020 − 12,987 = 7,033
9. Corey bought a pair of shoes for \$49, a shirt for \$28, and jeans for \$55. How much did he spend on his new clothes? \$132

Extra Practice

Lesson 2-5

Pages 74–75

For each problem, determine whether you need an estimate or an exact answer. Then solve.

1. A giant submarine sandwich can feed 13 students. Mr. Smith's science class is having a party for perfect attendance, and they want to order enough food to feed 37 students. How many subs will they need to order? estimate; 3 subs
2. Four friends are sharing 3 pizzas. Each pizza costs $12.96. How much will each person need to pay? exact answer; $9.72
3. A school spends $132 on art supplies for each student. There are 186 students in the school, and the school's art budget is $27,000. Does the school have enough money in the budget to cover the students' supplies? estimate; yes

Lesson 2-6

Pages 80–82

Add or subtract.

1. 2.4 + 4.7 = 7.1
2. 7.6 + 2.56 = 10.16
3. 0.78 − 0.04 = 0.74
4. 8 − 3.5 = 4.5
5. 5.14 + 3.66 8.80
6. 0.6 − 0.11 0.49
7. Brody, Elvio, Jamil and Tito were on the relay team for track and field. The table lists their times. What was the team's total time? 232.53 s

Name	Time (in seconds)
Brody	58.6
Elvio	57.93
Jamil	59.2
Tito	56.8

Lesson 2-7 2. associative 3. commutative

Pages 84–87

Identify the addition property used to rewrite each problem.

1. 10 + 5 = 5 + 10 commutative
2. (22 + 50) + 25 = 22 + (50 + 25)
3. 9 + 23 + 75 = 9 + 75 + 23
4. 45 + 0 + 5 = 45 + 5 identity

Use properties of addition to find each sum mentally. Show your steps and identify the properties that you used.

5. 5 + 30 + 11
6. 22 + 54 + 6
7. 3.5 + 7.6 + 19.5
8. 10.6 + 74 + 2
9. 49 + 27
10. 50.4 + 13.6 + 4.5

5–10. See Extra Practice Answer Appendix.

Find the value that makes each sentence true.

11. 21 + (45 + 7) = 7 + (21 + ■) 45
12. 13.3 + 2.6 + 6 = ■ + 21 0.9
13. 52 + 0 = ■ 52
14. 17 + 32 + 3 = 17 + ■ + 32 3

Lesson 2-8

Pages 88–91

Add or subtract mentally. Use compensation.

1. 43 + 21 64
2. 57 + 35 92
3. 79 − 31 48
4. 88 − 29 59
5. 25 − 15 10
6. 205 + 675 880
7. 4.3 − 3.2 1.1
8. 95 − 77 18
9. 29.4 + 22.6 52
10. 74.2 − 41.2 33
11. 59.4 + 38.6 98
12. 60.5 − 20.3 40.2
13. 398 + 492 890
13. 62.6 − 41.9 20.7
14. 492 − 398 94
15. In a fish tank, one angelfish measures 5.7 inches and another one measures 4.9 inches. What is the total length of both angelfish? 10.6 in.

Lesson 3-1

Pages 103–105

Find each product mentally.

1. 4 × 30 120
2. 70 × 3 210
3. 22 × 10 220
4. 50 × 40 2,000
5. 300 × 5 1,500
6. 620 × 10 6,200
7. 30 × 400 12,000
8. 800 × 700 560,000
9. 1,000 × 40 40,000
10. 4,000 × 5 20,000
11. 300 × 70 21,000
12. 25 × 500 12,500
13. 25 × 20 500
14. 600 × 600 360,000
15. 3,000 × 20 60,000
16. Celeste is making bracelets for her friends. Each bracelet uses 50 beads. If she wants to make 20 bracelets, how many beads does she need? 1,000 beads

Lesson 3-2

Pages 108–111

Rewrite each expression using the Distributive Property. Then evaluate. 1–6. See Extra Practice Answer Appendix.

1. 5 × (8 + 2)
2. 3 × (20 + 7)
3. 8 × (40 + 2)
4. 4 × (7 + 7)
5. 6 × (5 + 9)
6. 2 × (90 + 40)

7–15. See Extra Practice Answer Appendix.

Find each product mentally using the Distributive Property. Show the steps that you used.

7. 3 × 12
8. 5 × 48
9. 7 × 23
10. 2 × 76
11. 33 × 6
12. 94 × 5
13. 2 × 43
14. 55 × 6
15. Arnaldo is packing 8 red model cars and 5 blue model cars into each box. If he needs to pack 25 boxes, how many model cars will he need? Use the Distributive Property. Show your steps.
16. Maurice is a sports cards dealer. On Tuesday, he sold 13 cards that cost $15 each. He also sold 10 cards that cost $8 each. How much money did Maurice make on Tuesday? $275

Extra Practice

Lesson 3-3

Pages 112–115

Estimate by rounding. Show your work.

1. 38×5; $40 \times 5 = 200$
2. 52×7; $50 \times 10 = 500$
3. 49×79; $50 \times 80 = 4,000$
4. 102×38; $100 \times 40 = 4,000$
5. 320×73; $300 \times 70 = 21,000$
6. 320×17; $300 \times 20 = 6,000$
7. 79×59; $80 \times 60 = 4,800$
8. 520×437; $500 \times 400 = 200,000$
9. 289×132; $300 \times 100 = 30,000$

Estimate by using compatible numbers. Show your work.

10. 85 × 221 **11.** 118 × 94 **12.** 327 × 75

13. Thi's class is ordering books for the reading club. Each book costs $7.55. If there are 12 people in the reading club, about how much will the books cost? Show how you estimated. Sample answer: 10 × $8 = $80

10. 100 × 200 = 20,000 11. 100 × 90 = 90,000 12. 300 × 70 = 21,000

Lesson 3-4

Pages 116–118

Multiply.

1. 32×8 256
2. 47×6 282
3. 257×5 1,285
4. 442×2 884

5. 321 × 4 1,284 **6.** 63 × 5 315 **7.** 7 × 321 2,247 **8.** 94 × 2 188

9. Willy wants to buy diet soda for 6 people. The sodas cost $1.39 each and he has $10. Will he have enough money? How much will be left over? Yes; $1.66

Lesson 3-5

Pages 120–121

Solve. Use the *draw a picture* strategy.

1. Denitra is making bracelets from a piece of string that is 50 inches long. After she cuts eight equal size pieces, she has 2 inches left. How long was each piece? 6 inches
2. Mr. Morris is hanging a light from a ceiling. The height from the ceiling to the floor is 12 feet. If the fixture is 2 feet 4 inches from the ceiling, how far is the fixture to the floor? 9 ft 8 in.
4. A bike trail has markers at every other mile beginning with mile one. There is also one at the end of the trail. The trail is 16.3 miles long. How many markers are there? 9 markers

Lesson 3-6

Pages 122–124

Multiply.

1. 45×41 1,845
2. 62×68 4,216
3. 17×59 1,003
4. 172×48 8,256

5. 17 × 13 221 **6.** 56 × 72 4,032

7. 473 × 59 27,907 **8.** 182 × 35 6,370

9. Kate swims 18 laps every day in the school's pool. The length of the pool is 50 meters. How many meters will she swim in 28 days? 25,200 meters

Lesson 3-7

Pages 126–129

Identify the multiplication property used to rewrite each problem. 3. commutative 4. associative

1. 13 × 4 = 4 × 13 commutative **2.** 46 = 1 × 46 identity

3. 7 × 15 × 42 = 7 × 42 × 15 **4.** 5 × (8 × 10) = (5 × 8) × 10

Use properties of multiplication to find each product mentally. Show your steps and identify the properties that you used.

5. 10 × 4 × 7 **6.** 15 × (4 × 5) **7.** 100 × 32 × 3

8. 4 × (5 × 18) **9.** 2 × 24 × 5 **10.** 25 × (4 × 17)

11. Colby delivers papers every weekday. It takes him 80 minutes each day. If he works 5 days a week for 4 weeks, how many total minutes will it take him to deliver the papers? 1,600 minutes

5–10. See Extra Practice Answer Appendix.

Lesson 3-8

Pages 132–135

Estimate by rounding.

1. $2.30 × 8; $2 × 8 = $16
2. $5.87 × 4; $6 × 4 = $24
3. $38.09 × 6; $40 × 6 = $240
4. $19.95 × 3; $20 × 3 = $60
5. 3,272 × 9; 3,000 × 9 = 27,000
6. 485 × 724; 500 × 700 = 350,000
7. Lauren bought 3.2 pounds of lunch meat. It costs $4 per pound. About how much did Lauren pay for the lunch meat? $4 × 3 = $12
8. Rodrigo is buying DVDs. He buys two DVDs that cost $19.98 each and three that cost $22.50 each. Estimate the total cost of the DVDs. $100

Extra Practice

Lesson 3-9

Pages 136–137

Solve each problem. If there is extra information, identify it. If there is not enough information, tell what information is needed. 1–3. See Extra Practice Answer Appendix.

1. Hayden purchases a new bicycle for $149. The color of the bicycle is blue with red stripes. He needs to make 12 monthly payments of $9 to pay off the balance on the bike. How much was the down payment?
2. Shawnel and Cynthiana are participating in a magazine sale. Each magazine subscription costs $2 per week. How many more magazine subscriptions did Cynthiana sell than Shawnel?

Person	Subscriptions
Shawnel	38
Cynthiana	77

3. An arts and crafts store sells three sizes of candles. The prices for the candles are $1.50 for the small size, $2.50 for the medium size, and $5.00 for the large size. The store averages $335 in candle sales each week. How many large candles do they sell on average per week?

Lesson 4-1 8. 2 9. 14,000 10. 9,000 11. 300 12. 7,000

Pages 149–151

Divide mentally.

1. 400 ÷ 4 100
2. 600 ÷ 3 200
3. 270 ÷ 10 27
4. 160 ÷ 8 20
5. 5,400 ÷ 6 900
6. 800 ÷ 8 100
7. 2,700 ÷ 9 300
8. 16,000 ÷ 8,000
9. 28,000 ÷ 2
10. 45,000 ÷ 5
11. 90,000 ÷ 300
12. 42,000 ÷ 6
13. Griffen made $350 doing yard work. If he makes $10 per hour, how many hours did he work? 35 hours

Lesson 4-2 1–12. See Extra Practice Answer Appendix.

Pages 152–155

Estimate by using compatible numbers. Show your work.

1. 277 ÷ 3
2. 778 ÷ 21
3. 990 ÷ 333
4. 721 ÷ 34
5. 110 ÷ 9
6. 320 ÷ 37
7. 499 ÷ 23
8. 655 ÷ 222
9. 5,322 ÷ 63
10. 8,672 ÷ 218
11. 4,776 ÷ 239
12. 21,356 ÷ 3,200
13. Mr. Jerome can drive 320 miles on one tank of gas. If his gas tank holds 11 gallons of gasoline, about how many miles can he drive on one gallon? Show how you estimated. 30 miles; 330 ÷ 11 = 30

Lesson 4-3

Pages 158–161

Divide.

1. 76 ÷ 4 19
2. 235 ÷ 5 47
3. 244 ÷ 8 30 R4
4. 333 ÷ 2 166 R1
5. 222 ÷ 3 74
6. 632 ÷ 4 158
7. 933 ÷ 3 311
8. 420 ÷ 4 105
9. 302 ÷ 4 75 R2
10. 622 ÷ 3 207 R1
11. 721 ÷ 7 103
12. 432 ÷ 6 72
13. Trey used a total of 13,335 Calories for the week. On average, how many Calories a day did he use? 1,905 Calories per day
14. If Trey eats 3 meals a day, how many Calories per meal can he have? 635 Calories

Lesson 4-4

Pages 162–164

Divide.

1. 73 ÷ 11 6 R7
2. 81 ÷ 30 2 R21
3. 43 ÷ 13 3 R4
4. 82 ÷ 44 1 R38
5. 443 ÷ 66 6 R47
6. 211 ÷ 17 12 R7
7. 525 ÷ 75 7
8. 321 ÷ 11 29 R2
9. 150 ÷ 30 5
10. 756 ÷ 50 15 R6
11. 923 ÷ 71 13
12. 388 ÷ 24 16 R4
13. Paz's class is making birdhouses for a project. They have 524 inches of wood. If each birdhouse takes 24 inches to complete, how many birdhouses can they build? What does your remainder represent? 21 birdhouses; the remaining wood

Lesson 4-5

Pages 166–167

Solve. Use the *act it out* strategy.

1. The top three finishers in the local swimming competition were Melanie, Yasmin, and Francisca. In how many different ways can first, second, and third place be awarded? 6 ways
2. Elio's mother asked him to roll the family's extra change. The table shows the coins he rolled, how many rolls he made, and the value of money in the rolls. How many total coins did Elio roll? 300 coins

Coin	Number of rolls	Value of coins (in dollars)
Quarter	2	20.00
Dime	2	10.00
Nickel	3	6.00

Extra Practice

1. 3 T-shirts; remainder 2.03 means that there is $2.03 left over.

Lesson 4-6 2. 21 necklaces; remainder 1 bag of beads

Pages 170–173

Solve. Tell how you interpreted the remainder.

1. Deborah decided to purchase T-shirts at an amusement park to give as souvenirs. How many T-shirts can she buy with $35?

2. It takes 5 bags of beads to make 3 necklaces. How many necklaces can be made with 36 bags of beads?
3. Mrs. Heaton cuts her pie into 7 pieces. She needs to have 83 pieces for a charity event. How many pies must she bake to have enough pieces? How many pieces will be left over? 12 pies; 1 piece of pie left over

Lesson 4-7

Pages 174–176

Estimate.

1. $5\overline{)\$8.25}$ $\$10 \div 5 = \$2$
2. $7\overline{)\$19.88}$ $\$21 \div 7 = \$3$
3. $2\overline{)\$33.50}$ $\$30 \div 2 = \$15$
4. Papina, Malik, and Silvia made a total of $63.21 at a yard sale. They divide the money evenly. About how much does each person get? $\$60 \div 3 = \$20$

Lesson 4-8

Pages 180–181

Use any strategy to solve each problem.

1. An artist painted twice as many pieces on Tuesday as he did on Monday. He painted 36 pieces total on the two days. How many did he paint on Monday? 12 pieces
2. Ruth has 43 cents in coins in her pocket. If you know that one of the coins is a quarter and she has six coins in her pocket, what are the other coins? 1 dime, 1 nickel, 3 pennies
3. Luz is saving up to buy a pair of inline skates that cost $34.98. If she saves $5.00 each week, how many weeks will it take until she can buy the skates? 7 weeks
4. Amiel is heading out for his daily jog. He needs to be home by 6:15 P.M. to do his homework. It takes him 15 minutes to warm up, 45 minutes to jog, and 10 minutes to cool down. What time should he leave for his jog? 5:05 P.M.
5. Akiko is buying books to hold her stamp collection. Each book can hold 120 stamps. If she has 76 envelopes that contain 4 stamps each, how many books will she need? 3 books

Lesson 5-1

Pages 193–195

Evaluate each expression if $x = 4$ and $y = 7$.

1. $x + 6$ 10
2. $3 + y$ 10
3. $2 + x$ 6
4. $y + 27$ 34
5. $17 + y$ 24
6. $x + 21$ 25
7. $x + 29$ 33
8. $x + y$ 11

Write an expression for the real-world situation. Then evaluate it.

9. Sareeta is t years old. Her sister is 6 years older. If $t = 10$, how old is Sareeta's sister? 16 years old

Lesson 5-2 3. 630 seconds or 10 minutes 30 seconds

Pages 196–197

Solve. Use the *solve a simpler problem* strategy.

1. For a play, five students can paint 5 props in 5 hours. At this rate, how many props can 7 students paint in 10 hours? 14 props
2. What is the sum of the whole numbers from 10 through 19? 20 through 29? 30 through 39? Can you predict the sum of the numbers 50 through 59? 145; 245; 345; 545
3. Monty is cutting wood for shelves. He has 40 feet of lumber. Each shelf needs to be 5 feet long. If each cut takes 90 seconds, how long will it take Monty to make the cuts?
4. A newspaper delivery person can fit 35 newspapers into their carry bag on Monday through Saturday. On Sunday they can fit 21 papers. They deliver the newspaper to 88 customers every day. How many times do they have to load their carry bag on Wednesdays? 3 times

Lesson 5-3

Pages 198–201

Evaluate each expression if $x = 5$ and $y = 3$.

1. $3x$ 15
2. $6y$ 18
3. $7x$ 35
4. $13y$ 39

Evaluate each expression if $a = 9$ and $b = 5$.

5. $4b$ 20
6. $11a$ 99
7. $20b$ 100
8. $8a$ 72
9. $17b$ 85
10. $31a$ 279
11. $45b$ 225
12. $9b$ 45
13. Mei can walk 3 miles in one hour. Saturday she walked for t hours. Write an expression to show the distance she walked. $3t$
14. Mrs. Turner is providing fruit slices for the football team. She can get 8 slices from one orange. Write an expression to show how many slices she can get from f oranges. How many slices can Mrs. Turner get from 15 oranges? $8f$; 120 slices

Lesson 5-4

Pages 202–204

Write an expression for each phrase. 6. $m + 5$

1. half of c $c \div 2$ **2.** 12 times w $12w$ **3.** 19 more than k $k + 19$

4. 20 less than x $x - 20$ **5.** twice p $2p$ **6.** the sum of m and 5

Evaluate each expression if $r = 3$, $s = 5$, and $t = 9$.

7. $r \times 31$ 93 **8.** $13t$ 117 **9.** $4r$ 12 **10.** $t \div 3 \times s$ 15

11. There were t questions on a test. Eva missed 4 questions. If there were 35 questions on the test, write and evaluate an expression for the number of questions answered correctly. $t - 4$; 31 questions

Lesson 5-5

2. Marlo: 16 years old, Naomi: 8 years old

Pages 206–207

Use any strategy to solve each problem.

1. Jonas' parents give him $15 each week for school lunches. If Jonas buys one of each item every day, how much money does he have left on Friday? $0.50

Item	Price (in dollars)
pizza	1.50
drink	0.65
fruit	0.75

2. Marlo is twice as old as his sister Naomi. Four years ago he was three times as old. What are their ages now?

3. A large commercial jet seats 416 passengers. On a recent flight, there was one empty seat for every three passengers. How many passengers were on the flight? 312 passengers

Lesson 5-6

Pages 210–213

Copy and complete each function table for each real-world situation.

1. Cora has 11 more trains than Luis.

Input (x)	$x + 11$	Output
12	12 + 11	23
14	14 + 11	25
17	17 + 11	29

2. Each package weighs 10 pounds.

Input (x)	$10x$	Output
7	10 × 7	70
11	10 × 11	110
15	10 × 15	150

Lesson 5-7

Pages 218–222

Evaluate each expression.

1. $(14 \times 7) - 3$ 95 **2.** $14 \times (7 - 3)$ 56 **3.** $7 + (2 \times 9)$ 25

4. $(7 + 2) \times 9$ 81 **5.** $(23 + 17) \times 5$ 200 **6.** $23 + (17 \times 5)$ 108

7. Mrs. Walker is making banners for the middle school sports teams. She needs 8 yards of gold fabric and 6 yards of maroon fabric. The gold fabric costs $6 per yard and the maroon fabric costs $10 per yard. How much will she spend for the fabric? $108

Lesson 6-1

Pages 237–239

Solve each equation. Check your solution.

1. $x + 8 = 14$ 6 **2.** $7 - y = 2$ 5 **3.** $e + 15 = 29$ 14 **4.** $q + 4 = 17$ 13

5. $17 - w = 5$ 12 **6.** $9 + h = 21$ 12 **7.** $t - 19 = 6$ 25 **8.** $29 - y = 1$ 28

Write an equation and then solve. Check your solution.

9. Lei is thinking of a number. Elsa incorrectly guessed the number to be 25. Lei said the difference between the two numbers is 36. What was her number?

10. The school's lacrosse team has won 5 straight games. Their record is now 13 wins and 4 losses. What was their record before the winning streak?

11. Tyran owns 24 movies. He bought 11 with his own money. The other movies were gifts from others. How many did he receive as gifts?

9–11. See Extra Practice Answer Appendix.

Lesson 6-2

Pages 244–247

Solve each equation. Check your solution.

1. $6c = 24$ 4 **2.** $21 = 3c$ 7 **3.** $9g = 45$ 5 **4.** $66 = 2p$ 33

5. $17y = 102$ 6 **6.** $93 = 31h$ 3 **7.** $49 = 7k$ 7 **8.** $21s = 42$ 2

9. $30p = 330$; 11 players

Write an equation and then solve. Check your solution.

9. Every player on a basketball team practiced for 30 hours during the two week summer camp. The team practiced for a total of 330 hours. How many players are on the basketball team?

10. A shoe store sold 84 pairs of shoes last weekend. Each clerk sold the same number of shoes. There are 7 clerks at the store. How many pairs of shoes did each sell? $7s = 84$; 12 pairs of shoes

Lesson 6-3

Pages 248–249

Solve. Use the *make a table* strategy.

1. Francisco is 17 years old. His grandfather is 77. How old will Francisco's grandfather be when he is exactly 4 times as old as Francisco? 80 years old
2. The first week of track practice Cesar ran the 400 meter dash in 1 minute 8 seconds. The third week he ran the 400 meter dash in 1 minute 5 seconds. He continued this pattern until the end of the season. How fast could Cesar run the 400 meter dash in week 9? 56 seconds
3. Marsha's little brother tells her he will clean her room every day for the next two weeks if she pays him by doubling the amount of money paid from the day before. He offers to start for $0.10. How much will he make on the seventh day? $6.40
4. If Marsha agrees to his plan, did she make a good deal? Explain. See Extra Practice Answer Appendix.

Lesson 6-4

Pages 250–252

Name the ordered pair for each point.

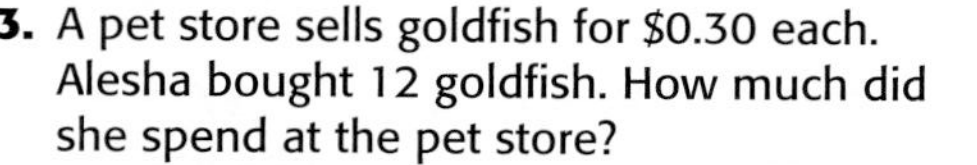

1. *B* (7,7) **2.** *F* (1, 2) **3.** *E* (2, 5)

4. *A* (5, 2) **5.** *K* (3, 1) **6.** *G* (5, 5)

7. Suppose point *C* was moved one unit to the right and 2 units down. After the move what point will be the same as point *C*? point *A*
8. Garcia located a point that was 6 points to the right of the origin and 3 points above the origin. What was the ordered pair? (6, 3)

Lesson 6-5 1–10. See Extra Practice Answer Appendix.

Pages 254–257

Graph and label each point on a coordinate grid.

1. *W* (3, 4) **2.** *R* (1, 8) **3.** *H* (7, 3) **4.** *T* (5, 5)

5. *B* (5, 2) **6.** *J* (3, 6) **7.** *P* (6, 8) **8.** *C* (2, 4)

9. Mr. Rollins wants to plant trees. Each tree costs $25, and he must pay a delivery charge of $10. Given the function rule $25t + 10$, make a function table to find the total amount Mr. Rollins would pay if he purchased 3 trees, 4 trees, 5 trees, and 6 trees.
10. The Williams family is taking a trip. They travel for 20 miles before they begin timing the length of the trip. Given the function rule $55h + 20$, make a function table to find the distance traveled if they drove for 3 hours, 4 hours, 5 hours, and 6 hours.

Lesson 6-6 1–4. See Extra Practice Answer Appendix.

Pages 260–262

Solve using a function table or equation.

1. A vendor sells gyros. How much would it cost for a group of 6 people to each eat one gyro?
2. On average Elizabeth reads 82 pages of her book each night. If her book is 548 pages, how long will it take her to read the entire book?
3. A pet store sells goldfish for $0.30 each. Alesha bought 12 goldfish. How much did she spend at the pet store?
4. A pumpkin pie recipe calls for 2 cups of sugar. How much sugar is needed to make 4 pumpkin pies?

Lesson 6-7 1. Olinda: vanilla; Danica: chocolate; Kimi: strawberry

Pages 266–267

Use any strategy to solve each problem.

1. Olinda, Danica, and Kimi each like different flavors of ice cream. The flavors they like are vanilla, chocolate, and strawberry. Danica does not like vanilla. Kimi does not like chocolate or vanilla. What type of ice cream does each girl like?
2. A store is selling a television at a clearance price. The clearance price of the television is listed with its original price. If the store sold 7 televisions, what was the total difference between selling them at clearance price and selling them at regular price? $1,400

Was $650
NOW $450

3. Yasu is painting eggs for the local egg hunt. He can paint 3 eggs in 20 minutes. How many eggs can he paint in 1 hour and 40 minutes? 15 eggs

Lesson 7-1

Pages 279–281

Find the mean, median, and mode of each set of data.

1. points scored by a basketball team: 55, 67, 55, 96, 87 mean: 72; median: 67; mode: 55
2. weight of rocks in pounds: 4, 12, 45, 17, 12 mean: 18; median: 12; mode: 12
3. cups of flour: 9, 2.5, 4.25, 2.5, 1.75 mean: 4; median: 2.5; mode: 2.5

Lesson 7-2

Pages 282–283

Use any strategy to solve each problem.

1. Henry bought two greeting cards. One card was $0.50 more than the other. The total cost was $7.00. How much did Henry spend for each card? $3.25; $3.75
2. Waban, Josie, and Jacylyn all like different types of books. Josie does not like mysteries or biographies. Jacylyn does not like mysteries or fairytales. Which type of book does each like to read? Waban: mysteries; Josie: fairytales; Jacylyn: biographies
3. Wanda wants to drive 300 miles to visit her brother. If she can drive 25 miles on one gallon of gasoline, how many gallons of gasoline will she need to make the trip? 12 gallons

Lesson 7-3

Pages 284–288

Draw a line plot for each set of data. Then find the median, mode, range, and any outliers of the data shown in the line plot. 1–4. See Extra Practice Answer Appendix.

1.

Student Height in inches for Mrs. Foster's 5th grade class			
52	48	52	51
52	65	58	48
60	45	50	52
56	48	53	58
62	49	51	49

2.

Daily Low Temperatures for January				
23	17	30	20	17
14	22	31	32	22
32	20	8	31	32
33	27	15	32	30
32	28	20	40	27
33	29	18	14	15

3.

Distances of Paper Airplanes (ft)					
1	5	5	8	3	2
1	4	3	3	6	9
0	2	2	6	3	1
4	7	5	2	4	8

4.

Number of Birds Counted			
30	20	18	22
20	18	21	23
20	20	21	19
18	19	20	23

Lesson 7-4 1, 2. See Extra Practice Answer Appendix.

Pages 289–292

The following are speed limits for different roads located in a city's limits:

55, 35, 25, 25, 35, 45, 40, 40, 25, 20, 25, 50, 35, 40, 25, 25

1. Make a frequency table of the data.
2. Find the median, mode, and range of the data. Identify any outliers.

Lesson 7-5 1–3. See Extra Practice Answer Appendix.

Pages 294–298

The table shows the cost of athletic shoes.

Athletic Shoe Prices (in dollars)				
75	60	60	110	60
100	90	90	85	45
90	75	65	65	55
60	85	110	60	80

1. Choose an appropriate scale and interval size for a frequency table that will represent the sales. Describe the intervals.
2. Create a frequency table using the scale and interval size you described.
3. Write a sentence or two to describe how the prices are distributed among the intervals.

Lesson 7-6 1. See Extra Practice Answer Appendix.

Pages 299–303

The table shows the number of each type of pie sold at a restaurant during lunch.

Pie Sales	
Flavor	Number
cherry pie	3
pumpkin pie	8
pecan pie	7
raspberry pie	6
apple pie	10

1. Make a bar graph of the data. Describe the scale and interval size that you used.
2. Which pie was purchased the most? Apple
3. Which pie represents the median number sold? Explain. Pecan; half the flavors sold more and half the flavors sold less.

For Exercises 4 and 5, use the bar graph below.

4. Based on the graph below, which state has about twice the area as Kansas? Which state is about $\frac{1}{3}$ the size of Texas? California; Kansas

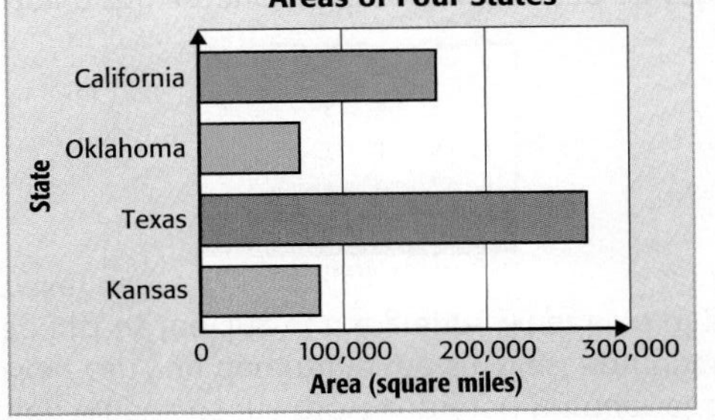

5. About how many more people live in California than Oklahoma? Sample answer: 85,000

Lesson 7-7 1–5. See Extra Practice Answer Appendix.

Pages 306–310

The table shows the amount of growth of two sunflower plants Juanita grew for her science fair project.

Sunflower growth control plant													
Week	0	1	2	3	4	5	6	7	8	9	10	11	12
Height (inches)	0	7	14	27	40	52	68	82	90	99	100	101	101
Sunflower growth experimental plant													
Height (inches)	0	3	10	15	18	21	24	28	28	28	32	32	32

1. Make a double line graph of the data.
2. What is the scale of each axis?
3. Would your scale be different if you only had the top data to graph? Explain.
4. Write a sentence or two for each line describing the changes over time.
5. Give a possible explanation for the differences between the two lines.

Lesson 7-8

Pages 312–317

Which type of graph would you use to display the data in each table? Write *line plot, bar graph, double bar graph, line graph, double line graph*, or *pictograph*. Explain why. Then make the graph. 1–2. See Extra Practice Answer Appendix for graphs.

1. bar graph

Students' Favorite Drinks In School Cafeteria	
White Milk	157
Chocolate Milk	93
Water	45
Orange Juice	140
Apple Juice	65

2. double bar graph

Neighborhood Pets	Cats	Dogs
House 1	2	0
House 2	0	3
House 3	1	2
House 4	2	2
House 5	3	0
House 6	0	1
House 7	0	0
House 8	3	1

3. You want to show your friends how easy it is to save money and what happens to that money over time. Which type of graph would be best to display the data? Explain.
4. Orlando took a survey of his classmates' favorite cafeteria food. What type of graph should he use if he wants to present the data to the principal? Explain. 3-4. See Extra Practice Answer Appendix.

Lesson 7-9

Pages 320–321

Solve by using a graph. 1–2. See Extra Practice Answer Appendix.

1. The table shows the number of books read by students during the summer. What was the most common number of books to read? How can you determine the smallest amount of books read just by looking at the graph? What kind of graph did you make?

Number of Books Read					
5	4	1	6	7	4
3	2	3	1	4	2
2	1	3	4	5	9
2	4	5	3	3	4

2. Ty wrote down the amount of time that he read on school nights. What day was the peak of his reading? What kind of graph did you make? How can you determine the peak of his reading just by looking at the graph?

Day of the Week	Sunday	Monday	Tuesday	Wednesday	Thursday
Time (hours)	2	1.5	3.5	2.5	1

Lesson 8-1 3. $\frac{1}{6}$; each person receives $\frac{1}{6}$ of the pizza.

Pages 333–335

Represent each situation using a fraction. Then solve.

1. Seven gallons of water are needed to wash 9 cars. How much water was needed to wash each car? $\frac{7}{9}$; each car uses $\frac{7}{9}$ gallons of the water.
2. Three tons of sand is put into 4 volleyball courts. How many tons of sand did each court receive? $\frac{3}{4}$; each court receives $\frac{3}{4}$ ton of the sand.
3. One pizza is divided between 6 people. How much pizza did each person receive?

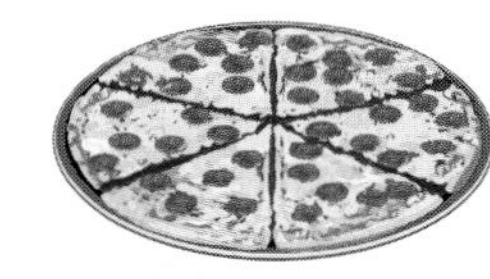

4. Twenty six bags of soil are used to fill in 6 holes. How many bags of soil does each hole use? $\frac{26}{6}$ or $4\frac{2}{6}$; each hole gets $\frac{26}{6}$ or $4\frac{2}{6}$ bags of soil.

Lesson 8-2

Pages 338–342

Write each improper fraction as a mixed number.

1. $\frac{6}{5}$ $1\frac{1}{5}$
2. $\frac{7}{2}$ $3\frac{1}{2}$
3. $\frac{19}{8}$ $2\frac{3}{8}$
4. $\frac{42}{5}$ $8\frac{2}{5}$
5. $\frac{27}{7}$ $3\frac{6}{7}$
6. $\frac{15}{4}$ $3\frac{3}{4}$
7. $\frac{8}{7}$ $1\frac{1}{7}$
8. $\frac{21}{8}$ $2\frac{5}{8}$
9. $\frac{10}{3}$ $3\frac{1}{3}$
10. $\frac{44}{6}$ $7\frac{2}{6}$
11. $\frac{11}{3}$ $3\frac{2}{3}$
12. $\frac{38}{5}$ $7\frac{3}{5}$

Lesson 8-3

Pages 344–345

Solve by *using logical reasoning*.

1. In a class of 30 students, 18 say their favorite subject is math, 5 say their favorite subject is social studies, and 3 say they love both math and social studies. How many students have favorite subjects other than math or social studies? 10 students
2. In a school of 500 students, 185 students are in the band, 300 are on sports teams, and 160 participate in both activities. How many students are involved in either band or sports? 325 students
3. There were six dogs, four cats, and two snakes in a vet's office. Two people owned a cat and dog, and one person owned a dog and snake. If no one else owned multiple animals, how many people were in the office? 9 people

Lesson 8-4

Pages 346–348

Write each mixed number as an improper fraction.

1. $6\frac{1}{2}$ $\frac{13}{2}$ **2.** $4\frac{2}{3}$ $\frac{14}{3}$ **3.** $9\frac{5}{7}$ $\frac{68}{7}$ **4.** $7\frac{4}{9}$ $\frac{67}{9}$

5. $2\frac{5}{8}$ $\frac{21}{8}$ **6.** $5\frac{2}{13}$ $\frac{67}{13}$ **7.** $2\frac{3}{5}$ $\frac{13}{5}$ **8.** $4\frac{7}{8}$ $\frac{39}{8}$

9. $3\frac{7}{12}$ $\frac{43}{12}$ **10.** $1\frac{5}{6}$ $\frac{11}{6}$ **11.** $13\frac{5}{12}$ $\frac{161}{12}$ **12.** $5\frac{1}{4}$ $\frac{21}{4}$

13. Ines can make $4\frac{1}{3}$ necklaces out of one bag of beads. Write this number as an improper fraction. $\frac{13}{3}$

Lesson 8-5

Pages 350–353

Replace each ● with < or > to make a true statement.

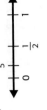

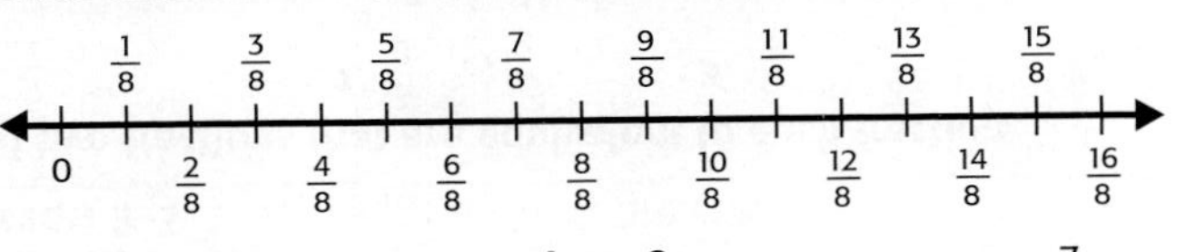

1. $\frac{5}{8}$ ● $\frac{3}{8}$ > **2.** $2\frac{4}{8}$ ● $2\frac{2}{8}$ > **3.** $10\frac{7}{8}$ ● $10\frac{5}{8}$ >

Replace each ● with < or > to make a true statement.

4. $\frac{6}{9}$ ● $\frac{4}{9}$ > **5.** $\frac{9}{5}$ ● $3\frac{5}{9}$ < **6.** $10\frac{3}{4}$ ● $2\frac{1}{3}$ >

5. $\frac{2}{3}$ ● $\frac{1}{2}$ > **6.** $2\frac{5}{8}$ ● $1\frac{1}{4}$ < **7.** $\frac{21}{3}$ ● $7\frac{1}{8}$ <

8. Ricky said he could make $\frac{4}{5}$ of the baskets he shot at practice. Omar said he could make $\frac{6}{7}$ of the baskets he shot. Who claimed to make more baskets at practice? Omar

Lesson 8-6

Pages 356–359

State whether each fraction is closest to 0, $\frac{1}{2}$, or 1.

1. $\frac{7}{9}$ 1

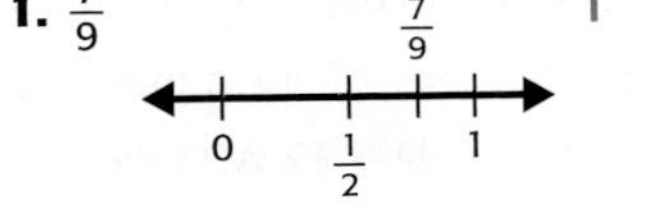

2. $\frac{1}{5}$ 0

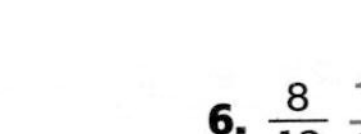

Round each fraction to 0, $\frac{1}{2}$, or 1.

3. $\frac{4}{13}$ $\frac{1}{2}$ **4.** $\frac{5}{7}$ $\frac{1}{2}$ **5.** $\frac{12}{15}$ 1 **6.** $\frac{8}{12}$ $\frac{1}{2}$

7. $\frac{7}{11}$ $\frac{1}{2}$ **8.** $\frac{6}{10}$ $\frac{1}{2}$ **9.** $\frac{15}{17}$ 1 **10.** $\frac{1}{16}$ 0

11. Lewis has finished running $\frac{5}{8}$ of a mile. Has he run half a mile or almost all of a mile? half a mile

Lesson 8-7

Pages 360–361

Use any strategy to solve each problem.

1. Billiards players use the dots on the edge of the table to guide their shots. If there are 6 dots on each side of the table and 3 dots on each end, how many total dots are there around the perimeter of the billiards table? 18 dots
2. What two positive integers have a sum of 17 and a product of 72? 9 and 8
3. A salesperson at a department store makes the following commissions. In one day, the sales person sold 8 shirts, 3 pairs of pants, and 4 pairs of shoes. How much did the salesperson make in commissions on that day? $56

Article of Clothing	Commission
Shirt	$2
Pants	$4
Shoes	$7

Lesson 9-1

Pages 373–375

Find the common factors of each set of numbers.

1. 7, 28 1,7 **2.** 12, 40 1,2,4 **3.** 6, 30 1,2,3,6 **4.** 27, 45 1,3,9

Find the GCF of each set of numbers.

5. 6, 18 6 **6.** 20, 24 4 **7.** 44, 12 4 **8.** 35, 14 7

9. There are 36 dogs and 48 cats in a pet show. The show planner wants to put an equal number of dogs and cats in each row. What is the greatest number of cats that can be in each row? 12 cats

Lesson 9-2
Pages 378–381

Tell whether each number is *prime* or *composite*.

1. 12 composite 2. 23 prime 3. 28 composite 4. 30 composite
5. 55 composite 6. 43 prime 7. 17 prime 8. 62 composite

9. Kaya wants to arrange her 12 field hockey trophies on a shelf. How many different ways can she arrange her trophies so an equal number of trophies are in each row? List the ways. 3 different ways; 12 rows of 1, 6 rows of 2, 4 rows of 3
10. What is the only even prime number? 2

Lesson 9-3 1–8. Sample answers are given.
Pages 382–384

Find two fractions that are equivalent to each fraction.

1. $\frac{6}{7}$ $\frac{12}{14}, \frac{18}{21}$ 2. $\frac{3}{9}$ $\frac{6}{18}, \frac{9}{27}$ 3. $\frac{8}{9}$ $\frac{16}{18}, \frac{24}{27}$ 4. $\frac{3}{10}$ $\frac{6}{20}, \frac{9}{30}$
5. $\frac{6}{18}$ $\frac{3}{9}, \frac{1}{3}$ 6. $\frac{8}{14}$ $\frac{4}{7}, \frac{16}{28}$ 7. $\frac{4}{20}$ $\frac{2}{10}, \frac{1}{5}$ 8. $\frac{7}{8}$ $\frac{14}{16}, \frac{21}{24}$

9. Khalid wants to buy $\frac{24}{32}$ of a yard of chain. How many fourths of a yard is this? $\frac{3}{4}$
10. A craft project takes $\frac{16}{24}$ of a yard of fabric. Ito wants to buy enough for one project. The store only sells fabric in thirds. How many thirds should Ito buy? 2

Lesson 9-4
Pages 386–389

Write each fraction in simplest form. If the fraction is already in simplest form, write *simplified*.

1. $\frac{4}{6}$ $\frac{2}{3}$ 2. $\frac{4}{10}$ $\frac{2}{5}$ 3. $\frac{9}{21}$ $\frac{3}{7}$ 4. $\frac{8}{12}$ $\frac{2}{3}$
5. $\frac{12}{32}$ $\frac{3}{8}$ 6. $\frac{17}{35}$ simplified 7. $\frac{20}{45}$ $\frac{4}{9}$ 8. $\frac{6}{42}$ $\frac{1}{7}$
9. $\frac{22}{44}$ $\frac{1}{2}$ 10. $\frac{9}{12}$ $\frac{3}{4}$ 11. $\frac{5}{15}$ $\frac{1}{3}$ 12. $\frac{10}{25}$ $\frac{2}{5}$

13. Victoria has 16 white socks, 10 pink socks, 4 green socks and 6 blue socks in her drawer. Express in simplest form the fraction of socks in her drawer that are white; pink; blue. $\frac{4}{9}$ white; $\frac{5}{18}$ pink; $\frac{1}{6}$ blue
14. Marta and Nicki were sharing a pizza. Marta wanted $\frac{1}{4}$ of the pizza and Nicki wanted $\frac{3}{8}$ of the pizza. Should they get the pizza cut into 4 or 8 pieces? How many pieces would each girl get? 8; Marta, 2 pieces; Nicki, 3 pieces

Lesson 9-5
Pages 391–393

Write each decimal as a fraction in simplest form.

1. 0.5 $\frac{1}{2}$ 2. 0.7 $\frac{7}{10}$ 3. 0.13 $\frac{13}{100}$ 4. 0.75 $\frac{3}{4}$
5. 0.321 $\frac{321}{1000}$ 6. 0.340 $\frac{17}{50}$ 7. 0.08 $\frac{2}{25}$ 8. 0.50 $\frac{1}{2}$

9. In 1911, Ty Cobbs' batting average was 0.420. Write this rate as a fraction in simplest form. $\frac{21}{50}$

Lesson 9-6
Pages 394–395

Solve. Use the *look for a pattern* strategy.

1. Look at the pattern below.

   17, 58, 99, 140

   Describe the rule for determining the last 3 numbers shown in this pattern. Each number is 41 more than the previous number.
2. Mrs. Hintz's fifth grade class is raising money for the American Red Cross. They raise $66 the first week. The next two weeks are shown on the table. If this pattern continues, how much should the class expect to raise in the fourth week? $129

Week	1	2	3
Amount raised ($)	66	87	108

3. Jalen's test scores are continually improving. Here is a record of four of his first five tests. Based on the pattern, what was his third test score? 75

Test 1	Test 2	Test 3	Test 4	Test 5
63	69	■	81	87

Lesson 9-7
Pages 396–399

List multiples to find the first two common multiples of each pair of numbers.

1. 3 and 6 6, 12 2. 4 and 16 16, 32 3. 5 and 20 20, 40 4. 7 and 14 14, 28

Find the LCM of each set of numbers.

5. 4 and 5 20 6. 7 and 9 63 7. 4, 6, and 8 24 8. 7 and 15 105
9. The ages of Mrs. Thorne's children are 6, 8, and 12. What is the least common multiple of their ages? 24

Lesson 9-8 1. Brad–baseball, Landon–tennis, Amanda–basketball Pages 400–401

Use any strategy to solve each problem.

1. Brad, Landon, and Amanda each play different sports. Amanda does not play baseball or tennis. Landon does not play basketball or baseball. What sport does each person play?
2. A DNA strip follows this pattern: TCTTCGTCTTCGT _ _ _ What three letters finish the pattern? CTT
3. A total of 42 students were on the quiz bowl team. There were twice as many boys as girls. How many girls were on the team? 14 girls

Lesson 9-9 2. $\frac{9}{24} > \frac{2}{24}$ 3. $\frac{5}{10} > \frac{3}{10}$ 4. $\frac{7}{21} < \frac{12}{21}$ Pages 404–407

Compare each pair of fractions using models or the LCD.

1. $\frac{1}{2}$ and $\frac{5}{6}$ $\frac{3}{6} < \frac{5}{6}$ 2. $\frac{3}{8}$ and $\frac{1}{12}$ 3. $\frac{1}{2}$ and $\frac{3}{10}$ 4. $\frac{1}{3}$ and $\frac{4}{7}$

Replace each ● with <, >, or = to make a true statement.

5. $\frac{3}{4}$ ● $\frac{2}{3}$ > 6. $\frac{5}{8}$ ● $\frac{10}{16}$ = 7. $\frac{3}{8}$ ● $\frac{1}{3}$ > 8. $\frac{5}{9}$ ● $\frac{7}{12}$ <

9. Mr. Torres assigned thirty math problems for homework. Aisha worked for $\frac{1}{3}$ of an hour, Taro worked for $\frac{2}{5}$ of an hour, and Lucas worked for $\frac{1}{2}$ of an hour. Who worked the longest on the math homework? Lucas
10. Marcela made punch for the class party. She used $\frac{2}{3}$ quart of orange juice and $\frac{3}{4}$ quart of grape juice. Did she use more orange juice or more grape juice? Explain. More grape juice; $\frac{3}{4} = \frac{9}{12}$ and $\frac{2}{3} = \frac{8}{12}$, so $\frac{3}{4} > \frac{2}{3}$.

Lesson 10-1 Pages 423–425

Add. Write each sum in the simplest form.

1. $\frac{3}{6} + \frac{5}{6}$ $1\frac{1}{3}$ 2. $\frac{7}{15} + \frac{11}{15}$ $1\frac{1}{5}$ 3. $\frac{2}{8} + \frac{4}{8}$ $\frac{3}{4}$ 4. $\frac{2}{4} + \frac{4}{4}$ $1\frac{1}{2}$
5. $\frac{7}{5} + \frac{2}{5}$ $1\frac{4}{5}$ 6. $\frac{7}{13} + \frac{3}{13}$ $\frac{10}{13}$ 7. $\frac{2}{9} + \frac{7}{9}$ $\frac{9}{9}$ or 1 8. $\frac{11}{20} + \frac{17}{20}$ $1\frac{2}{5}$

9. Mr. Chang and his daughter Ping were building shelves for her room. One day they worked $\frac{2}{3}$ of an hour, and the second day they worked twice as long. How much total time did they work on the shelves? 2 hours
10. Delmar was mixing paint to use on a school project. He mixed $\frac{3}{4}$ gallon of white paint, $\frac{3}{4}$ gallon of red paint, and $\frac{2}{4}$ gallon of yellow paint. How much total paint did Delmar have? $\frac{8}{4}$ or 2 gallons

Lesson 10-2 1–8. See students' work for tiles or pictures. Pages 428–431

Subtract. Write each difference in simplest form. Check your answer by using fraction tiles or drawing a picture.

1. $\frac{3}{6} - \frac{2}{6}$ $\frac{1}{6}$ 2. $\frac{12}{15} - \frac{11}{15}$ $\frac{1}{15}$ 3. $\frac{7}{8} - \frac{4}{8}$ $\frac{3}{8}$
4. $\frac{3}{4} - \frac{1}{4}$ $\frac{1}{2}$ 5. $\frac{7}{5} - \frac{2}{5}$ $\frac{5}{5}$ or 1 6. $\frac{7}{13} - \frac{3}{13}$ $\frac{4}{13}$
7. $\frac{9}{9} - \frac{7}{9}$ $\frac{2}{9}$ 8. $\frac{19}{20} - \frac{11}{20}$ $\frac{2}{5}$ 9. $\frac{15}{16} - \frac{3}{16}$ $\frac{12}{16}$ or $\frac{3}{4}$

10. Ken runs $\frac{3}{8}$ of a mile. Isabel runs $\frac{5}{8}$ of a mile in the same time. How much farther does Isabel run? $\frac{1}{4}$ mile

Lesson 10-3 Pages 434–436

Add. Write in simplest form.

1. $\frac{5}{14} + \frac{1}{7}$ $\frac{1}{2}$ 2. $\frac{1}{3} + \frac{1}{2}$ $\frac{5}{6}$ 3. $\frac{2}{9} + \frac{1}{3}$ $\frac{5}{9}$
4. $\frac{1}{2} + \frac{3}{4}$ $1\frac{1}{4}$ 5. $\frac{1}{4} + \frac{3}{12}$ $\frac{1}{2}$ 6. $\frac{9}{12} + \frac{13}{24}$ $1\frac{7}{24}$
7. $\frac{8}{15} + \frac{2}{3}$ $1\frac{1}{5}$ 8. $\frac{5}{14} + \frac{11}{28}$ $\frac{3}{4}$ 9. $\frac{7}{16} + \frac{3}{4}$ $1\frac{3}{16}$

10. Ahmed ate $\frac{2}{5}$ of the cookies and Sarah ate $\frac{1}{3}$ of the cookies. What fraction of the cookies were eaten altogether? $\frac{11}{15}$

Lesson 10-4 Pages 439–441

Subtract. Write in simplest form.

1. $\frac{13}{20} - \frac{3}{10}$ $\frac{7}{20}$ 2. $\frac{5}{9} - \frac{1}{3}$ $\frac{2}{9}$ 3. $\frac{5}{8} - \frac{2}{5}$ $\frac{9}{40}$
4. $\frac{3}{4} - \frac{1}{2}$ $\frac{1}{4}$ 5. $\frac{7}{8} - \frac{3}{16}$ $\frac{11}{16}$ 6. $\frac{2}{3} - \frac{1}{6}$ $\frac{1}{2}$
7. $\frac{9}{16} - \frac{1}{2}$ $\frac{1}{16}$ 8. $\frac{5}{8} - \frac{11}{20}$ $\frac{3}{40}$ 9. $\frac{9}{12} - \frac{2}{3}$ $\frac{1}{12}$

10. Terrell finished $\frac{4}{9}$ of his report on Wednesday and $\frac{1}{3}$ of his report on Thursday. What fraction of the report does Terrell have left to finish? $\frac{1}{9}$

Lesson 10-5
Pages 442–443

Solve. Determine which answer is reasonable.

1. Teak wants to buy a new skateboard with special wheels. The skateboard costs $38.45, the wheels cost $8.95, and the tools needed to install them are $10.49. Which is a more reasonable estimate for the money Teak needs to save: $55, $60, or $65? **$60**
2. A shoe store had a total of 3,868 pairs of shoes in stock. A week later, 997 pairs of shoes were sold. Which is a more reasonable estimate for the number of pairs of shoes remaining in the store: 3,000 or 2,500? **3,000 pairs**
3. After school, Trina spends $\frac{2}{4}$ of an hour cleaning her room, $\frac{3}{4}$ of an hour practicing the flute, and $\frac{3}{4}$ of an hour doing her homework. Which is a more reasonable estimate for the amount of time she has spent working: 1 hour, 2 hours or 3 hours? **2 hours**

Lesson 10-6
Pages 444–446

Estimate. **1–9. See Extra Practice Answer Appendix.**

1. $3\frac{4}{9} + 7\frac{2}{9}$
2. $10\frac{3}{11} - 4\frac{2}{11}$
3. $5\frac{7}{12} + 7\frac{2}{3}$
4. $10\frac{2}{11} - 3\frac{3}{22}$
5. $7\frac{5}{6} - 4\frac{1}{6}$
6. $7\frac{7}{15} + 4\frac{6}{15}$
7. $6\frac{5}{8} - 5\frac{1}{4}$
8. $19\frac{1}{15} + 11\frac{1}{15}$
9. $4\frac{5}{7} - 1\frac{6}{7}$
10. Clarissa's first long jump attempt was $4\frac{5}{6}$ feet. Her second attempt was $5\frac{1}{2}$ feet. About how much longer was Clarissa's second attempt? **About $\frac{1}{2}$ ft**

Lesson 10-7 1–9. See students' work for tiles or drawings.
Pages 448–451

Add. Write each sum in simplest form. Check your answer by using fraction tiles or drawing a picture.

1. $2\frac{4}{7} + 6\frac{2}{7}$ **$8\frac{6}{7}$**
2. $8\frac{1}{3} + 2\frac{2}{9}$ **$10\frac{5}{9}$**
3. $3\frac{7}{10} + 5\frac{4}{5}$ **$9\frac{1}{2}$**
4. $6\frac{1}{5} + 12\frac{9}{20}$ **$18\frac{13}{20}$**
5. $1\frac{1}{8} + 2\frac{5}{8}$ **$3\frac{3}{4}$**
6. $7\frac{7}{17} + 6\frac{6}{17}$ **$13\frac{13}{17}$**
7. $4\frac{1}{2} + 3\frac{2}{10}$ **$7\frac{7}{10}$**
8. $17\frac{1}{13} + 13\frac{1}{13}$ **$30\frac{2}{13}$**
9. $2\frac{4}{6} + 1\frac{2}{3}$ **$4\frac{1}{3}$**
10. Mr. Woods needs $1\frac{3}{4}$ pounds of ground beef to make hamburgers and $2\frac{1}{2}$ pounds to make meatloaf. How much ground beef does Mr. Woods need altogether? **$4\frac{1}{4}$ pounds**

Lesson 10-8 1–6. See students' work for tiles or drawings.
Pages 452–454

Subtract. Write each difference in simplest form. Check your answer by using fraction tiles or drawing a picture.

1. $7\frac{9}{10} - 4\frac{7}{10}$ **$3\frac{1}{5}$**
2. $10\frac{4}{7} - 2\frac{3}{7}$ **$8\frac{1}{7}$**
3. $9\frac{2}{3} - 7\frac{7}{12}$ **$2\frac{1}{12}$**
4. $16\frac{1}{3} - 12\frac{4}{27}$ **$4\frac{5}{27}$**
5. $7\frac{5}{9} - 2\frac{4}{9}$ **$5\frac{1}{9}$**
6. $7\frac{7}{19} - 6\frac{6}{19}$ **$1\frac{1}{19}$**
7. The average rainfall in Abilene for the month of August is $2\frac{4}{5}$ inches. The average rainfall in Zapata is $1\frac{7}{10}$ inches. What is the difference in the average amount of rainfall between the two cities? **$1\frac{1}{10}$ in.**

Lesson 10-9
Pages 456–457

Use any strategy to solve each problem.

1. A one topping pizza with eight slices costs $6. If the cost per slice remains the same, how much would a one topping pizza with fourteen slices cost? **$10.50**
2. What is the next figure in the pattern? → ← ↑ ↓ → ←
3. At the Henderson's garage sale, they are selling T-shirts for $0.80 each and bicycles for $15.50 each. If someone bought 3 T-shirts and 1 bicycle, how much did they spend at the garage sale? **$17.90**

Lesson 10-10 1–8. See students' work for tiles or drawings.
Pages 458–461

Subtract. Write each difference in simplest form. Check your answer by using fraction tiles or drawing a picture.

1. $9\frac{2}{6} - 5\frac{5}{6}$ **$3\frac{1}{2}$**
2. $8\frac{4}{9} - 6\frac{7}{9}$ **$1\frac{2}{3}$**
3. $5\frac{1}{5} - 1\frac{2}{5}$ **$3\frac{4}{5}$**
4. $7\frac{1}{3} - 3\frac{2}{3}$ **$3\frac{2}{3}$**
5. $13 - 10\frac{5}{8}$ **$2\frac{3}{8}$**
6. $15\frac{1}{4} - 12\frac{3}{4}$ **$2\frac{1}{2}$**
7. $10\frac{3}{7} - 5\frac{5}{7}$ **$4\frac{5}{7}$**
8. $15 - 11\frac{7}{10}$ **$3\frac{3}{10}$**
9. Hala's dog Max weighs $45\frac{3}{8}$ pounds. Berto's dog Teddy weighs $23\frac{5}{8}$ pounds. How much more does Max weigh than Teddy? **$21\frac{3}{4}$ lb**

Lesson 11-1
Pages 477–480

Complete.

1. 4 ft = ■ in. **48**
2. 14 yd = ■ in. **504**
3. 39 ft = ■ yd **13**
4. 132 in. = ■ ft. **11**
5. 24 yd 3 ft = ■ ft **75**
6. 8 ft 24 in. = ■ ft **10**
7. The beluga whale grows to be about 15 feet in length. What is the length of the whale in yards? In inches? **5 yards; 180 inches**

Lesson 11-2
Pages 482–483

Solve. Use the *draw a diagram* strategy.

1. Jai is taking her dog for a walk. She leaves the house, turns left and walks three blocks. Then she turns right, walks three blocks, turns left, walks 2 more blocks, then turns left again and walks 5 blocks. How far from home is she? 7 blocks
2. Mr. Costa is making cookies for a party. He has two cookie sheets. One is 14 inches wide by 16 inches long and the other is 12 inches by 18 inches. If each cookie is 2 inches in diameter and he places them 1 inch apart, which cookie sheet holds more cookies? 14 in. by 16 in.

Lesson 11-3
Pages 484–487

Complete. 4. 1; 1,000

1. 80 oz = ■ lb 5 **2.** 3 T = ■ lb 6,000 **3.** 12 lb = ■ oz 192
4. 3,000 lb = ■ T ■ lb **5.** 23 lb 48 oz = ■ lb 26 **6.** 144 oz = ■ lb 9
7. Mrs. Wilson needs 240 ounces of potatoes for her school potluck dinner. How many pounds of potatoes does she need? 15 pounds

Lesson 11-4
Pages 488–490

Complete. 9. 2; 6

1. 6 c = ■ fl oz 48 **2.** 6 gal = ■ fl oz 768 **3.** 34 c = ■ pt 17
4. 8 qt = ■ gal 2 **5.** 5 qt 3 c = ■ c 23 **6.** 16 pt = ■ qt 8
7. 9 c = ■ pt ■ c 4; 1 **8.** 7 gal = ■ qt 28 **9.** 22 fl oz = ■ c ■ fl oz
10. Alvar's mother brought home 24 bottles of water. Each bottle contained 20 ounces. How many quarts of water did she bring home? 15 quarts
11. Mr. Chen's car holds $12\frac{1}{2}$ gallons of gasoline. How many quarts is this? How many fluid ounces? 50 qt; 1,600 fl oz

Lesson 11-5
Pages 492–495

Complete. 4. 33; 10 6. 458; 5

1. 660 s = ■ min 11 **2.** 3 wk = ■ d 21 **3.** 1,825 d = ■ y 5
4. 1,990 s = ■ min ■ s **5.** 240 min = ■ h 4 **6.** 3,211 d = ■ wk ■ d
7. The average lifespan of a Border Collie is 13 years. The average lifespan of a Jack Russell Terrier is 163 months. On average, which breed of dog lives longer? How much longer? Jack Russell Terrier; about 7 months longer

Lesson 11-6
Pages 496–497

Use any strategy to solve each problem.

1. Mount Kilimanjaro, the highest mountain in Tanzania, is 5,895 meters tall. Mount Meru, which is near Kilimanjaro, is 4,566 meters tall. What is the difference in height between the two? 1,329 meters
2. Tory's cow is 3 times heavier than Tom's. If Tory's cow weighs 840 pounds, how much does Tom's cow weigh? 280 pounds
3. Marla and Angelina are hiking. They can hike 6 miles in 2 hours, 9 miles in 3 hours, and 12 miles in 4 hours. How many miles can they hike in 5 hours? 15 miles
4. Mr. Stevens grades a test with 20 questions. Each correct answer is worth 2 points. Each wrong answer takes one point away from the total. Lana's score is 25. Continue the table to find how many of her answers are correct. 15 questions. See Extra Practice Answer Appendix for table.

Number Correct	20	19	18
Number Wrong	0	1	2
Total Score	40	37	34

Lesson 11-7 4. 10 hours 33 minutes
Pages 500–503

Find the elapsed time. 1. 5 hours 15 minutes 2. 18 hours 45 minutes

1. 7:00 A.M. to 12:15 P.M. **2.** 1:30 P.M. to 8:15 A.M.
3. 4:46 P.M. to 5:39 P.M. 53 minutes **4.** 8:04 P.M. to 6:37 A.M.
5. Bryce started babysitting at 6:45 P.M. and finished at 9:54 P.M. How long did he babysit? 3 hours 9 minutes

Lesson 12-1
Pages 517–521

Complete.

1. 6 cm = ■ mm 60 **2.** 4,000 mm = ■ m 4 **3.** 700 cm = ■ m 7
4. 5 m = ■ cm 500 **5.** 14,000 mm = ■ m 14 **6.** 18 cm = ■ mm 180

Select an appropriate unit to measure the length of each of the following. Write *millimeter, centimeter, meter,* or *kilometer.* 9. centimeter

7. lightpole meter **8.** notebook centimeter **9.** postage stamp
10. Mira has a cordless phone that allows her to talk up to 20 meters from the base of the phone. Can she continue to talk on the phone while going to her mail box which is 2,200 centimeters away from the base of the phone? Explain. No; 20 m = 2,000 cm so 2,200 > 2,000 cm

Lesson 12-2 1–3. See Extra Practice Answer Appendix.

Pages 522–523

Solve. Determine *reasonable* answers.

1. A label on a mountain bike states that the weight of the bike is 100 pounds. Is this label accurate? Explain.
2. Mrs. Cashman estimates that she uses a cup and a half of sugar in her pumpkin pie recipe. Does this seem like a reasonable amount to use? Explain.
3. Parker is at the lumber yard looking at plywood to build a toy chest. The toy chest needs 36 square feet of lumber to build it. The plywood comes in sheets of 4 feet × 8 feet. Parker reasons that 4 sheets of plywood will be just enough. Is this a reasonable assumption? Explain.
4. Shaniqua was measuring her locker to see if her books would fit. She claimed her notebooks were 21 centimeters wide and 30 centimeters long. Is she correct? Explain. Yes; since 2.54 cm ≈ 1 in., 21 cm ≈ 9 in.

Lesson 12-3

Pages 524–526

Complete.

1. 4 g = ■ mg 4,000
2. 9 kg = ■ g 9,000
3. 12 g = ■ mg 12,000
4. 6,000 g = ■ kg 6
5. 2,000 mg = ■ kg 2
6. 1 kg = ■ g 1,000
7. Which is a more reasonable estimate for the mass of a stapler: 130 milligrams, 130 grams, or 130 kilograms? 130 grams
8. A sugar company donated 50 kg of sugar to a local high school. If the sugar was divided into equal bags of 250 g, how many bags are there? 200 bags

Lesson 12-4

Pages 527–530

Complete.

1. 40 L = ■ mL 40,000
2. 8,000 mL = ■ L 8
3. 7 L = ■ mL 7,000
4. 4,000 mL = ■ L 4
5. 5 L = ■ mL 5,000
6. 8 L = ■ mL 8,000
7. Which metric unit would you use to measure the capacity of a bath tub? liter
8. A coffee mug holds 600 milliliters. Find the capacity in liters. 0.6 L
9. Jenn bought 6 bottles of juice that were marked 750 mL. How many liters of juice did she buy? 4.5 L

Lesson 12-5

Pages 533–535

Write an integer to represent each situation. Then graph the integer on a number line. See Extra Practice Answer Appendix for graphs.

1. spent $12 on a CD −12
2. 8 degrees warmer +8 or 8
3. The puppy gained 2 pounds +2 or 2
4. lost $10 −10

Write an integer to represent each situation. Then write its opposite.

5. earned $56 mowing grass +56 or 56; −56
6. scored a three point basket in basketball +3 or 3; −3
7. 40 plants were dead −40; +40 or 40
8. 2 inches of rain in a gauge +2 or 2; −2

Lesson 12-6

Pages 537–541

Choose the more reasonable temperature for each situation.

1. skiing: 56°F or 7°C 7°C
2. frozen fish: 40°F or 0°C 0°C
3. July 4th in Florida: 18°C or 92°F 92°F
4. playing tennis: 5°C or 75°F 75°F

The table shows the highest recorded temperatures for several U.S. states.

State	Temperature (°F)	State	Temperature (°F)
Alabama	112	Florida	109
Connecticut	100	Idaho	118
Arizona	128	California	134
Arkansas	120	Texas	120
Colorado	118	Maine	105

Source: Fact Monster

5. How much greater is California's highest temperature than Maine's highest temperature? 29°F
6. How much greater is Arizona's highest temperature than Florida's highest temperature? 19°F

Lesson 12-7
Pages 544–545

Use any strategy to solve each problem.

1. Tyler runs for 8 minutes then walks for 4 minutes. How many sets of this pattern will he complete if he exercises for 65 minutes? **5**
2. Tickets for a movie cost $3 for children and $5 for adults. The movie took in $126 in one showing. At that showing there were 12 children. How many adults were there? **18 adults**
3. The Empire State Building is 1,250 ft tall. How many inches is half of the building? **7,500 inches**
4. Gary claimed that he is older than Diane. Diane is twice as old as Marty. Marty is 3 years short of being half as old as Gary. Is Gary's claim true? **yes**

Lesson 13-1 **1. Ray; $\overrightarrow{WX}$ 2. point B 3. line; $\overleftrightarrow{GH}$**
Pages 557–560

Identify each figure. Then name it using symbols.

1. W X
2. •B
3. G H

4. Are these two lines parallel? Explain your answer.

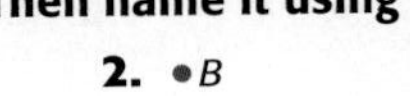
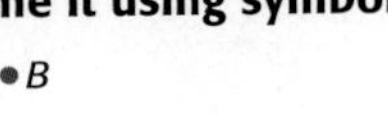

No, if they are extended, they will eventually intersect.

Lesson 13-2
Pages 562–563

Solve. Use *logical reasoning*.

1. If Tiara continues making the figures shown below, how many triangular blocks will be in the fifth figure? **15 triangular blocks**

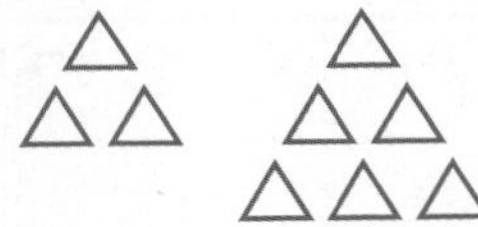

2. Sebastian made 44 more necklaces than Tina made. Together they made 196 necklaces. How many necklaces did Tina make? **76 necklaces**
3. Quinn, Andy, and Chase are friends with three different hobbies: motocross, art, and skating. Andy has no artistic skill. Chase can not draw or skate. Quinn is a tremendous painter. Who is the friend that rides motocross? **Chase**
4. There are three fish bowls with five fish in each bowl. Two of the bowls have two orange fish, two bowls have two yellow fish, two bowls have two gold fish and all three have one silver fish. What are the colors of fish in each bowl?
See Extra Practice Answer Appendix.

Lesson 13-3
Pages 566–569

Measure the sides of each triangle. Then find the number of congruent sides. State whether any of the sides appear to be perpendicular. Write yes or no.

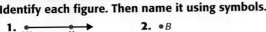

1. **0; yes**
2. **2; no**
3. **3; no**
4. **2; no**

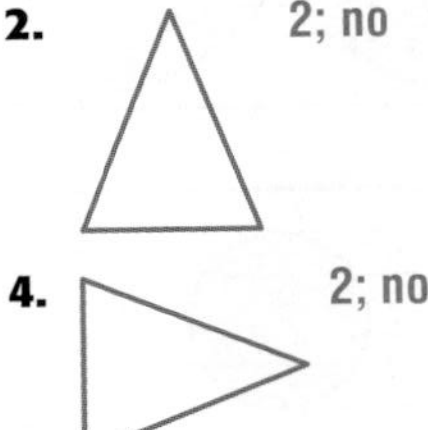

Lesson 13-4
Pages 570–574

Determine whether each statement is *true* or *false*. Explain.

1. Some rhombi are rectangles.
2. Some trapezoids are parallelograms.
3. All parallelograms are rectangles.
4. All squares are rhombi.
True; squares have 4 equal sides.

1. True; a rhombus that has all right angles is a rectangle.
2. False; trapezoids do not have two sets of parallel sides.
3. False; not all parallelograms have 90° angles.

Lesson 13-5
Pages 576–577

Use any strategy to solve each problem.

1. Seven trains pass through a town every day. The times for the first four trains are 9:10 A.M., 9:45 A.M., 10:20 A.M., and 10:55 A.M. At what time will the last train of the day pass through the town? **12:40 P.M.**
2. There are 12 pieces of red candy in a jar for every 8 pieces of blue candy. If there are 60 pieces of red candy in the jar, how many total pieces of candy are in the jar? **100**
3. Ramous' batting average is 0.050 points higher than Albert's. Albert's average is 0.180 points lower than Rashid's. List the players in order of their batting average from least to greatest. **Rashid, Ramous, Albert**
4. The Fibonacci Sequence is a special mathematical sequence that occurs frequently in nature. The first six numbers of the sequence are 1, 1, 2, 3, 5, and 8. What is the seventh term? The tenth?
13; 55

Lesson 13-6
Pages 578–581

Graph each figure and the translation described. Then write the ordered pairs for the vertices of the translation image.

1. triangle *XYZ* with vertices *X*(3, 2), *Y*(5, 4), *Z*(2, 6); translated 2 units right *X*(5, 2), *Y*(7, 4), *Z*(4, 6)
2. quadrilateral *LMNO* with vertices *L*(1, 8), *M*(1, 6), *N*(5, 6), *O*(5, 8); translated 3 units up *L*(1, 11), *M*(1, 9), *N*(5, 9), *O*(5, 11)
3. triangle *KLM* with vertices *K*(2, 5), *L*(4, 7), and *M*(5, 5); translated 3 units right, 4 units down *K*(5,1), *L*(7,3), *M*(8,1)
4. triangle *ABC* with vertices *A*(3, 6), *B*(3, 9), *C*(7, 6); translated 2 units left and 3 units down *A*(1, 3), *B*(1, 6), *C*(5, 3)

Lesson 13-7 1. (7, 1), (5, 1), (7, 6), (5, 6)
Pages 582–585

Graph each figure after a reflection across the line. Then write the ordered pairs for the vertices of the relection image. 2. (2, 7), (6, 7), (2, 5)

1.
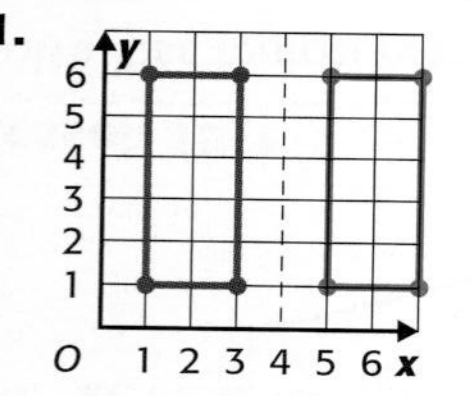

2.
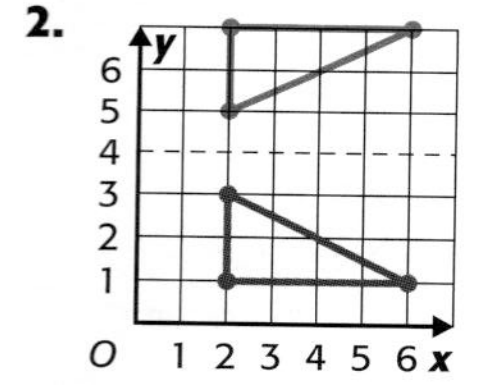

Lesson 13-8 1. *A*(6, 3), *B*(8, 1), *C*(4, 1) 2. *A*(6, 3), *B*(4, 5), *C*(8, 5)
Pages 586–590

Graph the triangle after each rotation. Then write the ordered pairs for the vertices of the rotation image. 3. *A*(2, 3), *B*(0, 5), *C*(4, 3)

1. 90′ clockwise about point *C*
2. 90′ counterclockwise about point *B*
3. 90′ counterclockwise about point *A*

Lesson 13-9
Pages 591–593

Determine whether each transformation is a *translation*, *reflection*, or *rotation*.

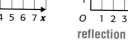

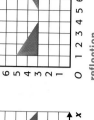

1.
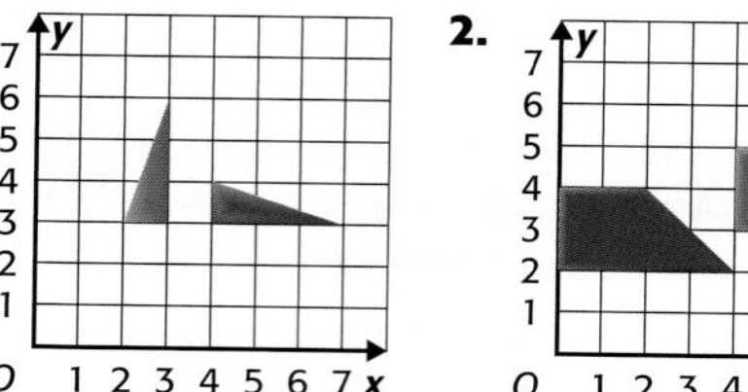
rotation

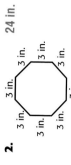

2.
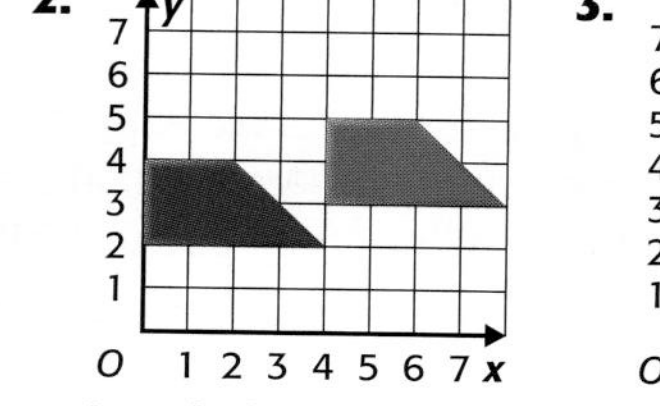
translation

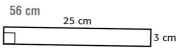

3.
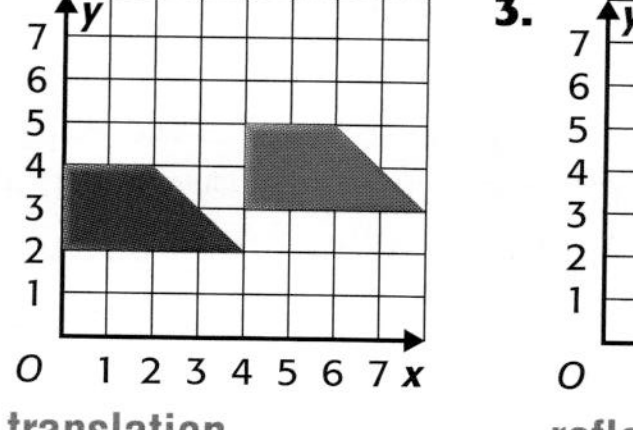
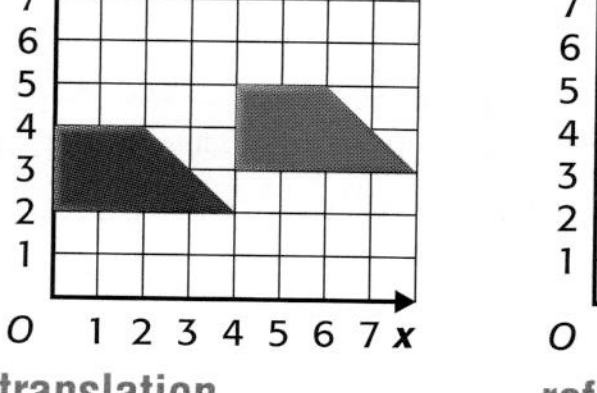
reflection

Lesson 14-1
Pages 608–611

Find the perimeter of each figure.

1. 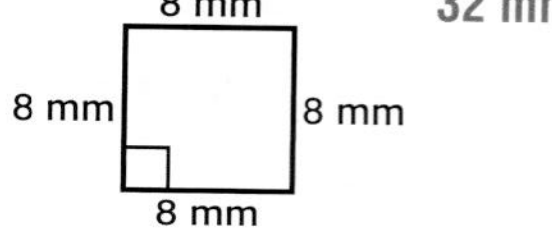

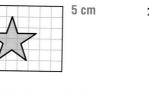

32 mm

2. 3 in. sides (octagon) 24 in.

3. 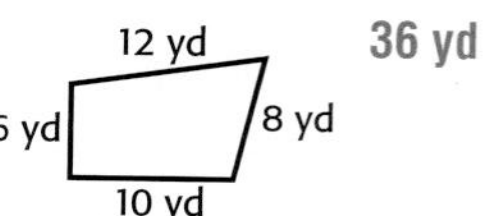
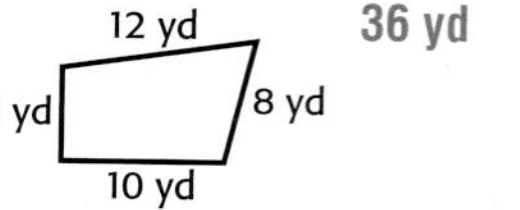

36 yd

4. 56 cm
25 cm
3 cm

Lesson 14-2
Pages 612–615

Estimate the area of each figure. Each square represents 1 square centimeter.

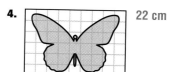

1. 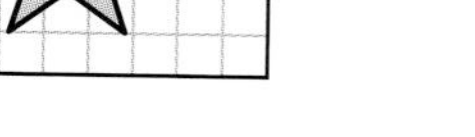
5 cm

2. 10 cm

3. 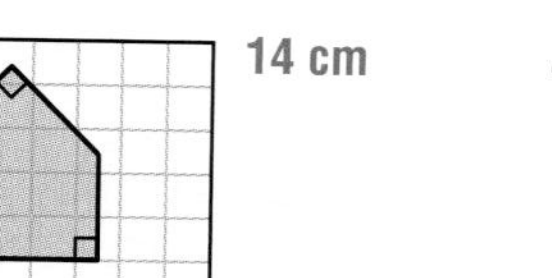
14 cm

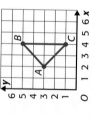

4. 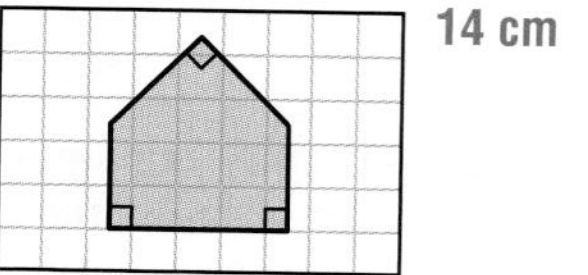
22 cm

Lesson 14-3 9. 12 inches; 24 inches

Pages 616–619

Find the area of each rectangle.

1. 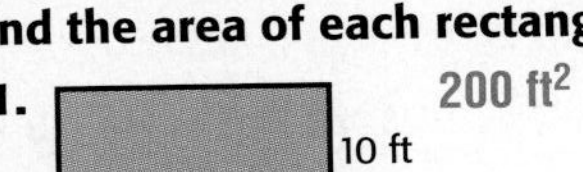 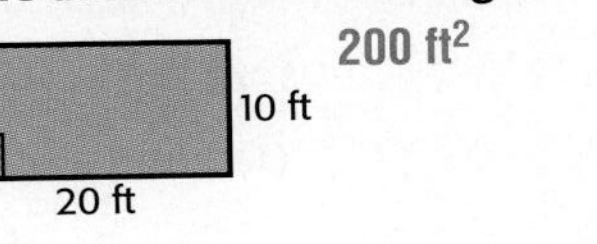

200 ft²

2. 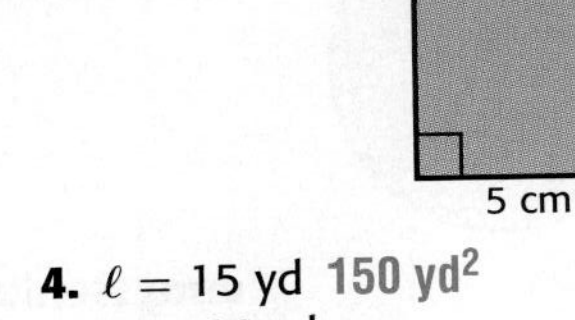

25 cm²

3. $\ell = 6$ cm, $w = 12$ cm 72 cm²

4. $\ell = 15$ yd, $w = 10$ yd 150 yd²

5. $\ell = 7$ ft, $w = 21$ ft 147 ft²

6. Mrs. Ortega is painting three walls in a room. The walls are 8 feet high and 13 feet long. One gallon of paint will cover 350 ft². If she buys one gallon of paint, will she have enough? Explain. Yes; the area of the walls is only 312 ft².

Lesson 14-4

Pages 624–627

Describe parts of each figure that are parallel and congruent. Then identify the figure. 1–3. See Extra Practice Answer Appendix.

1.  

2. 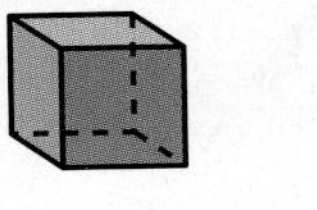

3. 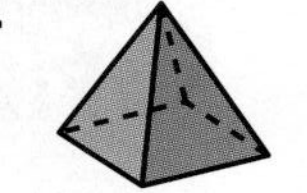

Lesson 14-5

Pages 628–629

Solve. Use the *make a model* strategy

1. Ms. Jacobson is passing out notebooks to her class of 27 students. She has four different colors of notebooks; red, green, blue, and yellow. If she passes out a red notebook to every fourth student, how many red notebooks does she pass out? 6 red notebooks

2. The students in Mr. Lincoln's gym class were asked to run around three cones placed in a line. The students must run down and back to complete one run. How many times will the students go between the cones in their attempt to complete six runs? 24 times for 6 runs

3. Pentominoes are tiles made by placing five squares in different designs. One way to place the squares is in a straight line. Another is to form an L. How many different designs are there? 12

Lesson 14-6

Pages 631–635

Find the volume of each prism.

1. 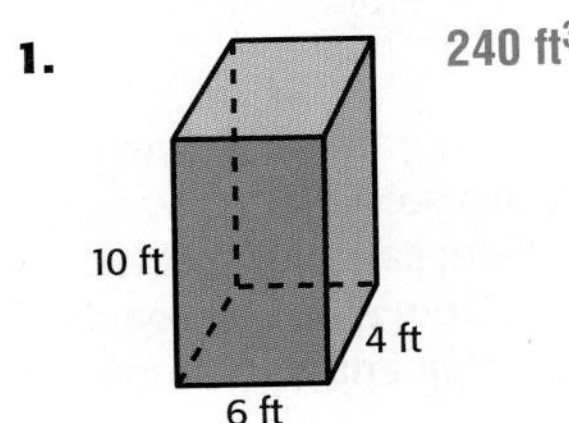

240 ft³

2. 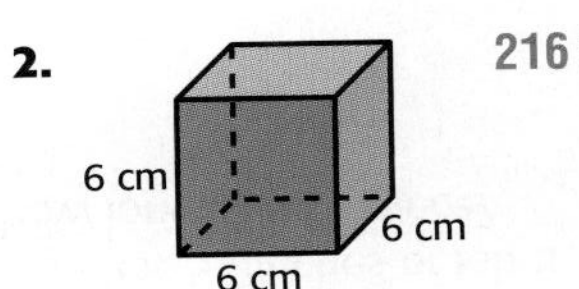

216 ft³

3. Prism A has dimensions of 9 yards × 6 yards × 3 yards and Prism B has dimensions of 3 yards × 2 yards × 1 yard. How much larger is the volume of Prism A than Prism B in cubic feet? 4212 ft³

Lesson 14-7

Pages 640–643

Find the surface area of each rectangular prism.

1. 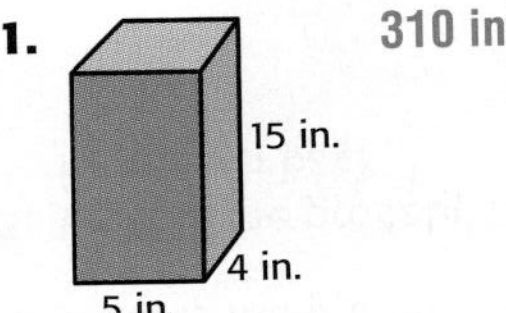

310 in²

2. 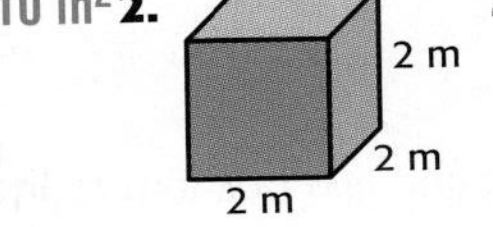

24 m²

3. 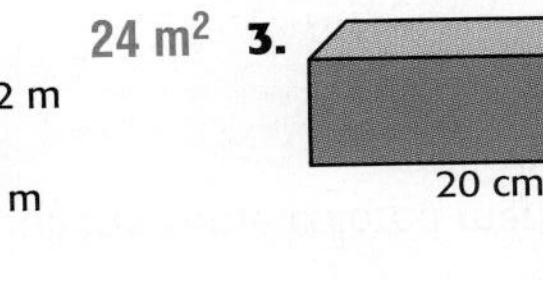 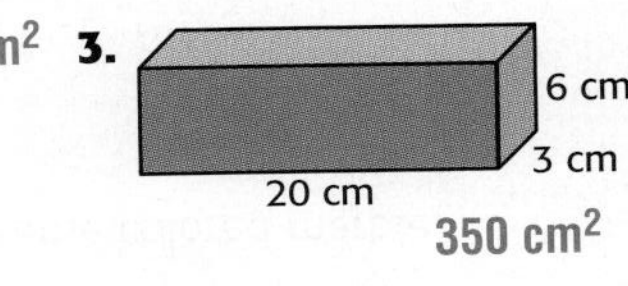

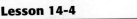

350 cm²

4. Natalie finds the measurements of a rectangular prism. The length is 13 feet, the width is 7 feet, and the height is 9 feet. Find the surface area. 542 ft²

Lesson 14-8

Pages 644–647

Determine whether you need to find the perimeter, area, or volume. Then solve. 1. perimeter; 2,472 ft

1. The basketball team warms up by running around the gym, which is 120 feet by 86 feet. If Chet runs 6 laps, how far has he run?

2. Freda is laying mulch in her garden. The garden is 8 feet by 12 feet and the mulch should be 3 inches deep. How much mulch does she need? volume; 24 ft³

3. Maya wants new carpet for her bedroom. The room is 5 yards wide and 4 yards long. The carpet she wants costs $23.00 per square yard. How much will it cost to carpet her room? area; $460.00

Lesson 14-9 1. yes; 11 stuffed animals

Pages 648–649

Use any strategy to solve each problem.

1. Tamika has 33 stuffed animals. She gave $\frac{1}{3}$ to her sister and $\frac{1}{2}$ of the rest to charity. She says she has more than 10 stuffed animals left. Is she correct? How many stuffed animals are left?
2. Mr. Ruiz is making cookies. If each batch of cookies requires 14 ounces of milk, how many quarts of milk will he need to make 8 batches? 7 quarts
3. The middle school soccer team had the following record for the past five years. What fraction of the games did they win? $\frac{46}{75}$

Year	2002	2003	2004	2005	2006
Won	12	10	4	7	13
Lost	3	5	11	8	2

Lesson 15-1 2. 1, 2, 3, 4, 5

Pages 661–663

List the possible outcomes in each probability experiment.

1. spinning the spinner A, B, C, D

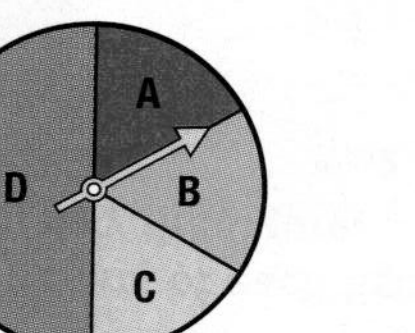

2. choosing one number out of a bowl

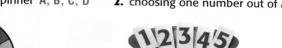

3. Sarah randomly chose one letter from the word BEEKEEPER. Which letter did she most likely pick? How likely is it that she chose a vowel? E; very likely

Lesson 15-2

Pages 668–672

The spinner is spun once. Find the probability of each event. Write as a fraction in simplest form.

1. $P(1)$ $\frac{1}{2}$
2. $P(2)$ $\frac{1}{4}$
3. $P(\text{prime number})$ $\frac{1}{2}$
4. $P(\text{odd number})$ $\frac{3}{4}$

Lesson 15-3

Pages 674–675

Solve by making an organized list.

1. Two years ago, Mr. Braxton counted seven hickory trees in his yard. Last year he counted 14 trees in his yard. This spring he counted 28 hickory trees. In how many years will there be 224 hickory trees? 3 years
2. Thomas has four books colored blue, red, green, and yellow. How many different ways can he combine them on a shelf? 24 different ways

Lesson 15-4 See Extra Practice Answer Appendix for tree diagram.

Pages 677–680

Two bags each contain three different colored marbles: green, blue, and yellow. Make a tree diagram to show all possible outcomes if you choose a marble from each bag.

1. What is the probability of pulling a green marble from the first bag, then a blue marble from the second bag? $\frac{1}{9}$
2. What is the probability of pulling a yellow marble from each bag? $\frac{1}{9}$
3. What is the probability that you will pull the same colored marble from each bag? $\frac{1}{3}$

Lesson 15-5

Pages 682–683

Use any strategy to solve each problem. 2. No, trains do not travel at 182 mph.

1. Sydney has been randomly tossing a coin. She has landed on heads 16 times and tails 8 times. Based on these results, if she tosses a coin what is the probability that she will land on tails? $\frac{1}{3}$
2. A train engineer said that he traveled 1,458 miles in his train during a single 8 hour work day. Is his claim reasonable? Explain.
3. Mona is cutting different size pieces of fabric for a quilt. The first piece is 1 inch long, the second piece is 2 inches long, the third piece is 4 inches long, and so on. If she has 55 inches of fabric, how many pieces can she cut, and how long is each piece? 5 pieces; 1 in., 2 in., 4 in., 8 in., 16 in.

Page R2, Extra Practice, Lesson 1-1

1. ten thousands; 50,000
2. hundred thousands; 300,000
3. ten millions; 80,000,000
4. billions; 5,000,000,000
5. hundred billions; 400,000,000,000
6. ten thousands; 00,000
9. 800,000 + 50,000 + 100 + 20; eight hundred fifty thousand, one hundred twenty
10. 30,000,000 + 300,000 + 30,000 + 5,000 + 10 + 2; thirty million, three hundred thirty-five thousand, twelve
11. 60,000,000,000 + 1,000,000,000 + 800,000,000 + 50,000,000 + 2,000 + 50; sixty-one billion, eight hundred fifty million, two thousand, fifty

Page R2, Extra Practice, Lesson 1-3

1. 200 m dash: 53.7, 800 m dash 2.02 min; The shortest race would take the least amount of time.

Page R4, Extra Practice, Lesson 1-7

3. 2,335, 2,893, 2,984, 4,367, 4,387
4. 1.9, 2.7, 3.8, 5.6, 5.9
5. 51,092, 52,456, 59,033, 59,999
6. 61.99, 63.09, 63.10, 68.47
7. 0.044, 0.444, 4.44, 44.4, 444
8. 0.772, 7.27, 7.79, 76.903, 77.5
9. 5.7, 5.77, 7.5, 7.55
10. 8.96, 8.9, 9, 9.001, 9.01

Page R4, Extra Practice, Lesson 1-8

1. 3 cars and 2 motorcycles
3. 9 quarters and 5 nickels

Page R6, Extra Practice, Lesson 2-7

5. 46

$5 + 30 + 11 = (5 + 30) + 11$ Associative Property
$= 35 + 11$ Add 5 and 30 mentally
$= 46$ Add 35 and 11 mentally

6. 82

$22 + 54 + 6 = 22 + (54 + 6)$ Associative Property
$= 22 + 60$ Add 54 and 7 mentally
$= 82$ Add 22 and 60 mentally

7. 30.6

$3.5 + 7.6 + 19.5$
$= 3.5 + 19.5 + 7.6$ Commutative Property
$= (3.5 + 19.5) + 7.6$ Associative Property
$= 23.0 + 7.6$ Add 3.5 and 19.5 mentally
$= 30.6$ Add 23.0 and 7.6 mentally

8. 86.6

$10.6 + 74 + 2$
$= 10.6 + (74 + 2)$ Associative Property
$= 10.6 + 76$ Add 74 + 2 mentally
$= 86.6$ Add 10.6 + 19.5 mentally

9. 76

$49 + 27$
$= (49 + 1) + 26$ Associative Property
$= 50 + 26$ Add 49 + 1 mentally
$= 76$ Add 50 + 26 mentally

10. 68.5

$50.4 + 13.6 + 4.5$
$= (50.4 + 13.6) + 4.5$ Associative Property
$= 64 + 4.5$ Add 50.4 + 13.6 mentally
$= 68.5$ Add 64 + 4.5 mentally

Page R7, Extra Practice, Lesson 3-2

Sample answers are given

1. 50; $(5 \times 8) + (5 \times 2)$
2. 81; $(3 \times 20) + (3 \times 7)$
3. 336; $(8 \times 40) + (8 \times 2)$
4. 56; $(4 \times 7) + (4 \times 7)$
5. 84; $(6 \times 5) + (6 \times 9)$
6. 260; $(2 \times 90) + (2 \times 40)$
7. $3 \times 12 = 3 \times (10 + 2)$
$= (3 \times 10) + (3 \times 2)$
$= 30 + 6$
$= 36$
8. $5 \times 48 = 5 \times (40 + 8)$
$= (5 \times 40) + (5 \times 8)$
$= 200 + 40$
$= 240$
9. $7 \times 23 = 7 \times (20 + 3)$
$= (7 \times 20) + (7 \times 3)$
$= 140 + 21$
$= 161$
10. $2 \times 76 = 2 \times (70 + 6)$
$= (2 \times 70) + (2 \times 6)$
$= 140 + 12$
$= 152$
11. $33 \times 6 = (30 + 3) \times 6$
$= (30 \times 6) + (3 \times 6)$
$= 180 + 18$
$= 198$
12. $94 \times 5 = (90 + 4) \times 5$
$= (90 \times 5) + (4 \times 5)$
$= 450 + 20$
$= 470$
13. $2 \times 43 = 2 \times (40 + 3)$
$= (2 \times 40) + (2 \times 3)$
$= 80 + 6$
$= 86$
14. $55 \times 6 = (50 + 5) \times 6$
$= (50 \times 6) + (5 \times 6)$
$= 300 + 30$
$= 330$
15. 325 model cars; $25(8 + 5) = (25 \times 8) + (25 \times 5)$
$= 200 + 125$
$= 325$

Page R9, Extra Practice, Lesson 3-7

5. $10 \times 4 \times 7 = 10 \times (4 \times 7)$ Associative property
$= 10 \times 28$ find 4 × 7 mentally
$= 280$ find 10 × 28 mentally
6. $15 \times (4 \times 5) = (15 \times 4) \times 5$ Associative Property
$= 60 \times 5$ find 15 × 4 mentally
$= 300$ find 60 × 5 mentally
7. $100 \times 32 \times 3 = 100 \times 3 \times 32$ Commutative Property
$= (100 \times 3) \times 32$ Associative Property
$= 300 \times 32$ find 100 × 3 mentally
$= 9600$ find 300 × 32 mentally
8. $4 \times (5 \times 18) = (4 \times 5) \times 18$ Associative Property
$= 20 \times 18$ find 4 × 5 mentally
$= 360$ find 20 × 18 mentally
9. $2 \times 24 \times 5 = 2 \times 5 \times 24$ Commutative Property
$= (2 \times 5) \times 24$ Associative Property
$= 10 \times 24$ find 2 × 5 mentally
$= 240$ find 10 × 24 mentally
10. $25 \times (4 \times 17) = (25 \times 4) \times 17$ Associative Property
$= 100 \times 17$ find 25 × 4 mentally
$= 1700$ find 100 × 17 mentally

Page R10, Extra Practice, Lesson 3-9

1. \$41; extra information; color of the bicycle
2. 39 more subscriptions; extra information; magazine subscription cost
3. missing information; amount of small and medium candles sold per week

Page R10, Extra Practice, Lesson 4-2

1. $300 \div 3 = 100$
2. $800 \div 20 = 40$
3. $999 \div 333 = 3$
4. $680 \div 34 = 20$
5. $110 \div 10 = 11$
6. $320 \div 32 = 10$
7. $460 \div 23 = 20$
8. $666 \div 222 = 3$
9. $5{,}400 \div 60 = 90$
10. $8{,}720 \div 218 = 40$
11. $4{,}800 \div 240 = 20$
12. $21{,}000 \div 3{,}000 = 7$

Page R15, Extra Practice, Lesson 6-1

9. $n - 25 = 36$; Lei's number is 61.
10. $13 = w + 5$; 8 wins, 4 losses
11. $24 = 11 + g$; 13 movies

Page R16, Extra Practice, Lesson 6-3

4. Sample answer: No. She would have paid him \$1,638.30 at the end of the two weeks.

Page R16, Extra Practice, Lesson 6-5

1–8.

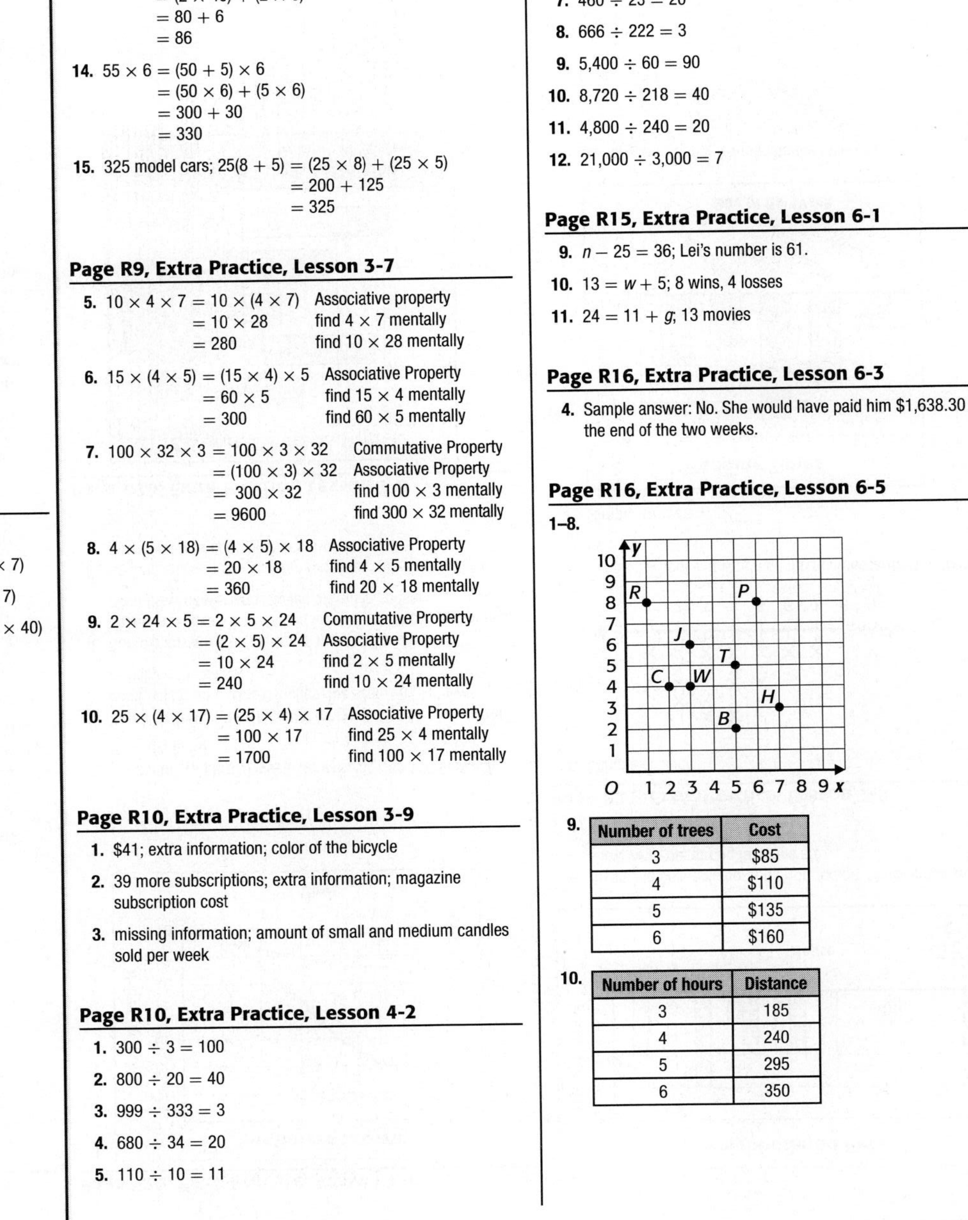

9.

Number of trees	Cost
3	\$85
4	\$110
5	\$135
6	\$160

10.

Number of hours	Distance
3	185
4	240
5	295
6	350

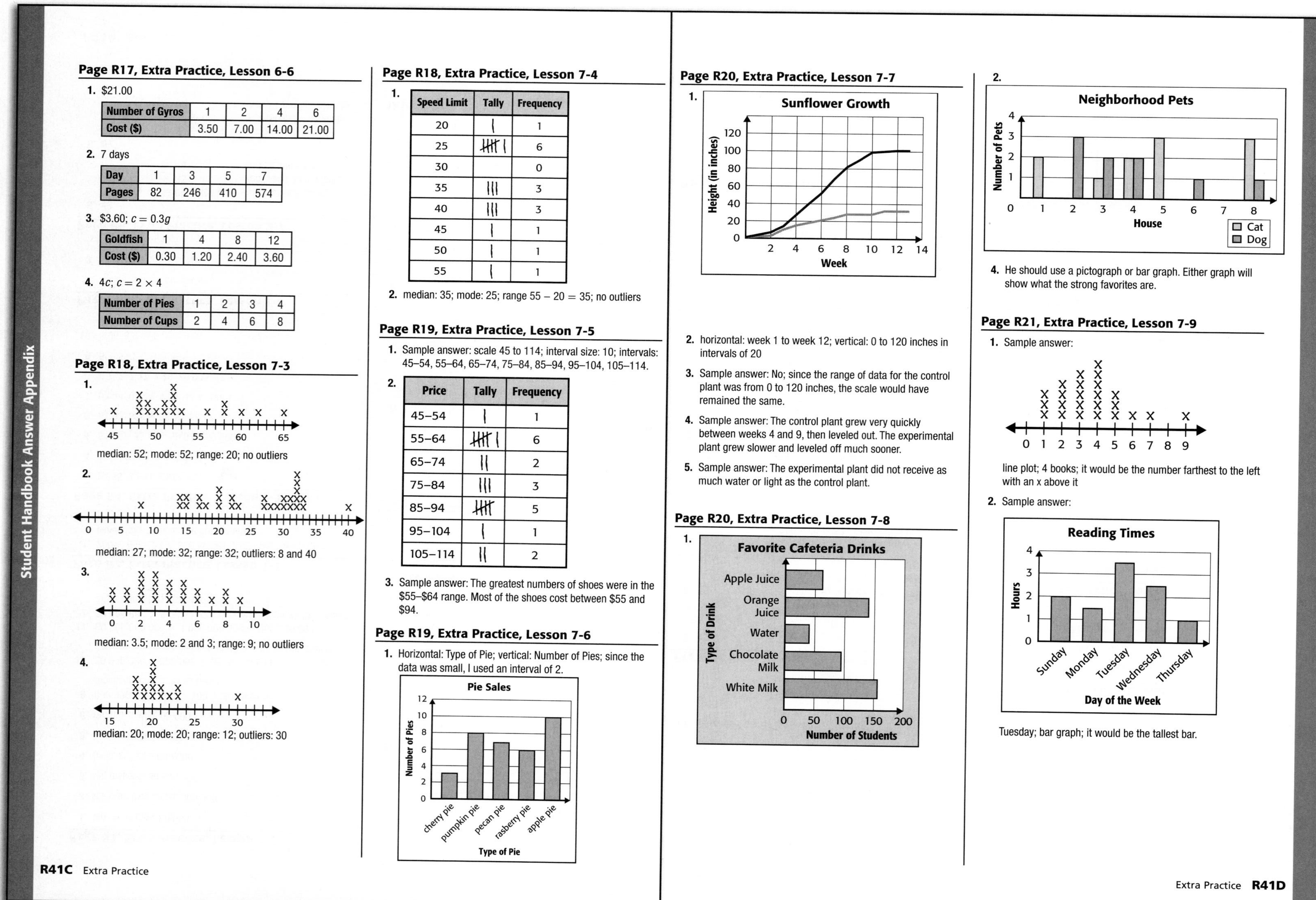

Student Handbook Answer Appendix

Page R17, Extra Practice, Lesson 6-6

1. $21.00

Number of Gyros	1	2	4	6
Cost ($)	3.50	7.00	14.00	21.00

2. 7 days

Day	1	3	5	7
Pages	82	246	410	574

3. $3.60; $c = 0.3g$

Goldfish	1	4	8	12
Cost ($)	0.30	1.20	2.40	3.60

4. $4c$; $c = 2 \times 4$

Number of Pies	1	2	3	4
Number of Cups	2	4	6	8

Page R18, Extra Practice, Lesson 7-3

1.

median: 52; mode: 52; range: 20; no outliers

2.

median: 27; mode: 32; range: 32; outliers: 8 and 40

3.

median: 3.5; mode: 2 and 3; range: 9; no outliers

4.

median: 20; mode: 20; range: 12; outliers: 30

Page R18, Extra Practice, Lesson 7-4

1.

Speed Limit	Tally	Frequency
20	|	1
25	~~||||~~ |	6
30		0
35	|||	3
40	|||	3
45	|	1
50	|	1
55	|	1

2. median: 35; mode: 25; range 55 − 20 = 35; no outliers

Page R19, Extra Practice, Lesson 7-5

1. Sample answer: scale 45 to 114; interval size: 10; intervals: 45–54, 55–64, 65–74, 75–84, 85–94, 95–104, 105–114.

2.

Price	Tally	Frequency
45–54	|	1
55–64	~~||||~~ |	6
65–74	||	2
75–84	|||	3
85–94	~~||||~~	5
95–104	|	1
105–114	||	2

3. Sample answer: The greatest numbers of shoes were in the $55–$64 range. Most of the shoes cost between $55 and $94.

Page R19, Extra Practice, Lesson 7-6

1. Horizontal: Type of Pie; vertical: Number of Pies; since the data was small, I used an interval of 2.

R41C Extra Practice

Page R20, Extra Practice, Lesson 7-7

1.

2. horizontal: week 1 to week 12; vertical: 0 to 120 inches in intervals of 20

3. Sample answer: No; since the range of data for the control plant was from 0 to 120 inches, the scale would have remained the same.

4. Sample answer: The control plant grew very quickly between weeks 4 and 9, then leveled out. The experimental plant grew slower and leveled off much sooner.

5. Sample answer: The experimental plant did not receive as much water or light as the control plant.

Page R20, Extra Practice, Lesson 7-8

1.

2.

4. He should use a pictograph or bar graph. Either graph will show what the strong favorites are.

Page R21, Extra Practice, Lesson 7-9

1. Sample answer:

line plot; 4 books; it would be the number farthest to the left with an x above it

2. Sample answer:

Tuesday; bar graph; it would be the tallest bar.

Extra Practice R41D

Page R28, Extra Practice, Lesson 10-6

1. Sample answer: $3 + 7 = 10$
2. Sample answer: $10 - 4 = 6$
3. Sample answer: $6 + 8 = 14$
4. Sample answer: $10 - 3 = 7$
5. Sample answer: $8 - 4 = 4$
6. Sample answer: $7 + 4 = 11$
7. Sample answer: $7 - 5 = 2$
8. Sample answer: $19 + 11 = 30$
9. Sample answer: $5 - 2 = 3$

Page R31, Extra Practice, Lesson 11-6

4.

Number Correct	20	19	18	17	16	15
Number Wrong	0	1	2	3	4	5
Total Score	40	37	34	31	28	25

Page R32, Extra Practice, Lesson 12-2

1. No; it is more likely to be in the 30–40 pound range.
2. Yes, since it is a reasonable amount to add in a recipe.
3. No, a 4×8 sheet is 32 sq ft. So he would need 2 sheets maximum.

Page R33, Extra Practice, Lesson 12-5

1.

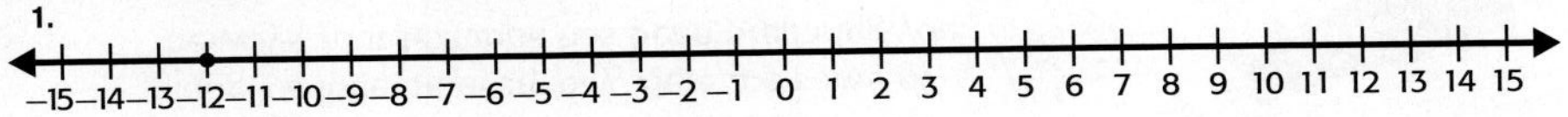

2.

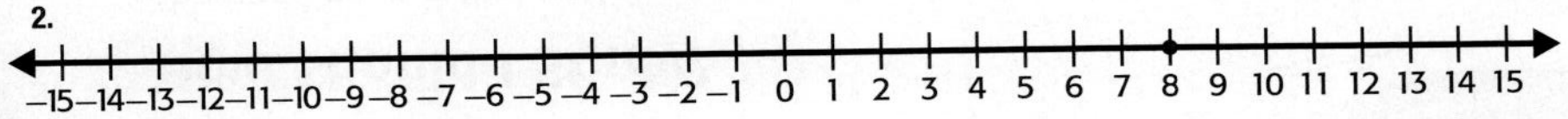

3.

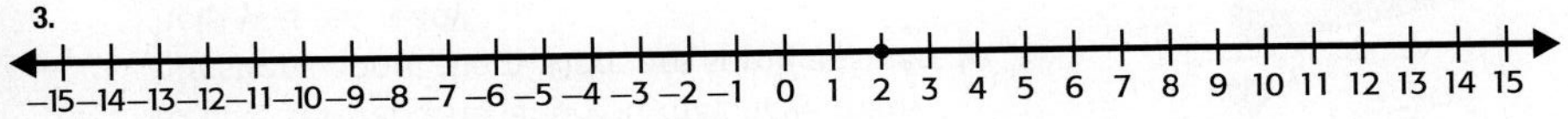

4.

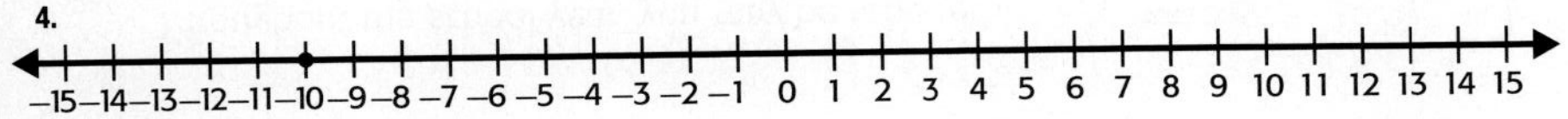

Page R34, Extra Practice, Lesson 13-2

4. One bowl has 2 yellow fish, 2 orange fish, and 1 silver fish; one bowl has 2 gold fish, 2 orange fish, and 1 silver fish; one bowl has 2 yellow fish, 2 gold fish, and 1 silver fish.

Page R38, Extra Practice, Lesson 14-4

1. Sample answer; the circular bases are parallel and congruent; cylinder.
2. Sample answer; all opposite sides and edges are parallel and congruent; cube.
3. Sample answer; opposite edges in the square bases are parallel and congruent, side triangles are congruent, legs on each triangle are congruent; pyramid.

Page R41, Extra Practice, Lesson 15-4

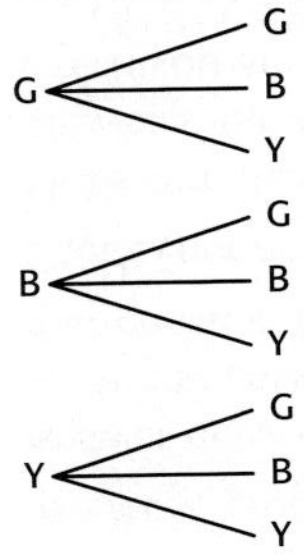

Preparing for Standardized Tests

Throughout the school year, you may be required to take several tests, and you may have many questions about them. Here are some answers to help you get ready.

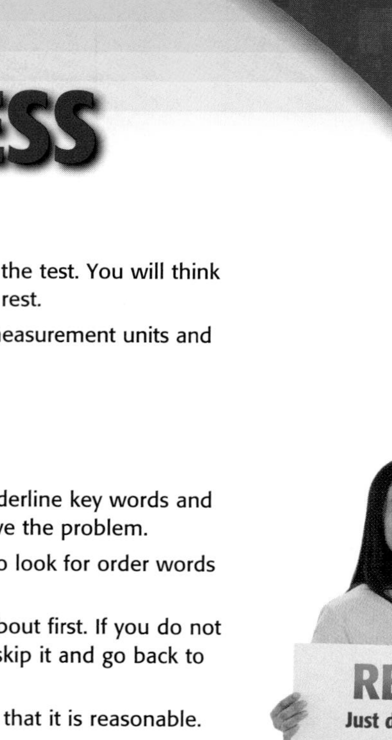

How Should I Study?

The good news is that you've been studying all along– a little bit every day. Here are some of the ways your textbook has been preparing you.

- **Every Day** The lessons had multiple-choice practice questions.
- **Every Week** The Mid-Chapter Check and Chapter Test also had several multiple-choice practice questions.
- **Every Month** The Test Practice pages at the end of each chapter had even more questions, including short-response and extended-response questions.

Are There Other Ways to Review?

Absolutely! The following pages contain even more practice for standardized tests.

Tips for SUCCESS

Before the Test

- Go to bed early the night before the test. You will think more clearly after a good night's rest.
- Become familiar with common measurement units and when they should be used.
- Think positively.

During the Test

- Read each problem carefully. Underline key words and think about different ways to solve the problem.
- Watch for key words like *not.* Also look for order words like *least, greatest, first,* and *last.*
- Answer questions you are sure about first. If you do not know the answer to a question, skip it and go back to that question later.
- Check your answer to make sure that it is reasonable.
- Make sure that the number of the question on the answer sheet matches the number of the question on which you are working in your test booklet.

Whatever you do...

- Don't try to do it all in your head. If no figure is provided, draw one.
- Don't rush. Try to work at a steady pace.
- Don't give up. Some problems may seem hard to you, but you may be able to figure out what to do if you read each question carefully or try another strategy.

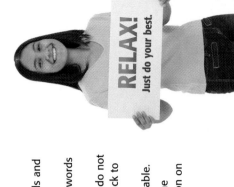

RELAX!
Just do your best.

Multiple-Choice Questions

Incomplete shading
(A) (B) (C) (D)
Too light shading
(A) (B) (C) (D)
Correct shading
(A) (B) (C) (D)

Multiple-choice questions are the most common type of questions on standardized tests. You are asked to choose the best answer from four possible answers.

To record a multiple-choice answer, you may be asked to shade in a bubble that is a circle or an oval. Always make sure that your shading is dark enough and completely covers the bubble.

Example

1 The table shows the price of cheese per pound at a local farmers' market.

Amount (lb)	Price
1	$5
2	$10
3	$15

If the price increases at the same rate, how much would you pay for 5 pounds of cheese?

A $35 **B** $25 **C** $20 **D** $15

STRATEGY
Patterns Can you find a pattern to solve the problem?

Read the Problem Carefully You know the price of cheese per pound in dollars. Find how much you will pay if you buy 5 pounds of cheese.

Solve the Problem Look for a pattern. One pound of cheese costs $5. Two pounds cost $10. Three pounds cost $15. So, for each pound of cheese, the price increases by $5.

Extend the pattern to find the price of five pounds of cheese.

4 pounds ⟶ $15 + $5 or $20
5 pounds ⟶ $20 + $5 or $25

So, 5 pounds of cheese will cost $25.

The correct choice is B.

STRATEGY
Key Words When reading a question, look for words such as *not* or *both*.

Example

2 The shaded part of the figure below represents the fraction $\frac{2}{3}$.

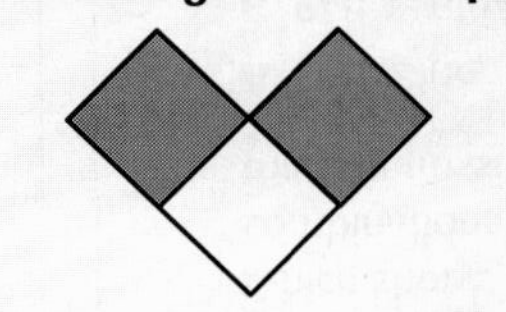

Which fraction is NOT equivalent to $\frac{2}{3}$?

F $\frac{6}{9}$ **G** $\frac{4}{6}$ **H** $\frac{2}{6}$ **J** $\frac{10}{15}$

Read the Problem Carefully You are asked to use the diagram to find which fraction is NOT equivalent to $\frac{2}{3}$.

Solve the Problem Find the fraction that is not equivalent to $\frac{2}{3}$.

$\frac{2}{3} \times \frac{3}{3} = \frac{6}{9}$ ⟵ equivalent
$\frac{2}{3} \times \frac{1}{2} = \frac{2}{6}$ ⟵ NOT equivalent
$\frac{2}{3} \times \frac{2}{2} = \frac{4}{6}$ ⟵ equivalent
$\frac{2}{3} \times \frac{5}{5} = \frac{10}{15}$ ⟵ equivalent

The correct choice is H.

STRATEGY
Work Backward Can you work backward from the total to find the unit cost?

Example

3 A book has five chapters. Each chapter has 5 more pages than the previous chapter. Chapter 5 has 38 pages. How many pages were in Chapter 2?

A 18 **B** 23 **C** 25 **D** 33

Read the Problem Carefully You are asked to find the number of pages in Chapter 2. You know how many pages were in Chapter 5.

Solve the Problem You need to find the number of pages in Chapter 2. To find the number of pages, count backward by five.

Chapter 5	38 pages	
Chapter 4	33 pages	−5
Chapter 3	28 pages	−5
Chapter 2	23 pages	−5

The correct choice is B.

Preparing for Standardized Tests

Multiple-Choice Practice

DIRECTIONS
Read each question. Choose the best answer.

1. A car wash company charges $8 per car. If 94 cars were washed in one day, how much money would the company collect? A

A $752
B $740
C $702
D $688

2. Which fractional part of the model is shaded? G

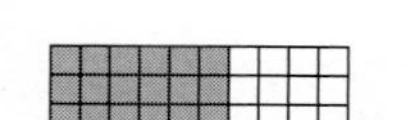

F $\frac{53}{1,000}$ **H** $\frac{53}{10}$
G $\frac{53}{100}$ **J** 53

3. Which group shows all the numbers that are common factors of 24 and 32? A

A 1, 2, 4, 8
B 1, 2, 3, 4, 8
C 1, 2, 4, 6, 8
D 1, 2, 4, 8, 12

4. Brittany is having a party on a date in May that is NOT a prime number. Which of the following could be the date of her party? H

F May 11 **H** May 21
G May 17 **J** May 31

5. The table shows how much money Mrs. Stoehr spends on bus fare. A

Bus Fare	
Number of Weeks	Total Amount Spent ($)
4	48
5	60
6	72
7	84

What is the relationship between the number of weeks and the total amount spent?

A The total amount spent is 12 times the number of weeks.
B The number of weeks is 44 less than the total amount spent.
C The total amount spent is 55 more than the number of weeks.
D The number of weeks is 12 times the total amount spent.

6. Which figure does NOT contain any right angles? F

F
G
H
J

7. Suppose the temperature outside at 5:15 P.M. was 54°F. By midnight, the temperature was 37 °F. How many degrees did the temperature drop by midnight? B

A 13°F
B 17°F
C 23°F
D 27°F

8. Which pair of moons shows only a translation? F

F
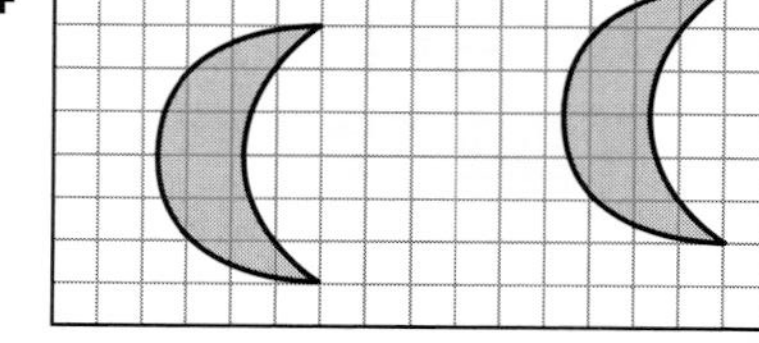

G
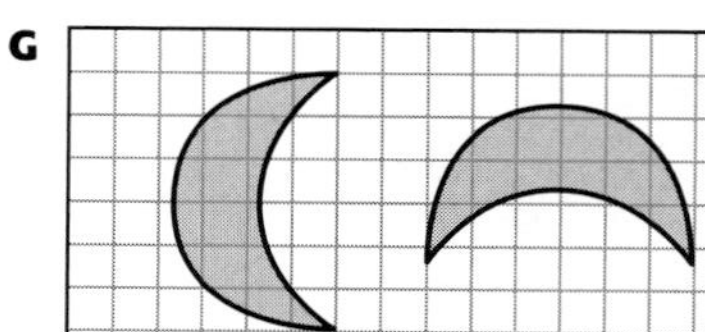

H
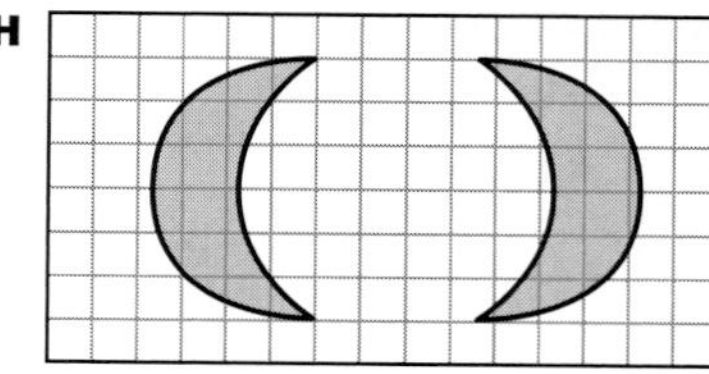

J
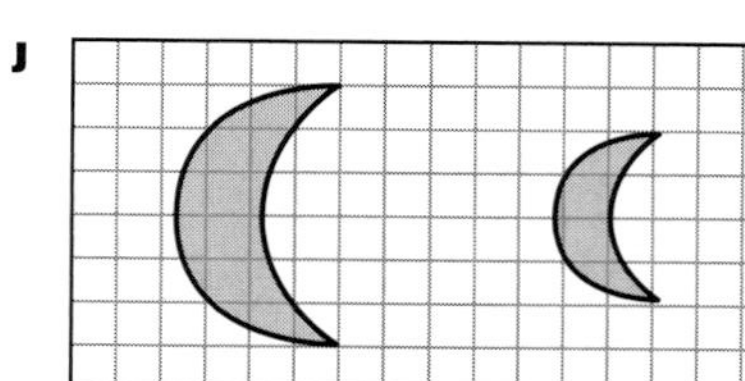
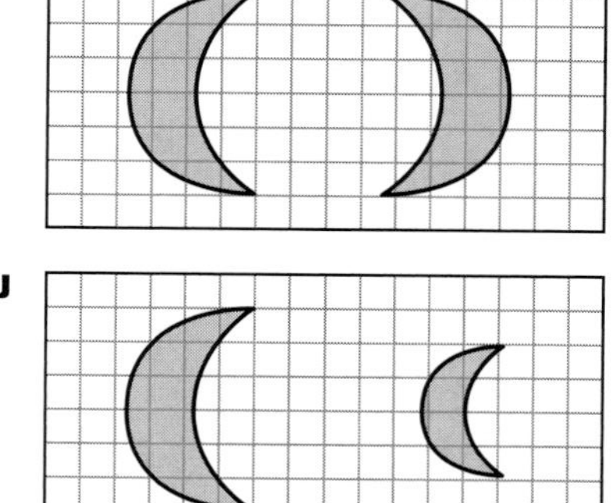

9. What fractional part of a kilogram is a gram? D

A $\frac{1}{4}$
B $\frac{1}{10}$
C $\frac{1}{100}$
D $\frac{1}{1,000}$

10. Nico has 10 letter cards that spell the word *ELEMENTARY* when put together. If he picks one card without looking, what is the probability that it will have the letter *E* on it? F

F $\frac{3}{10}$ **H** $\frac{3}{5}$
G $\frac{2}{5}$ **J** $\frac{7}{10}$

11. Paulo spun each spinner once.

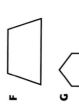

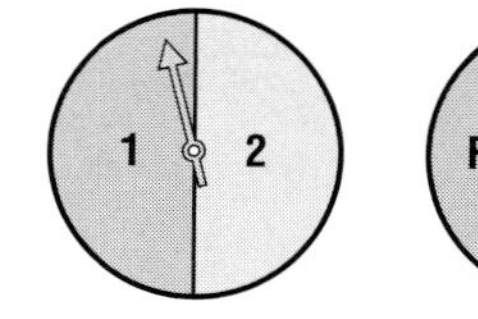

Which shows all the unique combinations of letters and numbers that are possible? C

A Red, Blue, 1, 2
B Red 1, Blue 2, Red 1
C Red 1, Blue 1, Red 2, Blue 2
D Blue Red, Red Blue, 21, 12

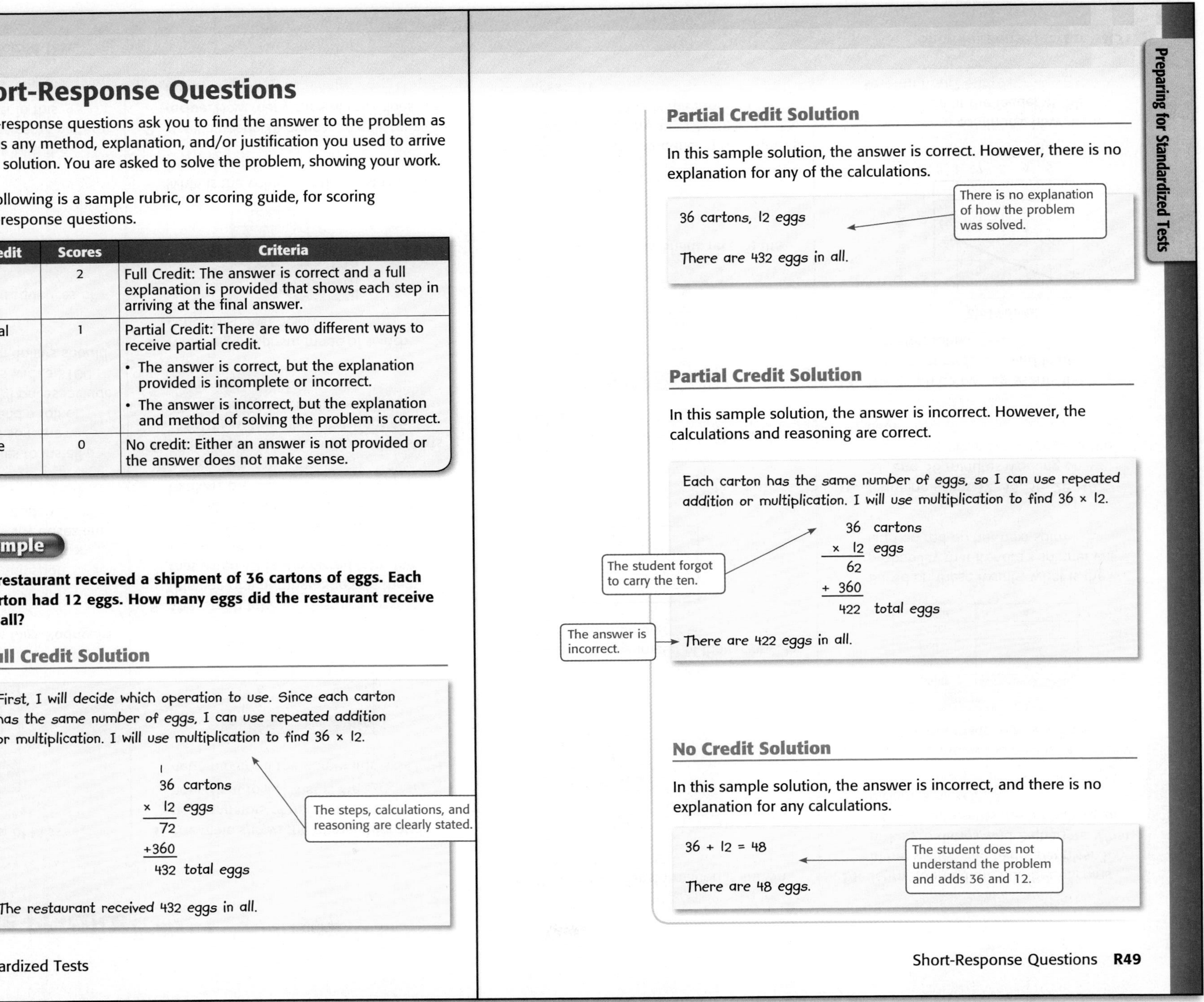

Short-Response Questions

Short-response questions ask you to find the answer to the problem as well as any method, explanation, and/or justification you used to arrive at the solution. You are asked to solve the problem, showing your work.

The following is a sample rubric, or scoring guide, for scoring short-response questions.

Credit	Scores	Criteria
Full	2	Full Credit: The answer is correct and a full explanation is provided that shows each step in arriving at the final answer.
Partial	1	Partial Credit: There are two different ways to receive partial credit. • The answer is correct, but the explanation provided is incomplete or incorrect. • The answer is incorrect, but the explanation and method of solving the problem is correct.
None	0	No credit: Either an answer is not provided or the answer does not make sense.

Example

1 A restaurant received a shipment of 36 cartons of eggs. Each carton had 12 eggs. How many eggs did the restaurant receive in all?

Full Credit Solution

First, I will decide which operation to use. Since each carton has the same number of eggs, I can use repeated addition or multiplication. I will use multiplication to find 36 × 12.

```
   1
   36  cartons
 × 12  eggs
   72
 +360
  432  total eggs
```

The restaurant received 432 eggs in all.

The steps, calculations, and reasoning are clearly stated.

The correct answer is given.

Partial Credit Solution

In this sample solution, the answer is correct. However, there is no explanation for any of the calculations.

36 cartons, 12 eggs

There are 432 eggs in all.

There is no explanation of how the problem was solved.

Partial Credit Solution

In this sample solution, the answer is incorrect. However, the calculations and reasoning are correct.

Each carton has the same number of eggs, so I can use repeated addition or multiplication. I will use multiplication to find 36 × 12.

```
   36  cartons
 × 12  eggs
   62
 + 360
  422  total eggs
```

There are 422 eggs in all.

The student forgot to carry the ten.

The answer is incorrect.

No Credit Solution

In this sample solution, the answer is incorrect, and there is no explanation for any calculations.

36 + 12 = 48

There are 48 eggs.

The student does not understand the problem and adds 36 and 12.

Short-Response Practice

DIRECTIONS
Solve each problem.

1. The table shows the cost of Miss Rodriguez's lunch items.

Lunch	
Item	**Cost**
Sandwich	$3.85
Salad	$0.90
Pudding	$0.63
Iced Tea	$1.10

She has a $5 bill in her pocket. How much more money does Miss Rodriguez need? $1.48

2. Buses are being used to transport students on a field trip. Each bus can hold 62 students. How many buses are needed to transport 180 students? 3 buses

3. Mr. Solis is buying supplies to install a ceiling fan. The fan costs $64, the support brace costs $8, and a roll of electrical tape costs $2. All prices include sales tax. If Mr. Solis pays with a $100 bill, how much change in dollars should he receive? $26

4. Look for a pattern in the sequences of numbers shown below.

3, 6, 9, 12, 15, 18, …

5, 10, 15, 20, 25, …

8, 16, 24, 32, 40, 48, …

Another sequence begins with the number 4 and follows the same pattern. Which is the third number in this sequence? 12

5. The table shows the numerators and denominators of fractions that are equivalent to $\frac{2}{3}$. What is the denominator if the numerator is 54? 81

Numerator	Denominator
2	3
6	9
18	27
54	?

6. Mrs. Smith told her class she was thinking of a number. She told them that when 12 is subtracted from the number and the result is doubled, the final number is 26. What was the original number that Mrs. Smith was thinking of? 25

7. Sarika wants to go to a movie that starts at 9:10 P.M. The movie is 1 hour 45 minutes long. At what time will the movie end? 10:55 P.M.

8. A rectangular prism made of 1-inch cubes is shown below.

What is the volume of the prism? 60 cubic inches

9. Natalie needs 24 ounces of milk for a recipe. How many cups of milk does she need? 3 cups

10. What single transformation is shown below? reflection

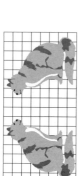

11. What is the perimeter of the rectangular field shown below? 260 yards

50 yd

80 yd

12. Shada's quiz scores are shown in the table.

Quiz	Score
1	84
2	90
3	88
4	92
5	89

On which quiz did Shada receive the median score? quiz 5

13. The ages of the students in Mr. Jeffrey's reading group are 11, 12, 10, 9, 11, 13, 12, and 11. What is the mode of the ages? 11

14. Jenny counted the number of coins in her wallet. She had 4 pennies, 3 nickels, 6 dimes, and 2 quarters. What fraction represents the probability of picking a nickel? $\frac{1}{5}$

15. The table shows the results of 20 spins that Kendra made with a spinner.

Spinner Results	
Color	**Number of Spins**
Blue	3
Red	8
Green	5
White	4

Based on these results, what is the probability that Kendra's spinner will land on red on her next spin? $\frac{2}{5}$

16. Jermaine spent 32, 38, 36, 28, 40, 33, and 36 minutes working on homework. What is the range of the data? 12

17. The graph below represents the number of birds at a bird feeder one afternoon.

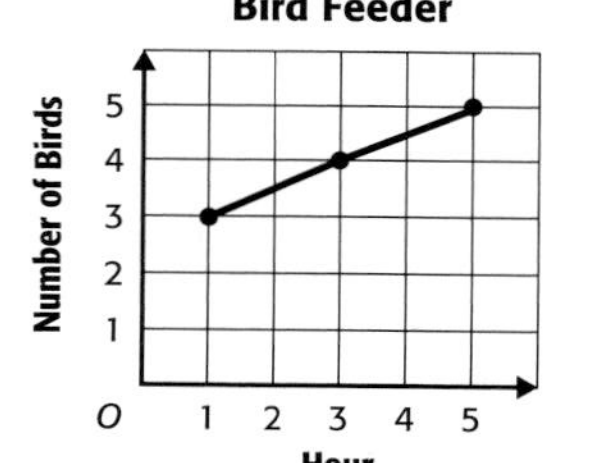

If the pattern continues, how many birds will be at the feeder at the seventh hour? 6 birds

Extended-Response Questions

Most extended-response questions have multiple parts. You must answer all parts to receive full credit.

In extended-response questions, you must show all of your work in solving the problem. A rubric is used to determine if you receive full, partial, or no credit. The following is a sample rubric for scoring extended-response questions.

Credit	Scores	Criteria
Full	4	Full Credit: The answer is correct and a full explanation is given that shows each step in finding the answer.
Partial	3, 2, 1	Partial Credit: Most of the solution is correct but it may have some mistakes in the explanation or solution. The more correct the solution, the greater the score.
None	0	No credit: Either an answer is not provided or the answer does not make sense.

Make sure that when the problem says to *show your work*, you show every part of your solution. This includes figures, graphs, and any explanations for your calculations.

Example

1 The bar graph shows the top speeds of four roller coasters. Explain how to use the bar graph to find the range of the roller coaster speeds shown.

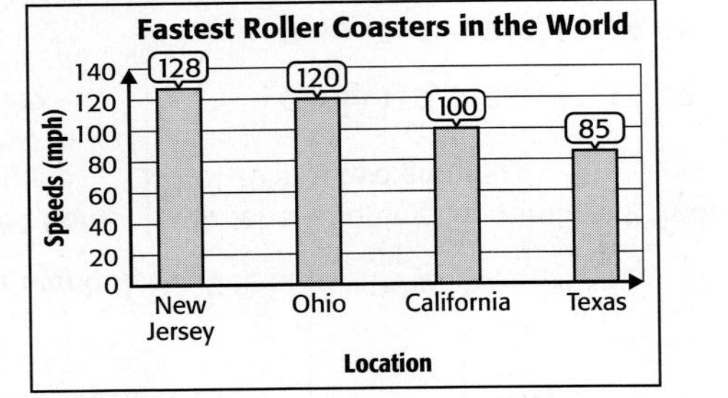

Full Credit Solution

In this sample answer, the student explains how to read the bar graph, what calculations need to be done and finds the correct solution.

The steps, calculations, and reasoning are clearly stated.

First, I will use the bar graph to find the fastest speed and slowest speed. Then I will find the difference of the two speeds.

The bar graph shows the speeds (mph) in each of the four states: New Jersey: 128, Ohio: 120, California: 100, and Texas: 85.

128 mph fastest roller coaster
− 85 mph slowest roller coaster
43 mph

The range of the given speeds is 43 mph.

The correct answer is given.

Partial Credit Solution

In this sample answer, the student explains what calculations need to be done. However, there is an error in the calculations.

The steps, calculations, and reasoning are clearly stated.

First, I will use the bar graphs to find the fastest speed and slowest speed. Then I will find the difference of the two speeds.

The bar graph shows the speeds (mph) in each of the four states: New Jersey: 128, Ohio: 120, California: 100, Texas: 85

128 mph − 85 mph = 143 mph

There is an error.
$128 - 85 \neq 143$

The range of the given speeds is 143 mph.

No Credit Solution

A solution for this problem that will receive no credit may include incorrect answers and an inaccurate explanation.

I will find the range by listing all of the speeds.
New Jersey: 128, Ohio: 120, California: 110, Texas: 85
228 + 120 + 110 + 85 = 433 mph

The range is 143 mph.

Preparing for Standardized Tests

Extended-Response Practice

DIRECTIONS:
Solve each problem. Show all your work. 1-13. See student's work.

1. Each month Carmina saves $24.80 from her paychecks. How can she estimate the amount of money she will save in 4 months? Sample answer: Round $24.80 to the nearest ten dollars and multiply by 4.

2. The table below shows the amount of rain in a city during a 3-month period.

Amount of Rainfall	
Month	Amount of Rain (centimeters)
1	15.1
2	18.5
3	20.2

Estimate the total rainfall in these three months. Explain how to find the difference between your estimate and the actual total rainfall. Sample answer: 55 cm

3. Write the instructions of how to make $4\frac{1}{5}$ into an improper fraction. Sample answer: Multiply the denominator (5) times the whole number (4) and add the numerator (1).

4. Shawnda needed 12 yards of fabric. How many feet of fabric did she need? What operation did you use to solve the problem? 36 feet

5. Jane is sorting the numbers 2 through 20 into two groups.

Group 1: 2, 3, 5, 7, 11, 13, 17

Group 2: 4, 6, 8, 9, 12, 14, 15, 16, 18

How is she sorting them? In which groups should she place 19 and 20?
19 – Group 1
20 – Group 2

6. The dimensions of a rectangle are shown. Find the area. Show your work. 36 square inches

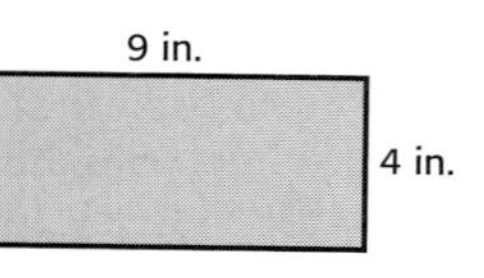

7. The figure below is made of 1-unit cubes. Describe how to find the volume of the figure.

Sample answer: Multiply the length (6) times the width (4) times the height (2).

8. Mykia's dance class started at 10:45 A.M. and ended at 12:00 P.M. How many hours and minutes was her dance class? Explain your reasoning. 1 hour 15 minutes

9. The coordinate grid below represents a playground.

Playground

O 1 2 3 4 5 6 7 8 9 x

A slide is at point S on the playground. A set of swings that is not shown on the grid is 4 units up from the slide. Explain how to find the coordinates of the swings. (5, 3)

10. The figure below is a rectangular prism.

Face *ABFE* is congruent to face CDHG. Name another two faces that are congruent. Explain why they are congruent.

11. The table shows the prices at a used media store including tax. Ty has $24 to spend at the store. List two combinations of items that he can buy. Show your work. Sample answer: 6 CDs; 4 DVDs and 1 CD

Item	Price
CD	$4
DVD	$5
Video Game	$6

12. The table shows the results of a survey.

Class Pets	
Pet	Number of Students
Cat	7
Dog	8
Fish	6
Bird	2

A student made the following graph to display the data.

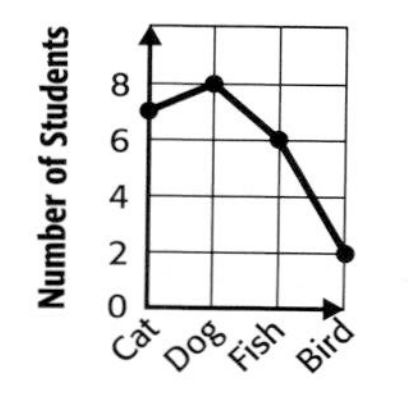

Explain why this type of a graph is not appropriate for the data shown in the table.

13. The graph shows how much time Jasmine spent on her project. How many total minutes were spent on this project? How many hours and minutes is this? Explain your reasoning. 5 hours 25 min.

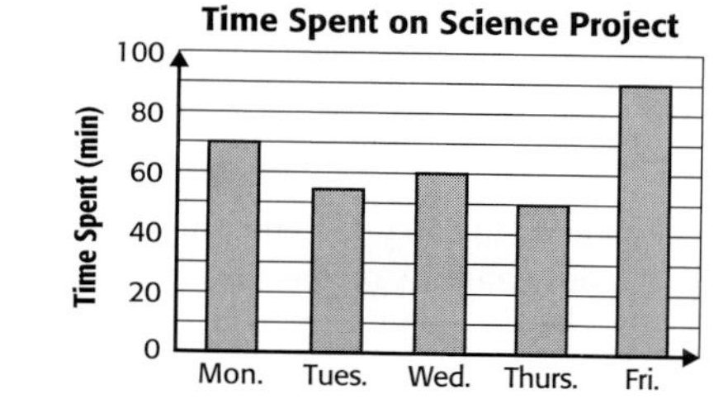

Concepts and Skills Bank

Percents as Fractions, and Decimals

Lesson Planner

Objective

Express percents as fractions and decimals.

Vocabulary

percent

Activate Prior Knowledge

Discuss situations in which students have encountered percents. Sample answers: discounts at stores, test scores

Using Student Page R56.

- Refer to Example 1: Using a hundreds grid, shade 75 out of 100 squares.
- **What is another way to write 75% as a fraction in simplest form?** Sample answer: write 75 as a fraction over 100 and divide both numbers by the same number until the fraction is in simplest form.
- Refer to Example 2: One way to write 32% as a decimal is to locate the decimal point and move it 2 places to the left.
- **Explain how to write 32% as a decimal.** Sample answer: Divide 32 by 100 to get 0.32 or move the decimal two places to the left.

Exercises 1–14 Have students work independently to solve the exercises.

Assess and Close

Give students real-world examples of percents, fractions, and decimals and have them write them in different forms.

Concepts and Skills

1 Percents as Fractions, and Decimals

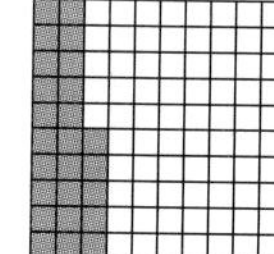

The model to the right shows 25 squares shaded out of 100. This can be written as the fraction $\frac{25}{100}$ or $\frac{1}{4}$. It can also be written as the decimal 0.25.

A **percent** is a ratio that compares a number to 100.
25% = 25 out of 100 or $\frac{25}{100}$.

EXAMPLE Write a percent as a fraction

1 **Write 75% as a fraction in simplest form.**

75% means "75 out of 100."

$75\% = \frac{75}{100}$ — Write as a fraction with a denominator of 100.

$= \frac{\overset{3}{\cancel{75}}}{\underset{4}{\cancel{100}}} = \frac{3}{4}$ — Simplify.

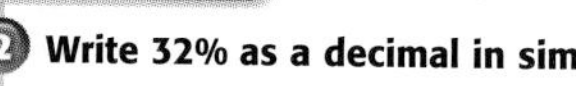

EXAMPLE Write a percent as a decimal

2 **Write 32% as a decimal in simplest form.**

32% means "32 out of 100."

32% = 0.32 — Write as a decimal.

Exercises

Write each percent as a fraction in simplest form.

1. 29% $\frac{29}{100}$ **2.** 30% $\frac{3}{10}$ **3.** 60% $\frac{3}{5}$ **4.** 84% $\frac{21}{25}$

5. 92% $\frac{23}{25}$ **6.** 8% $\frac{2}{25}$ **7.** 15% $\frac{3}{20}$ **8.** 22% $\frac{11}{50}$

Write each percent as a decimal.

9. 4% 0.04 **10.** 17% 0.17 **11.** 12% 0.12 **12.** 50% 0.50

13. Malak bought a box of colored paper clips. If 15% are green, what fraction of the paper clips are green? $\frac{3}{20}$

14. Of the students in a class, 65% have more than 1 pet. Write this amount as a decimal. 0.65

2 Squared Numbers

The product of a number and itself is the **square** of that number.

A square with an area of 16 square units is shown. The number 16 is a square number because the product of 4 and itself is 16.

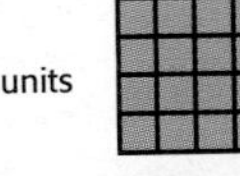

EXAMPLES

1 Find the square of 5.

5 × 5 = 25. Multiply 5 by itself.

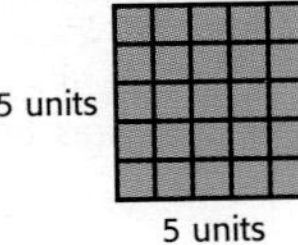

2 Use models to determine if 9 is a square number.

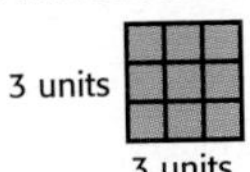

9 units can be arranged to make a square because 3 × 3 = 9.

Yes, 9 is a square number

Exercises

Find the square of each number.

1. 6 36
2. 10 100
3. 15 225
4. 12 144
5. 17 289
6. 22 484
7. 37 1,369
8. 50 2,500

Use models to determine if each number is a square number. Write yes or no.

9. 4 yes
10. 12 no
11. 17 no
12. 36 yes
13. 49 yes
14. 50 no
15. 64 yes
16. 81 yes

★17. How much greater is the area of a square that is 10 meters by 10 meters than the area of a square that is 9 meters by 9 meters? 9 square meters

18. A square garden has an area of 121 square feet. How much fencing is needed to place a fence around the entire garden? 44 feet

Concepts and Skills Bank

2 Squared Numbers

Lesson Planner

Objective

Find the square of a number and identify square numbers.

Vocabulary

square

Activate Prior Knowledge

Discuss the area of square figures and the formula used to find the area. Emphasize that squares have sides of equal length, so the area is always going to be a number multiplied by itself.

Using Student Page R57.

- Refer to Example 1: **What is one way to show the square of 5?** Sample answer: The square of 5 means 5^2 or 5 × 5 = 25.
- Refer to Example 2: A model can be used to determine if 9 is a square number by arranging 9 units to make a square. Manipulatives may be used to help students better understand this concept.

Exercises 1-18 Have students work independently to solve the exercises.

Assess and Close

Manipulatives are helpful to give students a better understanding of square numbers. Give students a random number of squares to see if the total is a square number. For example, give one student 15 squares and ask them to find out if 15 is a square number by making a model.

3 Congruent and Similar Triangles

Lesson Planner

Objective

Identify congruent and similar triangles.

Vocabulary

congruent triangles, similar triangles

Activate Prior Knowledge

Discuss what students know about the terms congruent and similar.

- **What have you already learned about the terms congruent and similar?** Sample answers: Congruent means the figures will have the same shape and size. Similar means the figures will have the same shape but different sizes.

Using Student Page R58.

- Refer to Example 1: The measure of the side lengths and the size of the angles in congruent triangles are always equal.
- **How can you tell if a triangle is congruent or similar?** Sample answer: Without a measuring device, it is hard to be exact. The best way is to compare both figures and look for noticeable differences or similarities.

Concepts and Skills

3 Congruent and Similar Triangles

Congruent and Similar Triangles — Key Concepts

Words If two triangles are congruent, they have the same angle measures and side lengths.

Model

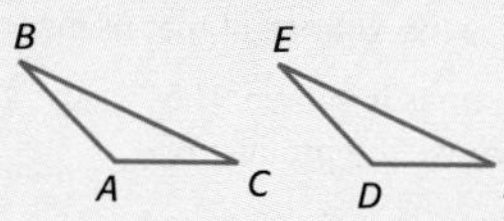

Symbols The symbol ≅ means congruent. $\triangle ABC \cong \triangle DEF$

Congruent sides: $\overline{AB} \cong \overline{DE}$; $\overline{AC} \cong \overline{DF}$; $\overline{BC} \cong \overline{EF}$

Congruent angles: $\angle A \cong \angle D$; $\angle B \cong \angle E$; $\angle C \cong \angle F$

Words If two triangles are similar, they have the same angle measures, but different side lengths.

Model

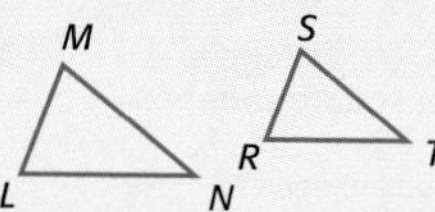

Symbols The symbol ~ means similar. $\triangle LMN \sim \triangle RST$

Congruent angles: $\angle L \cong \angle R$; $\angle M \cong \angle S$; $\angle N \cong \angle T$

note: Congruent figures are also similar.

EXAMPLE Congruent Triangles

1 **IF $\triangle JKM \cong \triangle STU$ name the congruent sides and angles.**

≅ **sides:** $\overline{JM} \cong \overline{SU}$; $\overline{KM} \cong \overline{TU}$; $\overline{JK} \cong \overline{ST}$

≅ **angles:** $\angle J \cong \angle S$; $\angle K \cong \angle T$; $\angle M \cong \angle U$

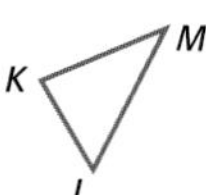

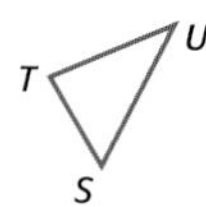

EXAMPLE Similar Triangles

2 **IF $\triangle MNP \sim \triangle ABC$ name the congruent angles.**

≅ **angles:** $\angle P \cong \angle C$; $\angle M \cong \angle A$; $\angle N \cong \angle B$

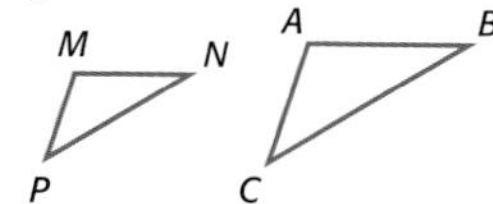

Exercises

Tell whether the triangles appear to be *congruent, similar,* or *neither.*

1.  congruent

2. 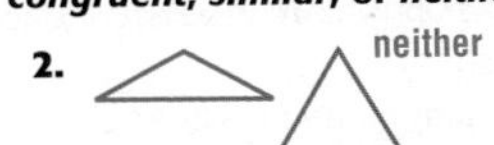 neither

3.  congruent

4.  similar

Identify the corresponding angle in the similar triangles shown.

5. ∠A ∠D
6. ∠F ∠C
7. ∠B ∠E
8. ∠D ∠A

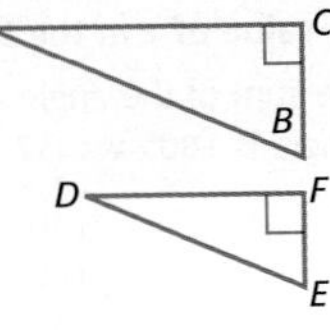

Identify the corresponding side in the congruent triangles shown.

9. $\overline{GH}$ $\overline{LK}$
10. $\overline{IH}$ $\overline{JK}$
11. $\overline{IJ}$ $\overline{GI}$
12. $\overline{GH}$ $\overline{LK}$

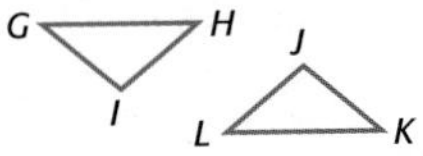

G H I J L K

Solve.

13. Two triangles are similar. The height of one triangle is 4 times greater than the other triangle. If the smaller triangle is 33 centimeters tall, how tall is the larger triangle? 132 cm

14. Mia is cutting out 12 triangles for a project. She decides to speed up the process by cutting multiple sheets of paper at once. Is Mia cutting congruent triangles or similar triangles? Explain. Sample Answer: Congruent; Each triangle will be the same size and have equal angle measurements.

15. Marcus is building a triangular frame for his garden. Before he cuts the wood for the frame, he draws the triangle shown. If one inch represents 2 feet, find the dimensions of the sides of the frame. Two sides will be 10 feet long and one side will be 8 feet long.

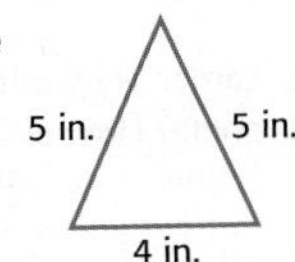

16. In Exercise 15, is Marcus' drawing similar or congruent to the frame he built? Explain. Sample Answer: Similar; the angles will be the same but the side lengths are different.

Concepts and Skills

Exercises 1- 16 Have students work independently as they: determine whether the figures are congruent or similar, identify corresponding angles, identify corresponding sides, and solve word problems.

Assess and Close

Have students use a ruler and a protractor to create two congruent triangles and two similar triangles.

4 Interior Angle Measures of Triangles

Lesson Planner

Objective

Find missing angle measures in triangles.

Vocabulary

triangle

Activate Prior Knowledge

Discuss what students already know about triangles.

- **What do all triangles have in common?** Sample answer: They are three sided figures.
- **What are different types of triangles?** Sample answer: acute, equilateral, isosceles, obtuse, right, and scalene

Using Student Page R60.

- Explain that the interior angles of a triangle add up to 180 degrees.
- **How can you find the measure of an interior angle of a triangle?** Sample answer: You could measure the angles. Or, if two of the angles are given, they could subtract the known angles from 180°.
- Refer to Example 1: In order to find a missing angle of a triangle, it is helpful to set up an equation showing what you know and do not know.

Exercises 1–8 Have students work independently to determine the interior angle measures of the triangles.

4 Interior Angle Measures of Triangles

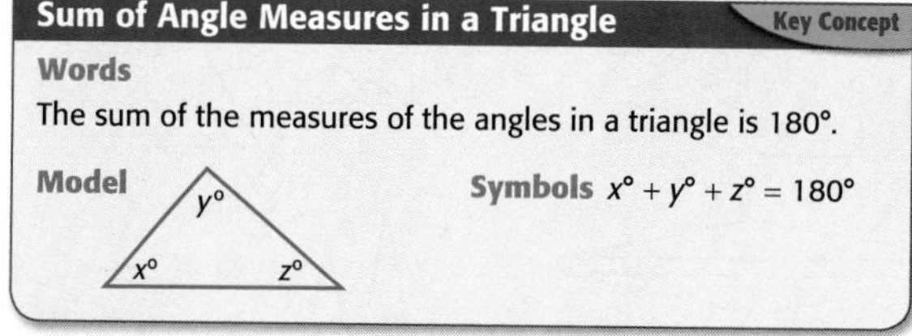
Sum of Angle Measures in a Triangle — Key Concept

Words
The sum of the measures of the angles in a triangle is 180°.

Model

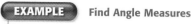

Symbols $x° + y° + z° = 180°$

EXAMPLE Find Angle Measures

1 **Find the value of x in the triangle.**

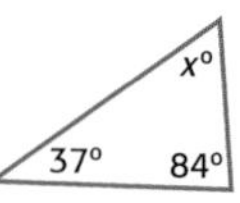

Since the sum of the angle measures in a triangle is 180°, $x + 37 + 84 = 180$.

$x + 37 + 84$	=	180	Write the equation.
$x + 121$	=	180	Add 37 and 84.
-121	=	-121	Subtract 121 from each side.
x	=	59	

So, the value of x is 59.

Exercises

Find the value of the missing angle x.

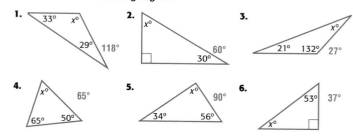

1. 33°, x°, 29° — 118°
2. x°, 60°, 30° — 60°
3. x°, 21°, 132° — 27°
4. x°, 65°, 50° — 65°
5. x°, 34°, 56° — 90°
6. 53°, x° — 37°

7. Lamar drew a triangle with three equal sides. What is the measure of each angle? How did you find the answer? 60°; The sum of the angles of a triangle is 180°, since all three angles are equal 180 ÷ 3 = 60.

8. Adrian was asked to draw a triangle in which each angle is 10° greater than the next angle. If the largest angle is 70°, what is the measure of the other two angles? How can you check your solution? 60°, 50°; Add all three angles to get 180°.

Assess and Close

Have students each draw a triangle and cut them out. After each student has a triangle, have them tear each angle of the triangle off to prove that the triangle's interior angles do add up to 180 degrees. Students should be able to show that all three angles will make a straight line, or a 180° angle. Have students find triangles throughout the room. Have them measure the interior angles to determine if the angles add up to 180°.

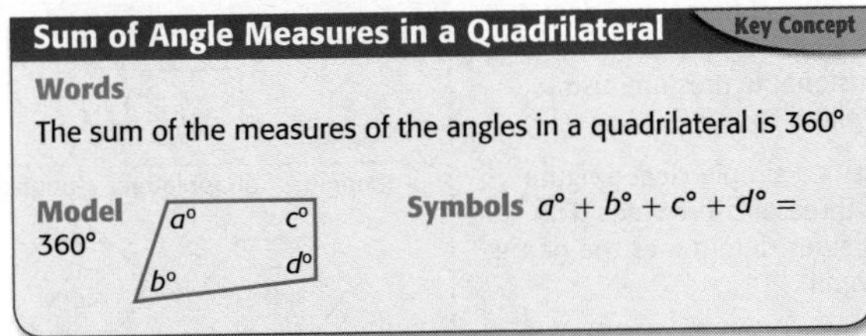

EXAMPLE Find Angle Measures

85° 65° x°

1 **Find the value of x in the quadrilateral.**

The sum of the angle measures in a quadrilateral is 360°.

$$\begin{aligned} x + 65 + 85 + 90 &= 360 \\ x + 240 &= 360 \quad \text{Add 65, 85, and 90.} \\ -240 &= -240 \quad \text{Subtract 240 from each side.} \\ \hline x &= 120 \end{aligned}$$

So, the value of x is 120.

Exercises

Algebra Find the value of x in each quadrilateral.

1. 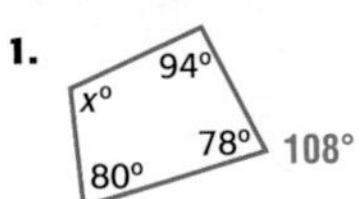

2. 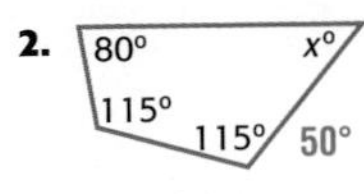

3. 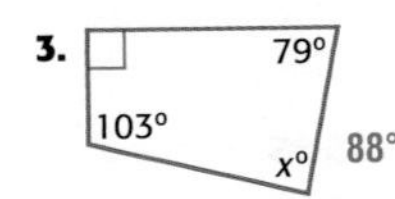

4. 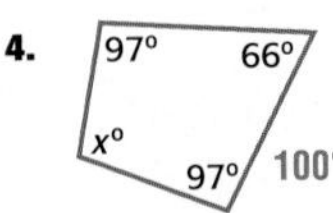

5. 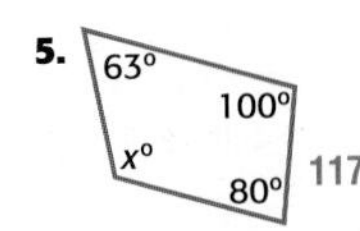

6. 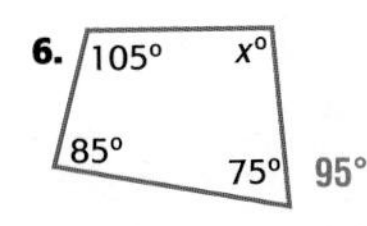

7. Jacob was asked to draw a quadrilateral in which each angle is 10° greater than the next angle. If the smallest angle is 75°, what is the measure of the other three angles? How can you check your solution? 85°, 95°, 105°; Add all four angles to get 360°.

Concepts and Skills Bank

5 Interior Angle Measures of Quadrilaterals

Lesson Planner

Objective

Find missing angle measures in quadrilaterals.

Vocabulary

quadrilateral

Activate Prior Knowledge

Discuss the properties of quadrilaterals.

- **What do all quadrilaterals have in common?** four sides, four angles

Using Student Page R61.

- Give students copies of various quadrilaterals. Some of them should have three angles labeled, the others should not have any angles labeled. Students can write equations or use protractors to find the measures of each of the four angles.
- **What is the sum of the angles of a quadrilateral?** 360°

Exercises 1–7 Have students compare their answers after completing Exercises 1 through 7 independently.

Assess and Close

Have students find objects in the classroom that are in the shapes of quadrilaterals. Have the students use a protractor to measure three of the angles of the quadrilateral and use algebra to find the measure of the fourth angle. Have students check their work by measuring the fourth angle with a protractor.

Concepts and Skills Bank

6 Two-Dimensional Figures

Lesson Planner

Objective

Identify and name polygons.

Vocabulary

polygon, triangle, quadrilateral, pentagon, hexagon, octagon

Activate Prior Knowledge

Show students examples and non-examples of polygons and ask them to categorize them. Have them justify their classifications.

Using Student Page R62.

- Have students draw examples and nonexamples of polygons. If possible, have the students give their polygons names based on the number of sides.
- **Give an example of a real-world object that is not a polygon.** Sample answers: bowl, Earth, cup

Exercises 1–6 Have students work independently to determine if the figures are polygons.

Concepts and Skills

6 Two-Dimensional Figures

A two-dimensional figure is a closed figure with length and width. Two-dimensional figures are also known as plane figures.

A **polygon** is a simple closed figure formed by three or more sides. The number of sides determines the name of the polygon.

A circle is not a polygon because it is a curve.

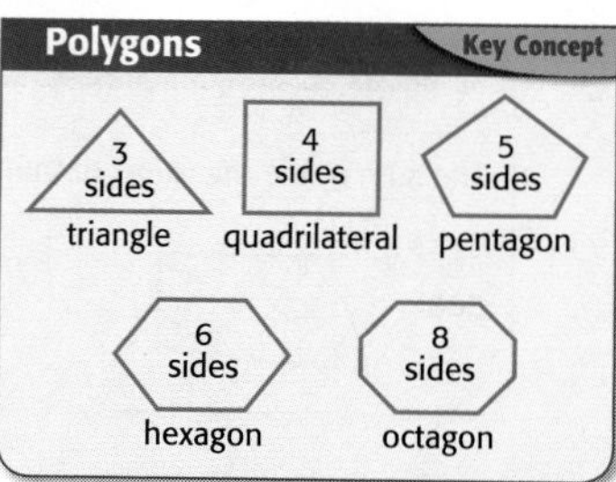

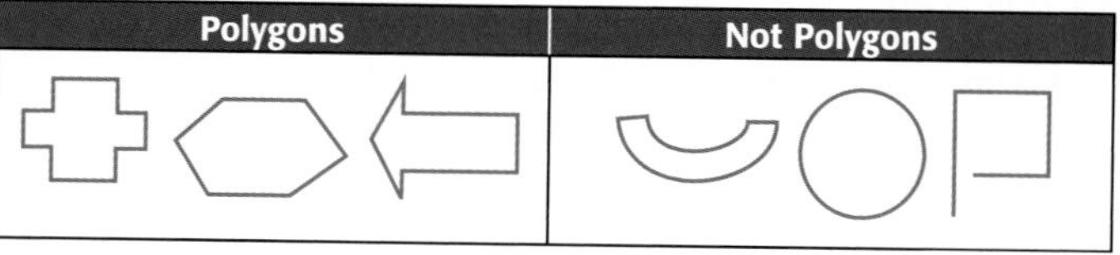

EXAMPLES

Tell whether each shape is a polygon. If it is a polygon, identify the polygon.

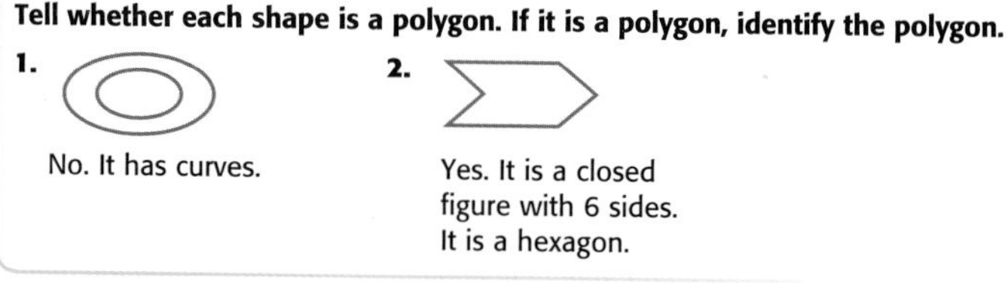

1. No. It has curves.

2. Yes. It is a closed figure with 6 sides. It is a hexagon.

Exercises

Tell whether each shape is a polygon. If it is a polygon, identify the polygon.

1. no

2. yes; octagon

3. no

Identify the type polygon for each sign.

4. yes; quadrilateral

5. yes; octagon

6. yes; pentagon

Assess and Close

Have students create two different drawings using figures. One drawing should only use only polygons. The other drawing should not contain any polygons.

7 Mean

The **mean** is a type of average. To find the mean of a set of data, you can add the data, then divide by the total number of data.

EXAMPLE Find the Mean

1 Find the mean of the following test scores: 75, 77, 89, 95, 66, 81, 54, 99

$75 + 77 + 89 + 95 + 66 + 81 + 54 + 99 = 636$ Add the data.

$= \frac{636}{8}$ Divide by the number of test scores.

$= 79.5$

So, the mean is 79.5.

Exercises

Find the mean.

1. Number of DVDs: 21, 23, 25, 27, 19 23
2. Test scores: 99, 87, 81, 95, 94, 84, 67 86.7
3. Number of pets: 2, 3, 7, 4, 5, 8, 6 5
4. Points scored: 11, 17, 34, 57, 14, 49, 35 31
5. Coins collected: 105, 112, 155, 142, 164, 187, 123 141.1
6. Yards gained: 751.1, 857.1, 801.4, 610.1 754.9
7. Miles traveled: 21.5, 25.9, 34.1, 24.7, 22.6 25.8
8. Students from Mrs. Whittier's class went on a field trip to collect different kinds of leaves for their science project. Use the chart to determine the mean number of leaves collected. 12 leaves

Student	Number of leaves
Manny	17
Tanya	4
Jai	7
Randy	11
Kelly	21

9. Trisha went to the mall and walked by several jewelry displays. There were 30 pairs of earrings in the first display. There were 40 necklaces in the next display. The third display had 25 rings. The final display had 50 bracelets. Find the mean number of jewelry in the displays. 36 pieces of jewelry

Concepts and Skills Bank

7 Mean

Lesson Planner

Objective

Find the mean of a data set.

Vocabulary

mean

Activate Prior Knowledge

Give students the set of values, {68, 75, 78, 72, 80}, and ask them to estimate what single value the set is "around". See students' work, around 75.

Using Student Page R63.

- Review with students how to determine the median of a set of data. Order the numbers from least to greatest, and then find the number in the middle.
- Discuss with students how to find the mean by adding all of the values in the set and dividing by the number of values that were added.
- **In your own words, explain a time when it would be helpful to find the mean of a data set.** Sample answers: charting statistics for athletes, examining a set of classroom test scores.

Exercises 1–9 Have students work independently as they find the mean for each of the exercises.

Assess and Close

Have students write their heights, in inches, on the board. Have them find the mean of the heights of every student in the class.

Concepts and Skills Bank

8 Stem-and-Leaf Plots

Lesson Planner

Objective

Display and analyze data using a stem-and-leaf plot.

Vocabulary

stem-and-leaf plot

Activate Prior Knowledge

Discuss some of the different ways to display data such as bar graphs, line graphs, and pictographs.

Using Student Page R64.

- Discuss with students the steps involved when creating a stem-and-leaf plot. Discuss what should be done if the range is 40 to 80 but there are no values in the 70s. Do you need a 7 in the stem? Yes, there would be a 7 stem, but no accompanying leaf.
- Discuss with students how to read a stem-and-leaf plot.
- **In Example 1, what is the greatest number in the set? the least number?** 51; 85

Exercises 1–5 Have students work independently as they create and analyze stem-and-leaf plots.

Concepts and Skills

8 Stem-and-Leaf Plots

A **stem-and-leaf plot** is a way to organize and distribute data.

- The leaf is the last digit of the number.
- The other digits to the left of the leaf form the stem.

For the numbers 21, 24, 35, and 38, 2 and 3 are the stems. The numbers 1, 4, 5 and 8 are the leaves.

Stem	Leaf
2	1 4
3	5 8

EXAMPLE

1 SPORTS Make a stem-and-leaf plot of the basketball scores below.
68, 52, 85, 64, 59, 51, 62, 66

51, 52, 59, 62, 64, 66, 68, 85 — Write the data from least to greatest.

51, 52, 59
62, 64, 66, 68
85
— Group the numbers with the same first digit.

Separate each stem from each leaf.

Stem	Leaf
5	1 2 9
6	2 4 6 8
7	
8	5

Exercises

Make a stem-and-leaf plot for each set of numbers. 1–2 See students' work

1. 83, 86, 99, 43, 75, 91

2. 33, 31, 62, 20, 32, 25

Write the set of numbers from least to greatest used to form each stem-and-leaf plot.

3. 4, 5, 8, 13, 14, 17, 26

Stem	Leaf
0	4 5 8
1	3 4 7
2	6

4. 41, 51, 52, 56, 58

Stem	Leaf
4	1
5	1 2 6 8

5. Sarah wants to use a stem-and-leaf plot to organize her test scores. List the digits that will make up the stem portions of the plot for the scores 80, 92, 88, 85, 76, 94, 98. 7, 8, 9

Assess and Close

Have students research the high temperatures for their city for the last fifteen days. Have them create a stem-and-leaf plot of the temperatures.

Photo Credits

Unless otherwise credited, all currency courtesy of the US Mint. **v** (br)Thomas Barwick/Getty Images; **vi** Doug Martin; **vii** (br)courtesy Dinah Zike, (others)Doug Martin; **x-xi** Kerrick James Photog/Getty Images; **xii-xiii** Miles Ertman/Masterfile; **xiv-xv** George H. H. Huey/CORBIS; **xvi-xvii** Taxi/Getty Images; **xviii-xix** Robert Landau/CORBIS; **xx-xxi** Richard Cummins/CORBIS; **xxii-xxiii** Eduardo Garcia/Getty Images; **xxiv-xxv** Darrell Gulin/Getty Images; **xxix** Eclipse Studios; **xxvii** Purestock/PunchStock; **xxviii** Tim Fuller; 1 Sandra Baker/Alamy Images; **2** Kenneth Murray/Photo Researchers; **3** Peter Griffith/Masterfile; **4** Alan Schein/Alamy Images; **5** Neal and Molly Jansen/Alamy Images; **6** Keith Srakocic/AP Images; **7** John Anderson/Alamy Images;
8 Bettman/CORBIS; **9** Andre Jenny/Alamy Images; **10** Dennis MacDonald/Alamy Images; **11** Jim Nicholson/Alamy Images; **12** Patrick Mallette/Alamy Images; **13** Courtesy North Carolina Museum of Art; **14-15** Richard Broadwell/Alamy Images; **17 19** CORBIS; **22** Darrell Gulin/Getty Images; **24** Ed-imaging; **28** A & L Sinibaldi/Stone/Getty Images; **30** Ed-Imaging; **32** Al Bello/Getty Images; **34** Dennis Flaherty/Getty Images; **36** Ed-Imaging; **38** Archivo Iconografico, S.A./CORBIS; **40-41** Melba Photo Agency/Punchstock; **44** Stephen Simpson/Getty Images; **45** (tr)Joseph T. Collins/Photo Researchers, (others) Ed-Imaging; **46** David Andrews/Tennessee Aquarium; **47** Ed-Imaging; **48** George Holton/Photo Researchers; **58-59** Getty Images; **61** A. Fifis/AP Images; **66** Ed-Imaging; **68** Flip De Nooyer/Minden Pictures; **70** Deborah Feingold/CORBIS; **74** Ed-Imaging ; **76-77** (bkgd)Janusz Wrobel/Alamy Images, (inset)Alan Jakubek/CORBIS; **78** Ed-Imaging; **80** Barry Gregg/CORBIS; **81** Bernard Annebicque/CORBIS; **82** John Lamb/Getty Images; **83** Ed-Imaging; **84** Richard Hutchings/CORBIS; **90** (tr)Christian Darkin/Photo Researchers, (others)Ed-Imaging; **91** Jeff Vanuga/CORBIS; **100-101** Antony Nagelmann/Getty Images; **103** Courtesy Schlitterbahn Waterpark Resort; **105** W. Treat Davidson/Photo Researchers; **108** Bob Krist/CORBIS; **109** Jim Zipp/Photo Researchers; **110** Ed-Imaging; **112** Norbert Rosing/National Geographic Image Collection; **115** Ed-Imaging; **116** Elyse Lewin/Getty Images; **117** Rich Reid/Getty Images; **120** Doug Menuez/Getty Images; **122** Creatas/PunchStock; **123** Bloomimage/CORBIS; **125 126** Ed-Imaging; **127** C Squared Studios/Getty Images; **130-131** (bkgd)Anthony Johnson/Getty Images, (inset)D. Hurst/Alamy Images; **132** Catapult/Getty Images; **136** Ed-Imaging; **146-147** Tom Brakefield/Getty Images; **149** Altrendo Nature/Getty Images; **150** Gary Neil Corbett/SuperStock; **151** Ed-Imaging; **152** Yellow Dog Productions/Getty Images; **158** Cedar Fair Entertainment Company; **164** (tr)Elliot Elliot/Getty Images, (others)Ed-Imaging; **166 168 169** Ed-Imaging; **170** Greg Pease/Getty Images; **172** Douglas Johns Studio/StockFood; **174** Thinkstock/CORBIS; **175** CORBIS; **176** Nick Koudis/Getty Images; **178-179** (bkgd)Everett C. Johnson/eStock Photo, (inset)CORBIS; **180** Ed-Imaging; **190-191** Richard Cummins/CORBIS; **195** Raymond Gehman/CORBIS; **196** Petrified Collection/Getty Images; **202** Doug Pensinger/Getty Images; **206** Ed-Imaging; **210** Millard H. Sharp/Photo Researchers; **212** Ed-Imaging; **216-217** Jeff Rotman/Getty Images; **221** Don Farrall/Getty Images; **232-233** Theo Allofs/CORBIS; **239** (r)George Doyle/Getty Images, (bl)Image Source/SuperStock; **245** (l)CORBIS, (r)C Squared Studios/Getty Images; **246** Bob Wickley/SuperStock; **247** Ryan McVay/Getty Images; **248** Ed-Imaging; **256** Patricio Robles Gil/Minden Pictures; **258-259** (bkgd)SIME s.a.s/eStock Photo, (inset)CORBIS; **260** Tom Stewart/CORBIS; **261** Brand X Pictures/PunchStock; **262 263 266** Ed-Imaging; **276-277** Taxi/Getty Images; **282** Ed-Imaging; **285** Purestock/Getty Images; **286** Eric Meola/Getty Images; **287** Ryan McVay/Getty Images; **288** Eric Meola/Getty Images; **292** Jean-Paul Ferrero/Minden Pictures; **296** Mark Raycroft/Minden Pictures; **297** John Strohsacker/Getty Images; **298** Friso Gentsch/CORBIS; **299** Margarette Mead/Getty Images; **301** DLILLC/CORBIS; **303** Ed-Imaging; **304-305** Tim Cuff/Alamy Images; **311** Ed-Imaging; **312** Jose Fuste Raga/CORBIS; **317** Ed-Imaging; **320** ThinkStock LLC/Index Stock Imagery; **330-331** Janis Christie/Getty Images; **341** (tr)Gerry Ellis/Getty Images, (others)Ed-imaging; **343** Ed-Imaging; **344** Ariel Skelley/CORBIS; **345** Photodisc/PunchStock; **346** Juniors Bildarchiv/Alamy Images; **347** David Steele/Getty Images; **348** Courtesy Burpee Museum of Natural History Rockford, IL; **350** Eising/Getty Images; **353** Ed-Imaging; **354-355** Getty Images; **356** age fotostock/SuperStock; **360** Ed-Imaging; **370-371** Arnaldo Pomodoro, Disk in the Form of a Desert Rose, Frederik Meijer Gardens & Sculpture Park cast 1999-2000. Gift of Fred and Lena Meijer. Photo by William J. Hebert; **373** Laura Doss/CORBIS; **375** Dr. Nick Kurzenko/Photo Researchers; **384** Ed-Imaging; **386** Gail Shumway/Getty Images; 388 Scenics of America/Getty Images; **393** Dorling Kindersley/Getty Images; **394** David Madison/Getty Images; **398** Wilfried Krecichwost/Getty Images; **399** (l)Paul Burns/Getty Images, (r)Ed-Imaging; **400** Ed-Imaging; **407** Ryan McVay/Getty Images; **408-409** (bkgd)Franck Jeannin/Alamy Images, (t)Oleg Moiseyenk/Alamy Images, (b)Getty Images; **418-419** Martin Harvey Cart/CORBIS; **425** Ingram Publishing/Alamy Images; **430** Geostock/Getty Images; **434** Laurence Mouton/Jupiter Images; **436** (l)Stockdisc/Getty Images, (r)image100 Ltd; **439** Samuel R. Maglione/Photo Researchers, Inc.; **442** Bob Daemmrich/PhotoEdit; **444** Cosmo Condina/Getty Images; **448** Lew Robertson/Jupiter Images; **449** Norgert Wu/Minden Pictures; **450** Ed-Imaging; **451** Purestock/Getty Images; **452** ImageShop/CORBIS; **453** (l)age fotostock/SuperStock, (r)Dan Johnson; **455 456** Ed-Imaging; **458** Darrell Gulin/CORBIS; **460** Pete Turner/Getty Images; **461** (l)Ed-Imaging, (r)Ben Blackenburg/CORBIS; **462-463** (bkgd)Getty Images, (t)Getty Images, (b)Philip James Corwin/CORBIS; **472-473** Robert Glusic/Getty Images; **475** C Squared Studios/Getty Images;

Photo Credits

Photo Credits **R65**

Photo Credits

Photo Credits

476 (tr)G.K. Vikki Hart/Getty Images, (bl)Photodisc/Getty Images, (others)C Squared Studios/Getty Images; **477** Randy Faris/CORBIS; **481** Ed-Imaging; **482** (t)National Geographic/Getty Images, (c)Getty Images, (b)Darlyne A Murawski/Getty Images; **484** Anup Shah/Getty Images; 488 Jose Luis Pelaez/Getty Images; **490** Ed-Imaging; **492** Marc Debnam/Getty Images; **494** Dennis MacDonald/Alamy Images; **496** Ed-Imaging; **498-499** EuroStyle Graphics/Alamy Images; **502** Ed-Imaging; **512-513** Tim De Waele/CORBIS; **515** Dorling Kindersley/Getty Images; **516** (c)Photos.com, (r)Jonathan Kitchen/Getty Images; **517** Laurence Parent Photography; **520** Chris Cheadle/Getty Images; **521** NASA/Photo Researchers; **522** C Borland/Getty Images; **524** Piotr Naskrecki/Minden Pictures; **525** CORBIS; **526** (l)Stockbyte/Getty Images, (tr)IT Stock/PunchStock, (others) Ed-Imaging; **527** Foodcollection/Getty Images; **528** Veronique Rolland/Getty Images; **529** Ed-Imaging; **535** Daniel J Cox/Getty Images; **537** Joe McDonald/Getty Images; **540** Ilene MacDonald/Alamy Images; **542-543** (bkgd)PhotoLink/Getty Images, (l)Museum of Flight/CORBIS, (r)CORBIS; **544** Ed-Imaging; **548** The McGraw-Hill Companies, Inc./Michael Scott photographer; **554-555** Eduardo Garcia/Getty Images; **557** Courtesy New Tech Kites; **559** Photodisc/Getty Images; **561** Ed-Imaging; **562** MTR Photography; **566** Andrew Ward/Getty Images; **567** Kazuyoshi Nomachi/CORBIS; **568** (tr)Matthias Kulka/CORBIS, (bl)Colin Mead Enterprises/Getty Images, (br)Ryman Cabannes/CORBIS; **569** (tr)Michael Houghton/StudiOhio, (br)Purestock/Getty Images; **570** Purestock/Getty Images; **573** (l)Ed-Imaging, (tr)Gail Mooney/CORBIS, (br) Ed-Imaging; **576** Blend Images/SuperStock; **585** Ed-Imaging; **586** image100/CORBIS; **589** (r)Creatas/PunchStock, (others)Getty Images; **591** Jon Arnold Images/Alamy Images; **592** MTR Photography; **593** Lew Robertson/CORBIS; **594-595** (bkgd)Robert Harding Picture Library/Alamy Images, (inset)Martin Moos/Lonely Planet Images; **598** David Frazier/CORBIS; **604-605** Darrell Gulin/Getty Images; **608** Photoalto/Photolibrary; **609** Jules Frazier/Getty Images; **610** Andrea Rugg/CORBIS; **612** Siede Preis/Getty Images; **616** United Veterans of America; **619** ASSOCIATED PRESS; **622** Ed-Imaging; **624** pixie/Emporis; **625** (c)Image Source Pink/Getty Images, (b)Paul Bricknell/Getty Images; **626 631** The McGraw-Hill Companies; **635** (yellow boots)Digital Vision/Getty Images, (others)C Squared Studios/Getty Images; **636-637** (bkgd)Elisabeth Coelfen/Alamy Images; **641** Judith Collins/Alamy Images; **644** Getty Images; **647** (tr)Purestock/Getty Images, (others)Ed-Imaging; **648** Ned Frisk/CORBIS; **658-659** Digital Vision/Getty Images; **664-665** Ace Stock Limited/Alamy Images; **666** Ed-Imaging; **669** Getty Images; **674** (l)Ryan McVay/Getty Images, (c)Getty Images, (r)CORBIS; **677** Nona Darryl Whittington/Darmar Enterprises; **679** Little Blue Wolf Productions/CORBIS; **680 681** Ed-Imaging; **682** George Doyle/Getty Images; **683** Masterfile; **LA0** Mark Steinmetz; **LA1** Amos Morgan/Getty Images; **LA3** PunchStock; **LA4** Ingram Publishing/Alamy Images; **LA5** Purestock/PunchStock; **LA6** imagebroker/Alamy; **LA8** Stockdisc/PunchStock; **LA9** Creatas/PunchStock; **LA10** (t)Stockdisc/PunchStock, (b)D. Hurst/Alamy Images; **LA11** Getty Images; **LA14** Oleg Raisky/Alamy Images; **LA17** Richard Herrmann/Getty Images; **LA18** G.K. & Vikki Hart/Getty Images; **LA21** CORBIS; **LA22** Getty Images; **LA23** C Squared Studios/Getty Images; **LA24** G.K. & Vikki Hart/Getty Images; **LA25** CORBIS/PunchStock; **P0** (tl)Getty Images, (cr)Punchstock, (bl)Bob Daemmrich/PhotoEdit; **P1** Tim Fuller; **P2** Reuters/CORBIS; **P3** Jason Reed/CORBIS; **P4** Mika/CORBIS; **P5** Ed-Imaging; **P6** Nati Harnik/AP Images; **P7** Ed-Imaging; **P8** Jeff Pape/New Bremen Giant Pumpkin Growers; **P9** STOCK4B/Getty Images; **R0** Eclipse Studios; **R43** Tim Fuller

T3 LWA-JDC/CORBIS; **T4** Doug Martin; **T5** (br)courtesy Dinah Zike, (others)Doug Martin; **T8** Bloom Works Inc./Alamy Images; **T12** CORBIS; **T13** Bananastock/PunchStock; **T14** Blend Images/Alamy Images; **ii–iii** Kerrick James Photog/Getty Images; **iv–v** Miles Ertman/Masterfile; **vi–vii** George H. H. Huey/CORBIS; **vii–ix** Taxi/Getty Images; **x–xi** Robert Landau/CORBIS; **xii–xiii** Richard Cummins/CORBIS; **xiv–xv** Eduardo Garcia/Getty Images; **xix** Purestock/PunchStock; **xvi–xvii** Darrell Gulin/Getty Images; **xx** Tim Fuller; **xxi** Eclipse Studios; **14H** Ed-Imaging; **17** Eclipse Studios; **20B** Ed-Imaging; **20** Eclipse Studios; **24 28 32** Eclipse Studios; **36B** Ed-Imaging; **36 42** Eclipse Studios; **58H** Ed-Imaging; **61 64 68** Eclipse Studios; **70B** Ed-Imaging; **80 84** Eclipse Studios; **88B** Ed-Imaging; **88** Eclipse Studios; **100H** Ed-Imaging; **103** Eclipse Studios; **108B** Ed-Imaging; **108 112** Eclipse Studios; **116B** Ed-Imaging; **116** Eclipse Studios; **122B** Ed-Imaging; **126 132** Eclipse Studios; **146H 149B** Ed-Imaging; **149** Eclipse Studios; **152B** Ed-Imaging; **152** Eclipse Studios; **158B** Ed-Imaging; **158 162** Eclipse Studios; **166B** Ed-Imaging; **170B** Daniel Dempster Photography/Alamy Images; **170 174 193 198** Eclipse Studios; **206B** Ed-Imaging; **210 218** Eclipse Studios; **232G** Ed-Imaging; **237 through 260** Eclipse Studios; **276G 276H** Ed-Imaging; **279** Eclipse Studios; **284B** Ed-Imaging; **284 289 294 306** Eclipse Studios; **320B** Michael Newman/PhotoEdit; **330H 333B** Ed-Imaging; **338** Eclipse Studios; **344B** Ed-Imaging; **344 346 350 356** Eclipse Studios; **370G 382B** Ed-Imaging; **382** Eclipse Studios; **386 404** Eclipse Studios; **418I 418J** Ed-Imaging; **423** Eclipse Studios; **428B 442B** Ed-Imaging; **442 448** Eclipse Studios; **452B** Ed-Imaging; **458** Eclipse Studios; **472G 477B** Ed-Imaging; **477** Eclipse Studios; **484B** Ed-Imaging; **484 492** Eclipse Studios; **496B** (l to r)Peter Bowater/Alamy Images, Trujillo-Paumier/Getty Images, Stockbyte Platinum/Getty Images, Michael Newman/PhotoEdit; **500** Eclipse Studios; **512H 517B** Ed-Imaging; **517** Eclipse Studios; **522B** (l)Michael Houghton/StudiOhio, (r)Ed-Imaging; **522 537** Eclipse Studios; **554G** (t)Getty Images, (b)The Canal, Robert, Hubert/The Bridgeman Art Library; **554H** (t)Ed-Imaging, (b)PhotoLink/Getty Images; **557 562** Eclipse Studios; **566B** Ed-Imaging; **566** Eclipse Studios; **567** Steve Vidler/SuperStock; **578 582 586 591** Eclipse Studios; **604I 604J 608B** Ed-Imaging; **608 612** Eclipse Studios; **616B** Ed-Imaging; **624B** (l)Getty Images, (c)CORBIS, (r)Andrea Jemolo/CORBIS; **628 631 640 644** Eclipse Studios; **658H** (t)Envision/CORBIS, (b)Colin Young-Wolff/PhotoEdit; **661 668** Eclipse Studios; **677B** Ed-Imaging; **677** Eclipse Studios; **LA10B LA14B** Ed-Imaging

Photo Credits

Glossary/Glosario

Math Online A mathematics multilingual glossary is available at www.macmillanmh.com. The glossary includes the following languages.

Arabic	Cantonese	Korean	Tagalog
Bengali	English	Russian	Urdu
Brazilian Portuguese	Haitian Creole	Spanish	Vietnamese
	Hmong		

Cómo usar el glosario en español:
1. Busca el término en inglés que desees encontrar.
2. El término en español, junto con la definición, se encuentran en la columna de la derecha.

English | Español

A

acute angle (p. 564) An *angle* with a measure between 0° and 90°.

ángulo agudo *Ángulo* que mide entre 0° y 90°.

acute triangle (p. 567) A *triangle* with all three *angles* less than 90°.

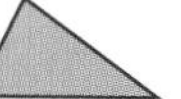

triángulo acutángulo *Triángulo* cuyos tres *ángulos* miden menos de 90°.

addition (p. 70) An operation on two or more *addends* that results in a *sum*.

$$9 + 3 = 12$$

sumar (suma) Operación en dos o más *sumandos* que resulta en una *suma*.

$$9 + 3 = 12$$

algebra (p. 193) A branch of mathematics that uses symbols, usually letters, to explore relationships between quantities.

álgebra Rama de las matemáticas que usa símbolos, generalmente letras para explorar relaciones entre cantidades.

algebraic expression (p. 193) A group of numbers, symbols, and variables that represent an operation or series of operations.

$$3x + 5 \text{ or } y + 5$$

expresión algebraica Grupo de números, símbolos y variables que representan una operación o una serie de operaciones.

$$3x + 5 \text{ o } y + 5$$

angle (p. 564) Two rays with a common endpoint.

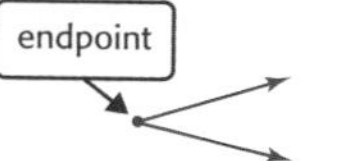

ángulo Dos rectas con un extremo común.

extremo

Glossary/Glosario

area (p. 612) The number of *square units* needed to cover the surface of a closed figure.

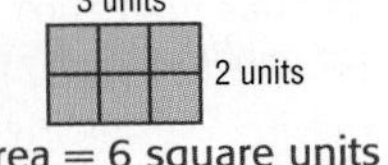

area = 6 square units

Associative Property of Addition (p. 84) Property that states that the way in which numbers are grouped does not change the sum.

Associative Property of Multiplication (p. 126) Property that states that the way in which factors are grouped does not change the product.

axis (p. 250) A horizontal or vertical number line on a graph. Plural is *axes*.

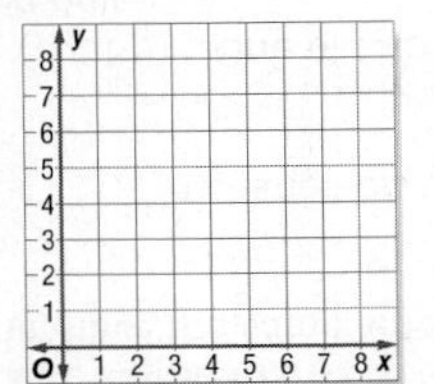

B

bar graph (p. 299) A graph that compares *data* by using bars to display the number of items in each group.

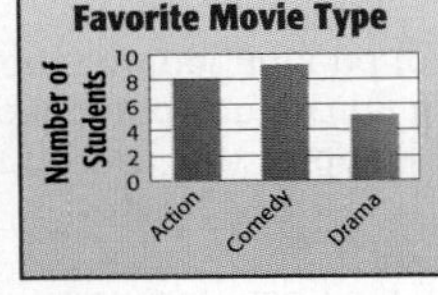

base (p. 624) One of two parallel congruent faces in a prism.

área Número de *unidades cuadradas* necesarias para cubrir la superficie de una figura cerrada.

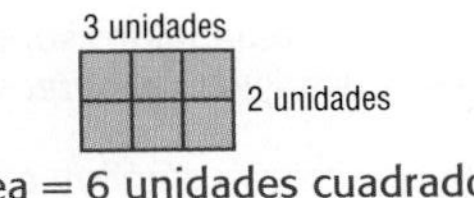

área = 6 unidades cuadrados

propiedad asociativa de la suma Propiedad que establece que la manera en que se agrupan los números no altera la suma.

propiedad asociativa de la multiplicación Propiedad que establece que la manera en que se agrupan los factores no altera el producto.

eje Recta numérica horizontal o vertical en una gráfica.

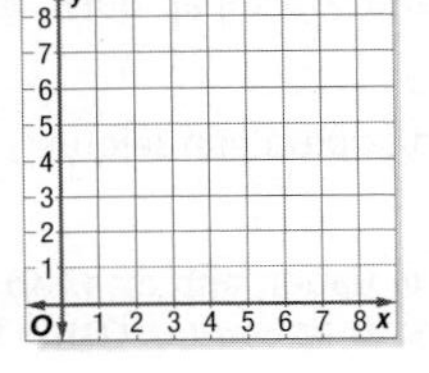

gráfica de barras Gráfica que compara *datos* usando barras para mostrar el número de artículos en cada grupo.

base Una de dos caras congruentes paralelas en un prisma.

C

capacity (p. 488) The amount a container can hold.

Celsius (°C) (p. 537) The unit used to measure temperature in the metric system.

centimeter (cm) (p. 517) A *metric unit* for measuring *length*.

100 centimeters = 1 meter

certain (p. 661) The probability that an event will definitely happen.

common denominator (p. 404) A number that is a multiple of the denominators of two or more fractions.

common factor (p. 373) A number that is a *factor* of two or more numbers.

3 is a common factor of 6 and 12.

common multiple (p. 396) A *whole number* that is a *multiple* of two or more numbers.

24 is a common multiple of 6 and 4.

Commutative Property of Addition (p. 84) Property that states that the order in which numbers are added does not change the sum.

Commutative Property of Multiplication (p. 126) Property that states that the order in which factors are multiplied does not change the product.

capacidad Cantidad que puede contener un envase.

Celsios (°C) Unidad que se usa para medir la temperatura en el sistema métrico.

centímetro (cm) *Unidad métrica* de *longitud*.

100 centímetros = 1 metro

cierto La probabilidad de que ocurra un evento.

denominador común Número que es múltiplo de los denominadores de dos o más fracciones.

factor común Un número *entero factor* de dos o más números.

3 es factor común de 6 y de 12.

múltiplo común *Número entero múltiplo* de dos o más números.

24 es un múltiplo común de 6 y 4.

propiedad conmutativa de la suma Propiedad que establece que el orden en que se suman los números no altera la suma.

propiedad conmutativa de la multiplicación Propiedad que establece que el orden en que se multiplican los factores no altera el producto.

compatible numbers (p. 64) Numbers in a problem that are easy to work with mentally.

720 and 90 are compatible numbers for division because $72 \div 9 = 8$.

compensation (p. 88) Adding a number to one addend and subtracting the same number from another addend to add mentally.

composite number (p. 376) A whole number that has more than two factors.

12 has the factors 1, 2, 3, 4, 6, and 12.

cone (p. 624) A solid that has a circular base and one curved surface from the base to a vertex.

congruent line segments (p. 559) Line segments that have the same length.

convert (p. 477) To change one unit to another.

coordinate (p. 250) One of two numbers in an *ordered pair*.

The 1 is the number on the *x*-axis, the 5 is on the *y*-axis. A coordinate can be positive or negative.

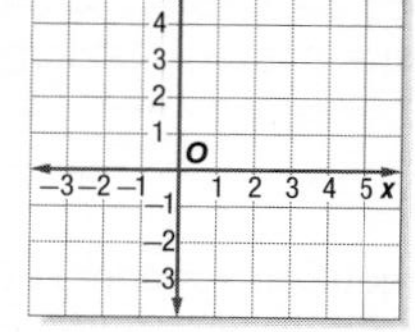

coordinate grid (p. 250) A grid that is formed when two number lines intersect at a right angle.

cube (p. 624) A rectangular *prism* with six faces that are congruent squares.

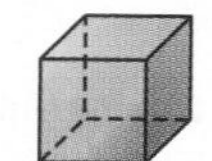

números compatibles Números en un problema con los cuales es fácil trabajar mentalmente.

720 y 90 son números compatibles en la división porque $72 \div 9 = 8$.

compensación Sumar un número a un sumando y restar el mismo número de otro sumando con el fin de sumar mentalmente.

número compuesto Número entero que tiene más de dos factores.

12 tiene a los factores 1, 2, 3, 4, 6 y 12.

cono Sólido con una base circular y una superficie curva desde la base hasta el vértice.

segmentos congruentes de recta Segmentos de recta que tienen la misma medida.

convertir Cambiar una unidad en otra.

coordenada Uno de los dos números de un *par ordenado*.

El 1 es el número en el eje *x* y el 5 está en el eje *y*. Una coordenada puede ser positiva o negativa.

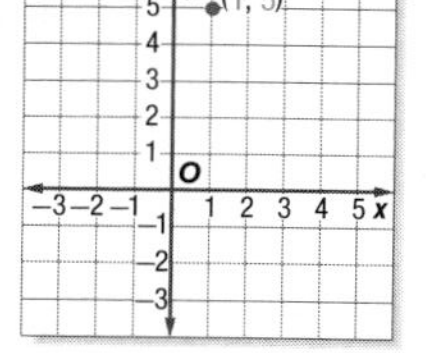

plano de coordenadas cuadriculado que se forma cuando dos rectas numéricas se intersecan a ángulos rectos.

cubo *Prisma* rectangular con seis caras que son cuadrados congruentes.

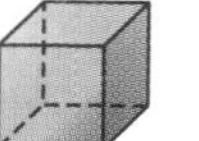

cubic unit (p. 631) A unit for measuring *volume*, such as a cubic inch or a cubic centimeter.

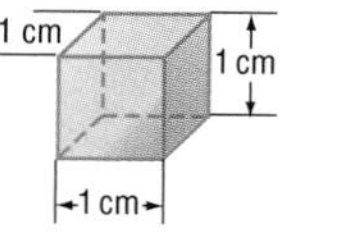

cup (p. 488) A *customary unit* of *capacity* equal to 8 fluid ounces.

customary units (p. 477) The units of measurement most often used in the United States. These include foot, pound, quart, and degrees Fahrenheit.

cylinder (p. 624) A solid with two parallel congruent circular bases and a curved surface that connects the bases.

D

data (p. 279) Pieces of information that are often numerical.

decimal (p. 26) A number that has a digit in the tenths place, hundredths place, and beyond.

decimal point (p. 26) A period separating the ones and the *tenths* in a decimal number.

0.8 or $3.77

defining the variable (p. 238) Choosing a variable to represent an unknown value.

degree (°) (pp. 537, 564) **a.** A unit of measure used to describe temperature. **b.** A unit for measuring *angles*.

denominator (p. 333) The bottom number in a *fraction*. It represents the number of parts in the whole.

In $\frac{5}{6}$, 6 is the denominator.

digit (p. 17) A symbol used to write numbers. The ten digits are 0, 1, 2, 3, 4, 5, 6, 7, 8, and 9.

unidad cúbica Unidad de *volumen*, como una pulgada cúbica o un centímetro cúbico.

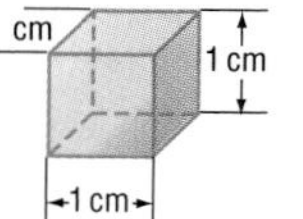

taza *Unidad inglesa* de *capacidad* igual a 8 onzas líquidas.

unidades inglesas Las unidades de medida de uso más frecuente en Estados Unidos. Incluyen el pie, la libra, el cuarto de galón y los grados Fahrenheit.

cilindro Sólido con dos bases paralelas y congruentes y una superficie curva que las conecta.

datos Piezas de información que con frecuencia son numéricas.

decimal Número que tiene un dígito en el lugar de las décimas, centésimas y más allá.

punto decimal Punto que separa las unidades y las *décimas* en un número decimal.

0.8 ó $3.77

definir la variable Elegir una variable para representar un valor desconocido.

grado (°) **a.** Unidad de medida que se usa para describir la temperatura. **b.** Unidad para medir ángulos.

denominador El número inferior en una *fracción*. Representa el número de partes en el todo.

En $\frac{5}{6}$, 6 es el denominador.

dígito Símbolo que se usa para escribir números. Los diez dígitos son 0, 1, 2, 3, 4, 5, 6, 7, 8 y 9.

Distributive Property (p. 108) To multiply a *sum* by a number, you can multiply each *addend* by the same number and add the *products*.

$8 \times (9 + 5) = (8 \times 9) + (8 \times 5)$

divide (division) (p. 149) An operation on two numbers in which the first number is split into the same number of equal groups as the second number.

12 ÷ 3 means 12 is divided into 3 equal size groups

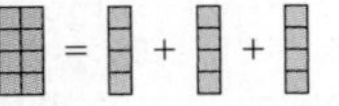

dividend (p. 149) A number that is being divided.

$3\overline{)429}$ 429 is the dividend

divisible (p. 149) Describes a number that can be divided into equal parts and has no remainder.

39 is divisible by 3 with no remainder.

divisor (p. 149) The number by which the dividend is being divided.

$3\overline{)19}$ 3 is the divisor

double bar graph (p. 300) A graph used to display two sets of data dealing with the same subject.

double line graph (p. 307) A graph used to display two different sets of data using a common scale.

propiedad distributiva Para multiplicar una *suma* por un número, puedes multiplicar cada *sumando* por el mismo número y sumar los *productos*.

$8 \times (9 + 5) = (8 \times 9) + (8 \times 5)$

dividir (división) Operación en dos números en que el primer número se separa en tantos grupos iguales como indica el segundo número.

12 ÷ 3 significa que 12 se divide en 3 grupos de igual tamaño.

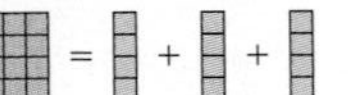

dividendo Número que se divide.

$3\overline{)429}$ 429 es el dividendo

divisible Describe un número que puede dividirse en partes iguales, sin residuo.

39 es divisible entre 3 sin residuo.

divisor Número entre el que se divide el dividendo.

$3\overline{)19}$ 3 es el divisor

gráfica de barras dobles Gráfica que se usa para mostrar dos conjuntos de datos que tienen que ver con el mismo tema.

gráfica lineal doble Gráfica que se usa para mostrar dos conjuntos diferentes de datos usando una escala común.

E

edge (p. 624) The *line segment* where two *faces* of a *3-dimensional figure* meet.

edge

elapsed time (p. 500) The difference in time between the start and the end of an event.

arista Segmento de recta donde concurren dos caras de una *figura tridimensional*.

arista

tiempo transcurrido La diferencia en tiempo entre el comienzo y el final de un evento.

equally likely (p. 661) Having the same chance of occurring.

In a coin toss you are equally likely to flip a head or a tail.

equals sign (p. 235) A symbol of equality, =.

equation (p. 235) A number sentence that contains an equal sign, showing that two expressions are equal.

equilateral triangle (p. 566) A *triangle* with three *congruent* sides.

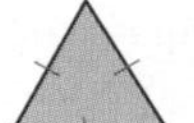

equivalent decimals (p. 37) Decimals that have the same value.

0.3 and 0.30

equivalent fractions (p. 382) *Fractions* that have the same value.

$\frac{3}{4} = \frac{6}{8} = \frac{9}{12}$

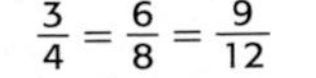

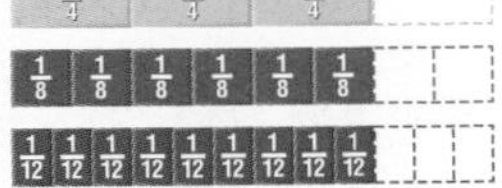

estimate (p. 64) A number close to an exact value. An estimate indicates *about* how much.

47 + 22 (round to 50 + 20)
The estimate is 70.

evaluate (p. 193) To find the *value* of an *expression* by replacing variables with numbers.

even number (p. 377) A whole number that is divisible by 2.

expanded form (p. 17) A way of writing a number as the sum of the values of its digits.

expression (p. 193) A combination of numbers, variables, and at least one operation.

equiprobable Que tienen la misma posibilidad de ocurrir.

Al lanzar una moneda, tienes la misma posibilidad de sacar cara o cruz.

signo de igualdad Símbolo de igual, =.

ecuación Expresión numérica que contiene un signo de igualdad que muestra que dos expresiones son iguales.

triángulo equilátero *Triángulo* con tres lados *congruentes*.

decimales equivalentes Decimales que tienen el mismo valor.

0.3 y 0.30

fracciones equivalentes *Fracciones* que representan el mismo número.

$\frac{3}{4} = \frac{6}{8} = \frac{9}{12}$

estimación Un número cercano a un valor exacto. Una estimación indica *aproximadamente* cuánto.

47 + 22 se redeondea a 50 + 20
La estimación es 70.

evaluar Calcular el *valor* de una expresión reemplazando las variables con números.

número par Número entero divisible entre 2.

forma desarrollada Una manera de escribir un número como la suma de los valores de sus dígitos.

expresión Combinación de números, variables y por lo menos una operación.

F

face (p. 624) The flat part of a 3-dimensional figure.

A square is a face of a cube.

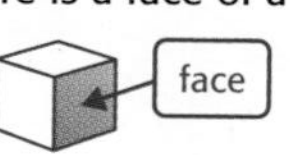

factor (p. 103) A number that is multiplied by another number.

Fahrenheit (°F) (p. 537) The unit used to measure temperature in the customary system.

favorable outcome (p. 668) Desired results in a *probability experiment*.

fluid ounce (p. 488) A *customary unit* of *capacity*.

foot (ft) (p. 477) A *customary unit* for measuring *length*. Plural is *feet*.

1 foot = 12 inches

fraction (p. 333) A number that represents part of a whole or part of a set.

$\frac{1}{2}, \frac{1}{3}, \frac{1}{4}, \frac{3}{4}$

frequency (p. 289) The number of times a result occurs or something happens in a set amount of time or collection of data.

frequency table (p. 289) A table for organizing a set of *data* that shows the number of times each result has occurred.

function (p. 210) A relationship between two variables in which one input quantity is paried with exactly one output quantity.

function rule (p. 210) An expression that describes the relationship between each input and output.

cara La parte llana de una figura tridimensional.

Un cuadrado es una cara de un cubo.

factor Número que se multiplica por otro número.

Fahrenheit Unidad que se usa para medir la temperatura en el sistema inglés.

resultados favorables Resultados deseados en un *experimento probabilístico*.

onzas líquidas *Unidad inglesa* de *capacidad*.

pie (pie) *Unidad inglesa* de *longitud*.

1 pie = 12 pulgadas

fracción Número que representa parte de un todo o parte de un conjunto.

$\frac{1}{2}, \frac{1}{3}, \frac{1}{4}, \frac{3}{4}$

frecuencia Número de veces que ocurre un resultado o sucede algo en un período de tiempo dado o en una colección de datos.

tabla de frecuencias Tabla para organizar un conjunto de *datos* que muestra el número de veces que ha ocurrido cada resultado.

función Relación entre dos variables en que una cantidad de entrada se relaciona exactamente con una cantidad de salida.

regla de funciones Expresión que describe la relación entre cada valor de entrada y cada valor de salida.

function table (p. 210) A table of ordered pairs that is based on a rule.

Rule: $8h = r$	
Input (h)	Output (r)
1	8
2	16
3	24
4	32

tabla de funciones Tabla de pares ordenados que se basa en una regla.

Regla: $8h = r$	
Entrada (h)	Salida (r)
1	8
2	16
3	24
4	32

G

gallon (gal) (p. 488) A *customary unit* for measuring *capacity* for liquids.

1 gallon = 4 quarts

gram (g) (p. 524) A *metric unit* for measuring *mass*.

graph (p. 254) Place a point named by an ordered pair on a coordinate grid.

greater than > (p. 20) An inequality relationship showing that the number on the left of the symbol is greater than the number on the right.

$5 > 3$

5 is greater than 3

Greatest Common Factor (GCF) (p. 374) The greatest of the common factors of two or more numbers.

The greatest common factor of 12, 18, and 30 is 6.

galón (gal) Unidad de *medida inglesa* de *capacidad* de líquidos.

1 galón = 4 cuartos

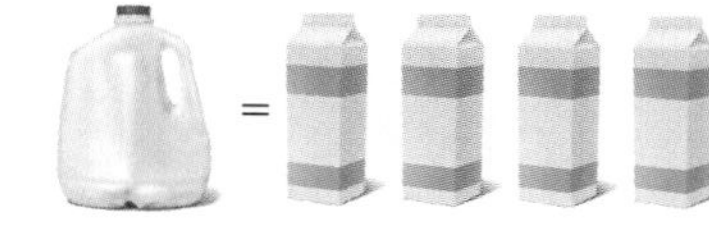

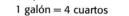

gramo (g) Una *unidad métrica* para medir *masa*.

graficar Colocar un punto indicado por un par ordenado en un plano de coordenadas.

mayor que > Relación de desigualdad que muestra que el número a la izquierda del símbolo es mayor que el número a la derecha.

$5 > 3$

5 es mayor que 3

máximo común divisor (MCD) El mayor de los factores comunes de dos o más números.

El máximo común divisor de 12, 18 y 30 es 6.

H

horizontal axis (p. 250) The axis in a coordinate plane that runs left and right (↔). Also known as the *x*-axis.

eje horizontal Eje en un plano de coordenadas que va de izquierda a derecha (↔). También conocido como eje *x*.

hundredth (p. 28) A place value position. One of one hundred equal parts.

In the number 0.57, 7 is in the hundredths place.

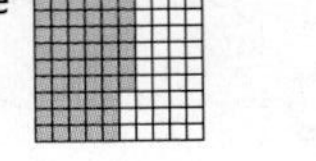

I

Identity Property of Addition (p. 84) Property that states that the sum of any number and 0 equals the number.

Identity Property of Multiplication (p. 126) Property that states that the product of any number and 1 equals the factor.

image (p. 578) The resulting image after a geometric figure has been transformed.

impossible (p. 661) There is no chance an event will happen. An *outcome* or *event* is impossible if it has a *probability* of 0.

It is impossible to choose a yellow tile.

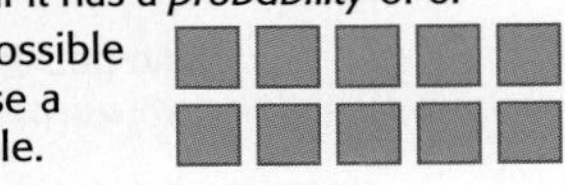

improper fraction (p. 337) A fraction with a numerator that is greater than or equal to the denominator.

$\frac{17}{3}$ or $\frac{5}{5}$

inch (in.) (p. 477) A *customary unit* for measuring *length*. The plural is *inches*.

inequality (p. 20) Two quantities that are not equal.

integer (p. 533) Whole numbers and their opposites, including zero.

...−3, −2, −1, 0, 1, 2, 3...

intersecting lines (p. 558) *Lines* that meet or cross at a common *point*.

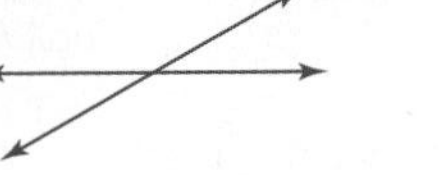

centésima Valor de posición. Una de cien partes iguales.

En el número 0.57, 7 está en el lugar de las centésimas.

propiedad de identidad de la suma Propiedad que establece que la suma de cualquier número y 0 es igual al número.

propiedad de identidad de la multiplicación Propiedad que establece que el producto de cualquier número por 0 es igual al factor.

imagen La imagen que resulta después de transformar una figura geométrica.

imposible Un *resultado* o un *evento* es imposible si tiene una *probabilidad* igual a 0.

Es imposible que elijas un azulejo amarillo.

fracción impropia Fracción con un numerador mayor que o igual al denominador.

$\frac{17}{3}$ o $\frac{5}{5}$

pulgada (pulg) *Unidad inglesa* de *longitud*.

desigualdad Dos cantidades que no son iguales.

entero Los números enteros y sus opuestos, incluyendo el cero.

...−3, −2, −1, 0, 1, 2, 3...

rectas secantes *Rectas* que se intersecan o se cruzan en un *punto* común.

interval (p. 294) The distance between successive values on a scale.

isosceles triangle (p. 566) A *triangle* with at least 2 *sides* of the same *length*.

K

kilogram (kg) (p. 524) A *metric unit* for measuring *mass*.

kilometer (km) (p. 517) A *metric unit* for measuring *length*.

L

Least Common Denominator (LCD) (p. 404) The *least common multiple* of the *denominators* of two or more *fractions*.

$\frac{1}{12}, \frac{1}{6}, \frac{1}{8}$; LCD is 24.

Least Common Multiple (LCM) (p. 397) The smallest *whole number* greater than 0 that is a common *multiple* of each of two or more numbers.

The LCM of 2 and 3 is 6.

length (p. 475) Measurement of the distance between two points.

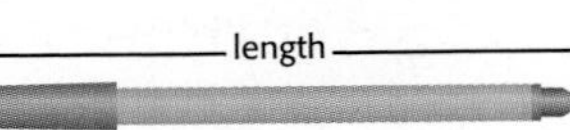

less than < (p. 20) The number on the left side of the symbol is smaller than the number on the right side.

$4 < 7$

4 is smaller than 7

like fractions (p. 421) Fractions that have the same denominator.

$\frac{1}{5}$ and $\frac{2}{5}$

intervalo Distancia entre dos valores sucesivos en una escala.

triángulo isósceles *Triángulo* que tiene por lo menos 2 *lados* del mismo largo.

kilogramo (kg) *Unidad métrica* de *masa*.

kilómetro (km) *Unidad métrica* de *longitud*.

mínimo común denominador (mcd) El *mínimo común múltiplo* de los *denominadores* de dos o más *fracciones*.

$\frac{1}{12}, \frac{1}{6}, \frac{1}{8}$; el mcd es 24.

mínimo común múltiplo (mcm) El menor *número entero*, mayor que 0, *múltiplo* común de dos o más números.

El mcm de 2 y 3 es 6.

longitud Medida de la distancia entre dos puntos.

longitud

menor que < El número a la izquierda del símbolo es más pequeño que el número a su derecha.

$4 < 7$

4 es menor que 7

fracciones semejantes Fracciones que tienen el mismo denominador.

$\frac{1}{5}$ y $\frac{2}{5}$

likely (p. 662) An event that will probably happen.

It is likely you will choose a red cube.

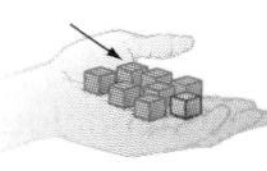

line (p. 557) A set of *points* that form a straight path that goes on forever in opposite directions.

line graph (p. 306) A graph that uses points connected by *line segments* to show changes in data over time.

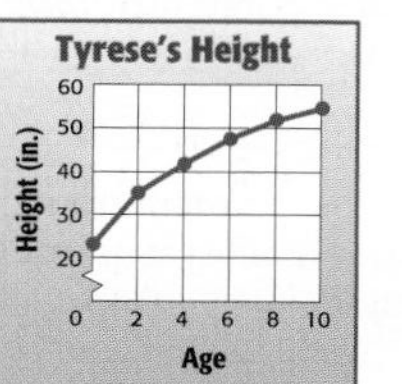

line of reflection (p. 582) The line an image is reflected over.

line plot (p. 284) A graph that uses columns of Xs above a *number line* to show the number of times values in a set of data occur.

line segment (p. 557) A part of a *line* that connects two points.

liter (L) (p. 527) A *metric unit* for measuring *volume* or *capacity*.

1 liter = 1,000 milliliters

M

mass (p. 524) Measure of the amount of matter in an object.

posible Un evento que probablemente sucederá.

Es posible que elijas un cubo rojo.

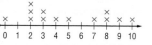

recta Conjunto de *puntos* que forman una trayectoria recta sin fin en direcciones opuestas.

gráfica lineal Gráfica que usa puntos unidos por *segmentos de recta* para mostrar cambios en los datos con el tiempo.

línea de reflexión Línea sobre la cual se refleja una imagen.

esquema lineal Gráfica que usa columnas de X sobre una *recta numérica* para mostrar el número de veces que en un conjunto de datos.

segmento de recta Parte de una *recta* que conecta dos puntos.

litro (L) *Unidad métrica* de *volumen* o *capacidad*.

1 litro = 1,000 mililitros

masa Medida de la cantidad de material en un objeto. Dos ejemplos de unidades de esta medida son la libra y el kilogramo.

mean (p. 279) The quotient found by adding the numbers in a set of data and dividing this sum by the amount of numbers in the data set.

median (p. 279) The middle number in a set of data that has been written in order from least to greatest. If the set contains an even number of numbers, the median is the number exactly halfway between the two middle numbers.

3, 4, 6, 8, 9, 9

The median is $7 = \frac{(6 + 8)}{2}$.

meter (p. 517) A *metric unit* used to measure length.

metric system (SI) (p. 517) The decimal system of measurement. Includes units such as meter, gram, liter, and degrees Celsius.

mile (mi) (p. 477) A *customary unit* of measure for length.

1 mile = 5,280 feet

milligram (mg) (p. 524) A *metric unit* used to measure *mass*.

1,000 milligrams = 1 gram

milliliter (mL) (p. 527) A *metric unit* used for measuring *capacity*.

1,000 milliliters = 1 liter

millimeter (mm) (p. 517) A *metric unit* used for measuring *length*.

1,000 millimeters = 1 meter

mode (p. 279) The number(s) that occurs most often in a set of data.

7, 4, 7, 10, 7, and 2 The mode is 7.

multiple (multiples) (p. 396) A multiple of a number is the *product* of that number and any whole number.

15 is a multiple of 5 because $3 \times 5 = 15$.

media Cociente que se calcula sumando los números en un conjunto de datos y dividiendo esta suma entre el número de sumandos.

mediana Número central de un conjunto de datos escritos en orden de menor a mayor. Si el conjunto contiene una cantidad par de números, la mediana es el número que está exactamente a mitad de camino entre los dos números centrales.

3, 4, 6, 8, 9, 9

La mediana es $7 = \frac{(6 + 8)}{2}$.

metro *Unidad métrica* que se usa para medir la longitud.

sistema métrico (sm) Sistema de medición que se basa en potencias de 10 el cual incluye unidades como el metro, el gramo, el litro y los grados Celsius.

milla (mi) *Unidad inglesa* de longitud.

1 milla = 5,280 pies

miligramo (mg) *Unidad métrica* de *masa*.

1,000 miligramos = 1 gramo

mililitro (mL) *Unidad métrica* de *capacidad*.

1,000 mililitros = 1 litro

milímetro (mm) *Unidad métrica* de *longitud*.

1,000 milímetros = 1 metro

moda Número o números que ocurren con mayor frecuencia en un conjunto de datos.

7, 4, 7, 10, 7, y 2 La moda es 7.

múltiplo (múltiplos) Un múltiplo de un número es el *producto* de ese número por cualquier otro número entero.

15 es múltiplo de 5 porque $3 \times 5 = 15$.

multiplication (p. 103) An operation on two numbers to find their *product*. It can be thought of as repeated *addition*.

4 × 3 is another way to write the *sum* of four 3s, which is 3 + 3 + 3 + 3 or 12.

N

negative integer (p. 533) Integers less than zero. Written with a − sign.

negative number (p. 533) Numbers less than zero.

number line (p. 20) A line that represents numbers as points.

0 1 2 3 4 5 6 7 8 9 10

numerator (p. 333) The top number in a *fraction*; the part of the fraction that tells the number of parts you have.

numerical expression (p. 193) A combination of numbers and operations.

O

obtuse angle (p. 564) An *angle* that measures between 90° and 180°.

obtuse triangle (p. 567) A *triangle* with one *obtuse angle*.

odd number (p. 377) A number that is not divisible by 2; such a number has 1, 3, 5, 7, or 9 in the ones place.

operation (p. 190) A mathematical process such as addition (+), subtraction (−), multiplication (×), division (÷), and raising to a power.

multiplicación Operación que se realiza en dos números para calcular su *producto*. También se puede interpretar como una *suma* repetida.

4 × 3 es otra forma de escribir la *suma* de cuatro veces 3, la cual es 3 + 3 + 3 + 3 o 12.

entero negativo Enteros menores que cero. Se escriben con un signo −.

número negativo Números menores que cero.

recta numérica Recta que representa números como puntos.

0 1 2 3 4 5 6 7 8 9 10

numerador Número que se escribe arriba de la barra de *fracción*; la parte de la fracción que indica el número de partes que tienes.

expresión numérica Combinación de números y operaciones.

ángulo obtuso *Ángulo* que mide entre 90° y 180°.

triángulo obtusángulo *Triángulo* con un *ángulo obtuso*.

número impar Número que no es divisible entre 2, tal número tiene 1, 3, 5, 7 ó 9 en el lugar de las unidades.

operación Proceso matemático como la suma (+), la resta (−), la multiplicación (×), la división (÷) y la potenciación.

opposite integers (p. 534) Two different integers that are the same distance from 0 on a number line.

5 and −5

ordered pair (p. 250) A pair of numbers that is used to name a point on the coordinate grid.

origin (p. 250) The point (0, 0) on a *coordinate grid* where the vertical axis meets the horizontal axis.

ounce (oz) (p. 484) A *customary unit* for measuring *weight* or *capacity*.

outcome (p. 661) A possible result of a probability experiment.

outlier (p. 285) A number in a set of data that is much larger or much smaller than most of the other numbers in the set.

P

parallel lines (p. 558) Lines that are the same distance apart. Parallel lines do not intersect.

parallelogram (p. 571) A quadrilateral with four sides in which each pair of opposite sides are parallel and congruent.

enteros opuestos Dos enteros diferentes que equidistan de 0 en una recta numérica.

5 y −5

par ordenado Par de números que se usan para nombrar un punto en un cuadriculado de coordenadas.

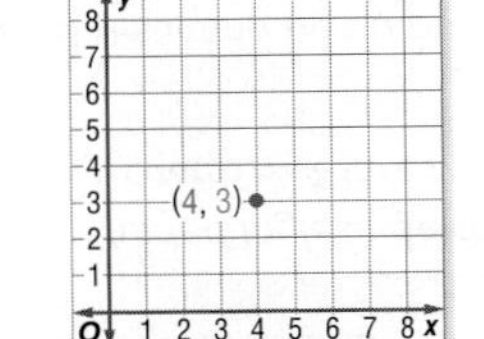

origen El punto (0, 0) en un *cuadriculado de coordenadas* donde el *eje* vertical interseca el eje horizontal.

onza (oz) *Unidad inglesa* de *peso* o *capacidad*.

resultado Resultado posible de un experimento probabilístico.

valor atípico Número en un conjunto de datos que es mucho mayor o mucho menor que la mayoría de los otros números del conjunto.

rectas paralelas Rectas separadas por la misma distancia. Las rectas paralelas no se intersecan.

paralelogramo Cuadrilátero de cuatro lados en que cada par de lados opuestos son paralelos y congruentes.

perimeter (p. 608) The *distance* around a polygon.

period (p. 17) Each group of three digits on a place-value chart.

perpendicular lines (p. 558) *Lines* that cross each other at *right angles*.

pint (pt) (p. 488) A customary *unit* for measuring *capacity*.

1 pint = 2 cups

place value (p. 17) The value given to a digit by its position in a number.

place-value chart (p. 17) A chart that shows the value of the digits in a number.

plane (p. 557) A flat surface that goes on forever in all directions.

point (p. 557) An exact location in space that is represented by a dot.

polygon (p. 608) A closed figure made up of line segments that do not cross each other.

polyhedron (p. 624) A three-dimensional figure with faces that are polygons.

positive integer (p. 533) Integers greater than zero. They can be written with or without a + sign.

positive number (p. 533) Numbers that are greater than zero.

possible outcomes (p. 677) Any of the results that could occur in an experiment.

pound (lb) (p. 484) A *customary unit* for measuring *weight* or *mass*.

1 pound = 16 ounces

perímetro *Distancia* alrededor de un polígono.

período Cada grupo de tres dígitos en una tabla de valor de posición.

rectas perpendiculares *Rectas* que se cruzan a *ángulos rectos*.

pinta (pt) *Unidad inglesa* de *capacidad*.

1 pinta = 2 tazas

valor de posición Valor dado a un dígito según su posición en el número.

tabla de valor de posición Tabla que muestra el valor de los dígitos en un número.

plano Superficie plana que se extiende infinitamente en todas direcciones.

punto Ubicación exacta en el espacio que se representa con un marca puntual.

polígono Figura cerrada compuesta por segmentos de recta que no se intersecan.

poliedro Figura tridimensional con caras en forma de polígonos.

entero positivo Enteros mayores que cero. Se pueden escribir con o sin el signo +.

número positivo Números mayores que cero.

resultados posibles Cualquiera de los resultados que puede ocurrir en un experimento.

libra (lb) *Unidad inglesa* de *peso* o *masa*.

1 libra = 16 onzas

prime factorization (p. 379) A way of expressing a *composite number* as a product of its *prime factors*.

prime number (p. 376) A *whole number* with exactly two *factors*, 1 and itself.

7, 13, and 19

prism (p. 624) A polyhedron with two *parallel, congruent faces,* called *bases*.

probability (p. 661) The chance that an event will happen. It can be described as a number from 0 to 1.

probability experiment (p. 661) An experiment to determine the chance that an event will happen.

product (p. 103) The answer to a multiplication problem.

proper fraction (p. 338) A fraction in which the numerator is less than the denominator.

$\frac{1}{2}$

factorización prima Una manera de escribir un *número compuesto* como un producto de sus *factores primos*.

número primo *Número entero* que tiene exactamente dos *factores*, 1 y sí mismo.

7, 13, y 19

prisma Poliedro con dos *caras paralelas* y *congruentes* llamadas *bases*.

probabilidad La posibilidad de que ocurra un evento. Se puede describir como un número de 0 a 1.

experimento probabilístico Experimento para determinar la posibilidad de que ocurra un evento.

producto Repuesta a un problema de multiplicación.

fracción propia Fracción en que el numerador es menor que el denominador.

$\frac{1}{2}$

Q

quadrilateral (p. 570) A polygon that has 4 sides and 4 angles.

square, rectangle, and parallelogram

quart (qt) (p. 488) A *customary unit* for measuring *capacity*.

1 quart = 4 cups

quotient (p. 149) The result of a *division* problem.

cuadrilátero Polígono con 4 lados y 4 ángulos.

cuadrado, rectángulo y paralelogramo

cuarto (ct) *Unidad inglesa* de *capacidad*.

1 cuarto = 4 tazas

cociente El resultado de un problema de *división*.

R

range (p. 285) The *difference* between the greatest and the least values in a set of data.

rango La *diferencia* entre el mayor y el menor de los valores en un conjunto de datos.

ray (p. 557) A line that has one endpoint and goes on forever in only one direction.

rectangle (p. 571) A *quadrilateral* with four *right angles*; opposite *sides* are equal and *parallel*.

rectangular prism (p. 624) A polyhedron with six rectangular faces.

reflection (p. 582) An figure that is flipped over a line to create a mirror image of the figure.

remainder (p. 159) The number that is left after one whole number is divided by another.

rhombus (p. 571) A *parallelogram* with four *congruent sides*.

right angle (p. 564) An *angle* with a measure of 90°.

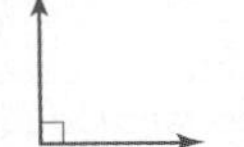

right triangle (p. 567) A *triangle* with one *right angle*.

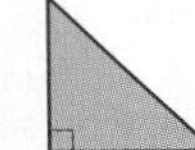

rotation (p. 586) Rotating a figure about a point.

round (p. 61) To find the approximate value of a number.

6.38 rounded to the nearest tenth is 6.4.

rayo Recta con un extremo y la cual se extiende infinitamente en una sola dirección.

rectángulo *Cuadrilátero* con cuatro *ángulo rectos*; los *lados* opuestos son iguales y *paralelos*.

prisma rectangular Poliedro con seis caras rectangulares.

reflexión Figura que se vuelca sobre una línea para crear una imagen especular de la figura.

residuo Número que queda después de dividir un número entero entre otro número entero.

rombo *Paralelogramo* con cuatro *lados congruentes*.

ángulo recto *Ángulo* que mide 90°.

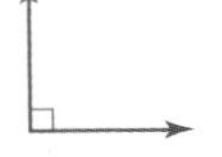

triángulo rectángulo *Triángulo* con un *ángulo recto*.

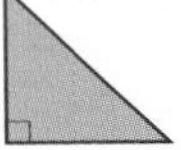

rotación Rotar una figura alrededor de un punto.

redondear Calcular el valor aproximado de un número.

6.38 redondeado a la décima más cercana es 6.4.

S

scale (p. 294) A set of numbers that includes the least and greatest values separated by equal intervals.

escala Conjunto de números que incluye los valores menor y mayor separados por intervalos iguales.

scalene triangle (p. 566) A *triangle* with no *congruent sides*.

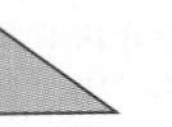

simplest form (p. 386) A fraction in which the GCF of the numerator and the denominator is 1.

solution (p. 235) The value of a variable that makes an equation true. The solution of $12 = x + 7$ is 5.

solve (p. 235) To replace a variable with a value that results in a true sentence.

square (p. 571) A rectangle with four *congruent sides*.

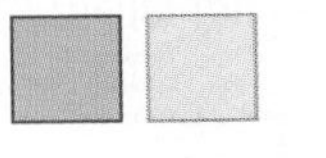

square unit (p. 612) A unit for measuring *area*, such as *square inch* or *square centimeter*.

standard form (p. 17) The usual or common way to write a number using digits.

subtraction (subtract) (p. 64) An operation on two numbers that tells how many are left (*difference*), when some or all are taken away. Subtraction is also used to compare two numbers.

$$14 - 8 = 6$$

sum (p. 64) The answer to an addition problem.

surface area (p. 640) The sum of the areas of all the faces of a prism.

triángulo escaleno *Triángulo* sin *lados congruentes*.

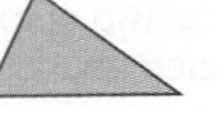

forma reducida Fracción en que el MCD del numerador y del denominador es 1.

solución Valor de una variable que hace verdadera la ecuación. La solución de $12 = x + 7$ es 5.

resolver Despejar una variable y reemplazar este valor en la variable para hacer verdadera la ecuación.

cuadrado Rectángulo con cuatro *lados congruentes*.

unidad cuadrada Unidad de *área*, como una *pulgada cuadrada* o un *centímetro cuadrado*.

forma estándar La manera usual o común de escribir un número usando dígitos.

restar (resta) Operación que se realiza en dos números y que indica cuántos quedan (*diferencia*), cuando se eliminan algunos o todos. La resta también se usa para comparar dos números.

$$14 - 8 = 6$$

suma Respuesta a un problema de suma.

área total La suma de todas las área de todas las caras de un prisma.

T

tally mark(s) (p. 289) A mark made to keep track and display data recorded from a survey.

marcas(s) de conteo Marca que se hace para llevar la cuenta y representar datos reunidos en una encuesta.

tenth (p. 33) A place value in a decimal number or one of ten equal parts or $\frac{1}{10}$.

thousandth(s) (p. 33) One of a thousand equal parts or $\frac{1}{1,000}$. Also refers to a place value in a decimal number.
In the decimal 0.789, the 9 is in the thousandth place.

three-dimensional figure (p. 624) A solid figure that has *length*, *width*, and *height*.

ton (T) (p. 484) A customary unit to measure weight. 1 ton = 2,000 pounds

transformation (p. 578) A movement of a figure that does not change the size or shape of the figure.

translation (p. 578) Sliding a figure in a straight line horizontally, vertically, or diagonally.

trapezoid (p. 571) A *quadrilateral* with exactly one pair of *parallel* sides.

tree diagram (p. 677) A diagram that shows all the *possible outcomes* of an event.

triangle (p. 566) A *polygon* with three sides and three angles.

triangular prism (p. 624) A prism that has triangular bases.

U

unlike fractions (p. 432) Fractions that have different denominators.

unlikely (p. 662) An event that is improbable or will probably *not* happen.

It is unlikely you will choose a blue cube.

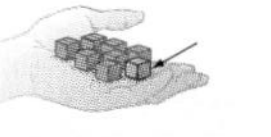

décima Valor de posición en un número decimal o una de diez partes iguales ó $\frac{1}{10}$.

milésima(s) Una de mil partes iguales ó $\frac{1}{1,000}$. También se refiere a un valor de posición en un número decimal.
En el decimal 0.789, el 9 está en el lugar de las milésimas.

figura tridimensional Figura sólida que tiene *largo, ancho* y *alto*.

tonelada (T) Unidad inglesa de peso
1 tonelada = 2,000 libras

transformación Movimiento de una figura que no cambia el tamaño o la forma de la figura.

traslación Deslizar una figura horizontal, vertical o diagonalmente en línea recta.

trapecio *Cuadrilátero* con exactamente un par de lados *paralelos*.

diagrama de árbol Diagrama que muestra todos los *resultados posibles* de un evento.

triángulo *Polígono* con tres lados y tres ángulos.

prisma triangular Prisma con bases triangulares.

fracciones no semejantes Fracciones que tienen denominadores diferentes.

improbable Evento que es improbable o que es probable que *no* suceda.

Es improbable que elijas un cubo azul.

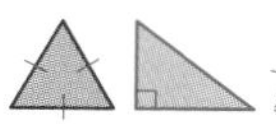

V

value (p. 17) A number amount or the worth of an object.

variable (p. 193) A letter or symbol used to represent an unknown quantity.

vertex (pp. 564, 624) **a.** The *point* where two rays meet in an *angle*. **b.** The point on a three-dimensional figure where 3 or more edges meet.

vertical axis (p. 250) A vertical number line on a graph (↕). Also known as the *y*-axis.

volume (p. 631) The amount of space that a *3-dimensional figure* contains.

W

weight (p. 484) A measurement that tells how heavy an object is.

whole number (p. 20) The numbers 0, 1, 2, 3, 4…

width (p. 616) The measurement of distance from side to side telling how wide.

X

***x*-axis** (p. 250) The horizontal axis (↔) in a coordinate plane.

***x*-coordinate** (p. 250) The first part of an ordered pair that indicates how far to the right or left of the *y*-axis the corresponding point is.

Y

yard (p. 477) A *customary unit* of *length* equal to 3 feet or 36 inches.

***y*-axis** (p. 250) The vertical axis (↕) in a coordinate plane.

***y*-coordinate** (p. 250) The second part of an ordered pair that indicates how far above or below the *x*-axis the corresponding point is.

valor Cantidad numérica o lo que vale un objeto.

variable Letra o un símbolo que se usa para representar una cantidad desconocida.

vértice **a.** *Punto* donde concurren dos rayos de un *ángulo*. **b.** *Punto* en *una figura tridimensional* donde se intersecan 3 ó más aristas.

eje vertical Recta numérica vertical en una gráfica (↕). También conocido como eje *y*.

volumen Cantidad de espacio que contiene una *figura tridimensional*.

peso Medida que indica la pesadez un cuerpo.

número entero Los números 0, 1, 2, 3, 4…

ancho Medida de la distancia de lado a lado y que indica amplitud.

eje *x* Eje horizontal (↔) en un plano de coordenadas.

coordenada *x* Primera parte de un par ordenado que indica la distancia a que está el punto correspondiente a la derecha del eje *y*.

yarda *Unidad inglesa* de *longitud* igual a 3 pies ó 36 pulgadas.

eje *y* El eje vertical (↕) en un plano de coordenadas.

coordenada *y* Segunda parte de un par ordenado que indica la distancia a que está el punto correspondiente por encima del eje *x*.

Index

Index

B

Index

D

Index

E

H

Index

M

N

O